Date D.

The Complete Antiques Price List

RALPH & TERRY KOVEL

authors of KNOW YOUR ANTIQUES, etc.

SIXTH EDITION
THE COMPLETE ANTIQUES PRICE LIST

Cover illustration
courtesy of National Gallery of Art
Washington, D.C.

Books by Ralph M. and Terry H. Kovel

The Complete Antiques Price List

Know Your Antiques

American Country Furniture 1780–1875

Dictionary of Marks—Pottery and Porcelain

The Official Bottle Price List

SIXTH EDITION
THE COMPLETE

ANTIQUES PRICE LIST

**A guide to the 1973–1974 market
for professionals, dealers, and collectors**

by Ralph M. and Terry H. Kovel
ILLUSTRATED

CROWN PUBLISHERS, INC., NEW YORK

Printed in the United States of America
Published simultaneously in Canada by General Publishing Company Limited

INTRODUCTION

Antique prices have been rising steadily through the past years, and 1972–73 saw no change in the trend. The added taxes in England, the devaluation of the dollar, and the pressures of inflation have all joined to push up the prices of antiques in the United States. Prints and pictures of all types have increased sharply. Fine American furniture and art have risen in price by the greatest percentage. It almost seems that an advanced collector or a museum will pay any price for an important item, but at the same time, an average piece remains part of the slowly rising art and antique market. Croesus glass prices went up about 25 percent this year. Bottles, art glass, pressed glass, and the other standard antique items increased only slightly. Art pottery has become a specialist's market, with the unusual or early pieces of Rookwood, Weller, Owens, Ohr, Roseville, Van Briggle, and other potteries bringing prices in the hundreds of dollars. The more ordinary pieces by the same factories bring prices that are in line with those of last year. Depression glass and "Occupied Japan" wares are still low priced, but as the collector's interest increases, reproductions are being made. The prices of Victorian gold items and Art Deco precious stone pieces have risen more rapidly than those of other jewelry. Hummel and Royal Doulton figurines are gaining interest, and the number offered for sale has increased. Collector plates and other limited edition items continue to be produced by dozens of old and new companies, and now the price rise seems to be determined by the importance of the artist or the company. The limited edition market seems confused, with no clear price trends appearing this year.

Prices of advertising items seem to have leveled off, especially for signs, but tin boxes continue to gain in price. Celebrity items and radio giveaways have also gained in value.

GUIDE TO USE

There are just a few simple rules to follow in using this book. Each listing is arranged in the following manner: CATEGORY (such as pressed glass, silver, or furniture); OBJECT (such as vase, spoon, table); DESCRIPTION (which includes as much information as possible about size, age, color, and pattern). All items are presumed perfect unless otherwise noted. Leaf through the book and examine the various category headings. Most of them are exactly as one would expect.

Several special categories were formed to make a more sensible listing of items possible. "Fire" includes andirons, fire fighting equipment, fireplace equipment, and related pieces. "Household," "kitchen," and "tool" include the various special equipment. It seemed impossible to expect the casual collector to know the proper name for each variety of tool, such as an "adze" or a "trefine," so we have lumped them in the special categories.

This book has several idiosyncrasies of style that must be noted before it can be used properly. The prices are compiled by computer, and the machine has dictated several strange rules. Everything in the book is listed alphabetically according to the IBM alphabetic system. This means that words such as "dr." are alphabetized as "D-R," not as "D-O-C-T-O-R." A quick glance at a listing will make this clear, as the alphabetizing is consistent throughout the book.

We have made several editorial decisions that affect the use of the book. A bowl is a bowl and not a dish unless it is a special type of dish such as a sauce dish. A butter dish is called a "butter" and a celery dish a "celery." Small figures are listed as "figurines"; large floor-standing figures are called "statues." Medical and dental tools are listed under "medical" and "dental." "Sewing tools" include thimbles, needles, sewing boxes, sewing birds, and related items. "Textile" includes all fabric items such as coverlets, samplers, rugs, and clothing. All of these are also indexed under their proper names to direct the reader to the textile section.

Many new categories have been added this year. The most important of these are Shaker (this includes all types of small Shaker items, but not Shaker furniture, which is still to be found under the heading "furniture"); Galle pottery; and the many American art potteries such as Ohr, Brouwer, Marblehead, Owens, and others listed by name.

We have added several new features this year. Factory marks for glass and pottery have been included with many of the paragraphs about the factories. Only the marks most commonly used by the firm are given. More descriptive paragraphs have been included, and there now is extensive internal indexing which should make it easier to find a specific item. Several categories such as "milk glass" and "bottles" include special reference numbers. These numbers refer the reader to the most widely known books about the category. When these numbers appear, the name of the special book is given in the paragraph heading. All of these numbers take the form "B-22, C-103," and so forth. The letter is the author's initial; the number refers to a picture in the author's book.

All black and white pictures in THE COMPLETE ANTIQUES PRICE LIST are of antiques sold during the past year. The prices are as reported by the seller. Each piece pictured is listed with the word "illus." as part of the description. Pictures are placed as close to the price listing as is possible. Color pictures are all of museum items, and no prices are given for these antiques.

All prices listed in this book were recorded from antique shows, sales, flea markets, and auctions between June 1972 and June 1973. The prices have been taken from sales in all parts of the country, and variations are sometimes due to the geographic differences in pricing. Antiques of top quality tend to be most expensive near the town where they originated because the local collectors are informed about them. Bottles and advertising items seem higher priced in the West. We have tred to be accurate in all of the prices reported, but we cannot be responsible for any errors that may have occurred. We welcome any suggestions for future editions of this book, but cannot answer letters asking for advice or appraisals.

PICTURE ACKNOWLEDGMENTS

The black and white pictures were taken in many parts of the country. The dealers who helped with this chore and loaned items to be pictured were:

The Antique; Robert and Cynthia Baker; Kenneth Cline; Collin Antiques; Decker Antiques; H. C. Dedrick; Dunbar's Distant View Farm Antiques; Dixie and Dana Franklin; Gable Galleries; Gaier House Antiques; Gillespie's; The Griffin; H and M Antiques; Rebecca Hahn Antiques; Bernard Harter; Hillsway House Antiques; Allan Hodges; House of Antiques; Jamieson's; Ted Kromer; Peter Nelson Antiques; Oak Tree; Opera House Antiques, Granville, Ohio; Kenneth Parrish; Jay Pawlak; The Queen's Attic (Mary Shutt Warther); The Reynolds; Rhea's; Jenny Roberts; Opal Sallee; E. C. Selman; Seven Acres; Spare Parts; Lewis Stotz; Sy's Antiques; Tally Ho Antiques; Unicorns Antiques; Fran Weiss; Marie Wetzel; Betty Whetson; Anne McCullough Wichert; Wilhelm's Antiques; Barbara Woodruff; R. W. Woodruff; Worldwide Antiques; Robert W. Young.

COLOR PICTURES

The color pictures in the sixth edition of THE COMPLETE AN-TIQUES PRICE LIST are skillfully, accurately rendered watercolor drawings of American antiques. This remarkable collection of paintings is from the Index of American Design, which can be found at the National Gallery of Art in Washington, D.C. The Index was a WPA (Works Progress Administration) project begun in 1935. Pictures were drawn by about three hundred artists commissioned in thirty-five states, who worked on the project until it was terminated in 1941. There are more than seventeen thousand drawings in the Index collection, representing some of the best of the decorative arts of America. Collectors can still see the original drawings at the National Gallery of Art in Washington or at one of the special exhibits set up in various museums across the country.

The cover drawing of a country kitchen is from the collection of the Index of American Design, National Gallery of Art, Washington, D.C. It is a composite drawing of a rural kitchen of the 1890–1910 period. The room is filled with objects assembled from various sources. Notice the dutch tile wallpaper, popular during the 1890s. The drawing is one of a series by Perkins Harnly.

Our special thanks to the staff of the Index of American Design, especially Cathy Kissane and Lina Steele. Extra gratitude to Mr. Curt Opliger of the City of Los Angeles Municipal Art Gallery, who helped us photograph the kitchen interior scene on display at the gallery.

DEDICATION

TO
R. Mallory
always first
and of course
our paleobiologist
and junior account executive

ABC Plates or Children's Alphabet Plates were popular from 1780 to 1860. The letters on the plate were meant as teaching aids for the children who were learning to read. The plates were made of pottery, porcelain, metal, or glass.

ABC, Creamer, White, Germany	8.00
ABC, Dish, Bopeep, Deep	28.00
ABC, Dish, Feeding, Bopeep Center	26.00
ABC, Knife, Fork, Spoon, Child's	6.50
ABC, Mug, Bunnies, Roosters, Germany	8.00
ABC, Mug, Child's, Austria	4.00
ABC, Mug, Farm Animals, Children, Silver Plate, Forbes Silver Co.	27.00
ABC, Plate, 'A Timely Rescue, 'Cream, Brown	25.00
ABC, Plate, Alphabet Around Rim In Gold Letters, Beaded Edge, Milk Glass	20.00
ABC, Plate, Aluminum, 6 1/2 In.	7.50
ABC, Plate, Bopeep, Pressed Glass, Clear	22.00
ABC, Plate, Brown & White Clock, Dated 1882, Porcelain, 8 In.	18.00
ABC, Plate, Brownies Washing Dishes, Dated 1896, Tin, 9 In.	33.00
ABC, Plate, Bulldog In Center, Clear Glass, 6 1/2 In.Diameter	18.00
ABC, Plate, Bulldog, Amber	25.00
ABC, Plate, Bulldog, Clear	20.00
ABC, Plate, Cat Center, Alphabet Rim, 7 In.	15.00
ABC, Plate, Chicken Center, 6 In.	35.00
ABC, Plate, Chicken With Chicks	25.00
ABC, Plate, Chicks, Hens, Roosters, Alphabet Raised Border, Gold, 7 In.	10.00
ABC, Plate, Clear, Child Intaglio Center, Clay's Crystal Works, 8 In.	30.00
ABC, Plate, Clockface, 7 In.	18.00 To 24.00
ABC, Plate, 'Come Into The Garden Maude, 'Mother & Kittens, Cobalt	35.00
ABC, Plate, Cream, Blue Indian Scene, Signed Candlefish, Porcelain, England	15.00
ABC, Plate, Crusoe, Friday, Tunstall, England	35.00
ABC, Plate, Dog's Face Center	35.00
ABC, Plate, Embossed Alphabet Border, Marked J & G Meakin	25.00
ABC, Plate, Emma, Blue	25.00
ABC, Plate, Emma, Pressed Glass, Clear	35.00 To 38.00
ABC, Plate, Feeding Dish, Baby's, Little Bopeep, Numerals	24.50
ABC, Plate, Garfield	25.00
ABC, Plate, Girl & Puppies, 7 In.	20.00
ABC, Plate, Girl Center, Amber Glass, 6 1/2 In.	25.00
ABC, Plate, Going To Market, Raised Letters, Staffordshire	24.00
ABC, Plate, Going To Market, Soft Paste, 7 In.	24.00
ABC, Plate, Green Center, Children Playing In Meadow, England	18.00
ABC, Plate, Green Center, Little Girls Under Large Umbrella, England	18.00
ABC, Plate, Hen With Chicks	25.00
ABC, Plate, Hi Diddle, Tin	25.00
ABC, Plate, Hunters, Dogs, Deer	27.00
ABC, Plate, Lamb's, 6 In.	40.00
ABC, Plate, Little Jack Horner, Tunstall, England, 7 1/4 In.	16.00
ABC, Plate, Maiden Forlorn, Germany	17.50
ABC, Plate, Maj.Gen.Geo.Meade, Civil War	26.00
ABC, Plate, Months, Days, Numerals, Clock Center, Pressed Glass, Clear	38.00
ABC, Plate, Parrot On Swing, Two Girls & Dog	16.50
ABC, Plate, Peacock, Incised Elsmore & Son, England, 7 In.	20.00
ABC, Plate, Rabbit, Running, Frosted Center	25.00
ABC, Plate, Red Riding Hood Starting, Impressed Wood, 7 1/2 In.	22.00
ABC, Plate, Robinson Crusoe, Soft Paste, 6 1/2 In.	25.00
ABC, Plate, Running Rabbit, Frosted Center	25.00
ABC, Plate, Sancho Panza, Dapple, Frosted	25.00 To 36.00
ABC, Plate, Slipware	200.00
ABC, Plate, Star Center, Pressed Glass, Clear	25.00
ABC, Plate, Swing Swong, Boy In Swing, Elsmore, England	25.00
ABC, Plate, The Camel, Staffordshire	37.50
ABC, Plate, The Gleaners, Picture Of Mother & Children In Field, English	23.50
ABC, Plate, Titmouse	16.50
ABC, Plate, Two Children & Dog	27.00
ABC, Plate, Two Children In Dog Cart	25.00
ABC, Plate, Wandering Pie, Bird On Branch, Bird In Flight	25.00
ABC, Plate, Washington Profile & Bust, 13 Stars, Tin	15.00

ABC, Plate, White, Raised Letters, William Penn, Blue Suit, 7 1/2 In. 28.00
ABC, Plate, 'Who Killed Cock Robin, 'Tin ....23.00 To 24.00
ABC, Plate, Wild Animal Series, Tiger, English 22.00
ABC, Plate, Wild Animals, C.1880, 8 In. 30.00
ABC, Plate, Young Men And Ladies In A Rowboat 27.00

*Adams China was made by William Adams and Sons of Staffordshire,
England.The firm was founded in 1769 and is still working.*

Adams, Barrel, Biscuit, Black Jasper, White Figures, Relief 110.00
Adams, Biscuit Barrel, Dark Blue Jasper, White Decoration In Relief 85.00
Adams, Bowl, Dr.Syntax Reading His Tour, Marked, England 28.00
Adams, Cup & Saucer, Handleless, Deep Blue, Pagoda 27.50
Adams, Cup & Saucer, Handleless, Rose 22.50
Adams, Cup & Saucer, Miniature 15.00
Adams, Cup Plate, Black, Soft Paste, Farm Scene, Circa 1830 .... 25.00
Adams, Cup Plate, Dark Blue, Sheep & Flowers 25.00
Adams, Cup Plate, Pink, Log Cabins 15.00
Adams, Cup Plate, Pink, The Sea 15.00
Adams, Dish, Blue, Boy On Pony With Sheep, Rectangular, Deep 65.00
Adams, Eggcup, Blue, Ocher, Stylized Flowers, Pair 10.00
Adams, Jar, Cracker, The Hunt, White On Blue, Tunstall, England 50.00
Adams, Pitcher, Coolidge Home, Plymouth, Vt., Name Ruth, Blue & White 29.00
Adams, Pitcher, Cries Of London, Hot Spice Gingerbread, New Mackerel 28.00
Adams, Pitcher, Cries Of London, Scenes, 6 3/4 In. 28.00
Adams, Pitcher, Jeddo Pattern, Signed, 1855, 6 In. 80.00
Adams, Pitcher, Mulberry, Athens, Ironstone, 7 3/4 In.High 25.00
Adams, Pitcher, Pink, Cone Shape, 8 In. 12.00
Adams, Plate, Andalusia, Pink, 8 In. 8.00
Adams, Plate, Bunker Hill Monument, Blue, White, Historical, 10 In. 15.00
Adams, Plate, Child's, Horses, 4 3/4 In. 32.50
Adams, Plate, Cries Of London, Cherry Sellers, 10 In. 15.00
Adams, Plate, Cries Of London, Pea Sellers, 10 In. 15.00
Adams, Plate, Cries Of London, Strawberries 20.00
Adams, Plate, Cries Of London, Turnips & Carrots Ho, By Wealty, 10 1/2 In. 27.50
Adams, Plate, Currier & Ives, Home To Thanksgiving, 10 1/2 In. 17.50
Adams, Plate, Currier & Ives, The Rocky Mountains, 10 1/2 In. 17.50
Adams, Plate, Currier & Ives, Yosemite Valley, 10 1/2 In. 17.50
Adams, Plate, Dr.Syntax Sells Grizzle, Silver Luster Border, 9 In. 65.00
Adams, Plate, Flat Bowl Shape, Dark Blue Flowers, Red, Green, Incised 19.00
Adams, Plate, Hawthornden Edinburghshire, Blue, White, Staffordshire 45.00
Adams, Plate, Indian Tree, Blue & Red, 9 In. 15.00
Adams, Plate, Jeddo Pattern, Ironstone, 9 1/4 In. 18.00
Adams, Plate, Jeddo Pattern, Signed, 1855, 10 In. 25.00
Adams, Plate, King's Rose, 9 3/8 In. 40.00
Adams, Plate, Men In Boat, Blue, 9 In. 55.00
Adams, Plate, Old Curiosity Shop, Dickens Series, Transfer Scene 15.00
Adams, Plate, Palestine Pattern, Blue & White, 10 1/2 In. 15.00
Adams, Plate, Pickwick, Christmas Eve At Mr.Wardles, England 25.00
Adams, Plate, Pink, Seasons, 10 1/2 In.Diameter 15.00
Adams, Plate, Rose, Circa 1820-1840, 9 1/2 In.Diameter 50.00
Adams, Plate, Rose, 7 1/4 In.Diameter 12.50
Adams, Plate, Rose, 8 1/2 In.Diameter 25.00
Adams, Plate, State Capitol, Columbus.Ohio, Floral Border, Blue, White 27.00
Adams, Plate, Tonquin, Flow Blue, 8 1/2 In. 24.00
Adams, Platter, Historical Blue, Regent Street, 13 1/2 In. 145.00
Adams, Platter, Tonquin, Flow Blue, Ironstone, 10 X 14 In. 49.40
Adams, Platter, Turkey, Light Blue, Courtyard Scene, C.1850 .... 75.00
Adams, Saucer, Deep Blue, Seashells 22.50
Adams, Soup, Rose, 10 1/2 In.Diameter 60.00
Adams, Soup, Spanish Convent, Pink, Staffordshire 16.00
Adams, Tile, Plymouth Rock, 6 In.Square 22.00
Adams, Tureen, Historical Blue, Staffordshire, 6 1/2 In. 45.00
    Advertising Card, see Card, Advertising

*Agata Glass was made by Joseph Locke of the New England Glass
Company of Cambridge, Massachusetts, after 1885.A metallic stain was*

applied to New England Peachblow and the mottled design characteristic
of Agata appeared.

Agata, **Tumbler**, Gold Tracery, Blue-Black Oil Spots 595.00
Agata, **Tumbler**, 3 3/4 In.High .... *Illus* 485.00
Agata, **Vase**, Green Opaque, Vertical Ribs, Metallic Stain At Top, 4 1/4 In. 450.00
Agata, **Vase**, Lily 1275.00
Agate, **Bottle**, Snuff, Brown, Carved In Long Life Symbols, Animals, C.1821 .... 245.00
Agate, **Seal**, Desk, Banded Handle, Silver End, Initial T 12.00

Akro Agate Glass was made in Clarksburg, West Virginia, from 1932 to
1951. Before that time the firm made children's glass marbles.Most of the
glass is marked with a crow flying through the letter A.

Akro Agate, **Ashtray**, Blue Leaf 7.00
Akro Agate, **Box**, Powder, Blue, Four Raised Scotties, Dome Lid 30.00
Akro Agate, **Box**, Powder, Figural, Lady In Formal Dress, Blue, 6 1/2 In. 17.00
Akro Agate, **Box**, Powder, Raised Scottie On Lid, Scotties Around Sides, 1920 .... 30.00
Akro Agate, **Cornucopia**, Blue Green, White Mottle 9.50
Akro Agate, **Cornucopia**, Orange, White Mottle 9.50
Akro Agate, **Creamer**, Child's, Pink Opaque, Cover, Mark 6.00

Agata, Tumbler, 3 3/4 In.High

Akro Agate, **Creamer**, White, Toy 2.50
Akro Agate, **Dishes**, Child's 12.50
Akro Agate, **Lemonade Set**, Child's, Emerald Green, 6 Piece 20.00
Akro Agate, **Pitcher**, Child's, Green 3.50
Akro Agate, **Planter**, Green, 6 X 3 In. .... 5.00 To 8.50
Akro Agate, **Powder**, Cover, Colonial Lady 45.00
Akro Agate, **Toothpick**, Blue, White, Urn Shape 5.00
Akro Agate, **Tumbler**, Child's, Green 3.00
Akro Agate, **Vase**, Green & White, 6 In. 8.50
Akro Agate, **Vase**, Green, White, Floral 12.00
Akro Agate, **Vase**, Green, 4 1/4 In.High, Pair 7.00
Akro Agate, **Vase**, Hand, Green & White 9.50
Akro Agate, **Vase**, Orange, White Flowers 9.00
Alabaster, **Figurine**, Two Stallions In Combat, 17 In.Long, 14 In.High 75.00
Alabaster, **Relief**, St.Christopher, Malines, Polychrome, Gilt, C.1550 .... 950.00
Alabaster, **Urn**, Covered, Italian, White, Double Ribbon Handles, Pair 120.00

Albums were popular in Victorian times to hold the myriad pictures and
cutouts favored by the collectors.All sorts of scrapbooks and albums can
still be found.

Album, **Card**, Leather, Tooled, Brass Hinge Clasp, Medallions, 1870 .... 19.00
Album, **Card**, Trade, School, Reward, Circa 1880, 335 .... 45.00
Album, **Christmas & New Year Cards**, 275 .... 42.50
Album, **Fairy**, 23 Miniature Tintypes, Red Leather, Pat.1867, 1 7/8 In.Square 59.50
Album, **Good Luck Symbols**, Horseshoes, Wishbones, Shamrocks, 135 .... 25.00
Album, **Maroon Plush**, Brass Bamboo & Foliage At Corners & Center, Clasp 18.00
Album, **Padded Maroon Plush**, Horseshoe & Poppies Decoration, Metal Clasp 17.00
Album, **Photo**, Black Lacquer, Engraved, Mother-Of-Pearl Inlay, Phoenix, Japan 35.00
Album, **Photo**, Blue Velvet Back, Celluloid Front, Embossed Floral, Latch 12.75

Album, Photo, Blue Velvet, Metal Corners, Crest, Dated Dec.25, 1892 .... 20.00
Album, Photo, Leather 15.00
Album, Photo, Leather, Gold Edges, Brass Clasp, 31 Pictures 8.75
Album, Photo, Musical, Tooled Floral, Scenic Decor On Pages, Clasp 65.00
Album, Photo, Red Plush, Latch, 10 1/2 X 7 1/2 In. 12.50
Album, Photo, Rose Velvet Back, Celluloid Front, Allover Scene, Women, Latch 20.00
Album, Postcard, Clapsaddle, Tuck, Satin, Etc., Santa, 75 .... 150.00
Album, Postcard, Greetings, Views, 102 .... 20.00
Album, Postcard, Tucks, Holidays, Tinsels, Embossed, Scenics, 304 Cards 46.50
Album, Postcard, U.S.Street Views, Cars, Trolley, Horse Drawn Vehicles, 320 .... 45.00
Album, Postcard, Views Of Massachusetts, C.1900, 52 .... 7.00
Album, Scrapbook, Trade Cards, Victorian, 100 Pages 39.00
Album, Velour, Emerald Green, White Celluloid Carnations, Gilt Clasp 28.00

*Alexandrite glass was first made by Thomas Webb & Sons at the beginning
of the 20th century. It is a transparent glass shading from pale yellow to
rose to blue. Stevens & Williams later produced Alexandrite glassware
by plating a transparent yellow body with rose and blue glass.*
Alexandrite, Rose Bowl, Honeycomb Pattern, Neck In Shape Of 6 Point Star 575.00
Alexandrite, Vase, Applied Rigaree, Diamond Quilted, 4 In.High 375.00
Alexandrite, Vase, Diamond Quilted, Amber To Rose To Blue, 4 In.High 375.00

*Amber Glass is the name of any glassware with the proper yellow-brown
shade. It was a popular color after the Civil War.*
Amber Glass, Basket, Embossed Basket Weave, Mica Flakes, Twisted Handle 52.00
Amber Glass, Bathtub, Sietz, Daisy & Button, Light Golden 67.50
Amber Glass, Bell, Crystal Corset Shape Handle, Clapper, 10 In.High 85.00
Amber Glass, Bell, Dinner, Clear Handle 14.50
Amber Glass, Berry Set, Daisy & Button, Panels, 7 Piece .... 185.00 To 200.00
Amber Glass, Berry Set, Hobnail With Fan, 13 Piece 125.00
Amber Glass, Bowl, Berry, Amberette, 10 In. 35.00
Amber Glass, Bowl, Berry, Three Panels, Straight Sides, 7 In. 22.50
Amber Glass, Bowl, Daisy & Button, Cradle Shape, 9 1/2 In.Long 55.00
Amber Glass, Bowl, Diamond-Quilted, 8 In. 17.00
Amber Glass, Bowl, Fruit, Pedestal, Scalloped, Drapery, Floral Checkerboards 30.00
Amber Glass, Bowl, Fruit, Three Panels, Pedestal Base 29.50
Amber Glass, Bowl, Ohio, Welded Rim, 5 1/4 In.Diameter 100.00
Amber Glass, Bowl, Punch, Hand-Painted Enamel Floral, Cover, Spear Finial 125.00
Amber Glass, Bowl, Wildflower, Square, 7 1/2 In. 20.00
Amber Glass, Butter, Diamond Point Loop, Cover 22.50
Amber Glass, Butter, Star & Button, Cover 35.00
Amber Glass, Butter, Victorian Stove, Covered 35.00
Amber Glass, Cake Stand, Cut Frosted Flowers, High Center Handle 21.00
Amber Glass, Cake Stand, Thumbprint, Daisy & Button 65.00
Amber Glass, Cake Stand, 8 1/2 In. 18.50
Amber Glass, Candlestick, Etched Grapes, Floral, Vines, 10 3/4 In.High 55.00
Amber Glass, Candlestick, 8 1/4 In., Pair 25.00
Amber Glass, Carafe, Water, Thumbprint, Tumbler 30.00
Amber Glass, Castor, Pickle, Cane, Pewter Frame & Tongs 72.50
Amber Glass, Celery Vase, Daisy & Button, Crossbar 48.00
Amber Glass, Cigarette Holder, Orange, Signed Czechoslovakia, 5 In.Long 18.00
Amber Glass, Compote, Cover, Random Reeding In Green, Flint 100.00
Amber Glass, Compote, Daisy & Button, Crossbars 45.00
Amber Glass, Compote, Lacy Open Edge, Fine Cut, Pedestal Flared Base 27.50
Amber Glass, Compote, Three Panel Pattern, Low Standard, 10 In.Diameter 28.00
Amber Glass, Compote, Valencia Waffle, Cover, 9 In.High, 8 In.Square 50.00
Amber Glass, Console Set, 6 1/2 In.Candlesticks 10.00
Amber Glass, Creamer, Daisy & Button With Crossbar .... 20.00 To 34.00
Amber Glass, Creamer, Leaves & Cherries, 3 Panel 16.50
Amber Glass, Creamer, Medallion 25.00
Amber Glass, Creamer, Pointed Hobnail 18.00
Amber Glass, Creamer, Thumbprint, Square Top, Blue Rib Handle, New England 250.00
Amber Glass, Creamer, Wildflower 22.00
Amber Glass, Cruet, Castle, Deer, Trees, Cut, Bohemian 45.00
Amber Glass, Cruet, Stopper 45.00
Amber Glass, Cup & Saucer, Thistle & Leaf Decor, Enameled, Gold, Signed 145.00

Amber Glass, **Cuspidor**, Ellenville, Swag Pattern 115.00
Amber Glass, **Cuspidor**, Lady's, Clear, No Design, 4 1/4 In.High 95.00
Amber Glass, **Decanter**, Silver Overlay, 9 1/4 In.High 48.00
Amber Glass, **Dish**, Candy, Cambridge 6.00
Amber Glass, **Dish**, Chicken Covered, Geometric Base .... 27.50 To 30.00
Amber Glass, **Dish**, Daisy & Button, V Ornament, Oblong 25.00
Amber Glass, **Dish**, Hen Cover, White Milk Glass Head, Clear, 5 In. 60.00
Amber Glass, **Dish**, Open, Spirea Band, 9 X 6 In. 8.00
Amber Glass, **Epergne**, Mirror Base, Blue Trim 22.50
Amber Glass, **Figurine**, Bird, Carved, Cherry, Fitted Wooden Stand, China, Pair 195.00
Amber Glass, **Figurine**, Buddha, Gillinder, 6 In. 49.00
Amber Glass, **Goblet**, Basket Weave 21.00
Amber Glass, **Goblet**, Diamond-Quilted 15.00
Amber Glass, **Goblet**, Prism & Daisy Bar 21.50
Amber Glass, **Hat**, Daisy & Button 16.00
Amber Glass, **Hat**, Derby, Folded Rim, Open Pontil, South Jersey, 6 In.High 125.00
Amber Glass, **Inkwell**, Paneled Cut, Teapot Shape, Hinged Cover, Pen In Spout 28.50
Amber Glass, **Jar**, Enamel, Woman In Period Clothes, Applied Prunts, Finial 75.00
Amber Glass, **Jar**, Powder, Footed, Blue Cover 3.95
Amber Glass, **Jar**, Tobacco, 'Globe-Detroit, ' Barrel 30.00
Amber Glass, **Kettle**, Gypsy, Footed, Wire Bail, 3 1/2 In. 18.00
Amber Glass, **Lamp**, Oil, Ribbed, Chimney, Small 6.00
Amber Glass, **Match Holder**, Cane, Double, Hanging, Place For Used Matches 35.00
Amber Glass, **Mug**, Child's, Butterflies 20.00
Amber Glass, **Mug**, Child's, Cube & Daisy 17.00
Amber Glass, **Mug**, Child's, Deer & Tree 25.00
Amber Glass, **Mug**, Crossed Cords & Prisms 18.00
Amber Glass, **Mug**, Deer & Dog 23.00
Amber Glass, **Mug**, Hobnail .... 12.50 To 15.00
Amber Glass, **Mug**, Trees, Birds, Owl, Pleated Base, Square Knob Handle 17.50
Amber Glass, **Mug**, Wheat & Barley .... 25.00 To 30.00
Amber Glass, **Perfume**, Blown, Bubble Stopper, Enameled Floral 30.00
Amber Glass, **Pitcher**, Blue, White, & Coral Floral, Lacy Gold Foliage, 3 In. 35.00
Amber Glass, **Pitcher**, Daisy & Button With Crossbar, 8 In.High 27.50
Amber Glass, **Pitcher**, Daisy & Button, Amber Handle, Tankard, 9 In. 67.50
Amber Glass, **Pitcher**, Light Blue Applied Handle, Bulbous, 8 In.High 57.00
Amber Glass, **Pitcher**, Water, Daisy & Button Band, Plain Panels 25.00
Amber Glass, **Pitcher**, Water, Daisy & Button With Crossbar 38.00
Amber Glass, **Pitcher**, Water, Frosted Etchings Of Flowers 13.50
Amber Glass, **Pitcher**, Water, Hummingbird 42.00
Amber Glass, **Pitcher**, Water, Inverted Panel, Applied Handle, Blown 55.00
Amber Glass, **Pitcher**, Water, Inverted Thumbprint, Reeded Clear Handle 75.00
Amber Glass, **Pitcher**, Water, Primrose 28.00
Amber Glass, **Pitcher**, Water, Zipper .... 24.00 To 38.00
Amber Glass, **Plate**, Barley, 6 In. 40.00
Amber Glass, **Plate**, Bread, Queen Victoria Jubilee, 1837-1887, 9 1/2 In. 20.00
Amber Glass, **Plate**, Cake, Fine Cut, Pedestal Base 25.00
Amber Glass, **Plate**, Cake, Willow Oak 25.00
Amber Glass, **Plate**, Daisy & Button, 7 In. 18.00
Amber Glass, **Plate**, Daisy & Button, 7 In.Square 10.00
Amber Glass, **Plate**, Dinner, Daisy & Button 22.50
Amber Glass, **Plate**, Grant Peace, Round, 10 In. 35.00
Amber Glass, **Plate**, Manhattan, 11 In.Diameter 3.50
Amber Glass, **Plate**, Maple Leaf, 11 In. 32.50
Amber Glass, **Plate**, Primrose, 6 7/8 In. 18.00
Amber Glass, **Plate**, Wild Flower, 9 5/8 In. 30.00
Amber Glass, **Plate**, 1, 000-Eye, Diaper Corners, 10 In. 18.00
Amber Glass, **Relish**, Block, Oval 22.50
Amber Glass, **Relish**, Two Panel 10.50
Amber Glass, **Rose Bowl**, Hobnail, Fluted Rim, Honey Color 28.00
Amber Glass, **Salt & Pepper**, Hobnail, Silver Plate Top 10.00
Amber Glass, **Salt Dip**, Design, Flat Surface, Sanded 75.00
Amber Glass, **Salt Dip**, Goose 8.50
Amber Glass, **Sandal**, 4 1/2 In.Long 25.00
Amber Glass, **Sauce**, Daisy & Button, Panels, Set Of 10 .... 175.00
Amber Glass, **Sauce**, Daisy & Button, 4 In.Square 4.00

Amber Glass, **Sauce**, Rose Sprig, Footed 7.50
Amber Glass, **Shaker**, Salt, Daisy & Button, Crossbar 12.00
Amber Glass, **Shaker**, Salt, Pointed Hobnail 12.00
Amber Glass, **Shaker**, Sugar, Swirled Panels, Tin Top 30.00
Amber Glass, **Shoe**, Baby's, Daisy & Button 15.00
Amber Glass, **Shoe**, Daisy & Button 8.00
Amber Glass, **Shoe**, Daisy & Button, Patent Oct.19, 1886 .... 29.00
Amber Glass, **Shoe**, High, Marked 26.00
Amber Glass, **Shoe**, High, Ribbed 32.50
Amber Glass, **Spittoon**, Lady's, No Design, Pontil, 4 1/4 In.High 95.00
Amber Glass, **Spooner**, Inverted Thumbprint 14.00
Amber Glass, **Spooner**, Inverted Thumbprint, 1880 .... 23.00
Amber Glass, **Spooner**, Inverted Thumbprint, Enamel Floral, Leaves 45.00
Amber Glass, **Spooner**, Three Panel 17.50
Amber Glass, **Stein**, Applied Green Blue Rosettes, Pewter Top, Dated 12-24-88 .... 67.50
Amber Glass, **Sugar & Creamer**, Medallion Pattern 58.00
Amber Glass, **Sugar**, Cane, Cover 37.00
Amber Glass, **Sugar**, Daisy & Button, Crossbar, Cover 47.00
Amber Glass, **Swan**, Openwork Wings, Pair 60.00
Amber Glass, **Syrup**, Embossed Scene, Bird, Tree, Nest 75.00
Amber Glass, **Syrup**, Glass Top 30.00
Amber Glass, **Syrup**, Inverted Thumbprint, Pewter Top 55.00
Amber Glass, **Syrup**, Inverted Thumbprint, Standard, Pewter Lid 68.50
Amber Glass, **Syrup**, Thumbprint, Pewter Lid, Patent Date 27.00
Amber Glass, **Toothpick**, Daisy & Button, Cradle 27.00
Amber Glass, **Toothpick**, Hive, Bees 14.50
Amber Glass, **Toothpick**, Honey Color 18.50
Amber Glass, **Toothpick**, Inverted Thumbprint, Applied Blue Rigaree Feet 35.00
Amber Glass, **Toothpick**, Monkeys On Tree Trunk 17.00
Amber Glass, **Toothpick**, Moon & Star 10.00
Amber Glass, **Toothpick**, Mortar Cannon 17.00
Amber Glass, **Toothpick**, Swirls 8.50
Amber Glass, **Toothpick**, Yellow & White Daisies, Swirls, Crimped, Flared Top 48.50
Amber Glass, **Tray & Six Goblets**, Basket Weave 120.00
Amber Glass, **Tray**, Bread, Deer And Pine Tree 39.00
Amber Glass, **Tray**, Dresser, Two Covered Boxes, Pair Three Mold Candlesticks 37.50
Amber Glass, **Tray**, For Water Glasses, Hobnail 75.00
Amber Glass, **Tray**, Primrose 20.00
Amber Glass, **Tray**, Water, Daisy & Button 25.00
Amber Glass, **Tray**, Water, Primrose 28.50
Amber Glass, **Tray**, 1, 000-Eye, 11 X 8 In. 25.00
Amber Glass, **Tumbler & Tumble-Up**, Nickle Rim 10.00
Amber Glass, **Tumbler**, Inverted Thumbprint 16.00
Amber Glass, **Tumbler**, Pointed Hobnail 12.00
Amber Glass, **Tumbler**, Shell & Jewel 18.50
Amber Glass, **Tumbler**, Wheat & Barley 16.00
Amber Glass, **Tumbler**, Wildflower 30.00
Amber Glass, **Tumbler**, Windflower 25.00
Amber Glass, **Vase**, Bud, Round Base, Heavy Lip, 9 In. 4.50
Amber Glass, **Vase**, Diamond Pattern, Scalloped Top & Base, 10 In.High 20.00
Amber Glass, **Vase**, Enamel, Wright Brothers Type Airplane Over Forest, Blown 50.00
Amber Glass, **Vase**, Frosted, Narrow Gold Rim, Coralene Bird On Branch, Pair 40.00
Amber Glass, **Vase**, Hand, Daisy & Button 19.00
Amber Glass, **Vase**, Open Mouth Fish, 3 1/2 In. 15.00
Amber Glass, **Vase**, Ovoid Paneled Body, Enamel Floral, Dragon, Blue Pedestal 75.00
Amber Glass, **Vase**, White & Gold Enamel Leaves, Daisies, Squatty, Pair 48.00
Amber Glass, **Wine**, Blue Applied Teardrops, Dot Trim, Set Of 6 .... 75.00
    Amber, Bottle, see also Bottle, Amber
Amber, **Bottle**, Snuff, Flattened, Opaque Brown, Quartz Stopper, C.1850 .... 80.00

*Amberina is a two-toned glassware made from 1883 to about 1900.It was
patented by Joseph Locke of the New England Glass Company.The
glass shades from red to amber.*
    Amberina, see also Mt.Washington, Baccarat, Plated Amberina, Bluerina
Amberina, **Basket**, Hobnail, Three Amber Feet, Sides Berry Prunts 1450.00
Amberina, **Bonbon**, Fluted, Ruffled, 6 In.Diameter 100.00

Amberina, **Bottle**, Water, Rigaree Around Neck, Tricorner Opening, New England 195.00
Amberina, **Bowl**, Finger, Fuchsia, Crimped Top, New England 125.00
Amberina, **Bowl**, Finger, Fuchsia, Flared Top, New England 125.00
Amberina, **Bowl**, Finger, Fuchsia, Scalloped 85.00
Amberina, **Bowl**, Finger, Inverted Thumbprint .... 65.00 To 95.00
Amberina, **Bowl**, Fluted, Applied Handles 165.00
Amberina, **Bowl**, Fuchsia, Diamond-Quilted, 7 In.Diameter 230.00
Amberina, **Bowl**, Fuchsia, Ribs, Swirls, Bulbous, Square Rim, Polished Pontil 250.00
Amberina, **Bowl**, Fuchsia, Triangular, Mt.Washington 175.00
Amberina, **Bowl**, Inverted Thumbprint, Red At Base, 2 1/2 X 5 In. 85.00
Amberina, **Bowl**, Open Rose, Marked Imperial 50.00
Amberina, **Bowl**, Swirls, Gold Floral, Turned In Crimped Top, Mt.Washington 295.00
Amberina, **Butter Pat**, Daisy & Button, New England 60.00
Amberina, **Butter Pat**, Daisy & Button, Sandwich 55.00
Amberina, **Candlestick**, Footed, Nine Point Star Cut 18.00
Amberina, **Canoe**, Daisy & Button, 8 In.Long 140.00
Amberina, **Canoe**, Fuchsia, Daisy & Button, Flint 110.00
Amberina, **Celery**, Diamond-Quilted, Deep Red At Top 275.00
Amberina, **Celery**, Elongated Thumbprint, Scalloped Top 72.50
Amberina, **Celery**, Fuchsia To Dark Amber 265.00
Amberina, **Celery**, Fuchsia, Diamond-Quilted, Scalloped, Mt.Washington 165.00
Amberina, **Celery**, Fuchsia, Inverted Thumbprint, New England 165.00
Amberina, **Celery**, Inverted Thumbprint, Scalloped Rim, Polished Pontil 100.00
Amberina, **Celery**, Reversed, Three Amber Feet 500.00
Amberina, **Celery**, Rose, Fuchsia, Square, 6 1/2 In.High 165.00
Amberina, **Celery**, Ruffled Top, 6 In. 95.00
Amberina, **Celery**, Scalloped Top 155.00
Amberina, **Celery**, Thumbprint, Cranberry To Honey Amber 126.00
Amberina, **Cologne**, Baccarat Swirl, Stopper, 7 In.High 60.00
Amberina, **Compote**, Honeycomb, Red, Amber, Green, Blue, Footed, Cambridge 110.00
Amberina, **Creamer**, Amber, Ruffled Top, Diamond-Quilted, 4 1/2 In. 250.00
Amberina, **Creamer**, Diamond-Quilted 165.00
Amberina, **Creamer**, Fuchsia, Inverted Thumbprint, New England 195.00
Amberina, **Creamer**, Inverted Thumbprint, Amber Reeded Handle 65.00
Amberina, **Creamer**, Melon Shape, Amber Green Handle 160.00
Amberina, **Cruet**, Brandy, Inverted Thumbprint 90.00
Amberina, **Cruet**, Diamond-Quilted 135.00
Amberina, **Cruet**, Fuchsia, Bulbous, Squat, Stopper, 6 1/2 In. 225.00
Amberina, **Cruet**, Inverted Rib, Three Lips, Faceted Stopper, New England 165.00
Amberina, **Cruet**, Inverted Thumbprint, Amber Stopper & Handle 145.00
Amberina, **Cruet**, Inverted Thumbprint, Clear Stopper, Ribbed Handle 70.00
Amberina, **Cup**, Punch, Inverted Thumbprint 43.00
Amberina, **Cup**, Punch, Inverted Thumbprint, Reeded Handle 95.00
Amberina, **Cup**, Punch, Thumbprint, Amber Hand 47.00
Amberina, **Decanter**, Fuchsia, Thumprints, Applied Amber Rigaree On Neck, 1884 .... 225.00
Amberina, **Decanter**, Reverse, Squat, Stopper, 18 In. X 4 3/4 In.High 125.00
Amberina, **Decanter**, Stopper 95.00
Amberina, **Dish**, Cheese, Inverted Thumbprint, Cover 385.00
Amberina, **Dish**, Daisy & Button, Scalloped Ends, 6 In.Square 110.00
Amberina, **Dish**, Flare-Out Sides, Signed Cambridge, 9 In. 150.00
Amberina, **Goblet**, Inverted Thumbprint 75.00
Amberina, **Hat**, Jack-In-The-Pulpit Shape, Raspberry Pattern, Ruffled, Pair 170.00
Amberina, **Ice Cream Set**, Fuchsia, Daisy & Button, Square Plates, 7 Piece 725.00
Amberina, **Juice**, Enameled 85.00
Amberina, **Lampshade**, Gas, Honeycomb Pattern, Opalescent, Scalloped Edge 35.00
Amberina, **Muffineer**, Inverted Thumbprint, Enameled Flowers 135.00
Amberina, **Muffineer**, Thumbprint, Pewter Top 90.00
Amberina, **Mug**, Handled, Fuchsia, Etched Flowers, 3 7/8 In.High 275.00
Amberina, **Mustard Pot**, Brass Lid, 3 1/2 In. 24.00
Amberina, **Perfume**, Footed, Ground Stopper, Etched Design, 6 1/4 In.High 32.00
Amberina, **Pitcher**, Bulbous, Clear Applied Handle, Ground Pontil 25.00
Amberina, **Pitcher**, Deep Fuchsia, Crimped Amber Handle, Hand Blown 195.00
Amberina, **Pitcher**, Fuchsia, Diamond-Quilted, Reeded Handle, Tankard, 4 In. 88.00
Amberina, **Pitcher**, Inverted Thumbprint, Reeded Handle, Ground Pontil 175.00
Amberina, **Pitcher**, Reverse, Diamond-Quilted, Amber Ribbed Handle, 5 In. 80.00
Amberina, **Pitcher**, Square Top, Swirled, Amber Reeded Handle, Mt.Washington 125.00

Amberina, Pitcher, Tankard, Expanded Diamond, 7 In.High 225.00
Amberina, Pitcher, Water, Bulbous Swirl, Square Amber Handle 200.00
Amberina, Pitcher, Water, Diamond-Quilted, Enameled, Reeded Handle 225.00
Amberina, Pitcher, Water, Diamond-Quilted, Tankard, 8 3/4 In.High 350.00
Amberina, Pitcher, Water, Fuchsia, Inverted Thumbprint, New England 225.00
Amberina, Pitcher, Water, Inverted Thumbprint, Blue Handle, 9 1/2 In. 200.00
Amberina, Pitcher, Water, Inverted Thumbprint, Reed Handle, Square Top 200.00
Amberina, Pitcher, Water, Inverted Thumbprint, Ruffled Rim, Reed Handle 285.00
Amberina, Pitcher, Water, Inverted Thumbprint, 9 1/2 In.High 200.00
Amberina, Pitcher, Water, Quilted, Tankard Shape, 8 3/4 In.High 350.00
Amberina, Pitcher, Water, Scoop Shape Mouth, Inverted Thumbprint 165.00
Amberina, Pitcher, Water, White Enameling 165.00
Amberina, Plate, Expanded Diamond, 7 In. 145.00
Amberina, Rose Bowl, Fuchsia, Applied Amber Rigaree, Diamond-Quilted 285.00
Amberina, Salt & Pepper, Melon Ribbed, Diamond-Quilted, Reverse, Pair 110.00
Amberina, Salt, Squirrel & Tree Trunk 37.50
Amberina, Saltshaker, Baby Inverted Thumbprint, Barrel Shape, Pewter Top 75.00
Amberina, Sauce, Daisy & Button, Scalloped Edge, 5 In.Square 70.00
Amberina, Sauce, Daisy & Button, 5 In.Square 57.50
Amberina, Sauce, Diamond-Quilted, New England Glass Co. 75.00
Amberina, Sauce, Square, Flint 67.00
Amberina, Sauce, Venetian Diamond Pattern, New England Glass Co. 75.00
Amberina, Spooner, Shaded, By N.E.Glass Co. 225.00
Amberina, Tieback, 3 In., Pair 35.00
Amberina, Toothpick, Cranberry Halfway Down, Cut Panels At Base, Flashed 50.00
Amberina, Toothpick, Daisy & Button, Footed, Sandwich 125.00
Amberina, Toothpick, Flashed, Ruby Comes Halfway Down, Cut Paneled Base 50.00
Amberina, Toothpick, Four Cornered 120.00
Amberina, Toothpick, Fuchsia, Venetian Diamond, Square Top 150.00
Amberina, Toothpick, Fuchsia, Venetian Diamond, Tricorner .... 145.00 To 185.00
Amberina, Toothpick, Venetian Diamond, New England Glass Co. 135.00
Amberina, Toothpick, Venetian Diamond, Square Mouth, New England 110.00
Amberina, Tray, Card, Handle 37.00
Amberina, Tray, Celery, Pineapple & Fan 45.00
Amberina, Tumble-Up, Inverted Thumbprint, Yellow To Fuchsia, Reverse 250.00
Amberina, Tumbler, Baby Thumbprint 55.00
Amberina, Tumbler, Deep Fuchsia, Diamond-Quilted 95.00
Amberina, Tumbler, Diamond-Quilted, Enameled 100.00
Amberina, Tumbler, Diamond-Quilted, New England 65.00
Amberina, Tumbler, Diamond-Quilted, Thumbprint 95.00
Amberina, Tumbler, Expanded Diamond 85.00
Amberina, Tumbler, Expanded Diamond, Mt.Washington 70.00
Amberina, Tumbler, Fuchsia, Deep Color 95.00
Amberina, Tumbler, Fuchsia, Diamond-Quilted 95.00
Amberina, Tumbler, Fuchsia, Diamond-Quilted, Polished Pontil 75.00
Amberina, Tumbler, Fuchsia, Expanded Diamond, Ruby To Fuchsia To Amber 85.00
Amberina, Tumbler, Fuchsia, Inverted Thumbprint 40.00
Amberina, Tumbler, Fuchsia, Panels 74.50
Amberina, Tumbler, Fuchsia, Signed Libbey 140.00
Amberina, Tumbler, Fuchsia, Venetian Diamond 75.00
Amberina, Tumbler, Inverted Thumbprint 40.00
Amberina, Tumbler, Inverted Thumbprint, New England 88.00
Amberina, Tumbler, Juice, Overall Enameling 85.00
Amberina, Tumbler, New England, Thumbprint 85.00
Amberina, Tumbler, Optic Diamond Pattern 85.00
Amberina, Tumbler, Set Of 6 .... 390.00
Amberina, Tumbler, Swirls 37.50
Amberina, Tumbler, Venetian Diamond Pattern 85.00
Amberina, Vase, Applied Rigaree, New England Glass Co. 425.00
Amberina, Vase, Bud, Signed Libbey, 11 In.High 295.00
Amberina, Vase, Coin Spot Pattern, Blown, Petal Feet 85.00
Amberina, Vase, Fuchsia, Fluted Top, Signed Libbey 350.00
Amberina, Vase, Fuchsia, Ribbed, Three Pour Top, 9 In. 185.00
Amberina, Vase, Hobnails, Ruffled, Footed, 6 In.High 150.00
Amberina, Vase, Inverted Swirl, Enamel Pink & White Floral, Crimped Feet 115.00
Amberina, Vase, Inverted Thumbprint, Square Top, 6 3/4 In. 150.00

Amberina, Vase, Inverted Thumbprint, Violet, Bulbous, 5 1/2 In. 45.00
Amberina, Vase, Jack-In-The-Pulpit, Cranberry To Golden Amber, Footed, Pair 295.00
Amberina, Vase, Jack-In-The-Pulpit, Signed Libbey 285.00
Amberina, Vase, Lily, Fuchsia, Ribbed, 8 In. 250.00
Amberina, Vase, Lily, New England, Ribbing, Signed Reed & Barton Holder 135.00
Amberina, Vase, Lily, New England, 10 In.High 220.00
Amberina, Vase, Lily, Pair 495.00
Amberina, Vase, Lily, Vertical Ribs, Libbey, 10 In. 85.00
Amberina, Vase, Morning Glory, 5 1/2 In. 125.00
Amberina, Vase, Reversed, Raised Swirl, Clear Rigaree Trim 68.00
Amberina, Vase, Serpent Coiled Around Center, Footed, 10 In. 145.00
Amberina, Vase, Trumpet, Swirl, Cranberry To Golden Amber, Foot, Ribbed 210.00
Amberina, Vase, Tulip, Libbey, 11 In. 395.00
Amberina, Water Set, Amber Handle, 7 Piece 550.00
Amberina, Water Set, Applied Reeded Handle, 7 In.High, 5 Piece 200.00
Amberina, Water Set, Fuchsia, Swirl Ribs, Amberina Handle, 7 Piece 725.00
Amberina, Whiskey 125.00
American Crystal, see Collector, Plate
American Encaustic Tiling Co., Ashtray, N.Y., Green Frog 15.00

*Amethyst Glass is any of the many glasswares made in the proper dark purple
shade.It was a color popular after the Civil War.*

Amethyst Glass, Atomizer, Multicolor Enameling 36.00
Amethyst Glass, Bell, Glass Clapper, 5 1/2 In.High 37.50
Amethyst Glass, Bowl, Double Stem Rose, Scalloped Top, Footed, 4 In.High 38.00
Black Amethyst, Bowl, Fluted Top, 11 1/2 In.Diameter 25.00
Amethyst Glass, Bowl, Grape & Flower Design, Cut To Clear, 12 In.Diameter 45.00
Amethyst Glass, Bowl, Stretch, 9 1/2 In. 24.00
Amethyst Glass, Bowl, Three Fruit Pattern, 8 In.Diameter, 3 1/2 In.High 40.00
Amethyst Glass, Bowl, Water Lilies, Cattails, Crimp Fluted Scalloped Edge 39.50
Amethyst Glass, Box, Trinket, Gold Decoration 35.00
Amethyst Glass, Candleholder, Laced With 1/2 In.Gold Trim 19.00
Amethyst Glass, Candlestick, Stamped Gold Filigree Decorative Band, Pair 45.00
Amethyst Glass, Candlestick, Twisted Stem, Pair 30.00
Amethyst Glass, Candy, Cover, 9 In.High 15.00
Amethyst Glass, Cologne, Sandwich 75.00
Amethyst Glass, Compote, Controlled Bubbles, Frilly Rim 35.00
Amethyst Glass, Compote, Open 15.00
Amethyst Glass, Compote, Polished Pontil 15.00
Amethyst Glass, Creamer, Daisy & Button, Triangular 15.00
Amethyst Glass, Decanter, Bar, Stopper, Eight Panels Around Side 160.00
Amethyst Glass, Decanter, Blown, Clear Stopper, 5 Cordials 20.00
Amethyst Glass, Decanter, Wine, Raised Grapes & Leaves, Matching Stopper 10.00
Amethyst Glass, Dish, Hen On Nest Cover, White Head 27.50
Amethyst Glass, Dish, Stretch Glass, Iridescent, Hat Shape 20.00
Amethyst Glass, Finger Bowl 4.00
Amethyst Glass, Hatchet, Embossed Indian's Head, Beading, 7 1/4 In.Long 24.00
Amethyst Glass, Inkwell, Hinged Lid, 8 Sided 40.00
Amethyst Glass, Inkwell, Paneled, Spout, Brass Lid, Pittsburgh 230.00
Amethyst Glass, Jug, Claret, Pink & White Enamel Floral, Art Nouveau Top 125.00
Amethyst Glass, Mug, Child's, George Washington & Lafayette 40.00
Amethyst Glass, Mug, Commemorative, Washington & Lafayette 35.00
Amethyst Glass, Perfume, Pink & Green Enameling, Stemmed, 6 1/4 In. 22.50
Amethyst Glass, Pitcher & Bowl Set, Enameled Flowers 65.00
Amethyst Glass, Pitcher, Applied Handle, Purple, 9 1/2 In.High 275.00
Amethyst Glass, Plate, Octagon, 10 In.Diameter 4.50
Amethyst Glass, Plate, Opalescent, Pond, Lilies, Scalloped, 11 In.Diameter 10.00
Amethyst Glass, Plate, Two Handles, 10 1/2 In.Diameter 15.00
Amethyst Glass, Rose Bowl, Dutch Girl Pouring Water, Ground Pontil, Ribbed 115.00
Amethyst Glass, Sauce, Diamond-Quilted 9.50
Amethyst Glass, Shot Glass, 2 Oz. 5.00
Amethyst Glass, Spooner, Pink & Blue Enamel Floral 18.00
Amethyst Glass, Sugar & Creamer, Footed, Salesman's Sample, 2 3/4 In. 15.00
Amethyst Glass, Tumbler, Enameled Daisies 25.00
Amethyst Glass, Vase, White Enameling, Hand Blown 23.50
Amethyst Glass, Wine Set, Enamel Floral, 7 Piece 48.00

Amethyst Glass, Wine Set, Farber Chrome Holders, 7 Piece 55.00
   Amphora, see Teplitz
   Andiron, many related fireplace items are under Fire
Ansbach, Cup & Saucer, Miniature, C.1770 .... *Illus* 250.00
   Apothecary jar, see Bottle
   Apple Peeler, see Kitchen, Peeler, Apple
Argy Rousseau, Box, Covered, Raised Floral, Yellow, Orange, & Brown, Signed 450.00
Argy Rousseau, Compote, Swans, Spread Wings, Signed, 4 In.High 375.00

Art Deco or Art Moderne is a style started at the Paris Exposition
of 1925. All types of furniture, and decorative arts, jewelry, bookbindings, and
even games, were designed in this style.

Art Deco, Ashtray, Harlequin Figure Seated, Legs Spread, Porcelain 12.50
Art Deco, Ashtray, Marble, Green, Afghan Hound On Top 15.00
Art Deco, Ashtray, Marble, Lizard Lying On Top, Free Form 12.50
Art Deco, Bookend, Bronzed White Metal, Female Nudes, Pair 20.00
Art Deco, Bookend, Fantail Pigeon, Bronze, Marble, G.Garreau, Pair 120.00
Art Deco, Bookend, Reclining Nude, Flowing Hair, Brass, Pair 45.00
Art Deco, Bottle, Charcoal Gray, 5 In. 17.50
Art Deco, Bowl, Black Glass Rim, Frieze Of Lions At Center, D'Avensen, 1930 .... 150.00
Art Deco, Box, Cigarette, Sterling, Rectangular, Chased, Georg Jensen, C.1930 .... 425.00
Art Deco, Box, Covered, Round, Wiener Werkstatte, Josef Hoffman, C.1920, Pair 1050.00
Art Deco, Calendar, Perpetual, Brass, Ivory, Dated 23.50
Art Deco, Candelabrum, White, Ceramic, Nude Dancer, Blythe, Circa 1920 .... 16.00
Art Deco, Case & Lighter, Cigarette, Sterling, Green & Black Enamel 65.00
Art Deco, Case, Cigarette, Silver, Gold, & Enamel, Black, Starr, & Frost, C.1925 .... 400.00
Art Deco, Case, Cigarette, Sterling, Green Enamel, Sun Ray Motif 125.00
Art Deco, Centerpiece, Mottled Glass, Iron, 8 1/2 In. .... *Illus* 225.00
Art Deco, Chandelier, Chrome & Milk Glass, Round, 7 Pendants, Brandt, C.1930 .... 650.00
Art Deco, Compact On Chain, Silver, Enamel, Square 7.50
Art Deco, Compact, Embossed, Filigree, Green Enamel, Sterling 12.50
Art Deco, Compact, French, Gold, Rectangular, Enamel, Diamonds, Cartier, C.1930 ...... 400.00
Art Deco, Compact, Miniature, French, Gold, Enamel Oriental Scene, C.1920 .... 275.00
Art Deco, Figurine, Champagne Lady, Bronze, Ivory, F.Preiss, C.1930 .... 900.00
Art Deco, Figurine, Dancing Female Nude, Bronze, Ivory, D.Chiparus, C.1920 .... 1600.00
Art Deco, Figurine, Dancing Girl, Bronze, Ivory Hands & Face, 9 In.High 175.00
Art Deco, Figurine, Dancing Lady, Ivory & Bronze, Signed, C.1920, 15 In.High 375.00
Art Deco, Figurine, Egyptian Woman, Seated, Glass Paperweight In Lap, Metal 25.00
Art Deco, Figurine, Female Bareback Rider, Composition, Archipenko, C.1935 .... 3000.00
Art Deco, Figurine, Girl In Grecian Dress, Bronze, Marble, Chiparus, C.1930 .... 250.00
Art Deco, Figurine, Girl In Sailor Suit, Bronze, Lucite, Lorenzl, C.1935 .... 100.00
Art Deco, Figurine, Horse & Rider, Silver Bronze, Ivory, La Faquays, C.1925 .... 850.00
Art Deco, Figurine, Kneeling Nude Female, Bronze, J.Martel, C.1925 .... 450.00
Art Deco, Figurine, Little Confidence, Italian Obsidian, Shonnard, C.1920 .... 200.00
Art Deco, Figurine, Nude Female Jumping Rope, Bronze, Marble, A.Doni, C.1930 .... 100.00
Art Deco, Figurine, Semidraped, Turban & Beads, Bronze, Marble, Allman, C.1935 .... 550.00
Art Deco, Figurine, Siamese Dancer, Bronze, Ivory Hands, Face, Onyx Base 250.00
Art Deco, Figurine, Silvered Bronze, C.1930, 27 In.Long .... *Illus* 600.00
Art Deco, Figurine, Spanish Dancing Girl, Ivory Over Metal, Onyx Base 22.50
Art Deco, Figurine, Two Deer, Pottery, Cream Glaze, French Artist 56.00
Art Deco, Figurine, Woman, Opaque Glass, Holds Gown, Signed Etling, France 115.00
Art Deco, Flower Frog, Dancing Lady In Hoop, Isadora Duncan Type, Porcelain 18.00
Art Deco, Group, Young Woman, 2 Greyhounds, D.H.Chiparus, Marble Base 225.00
Art Deco, Lamp Base, Fluted Column, Flower Form, Bronze White Metal, 14 In. 16.00
Art Deco, Lamp Base, Mottle Orange Onyx Column, Harp Finial, Metal, 15 In. 20.00
Art Deco, Lamp Base, Ram Heads, Laurel Wreath, Harp Finial, 17 In. 15.00
Art Deco, Lamp, Bronze Nude, Controlled Bubble Impregnated Ball 35.00
Art Deco, Lamp, Dancing Girl, Ivory Face, Black Base, Metal 15.00
Art Deco, Lamp, Desk, Gooseneck, Embossed Flower Form Base 9.00
Art Deco, Lamp, Frosted Glass, Dancing Couple, Metal Filigree Beaded Shade 20.00
Art Deco, Lamp, Reclining Maiden Holds Amber Globe, Metal, 13 X 14 In.Long 37.50
Art Deco, Lamp, Table, Three Nudes, Bronzed Metal, Hold Globe Shade, 13 In. 80.00
Art Deco, Lamp, Two Nudes Hold Pink Satin Ball Shade, Dated 1927 .... 49.00
Art Deco, Lighter, Cigarette, Agate, Quadrangular, Gray, 4 Cabochon Sapphires 220.00
Art Deco, Lighter, Cigarette, Sterling, Green Enamel, Dunhill 65.00
Art Deco, Luminiere, Bronzed Metal & Glass, Hexagonal, Cameo Cut Diana, Deer 70.00

Art Deco, Mannequin Head, Frosted Glass, Young Man, Metal Mount, 13 In. 150.00
Art Deco, Perfume, Atomizer, Black Enamel, Geometric, Cut Glass, Steel Base 12.00
Art Deco, Perfume, Crystal, 6 In.High 45.00
Art Deco, Perfume, Opaque Black, Crystal Stopper 12.00
Art Deco, Tea Set, Rattan Handles, M.Daurat, C.1925, 3 Piece 850.00
Art Deco, Vase, Beaker Form, Cut Moose On Acid Etched, F.R.Karhula, C.1935 .... 200.00
Art Deco, Vase, Blue, 1925, 7 In.High 22.00
Art Deco, Vase, Bulbous, Gold Glass, 5 In.High 17.50
Art Deco, Vase, Mottled Glass, Iron, 12 In.High .... *Illus* 300.00

Ansbach, Cup & Saucer,
Miniature, C.1770
See Page 10

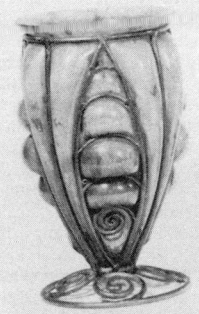

Art Deco, Vase,
Mottled Glass, Iron, 12 In.High

Art Deco, Centerpiece,
Mottled Glass, Iron, 8 1/2 In.
See Page 10

Art Deco, Figurine,
Silvered Bronze,
C.1930, 27 In.Long
See Page 10

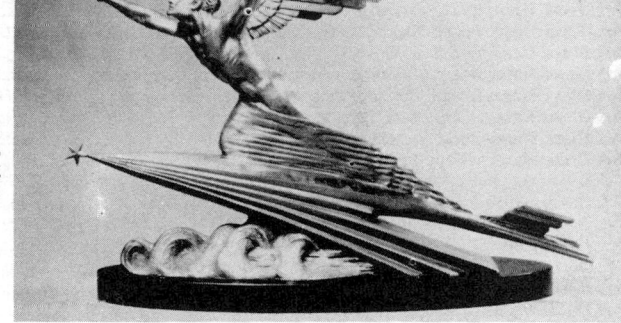

Art Deco, Vase, Ovoid, Allover Butterflies, Punchwork Ground, Signed 50.00
Art Deco, Vase, Pyriform, Coral Glaze, Deer, Jean Mayodon, 1926 .... 200.00
Art Deco, Vase, Tapering, Classical Figures Frieze, G.Defeure, C.1925, Pair 100.00

> *Art Glass means any of the many forms of glassware made during the late
> nineteenth century or early twentieth century.These wares were expensive and
> made in limited production.Art Glass is not the typical commercial
> glassware that was made in large quantities, and most of the Art Glass was
> produced by hand methods.*

Art Glass, see also Schneider, Nash
Art Glass, see also separate headings such as Burmese, etc.
Art Glass, Basket, Aqua Crimped Top, Vaseline Applied Handle 225.00
Art Glass, Basket, Frosted, Applied Red Cherries 120.00
Art Glass, Basket, Medium Blue Interior, Frilly Rim, Glass Loop Handle 49.00
Art Glass, Basket, Miniature, Ruffled Butterscotch Interior, White Exterior 30.00
Art Glass, Basket, Miniature, Ruffled Rose Interior, White Exterior 25.00
Art Glass, Basket, Opaque White, Applied Amber Leaves, Pink Fruit, Crimped 100.00

Art Glass, Basket, Pink Overlay, White Hobnail, Amber Border, Pink Lining 55.00
Art Glass, Basket, Speckled Mica, Twisted Clear Handle, White Luster, Ruffle 98.00
Art Glass, Basket, Yellow, Orange, Clear Overlay, Twisted Handle 47.50
Art Glass, Bowl, Davidson, Brown Swirls, 9 In. 30.00
Art Glass, Bowl, Elongated Fleur-De-Lis, Clover Leaf Opening, Gold Lining 110.00
Art Glass, Bowl, Honesdale-Type, Emerald Green, Gold, Floral 60.00
Art Glass, Bowl, Ruffled Rim, Cranberry Opalescent, Applied Feet, Flint 65.00
Art Glass, Bowl, Tangerine & Cobalt, French, 9 X 6 In. 35.00
Art Glass, Bowl, Yellow, Opaque, Rose Edge, Hobbs, Brockunier Co., Wheeling 135.00
Art Glass, Compote, Cranberry To Clear, Teardrop In Stem, France, 15 In.High 150.00
Art Glass, Cruet, Vinegar, Blue, Clear Handle & Stopper 47.50
Art Glass, Cruet, Vinegar, Deep Blue, Clear Stopper & Handle 50.00
Art Glass, Ewer, Three Layer, Applied Handle, English, C.1860 .... 90.00
Art Glass, Hat, Turned Down Crimped Top, Applied Pink, Threaded Bow, 6 In. 24.00
Art Glass, Inkwell, Purple, Iridescent, Hinged Top, Square Shape 80.00
Art Glass, Jar, Powder, Green Glass, Enamel Floral, Gold, Hinged Cover 75.00
Art Glass, Light Shade, Frosted To Purple, Signed Rothodes, France, Pair 45.00
Art Glass, Muffineer, Blown, Silver Top, Amethyst, C.1860 .... 60.00
Art Glass, Muffineer, Blown, Vertical Striations, 3 Color, Silver Top 55.00
Art Glass, Pitcher, Pink Shading To Pale Yellow, Ruffled Top, Reed Handle 55.00
Art Glass, Pitcher, Yellow To Pink Top, Applied Reeded Handle 45.00
Art Glass, Salt, Cranberry, Trefoil Top, Vaseline Ruffles & Berry Prunt 40.00
Art Glass, Shade For Lamp, Pink, Rib, Glass Petals Around Edge, 4 1/4 In. 13.50
Art Glass, Shade, Frosted, Mottled Blue, Apricot, Signed G.V.Croismare, Pair 55.00
Art Glass, Shade, Luster, Butterscotch Snakeskin On White, Signed, Pair 110.00
Art Glass, Shade, White, Iridescent & Opalescent, 5 1/4 In. 8.00
Art Glass, Shaker, Salt, Ribbed Spiral, Blue Opalescent 24.00
Art Glass, Tumbler, Rainbow, Three Colors, Floral Decoration 950.00
Art Glass, Urn, Gold Iridescent, Applied Blue Iridescent Handles, Rim 58.00
Art Glass, Vase, Amethyst To Clear, Gold Enamel, Threads, 12 1/4 In., Pair 75.00
Art Glass, Vase, Drag Loop, Green, Gold, Orange, Iridescent, 6 1/2 In.High 175.00
Art Glass, Vase, Orange, Molded Star Base, Square, 4 3/4 In.High 22.50
Art Glass, Vase, Orange, Pink, Green, Ornate Brass Frame & Foot, Lorranz 70.00
Art Glass, Vase, Overlay, Amber Ruffled Top, Pink Interior, Enameled 65.00
Art Glass, Vase, Purple Swirls, Green Iridescent, Pair 185.00
Art Glass, Vase, Red Swirl On Pink, Five Glass Feet, Cased, 4 1/2 In.High 65.00
Art Glass, Vase, Rubena Verde Coloring, 5 1/2 In. 25.00
Art Glass, Vase, Signed Carillo, France, 5 In.High 100.00
Art Glass, Vase, Stick, Loetz Type, Iridescent Green, Red, Purple, 8 1/2 In. 100.00
Art Glass, Vase, Stick, Signed Deley, French, 16 In.High 60.00
Art Glass, Vase, Tiffany Style, Pastel, Crystal, Oval, Pulpit Top 27.00

Art Nouveau, a style characterized by free-flowing organic design, reached
its zenith between 1895 and 1905. The style encompassed all decorative and
functional arts from architecture to furniture and posters.
Art Nouveau, see also Glass, Furniture, etc.
Art Nouveau, see also Royal Dux, Schneider, Faberge
Art Nouveau, Ashtray, Nudes On Frosted Glass, Pierced Brass Trim, Footed 30.00
Art Nouveau, Basket, Bonbon, Silver, 3 In.High 5.00
Art Nouveau, Bookend, Dancing Girl, Metal, Pair 22.50
Art Nouveau, Bookend, Flowers, Roycroft, Signed, Pair 16.00
Art Nouveau, Bookend, Nude Girl Stands In Pond, Frog, Bronzed Metal, Pair 45.00
Art Nouveau, Bookend, Sliding, Mahogany, Sterling End, Pair 22.50
Art Nouveau, Bowl, Free Form, Cobalt, Silver Mica, Applied Pewter Floral 110.00
Art Nouveau, Bowl, Iridescent, Rectangular, Blue & Amber, 9 1/2 In.Long 70.00
Art Nouveau, Box, Jewel, Metal, Beveled Glass Top, Miniature Portrait 10.00
Art Nouveau, Box, Jewel, Signed B. & W. 8.00
Art Nouveau, Box, Jewel, Victorian, Dutch Girl, Windmill, Brass, Hinged, Footed 18.50
Art Nouveau, Buckle, Embossed Work, Three Different Sets 16.00
Art Nouveau, Buckle, Flowing Floral Work, Cherub 7.50
Art Nouveau, Buckle, Flowing Floral Work, Flaming Urns & Wings 7.50
Art Nouveau, Buckle, Silver 15.00
Art Nouveau, Candlestick, Floral, Metal-Gilt, Footed, 7 1/2 In.High, Pair 25.00
Art Nouveau, Cane Handle, Figural, Lady's Head, Silver 10.00
Art Nouveau, Casket, Jewel, Bronze, Velvet Lined 35.00
Art Nouveau, Chest, Jewel, Brass, Lined 250.00

Art Nouveau, **Compote**, Crystal, Paperweight Base, Teardrop In Base, Kosta 29.00
Art Nouveau, **Desk Set**, Bronze, 5 Piece 45.00
Art Nouveau, **Dish**, Soap, Nude 16.50
Art Nouveau, **Figurine**, Old Man, Chinese, Brass, 7 1/4 In.Tall 60.00
Art Nouveau, **Flower Frog**, Dancing Nude With Drape, Porcelain, Germany, 9 In. 25.00
Art Nouveau, **Flower Holder**, Draped Nude Figure, Green Glass, 8 1/2 In.High 30.00
Art Nouveau, **Frame**, Floral, Ivory Color, Metal, 10 1/2 In.High 32.00
Art Nouveau, **Lamp**, Basket, Beaded White Crystal Top, Covered Colored Fruit 150.00
Art Nouveau, **Lamp**, Bronze, Nude Dancing With Drape, Camphor Flame Globe 35.00
Art Nouveau, **Lamp**, Desk, Woman Figure, Signed, Art Glass Shade 110.00
Art Nouveau, **Lamp**, Draped Woman Holds Frosted Shade, Bronze, Marble Base 80.00
Art Nouveau, **Lamp**, Gilt Nymph Supports Pedestal With Globe Of Cased Glass 37.50
Art Nouveau, **Lamp**, Perfume, Mottled Orange & Yellow, Bronze Base, Rouj Paris 125.00
Art Nouveau, **Lamp**, Table, Iris Decoration, Pairpoint, 1i In.X 21 In.High 450.00
Art Nouveau, **Mirror**, Hand, Evangeline, Sterling, Unger Bros., Woman 125.00
Art Nouveau, **Nail File**, Sterling Silver, Flowing-Haired Maiden, Flowers 10.00
Art Nouveau, **Necklace**, 14k Gold Pendant Set With 5 1/2 Carat Peridot 275.00
Art Nouveau, **Paper Clip**, Full Figure Woman, Iron, 3 1/2 In. 12.00
Art Nouveau, **Pen**, Ink, Waterman, 14k Gold 125.00
Art Nouveau, **Perfume**, Lalique Type, Embossed Mistletoe 18.50
Art Nouveau, **Pitcher**, Water, Raised Applied Iris, Beading, Scrolled, 1890 .... 29.50
Art Nouveau, **Plaque**, Bronze, Profile Of Young Girl, Signed C.Flamand, 1904 .... 150.00
Art Nouveau, **Plate**, Bronze, Sterling Wreath Overlay, 6 In. 16.00
Art Nouveau, **Purse**, Coin, Sterling, 14k Rose & Yellow Gold Inlay, Bracelet 35.00
Art Nouveau, **Serving Set**, Amston Sterling, 9 In., 2 Piece 39.00
Art Nouveau, **Shade**, Lamp, Slag, Metal 75.00
Art Nouveau, **Statuette**, Nude Dancing Female, Gilt Metal, 21 In.High 100.00
Art Nouveau, **Tazza**, Bronze, 8 In. 55.00
Art Nouveau, **Tray**, Crumb, Brush, Embossed Women's Heads, Flowing Hair, Brass 45.00
Art Nouveau, **Tray**, Pewter, Flowing Lady, Iris & Leaves 125.00
Art Nouveau, **Tray**, Pewterlike Finish, Woman With Flowing Hair 12.50
Art Nouveau, **Tray**, Pin, Bronze, Signed Gurschner Vienne, Sleeping Maiden 300.00
Art Nouveau, **Tray**, Pin, Shell Shape, Bronze Plated 10.50
Art Nouveau, **Vase**, Blue Ground, Flapper's Face In Gold Cartouche, Huebach 62.50
Art Nouveau, **Vase**, Brass, Flower Design, 2 Handle, 10 3/4 In.Tall 22.50
Art Nouveau, **Vase**, Bronze, Sterling Floral Overlay, 1912, 6 1/4 In.High 37.00
Art Nouveau, **Vase**, Cabinet, Hornberg, Flapper's Head In Gold Filigree 65.00
Art Nouveau, **Vase**, Draped Nudes, White Cased, 15 In. 75.00
Art Nouveau, **Vase**, Enamel Decor, Clear To Amethyst, Blown, Pair 85.00
Art Nouveau, **Vase**, Floral, Leaves, Brown With Gold Crosshatching At Base 35.00
Art Nouveau, **Vase**, Gilt Bronze, Signed A.Makionne, Chased Floral, 8 1/2 In. 80.00
Art Nouveau, **Vase**, Girl's Portrait, Double Handled, Chocolate & Cream Tones 65.00
Art Nouveau, **Vase**, Green Satin Glass, Silver Overlay Of Berries & Leaves 55.00
Art Nouveau, **Vase**, Inscribed Hawkes, Sterling Base Impressed Gorhams 1857 .... 100.00
Art Nouveau, **Vase**, Open Flower With Buds, Ornate, Bronze, 6 1/2 In.High 65.00
Art Nouveau, **Vase**, Pottery, Gilt Bronze, Lamarre, 1898 .... *Illus* 2100.00
Art Nouveau, **Vase**, Pottery, Urn Shape, Contiguous Mythological Handles 200.00
Art Nouveau, **Vase**, Rubina Satin Glass, Overlay Silver Iris, 10 1/2 In.High 75.00

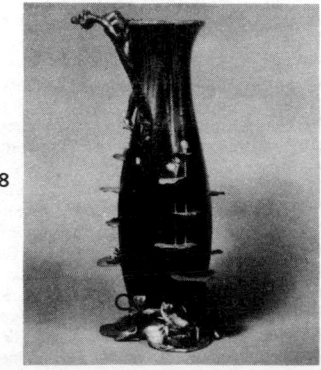

Art Nouveau, Vase, Pottery, Gilt Bronze, Lamarre, 1898

Art Nouveau, Vase, Shape Woman's Head, Flowing Hair, Green Porcelain, Bronze 125.00
Art Nouveau, Vase, Silver Deposit, Leaf Motifs, Dark Green, 13 3/4 In. 150.00
Art Nouveau, Vase, Sterling On Bronze, Pat.Aug.27, '12, 6 In.High 25.00
Art Nouveau, Vase, Sterling Silver, Porcelain Base, Child, Dragonflies 37.50

Aurene Glass was made by Frederick Carder of New York about 1904. AURENE
It is an iridescent gold glass, usually marked Aurene or Steuben.

Aurene, see also Steuben
Aurene, Atomizer, Blue, Unsigned Steuben 150.00
Aurene, Atomizer, Iridescent, Devilbiss, Steuben, Blue Finial, 10 In. 160.00
Aurene, Basket, Gold, Signed, Numbered, Paper Label, 7 X 7 1/2 In.High 595.00
Aurene, Bowl & Underplate, Finger, Gold, Signed 195.00
Aurene, Bowl, Blue, Fully Signed 395.00
Aurene, Bowl, Blue, No.2687, Signed, 12 In. 450.00
Aurene, Bowl, Blue, Signed, 13 1/2 In. .... 295.00 To 450.00
Aurene, Bowl, Flared, 6 In.Diameter 110.00
Aurene, Bowl, Folded In Rim, Blue, Footed, Shallow, 2 In.High, 7 In.Wide 285.00
Aurene, Bowl, Gold Iridescent, Flaring, Pedestal, 5 In.Tall, 12 In.Diameter 175.00
Aurene, Bowl, Gold Iridescent, Rolled Over Edges, Signed, 1i In. 275.00
Aurene, Bowl, Gold, Calcite, Rolled Edge, 8 In. 75.00
Aurene, Bowl, Green Gold, Blue & Rose Highlights, Signed 185.00
Aurene, Bowl, On Calcite, Curved Sides, Steuben, 12 X 5 In.High 195.00
Aurene, Bowl, On Calcite, Curved Sides, 1i In. 195.00
Aurene, Bowl, On Calcite, Steuben, 12 1/2 In. 150.00
Aurene, Bowl, Pair Candlesticks, Blue, Steuben, Signed 950.00
Aurene, Bowl, 7 3/4 In.Diameter 120.00
Aurene, Candlestick, Futuristic Shape, Signed, 4 In.High 125.00
Aurene, Candlestick, Gold, Twisted, Signed, 9 In.High, Pair 395.00
Aurene, Champagne, Gold, Swirl, Signed 195.00
Aurene, Cologne, Blue, Iridescent, Steeple Stopper 450.00
Aurene, Compote, Gold, Signed 175.00
Aurene, Console Set, Blue, Bowl, Pair Candlesticks, Signed 1095.00
Aurene, Cordial, Gold, Blue Highlights, Pedestal Base, Signed, No.2827 .... 110.00
Aurene, Cordial, Gold, Blue Iridized, Signed 145.00
Aurene, Cup & Saucer, Demitasse, Gold, Iridescent, Pink & Blue Highlights 295.00
Aurene, Darner, Blue, One Mottled Area, Steuben, 7 In.Long 100.00
Aurene, Darner, Stocking, Blue 110.00
Aurene, Dish, Centerpiece, Signed, 1 1/2 X 10 1/4 In.Diameter 110.00
Aurene, Dish, Flared, Scalloped, Purple, Red, Signed, 3 In.High 145.00
Aurene, Dish, Gold, Amethyst Highlights, Ruffled, 5 In. 145.00
Aurene, Goblet, Gold Satin Ground, Blue, Purple, Green Iridescent 135.00
Aurene, Goblet, Gold, Twisted Stem, Blue Highlights 135.00
Aurene, Goblet, Gold, Twisted Stem, Multicolor Highlights, Steuben, 6 In. 250.00
Aurene, Lamp, Buffet, Gold Iridescent, Trumpet Shade, Gold Base, 15 In., Pair 185.00
Aurene, Perfume, Gold Iridescence, 7 1/2 In.High 75.00
Aurene, Perfume, Gold, Mushroom Shape Stopper, Steuben, 6 In.High 350.00
Aurene, Perfume, Melon Rib, Gold, Blue Highlights, Signed & Numbered 210.00
Aurene, Perfume, Melon Shape, Gold, Signed, Stopper 210.00
Aurene, Rose Bowl, Blue, Signed 225.00
Aurene, Rose Bowl, Platinum & Green, Signed, 2 1/4 In.High 450.00
Aurene, Salt, Gold, Open, Signed 95.00
Aurene, Salt, Steuben, Pedestal 95.00
Aurene, Shade, Brown, Applied Silvery Band, Brown & White Rickrack, Signed 125.00
Aurene, Shade, Gold, Ruffled Top, Pink Highlights, 7 1/2 In.Diameter 55.00
Aurene, Sherbet, Gold, Blue Iridescence, Twist Stem, Steuben 125.00
Aurene, Sherbet, Gold, Multicolor Highlights, Underplate, Steuben 325.00
Aurene, Urn, Blue, Footed, 7 In.High 475.00
Aurene, Urn, Blue, Two Handles, Steuben, 12 In.High 650.00
Aurene, Vase, Applied Chrysanthemumlike Flower & Stem, Blue, 6 In. 65.00
Aurene, Vase, Blue Iridescent, Paneled, Flaring Rim, Signed, 5 1/4 In. 325.00
Aurene, Vase, Blue Iridescent, Ribs, Sterling Silver, Art Nouveau Holder 175.00
Aurene, Vase, Blue Iridescent, Signed, 10 In.High 325.00
Aurene, Vase, Blue, Gold Iridescent, Silver Iridescent Lining, Ruffled 245.00
Aurene, Vase, Blue, Ribbed Shade Type, Peacock Color, Signed 275.00
Aurene, Vase, Blue, Ribbed, Signed & Numbered .... 225.00 To 275.00
Aurene, Vase, Blue, Ribbed, Silver Holder, 9 In.High 175.00

Aurene, Vase, Blue, Ribbed, Vibrant Peacock Color, Signed, Steuben 225.00
Aurene, Vase, Blue, Ruffled Top, Round Base, Steuben, 10 In.High 425.00
Aurene, Vase, Blue, Signed, 7 In.High 250.00
Aurene, Vase, Blue, Three Stems, Signed & Numbered, Steuben 350.00
Aurene, Vase, Bud, Blue, Flared Lip, Signed, Numbered, 10 1/2 In. 200.00
Aurene, Vase, Bud, Gold Iridescent, Dolphin Holder, 9 3/4 In.High 125.00
Aurene, Vase, Bud, 8 In.High 85.00
Aurene, Vase, Gold, Bowl Shape, Steuben, 6 In. 300.00
Aurene, Vase, Gold, Bulbous, 4 In.High, 2 1/2 In.Wide 185.00
Aurene, Vase, Gold, Green Hooked Feathers, 2 1/2 In. 450.00
Aurene, Vase, Gold, Iridescent Blue & Lavender Shades, Corset Shape 195.00
Aurene, Vase, Gold, Red Purple Highlights, Steuben, 3 In. 135.00
Aurene, Vase, Gold, Ribbed, Signed, 6 In.High 110.00
Aurene, Vase, Lily, Blue, Purple, Gold, Signed, Numbered, 10 In.High 250.00
Aurene, Vase, Lily, Ivrene, Signed 500.00
Aurene, Vase, Signed, Steuben, 3 X 2 3/4 In.High 195.00
Aurene, Vase, Stick, Blue, Gold, Signed, No.2556, 10 In. 195.00
Aurene, Vase, Stick, Blue, Gold Iridescent, Serrated Top Edge 124.00
Aurene, Vase, Stick, Gold, Signed, Numbered, 8 In. 75.00
Aurene, Vase, Tapered Body, Flared Top, Steuben, Unsigned, 10 In. 235.00
Aurene, Vase, Three Stump, Gold, Purple, Blues, Greens, Signed, Steuben 150.00
Aurene, Wine, Blue & Gold Iridescent, Signed 110.00
Aurene, Wine, Gold & Blue Iridescent 75.00
Austria, see Royal Dux, Kauffmann, Porcelain

Auto parts and accessories are collectors' items today.
Auto, Boyce Moto Meter, Chevrolet 12.00
Auto, Carrier, Running Board, Luggage, Folding 15.00
Auto, Carrier, Running Board, Model T 10.00
Auto, Dash With Speedometer, Model A 10.00
Auto, Defroster, Alcohol Lamp, For Windshield, Tin, Glass Bottle, 1920s 6.00
Auto, Gauge, Tire, Shrader 4.00
Auto, Headlight, 1929 Lasalle, Mounted, Tie Bar, Mounting Bar, Brackets 285.00
Auto, Hood Ornament, Greyhound, 9 1/2 In.Long 15.00
Auto, Horn, Arooga, Crank Type, 1905 .... 22.00
Auto, Horn, Brass, C.1918 .... 85.00
Auto, Horn, Brass, Rubber Squeeze Ball 35.00
Auto, Horn, Hand Crank, Claxton, Seiss Co., Toledo, Pat.1914 .... 15.00
Auto, Horn, Klazon 17.50
Auto, Knob For Gear Shift, Marked Ford, Dallas, Star, 1836-1936 .... 10.00
Auto, Lamp, Cadillac, Brass 45.00
Auto, Lamp, Model T, Kerosene, Clear Bullet Lens 22.50
Auto, Lamp, Side, Kerosene, Ford, Model T 12.50
Auto, Lamp, Side, Square, Rounded Top & Bottom, C.1915, 12 1/2 In.High, Pair 125.00
Auto, Lamp, Solar 25.00
Auto, Lantern, Kerosene, Black Paint, Red Reflector, Dated 1909 .... 35.00
Auto, Lantern, Oil Burner, Beveled Glasses, For Ford, Patent 1908, 10 1/2 In. 45.00
Auto, License Plate, Alaska, 1968, The Great Land Motto, Set 2.50
Auto, License Plate, Connecticut, 1924 .... 3.00
Auto, License Plate, Indiana, 1913 To 1970 .... 170.00
Auto, License Plate, New Hampshire, 1917, Porcelain 8.50
Auto, License Plate, New Hampshire, 1919 .... 5.00
Auto, License Plate, Pennsylvania, 1913, Porcelain, Keystone Tag 15.00
Auto, Luggage Rack, For Running Board, Folding 15.00
Auto, Meter, Motor, American Lafrance, Boyce 12.00
Auto, Ornament Cap, Bird, Hudson 12.00
Auto, Ornament Cap, Flying Lady, Hupmobile, Circa 1920 .... 18.00
Auto, Ornament Cap, Indian, Pontiac 22.00
Auto, Ornament Cap, Mermaid, DeSoto 15.00
Auto, Ornament Cap, Ram, Dodge 20.00
Auto, Rack, Luggage, For Running Board, Model T Ford 7.50
Auto, Radiator Cap, Boyce Ford Thermometer, With Wings 15.00
Auto, Radiator Cap, Eagle 20.00
Auto, Radiator Cap, Flying Ram From 1932 Dodge 15.00
Auto, Radiator Cap, Indian Head From Pontiac 15.00
Auto, Radiator Cap, Maxwell 10.00

Auto, **Radiator Cap**, Model T, Boyce Motometer 15.00
Auto, **Radiator Name Plate**, Maxwell 6.00
Auto, **Radiator Name Plate**, Oakland 8.50
Auto, **Sidelight**, Cadillac, Electric, Brass, 7 In., Pair 65.00
Auto, **Trouble Spotlight Combination**, Model T Ford 12.00
Auto, **Vase**, Clear 5.00
Auto, **Vase**, Pewterlike Metal, Bracket To Attach 7.00
Auto, **Wrench**, 'Ford' In Script 2.00
Aventurine, Syrup, Green 300.00
Aventurine, Tumbler, Blue, White Cased 35.00
Aventurine, Vase, Chrome Green, Tricorner Top 200.00
Aventurine, Vase, Red, Silver Deposit, 7 1/2 In.High 100.00
   Avon, see Bottle, Avon
Baby Carriage, Wicker, C.1870 .... 75.00
Baby Carriage, Wicker, Ornate 195.00

Baccarat Glass was made in France by La Compagnie des
Cristalleries de Baccarat, located about 150 miles from Paris. The
factory was started in 1765. The firm went bankrupt and began operating about
1822. Famous Cane and Millefiori paperweights were made there during the
1860-1880 period. The firm is still working near Paris making paperweights
and glasswares.

Baccarat Type, Syrup, Swirl, Bulbous, Clear, Notched Handle, Silver Top 25.00
Baccarat, Bobeche, Crystal, Square 7.00
Baccarat, Bottle, Diamond Point Swirl, Rose Teinte, Set Of 4 Graduated 75.00
Baccarat, Bottle, Dresser, Amberina, Swirl Pattern, 5 1/2 In.High 34.50
Baccarat, Bottle, Dresser, Amberina, 5 1/2 In.High 37.50
Baccarat, Bottle, Rubina Swirl, Stopper, 7 In.High 32.00
Baccarat, Bottle, Scent, Barrel Shape, Stopper 17.50
Baccarat, Bottle, Scent, Hexagon, Cut Stopper 15.00
Baccarat, Bottle, Scent, Turtle Shape, Frosted Sides, Cut Stopper 15.00
Baccarat, Bowl, Amberina Swirl Pattern, Fluted & Rolled Edge, 6 1/2 In. 35.00
Baccarat, Bowl, Amberina Swirl Pattern, Signed, 6 1/4 In.Diameter 37.50
Baccarat, Bowl, Engraved Daisies, Leaves, Gold, 9 1/2 In. X 4 1/2 In.High 35.00
Baccarat, Bowl, Salad, Star Swirl, Copper Rim, 7 In. 57.50
Baccarat, Candelabrum, Swirl Crystal, Prisms, 4 Candle 225.00
Baccarat, Candleholder, Electric Blue, Signed, 6 X 1 3/4 In.High 20.00
Baccarat, Candlestick, Swirl, Crystal, Flint, Signed, 8 In.High, Pair 42.00
Baccarat, Candlestick, Ten Prisms On Bobeche, Pair 120.00
Baccarat, Cologne, Cobalt, Bowtie Shape, Signed 30.00
Baccarat, Cologne, Cranberry, Gold Edging & Trim, Cut Faceted Stopper, Label ... 45.00
Baccarat, Cologne, Pink Swirls 15.00
Baccarat, Cologne, Sapphire Blue Swirl, Stopper 38.00
Baccarat, Compote, Amberina Swirl, Signed 30.00
Baccarat, Compote, Crystal, Bronze Lady Stem, Bronze Foot, By Renaud 135.00
Baccarat, Compote, Diagonal Block Pattern, Amber, Signed, 1890, Open 138.50
Baccarat, Compote, Green, Swirled, Signed 18.50
Baccarat, Compote, Swirls, Aqua, Scalloped Rim, Signed 28.00
Baccarat, Decanter, Clear, Swirl, Gold Trim, Stopper 40.00
Baccarat, Decanter, Etched Design, Signed, 14 In. 60.00
Baccarat, Decanter, Oval Cutting, Blown Stopper, 10 In. 27.50
Baccarat, Dish, Candy, Yellow Swirled, Pedestal, Signed, 5 1/2 In. 15.00
Baccarat, Dish, Center, Clear To Salmon, Color Swirl, Scalloped Top, Signed 48.00
Baccarat, Goblet, Allover Etching, Footed, Signed 16.00
Baccarat, Holder, Nail Buffer, Amberina Swirl 10.00
Baccarat, Inkwell, Swirled, Hinged Dome, Brass Cover, 4 In.Diameter 55.00
Baccarat, Jar, Dresser, Swirled Red Shading To Amber, Finial, 4 In. 29.50
Baccarat, Jar, Powder, Lid, Amberina, Signed 55.00
Baccarat, Juice Set, Flowers, Ivy, Unsigned, Stopper, 6 Glasses 75.00
Baccarat, Lamp Globe, Green Ferns, Outlined In Gold, Signed, 7 In.Diameter 56.00
Baccarat, Lamp, Fairy, Pink Swirl, Signed, 6 X 4 In.High 195.00
Baccarat, Lamp, Kerosene, Milk Glass, Hand-Painted, Bronze, Signed, 16 In. 150.00
Baccarat, Letter Opener, Clear Crystal, Signed, 9 In.Long 25.00
Baccarat, Paperweight, Abraham Lincoln, Sulfide, Clear, Hexagon, 1954 .... 300.00
Baccarat, Paperweight, Adlai Stevenson 62.50
Baccarat, Paperweight, Adlai Stevenson, Overlay 225.00

Baccarat, Paperweight, Adlai Stevenson, Sulfide 100.00
Baccarat, Paperweight, Adlai Stevenson, Sulfide, 7 Windows, Wine Red 70.00
Baccarat, Paperweight, Andrew Jackson 47.50
Baccarat, Paperweight, Andrew Jackson, Sulfide 47.50
Baccarat, Paperweight, Benjamin Franklin, 1954, Sulfide, 7 Windows, Blue 450.00
Baccarat, Paperweight, Bouquet Of White Double Clematis, Stars, Star Cut 1000.00
Baccarat, Paperweight, Bouquet Of 2 Pansies, Flat, Star Cut Base 2000.00
Baccarat, Paperweight, Butterfly, Amethyst, Alternating Canes, Muslin Ground 650.00
Baccarat, Paperweight, Butterfly, Clear, Red & White Canes, Star Cut Base 850.00
Baccarat, Paperweight, Canes, Flat, 3 In. 49.00
Baccarat, Paperweight, Canes & Florette, Millefiori Canes, Garlands 120.00
Baccarat, Paperweight, Center Cane, Four Rows Of Canes, Coral, Blue, Green 180.00
Baccarat, Paperweight, Centurian, Zodiac Series, Sulfide 35.00
Baccarat, Paperweight, Church, Zodiac Silhouettes 120.00
Baccarat, Paperweight, Circlets Of Canes, Dated & Signed 550.00
Baccarat, Paperweight, Comte De Chambord, Sulfide, Clear Ground 125.00
Baccarat, Paperweight, Concentric Canes, Stars, Green, Blue, White, & Red 220.00
Baccarat, Paperweight, Concentric Canes, 2 In.Diameter .... 125.00 To 150.00
Baccarat, Paperweight, Concentric Circles Of Canes 140.00
Baccarat, Paperweight, Concentric Circlets Of Canes, Signed & Dated 55.00
Baccarat, Paperweight, Concentric, Red, Green, & White, 2 In.Diameter 225.00
Baccarat, Paperweight, Crow's Foot & Stardust Canes, Concentric, Faceted 375.00
Baccarat, Paperweight, Dogwood, Pink & White, Red Whorl, Star Cut Base 525.00
Baccarat, Paperweight, Eisenhower, Cobalt Ground, Hexagon, 1955 .... 300.00 To 400.00
Baccarat, Paperweight, Eleanor Roosevelt .... 47.50 To 78.00
Baccarat, Paperweight, Florette, Clear, Concentric Millefiori Canes 150.00
Baccarat, Paperweight, Florette, Millefiori Canes, Loops 100.00
Baccarat, Paperweight, Florette, Millefiori, Stardust Canes, White, Yellow 120.00
Baccarat, Paperweight, Florette, Miniature, Concentric Millefiori Canes 60.00
Baccarat, Paperweight, George Washington, 1953, Sulfide, 7 Windows, Green 175.00
Baccarat, Paperweight, George Washington, 1954, Sulfide, Red Ground, Hexagon 325.00
Baccarat, Paperweight, Green Snake, Clear, Mercurial Bubbles 2000.00
Baccarat, Paperweight, Gridel Silhouettes With Rooster 150.00
Baccarat, Paperweight, Gridel Silhouettes With Squirrel 150.00
Baccarat, Paperweight, Herbert Hoover .... 62.50 To 80.00
Baccarat, Paperweight, Huntsman, Sulfide, Faceted .... *Illus* 475.00
Baccarat, Paperweight, James Monroe 62.50
Baccarat, Paperweight, Joan Of Arc, Sulfide .... *Illus* 1500.00

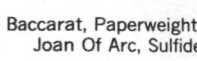

Baccarat, Paperweight,
Huntsman, Sulfide,
Faceted

Baccarat, Paperweight,
Joan Of Arc, Sulfide

Baccarat, Paperweight, John F.Kennedy, 1963, Sulfide, Diamond Facets, Purple 200.00
Baccarat, Paperweight, John F.Kennedy, 1963, Sulfide, 7 Windows, Blue 135.00
Baccarat, Paperweight, Mauve & Black Pansy, Red Whorl, Star Cut Base 150.00
Baccarat, Paperweight, Mauve & Yellow Pansy, Green, Star Cut Base 150.00
Baccarat, Paperweight, Mauve & Yellow Pansy, Miniature, Star Cut Base 130.00
Baccarat, Paperweight, Mauve & Yellow Pansy, 7 Windows, Green Leaves 175.00
Baccarat, Paperweight, Mauve, Yellow, & Black Pansy, Star Cut Base 150.00
Baccarat, Paperweight, Millefiori, Zodiac Signs 120.00
Baccarat, Paperweight, Monroe 95.00
Baccarat, Paperweight, Monroe, Overlay 225.00
Baccarat, Paperweight, Mushroom, White Latticinio Cable, Star Cut Base 350.00
Baccarat, Paperweight, Mushroom, White Latticinio Threads, Star Cut Base 125.00
Baccarat, Paperweight, Pansy With Two Buds 175.00

Baccarat, Paperweight, Pansy, Mauve, Stardust Stamens, Star Cut Base 175.00
Baccarat, Paperweight, Pansy, 3 In.Diameter 175.00
Baccarat, Paperweight, Pope John XXIII, Overlay 175.00
Baccarat, Paperweight, Pope John XXIII, Sulfide 95.00
Baccarat, Paperweight, Pope John XXIII, 1963, Sulfide, 7 Windows, Amber 80.00
Baccarat, Paperweight, Pope Pius XII 120.00
Baccarat, Paperweight, Primrose, Blue & White, Red Whorl, Star Cut Base 200.00
Baccarat, Paperweight, Primrose, Blue, White, & Green, Yellow Whorl, Star Cut 300.00
Baccarat, Paperweight, Queen Elizabeth II & Philip, Sulfide, 7 Windows 225.00
Baccarat, Paperweight, Queen Elizabeth II, Sulfide, 5 Windows, Overlay 250.00
Baccarat, Paperweight, Red & Black Snake, Blue & Mottled Ground 300.00
Baccarat, Paperweight. Red Clematis Bud, Star Cut Base 650.00
Baccarat, Paperweight, Robert E.Lee, 1954, Sulfide, 7 Windows, Blue 175.00
Baccarat, Paperweight, Robert E.Lee, 1955, Sulfide, Gray Ground, Hexagon 250.00
Baccarat, Paperweight, Rooster, Gridel 150.00
Baccarat, Paperweight, Shell Motif, Sulfide, Faceted 220.00
Baccarat, Paperweight, Silhouettes Of Animals & 2 Birds, Millefiori, 1848 .... 525.00
Baccarat, Paperweight, Silhouettes Of Devil & Animals, Millefiori, 1848 .... 500.00
Baccarat, Paperweight, Silhouettes Of Goat, Cock, & 2 Birds, Millefiori 160.00
Baccarat, Paperweight, Silhouettes Of Hunter, Devil, & Animals, Dated 1848 .... 475.00
Baccarat, Paperweight, Snake .... *Illus* 300.00
Baccarat, Paperweight, Squirrel, Gridel 150.00
Baccarat, Paperweight, Sulfide .... *Illus* 125.00
Baccarat, Paperweight, Sulfide, Herbert Hoover, Limited Edition 175.00
Baccarat, Paperweight, Sulfide, Libra, Faceted, Deep Blue Ground 45.00
Baccarat, Paperweight, T.Roosevelt, Sulfide, Purple, Hexagon .... 85.00 To 150.00
Baccarat, Paperweight, Theodore Roosevelt 85.00
Baccarat, Paperweight, Thomas Jefferson, 1953, Sulfide, 7 Windows, Blue 190.00
Baccarat, Paperweight, White & Red Florette, Miniature, Millefiori Canes 80.00
Baccarat, Paperweight, White Clematis Bud, Star Cut Base 550.00
Baccarat, Paperweight, White Double Clematis, Canes, 7 Windows 450.00
Baccarat, Paperweight, White Double Clematis, Clear, Star Cut Base 1500.00
Baccarat, Paperweight, White Double Clematis, Star Cut Base, Red Whorl 450.00
Baccarat, Paperweight, Will Rogers, 1966, Sulfide, Amber .... 70.00 To 120.00
Baccarat, Paperweight, Woodrow Wilson 50.00
Baccarat, Paperweight, Woodrow Wilson, Yellow Overlay .... *Illus* 160.00

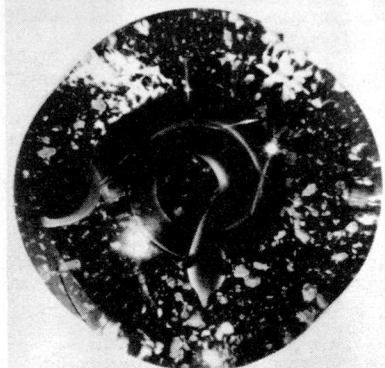

Baccarat, Paperweight, Snake

Baccarat, Paperweight,
Woodrow Wilson,
Yellow Overlay

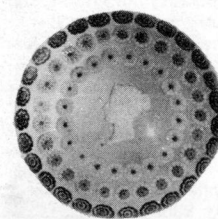

Baccarat, Paperweight, Sulfide

Baccarat, Paperweight, Zodiac, Sulfide Centurian, Faceted, Star Cut Base	35.00
Baccarat, Perfume, Acid Etched Design, Signed, 5 1/2 In.High	28.00
Baccarat, Perfume, Amber Swirl, Signed	45.00
Baccarat, Perfume, Amberina To Clear To Cranberry, Swirl, Stopper	48.00
Baccarat, Perfume, Amethyst Fan Stopper, Signed Guerlain, Paris, Footed	25.00
Baccarat, Perfume, Blue, Fan Shape Stopper, Signed Guerlain	16.00
Baccarat, Perfume, Blue, Opaline, Gold Stripes & Stars, French	45.00
Baccarat, Perfume, Clear, Reliefs, Stopper, Signed	15.00
Baccarat, Perfume, Color Swirl, Clear To Cranberry, Stopper	48.00
Baccarat, Perfume, Embossed Pattern, Blue Trim, Signed, 6 1/4 In.High	30.00
Baccarat, Perfume, Swirl, Clear, Hinged Sterling Cover, 5 In.High	28.00
Baccarat, Pitcher, Clear Crystal, Pontil, 12 In.	50.00
Baccarat, Plate, Amberina, Swirl Pattern, Signed, 7 1/4 In.Diameter	27.50
Baccarat, Plate, Pink To Peach Shading, Signed, 7 In.Diameter	37.50
Baccarat, Relish, Oval Swirl, Rose Teinte, Signed	35.00
Baccarat, Relish, Signed, Amberina Swirl, 7 1/2 X 3 1/2 In.	28.00
Baccarat, Ring Tree, Depose, Vaseline Swirl, 4 In.Wide, 3 In.High	15.00
Baccarat, Salt, Master, Ruby To Clear, Signed	35.00
Baccarat, Syrup, Swirl, Bulbous, Notched Handle, New Silver Plate Top	23.50
Baccarat, Tray, Dresser, Amberina	52.50
Baccarat, Tumbler, Amberina Swirl, Pedestal Base	40.00
Baccarat, Tumbler, Rose Teinte Swirl, Flint, Signed	22.00
Baccarat, Tumbler, Rubena Swirls, Fine Cut, Signed	18.00
Baccarat, Vase, Allover Scrolled Intaglio, Signed, 8 In.	28.00
Baccarat, Vase, Crackle Cranberry Glass, Footed, Label, 6 1/2 In.High	65.00
Baccarat, Vase, Trumpet Shape, Swirls, Footed & Handled Bronze Holder	40.00
Baccarat, Wine, Etched Unicorn, Birds, Foxes, Insects, Vines	28.50
Bag, Beaded, see Beaded Bag	

*The Whiting numbers refer to the book 'old Iron Still Banks' by
Hubert B. Whiting.*

Bank, Add A Coin Register	3.75
Bank, Advertising, Coffee, Tin	5.00
Bank, Advertising, Pittsburgh Paints, Embossed, Glass	5.00
Bank, Apollo, U.S.A., Cast Iron, Commemorative	4.00
Bank, Army Sergeant, Whistle In Hand	5.00
Bank, Aunt Jemima, Cast Iron, 5 In.	26.00
Bank, Auto, Dated 1927, Still, 6 In.Long	15.00
Bank, Bank Building, Iron, 5 In. *Illus*	22.50
Bank, Bank Building, Openwork, Iron	15.00
Bank, Bank Building, Painted Silver, Iron, 5 1/4 In.High	16.75
Bank, Barrel, Blatz Beer	18.00
Bank, Barrel, Happy Days, Tin, Chein	7.00
Bank, Barrel, Metal, 1920s	3.75
Bank, Baseball Player, Cast Iron, Wh-10	45.00
Bank, Basket, Two Handles, Iron	40.00
Bank, Battleship Maine, Iron	50.00

Bank, Bank Building, Iron, 5 In.

Bank, Bear & Beehive, Iron	75.00
Bank, Bear On Green Barrel, Porcelain	22.50
Bank, Bear, Iron, 5 1/2 In.High	25.00
Bank, Bear, Standing, Cast Iron, Whiting-330	35.00
Bank, Bear, Standing, Iron, 6 1/4 In.	55.00
Bank, Bear, Standing, Metal, 5 1/2 In.Tall	29.00
Bank, Book, Leather Bound, 1920s	3.75
Bank, Boy Scout, Cast Iron, Wh-14	30.00
Bank, Buffalo, Iron	25.00
Bank, Bugs Bunny Leaning Against Tree Trunk	16.00
Bank, Building, Cupola, Metal	18.50
Bank, Bulldog's Head, Pottery, Brown, 3 1/2 In.High	22.50
Bank, Bust Of Pershing, Patent 1918, Bronzed Iron	25.00
Bank, Buster Brown, High Hat, Cast Iron, Wh-259	45.00
Bank, Buster Brown, Tige, Iron	55.00
Bank, Camel, Gold Gilt, Iron	50.00
Bank, Camel, Iron, 4 3/4 In.High	24.75
Bank, Capitol, Budget, Metal, 6 1/2 X 2 1/2 X 2 In.	2.50
Bank, Carnival Glass, Marigold, Coin Shape, Eagle In Relief	10.00
Bank, Cash Register, Tin, Brass Finish, Security, Mechanical	23.50
Bank, Cat, Grapette, Label	5.00
Bank, Cat, Sitting, Cast Iron, 4 In.Tall	18.00
Bank, Cat, Staffordshire, 4 1/2 In. .... Illus	45.00

Bank, Cat, Staffordshire, 4 1/2 In.

Bank, Centennial, Liberty Bell, 1776-1876, Patented 1875	25.00
Bank, Chest, Maroon & Gold, Bristol County Trust Co., Taunton, Mass., Steel	4.95
Bank, Church, Chein, Tin	8.00 To 14.00
Bank, Clown, Chein, Tin	15.00
Bank, Clown, Crooked Hat, Iron	50.00
Bank, Clown, Grapette	2.50
Bank, Coin Deposit, Iron	16.00
Bank, Coin, Oval, 1920s	3.75
Bank, Columbian Exposition Administration Bldg., Iron, Semimechanical	85.00
Bank, Combination Safe, Junior Bank, Black, Tin	3.00
Bank, Commonwealth, Three Coin, Patent 1905, Tin, 5 In.High	22.50
Bank, Cottage, Pottery, Man At Left, Woman At Right, Children	22.50
Bank, Cow, Iron	50.00
Bank, Crown Shape, 1953, Metal	18.00
Bank, Crown, Iron	50.00
Bank, Davy Crockett, Pony Express, Canvas	3.50
Bank, Deer, Antlers Twist Bolt, Cast Iron, Wh-195	40.00
Bank, Deer, Iron	27.50
Bank, Deposit, Cast Iron, Wh-371	30.00
Bank, Diamond Safe, Iron, Opens With Key	22.00
Bank, Dime Register, Chein	10.00
Bank, Dime, Popeye	22.00
Bank, Doe, Cast Iron, Wh-195	21.00

Bank, **Dog In Tub**, Iron 45.00
Bank, **Dog With Pack On Back**, Iron, Wh-106 .... 25.00 To 29.00
Bank, **Dog**, Fido, Iron .... 25.00 To 37.00
Bank, **Dog**, Retriever, Cast Iron 17.50
Bank, **Dog**, Scottie, Metal 9.00
Bank, **Donkey**, Cast Iron, Wh-193 .... 40.00
Bank, **Donkey**, Molded Saddle & Bridle, Some Gold Paint, Iron, Still 20.00
Bank, **Donkey**, Saddle & Bridle, Iron, Gold Paint 14.00
Bank, **Donkey**, Standing, Saddle Marked Texas 1915, Lock On Saddlebag 15.00
Bank, **Donkey**, With Saddle, Green Paint 27.50
Bank, **Duck On Tub**, Iron 32.00
Bank, **Dutch Cleanser** 8.50
Bank, **Eight Drawers**, Red Velvet Lining, Union Clothing Co., Iron 100.00
Bank, **Elephant**, Cast Iron, Wh-67 .... 22.00 To 28.00
Bank, **Elephant**, Glass, 7 1/2 In.High 7.50
Bank, **Elephant**, Grapette 2.50
Bank, **Elephant**, Howdah, Iron 18.00
Bank, **Elephant**, On Hind Legs On Circus Tub, Cast Iron, Wh-60 .... 35.00
Bank, **English Crown**, Elizabeth, 1953 .... 25.00
Bank, **Elephant**, Slot On Back, Metal 17.50
Bank, **Fido**, Paint, Iron 13.50
Bank, **First Savings & Loan**, Lubbock, Texas, Laughing Santa, Chimney, Metal ... 8.50
Bank, **Flatiron Building**, Iron, 5 1/2 In. 35.00
Bank, **Globe Of World**, Chein 12.00
Bank, **Globe**, Amber Glass 6.00
Bank, **Globe**, Semimechanical, On Arc Stand, Iron 45.00
Bank, **Graf Zeppelin**, Slot Top Rear, Iron 50.00
Bank, **Grand Piano**, Red Enamel, Tammany 125.00
Bank, **Horse**, Black Beauty, Cast Iron, Wh-62 .... 40.00
Bank, **Horse**, Bronze Metal, 12 In.Long 10.00
Bank, **Horse**, Plain, Cast Iron 25.00
Bank, **Horse**, Prancing, Cast Iron, Wh-77 .... 15.00 To 40.00
Bank, **House**, Bisque, French 28.00
Bank, **House**, Cast Iron, Wh-357 .... 25.00
Bank, **House**, Iron 16.00
Bank, **Ideal Safe Deposit** 35.00
Bank, **Kitten With Bowtie**, Chalk, Decoration 70.00
Bank, **Kitten**, Iron 23.50
Bank, **Liberty Bell**, Amber Glass, Patent Sept.22, 1885, Tin Lid, 4 1/2 In.High ... 25.00
Bank, **Liberty Bell**, Glass, Tin Screw On Base, Marked Robinson & Leoble 30.00
Bank, **Liberty Bell**, Iron 35.00
Bank, **Liberty Bell**, Marigold 5.00
Bank, **Liberty Bell**, Metal, C.1919 .... 5.50
Bank, **Liberty Bell**, Patent Date, 1919 .... 12.00
Bank, **Liberty Bell**, Stoughton Trust, Metal 9.00
Bank, **Liberty Bell**, 1919, Copper 10.00
Bank, **Lion Head**, Bennington Type 25.00
Bank, **Lion On Tub**, Cast Iron, Gold Gilt, 4 1/4 In.High, Wh-61 .... 35.00
Bank, **Lion**, Cast Iron, Wh-89 .... 27.00
Bank, **Lion**, Iron, 6 In. 30.00
Bank, **Lion**, Medium Size, Cast Iron, Wh-90 .... 33.00
Bank, **Lion**, Standing, Iron, Wh-91 .... 16.75 To 19.00
Bank, **Lion**, Standing, Iron, 4 1/2 X 3 1/2 In.High 16.75
Bank, **Log Cabin**, Glass, Pittsburgh Paints 12.00
Bank, **Log Cabin**, Pottery, Brown, 2 1/2 In.High 20.00
Bank, **Mailbox**, Cast Iron, Wh-126 .... 28.00
Bank, **Mailbox**, Iron 11.00

*Mechanical Banks were first made about 1870. Any bank with moving parts
is considered mechanical, although those most collected are the metal banks made
before World War I. Reproductions are being made.*

Bank, **Mechanical**, Always Did Spise A Mule 135.00
Bank, **Mechanical**, Beehive, Registers Dime, Iron 110.00
Bank, **Mechanical**, Cash Register, Uncle Sam's, Store, Tin 35.00
Bank, **Mechanical**, Clown, Chein 15.00
Bank, **Mechanical**, Coffee Grinder, Little Tot Label On Drawer, Iron & Wood ... 250.00

Bank, Mechanical, Dinah, Iron .... 180.00 To 295.00
Bank, Mechanical, Dog On Turntable ....95.00 To 125.00
Bank, Mechanical, Dog, Speaking 200.00
Bank, Mechanical, Elephant 25.00
Bank, Mechanical, Elephant Lifts Trunk, Chein 25.00
Bank, Mechanical, Elephant, Howdah, Movable Trunk 45.00
Bank, Mechanical, Elephant, Man In Howdah, Iron 140.00
Bank, Mechanical, Elephant, Movable Trunk, Iron 85.00
Bank, Mechanical, Gambling Machine, Las Vegas 22.00
Bank, Mechanical, Hall's Excelsior, Iron 85.00
Bank, Mechanical, Harry Lauder, Painted 95.00
Bank, Mechanical, Hometown Battery, Possums On Batter's Shirt, 1888 .... 165.00
Bank, Mechanical, Independence Hall Tower, Liberty Proclaimed July 4, 1776 .... 125.00
Bank, Mechanical, Jolly Nigger, Patent 1882, Shepard Hardware, Buffalo 100.00
Bank, Mechanical, Jolly Nigger, Signed 75.00
Bank, Mechanical, Little Joe, Iron ....70.00 To 185.00
Bank, Mechanical, Monkey, Tips Hat, Red Coat, Chein, Tin .... 16.50 To 48.00
Bank, Mechanical, Organ Monkey, Iron 150.00
Bank, Mechanical, Rabbit, Uncle Wiggily, Chein 18.00
Bank, Mechanical, Rocket Ship, Shoots Coin Into Planet 35.00
Bank, Mechanical, Southern Comfort Whiskey, Man Shooting Into Glass 35.00
Bank, Mechanical, Speaking Dog, Lever Moves Tail & Mouth, Pat.1885, Iron 150.00
Bank, Mechanical, Tammany, Dated June 8, 1875 ....50.00 To 125.00
Bank, Mechanical, Teddy & The Bear, Painted 225.00
Bank, Mechanical, Trick Dog, Pat.1888, Few Chips On Paint 125.00
Bank, Mechanical, Uncle Sam, Nickel 15.00
Bank, Mechanical, Uncle Sam, Register Bank, Three Coin 27.50
Bank, Mechanical, Uncle Sam, Steel, 1930s 17.00
Bank, Mechanical, Wireless 150.00
Bank, Mickey Mouse, Dime Register, 1939 .... 40.00
Bank, Middy Bank, Iron 49.00
Bank, Model T Ford, License Plate 1927, Marked Morris Plan Bank & Banking 9.75
Bank, Moneybag, Bedford, Ohio, 1962, Ceramic 4.00
Bank, Monkey, Tin 15.00
Bank, Mutt & Jeff, Iron ....50.00 To 55.00
Bank, New Geneva, Decorated, 6 In.High 80.00
Bank, Owl, Be Wise, Carnival Glass 18.00
Bank, Picnic Hamper, Pottery, Mottled, Two Gray Mice 25.00
Bank, Pig, Bisque 12.00
Bank, Pig, Cobalt Blue Wavy Glass, 5 X 3 In. 5.00
Bank, Pig, Decker, Cast Iron, Wh-82 ....25.50 To 35.00
Bank, Pig, Iron, 'Deckers Iowana'On Sides 25.00
Bank, Pig, Napier, Silver Plate, Patent Pending, 4 X 3 1/4 In. 8.50
Bank, Pig, Porky, Gold Metal, Enamel 8.00
Bank, Pig, Sitting, Cast Iron, Wh-179 ....22.50 To 30.00
Bank, Pig, Standing Up, Cast Iron 25.00
Bank, Pig, Standing, Brass, 5 3/4 In.Long 40.00
Bank, Pig, Standing, Nickel Plated Cast Iron, 6 3/4 In.Long 35.00
Bank, Pirate Treasure Chest, Gold, Iron, 3 3/4 In.Long 17.00
Bank, Popeye, Ceramic, Hole For His Pipe, 9 In. 6.00
Bank, Popeye, Dime, 1929 .... 15.00
Bank, Pottery, 1920s 3.75
Bank, Prancing Horse, Cast Iron, Wh-77 .... 21.00
Bank, Presto, Cast Iron, Wh-426 .... 25.00
Bank, Presto, Iron, Round Tower, Side Wings, Wh-427 .... 14.75
Bank, Puppy, Painted, Patent 1914, Iron 25.00
Bank, Radio, Iron 38.00
Bank, Refrigerator, C.1930, Lead 14.00
Bank, Refrigerator, Electrolux, White, Metal, 4 In.High 8.75
Bank, Refrigerator, Lead, 1930s 14.00
Bank, Rooster, Cast Iron, Wh-187 .... 30.00
Bank, Safe, Cast Iron, 1896, 3 1/4 In.High 15.00
Bank, Safe, Combination Lock, Boom Safe, Made By Kenton, Repainted, Iron 12.75
Bank, Safe, Combination Lock, Cast Iron 13.00
Bank, Safe, Combination Lock, Tin 5.00
Bank, Safe, Openwork Design, Iron 10.75

Bank, Safe, Openwork Design, Pat.1888, Iron, Key, 3 1/4 In.High 12.75
Bank, Safe, Security Safe Deposit, Combination, Cast Iron 12.50
Bank, Safe, Security Safe Deposit, Combination, Dated Mar.1, 1887, Cast Iron 30.00
Bank, Safe, Sport, Patent 1880, Cast Iron, Wh-374 .... 25.00
Bank, Safe, The Daisy, Cast Iron, 2 In.High 15.00
Bank, Sailor Carrying His Bag, Ceramic, 4 In. 3.00
Bank, Santa Claus, Ceramic, Red & White With Gold Belt & Bell 4.00
Bank, Santa With Tree, 5 1/2 In. 200.00
Bank, Save & Smile Money Box, Iron 170.00
Bank, Schoolhouse Shape, Painted, Wooden 45.00
Bank, Sharecropper, Iron 40.00
Bank, Sheep, Cast Iron 27.50
Bank, St.Bernard, Iron 42.00
Bank, State Bank, Hinged Door, Lock & Key, Cast Iron, Wh-445 .... 45.00
Bank, State Bank, Painted, Cast Iron, 3 X 4 X 6 In. 20.00
Bank, Statue Of Liberty, Cast Iron, 6 In.High .... 12.00 To 25.00
Bank, Stoneware, Decorated With 19 Blue Stars, 6 1/2 In.High 100.00
Bank, Stove, Gas, Iron 35.00
Bank, Stove, Porcelain & Iron, Brown, Fobrux, French 25.00
Bank, Tally Ho, Iron .... 75.00 To 80.00
Bank, Teller, Metal, 1920s 3.75
Bank, Three Little Pigs, Green, Brass Fittings, Key 8.50
Bank, Three Sections, Cashier, Manager, Frosted Glass Panel, Etched, Iron 450.00
Bank, Thrifty Pig, Cast Iron, Wh-75 .... 45.00
Bank, Turkey, Cast Iron, Small Size, Wh-193 .... 33.00
Bank, U.S.Mailbox, Green, Gilt Flying Eagle, Dated Feb.2, 1875, Iron 25.00
Bank, U.S.Mailbox, Green, Gold Eagle & Lettering 28.50
Bank, U.S.Mailbox, Iron, 4 In.High .... 12.75 To 14.75
Bank, Uncle Sam, Ceramic 5.00
Bank, Victorian House, Cast Iron, Wh-366 .... 45.00
Bank, Westminster Abbey, Iron, Still 75.00
Bank, Woolworth Building, Iron .... 28.00 To 35.00
Bank, 4-4-4, Cast Iron, Wh-306 .... 27.00
Barometer-Thermometer, Italian, 18th Century Style, Round Dial, Gilt 120.00
Barometer-Thermometer, Victorian, Mahogany, John Curotti, Baluster, C.1850 .... 200.00
Barometer, Adie & Son, Edinburgh, Stick, Brass Scales, Sliding, Mahogany, 1850 .... 225.00
Barometer, Banjo, English, Marquetry, Mahogany, Bellflower Inlay, C.1850 .... 275.00
Barometer, Black Japanned, Gilt Chinoiserie, Fra Searle, C.1790 .... 80.00
Barometer, Brass Case, Barometer & Temperature, 5 In.Diameter 30.00
Barometer, Diamond Shape, Milk Glass Case, Ogee Carved Wood Frame, C.1820 .... 90.00
Barometer, English, Mahogany, Stick, Cary, C.1850 .... 160.00
Barometer, Federal, Boston, C.1850, 38 In.Long .... *Illus* 450.00
Barometer, Federal, Mahogany, J.Tadeo, N.Y., Swanneck Cresting, C.1820 .... 600.00
Barometer, Italian, Gilt Wood, Hunting Trophy On Frame, C.1750 .... 225.00
Barometer, Louis XVI Style, Verre Eglomise, Lozenge Shape, Gold, Blue 225.00
Barometer, Mahogany, Brass Bezel, Taylor, 1925, England, 8 In.Diameter 30.00

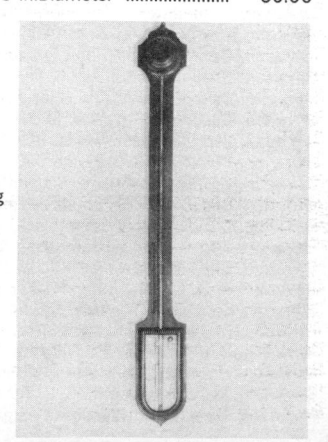

Barometer, Federal, Boston, C.1850, 38 In.Long

Barometer, Mahogany, Wheel, Grimondi, Halifax, C.1750 .... 275.00
Barometer, Short & Mason, Brass Case, 6 1/2 In.Diameter 40.00
Barometer, Victorian, Mother-Of-Pearl Inlaid Rosewood, Banjo, Silver Scale 170.00
    Barr, see Worcester

Basalt is a black stoneware made by mixing iron and oxides into a basic
clay. It is very hard and can be finished on a lathe. Wedgwood developed
his famous black basalt in 1769, which was an improvement on a similar ware made
in Staffordshire, England, as early as 1740. Basalt is still being made in
England and on the Continent.
Basalt, Figurine, Cat, Black, Amber Glass Eyes, 3 In.Long 30.00
Basalt, Figurine, Cat, Glass Eyes, 4 In. 85.00
Basalt, Figurine, Cat, 3 In.Long 25.00
Basalt, Figurine, Dog, Glass Eyes, 4 In. 89.00
Basalt, Teapot, Black, Classical Figure & Geometrics, Slide Lid 100.00
Batman, Bank, Modeled As Batman, Square Base Inscribed 'Batman' 60.00
Batman, Mug, Milk Glass 2.50
Batman, Pin, Batman & Robin Society, Member, Pictures, 3 1/2 In. .... .75

Battersea Enamels are enamels painted on copper and made in the Battersea
District of London from about 1750 to 1756. Many similar enamels are
mistakenly called Battersea.
Battersea, Box, Blue, Birds, Nest, Bushes, Fern, 'Esteem The Giver, '2 In. 225.00
Battersea, Box, Blue, White Lid, Star, Red, Blue, Green Floral, 1 7/8 In. 200.00
Battersea, Box, Cobalt, White Lid, 'Unto The End I Love My Friend' 250.00
Battersea, Box, Enamel, Angel On Swing, 1 1/2 X 3/4 In.High 125.00
Battersea, Box, Pink, Floral, Man Fishing, Boat, Water, Buildings, 2 1/2 In. 250.00
Battersea, Box, Pug Dog Face Forms Box, Top, Pug Dog Walks In Street, 2 In. 395.00
Battersea, Box, Roses, Oval 68.00
Battersea, Doorknob, Round, Admiral Lord Horatio Nelson, C.1800, Pair 350.00
Battersea, Doorknob, Round, Memorial, White Urn On Blue, C.1780, Pair 100.00
Battersea, Nutmeg Grater, Egg Shape, Pink, Yellow Floral, Red Roses, Leaves 225.00
Battersea, Plaque, Two Greyhounds, Says Final Tie, Waterloo Cup 1892, 13 In. 250.00
Battersea, Salt, Open, Enamel On Copper, Ruffled Edge, Spoon, Circa 1670 .... 90.00
Battersea, Saltshaker, Enamel On Copper, Insects, Animals, Floral, 1750, Pair 85.00

Bavaria was a district where many types of pottery and porcelain were made
for centuries. The word 'bavaria' appears on many pieces of
nineteenth-century china. The words 'bavaria, Germany, ' appeared
after 1871.
Bavarian, see also Rosenthal
Bavarian, Bowl, Blue In White, Pierced Openwork Sides, Carl Schumann Mark 25.00
Bavarian, Bowl, Green Ground, Pond Lilies & Iris, Luster Finish 25.00
Bavarian, Bowl, Painting Of Troubadour & Lady, Incised Metz Schust 18.50
Bavarian, Bowl, Pear & Apple Center, Gold Design Edge, 8 1/4 In. 8.00
Bavarian, Box, Collar Button, Hand-Painted Roses 11.50
Bavarian, Cachepot, Square, Floral Medallion Sides, Ball Feet, Pair 45.00
Bavarian, Celery, Hand-Painted White Roses, Gold Band Self Handles 8.50
Bavarian, Cereal, Child's, Pink Luster, Children Playing, 6 In. 7.50
Bavarian, Chocolate Pot, Red & Green Grapes, Artist-Signed 48.00
Bavarian, Chocolate Pot, Six Cups & Saucers, Yellow, Orange, Dated 1917 .... 79.50
Bavarian, Chocolate Pot, Tan, Green, Roses, Four Cups & Saucers 52.50
Bavarian, Chocolate Pot, White, Blue, Pink Roses, Green, Signed Royal Bavaria 36.00
Bavarian, Chocolate Set, Pitcher, Six Handled Cups, Floral 45.00
Bavarian, Coffee Set, Brown, Scene, Copper Luster Trim, Neukerchner, 3 Piece 65.00
Bavarian, Cup & Saucer, Bouillon, Gold Fleur-De-Lis Band, Gold Handles 9.50
Bavarian, Cup & Saucer, Demitasse, Flowers, Gold Trim, U.S.Occupation 6.00
Bavarian, Cup & Saucer, Demitasse, Footed, Narcissus On Cream To Green, Gold 4.50
Bavarian, Cup, The Baronial 3.00
Bavarian, Dish, Child's, Pony, Wicker Chair, Two Toys 25.00
Bavarian, Dish, Oval, Pierced, Floral, 6 In. 4.50
Bavarian, Dish, Sardine, Four Raised Sardines, Artist Signed 35.00
Bavarian, Hair Receiver, Pink Roses 14.00
Bavarian, Hatpin Holder, Roses, White, Pink, Attached Saucer 18.00
Bavarian, Jar, Jam, Roses 8.50
Bavarian, Plate, Cake, Blossom Design, Pink, Red, Green, Marked, 9 In.Diameter 18.00

Bavarian, Plate, Cake, Open Handles, Grapes, Signed A.Koch	45.00
Bavarian, Plate, Cake, Pink Roses, Foliage, Signed Faune, Pierced Handles	15.00
Bavarian, Plate, Cupid & Lady In Rose Garden, 10 In.	18.00
Bavarian, Plate, Dessert, Floral, Pierced, Prince Regent, Set Of 4	16.00
Bavarian, Plate, Five Pink Roses, Foliage, Pink & Yellow Ground, Scrollwork	9.00
Bavarian, Plate, Four Large Pink Asters, Wide Blue Band, 8 5/8 In.	10.00
Bavarian, Plate, Game, Buck, Trees, Grass, Lake, Blue Sky, Pierced, 12 1/2 In.	45.00
Bavarian, Plate, Game, Doe, Trees, Grass, Lake, Blue Sky, Pierced, 12 1/2 In.	45.00
Bavarian, Plate, Game, Quail, Gold Edge, 9 1/2 In.Diameter	39.50
Bavarian, Plate, 'Give Us This Day, Etc., '3 Wheat Sprays, Scrolls, 9 5/8 In.	10.00
Bavarian, Plate, Gold Band Panels, Violet, Yellow, Blue Floral, Artist-Signed	12.00
Bavarian, Plate, Green & Cream Ground, Pink Roses, Z.S.G. Co., Mignon	28.00
Bavarian, Plate, Hand-Painted Pink Daisies, Gold Rim	10.00
Bavarian, Plate, Hand-Painted Pink Roses, Signed Mauvilles, P.S.A.G.	10.00
Bavarian, Plate, Hand-Painted Reclining Nude, Signed H.Wolf	25.00
Bavarian, Plate, Hand-Painted Red & Yellow Roses, Scalloped Rim, Z.S.	8.00
Bavarian, Plate, Hand-Painted Three Yellow Roses, Gold Rim	9.00
Bavarian, Plate, Narcissus, Leaves, Signed De Vries, 8 1/2 In.	10.00 To 12.00
Bavarian, Plate, Nuts & Leaves On Cream, Crown & Crossed Swords Mark	12.00
Bavarian, Plate, Orange Poppies, Hand-Painted, 6 In., Pair	12.50
Bavarian, Plate, Pheasant, Green, Tan, Gold Scalloped Rim, 9 1/2 In.	25.00
Bavarian, Plate, Pink & Red Roses, Foliage, Tinted Ground, Signed Gray	20.00
Bavarian, Plate, Pink & Yellow Ground, Five Pink Roses, Foliage, 7 7/8 In.	10.00
Bavarian, Plate, Pink Asters, Wide Blue Band, 8 5/8 In.	10.00
Bavarian, Plate, Pink Daisies, Foliage, Gold Rim, 8 1/4 In.	10.00
Bavarian, Plate, Pink Roses, Foliage, 7 1/8 In.	10.00
Bavarian, Plate, Portrait, Girl, Long Hair, Openwork Border, Gold Trim	26.00
Bavarian, Plate, Queen's Rose Center, Gold Edge, Floral, 8 Sided	2.50
Bavarian, Plate, Red & Yellow Currants, Foliage, Gold Scrollwork	12.00
Bavarian, Plate, Ribbon, Roses, 12 1/2 In.	22.00
Bavarian, Plate, Single Large Bird Standing, 10 In.	35.00
Bavarian, Plate, Violets, Gold Band Panels, 10 In.	12.00
Bavarian, Plate, Water Lily Decoration, Thomas, Sevres, Bavaria	10.00
Bavarian, Shaker, Sugar, Gold Design, Tan, Signed, 4 1/2 In.Tall	15.00
Bavarian, Sugar & Creamer, Hand-Painted Pink Roses, Gold Trim, ZS & Co.	14.50
Bavarian, Sugar & Creamer, Hand-Painted Violets, Openwork Gold Handles	28.00
Bavarian, Sugar & Creamer, Pastel Blue, Pink Roses, Gold Handles, Hexagon	35.00
Bavarian, Sugar & Creamer, Ribbon, Roses	12.00
Bavarian, Sugar, Creamer, & Tray, Stipple & Floral In Gold By Stouffer	45.00
Bavarian, Syrup, Autumn Leaves, Underplate	15.00
Bavarian, Syrup, Underplate, Pastel, Gold Trim	14.00
Bavarian, Table Set, Forget-Me-Nots, Footed, Tray, 6 Piece	59.00
Bavarian, Tea Tile, Hand-Painted Yellow Roses On Cerise & Green	8.00
Bavarian, Teapot, Pink & Yellow Roses, Gold, Plate, Prince Regent China	22.00
Bavarian, Toothpick, Pastel Floral, Oblong Shape	16.00
Bavarian, Tray, Bread, Enameled Pastel Floral, Artist-Signed	39.00
Bavarian, Tray, Perfume, Artist Signed, Pink Roses, Blue Forget-Me-Nots	12.00
Bayonet, see Weapon, Bayonet	
Beaded Bag, Beige With Floral, Brass Frame & Chain Handle	18.50
Beaded Bag, Black Beads, Suede Backing, Clamps To Belt	8.00
Beaded Bag, Black, Fringe, C.1914	12.00
Beaded Bag, Bluebird, Roses, Butterfly, Silver Frame, 6 1/2 In.	25.00
Beaded Bag, Carnival Glass, Beads, Tortoiseshell Frame, Silk Lining	25.00
Beaded Bag, Cobalt With Rose, Green, & Gold Floral	9.50
Beaded Bag, Design In Purple, Rose, Silver, Copper, Fringe, 6 3/4 X 8 In.	18.00
Beaded Bag, Drawstring	25.00
Beaded Bag, Floral, Needlework, Pinks	7.00
Beaded Bag, Green Glass Beads	8.00
Beaded Bag, Iridescent Crystal Beads In Swags, Silver Plate Fringe	12.00
Beaded Bag, Metal Frame, Fringe	12.50
Beaded Bag, Multicolor, Gilt Frame, Chain Handle	25.00
Beaded Bag, Purple, Carnival Glass Beads, C.1915	17.50
Beaded Bag, Silver Color Beads, Art Nouveau Trim, Patent 1901	8.00
Beaded Bag, Steel Beads, Dated 1863, French	15.00
Beaded Bag, White, Circa 1928	8.50
Beam, see Bottle, Beam	

Beck, Fish Set, Gold Border, Signed R.K.Beck, 4 Piece 55.00
Beck, Plate, Game, Birds At Water, Signed R.K.Beck, 8 3/4 In. 15.00
Beck, Plate, Game, Geese Flying, Signed R.K.Beck, 8 3/4 In. 15.00

*Beehive, Austria, or Beehive, Vienna, China includes all the many types
of decorated porcelain marked with the famous Beehive mark. The mark has
been used since the eighteenth century.*
Beehive, Bowl, Portrait, Oscar Schlegelmilch, Kaufmann-Type Scene On Red 48.00
Beehive, Candleholder, Floral, Gold Loop Handle, Signed, E.S.Prussia 20.00
Beehive, Dish, Portrait Of Girl On Bottom, Gold & Blue Trim, 5 1/4 In. 12.50
Beehive, Figurine, Girl, Man, Hold Flowers, 18th Century, Kolmar, 6 In., Pair 250.00
Beehive, Pitcher, Chrysanthemums, Green, Brown On White, Porcelain, 7 1/2 In. 7.50
Beehive, Plaque, Coquetry, Boudoir Scene, Octagonal, Royal Vienna, Gold Frame 365.00
Beehive, Plate, Center Medallion, Two Quail, Four Medallions, Game Birds 58.00
Beehive, Plate, Classical Center, Aqua, Signed, 8 1/4 In.Diameter 15.00
Beehive, Plate, Flamingo, 5 In.Diameter 11.00
Beehive, Plate, Long Billed Birds, Gold Bands, Blue Border, 10 5/8 In. 8.00
Beehive, Plate, Portrait, Signed Hausmann, 7 1/4 In. 30.00
Beehive, Plate, Portrait, Woman & Cherub, Pink Border, Marked 95.00
Beehive, Plate, Portrait, Woman, Burnette, Artist-Signed 35.00
Beehive, Plate, Portrait, Woman, Cherub, Pink, Gold, Signed, Marked 95.00
Beehive, Plate, Portrait, Woman, Gold, Signed Schmitt, Royal Vienna 185.00
Beehive, Plate, Soup, Red & White, 9 In., Marked Royal Vienna 16.00
Beehive, Plate, Two Nymphs In Stream, Artist Carl Larsen 18.00
Beehive, Saucer, Pink, Red, & Yellow Flowers 8.00
Beehive, Saucer, White, Gold, Red, Blue, & Yellow Geometric Design 8.00
Beehive, Tea Caddy, Rose Color, Flower Garlands, Porcelain, Mark Under Glaze 50.00
Beehive, Urn, Hand-Painted, Signed, 10 In. 100.00
Beehive, Vase, Beige Ground, Raised Gold Work, Portrait Oval By Wagner 85.00
Beehive, Vase, Portrait, Lady, Maroon, Gold, Marked 28.00
Beehive, Vase, The Gleaners, Rust & Gold Border, 10 In. 35.00
Beehive, Vase, Two Watteau Type Panels On Each Side, 5 In.High 80.00

Bells have been made of china, glass, or metal. All types are collected.
Bell, Advertising, New York Hotel, Ruby Glass, 5 1/2 In.High 35.00
Bell, Brass, Apostle, 3 In.High 40.00
Bell, Brass, Boxing Bell, Mounted On Board, 11 X 11 In. 21.00
Bell, Brass, Briscoe School, McShane Bell Foundry, Baltimore, Md., 1914 .... 2880.00
Bell, Brass, Chinese Claw-Type 6.00
Bell, Brass, Chinese, Dinner, On Stand 12.00
Bell, Brass, Elizabethian Lady, Bouffant Dress, 4 In.High 20.00
Bell, Brass, Elizabethian Lady, Feet Clapper, 3 1/2 In. 11.00
Bell, Brass, Figural, Jenny Lind, 2 Legs Are Clappers, 5 In.High 35.00
Bell, Brass, Girl, Hoop Shirt, Bonnet 7.00
Bell, Brass, Handle In Shape Of Bird, Marked China, 4 In.High 3.75
Bell, Brass, Lady In Old Fashioned Dress 17.50
Bell, Brass, Little Girl In Crinoline 12.50
Bell, Brass, Marie Antoinette 26.00
Bell, Brass, Mass, 4 Graduated In Square Cluster, Hand Grip 35.00
Bell, Brass, Puritan, 1492 .... *Illus* 10.00
Bell, Brass, Push, Turtle Base, Engraved Frogs, Bird Striker 27.50
Bell, Brass, San Diego Mission, Marked 1838, 3 In. 20.00
Bell, Brass, Ship's, Scrolling, Marked 1878, 5 In.High 30.00
Bell, Brass, Table, Lacquered 6.00
Bell, Brass, Table, Windmill 8.00
Bell, Brass, Wooden Handle, 10 1/2 In.High 32.00
Bell, Brass, 4 Disciples, Matthew, Marc, Lucas, & Johann Engraved 47.50
Bell, Call, Dresden, White, Raised Gold Leaves & Sprays 35.00
Bell, Camel, Brass, Iron Clapper, Embossed Birds 45.00
Bell, Camel, Brass, Single Clapper, Embossed Birds, 8 In.High 50.00
Bell, Camel, String Of 4 .... 20.00
Bell, Camel, Three Bells Inside, Embossed, Iron Link Chain, Brass 65.00
Bell, Camel, Two Part, One Bell Inside Other, Animal Design, 12 In.Long 60.00
Bell, Chinese Gong, On Stand, Mahogany, Padded Hammer, 24 In.Diameter 50.00
Bell, Christmas, Three Graduated Encircled In A Ring, Chain 20.00
Bell, Cobalt 8.45

Bell, Colonial, Brass, Iron Anchor Shape Clapper, Says Colonial 1832-1922 .... 20.00
Bell, Country Store, Spiral Spring Type, 2 1/3 In.Diameter 9.50
Bell, Cow's, Copper 5.00
Bell, Cow's, Handmade, Brass, 5 In. 7.00
Bell, Cow's, Iron 6.00
Bell, Cow's, Iron, Two On Leather Strap 15.00
Bell, Cow's, Mr.O.Star, Royal Oak, Mich., 4 In. .... *Illus* 35.00

Bell, Brass,
Puritan, 1492
See Page 26

Bell, Cow's, Mr.O.Star,
Royal Oak, Mich., 4 In.

Bell, Cow's, New England, 4 In.High 4.75
Bell, Cow's, Square, Leather Strap, Buckle 15.00
Bell, Cutter, Four Bells, Metal Strip, Pair 30.00
Bell, Desk, Beaded Around Bottom, Black Enamel Weighted Base, Brass 15.00
Bell, Desk, Brass, French, 4 1/2 In.High 17.50
Bell, Desk, School, Indian Picture 20.00
Bell, Desk, Teacher's, Patent 1856 .... 12.00
Bell, Diamond-Quilted, Cranberry & Opalescent, Swirled Handle, Pair 250.00
Bell, Dinner, Blue Luster, Blown, Feather Pattern, Clapper On Gold Chain 3.00
Bell, Dinner, Bronze, Brass Ferrule, Rosewood Handle, Bronze Finial 12.00
Bell, Dinner, Cast Iron, Yoke 25.00
Bell, Dinner, Cut Glass, Crystal Clapper, 5 In.High 20.00
Bell, Dinner, Red, Clear Handle With White Loopings, 13 In.High 70.00
Bell, Emerald Green 8.45
Bell, Enamel, Flower Panels, Glass Clapper, China, 1895 .... 35.00
Bell, Figure Of Napoleon, Brass, 5 1/2 In. 10.00
Bell, Flower, Bent Stem Is Handle, Porcelain 25.00
Bell, Goose, Brass, Double Clapper, Leather Strap 14.00
Bell, Hand, Brass, 11 1/2 In. 45.00
Bell, Horse Swingers, Three Bells In Brass With Center Plume 38.00
Bell, Hotel Front Desk, Patent 1885 .... 14.50
Bell, Inscribed Merry Christmas, Elizabeth Arden, Metal 8.00
Bell, Lady With Bonnet, Brass 12.50
Bell, Lady With Hoop Skirt, Brass, 3 1/2 In.Tall, 2 In.Diameter 15.00
Bell, Lady, Flounced Skirt, Tight-Fitting Bodice, Bonnet, Bronze 34.00
Bell, Lettered Colonial 1822, Brass 15.00
Bell, Marked U.S.N., Cast Bronze, Wrought Iron Hanger, 15 Lbs. 29.50
Bell, Mechanical, Turtle Shape Base, Carved Wood 19.50
Bell, Oriental Holy Man Handle, Brass 27.00
Bell, Oriental Temple, Brass, Set Of 6, Tap Stick 65.00
Bell, Patio, Brass, 9 In.Iron S Shaped Frame, 5 X 5 In. 65.00
Bell, Patio, Cast Iron, Wrought Iron Bracket, 8 In.Across, 13 Lbs. 12.50
Bell, Pearl, Chicago Exposition, 1893, 4 1/2 In. .... *Illus* 85.00
Bell, Porcelain, Band Of Roses, Leaf Top, Wooden Clapper, 4 In.High 23.00
Bell, Pull, Gong Type, Brass, 5 In.Diameter 23.00
Bell, Rattle, Inside Whistle In End, Carved Filligree 25.00
Bell, Remember Pearl Harbor, Signed 12.00
Bell, School, Brass, Wooden Handle, 6 1/2 In. .... 10.00 To 15.00
Bell, School, Brass, Wooden Handle, 7 1/2 In.High 6.50

Bell, Pearl, Chicago Exposition, 1893, 4 1/2 In.
See Page 27

Bell, School, Brass, Wooden Handle, 8 In.High, 5 In.Diameter	30.00
Bell, School, Brass, Wooden Handle, 10 X 4 1/2 In.	32.50
Bell, School, Brass, Wooden Handle, 10 1/4 In.	45.00
Bell, School, Brass, 6 In.	18.00
Bell, School, Flared, Brass, Wooden Handle, 3 In.Diameter	15.00
Bell, School, Nickel Plate, Black Wooden Handle, 3 1/4 In.Diameter	8.50
Bell, School, Nickel Plated Bronze, Black Wood Handle, 11 1/4 In.High	32.00
Bell, School, 7 In.High	12.00
Bell, Schoolmaster's, 5 1/2 In.High	8.50
Bell, Sheep, Brass	5.00
Bell, Silver Over Brass, 4 In.High	6.00
Bell, Sleigh, Brass, Embossed, 24 On Leather Strap	65.00
Bell, Sleigh, Brass, 4 On Strap	23.00
Bell, Sleigh, Brass, 30 On Strap	50.00
Bell, Sleigh, Brass, 31 On 92 In.Strap, Cotter Keys, Rivets Between Bells	200.00
Bell, Sleigh, Brass, 38 On Leather Strap	185.00
Bell, Sleigh, Engraved, String Of 18 Graduated	80.00
Bell, Sleigh, Four On Metal Strip, Pair	30.00
Bell, Sleigh, Nickel On Brass, String Of 35	35.00
Bell, Sleigh, Nickel Plated, 30 On Leather Strap	85.00
Bell, Sleigh, Plain, Etched, Graduated, Brass, 30 On Leather Strap	70.00
Bell, Sleigh, Rump, Four Brass, Double Leather Strap, Fittings, Loops	55.00
Bell, Sleigh, Six Graduated Bells On Metal Bar	25.00
Bell, Sleigh, Three Bells On Each Bar, Shaft	25.00
Bell, Sleigh, Three Clappers In Each, Set Of 3 On Strap	9.75
Bell, Sleigh, 8 Graduated On Strap	65.00
Bell, Sleigh, 16 Graduated Brass Bells, 2 1/4 To 3 In., 7 Ft.Leather Strap	195.00
Bell, Sleigh, 25 Brass Bells Riveted To Strap, Patent 1876, 6 Ft. Strap	95.00
Bell, Sleigh, 29 Brass Bells Riveted To 6 Ft. Strap	100.00
Bell, Sleigh, 30 Acorn Shaped Bells On Strap, Brass	55.00
Bell, Sleigh, 35 Bells, Strap, Brass	50.00
Bell, Sleigh, 50 Brass Bells, Leather Strap, 1 1/8 In.Diameter	75.00
Bell, Smoke, Blown, Diamond Checker Pattern, Ruffled Edge	20.00
Bell, Smoke, Blue Trim	18.00
Bell, Smoke, Clear To Cranberry, Ruffled Edge, Overshot, 4 In.Tall	24.00
Bell, Smoke, Fluted Edge, 8 In.Diameter	10.00
Bell, Smoke, Milk Glass, Fluted	6.50
Bell, Smoke, Milk Glass, 8 In.Diameter	10.00
Bell, Sterling Handle, Raised Flowers, 4 1/4 In.High	12.50
Bell, Store Door, On Strap, Iron, 3 3/4 In.	8.00
Bell, Table, Brass, Hammer	9.00
Bell, Table, Embossed, Black Metal Base, Footed, Push Button, Silver, 3 In.	4.50
Bell, Tap, Iron & Brass	4.75
Bell, Tap, On Ornate Iron Base	4.75
Bell, Tap, Wire Legs, Brass	8.00
Bell, Teacher's, Brass, Mahogany Handle, 12 In.High, 6 In.Diameter	30.00

Bell, Teacher's, Brass, Wooden Handle 23.00
Bell, Teacher's, Brass, 6 In.High, 3 1/8 In.Diameter 15.00
Bell, Teacher's, Desk, Iron, Scalloped Top, Brass Dome, 2 3/4 In. 16.00
Bell, Temple, Four Graduated Sizes, Dragon On Brass 150.00
Bell, Three On Stand, Oriental Motif, Hammer, China, 10 In.High 20.00
Bell, Town Crier, Rosewood Handle, 13 1/2 In.High 62.50
Bell, Trolley, Activated By Pull Cord, Brass, 12 In.Diameter 55.00
Bell, Trolley, Embossed 42 St. M & St. N.Ave., 1884, Brass 100.00
Bell, Trolley, Pull Cord, Brass, Mounting Brackets, Circa 1920, 12 In. 30.00
Bell, Trolley, Pull Cord, Brass, 7 In.Diameter 35.00
Bell, Wedding, Amber, Clear Handle, No Clapper, 8 In.High 85.00

Belleek China was made in Ireland, other European countries, and the United States. The glaze is creamy yellow and appears wet. The first Belleek was made in 1857.

Belleek, see also Lenox
Belleek, Basket, Applied Roses, Spaghetti Type, Signed Co.Fermagh, Belleek 95.00
Belleek, Bowl Of Roses, Irish, Green F Mark 150.00
Belleek, Bowl, Double Shell Pattern, Pink Edging Top & Bottom, Irish 22.50
Belleek, Bowl, Latticework Sides, Basket Weave Base, Roses On Sides, C.1900 .... 85.00
Belleek, Bowl, Spaghetti Ware, Applied Rope Edges, Flared 20.00
Belleek, Bowl, Spaghetti Ware, Oval, Applied Flowers 40.00
Belleek, Caldron, White, Yellow Luster, Two Handles, Irish, Second Black Mark 38.00
Belleek, Candy Dish, Floral, Lenox, Palette Mark, 5 In. 16.00
Belleek, Coffee Server, Silver Trim, Lenox, Green Mark, 7 In. 35.00
Belleek, Coffee Set, Basket Weave & Shamrock Design, Green Mark, 6 Cups 65.00
Belleek, Coffeepot, Limpet Pattern, Pearl Gloss, Yellow Trim 35.00
Belleek, Compote, Gold Flower Decor, American, Palette Mark 27.50
Belleek, Creamer, Basket Weave, Shamrocks, Branch Handle, Second Black Mark 24.50
Belleek, Creamer, Green Foliage, Basket Weave, Black Mark 25.00
Belleek, Creamer, Ivy Pattern, Twisted Handle, Second Mark 42.00
Belleek, Creamer, Mask, First Black Mark 75.00
Belleek, Creamer, Mermaid, Green Mark 12.00
Belleek, Creamer, Nautilus Shell, Black Mark 42.00
Belleek, Creamer, Shaded Rose & White, Rope Handle, Black Mark 27.00
Belleek, Creamer, Shamrock & Basket Weave, Brown & Green Twig Handle 30.00
Belleek, Creamer, Shell & Coral Pattern, Footed, Second Mark 30.00
Belleek, Creamer, Silver Overlay, Willet 12.00
Belleek, Creamer, Tridacna, Pink Trim, Gold Rim, Irish, First Black Mark 75.00
Belleek, Creamer, Wheat Pattern, First Black Mark 75.00
Belleek, Cup & Saucer, Coral Pattern, Matching Pie Plate 35.00
Belleek, Cup & Saucer, Cream With Pink, Second Black Mark, Set Of 4 .... 85.00
Belleek, Cup & Saucer, Demitasse 18.00
Belleek, Cup & Saucer, Harp Shamrock, C Mark 27.50
Belleek, Cup & Saucer, Hawthorne, First Mark & Registration, Irish 80.00
Belleek, Cup & Saucer, Neptune, Green Edge, First Black Mark .... 25.00 To 30.00
Belleek, Cup & Saucer, Neptune, Pink & White, Shell Feet, Irish, Black Mark 39.00
Belleek, Cup & Saucer, Neptune, Shell Feet, Black Mark, Irish 32.50
Belleek, Cup & Saucer, Neptune, White Green Edges & Handle, Footed 35.00
Belleek, Cup & Saucer, Pinecones, Pink Trim, Black Mark, Ireland 33.00
Belleek, Cup & Saucer, Shamrock Design, Green, Twig Handle 20.00
Belleek, Cup & Saucer, Shamrocks, Twig Handles 18.00
Belleek, Cup & Saucer, Shell Feet, Robinson & Cleaver, Belfast, Black Mark 37.50
Belleek, Cup & Saucer, Shell Form, Brown Shell Footed Cup, Willet 42.00
Belleek, Dish, Heart, Green Hound, Harp, Tower Mark, 6 In. 15.00
Belleek, Dish, Leaf Shape, Pearl Luster, 3 Legs, Belleek Co., Fermanagh 12.00
Belleek, Dish, Maple Leaf Shape, Cream Shading To Green, Second Black Mark 25.00
Belleek, Dish, Nut, Creamy Luster, Twig Feet, Green Mark 13.50
Belleek, Dish, Pink And Red Morning Glories, Gold, Ruffled, Willet 54.00
Belleek, Figurine, Leprechaun, Green Mark 18.00
Belleek, Figurine, Pig, Green Mark 15.00
Belleek, Figurine, Piglet, Green Mark 12.00
Belleek, Figurine, Terrier, Green Mark 10.00
Belleek, Figurine, Wolfhound On Cushion, Green Mark 35.00
Belleek, Flowerpot, Cream, Yellow Inside, Raised Ridges, Swirled, Black Mark 25.00
Belleek, Hatpin Holder, Art Nouveau Border Decoration, Willet 35.00

Belleek, Hatpin Holder, Trenton, New Jersey, City Seal, White, Gold Trim	23.50
Belleek, Hatpin Holder, Violet Design, Purple, Artist Initial, 5 In.High	39.50
Belleek, Jar, Cookie, Shamrock & Basket Weave, Black Mark	125.00
Belleek, Jar, Marmalade, Shamrock, Green Mark	18.00
Belleek, Jar, Tobacco, Allover Floral, Lenox	38.00
Belleek, Mug, Corn Decoration, 5 In.	30.00
Belleek, Mug, Dragon Handle, Lenox	38.00
Belleek, Mug, Green & Red Gooseberries	35.00
Belleek, Mustard, Shell & Shamrock	20.00
Belleek, Perfume, Reticulated, Moorish Style, Carved Scene, C.1870	100.00
Belleek, Pitcher, Basket Weave, Shamrock, Green Mark, 4 In.Tall	15.00
Belleek, Pitcher, Flower Design, Sea Monster Handle, Spout Man's Head, Mark	60.00
Belleek, Pitcher, Grape Pattern, Tankard Type, Willet	125.00
Belleek, Pitcher, Lemonade, Pink & Purple Grapes, Pink Ground, Willet	110.00
Belleek, Pitcher, Pearl Gloss, Limpet Pattern, Yellow Luster Trim	23.00
Belleek, Pitcher, Shamrock Design	15.00
Belleek, Pitcher, Shamrock, Basket Weave, Third Black Mark, Irish, 4 1/2 In.	32.50
Belleek, Pitcher, Shell, White, Shell Embossed Base, Orange Coral Handle	145.00
Belleek, Pitcher, First Black Mark, 6 In.	30.00
Belleek, Plate, Bread, Neptune, Green Edge, First Black Mark	45.00
Belleek, Plate, Cake, Shamrock Design, Green, Twig Handle, 10 1/2 In.Diameter	28.00
Belleek, Plate, Cone Pattern, Green Trim, Irish, 9 1/2 In.	45.00
Belleek, Plate, Limpet Cob, Irish, Third Mark	15.00
Belleek, Plate, Shell Pattern, Pearl Gloss, Yellow Trim, Handle, Green Mark	23.00
Belleek, Plate, Trinket, Heart Shape, Hand-Painted Flowers, Willet's Mark	22.00
Belleek, Platter, Twig Handles, Second Mark, 9 In.Diameter	40.00
Belleek, Pot, Honey, Bees, Shamrocks, Second Mark, 6 In.High	140.00
Belleek, Pot, Posy, White, Swirled Raised Ridges, Yellow Lined, Third Mark	25.00
Belleek, Rose Bowl, Pearlized, Irish, Second Black Mark	40.00
Belleek, Salt, Blue Ground, Pink Roses, Lenox, Set Of 6	19.00
Belleek, Salt, Gold, Iridescent Liner, Signed L In Circle, Set Of 6	22.00
Belleek, Salt, Gold, Pearlized Finish Inside, Willet	15.00
Belleek, Salt, Green, White Dots, Willet, 1 1/2 In.Diameter	5.00
Belleek, Salt, Heart Shape, Dainty Pansy In Center, Willet	8.50
Belleek, Salt, Heart, Dresden-Like Flowers, Hand-Painted, Willet	8.50
Belleek, Salt, Individual, Star Shape, Third Black Mark	12.50
Belleek, Salt, Light Green, Three Gold Feet, Lenox	8.00
Belleek, Salt, Master, Shell & Green Coral, Scalloped, Irish, 2nd Black Mark	38.00
Belleek, Salt, Open, Black Fermanagh Mark	6.50
Belleek, Salt, Pearlized, Willet	6.00
Belleek, Salt, Shamrock, Black Mark	10.00
Belleek, Salt, Shell & Coral, Irish, Second Mark	18.00
Belleek, Salt, Shell, Shamrocks, Scalloped, Black Mark	20.00
Belleek, Salt, Swan Shape, Willet, Serpent Mark	15.00
Belleek, Sugar & Creamer, Bacchus Heads, Grapes, Hound & Harp Mark	35.00
Belleek, Sugar & Creamer, Bacchus, Black Hound, Harp, Castle, Fermanagh	60.00
Belleek, Sugar & Creamer, Basket Weave, Shamrock, Green Mark, 3 1/2 In.	20.00
Belleek, Sugar & Creamer, Embossed Floral, Black Mark, Irish	35.00
Belleek, Sugar & Creamer, Floral, Irish, Third Black Mark	26.00
Belleek, Sugar & Creamer, Floral, 1915 Black Mark	48.00
Belleek, Sugar & Creamer, Gold Luster Interior, Brown Handles, Irish	30.00
Belleek, Sugar & Creamer, Ribbon Pattern, Second Mark	50.00
Belleek, Sugar & Creamer, Shamrock & Basket Weave, Second Black Mark	50.00
Belleek, Sugar & Creamer, Shamrock, Irish, Second Mark	45.00
Belleek, Sugar & Creamer, Shell Pattern, Signed Fermanagh Ireland	30.00
Belleek, Sugar & Creamer, Souvenir, Cork International Expo., 1903, Ireland	60.00
Belleek, Sugar, Bacchus, Open	27.00
Belleek, Sugar, Open, Black Mark, 4 In.	24.00
Belleek, Sugar, Open, Tridacna, Black Mark	37.00
Belleek, Sugar, Open, Yellow Luster Ribbon, Second Mark	25.00
Belleek, Tankard, Grape	125.00
Belleek, Tankard, Grape Clusters, Artist Signed, Willet, American, 14 In.	95.00
Belleek, Tankard, Red, Green, Purple Grapes, Artist Signed, Willet, C.1853	235.00
Belleek, Tea Set, Basket Weave & Shamrock Design, Green Mark, 6 Cups, Sauces	75.00
Belleek, Tea Set, Limpet, Black Mark, Pot, Sugar, Creamer, 8 Cup & Saucer	350.00
Belleek, Teakettle, Ivory, Pink Trim, Tridacna, First Black Mark	135.00

Belleek, Teapot, Basket Weave, Shamrock, Black Mark Signature 60.00
Belleek, Teapot, Coin Gold Decoration, Leaves, Butterfly, American 200.00
Belleek, Teapot, Cone, Irish, Second Black Mark 125.00
Belleek, Teapot, Creamer, Sugar, Coral Pattern, Second Black Mark 125.00
Belleek, Teapot, First Mark, Number 898 .... 275.00
Belleek, Teapot, Gold Around Lid & Spout, Irish, First Mark 115.00
Belleek, Teapot, Green Trim, Gold Rim, Hexagon, Irish, Second Black Mark 125.00
Belleek, Teapot, Hexagon, Pink Trim, Irish, Second Mark 60.00
Belleek, Teapot, Salmon Color, Gilt Bands, Brown Mark, Willet 55.00
Belleek, Teapot, Shamrock & Basket Weave, Brown & Green Twig Handle 65.00
Belleek, Teapot, Sugar, Creamer, Gold Ground, Multicolored Floral, Willet 150.00
Belleek, Teapot, Sugar, Creamer Shamrocks, Twig Handles, Black Mark 100.00
Belleek, Teapot, Tridacna Pattern, Pearl Gloss, Yellow Accents 35.00
Belleek, Teapot, Tridacna, Green Trim, Large Size 150.00
Belleek, Tray, Grass Pattern, Black Mark, 12 X 15 In. 115.00
Belleek, Tree Stump, Shamrocks, Second Mark, 6 1/4 In.High 55.00
Belleek, Vase, Flower Design, Yellow, White, Bulbous, 4 In.High 28.50
Belleek, Vase, Green Ground, Gold Trim, Portrait Of Josephine, 9 1/2 In. 68.00
Belleek, Vase, Hand-Painted Enamel Floral On Cream, Lenox Palette Mark 35.00
Belleek, Vase, Hand-Painted Floral, Bluebirds, Willet, 14 1/4 In. High 275.00
Belleek, Vase, Horn Of Plenty, Black Mark, Irish, 3 3/8 In.High 25.00
Belleek, Vase, Lake Scene, Swans, People On A Boat, 18 In. 100.00
Belleek, Vase, Mum Decoration, Willet, 16 In.High 165.00
Belleek, Vase, Owl, Irish, Green Mark 25.00
Belleek, Vase, Raised Flowers, Irish, 3 3/8 In. ....
Belleek, Vase, Seahorse, Yellow Luster Trim, Black Mark, Ireland 78.00
Belleek, Vase, Second Mark, 6 1/2 In. .... *Illus* 67.00

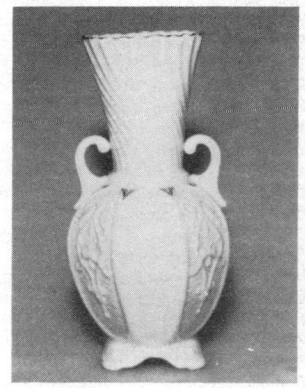

Belleek, Vase, Second Mark, 6 1/2 In.

Belleek, Vase, Shamrock Pattern, Flared Top, Green Mark, Ireland 25.00
Belleek, Vase, Spherical, Cabbage Roses, 10 In. 55.00
Belleek, Vase, Sunflower, Irish, 7 1/4 In. 75.00
Belleek, Vase, Thistle Motif, Green Mark, Irish, 8 1/4 In.High 125.00
Belleek, Vase, Tree Stump, Shamrock Pattern, Sectioned Top, Black Mark 35.00
Belleek, Vase, Two Colonial Musicians, Raised Gold Outlines, 15 In. 90.00
Belleek, Vase, Water Lilies, Art Nouveau, Willet, 9 1/2 In. 45.00

> *Bennington Ware was the product of two factories working in Bennington,*
> *Vermont. Both firms were out of business by 1896. The wares include the*
> *brown and yellow mottled pottery, Parian, Scroddle, Stoneware, Graniteware,*
> *Yellowware, and Staffordshire-like vases.*

Bennington, see also Rockingham
Bennington, Bottle, Figural, Mermaid 52.00
Bennington, Bottle, Toby, Marked, 1849 .... 370.00
Bennington, Bowl, Brown & White, Scroddleware, Pedestal 175.00
Bennington, Bowl, 10 In. 35.00
Bennington, Box, Trinket, Grapes In Relief, Parian 35.00
Bennington, Celery, Footed, Scalloped Top, 9 1/2 In.High 145.00
Bennington, Crock, Blue Leaf, Handle, E.Norton & Co. 38.00

Bennington, Cuspidor, Blue & Tan Marble, Diamond Pattern	250.00
Bennington, Cuspidor, Panel, Open Slot Side, 8 1/2 In.Diameter	21.00
Bennington, Cuspidor, Panels	31.50
Bennington, Cuspidor, Pineapple Design Around Base, Brown Glaze, 6 In.High	20.00
Bennington, Dish, Pudding, Flare-Out Sides, Brown Glaze, Yellow Mottling	55.00
Bennington, Dish, Soap, Brown, One Piece, Norton, 5 3/4 In.Long	20.00
Bennington, Doorknob, Pair	3.00
Bennington, Figurine, Draped Woman, Tinted Face, Hair, Applied Grapes, Parian	145.00
Bennington, Flask, Bible, Bennington Companion, 7 3/4 In.Long	375.00
Bennington, Flask, Bible, The Battle Of Bennington, 5 1/2 In.Long	285.00
Bennington, Footbath, Scalloped, Ribs, Flint, Circa 1849	850.00
Bennington, Jug, Blue Decoration, E.& L.P.Norton, 1861-1881, 3 Gallon	30.00
Bennington, Jug, Blue Tree, E. & L.P.Norton	38.00
Bennington, Pan, Mottled, Green, Brown, Yellow, Maple Leaves	37.50
Bennington, Pitcher, Grape Pattern	15.00
Bennington, Pitcher, Parian, Marked, 9 In.Tall	190.00
Bennington, Pitcher, Water, Brown	27.50
Bennington, Pitcher, Water, Bulbous Base, 10 3/4 In.High	35.00
Bennington, Pitcher, Water, Embossed Busts Of George Washington	75.00
Bennington, Pitcher, Water, Wreath Pattern	18.00
Bennington, Pitcher, Wild Rose	185.00
Bennington, Plate, Pie, Brown & Yellow Mottle, 11 In.	24.00
Bennington, Spittoon, Seashell Shape	29.00
Bennington, Syrup, Reliefs, Bulbous	12.00
Bennington, Vase, Bluebird Pattern, Pair	95.00
Bennington, Vase, Hand & Tulip, Parian	45.00
Bennington Type, Bottle, Fish Shape	10.00
Bennington Type, Candlestick, Squatty, Three Colors, Flint, Pair	20.00
Bennington Type, Figurine, Dog, Whippet, On Base	90.00
Bennington Type, Flask, Book, Green & Yellow Mottling, Departed Spirit	230.00
Bennington Type, Pitcher, Hound Handle, Eagle Under Spout, Hanging Game	75.00
Bennington Type, Syrup, Raised Design, Brown Glaze	15.00
Bennington Type, Teapot, Rebecca At The Well, Brown Glaze, 8 1/2 In.High	27.00

Berlin, a German porcelain factory, was started in 1751 by Wilhelm Kaspar Wegely. In 1763 the factory was taken over by Frederick the Great and became the Royal Berlin Porcelain Manufactory. It is still in operation today.

Berlin, Coffeepot, C.1765, 8 1/4 In.High	*Illus*	575.00
Berlin, Cup & Saucer, Blue, Floral, Gold, Dated 1847		35.00
Bicycle, Three Wheeled Buggy		350.00
Bicycle, Wood & Iron, Large Front Wheel, 10 1/4 In.Long		150.00

Bing and Grondahl is a famous Danish factory making fine porcelains from 1853 to the present. Their Christmas Plates are especially well known.

Bing & Grondahl, see also Collector, Plate

Bing & Grondahl, Figurine, Sea Gull, Free Standing, 4 In.Long		22.50
Bing & Grondahl, Vase, Gourd Shape, Cobalt, Irises, Artist Signed, Circa 1890		125.00
Binoculars, French, Enameled In Niello Technique, C.1875		150.00

Bisque is an unglazed baked porcelain. Finished Bisque has a slightly sandy texture with a dull finish. Some of it may be decorated with various colors. Bisque gained favor during the late Victorian era when thousands of Bisque figurines were made.

Bisque, Candelabra, 10 In.	*Illus*	175.00
Bisque, Chamberstick, Gold Roping Around Edge, Gold Butterfly Handle, Pair		30.00
Bisque, Creamer, Figural, Cow, White		28.50
Bisque, Creamer, Gold, Footed		15.00
Bisque, Dish, Heart, Blue, Enameled Flowers, Gold Trim, Fluted Edge		30.00
Bisque, Doll, Reclining Girl In Bathing Suit, Marked Germany		10.00
Bisque, Eggcup, Chick		15.00
Bisque, Figurine, Angel, Mounted On Maroon Velvet, Gold Frame		45.00
Bisque, Figurine, Bathing Beauty, Green Suit & Cap, Germany		13.50
Bisque, Figurine, Bear Couple, Says Isn't You Charley, C.1867, 5 1/2 In.		58.00

Bisque, Figurine, Blue Boy, 9 1/2 In.High	18.00
Bisque, Figurine, Boy & Girl In Wedding Clothes, French	98.00
Bisque, Figurine, Boy & Girl, Baskets, Pink, 3 1/2 In.Tall	55.00
Bisque, Figurine, Boy & Girl, White Hounds, Pair	20.00
Bisque, Figurine, Boy & Teddy Bear, Signed Ges Gesch	37.00
Bisque, Figurine, Boy, Holds Flowers, Satchel Over Shoulder, Germany, 7 In.	25.00
Bisque, Figurine, Cobbler, Gardner Decorated, Moscow, C.1885	200.00
Bisque, Figurine, Colonial Girl, Parasol, Pink	19.50
Bisque, Figurine, Discus Thrower, 9 In. _Illus_	120.00
Bisque, Figurine, Dog, Shaggy, Intaglio Eyes, Red Collar, Heubach	32.00
Bisque, Figurine, Dog, Spitz, White, Sitting, Curled Tail, Black Nose & Eyes	25.00
Bisque, Figurine, Dove, Green & Blue, Marked Colbert, 18 In.High, Pair	175.00
Bisque, Figurine, Eskimo Child, Baby Seal	9.00
Bisque, Figurine, Grumpy, Disney, 2 1/2 In.	6.00
Bisque, Figurine, Man In Spanish Costume & Guitar, Girl Dancer, Depose, Pair	125.00
Bisque, Figurine, Mutt & Jeff, 4 In.High, Pair	90.00
Bisque, Figurine, Negro Boy On Camel	12.50
Bisque, Figurine, Potty, Black Child Sitting, White Standing	17.50

Berlin, Coffeepot, C.1765, 8 1/4 In.High
See Page 32

Bisque, Candelabra, 10 In.
See Page 32

Bisque, Figurine, Discus Thrower, 9 In.

Bisque, Figurine, Sailor, Molded Cap, Painted Clothes, Japan	4.00
Bisque, Figurine, Seated Man & Woman, Germany	125.00
Bisque, Figurine, Soccer Player, 8 In.High	24.00
Bisque, Figurine, Woman Holding Child, Gardner Decorated, Moscow, C.1885	200.00
Bisque, Flower Holder, Figural, Boy In Costume Sits Near Flower, France	25.00
Bisque, Hatpin Holder, Hanging, Cameo Type Medallion, Pointed Shape	35.00
Bisque, Jar, Tobacco, Negro Boy's Head, 4 1/2 In.High	55.00
Bisque, Match Holder, Boots, Striker, 4 In.High	22.00
Bisque, Match Holder, Devil Sits At Base Of Cabbage, Pale Green	4.00
Bisque, Match Holder, Dutch Boy Alongside Beige Basket	32.50
Bisque, Match Holder, German, Boy, Dog, House, Pastel, Flowers, 7 X 4 In.	15.00
Bisque, Match Holder, Peasant Girl Alongside Wicker Basket	27.50
Bisque, Match Holder, Wall, 2 Chicks Peeking Out Of Pink Booties	27.00
Bisque, Match Holder, Wall, 2 Victorian Children, Pastel, C.1890	39.00
Bisque, Nodder, Oriental Woman Playing Stringed Instrument, 5 1/2 In.High	75.00
Bisque, Nodder, Santa, Germany	14.50
Bisque, Pastille Burner, Ann Hathaway Cottage, Signed W.H.Goss	35.00
Bisque, Pastille Burner, Robert Burns' Cottage, 5 1/2 X 3 1/2 In.High	18.00

Bisque, Piano Baby, Crawling, Raised Head, German, 7 In.Long	35.00
Bisque, Piano Baby, Creeping, White Dress, Blue Trim, One Foot Up, 12 1/4 In.	125.00
Bisque, Piano Baby, Heubach, Bonnet	110.00
Bisque, Piano Baby, Heubach, Girl Lying On Back, Feet In Air, Head On Pillow	195.00
Bisque, Piano Baby, Heubach, Lying On Stomach, Impressed Mark, 8 1/2 In.Long	150.00
Bisque, Piano Baby, Heubach, Molded Clothes, Holds Foot	395.00
Bisque, Piano Baby, Heubach, Seated, Signed, 7 1/4 In.High	95.00
Bisque, Piano Baby, On Side Holding Up Hand With Flower	85.00
Bisque, Piano Baby, Reclining On Back, French, 6 In.Long, 3 In.High	45.00
Bisque, Piano Baby, Seated, Holds Book, 4 1/2 In.High	35.00
Bisque, Piano Baby, 5 In.	23.00
Bisque, Pig, Japan, 3 1/2 In.Tall	7.50
Bisque, Pitcher, Pink, Warrior, 6 In.	40.00
Bisque, Salt & Pepper, Billikens, 3 1/2 In.High	3.50
Bisque, Salt, Open, Half Moon, Gray Side Smiles, Tan Side Serene	15.00
Bisque, Shoe, High, Tan, Cat On Toe, Mouse At Top, 3 1/4 In.Long	22.00
Bisque, Shoe, Shaped Like A Spaniel Dog, 7 In.Long	30.00
Bisque, Shoe, Two Green Frogs On Side Playing Guitar & Accordian	47.50
Bisque, Slipper, Blue, Embossed Top, Pink Floral, Green Leaves On Toe	8.00
Bisque, Slipper, Pearls & Leaves, 5 In.	12.50
Bisque, Toby Mug, Bacchus, Full Figure	22.00
Bisque, Toothpick, Bean Pot With Sitting Pink Pig, Germany	10.00
Bisque, Toothpick, Double, Pink Pig In Middle	20.00
Bisque, Toothpick, Egg Shape, Orange Floral, Gold Branch, Black Bird, Base	27.50
Bisque, Toothpick, Fairy, Child, Bird, Tree, Water, Green, White, 2 1/4 In.Tall	19.50
Bisque, Toothpick, Grotesque Gentlemen	12.00
Bisque, Toothpick, Victorian, Boy Standing On Boot, Tinted, Marked Germany	12.50
Bisque, Vase, Cupid By Blue Chicken, N In Circle, 7 In.	15.00
Bisque, Vase, Cupids On Side Of Large Open Conch Shell, 5 1/4 In.High	38.00

Black Amethyst Glass appears black until it is held to the light, and a dark purple can be seen. It was made in many factories from 1860 to the present time.

Black Amethyst, Bottle, Pinched, Sterling Overlay	35.00
Black Amethyst, Bottle, Seal, Embossed Ioii Vonpein	60.00
Black Amethyst, Bowl, Embossed Flowers Inside & Rim, Footed, 11 1/4 In.	22.00
Black Amethyst, Bowl, Separate Pedestal, Pair Candlesticks	16.00
Black Amethyst, Bowl, 7 In. X 4 In.High, Pair Candlesticks, 9 In.High	30.00
Black Amethyst, Compote, Silver Deposit Urns, Scrollwork	10.00
Black Amethyst, Compote, Underplate & Bowl, 2 Piece	45.00
Black Amethyst, Console Set, Bowl, Pedestal, Pair Candlesticks	18.00
Black Amethyst, Console Set, Center Handle, Footed Candlesticks	18.00
Black Amethyst, Console Set, Footed Bowl, Pair Candlesticks	17.50
Black Amethyst, Cup, Loving, Dancing Figures, 2 Handles	8.50
Black Amethyst, Dish, Footed, Greek Key Border, Signed In Cross	12.00
Black Amethyst, Dish, Nut, Footed, Tricornered Hobnail	12.00
Black Amethyst, Owl, Pressed, Marked D, 3 In.	8.00
Black Amethyst, Plate, Cake, Painted Peach Flowers With Gold, 10 In.	22.00
Black Amethyst, Plate, Silver Florals, Handled, 8 1/2 In.Diameter	6.00
Black Amethyst, Sugar & Creamer, Footed	10.00
Black Amethyst, Swan	18.50
Black Amethyst, Swan, Silver Trim, Marked Handmade Glassware L.E.Smith	38.00
Black Amethyst, Teaberry Gum Stand, Footed, 9 X 7 In.	14.00
Black Amethyst, Vase, Bead Pattern At Top, Tapered Center, 5 1/2 In.	6.00
Black Amethyst, Vase, Bud, Etched Gold Floral Band, Gold Trim, 10 1/4 In.	15.00
Black Amethyst, Vase, Bud, Ruffled Top, 8 In.	8.00
Black Amethyst, Vase, Bulbous, 9 1/2 In.High	9.50
Black Amethyst, Vase, Footed, 5 1/2 In.High	6.00
Black Amethyst, Vase, Painted Yellow Flower, 7 1/2 In.High	6.00
Black Amethyst, Vase, Platinum, Two Handles	20.00
Black Amethyst, Vase, Two Handles, 8 In.	15.50
Black Amethyst, Vase, Urn Shape, 9 5/8 In.High	20.00
Black Amethyst, Vase, 6 In.High, Pair	10.50
Black Amethyst, Vase, 8 1/4 In.High, Pair	10.50

Blown Glass was formed by forcing air through a rod into molten glass.

Early glass and some forms of Art Glass were hand blown. Other types of glass were molded or pressed. The McKearin numbers refer to the book American Glass by George and Helen McKearin.

Blown Glass, **Bottle**, Apothecary, Two Mold, Diamond Quilted, 19th Century 450.00
Blown Glass, **Bottle**, Condiment, Three Mold 50.00
Blown Glass, **Bowl**, Finger, Amethyst, 4 3/4 In.Diameter 12.50
Blown Glass, **Bowl**, Finger, Cobalt, 4 3/4 In.Diameter 12.50
Blown Glass, **Bowl**, Finger, Ruffle Top, Threaded, Polished Pontil, Green 17.50
Blown Glass, **Bowl**, Flower, Blue, Diamond Pattern, Scalloped, Applied Edge 25.00
Blown Glass, **Bowl**, Footed, Amber, Applied Handle, Ellenville, N.Y. 25.00
Blown Glass, **Bowl**, Footed, Expanded Panels, Folded Rim, 8 1/4 In.Diameter 60.00
Blown Glass, **Bowl**, Light Green, Welded Rim, 9 In.Diameter 90.00
Blown Glass, **Bowl**, McKearin G I-5, Shallow, Welded Rim 60.00
Blown Glass, **Bowl**, Milk, Miniature, Welded Rim 12.50
Blown Glass, **Bowl**, Swirl, Rib, Green, Ohio, C.1825, 9 1/2 In.Diameter 275.00
Blown Glass, **Bowl**, Three Mold, Folded Rim, Shallow Diamond Pattern, 6 In. 95.00
Blown Glass, **Bowl**, Tulip, Frosted, Polished Pontil, 6 In.Diameter 12.50
Blown Glass, **Box**, Powder, Scene On Lid, Sailboats, Trees, Mountains, Enamel 22.50
Blown Glass, **Candlestick**, Sandwich, Blown Column And Socket 200.00
Blown Glass, **Celery**, Gadrooned Swirl With Engraving 210.00
Blown Glass, **Celery**, Pittsburgh, Cut 190.00
Blown Glass, **Celery**, Pittsburgh, Expanded Oval Panels, Copper Wheel Etching 120.00
Blown Glass, **Creamer**, Footed, Applied Handle, Cobalt Blue 45.00
Blown Glass, **Creamer**, Miniature, Three Mold, Diamond & Rib, 3 In.High 140.00
Blown Glass, **Creamer**, Three Mold, Diamond & Rib, Clear, Applied Handle 55.00
Blown Glass, **Decanter**, Etched Fisherman, Pole, Nude Woman Watches, Pair 95.00
Blown Glass, **Dome**, Green, Bell Shape, C.1840, 16 In.Diameter 175.00
Blown Glass, **Flip**, McKearin G II-18, 4 1/2 In.High 135.00
Blown Glass, **Hat**, Blue, Open Pontil, 2 3/4 In.High 75.00
Blown Glass, **Hat**, Flared Sides, Ruby, 2 1/2 In.Tall 15.00
Blown Glass, **Hat**, Glass Band Inside Crown, Light Green 85.00
Blown Glass, **Hat**, Swirled, Clear, 5 In.Diameter, 2 1/4 In.Tall 14.00
Blown Glass, **Hat**, Three Mold, Diamond Sunburst, Folded Rim 35.00
Blown Glass, **Inkwell**, Cathedral Shape, Clear, Finial On Top 25.00
Blown Glass, **Inkwell**, Pitkin, Swirled To Left, Dark Olive Green 360.00
Blown Glass, **Jar**, Pittsburgh, Covered, Applied Blue Rings, Blue Finial 170.00
Blown Glass, **Jar**, Snuff, Olive Amber 42.50
Blown Glass, **Mug**, Baluster Shape, Applied Handle, Gold Letters, Green 35.00
Blown Glass, **Mug**, Child's, Ruby, Engraved, 'Love The Giver, 'Floral Reserve 20.00
Blown Glass, **Mug**, Spangled & Crackled Glass, Applied Handle, 4 1/2 In.Tall 19.00
Blown Glass, **Pan**, Milk, Deep Olive, Rolled Rim, Free-Blown 125.00
Blown Glass, **Pitcher**, Acid Etched, '1896, Mr.& Mrs.Frank W.B.Mahan' 30.00
Blown Glass, **Pitcher**, Milk, Inverted Panel, Fluted Top, Green 25.00
Blown Glass, **Pitcher**, Milk, Pillar, Pittsburgh, Applied Strap Handle 40.00
Blown Glass, **Pitcher**, Miniature, Pittsburgh, Clear, Applied Twist Handle 50.00
Blown Glass, **Pitcher**, Pittsburgh, Pillar, Swirled To Right, Hollow Handle 90.00
Blown Glass, **Pitcher**, Urn Shape, Clear, Swirled 15.00
Blown Glass, **Pitcher**, Water, Bulbous, Fine Rib, Applied Handle, Ground Pontil 75.00
Blown Glass, **Pitcher**, Water, Floral On Blue Band, Hand-Painted 17.50
Blown Glass, **Pitcher**, Water, Inverted Thumbprint, Amber, Bulbous 75.00
Blown Glass, **Pitcher**, Water, Midwestern, Swirled To Right, Tooled Edge 130.00
Blown Glass, **Pitcher**, Water, Pillar, Pittsburgh, Applied Strap Handle 110.00
Blown Glass, **Rolling Pin**, Milk White, Holds Water, Painted Forget-Me-Nots 15.00
Blown Glass, **Rose Bowl**, Green, Hand-Painted Enamel Scene Palm Trees 68.00
Blown Glass, **Rose Bowl**, Ruffled, Ribs, Pale Vaseline To Smoke, White Top 60.00
Blown Glass, **Salt & Pepper**, Ovals, Sterling Top, Clear, 2 1/2 In.High 7.00
Blown Glass, **Salt**, Expanded Diamond Pattern, Clear, Footed 45.00
Blown Glass, **Salt**, Expanded Diamond, Footed, Cobalt Blue To Violet 105.00
Blown Glass, **Salt**, Swirled To Right, Petal Base, Footed, Medium Green 310.00
Blown Glass, **Sugar**, McKearin G II-32, 3 Mold, Cobalt Base, Amethyst 750.00
Blown Glass, **Sugar**, Midwestern, Clear, Covered, Welded Rim On Cover 150.00
Blown Glass, **Sugar**, Three Mold, Amethyst, C.1815 .... *Illus* 4000.00
Blown Glass, **Sweetmeat**, Teardrop Stem, Flint, England, Set Of 6 .... 180.00
Blown Glass, **Syrup**, Flint, Applied Handle, Pewter Top 125.00
Blown Glass, **Vase**, Amethyst, Rough Pontil, Ruffled Top, White Flowers, Pair 35.00
Blown Glass, **Vase**, Etched Flower Design, Purple, 8 3/4 In.Tall, Pair 18.00

Blown Glass, Sugar, Three Mold, Amethyst, C.1815
See Page 35

Blown Glass, Vase, Yellow, White Ribbons, Clear Applied Handles	45.00
Blown Glass, Wine, Bucket Bowl, Applied Knop Stem & Foot, Flint	16.00
Blown Glass, Wine, Clear, Welded Rim, Expanded Flutes, Small Bowl	50.00
Blown Glass, Wine, Copper Wheel Decorated	18.50
Blown Glass, Wine, Ribbing & Copper Wheel Decoration	20.00

Blue Amberina, see Bluerina
Blue Glass, see Cobalt Blue
Blue Onion, see Onion

*Blue Willow Pattern has been made in England since 1780. The pattern
has been copied by factories in many countries, including Germany, Japan, and
the United States. It is still being made. Willow was named for a
pattern that pictures a bridge, birds, willow trees, and a Chinese landscape.*

Blue Willow, Bowl, Covered, Round, Morijama, 5 In.	11.00
Blue Willow, Butter, Covered, Dome, Buffalo	22.00
Blue Willow, Compote, Clear, Engraved Green	15.00
Blue Willow, Cup & Saucer, Farmer's, W.A.& Sons	25.00
Blue Willow, Dishes, Child's Set	12.50
Blue Willow, Food Warmer, Porcelain, Flat Container For Hot Water	10.00
Blue Willow, Gravy And Plate, Marked Barker Bros., England	14.00
Blue Willow, Gravy Boat, Buffalo Pottery, Signed, 1911	33.00
Blue Willow, Gravy Boat, Pattern In Base Of Boat, Arrow Shape Mark	25.00
Blue Willow, Jar, Biscuit, Barrel Shape, Silver Handle & Lid, Minton, Eng.	55.00
Blue Willow, Jug, Water, Handle, Japan	8.00 To 10.00
Blue Willow, Pitcher, Buffalo Pottery, Gold, Dated 1907, 6 In.High	35.00
Blue Willow, Pitcher, Burleighware, Burslem, England, 5 In.High	17.50
Blue Willow, Pitcher, Chinoiserie Pattern, Leeds Pearlware, 6 In.	65.00
Blue Willow, Pitcher, Covered, Buffalo Pottery, 1910	28.00
Blue Willow, Pitcher, Milk, Burleighware, Burslem, England	17.50
Blue Willow, Plate, Allerton, 9 3/4 In.	10.00
Blue Willow, Plate, Bread & Butter, Japan	1.00
Blue Willow, Plate, Buffalo Pottery, 1911, 6 In.	3.50
Blue Willow, Plate, Buffalo Pottery, 1911, 7 In.	4.00
Blue Willow, Plate, Buffalo Pottery, 9 In.	7.00 To 8.00
Blue Willow, Plate, Buffalo Pottery, 10 1/4 In.	12.50
Blue Willow, Plate, Burleighware, Burslem, England, 9 In.	5.00
Blue Willow, Plate, Burleighware, Burslem, England, 10 In.	6.00
Blue Willow, Plate, Dinner, Ridgway, 9 In.	15.00
Blue Willow, Plate, Divided, England	7.50
Blue Willow, Plate, 10 In.	7.50
Blue Willow, Platter, Buffalo Pottery, Dated 1905	37.00
Blue Willow, Platter, Ridgway, 9 1/2 X 12 In.	12.00
Blue Willow, Platter, Ridgway, 13 X 11 In.	16.00
Blue Willow, Saucer, Japan	1.00
Blue Willow, Soup, Buffalo Pottery, 1911	6.00
Blue Willow, Soup, Ridgway	10.00

Blue Willow, Teapot, Dog Finial 35.00
Blue Willow, Teapot, Ridgway 18.00
Blue Willow, Vegetable, Covered, Ridgway, 11 X 7 In. .... 28.50 To 29.50
Blue Willow, Washstand Set, England 55.00

Bluerina is a type of art glass which shades from light blue to ruby. It is often called Blue Amberina.
Bluerina, Sugar, Shaker 39.00
Bluerina, Tumbler, Rose To Light Blue, Inverted Thumbprint 70.00

Edward Marshall Boehm made pottery in Trenton, New Jersey, starting in 1949. His bird figurines have achieved worldwide recognition.
Boehm, Bird, American Redstarts, No.447, 12 In.High 400.00
Boehm, Bird, Baby Blue Bird, Signed, 3 1/2 In.Tall 175.00
Boehm, Bird, Baby Goldfinch, No.448, 4 1/4 In.High 375.00
Boehm, Bird, Baby Robin, No.437w, 3 1/2 In.High 600.00
Boehm, Bird, Nonpareil Buntings, No.446, 8 1/2 In.High 1300.00
Boehm, Bird, Sugar Birds 8000.00
Boehm, Bird, Varied Buntings 3000.00

Bohemian Glass is an ornate, overlay, or flashed glass made during the Victorian era. It has been reproduced in Bohemia, which is now a part of Czechoslovakia. Glass made from 1875 to 1900 is preferred by collectors.
Bohemian Glass, Bottle, Barber, Ruby, Deer & Castle 25.00
Bohemian Glass, Bottle, Ruby, Etched, 10 In.High 30.00
Bohemian Glass, Bottle, Ruby, Frosted Center, Red Birds, Blown, Stopper 30.00
Bohemian Glass, Bowl, Amber Cut To Clear, 5 1/2 In.High 90.00
Bohemian Glass, Bowl, Deer, Woods, & Birds, Flashed 55.00
Bohemian Glass, Bowl, Etched Lace, Blue Medallions, Dog, Rabbit, Castle 45.00
Bohemian Glass, Bowl, Finger, Ruby Flashed 10.00
Bohemian Glass, Bowl, Red & Green, Fluted & Pleated Rim, Taffeta, 11 In. 110.00
Bohemian Glass, Butter, Covered, Ruby, Deer & Castle 40.00
Bohemian Glass, Candleholder, Deer, Pine Trees, Ruby Flashed, 1900, Pair 62.50
Bohemian Glass, Candy, Covered, Cranberry Cut To Clear, 6 1/4 In. 95.00
Bohemian Glass, Cologne, Cobalt, Grapes, Leaves, Enamel, White, Gilt, Pontil 45.00
Bohemian Glass, Cordial, Vintage Pattern 19.00
Bohemian Glass, Decanter, Crystal, Red Flashed, Swirl Panels, Grapes, Leaves 45.00
Bohemian Glass, Decanter, Diamond Shape Red Panels, Cut Floral, Key & Lock 350.00
Bohemian Glass, Decanter, Red, Deer & Trees, Cut To Clear, Stopper, 8 In.High 145.00
Bohemian Glass, Decanter, Red, Vintage Decoration, Etched 65.00
Bohemian Glass, Decanter, Vintage Pattern, Numbered, 14 In.High, Pair 75.00
Bohemian Glass, Decanter, Vintage Pattern, Ruby & Clear, Stopper, Pair 110.00
Bohemian Glass, Dresser Set, Birds, Flowers, Blown, 3 Piece 77.00
Bohemian Glass, Goblet, Etched, Knob Stem 45.00
Bohemian Glass, Lamp, Ruby Cut To Clear, Flowers, Leaves, Bead Finial, Wired 175.00
Bohemian Glass, Lustre, Overlay, Pair 325.00
Bohemian Glass, Perfume, Flower & Leaf Design, Marked 50.00
Bohemian Glass, Perfume, Ruby, Clear & Ruby Rings, Gold Tracing, Stopper 18.00
Bohemian Glass, Pokal, Covered, Ruby, Doe & Stag, 13 1/4 In.High 400.00
Bohemian Glass, Pokal, Intaglio Cut Deer & Tree Decoration, Amber 180.00
Bohemian Glass, Pokal, Ruby, 19th Century, 31 In.High .... *Illus* 700.00
Bohemian Glass, Pokal, Scenic Decoration, Amber, Pair 160.00
Bohemian Glass, Spittoon, Lady's, Blue, Deer Scene, Amber Border, 3 In.High 38.00
Bohemian Glass, Toothpick, Red, Etched, Gold Trim 12.00
Bohemian Glass, Toothpick, Ruby, Deer & Castle 12.50
Bohemian Glass, Tumble-Up 30.00
Bohemian Glass, Tumble-Up, Allover Intaglio Cut Floral, Amber Overlay 55.00
Bohemian Glass, Tumbler, Ruby, Castle Scene 6.50
Bohemian Glass, Tumbler, Ruby, Etched Deer & Castle 14.50
Bohemian Glass, Tumbler, Vintage Etched Pattern, Footed 28.00
Bohemian Glass, Vase, Birds, Flowers, Leaves, White, Red, 13 1/2 In.Tall, Pair 115.00
Bohemian Glass, Vase, Cobalt, Decorated, Rough Pontil, Hollow Base, 1840 .... 65.00
Bohemian Glass, Vase, Cut Amber Panels, 5 In. 12.00
Bohemian Glass, Vase, Flowers, Copper Wheel Engraved, Band Of Daisies, Pair 195.00
Bohemian Glass, Vase, Green, Cut To Clear, Lilies Of The Valley, Overlay 65.00
Bohemian Glass, Vase, Royal Blue, Stag & Forest Scene, 13 In.High 75.00

Bohemian Glass, Pokal, Ruby, 19th Century, 31 In.High
See Page 37

Bohemian Glass, Vase, Ruby, Bird Design, 6 In.High	16.00
Bohemian Glass, Vase, Ruby, Deer, Bird, & Castle, 7 1/2 In.Across Top	60.00
Bohemian Glass, Vase, Ruby, Red Design, Frosted, 9 3/4 In.High	40.00
Bohemian Glass, Vase, Stags, Trees, Deeply Cut, 10 1/2 In.High	110.00
Bohemian Glass, Vase, Stags, Trees, Lookout Towers, Ground Pontil, 6 1/2 In.	57.50
Bohemian Glass, Wine Set, Ruby, Deer & Castle, Decanter 12 1/2 In., 7 Piece	95.00
Bohemian Glass, Wine, Vintage Pattern	15.00
Bone Dish, Blue & Yellow Floral, Marked Jones & Son, England, Set Of 4	20.00
Bone Dish, Colonial Pattern, Cobalt Blue & Orange Floral, Laughlin	3.00
Bone Dish, Forget-Me-Not Spray, Schwartzburg China, Pair	12.00
Book, Almanac, Ayer's Sarsaparilla, 1884, 36 Pages	3.50
Book, Almanac, Burdock Blood Bitters, 1839	2.75
Book, Almanac, Burdock Blood Bitters, 1888	2.75
Book, Almanac, Dr.Jayne's Medical, 1884, 48 Pages	3.50
Book, Almanac, Hostetter's, 1884	4.00
Book, Carter's Little Liver Pills, 1890	6.00
Book, Gene Autry, Big Little Book	4.00
Book, Hood's Sarsaparilla	3.00
Book, Ripley's Believe It Or Not, Big Little Book	3.50
Book, Tarzan Twins In The Jungle, Fast Action Book, 1938	12.00
Book, Zip Sanders, Big Little Book	2.00
Boston & Sandwich Co., see Sandwich, Fireglow, Lutz	

*Bottle collecting has become a major American hobby. There are several
general categories of bottles such as historic flasks, bitters, household, figural
and others.*

Bottle, Acme Beer, Amber, Cap, Label	5.00
Bottle, Ale, C.H.Evans & Sons, Dark Green	3.00
Bottle, Alkali, Opaque, Taylor Williams, Louisville, 12 In.	6.00
Bottle, Amber Chestnut, Rough Pontil, Bubbles In Glass, Blown, 5 1/4 In.	55.00
Bottle, Amber, Encased In Wicker, Raised Letters Say I.W.Harper	9.50
Bottle, Anodyne, Shaker, Paper Label	25.00
Bottle, Apothecary Jar, Free-Blown, Open Pontil, Tin Cap	15.00
Bottle, Apothecary, Blown, Amethyst	10.00
Bottle, Apothecary, Blown, Stopper, Clear, 8 1/2 In.High	5.00
Bottle, Apothecary, Blown, Stopper, Clear, 9 1/2 In.High	6.00
Bottle, Apothecary, Blown Stopper, Clear, 12 1/2 In.High	8.00
Bottle, Apothecary, Cobalt Blue	15.00
Bottle, Apothecary, Free-Blown, Rough Pontil, Glass Stopper, 10 In.	12.50
Bottle, Apothecary, Glass Label, Ground Stopper, Wide Mouth, 1840, Clear	8.95
Bottle, Apothecary, Gold Label, W.T.Co., U.S.A., Latin Name, 8 1/2 In.	8.00
Bottle, Apothecary, Gold Label, W.T.Co., U.S.A., Latin Name, 10 1/2 In.	10.00
Bottle, Apothecary, Green, Blown, Cut Stopper, 6 1/2 In.High	15.00

Bottle, Apothecary, Improved Pontil, Glass Stopper, Paper Label 6.00
Bottle, Apothecary, Lobeliae, Gold Border, Ground Stopper, Clear 25.00
Bottle, Apothecary, Made In Pennsylvania, Amber 3.50
Bottle, Apothecary, Made In Pennsylvania, Aqua 2.00
Bottle, Apothecary, Made In Pennsylvania, Clear 1.50
Bottle, Apothecary, Statue Of Liberty, Spread Winged Eagle, Clear 135.00
Bottle, Apothecary, White Label, Gold Bands, 8 Oz., Set Of 7 .... 40.00
Bottle, Aromatic Schnapps, Amber, Quart 18.00

Avon started in 1886 as the California Perfume Company. It was not
until 1929 that the name Avon was used. In 1939 it became the Avon
Products, Inc. Each year Avon sells many figural bottles filled with
cosmetic products. Ceramic, plastic, and glass bottles are made in limited
editions.

Bottle, Avon, After Shower Foam, 1965, Full & Boxed 49.00
Bottle, Avon, Apple Blossom Toilet Water, 2 Oz., 1940 .... 30.00
Bottle, Avon, Attention Powder Sachet, 1943 .... 15.00
Bottle, Avon, Avonette, 1953 .... 15.00
Bottle, Avon, Award, Banner, No.566, 30 X 36 In., 1966 .... 100.00
Bottle, Avon, Award, Bird Of Paradise Bracelet & Earrings, 1970 .... 20.00
Bottle, Avon, Award, Bird Of Paradise Pin, 1970 .... 10.00
Bottle, Avon, Award, Bird Of Paradise Scarf, 1970 .... 10.00
Bottle, Avon, Award, Charm Bracelet, 4 Charms, 1965 .... 50.00
Bottle, Avon, Award, Charm Bracelet, 5 Charms, 1965 .... 60.00
Bottle, Avon, Award, Charm Bracelet, 6 Charms, 1969 .... 75.00
Bottle, Avon, Award, Manager Pin, 11 Diamonds, 1961 .... 100.00
Bottle, Avon, Award, Pearl Pin, 1959 .... 20.00
Bottle, Avon, Award, Sales, Cream Sachet, 1962 .... 10.00
Bottle, Avon, Award, Sapphire Pin, 1960 .... 30.00
Bottle, Avon, Award, Shell Earrings, 1957 .... 5.00
Bottle, Avon, Award, Shell Pin, 1957 .... 5.00
Bottle, Avon, Award, Spoons Set, 7 Spoons, 1969 .... 75.00
Bottle, Avon, Bath Oil For Men, 1965, Full & Boxed 10.00
Bottle, Avon, Beauty Muff Set 85.00
Bottle, Avon, Birdhouse, 1969, Full & Boxed 4.99
Bottle, Avon, Blue Blazer Soap On A Rope, 1964, Full & Boxed 6.00
Bottle, Avon, Bowling Pin, 1960 .... 6.99
Bottle, Avon, Boxing Gloves, 1960, Full & Boxed 19.50
Bottle, Avon, Bright Night Beauty Dust With Perfume, 1956 .... 20.00
Bottle, Avon, Bright Night Powder Sachet, 1954, Full & Boxed 5.50
Bottle, Avon, Bright Night Powder Sachet, 1955 .... 6.00
Bottle, Avon, Bright Night Toilet Water, 1954, Full & Boxed 10.00
Bottle, Avon, Bureau Organizer Set, 1966 .... 29.95 To 40.00
Bottle, Avon, Buttons & Bows Cologne, 2 Oz., 1963, Full & Boxed 7.00
Bottle, Avon, C.P.C.Astringent, Ribbed, 4 Oz., 1936 .... 40.00
Bottle, Avon, C.P.C.Bleaching Cream, 2 Oz., 1934 .... 40.00
Bottle, Avon, C.P.C.Cleansing Cream, Ribbed, 1936 .... 55.00
Bottle, Avon, C.P.C.Compact, Green, Gold, 1936 .... 15.00
Bottle, Avon, C.P.C.Daphne Talc, Green, 1936 .... 20.00
Bottle, Avon, C.P.C.Dusting Powder, Square, 1930 .... 35.00
Bottle, Avon, C.P.C.Extract, Sweet Pea, White Paper Label, Ground Stopper 135.00
Bottle, Avon, C.P.C.Food Color Set, 6 Piece, 1935 .... 200.00
Bottle, Avon, C.P.C.Fruit Flavors 18.00
Bottle, Avon, C.P.C.Marionette Perfume, Glass Stopper, 1 Dram, 1936 .... 85.00
Bottle, Avon, C.P.C.Perfection Cologne, Flavor No.G, 1/2 Oz., 1936 .... 40.00
Bottle, Avon, C.P.C.Perfection Concentrated Coloring, Blue, Paper Label 45.00
Bottle, Avon, C.P.C.Perfection Flavors, No.G, 1936 .... 35.00
Bottle, Avon, C.P.C.Perfection Savory, 4 Oz., 1936 .... 50.00
Bottle, Avon, C.P.C.Powder Sachet, 1915 .... 70.00
Bottle, Avon, C.P.C.Talc, Slide Top, 1930 .... 30.00
Bottle, Avon, C.P.C.Tissue Cream, 2 Oz., 1934 .... 40.00
Bottle, Avon, C.P.C.Tooth Tablet, Milk Glass Base, Metal Cover 20.00
Bottle, Avon, C.P.C.Tooth Tablet, 1908 .... 150.00
Bottle, Avon, C.P.C.Vanishing Cream, 2 Oz., 1934, Full & Boxed 50.00
Bottle, Avon, C.P.C.Violet Bottle, Labels 30.00
Bottle, Avon, Cake Chest, Blue & Gold, Cake Pan 35.00

Bottle, Avon, Cameo Set, No Box 17.50
Bottle, Avon, Candle, Amber, 1965, Full & Boxed 8.00
Bottle, Avon, Christmas Ornament Set, 1964 .... 50.00
Bottle, Avon, Clean Shot, 1970, Full & Boxed 5.99
Bottle, Avon, Color Magic, 3 Piece Set, 1949 .... 30.00
Bottle, Avon, Coloring Set, Five Bottles, 4 1/2 Oz. 60.00
Bottle, Avon, Cotillion Cologne, Mist Yellow Bottom, 1961 .... 6.00
Bottle, Avon, Cotillion Cream Lotion & Cologne, 1951 .... 35.00
Bottle, Avon, Cotillion Powder Sachet, Pink, 1 1/4 Oz., 1958, Full & Boxed 6.00
Bottle, Avon, Cotillion Powder Sachet, 1946 .... 8.00
Bottle, Avon, Cotillion Toilet Water, 2 Oz., 1954, Full & Boxed 7.00
Bottle, Avon, Crystal Glory, 1962, Full & Boxed 6.00
Bottle, Avon, Daisies Won'T Tell Spray Cologne, 1957, Full & Boxed 7.00
Bottle, Avon, Daisy Won'T Tell Soap On Rope, Full & Boxed 10.00
Bottle, Avon, Decisions 19.50
Bottle, Avon, Elegante Powder Sachet, 1957, Full & Boxed 7.00
Bottle, Avon, Elegante Toilet Water, Full & Boxed 25.95
Bottle, Avon, Elysian Set, 1941 .... 50.00
Bottle, Avon, Flowertime Powder Sachet, 1949 .... 9.00
Bottle, Avon, For Young Hearts, 1945 .... 85.00
Bottle, Avon, Fragrance Jar, Flower, Pink, White 60.00
Bottle, Avon, Fragrant Ornament Set 35.00
Bottle, Avon, French Telephone 14.95
Bottle, Avon, Gentleman's Collection, 1968, Full & Boxed 9.00
Bottle, Avon, Gin & Crystal, Flat Top Caps 85.00
Bottle, Avon, Golden Heirloom Chest, 1968 .... 20.00
Bottle, Avon, Golden Promise Powder Sachet, Gold Metal Cap, 1948 .... 8.00
Bottle, Avon, Golf Bag, Full & Boxed 4.00
Bottle, Avon, Gun, Red, Full & Boxed 32.50
Bottle, Avon, Happy Hours Memento Set 85.00
Bottle, Avon, Happy Hours Star Bouquet Set 65.00
Bottle, Avon, Here's My Heart Powder Sachet, 1958 .... 7.00
Bottle, Avon, High Fashion Set, 1950, Boxed 22.50
Bottle, Avon, Island Lime, Dark Yellow Straw, 1966, Full & Boxed 49.00
Bottle, Avon, Just For Two, Full & Boxed 75.00
Bottle, Avon, Lady Slipper Soap, 1965, Full & Boxed 7.00
Bottle, Avon, Lavender Fragrance Jar, Glass Stopper, 6 3/4 In.Tall 125.00
Bottle, Avon, Manicure Tray, 1965 .... 4.50
Bottle, Avon, Marionette Toilet Water, 2 Oz., 1940 .... 30.00
Bottle, Avon, Nearness Cologne, 1/2 Oz., 1957, Full & Boxed 9.00
Bottle, Avon, Nearness Powder Sachet, 1954 .... 7.00
Bottle, Avon, Occur Powder Sachet, 1963 .... 7.00
Bottle, Avon, Perfection Glace Necklace, 1965 .... 6.99
Bottle, Avon, Perfection Glace Pin, 1965 .... 6.99
Bottle, Avon, Persian Wood Beauty Dust, 1956 .... 8.00
Bottle, Avon, Persian Wood Powder Sachet, 1957 .... 5.00
Bottle, Avon, Petipoint Perfume Glace, Full, Label 8.50
Bottle, Avon, Pipe Dream 12.50
Bottle, Avon, Quaintance Powder Sachet, 1948 .... 7.00
Bottle, Avon, Quaintance Powder Sachet, 1949, Full & Boxed 6.00
Bottle, Avon, Rainbow Wings 60.00
Bottle, Avon, Reception Set 50.00
Bottle, Avon, Regence Candle, 1968, Full 6.00
Bottle, Avon, Renaissance Trio 12.00
Bottle, Avon, Rose Fragrance Jar, Frosted Stopper, 1958 .... 15.00
Bottle, Avon, Scimitar, 1965 .... 7.50 To 15.00
Bottle, Avon, Somewhere Powder Sachet, 1967 .... 12.00
Bottle, Avon, Stagecoach, Embossed, 2 Oz., 1960 .... 10.00 To 20.00
Bottle, Avon, Steer Horn 12.99
Bottle, Avon, Stein, Silver, 6 Oz. 2.00
Bottle, Avon, Three Hearts On Cushion, 1966 .... 30.00
Bottle, Avon, Topaze Powder Sachet, 1959 .... 4.00
Bottle, Avon, Twin Tone Makeup Cream, White Milk Glass, Green Lid, 1943 .... 10.00
Bottle, Avon, Unforgettable Glace Pin, 1965 .... 10.00
Bottle, Avon, Viking Horn After Shave, 1966 .... 10.00
Bottle, Avon, Wild Rose Beauty Dust, 1957 .... 8.00

Bottle, Avon, Wild Rose Cologne, 1952 .... 15.00
Bottle, Avon, Wild Rose Cream Lotion, 1956 .... 5.00
Bottle, Avon, Wild Rose Perfume Oil, 1964, Full & Boxed 4.99
Bottle, Avon, Wild Rose Powder Sachet, 1953 .... 7.00
Bottle, Avon, Wild Rose Toilet Water, 2 Oz., Blue Cap, 1950 .... 9.00
Bottle, Avon, Wishing Powder Sachet, 1964 .... 6.00
Bottle, Baby's, Built In Thermometer, Eisele 7.00
Bottle, Baby's, Embossed Dog 3.50
Bottle, Bank, Christian Bros., Amber, 1 Qt. 35.00
Bottle, Bar, Diamond Thumbprint, Bar Lip, Pint 110.00
Bottle, Bar, Smocking, Lined, Flint, Bar Lip, Pint 15.00
Bottle, Darber, Amberina Coloring, Pewter Top, Baccarat 45.00
Bottle, Barber, Amethyst Glass, Enameled Daisies, Porcelain Stopper 52.00
Bottle, Barber, Amethyst, White & Gold Floral, Leaves, Pewter Shaker Top 45.00
Bottle, Barber, Amethyst, White Fleur-De-Lis, Inverted Cone Shape, Spout 65.00
Bottle, Barber, Black Ruby Glass, Enamel Leaves, Hand-Painted, Stopper 65.00
Bottle, Barber, Blown Design, Bulbous, Pewter Top, 5 1/2 In.Tall 18.50
Bottle, Barber, Blown, Silver Deposit, Brass Stopper, Honey Amber 47.50
Bottle, Barber, Bohemian Type, Cut Design To Clear, Spout, Red, 8 1/2 In.High ... 50.00
Bottle, Barber, Clambroth, E.W.Mark 20.00
Bottle, Barber, Clear Opalescent, White Stars & Stripes, Ground Pontil 45.00
Bottle, Barber, Cobalt Blue, Polished Pontil, Free-Blown, No Top, 8 3/4 In. 32.00
Bottle, Barber, Cranberry, Hobnail, Shaker Top, 7 3/4 In., Pair 150.00
Bottle, Barber, Emerald Green Glass, Bulbous, Metal Shaker, 5 1/2 In. 14.50
Bottle, Barber, End-Of-Day 92.50
Bottle, Barber, Glass Base, Chrome Center, Glass Top, Dated 1897, 3 Piece 24.50
Bottle, Barber, Hair Tonic & Bay Rum, Black 12.00
Bottle, Barber, Lady's Leg Neck, Hexagon Base, Glass Stopper, Milk Glass 22.50
Bottle, Barber, Milk Glass, Porcelain Stopper 12.00
Bottle, Barber, Red & White Enameled Decor, Double Rounded Body, Emerald 22.50
Bottle, Barber, Red Glass, Cutwork Panels On Neck 20.00
Bottle, Barber, Round, Milk Glass, Open Pontil, Blue, 8 1/2 In.High, Pair 50.00
Bottle, Barber, Stopper, Cobalt Blue, Pair 32.00
Bottle, Barber, Toilet Water, Black 12.00
Bottle, Barber, White & Orange Enamel Floral, Open Pontil, Blue, 7 In.High 30.00
Bottle, Barber, Witch Hazel, Bulbous Base, Milk Glass, Porcelain Top 20.00
Bottle, Barber, Witch Hazel, Hexagon, Milk Glass 14.00
Bottle, Barber, Witch Hazel, Pewter Spout, Clambroth 10.00
Bottle, Barber, Witch Hazel, Water, White Milk Glass, E.W., Inc., Pair 60.00

*Beam Bottles are made to hold Kentucky Straight Bourbon made by the
James B. Beam Distilling Company. The Beam series of ceramic
bottles began in 1953.*

Bottle, Beam, Blue, Slot, 1967 .... *Illus* 15.00
Bottle, Beam, Broadmoor, Regal China Specialty, 1968 .... *Illus* 9.00
Bottle, Beam, California Mission, 1970 .... *Illus* 50.00
Bottle, Beam, Centennial, Laramie, 1968 .... *Illus* 6.00
Bottle, Beam, Civil War, Pair 75.00
Bottle, Beam, Cocktail Shaker, 1953 .... 3.95
Bottle, Beam, Coffee Warmer, 1954 .... 10.00
Bottle, Beam, Coffee Warmer, 1956 .... 3.50
Bottle, Beam, Doe, 1963 .... 34.00
Bottle, Beam, Executive, Presidential, 1968 .... *Illus* 12.00
Bottle, Beam, Executive, 1955 .... 195.00
Bottle, Beam, Executive, 1957 .... 67.00
Bottle, Beam, Executive, 1957, Case 75.00
Bottle, Beam, Executive, 1958 .... 155.00
Bottle, Beam, Executive, 1960 .... 82.50
Bottle, Beam, Executive, 1960, Case 90.00
Bottle, Beam, Executive, 1961 .... 63.00
Bottle, Beam, Executive, 1961, Case 72.00
Bottle, Beam, Executive, 1963 .... 47.00
Bottle, Beam, Executive, 1965 .... 65.00
Bottle, Beam, Executive, 1965, Case 70.00
Bottle, Beam, Executive, 1966 .... 34.00
Bottle, Beam, Executive, 1966, Case 37.00

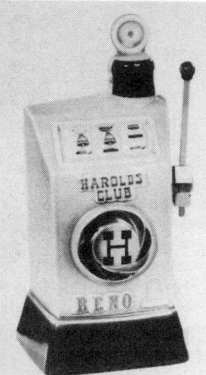

Bottle, Beam,
Blue Slot, 1967
See Page 41

Bottle, Beam, Broadmoor,
Regal China Specialty, 1968
See Page 41

Bottle, Beam,
California Mission, 1970
See Page 41

Bottle,
Beam, Centennial,
Laramie, 1968
See Page 41

Bottle, Beam,
Executive, Presidential,
1968
See Page 41

Bottle, Beam, Executive, 1967	16.95 To 18.00
Bottle, Beam, Executive, 1967, Case	15.00 To 19.00
Bottle, Beam, Executive, 1968	8.50
Bottle, Beam, Executive, 1968, Case	9.50
Bottle, Beam, Executive, 1969	9.00 To 10.00
Bottle, Beam, Executive, 1969, Case	10.00
Bottle, Beam, Executive, 1970	11.00
Bottle, Beam, Executive, 1970, Case	11.50
Bottle, Beam, Executive, 1971	13.00
Bottle, Beam, Executive, 1971, Case	14.00
Bottle, Beam, First Convention	10.95
Bottle, Beam, Fox, Green	39.00
Bottle, Beam, General Stark	19.95
Bottle, Beam, Hannah Duston	18.95
Bottle, Beam, Harold's Club V.I.P., 1967	35.00
Bottle, Beam, Harold's Club V.I.P., 1968	37.50
Bottle, Beam, Harold's Club V.I.P., 1969	70.00
Bottle, Beam, Horse, Brown, 1967	19.50
Bottle, Beam, Horse, Gray, 1967	19.50
Bottle, Beam, North Shore Club	29.50
Bottle, Beam, Pearl Harbor	11.95
Bottle, Beam, Pin, Wood Top, 1940	35.00
Bottle, Beam, Political Campaign, 1968, Elephant, Donkey, Pair	15.00
Bottle, Beam, Political, Donkey, 1966	15.00

Bottle, Beam, Political, Elephant, 1960 .... 15.00
Bottle, Beam, Ponderosa, 1972 .... 25.95
Bottle, Beam, Portland Rose 13.95
Bottle, Beam, Pro Football Hall Of Fame 13.95
Bottle, Beam, Ruidoso Downs, 1968 .... *Illus*   6.50
Bottle, Beam, St.Louis Arch 15.00
Bottle, Beam, St.Louis, 1964 .... 26.00
Bottle, Beam, Travelodge 9.95
Bottle, Beam, V.I.P., 1967 .... 50.00
Bottle, Beam, V.I.P., 1968 .... 50.00
Bottle, Beam, V.I.P., 1969 .... 80.00
Bottle, Beam, V.I.P., 1970, Case 49.95
Bottle, Beam, V.I.P., 1971, Case .... 49.95 To 55.00

Bottle, Beam, Ruidoso Downs, 1968

Bottle, Beam, Wyoming 55.00
Bottle, Beam, Yellowstone 12.95
Bottle, Beam, Yuma Rifle 37.50
Bottle, Beer, Blob Top, Embossed, Amber 2.50
Bottle, Beer, Blob Top, Embossed, Aqua 1.50
Bottle, Beer, English, Screw In Stopper, Embossed Brand Name 4.50
Bottle, Beer, F.& M.Schaeffer, N.Y., Embossed, Aqua, 10 In.High 3.00
Bottle, Beer, H.Jackel, Norwich, Conn., Metal Cap, Amber, 9 1/2 In.High 3.00
Bottle, Beer, Lithograph Label, Acme Beer, Nonfattening, Miniature, 3 In. 12.00
Bottle, Beer, Milk Glass, White, 11 In. 95.00
Bottle, Beer, Pottery, Incised Hennessey & Nolan 5.00
Bottle, Beer, Royal Ruby, 12 Oz. 7.00
Bottle, Beer, Ruby Red, Quart 7.50
Bottle, Beer, Schlitz, Miniature 2.00
Bottle, Beer, Schlitz, Royal Ruby, Label, 7 Oz. 18.00
Bottle, Bellows, Applied Collar, Handles, Button Prunt, Vermiform Rigaree 75.00
Bottle, Bitters, Abbott's 6.00
Bottle, Bitters, Angelica Bitter Tonic 20.00
Bottle, Bitters, Aromatic Schnapps, Amber, Quart 20.00
Bottle, Bitters, Atwood's Gourdic, Moses Atwood, Md., Round, Aqua 5.00
Bottle, Bitters, Atwood's Gourdic, Moses Atwood, Md., Round, Clear 5.00
Bottle, Bitters, Atwood's Jaundice, Aqua .... 3.25 To 12.50
Bottle, Bitters, Atwood's Jaundice, Free Sample, 4 In. 25.00
Bottle, Bitters, Atwood's, H.H.Hay 8.50
Bottle, Bitters, Baxter's Mandrake, Clear .... 5.00 To 8.50
Bottle, Bitters, Baxter's Mandrake, Aqua 5.00
Bottle, Bitters, Bishop's Wahoo, Amber 170.00
Bottle, Bitters, Bitterquelle 5.00
Bottle, Bitters, Boerhaves Holland, Aqua 32.00
Bottle, Bitters, Bourbon Whiskey, Puce 120.00
Bottle, Bitters, Brophy's 55.00
Bottle, Bitters, Brown's Iron, Embossed, Open Pontil 22.00
Bottle, Bitters, Burdock's Blood, Aqua 6.00

Bottle, Bitters, Burdock's Blood, Clear 10.00
Bottle, Bitters, Caroni 20.00
Bottle, Bitters, Clark's Sherry Wine 53.00
Bottle, Bitters, Curtis & Perkins Wild Cherry, Open Pontil, Stain, Aqua, Pint 40.00
Bottle, Bitters, Danziger Magen, Embossed R.B., Milk Glass 190.00
Bottle, Bitters, Doyle's Hop, Amber 22.00
Bottle, Bitters, Doyle's Hop, Embossed, Open Pontil 21.00
Bottle, Bitters, Dr.Baker's Restorative Life, Infolded Lip, Pontil, Blue 60.00
Bottle, Bitters, Dr.Flint's Quaker, Aqua 20.00
Bottle, Bitters, Dr.Hoofland's German, Liver Complaint, Cloudy 18.00
Bottle, Bitters, Dr.Hoofland's German, Open Pontil, Aqua 80.00
Bottle, Bitters, Dr.Hopkin's Union Stomach, Hartford, Conn., Embossed 33.00
Bottle, Bitters, Dr.Hostetter's Stomach .... 6.50 To 7.50
Bottle, Bitters, Dr.Langley's Root & Herb 27.00
Bottle, Bitters, Dr.Langley's, 99 Union, Embossed, Open Pontil 20.00
Bottle, Bitters, Dr.M.M.Fenner's Capital, Aqua 35.00
Bottle, Bitters, Dr.Owen's European Life, Detroit, Mich., Pontil, Aqua 110.00
Bottle, Bitters, Dr.S.B.H. 5.00
Bottle, Bitters, Dr.Simms Anticonstipation, Amber, 7 In.High 50.00
Bottle, Bitters, Dr.Stephen Jewett's Celebrated Health Restoring, Aqua 65.00
Bottle, Bitters, Dr.Stewart's Tonic, Labels 30.00
Bottle, Bitters, Dr.Stewart's, Label, Embossed, Contents, Amber 35.00
Bottle, Bitters, Dr.Wilson's Herbine, Label 35.00
Bottle, Bitters, Dr.Young's Wild Cherry 75.00
Bottle, Bitters, Dragon Brand Orange, Label, Blown In The Mold 15.00
Bottle, Bitters, Drake's Plantation, Dark Amber, 6 Log 35.00
Bottle, Bitters, Ed Wilder's 65.00
Bottle, Bitters, Electric Brand 12.00
Bottle, Bitters, Electric, Amber 10.00
Bottle, Bitters, Electric, Embossed, Open Pontil 16.00
Bottle, Bitters, Emerson's Botanic, Label, Open Pontil, 7 1/2 In.High 40.00
Bottle, Bitters, Ferro-China Bisleri 4.00
Bottle, Bitters, Fred Kalina, Quart .... *Illus* 75.00

Bottle, Bitters, Fred Kalina, Quart

Bottle, Bitters, German Hop, 1872, Reading, Mich., Amber 55.00
Bottle, Bitters, Globe Tonic, The, Embossed, Open Pontil 56.00
Bottle, Bitters, Goff's Herb 6.00
Bottle, Bitters, Greeley's Bourbon, Barrel, Long Bubbles Upper Portion, Puce 150.00
Bottle, Bitters, Greeley's Bourbon, Barrel, Wide Mouth, Puce 149.00
Bottle, Bitters, Hall's Catarrh Cure 2.00
Bottle, Bitters, Harter's Wild Cherry, Amber 35.00
Bottle, Bitters, Hentz Curative, Sample 22.00
Bottle, Bitters, Hi Hi, Three Sided 65.00
Bottle, Bitters, Hibbard's Wild Cherry, Aqua 90.00
Bottle, Bitters, Holtzermann's Stomach, Labels, Contents 145.00
Bottle, Bitters, Hostetter's, S.Mckee & Co.On Base, Dug, Amber 5.50
Bottle, Bitters, Iron Tonic, Label, Amber 15.00
Bottle, Bitters, J.M.Leonard, Wild Cherry, Bangor, Me., Label, 3 Mold 15.00
Bottle, Bitters, Jean Marie Farina, 333 Rue St.Honore, Barrel, Clear 60.00

Bottle, Bitters, Kaiser Wilhelm, Pontil, Clear	52.50
Bottle, Bitters, Kaufmann's Sulphur, Contents	10.00
Bottle, Bitters, Langley's, Root & Herb, Reverse 99 Union St.	36.50
Bottle, Bitters, Langley's, Slug Plate, Aqua, 6 1/4 X 2 3/8 In.	20.00
Bottle, Bitters, Langley's, 76 Union St., Open Pontil, Aqua, 8 1/2 In.High	50.00
Bottle, Bitters, Langley's, 99 Union St., Aqua	25.00
Bottle, Bitters, Lash's Kidney & Liver	12.00
Bottle, Bitters, Lash's, Amber	8.00
Bottle, Bitters, Lash's, Clear	6.00
Bottle, Bitters, Leipziger Burgunder Wein, Olive Green	35.00
Bottle, Bitters, Mapes, Contents	35.00
Bottle, Bitters, New England Pineapple, Footed, 7 1/4 In.High	55.00
Bottle, Bitters, Petzold's, Amber, 10 1/2 In.High	85.00
Bottle, Bitters, Pond's, An Unexcelled Laxative, Label	35.00
Bottle, Bitters, Pond's, Embossed, Paper Label	25.00
Bottle, Bitters, Richardson's	17.00
Bottle, Bitters, Roback's Barrel	100.00
Bottle, Bitters, Royal Pepsin	65.00
Bottle, Bitters, Rush's, Embossed, Open Pontil	32.00
Bottle, Bitters, S.O.Richardson's, Aqua	25.00
Bottle, Bitters, S.O.Richardson's, Open Pontil, Aqua	38.00
Bottle, Bitters, Sanborn's	60.00
Bottle, Bitters, St.Goddard Harb, St.Louis, Mo., Bubbly, Stain, Amber	55.00
Bottle, Bitters, Tippecanoe, H.H.Warner & Co.Patent Nov.20, 1983, Dark Amber	165.00
Bottle, Bitters, Tonita	15.00
Bottle, Bitters, Udolpho Wolfe's Schiedam Aromatic Schnapps, Emerald Green	15.00
Bottle, Bitters, Vermo Stomach, Clear	15.00
Bottle, Bitters, Vermo, Blown In Mold, Clear	15.00
Bottle, Bitters, Wahoo, Contents	8.00
Bottle, Bitters, Walker's Vinegar Bitters	5.00
Bottle, Bitters, Wallace's Tonic Stomach	45.00
Bottle, Bitters, 4 In 1 Bitters Co.	45.00
Bottle, Black Glass, Turn Mold, 3-Piece	2.50
Bottle, Blown, Union, Clasped Hands & Crest, Eagle With 13 Stars, Blue	50.00
Bottle, Blue Glass, Marked Laxol, A.J.White, N.Y., Pat.1894	3.95
Bottle, Brandy, Maraschino, 1870, Label, Applied Seal, Square, Sheared Top	6.00
Bottle, Carrie Nation, Clear	12.00
Bottle, Castor Oil, Flask Type, Cork Top, 5 1/2 In.High	5.00
Bottle, Cat Holding Mice, Paint, Milk Glass, 8 In.High	65.00
Bottle, Cathedral, Blue, Carter, Pint	35.00
Bottle, Chamberlain's Pain Balm For Rheumatism	5.00
Bottle, Chemical, Laboratory, Double Neck, Pontil	7.00
Bottle, Chemical, Rumford Chemical Works, Acid Phosphate, 8-Sided, Bluish	8.00
Bottle, Chestnut, Green Grass, New England	60.00
Bottle, Citrate Magnesia, Porcelain Stopper	2.00
Bottle, Clear, E.R.Durkee & Co., Belt & Mailed Gauntlet Design, Pat.1877	4.95
Bottle, Coachman, Van Dunck, Amber	115.00
Bottle, Coca-Cola, see Coca-Cola	
Bottle, Cod Liver Oil, Fish, Amber	75.00
Bottle, Codd, British, Marble In Neck, Embossed	7.25
Bottle, Codd, C.N.Ballinger, Monmouth, Embossed, Marble Stopper, Blown	4.95
Bottle, Codd, Marble In Neck, Embossed, Aqua	7.00
Bottle, Coff's Bitters, Aqua	10.00
Bottle, Cologne, Blue Ground, Flowers, Butterfly, Red Trim, Porcelain, France	22.00
Bottle, Cologne, Blue Stripes, White Lacy Threads, Cathedral Stopper	50.00
Bottle, Cologne, Bulbous Bottom, Long Thin Neck, Decorated, Milk Glass, Pair	35.00
Bottle, Cologne, Bull's-Eye, Flowers, Starred Bottom	20.00
Bottle, Cologne, Clear, 4 In.High	12.50
Bottle, Cologne, Eau De Cologne, W.E.Armstrong, Pewter Lid, Tapered, Label	9.00
Bottle, Cologne, Opalescent Hobnail, Bulbous Bottom, Round Stopper	13.00
Bottle, Cologne, Sterling Overlay, Stopper	10.00
Bottle, Cologne, Turkish Cologne For The Toilet, Figural Stopper, Clear	18.00
Bottle, Cosmetic, Colgate's Charmis Cold Cream, Jar, Lady In Peignoir	4.00
Bottle, Cosmetic, DeWitt's Toilet Creams, Rectangular, Cork, Label, Clear	1.50
Bottle, Cosmetic, Elysian Hair Curling Fluid, Rectangular, Cork, Clear	3.00
Bottle, Cosmetic, Harrison's Columbian Hair Dye, Open Pontil, Stain, Aqua	15.00

Bottle, Cosmetic, Palmer, Gold Embossed Screw Top, Green	10.00
Bottle, Cosmetic, Pompeian Massage Cream, Embossed, Ground Stopper, Clear	5.00
Bottle, Cosmetic, Quinine Hair Tonic, Metal Over Cork Top, Label, Clear	8.00
Bottle, Cosmetic, Rexall Hair Tonic, Rectangle, Brass Crown Cork Top, Amber	15.00
Bottle, Cosmetic, Stanhope's Instantaneous Liquid Shampoos, Cork, Aqua	4.00
Bottle, Cosmetic, Sweet Georgia Brown Cleansing Cream, Patent Date 1898	3.50
Bottle, Crystal Bottling, Geo.Martin, Tucson, Ariz., Clear, 7 3/4 In.	5.00
Bottle, Cupid Holds Cornucopia, Tinted, 5 1/2 In., Pair	46.50
Bottle, Dant, Fort Sill,Oklahoma *Illus*	12.00
Bottle, Decanter, Baroque, Quart	97.00
Bottle, Decanter, Blown, Cut Fluting Around Base, Gold Decoration	30.00
Bottle, Decanter, Clear & Chartreuse Overlay, Cut Cherry Branches, Pair	175.00
Bottle, Decanter, Double Neck Rings, Blown Molded, Quart	100.00
Bottle, Decanter, Four Compartment, 12 In.High	15.00
Bottle, Decanter, Four Parts Spirits, Blown, Mark France	35.00
Bottle, Decanter, Grape Design, Ruby Glass	40.00
Bottle, Decanter, Green, Amber Base & Stopper	16.00
Bottle, Decanter, Inverted Thumbprint, Hollow Blown Stopper, Blue	50.00
Bottle, Decanter, John Ruskin Cigars, Man's Head In Horseshoe, Color	20.00
Bottle, Decanter, Keene, Oliver Amber	295.00
Bottle, Decanter, McKearin G II-18, Mold-Blown, Quart, Pair	165.00
Bottle, Decanter, Old Mr.Boston, Bookends, Pair	10.00
Bottle, Decanter, Pittsburgh Pillar, Circa 1850, 12 In.	34.00
Bottle, Decanter, Roman Key Design, Frosted, Blue, 13 In.High	55.00
Bottle, Decanter, Russian, Purple Glass, Gilt, Faceted, C.1850	140.00
Bottle, Decanter, Santa, Signed Susie, Ceramic	8.50
Bottle, Decanter, Single Applied Ring At Neck, Heavy Fluting, Blue	22.50
Bottle, Decanter, Star, Diamond, Thumbprint, Cobalt Blue, Cut To Clear, 7 In.	35.00
Bottle, Decanter, Washington, Bar Lip	35.00
Bottle, Decanter, Wine, Enameled White Lilies Of The Valley, Green, Stopper	40.00
Bottle, Doyle's Bitters, Amber, 1872	32.00
Bottle, Dr.Haynes Arabian Balsam, E.Morgan & Sons, Providence, R.I., Aqua	2.75
Bottle, Dr.Peter's Blood Vitalizer, Tree Trademark, Clear, Oilcloth Case	16.00
Bottle, Dr.Stewart's Tonic Bitters, Amber, Labels	35.00
Bottle, Dr.Townsend's Sarsaparilla, Emerald Green, Iron Pontil	85.00
Bottle, Dr.W.B.Caldwell's Laxative, Pale Green, Cork Top, 7 1/2 In.High	8.00
Bottle, Dr.Wistar's Balsam	26.00
Bottle, Drake's Bitters, Five Log, Amber	72.00
Bottle, Dresser, Hand-Painted Violets, Panel Sides, Gold Trim, Milk Glass	25.00
Bottle, Dresser, Milk Glass, Embossed Flowers, Pair	60.00
Bottle, Drug, Embossed U.S.A.Hospital Dept, Three Mold, Olive Green	50.00
Bottle, Drug, New York Pharmacal Ass., Cobalt	8.00
Bottle, Drug, Specimen Jar, Whitall Tatum Co., Open Pontil, Clear, Pint	12.00
Bottle, Ezra Brooks, Birthday Club Bottle	18.95
Bottle, Ezra Brooks, Brahma Bull	14.59
Bottle, Ezra Brooks, Buffalo Hunt	12.50
Bottle, Ezra Brooks, Club Bottle, 1970	22.00
Bottle, Ezra Brooks, Fresno Grape	12.50
Bottle, Ezra Brooks, Go Big Red No.2	18.00
Bottle, Ezra Brooks, Golden Horseshoe	15.00
Bottle, Ezra Brooks, Golden Rooster No.1	55.00
Bottle, Ezra Brooks, Hereford	13.69
Bottle, Ezra Brooks, Hollywood Stars	21.95
Bottle, Ezra Brooks, Indianapolis Race Car, 1970 *Illus*	25.00
Bottle, Ezra Brooks, Kansas Jayhawk, 1969 *Illus*	12.00
Bottle, Ezra Brooks, Mr.Merchant, Jumping Man, 1970 *Illus*	17.00
Bottle, Ezra Brooks, Rooster Classic	12.50
Bottle, Ezra Brooks, Water Tower	12.50
Bottle, Ezra Brooks, Wheatshocker	8.00
Bottle, Ezra Brooks, White Turkey	21.95
Bottle, Figural, Banana, Metal Screw Cap, Clear, 7 5/8 In.High	11.00
Bottle, Figural, Bear, Kummel, Black Amethyst, 11 In.High	35.00
Bottle, Figural, Bear, Kummel, Green, 11 In.High	25.00
Bottle, Figural, Bear, Kummel, Light Amethyst	65.00
Bottle, Figural, Bear, Kummel, Milk Glass, 11 In.High	55.00
Bottle, Figural, Bear, Milk Glass, White, 11 In.High	95.00

Bottle, Dant,
Fort Sill, Oklahoma
See Page 46

Bottle, Ezra Brooks,
Kansas Jayhawk, 1969
See Page 46

Bottle, Ezra Brooks,
Indianapolis Race Car, 1970
See Page 46

Bottle, Ezra Brooks, Mr.Merchant,
Jumping Man, 1970
See Page 46

Bottle, Figural, Billiken	30.00
Bottle, Figural, Bird, Milk Glass, 10 In.High	12.00
Bottle, Figural, Boxing Glove, Pat.1889, Screw Cap, Clear	33.00
Bottle, Figural, Buddha, Vantine	35.00
Bottle, Figural, Bull Lying Down, Head Covers Opening	25.00
Bottle, Figural, Bunch Of Cigars, Amber	30.00 To 40.00
Bottle, Figural, Bunker Hill Monument	20.00
Bottle, Figural, Bust Of Man, Screw Opening, Black Amethyst	15.00
Bottle, Figural, Carrie Nation, Screw Cap, Clear	8.00
Bottle, Figural, Cat, Green Crystal, Raised Gold, 12 1/2 In.	6.50
Bottle, Figural, Cat, Pistachio, Cambridge, 8 In.High	16.00
Bottle, Figural, Cigar	8.50
Bottle, Figural, Cigar, Screw Cap, Amber, 5 In.	17.00
Bottle, Figural, Clamshell, Screw Cap	20.00
Bottle, Figural, Clamshell, Screw Cap, Paint	24.00
Bottle, Figural, Clothes Brush, Mark Germany, 6 In.Tall	16.50
Bottle, Figural, Coachman, Van Dunck's Genever, Amber	150.00
Bottle, Figural, Crying Baby	28.00 To 45.00
Bottle, Figural, Cucumber, Ceramic, Green & Yellow, 5 In.High	13.00
Bottle, Figural, Depression Shoe, Black	55.00
Bottle, Figural, Dog, Cabin Still	6.50
Bottle, Figural, Dog, Poodle, Screw Cap, Blue	10.50
Bottle, Figural, Drunk On Lamppost, Here's To Both Of You, Stopper, Number	25.00
Bottle, Figural, Dutch Slipper, Blue Cast	15.00
Bottle, Figural, Ear Of Corn, Screw Cap	20.00
Bottle, Figural, Elephant, Pouring Trunk, Porcelain, Cork Top, Bavaria	19.00

Bottle, Figural, Elk Tooth, Clear	50.00
Bottle, Figural, Fantasia	17.50
Bottle, Figural, Fantasia, Frosted	35.00
Bottle, Figural, Felix	18.00
Bottle, Figural, Fish, Lilly, Amber *Illus*	12.50
Bottle, Figural, French Cavalier	50.00
Bottle, Figural, French Cavalier, Miniature	25.00
Bottle, Figural, French Taxi, Frosted & Clear	100.00
Bottle, Figural, George Washington, Full Figure	12.00
Bottle, Figural, George Washington, Full Figure, Clear, 9 5/8 In.High	6.75
Bottle, Figural, George Washington, George Smith, Jr.	18.00
Bottle, Figural, George Washington, Screw Cap, Clear	8.00
Bottle, Figural, Grant's Tomb, Milk Glass, B-252	300.00
Bottle, Figural, Hat, Man's, 6 X 3 In.	15.00
Bottle, Figural, Hessian Soldier	28.00
Bottle, Figural, High Shoe, Blue Cast	15.00
Bottle, Figural, Idaho Potato	12.00
Bottle, Figural, Joan Of Arc On Horseback, Miniature	25.00
Bottle, Figural, Joan Of Arc, Embossed, Castagnon Nocaro, France, Clear	9.00
Bottle, Figural, Lady's Shoe, Lace On Side, Bennington Type	95.00
Bottle, Figural, Man In Overcoat, Hat Is Stopper, Brown, Porcelain	10.00
Bottle, Figural, Man's Slipper, Opaque Green	14.00
Bottle, Figural, Monk, Cloak Hood Forms Spout, Pottery, 8 In.High	67.50
Bottle, Figural, Moses, Honeymoon, Green	30.00
Bottle, Figural, Moses, Stopper Type, Clear, Quart	4.75
Bottle, Figural, Negro Waiter, Deponirt, Clear & Frosted	88.00
Bottle, Figural, Onion, Bubbly, Open Pontil, Olive	31.00
Bottle, Figural, Oyster Shell	35.00
Bottle, Figural, Oyster Shell, Screw Cap, Paint	25.00
Bottle, Figural, Pig, Good Old Bourbon In A Hog's-, Amber	155.00
Bottle, Figural, Potato, Patent Applied For, Screw Cap, Paint	23.00
Bottle, Figural, Riverboat Captain *Illus*	24.50

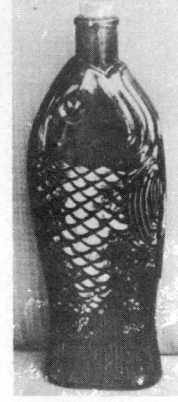

Bottle, Figural, Fish, Lilly, Amber

Bottle, Figural, Riverboat Captain

Bottle, Figural, Sad Hound	18.00
Bottle, Figural, Scallop Shell	27.50
Bottle, Figural, School Bell, Handle, 6 1/4 In.	8.50
Bottle, Figural, Shoe, Revenue Stamp On Sole, 4 1/2 In.High	22.50
Bottle, Figural, Sitting Bear, Dark Amber	40.00
Bottle, Figural, Statue Of Liberty, Milk Glass	98.00
Bottle, Figural, Teddy Bear, Green, 13 in.High	15.00
Bottle, Figural, Telephone, Upright, Black, Rubber Cord, 12 1/2 In.	20.00
Bottle, Figural, Train, Screw Opening	30.00
Bottle, Figural, Venus Rising From Sea, Screw Opening In Base, Frosted Blue	25.00
Bottle, Figural, Victor Emmanuel III	25.00
Bottle, Figural, Violin, Blue, 7 1/2 In.High	15.00
Bottle, Figural, Violin, Cobalt Blue, 8 In.High	1.25 To 2.98
Bottle, Figural, Violin, Cobalt, Label Advertising Vanilla	12.00

Bottle, Figural, Violin, Honey Amber, 8 3/4 In.High 15.00
Bottle, Figural, Violin, Music Notes, Open Pontil, Amethyst, 9 3/4 In.High 25.00
Bottle, Figural, Violin, Musical Notes On Back, Amethyst Glass 22.50
Bottle, Figural, Warrior's Head, Screw Opening, Black Amethyst 15.00
Bottle, Fish, Dark Amber 9.00
Bottle, Flask, Anchor & Sheaf Of Rye, Baltimore Glass Works, Amber, Quart 300.00
Bottle, Flask, Book, Spring Poems, The Four Swallows, 4 Bottles, Lock 18.00
Bottle, Flask, Bottom Encased In Pewter, Top Half In Leather, M.Volry, 1866 .... 7.95
Bottle, Flask, Bust Of Washington One Side, Eagle & Shield On Other, Clear 3.95
Bottle, Flask, Chestnut, Handle, Whittled, Amber 29.00
Bottle, Flask, Coffin, Diamond-Quilted, Bubbles, Applied Top, 5 In.High 4.50
Bottle, Flask, Cornucopia & Basket Of Flowers, Rough Pontil, Amber, 1/2 Pint 80.00
Bottle, Flask, Cornucopia & Urn 45.00
Bottle, Flask, Double Eagle, Aqua, 1/2 Pint 35.00
Bottle, Flask, Double, Engraved Fronds, Ferns, Bird, Date 1885, Cork Stoppers 70.00
Bottle, Flask, Dyottville Washington Taylor, Pint 49.00
Bottle, Flask, Eagle, Embossed, Amber 25.00
Bottle, Flask, Eagle, Wings Downward, 4 3/4 In.High 68.00
Bottle, Flask, For Pike's Peak & Eagle, Aqua, Pint 60.00
Bottle, Flask, For Pike's Peak, Sheared Neck, Iron Pontil, Aqua, 1/2 Pint 68.00
Bottle, Flask, Green, Imperial Pint 7.50
Bottle, Flask, Green, Silver Overlay, Cherub Finial, England 52.00
Bottle, Flask, Historical, Gen.Taylor, Washington, Sheared Lip, Aqua, Pint 75.00
Bottle, Flask, Lestoil, Amber 2.00
Bottle, Flask, Lestoil, Amethyst 2.00
Bottle, Flask, Lestoil, Green 2.00
Bottle, Flask, Man, Horse, Dog, Leather Shot, Brass, Dispenser 22.00
Bottle, Flask, McKearin C-15, Indian Shooting Bird & Eagle, Scent 100.00
Bottle, Flask, McKearin G I-31, Washington & Jackson, Amber, Pint 120.00
Bottle, Flask, McKearin G I-37, General Taylor Never Surrenders, Quart 60.00
Bottle, Flask, McKearin G I-42, A Little More Grape Captain Bragg, Quart 65.00
Bottle, Flask, McKearin G I-43, I Have Endeavored To Do My Duty, Quart 60.00
Bottle, Flask, McKearin G I-114, Byron & Scott, Olive Amber, 1/2 Pint 165.00
Bottle, Flask, McKearin G II-18, Pint 62.00
Bottle, Flask, McKearin G III-4, Cornucopia & Urn, Olive Green, Pint 75.00
Bottle, Flask, McKearin G III-4, Cornucopia, Golden Amber, Pint 67.50
Bottle, Flask, McKearin G IV-17, Masonic & Eagle, Keene, Stain, Aqua, Pint 250.00
Bottle, Flask, McKearin G VII-3, Coventry Sunburst, Olive 390.00
Bottle, Flask, McKearin G IX-2a, Scroll, Iron Pontil, Yellow Green, Quart 140.00
Bottle, Flask, Nailsea Type, Fine Diamond, Milk White Under Crystal 75.00
Bottle, Flask, Nailsea Type, Laydown, Blue & Mottled, 8 In.High 55.00
Bottle, Flask, Olive Green, Bubbly Glass, Cornucopia & Urn, Pint 75.00
Bottle, Flask, Perfume, Blue Green, Black Birds, Flowers, Fish, Persia, C.1780 .... 28.00
Bottle, Flask, Pewter & Glass, Screw Stopper, C.1866 .... 5.95
Bottle, Flask, Pewter Encased Bottom, Top Half Leather, Screw Stopper, 1866 .... 7.95
Bottle, Flask, Pistol Shape, Brass, Eagle, Shield 48.50
Bottle, Flask, Pocket, B.P.O.E., Embossed Elk Head, Clock, Pottery 30.00
Bottle, Flask, Pocket, Leather, Silver Design 18.00
Bottle, Flask, Pocket, Shape Of Amercan Eagle, B.P.O.E., Pottery 30.00
Bottle, Flask, Pumpkinseed, McCormick & Co.Extract, Spices, Clear, 1/2 Pint 20.00
Bottle, Flask, Regimental, German, Eagle On Top, Metal Casing, 1897 .... 125.00
Bottle, Flask, Ribs, Double Dipped In Olive Green, New England 230.00
Bottle, Flask, Saddle, 6 1/2 In. 10.00
Bottle, Flask, Scroll, Green Aqua, 1/2 Pint 60.00
Bottle, Flask, Sheaf Of Wheat & Westford Glass Co., Deep Amber 115.00
Bottle, Flask, Sheaf Of Wheat, Tibby Bros., Pitts., Pa.Base, Clear, 1/2 Pint 20.00
Bottle, Flask, Silver, Shape Of Cigar Holder, For 3 Cigars 25.00
Bottle, Flask, Strap, Amber, 6 In. 3.50
Bottle, Flask, Traveler's Companion, Ravenna, 8 Point Star, Blue 70.00
Bottle, Flask, Washington & Eagle & Shield, 1932, Clear, 9 In.High 3.95
Bottle, Flask, Washington & Taylor, Open Pontil, Aqua, Quart 45.00
Bottle, Flask, Water, Egyptian, Open Pontil 37.50
Bottle, Flask, Westford Glass Co., Sheath Rake & Fork Over Star, Pint 125.00
Bottle, Flask, Whiskey, Civil War Officer's Field, Pewter Cover Is Cup 12.50
Bottle, Flask, Whiskey, For Pocket, Swirled Ribs, Silver Plate, Screw Cap 7.50
Bottle, Flask, Women's Suffrage 9.75

Bottle, Food, Brooke's Lemos Sweetened Diluted Lemon Juice, 1906, Label 6.00
Bottle, Food, Canterbury Shaker, No.1 Syrup 17.00
Bottle, Food, Cherry Syrup, Recessed Glass Covered Label, 12 In.High 35.00
Bottle, Food, Chocolate Syrup, Decal Label, 12 In.High 18.00
Bottle, Food, Curtis & Moore's Orangeade Syrup, Metal Top, Red Paper Label 500.00
Bottle, Food, Horlick's Malted Milk, 6 Quart 8.50
Bottle, Food, Horlick's, Amethyst, 10 In. 7.00
Bottle, Food, Lemon Syrup, Decal Label, 12 In.High 18.00
Bottle, Food, Mellin's Food Co., Round, Embossed, Aqua & Clear, 6 In.High 1.00
Bottle, Food, Mellin's Food For Infants, Embossed Sample, Screw Cap, Aqua 3.50
Bottle, Food, Mellin's Infant's Food, Doliber Goodale & Co., Embossed, Aqua 5.00
Bottle, Food, Mellin's Infant's Food, Large Letters .... *Illus* 6.50
Bottle, Food, Mellin's, Free Sample, Aqua 4.50
Bottle, Food, Old Judge Coffee, 3 Pounds 5.00
Bottle, Food, Olive Oil, Open Pontil, Sheared Lip, Bubbly, Clear 15.00
Bottle, Food, Pineapple Syrup, Recessed Glass Covered Label, 12 In.High 35.00
Bottle, Food, Planter's, Block Letters, Round, Cork, Metal Closure, Amethyst 26.50
Bottle, Food, Professor Horsford's Baking Powder, Round, Cork, Clear, 6 In. 3.00
Bottle, Food, Raspberry Syrup, Gold & Black Label, 12 In.High 18.00
Bottle, Food, Rawleigh's Compound Extract Of Vanilla, Embossed, Aqua 3.00
Bottle, Food, Rope's Lemon New York, Rectangular, Clear, 5 In.High 1.50
Bottle, Food, Roses Lime Juice, Clear, 9 In. .... *Illus* 25.00
Bottle, Food, Roses West India Lime Juice, Embossed, Glass Stopper, Aqua 6.00
Bottle, Food, The 3 Millers Orangeade Syrup, Recessed Glass Label 50.00
Bottle, Food, Wan-Eta Cocoa, Amber, Quart 5.00
Bottle, Food, Wan-Eta Cocoa, Aqua, Quart 6.00
Bottle, Food, Wine Coca Syrup, Metal Top, Blue & White Paper Label, 11 In. 50.00

Bottle, Food, Mellin's Infant's Food,
Large Letters

Bottle, Food, Roses Lime Juice,
Clear, 9 In.

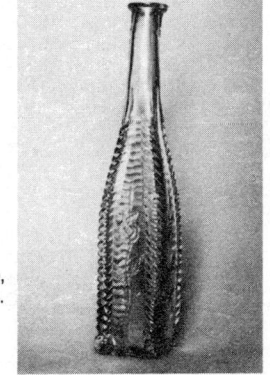

Bottle, Free-Blown, Half Post, Ground Stopper, Rectangular, C.1790, Clear 19.00
Bottle, Fruit Jar, Atlas E-Z Seal, Blue, Quart 15.00
Bottle, Fruit Jar, Atlas E-Z Seal, Clear, 1/2 Pint .... 2.00 To 2.75
Bottle, Fruit Jar, Atlas, Four-Leaf Clover Embossed, 1/2 Gallon 5.00
Bottle, Fruit Jar, Ball Ideal, Clear, 1/2 Pint 2.00
Bottle, Fruit Jar, Ball Standard, Script, Aqua, Quart .... 2.00 To 3.50
Bottle, Fruit Jar, Ball Standard, Script, Aqua, 1/2 Gallon .... 2.00 To 3.50
Bottle, Fruit Jar, Bamberger's, Sure Seal, Pint 8.00
Bottle, Fruit Jar, Banner, Patent, Feb.9, 1864, Aqua, Quart 50.00
Bottle, Fruit Jar, C.G.Co., Crystal, Quart 22.50
Bottle, Fruit Jar, Canadian Jewel, Zinc Band, Quart 4.50
Bottle, Fruit Jar, Chef, Picture, Closure, Pint 8.00
Bottle, Fruit Jar, Chef, Picture, Dated, Closure, Quart 6.00
Bottle, Fruit Jar, Cohansey, Patent, Feb.12, 1867, Widemouth 35.00
Bottle, Fruit Jar, Cohansey, Whittled, 1/2 Gallon 28.00
Bottle, Fruit Jar, Columbia, Clear, Pint .... 20.00 To 30.00
Bottle, Fruit Jar, Crown, Embossed, Clear, Pint 3.50
Bottle, Fruit Jar, Cunningham's & Ihmsen, Tin Lid, Blue, Quart 40.00
Bottle, Fruit Jar, D.G.Co., Embossed On Side & Lid, Zinc Band, Aqua, Quart 35.00

Bottle, Fruit Jar, Dandy, Amber, 1/2 Gallon 75.00
Bottle, Fruit Jar, Dillon G.Co., Fairmont, Ind., Green, 1/2 Gallon 10.00
Bottle, Fruit Jar, Dillon G.Co., Green, Quart 10.00
Bottle, Fruit Jar, Doolittle, Aqua 20.00
Bottle, Fruit Jar, Economy Sealer, Pat'D, Embossed, Whittled, Clear, Quart 16.00
Bottle, Fruit Jar, Embossed Beaver, Clear, No Lid, 2 Quart 25.00
Bottle, Fruit Jar, Empire, Quart 9.00
Bottle, Fruit Jar, Foster, Glass Lid, Purple, Pint 4.00
Bottle, Fruit Jar, Franklin Dexter, Half Gallon 30.00
Bottle, Fruit Jar, Franklin, Aqua, Quart 30.00
Bottle, Fruit Jar, Gaynor, Pint 9.00
Bottle, Fruit Jar, Gaynor, Quart 9.00
Bottle, Fruit Jar, Gilchrist, Aqua, Quart 12.00
Bottle, Fruit Jar, Globe, Dated May 25, 1886, Amber, One Quart 45.00
Bottle, Fruit Jar, Globe, Honey Amber, Quart .... 29.50 To 32.50
Bottle, Fruit Jar, H & R On Base, Whittled, Aqua, 1/2 Gallon 12.00
Bottle, Fruit Jar, H & R, Bubbles, Quart 9.00
Bottle, Fruit Jar, Hand Blown, Rolled Lip, Open Pontil, Aqua, 1/2 Gallon 125.00
Bottle, Fruit Jar, Hero Improved, Aqua, Quart 14.50
Bottle, Fruit Jar, Jelly, Tin Lid, Embossed Banner Jelly & Shield, Quart 9.50
Bottle, Fruit Jar, King, Embossed Oval, Clear, Pint 10.00
Bottle, Fruit Jar, Knowlton Vacuum 12.00
Bottle, Fruit Jar, Leotric, Aqua, Quart 3.50
Bottle, Fruit Jar, Light Green, Dated Nov.30, 1858, Mason, 2 Qt. 60.00
Bottle, Fruit Jar, Lightning, Amber, Dated 1883, One Quart 26.00
Bottle, Fruit Jar, Lightning, Amber, Quart .... 22.50 To 24.00
Bottle, Fruit Jar, Lightning, Aqua, Pint .... 1.00 To 2.00
Bottle, Fruit Jar, Lightning, Aqua, Quart 2.00
Bottle, Fruit Jar, Lightning, Aqua, 1/2 Gallon 2.50
Bottle, Fruit Jar, Lightning, Clear 1.00
Bottle, Fruit Jar, Ludlow's Patent 100.00
Bottle, Fruit Jar, Magic Star, Aqua, Quart 49.50
Bottle, Fruit Jar, Marion, The, Quart 9.50
Bottle, Fruit Jar, Mason Jar Of 1872 .... 22.00
Bottle, Fruit Jar, Mason, The, Aqua, 1/2 Gallon 3.50
Bottle, Fruit Jar, Mason, 1858 Patent, Olive Green, Screw Top 12.00
Bottle, Fruit Jar, Mason, 1858, 1/2 Gallon 4.50
Bottle, Fruit Jar, Mason's K.B.S.Co., Monogram, Aqua 6.00
Bottle, Fruit Jar, Mason's Patent, Nov.30th, 1858, Amber, 1/2 Gallon 10.00
Bottle, Fruit Jar, Mason's Patent, Nov.30th, 1858, Amethyst, 1/2 Gallon 10.00
Bottle, Fruit Jar, Mason's Patent, Nov.30th, 1858, Aqua .... 3.75 To 4.75
Bottle, Fruit Jar, Mason's Patent, Nov.30th, 1858, Cobalt Blue, 1/2 Gallon 10.00
Bottle, Fruit Jar, Mason's Patent, Nov.30th, 1858, Green, 1/2 Gallon 10.00
Bottle, Fruit Jar, Mason's S.G.Co., Monogram, Aqua, Quart 8.00
Bottle, Fruit Jar, Mason's S.G.Co., Monogram, Light Blue, Quart 18.50
Bottle, Fruit Jar, Midget, Mason's Patent Nov.30th, 1858, Iron Cross 9.50
Bottle, Fruit Jar, Millville, Quart 22.50
Bottle, Fruit Jar, Mission, Clear, Quart 4.00
Bottle, Fruit Jar, Patent Dec.17th, 1872 On Bottom, Clear, 1/2 Gallon 15.00
Bottle, Fruit Jar, Patented Dec.17th, 1872 On Bottom, Ground, Clear, 1/2 Pint 25.00
Bottle, Fruit Jar, Peoria Pottery 12.00
Bottle, Fruit Jar, Perfection, Clamp, Turning Amethyst, Quart 3.00
Bottle, Fruit Jar, Putnam, Amber, Quart 24.00
Bottle, Fruit Jar, Queen, Widemouth, Quart 1.00
Bottle, Fruit Jar, Reed's Patties, Wire Toggle Clamps Closure, 1/2 Gallon 16.00
Bottle, Fruit Jar, Royal, Clear, 1/2 Gallon 90.00
Bottle, Fruit Jar, Safe Seal, Blue, One Quart 4.00
Bottle, Fruit Jar, Safety, Amber, Pint 75.00
Bottle, Fruit Jar, Saratoga, Embossed, Dark Olive Green, 7 1/2 In.Tall 500.00
Bottle, Fruit Jar, Smalley Self Sealer, Widemouth, Half Gallon 5.00
Bottle, Fruit Jar, Smalley, Full Measure, Amber, Quart 22.00
Bottle, Fruit Jar, Snap Closure, Glass Top, Clear 5.00
Bottle, Fruit Jar, Spencer Patent, Whittled, No Closure, 2 Qt. 60.00
Bottle, Fruit Jar, Standard, W.Mc C & Co.In Reverse, Aqua, Quart 9.00
Bottle, Fruit Jar, Standard, W.Mc C & Co.In Reverse, Aqua, 1/2 Gallon 17.00
Bottle, Fruit Jar, Star Glass Co., New Albany, Ind., Bubbles, Quart 20.00

Bottle, Fruit Jar, Telephone, The, Whitney Glass Works, Quart, Light Blue 7.50
Bottle, Fruit Jar, Tillyer, Aqua, Quart 65.00
Bottle, Fruit Jar, Van Vliet, 1881, Aqua 135.00
Bottle, Fruit Jar, Wan-Eta, Amber, Quart 2.75
Bottle, Fruit Jar, Wears Jar, The, Clear, Quart 6.00
Bottle, Fruit Jar, Weir, Cream Stoneware, Metal Bail, Closure 6.00
Bottle, Fruit Jar, Woodbury Improved 24.00
Bottle, Gin, Amber, Star Mark On Bottom, Taper 17.00
Bottle, Gin, Case, Daniel Visser & Zonen Schiedam, Blown In Mold, Green 39.00
Bottle, Gin, Case, Flared Mouth, Open Pontil 30.00
Bottle, Gin, Case, Open Pontil, Light Green 15.00
Bottle, Gin, Case, P.Hoppe Schiedam, Sealed, Yellow Green 49.00
Bottle, Gin, Case, Rolled Flare Lip, Green 18.00
Bottle, Gin, Case, Vandenbergh & Co., Flare Lip, Sealed, Olive Green 42.50
Bottle, Gin, Daniel Visser, Zonen Schiedam, Seal, Label, Green 45.00
Bottle, Gin, Flared Lip, Open Pontil, Dark Olive 24.00
Bottle, Gin, Gordon's Dry 1.50
Bottle, Gin, London Jockey Clubhouse, Square Corners, Applied Collar, Green 170.00
Bottle, Gin, Silver Leaf Holland, Basket, Paper Label, Green, 14 In.High 10.00
Bottle, Ginger, Stoneware, English, Screw In Stopper 4.00
Bottle, Golden Wedding, Carnival Glass, Label 11.00
Bottle, Golfer, 12 In.High 35.00
Bottle, Grenadier, Eugene 12.50
Bottle, Grenadier, Lassal 29.00
Bottle, Grenadier, Napoleon 35.00
Bottle, Hand Blown, Jar, Stopper, Light Blue, 13 In. 22.00
Bottle, Hand Lotion, Embossed, Hinds 3.00
Bottle, Hobstar, Opalescent, Bulbous Bottom 6.50
Bottle, Hohenthal Brothers & Co., Indelible, N.Y., Pour Spout, Pontil, Olive 325.00
Bottle, Hot Water, Fulham Pottery, 11 In. .... *Illus* 39.00
Bottle, Household, Beaumont's Liquid Blueing, Embossed, Open Pontil 13.50
Bottle, Household, Wycoff & Co., Union Bluing, Aqua 3.50
Bottle, Ink, Barometric, Table, Inkwell, C-1309 .... 42.00
Bottle, Ink, Bell Shape, Pontil, Light Blue 25.00
Bottle, Ink, Bixby Mushroom 55.00
Bottle, Ink, Bixby, Cone, Aqua 2.00
Bottle, Ink, Blown, Pp, Squat, Round, Pewter Lid, Clear 50.00
Bottle, Ink, Blown, Sheared Top, Pen Rest, 2 X 2 In. 20.00
Bottle, Ink, Bristol Recorder, Amber 12.00
Bottle, Ink, Cardinal, Turtle, Aqua 45.00
Bottle, Ink, Carter's Cathedral, Pint 55.00
Bottle, Ink, Carter's Cathedral, Quart 45.00
Bottle, Ink, Carter's, Amber, 10 In.Tall 15.00
Bottle, Ink, Carter's, Man Seated, Head Is Stopper, Porcelain, Jan.6, 1914 .... 25.00
Bottle, Ink, Carter's, 1896 .... *Illus* 6.00
Bottle, Ink, Clear, Cone Shape, Marked Carter's, 2 1/2 In.High 2.50

Bottle, Hot Water,
Fulham Pottery, 11 In.

Bottle, Ink,
Carter's, 1896

Bottle, Ink, Clear, Sideway Opening, J. & I.E.M.	7.00
Bottle, Ink, Cone Bixby, Aqua	5.00
Bottle, Ink, Cone Shape, Aqua	2.50
Bottle, Ink, Cone Shape, Clear, Carter's No.5, 2 1/2 In.High	2.50
Bottle, Ink, Cone, Amber	2.50 To 8.00
Bottle, Ink, Cone, Aqua	1.50
Bottle, Ink, Cone, Cobalt	7.50
Bottle, Ink, Cone, Label, Contents	12.00
Bottle, Ink, Cone, Olive Green	18.00
Bottle, Ink, Cone, Pottery, 2 3/4 In.	18.00
Bottle, Ink, Conqueror Red Ink, Label, Pen Rest, Contents	20.00
Bottle, Ink, Cranberry, Iridescent Top, Brass Hinge & Rim	75.00
Bottle, Ink, Cut Glass, Waffle, Pyramid Top, 3 In.Square, 3 1/2 In.Tall	28.00
Bottle, Ink, Cylindrical, Deep Blue Green	15.00
Bottle, Ink, Cylindrical, Patent Feb.16, 1885, Green	19.00
Bottle, Ink, Cylindrical, Pontil, Aqua	10.00
Bottle, Ink, Eagle, Milk Glass, Label, Contents	12.00
Bottle, Ink, German Helmet, Black Amethyst	40.00
Bottle, Ink, German, Two Boys, Insert, C.1920	10.50
Bottle, Ink, Gers & Millman, Aqua	40.00
Bottle, Ink, Harrison's Columbian, Aqua	60.00
Bottle, Ink, Hoyt's Indelible, Paper Label, Cork, 2 X 1/2 In.	3.00
Bottle, Ink, J.& I.E.M., Aqua	12.00 To 14.00
Bottle, Ink, J.& I.E.M., Igloo, Green	15.00
Bottle, Ink, J.& I.E.M., Turtle, Aqua	22.00
Bottle, Ink, Ma Carter, Screw Cap	26.00
Bottle, Ink, Master International	15.00
Bottle, Ink, Master, Deep Blue Green	15.00
Bottle, Ink, Master, Edward's, Aqua	15.00
Bottle, Ink, Millville, Footed, White, Red, Green, Yellow, & Pink, Stopper	110.00
Bottle, Ink, Millville, Umbrella Top, Footed, Blue, Pink, Red, Green, & Yellow	140.00
Bottle, Ink, Paperweight, Canes Top & Bottom, White Friar, 6 In.High	180.00
Bottle, Ink, Sanford, Patent Date 1911, Pouring Spout, Labels, Brown, Quart	8.50
Bottle, Ink, Sanford's Indelible, Sample, Clear	10.00
Bottle, Ink, Sanford's, Label, Pint	10.00
Bottle, Ink, Sanford's, Wooden Box	35.00
Bottle, Ink, Stafford's, Master, Cobalt, Quart	8.00
Bottle, Ink, Stoddard Cone	85.00
Bottle, Ink, Stoddard Umbrella	80.00
Bottle, Ink, Teakettle, Pottery, Two Tone Tan	110.00
Bottle, Ink, Teapot, Penholder, Signed	8.50
Bottle, Ink, Umbrella, Open Pontil, Stain, Aqua	10.00
Bottle, Ink, Umbrella, Pontil, 10 Sided, Light Blue	22.00
Bottle, Ink, Umbrella, Sheared Lip, Amber	80.00
Bottle, Ink, Umbrella, Stoddard, Open Pontil, Amber	65.00
Bottle, Ink, Umbrella, 8 Sided, Open Pontil, Aqua	13.00 To 18.00
Bottle, Ink, Underwood's Inks, Metal Top, Label, Cobalt	25.00
Bottle, Ink, Underwood's, Aqua	10.00
Bottle, Ink, Washington Bust, Screw Cap, Blue	6.75
Bottle, Ink, Wharton's Inks, Nashville, Tenn.	5.00
Bottle, Jar, Biscuit, Mont Joy, Violets, Purple, Frosted, Etched	65.00
Bottle, Jar, Biscuit, Rose Design, Cream, Beige, Metal Cover, Handle	24.50
Bottle, Jar, Blown, Ground Pontil, Clear	12.00
Bottle, Jar, Doctor's, Pontil, Lid, Amethyst, 9 1/2 In.High	9.50
Bottle, Jar, Flowers, Butterflies, Cover, 7 1/2 In.Tall	52.50
Bottle, Jar, Free-Blown, Pontil, Plain Lip, Aqua, 8 In.Tall	28.00
Bottle, Jar, Leaves, Etched, Bulbous, Amber	15.00
Bottle, Jar, Pat.1866 On Base, Glass Lid With Knob On Top, Op, Clear	35.00
Bottle, Jar, Pickle, Some Cutting, Mushroom Shape Lid	19.00
Bottle, Jar, Planters Peanut, Barrel Shape, Label, Embossed Mr.Peanut	85.00
Bottle, Jar, Rose, Terra-Cotta, Allover Dragons, Flowers, Flower Bud Finial	35.00
Bottle, Jar, Samson Battery, Large Bubbles, Aqua	7.00
Bottle, Jar, Tobacco, Silver Bulldog On Lid	15.00
Bottle, Jug, Cobalt Floral & Swirl Decoration, Ottman Bros., 2 Gallon	30.00
Bottle, Jug, Thread Glass, Clear, Silver Plate Lid, Applied Handle, 8 In.Tall	36.00
Bottle, Keene, Pouring Lip, Barrel, Three Mold, Blown	150.00

Bottle, Kentucky Gentleman Soldier, Valley Forge Officer	9.95
Bottle, Kimmell's Tonic Herb, Label, Clear	10.00
Bottle, King's Gate Caernarvon Castle, Investiture Of Prince Charles, Pair	35.00
Bottle, Lionstone, Sodbuster .... *Illus*	24.50
Bottle, Liquor, Alternate Swirl & Notched Ribs, Stars, Flint	25.00
Bottle, Medicine, Ayer's Cherry Pectoral, Embossed, Open Pontil	30.00
Bottle, Medicine, Ayer's Cherry Pectoral, Pontil	20.00
Bottle, Medicine, Ayer's Hair Vigor, Blown In Mold, Blue	17.00
Bottle, Medicine, B.A.Fahnestock's Vermifuge, Embossed, Open Pontil	12.00
Bottle, Medicine, Barry's Tricopherous For The Skin & Hair, Embossed	23.00
Bottle, Medicine, Bauer's Instant Cough Cure	3.00
Bottle, Medicine, Bonpland's Fever & Ague Remedy, Embossed, Open Pontil	22.00
Bottle, Medicine, Brant's Indian Pulmonary Balsam, Open Pontil, Aqua	42.50
Bottle, Medicine, Castoria	2.00
Bottle, Medicine, Chapman's Genuine, Stoddard Glass, Olive Amber, 8 In.	300.00
Bottle, Medicine, Coco-Mariana, Squat, Paris, Dark Green	4.50
Bottle, Medicine, Coke Dandruff Cure	3.50 To 4.00
Bottle, Medicine, Compound Asiatic Balsam, Open Pontil, Wrapper	42.00
Bottle, Medicine, Cramer's Kidney Cure	6.00

Bottle, Lionstone, Sodbuster

Bottle, Medicine, Criswell's Bromo Pepsin	4.00
Bottle, Medicine, Crystal Tonic, Clear	9.00
Bottle, Medicine, Curtis & Perkins Cramp & Pain Killer	20.50 To 25.00
Bottle, Medicine, Cuticura System Of Blood & Skin Purification	2.50
Bottle, Medicine, Cuticura System Of Curing Constitutional Humors	7.00
Bottle, Medicine, Davis Vegetable Pain Killer, Embossed, Open Pontil	16.50
Bottle, Medicine, Dr.A.C.Daniel's Disinfectant, Curbo Negue, Cork, Clear	3.00
Bottle, Medicine, Dr.A.C.Daniel's Wonder Wocken Lotion, Paper Label, Clear	3.00
Bottle, Medicine, Dr.Baker's Pain Panacea, Rectangular, Aqua	18.50 To 68.50
Bottle, Medicine, Dr.Cumming's Vegetine, Oval, Aqua, 9 1/2 In.High	3.75
Bottle, Medicine, Dr.D.Jayne's Alternative, Embossed	25.00 To 26.00
Bottle, Medicine, Dr.D.Jayne's Alternative, Oval, Open Pontil, Aqua	20.00
Bottle, Medicine, Dr.D.Jayne's Expectorant, Embossed, Open Pontil	26.00
Bottle, Medicine, Dr.D.Jayne's Expectorant, Open Pontil, Dug	12.50
Bottle, Medicine, Dr.D.Jayne's Expectorant, Rectangular, Aqua	21.00 To 22.10
Bottle, Medicine, Dr.Elliott's Speedy Cure, Label	10.00
Bottle, Medicine, Dr.Graves' Heart Regulator, Cures Heart Disease	7.50
Bottle, Medicine, Dr.H.A.Ingrham's Nervine Pain Extract, Embossed	16.00
Bottle, Medicine, Dr.Kilmer's Cure	5.00
Bottle, Medicine, Dr.Kilmer's Cure, Small Size	2.00
Bottle, Medicine, Dr.Kilmer's Indian Cough Cure, Aqua, 5 3/4 In.Tall	22.00
Bottle, Medicine, Dr.Kilmer's Oceanweed Heart Remedy, Ice Blue	30.00
Bottle, Medicine, Dr.Kilmer's Specific	5.00
Bottle, Medicine, Dr.Kilmer's Swamp Root Cure Specific	3.50

Bottle, Medicine, Dr.Kilmer's Swamp Root, Full, Box 12.00
Bottle, Medicine, Dr.Kilmer's Swamp Root, Kidney, Liver, & Bladder Cure 3.50
Bottle, Medicine, Dr.Miles New Heart Cure, Embossed, Aqua 6.00
Bottle, Medicine, Dr.Ordway's Pain Destroyer, 12 Sided, Label, Aqua 12.00
Bottle, Medicine, Dr.Owen's London Horse Liniment, Michigan, Aqua 40.00
Bottle, Medicine, Dr.Pinkham's Emmenagogue, Whittled, Open Pontil, Aqua 40.00
Bottle, Medicine, Dr.Tebbet's Physiological Hair Regenerator, Amethyst 45.00
Bottle, Medicine, Dr.Thacher's Liver & Blood Syrup 4.50
Bottle, Medicine, Dr.Wistar's Balsam Of Wild Cherry, Embossed, Open Pontil 28.00
Bottle, Medicine, Dr.Wistar's Balsam Of Wild Cherry, Phila., Op, Aqua 23.00
Bottle, Medicine, Dyspepsia & Constipation Cure, L.A.Knight Label, Clear 4.00
Bottle, Medicine, Elliman's Royal Embrocation For Horses 15.00
Bottle, Medicine, F.Brown's Essence Of Jamaica Ginger, Embossed 17.50
Bottle, Medicine, Fellow's Compound Syrup Of Hypophosphates, Embossed, Aqua 9.00
Bottle, Medicine, Foley's Cure, Sample 3.00
Bottle, Medicine, Foley's Kidney & Bladder 10.00
Bottle, Medicine, Galen's Restorative Elixir, Label, Open Pontil, Aqua 25.00
Bottle, Medicine, Gardner's Liniment, Open Pontil 21.50
Bottle, Medicine, Genuine Essence, Embossed, Open Pontil 14.00
Bottle, Medicine, Glover's Distemper 4.00
Bottle, Medicine, Goodwin's Grand Grease Juice Quintessence Of Fat 35.00
Bottle, Medicine, Gray's Balsam Best Cough Cure 4.00
Bottle, Medicine, Hall's Catarrh 3.00
Bottle, Medicine, Hall's Hair Renewer, Embossed, Peacock Blue 20.00
Bottle, Medicine, Hansi's Cough Remedy, Rectangular, Cork, Crown 3.00
Bottle, Medicine, Holman's, Nature's Grand Restorative, Open Pontil, Aqua 30.00
Bottle, Medicine, Humphrey's Homeopathic No.20 Whooping Cough, Clear 3.00
Bottle, Medicine, Hunt's Liniment, Open Pontil, Green 22.00
Bottle, Medicine, Hunt's Liniment, Sing Sing, Embossed, Open Pontil 23.00
Bottle, Medicine, Hyatt's Life Balsam, N.Y., Aqua, 9 1/2 In.High 12.00
Bottle, Medicine, Improved Colic Remedy, Full, Box 7.00
Bottle, Medicine, International Colic Remedy, Full, Box 7.50
Bottle, Medicine, J.B.Wheatley's Compound Syrup, Dallasburg, Ky., OP, Aqua 24.00
Bottle, Medicine, John Wyeth & Bro., Embossed, Dose Cap, Cobalt Blue 35.00
Bottle, Medicine, Johnson's American Anodyne Liniment, Embosse .... 16.50 To 17.00
Bottle, Medicine, Kendall's Spavin Cure, Amber 2.50
Bottle, Medicine, Kodol Dysperia Cure, Label 2.50
Bottle, Medicine, Langenbach's Dysentery Cure, Embossed, Blob, Amber 17.50
Bottle, Medicine, Lawrence's Carminative, 12 Sided, Open Pontil, Cork, Aqua 18.00
Bottle, Medicine, Laxol, Cobalt 6.75
Bottle, Medicine, Lee's Cube Smelling, 2 3/4 In.High 8.00
Bottle, Medicine, Lockport Gargling Oil, N.Y., Emerald Green 8.00
Bottle, Medicine, Lyon's Kathairon For The Hair, Embossed, Open Pontil 23.00
Bottle, Medicine, Lyon's Powder, Open Pontil, Puce 84.00
Bottle, Medicine, Magic Arnica Liniment 3.50
Bottle, Medicine, Magic Mosquito Bite 9.00
Bottle, Medicine, Marsden's Asiatic Cholera Cure, Label, Contents, Stamp 20.50
Bottle, Medicine, Mexican Mustang Liniment, Embossed, Open Pontil 15.50
Bottle, Medicine, Mexican Mustang Liniment, Open Pontil 16.50
Bottle, Medicine, Morrison's Veterinary Fever Drops, Cork, Clear, Boxed 3.00
Bottle, Medicine, Mrs.S.A.Allen's World's Hair Restorer 10.95
Bottle, Medicine, Mrs.Winslow's Soothing Syrup 3.50
Bottle, Medicine, Mrs.Winslow's Soothing Syrup, Embossed, Open Pontil 14.00
Bottle, Medicine, Munyon's Inhaler Cure, Green 18.50
Bottle, Medicine, Nerve & Bone Liniment, Round, Open Pontil, Aqua 17.50
Bottle, Medicine, One Minute Cough Cure 5.00
Bottle, Medicine, One Night Cure 5.00
Bottle, Medicine, Paine's Celery Compound, Square, Iridescent, Amber 4.50
Bottle, Medicine, Peptenzyme Powder, Embossed, Labels, Screw Top, Cobalt 12.00
Bottle, Medicine, Piso's Cough & Cold, Full, Box 5.00
Bottle, Medicine, Piso's Cure For Consumption, Green 2.75
Bottle, Medicine, Piso's Cure, Amethyst 4.00
Bottle, Medicine, Piso's Cure, Aqua 4.00
Bottle, Medicine, Polar Star Cure 5.00
Bottle, Medicine, Primley's Iron & Wahoo Tonic, Ind., Square, Amber 15.00
Bottle, Medicine, Professor I.Hubert's Malvina Lotion, Toledo, Milk Glass 15.00

Bottle, Medicine, Professor Wood's Hair Restorer, Embossed, Open Pontil 30.00
Bottle, Medicine, Puratone Laxative 4.50
Bottle, Medicine, R.D.Porter's Genuine Oriental Life Liniment, Open Pontil 17.50
Bottle, Medicine, R.D.Porter's Genuine Oriental Life Liniment, Round, Aqua 17.50
Bottle, Medicine, R.R.Radway & Co., Embossed, Open Pontil 13.00
Bottle, Medicine, R.R.Radway, Act Of Congress 4.50
Bottle, Medicine, Radway's Ready Relief, Full, Box 6.50
Bottle, Medicine, Robt.Turlington, Balsam Of Life, Jany, London On Sides 8.50
Bottle, Medicine, Rohrer's Wild Cherry Tonic Expectoral, Whittled, Amber 135.00
Bottle, Medicine, Sanitol For The Teeth 7.00
Bottle, Medicine, Sauer's Liniment, Paper Label, Round, Contents, 5 1/4 In. 2.00
Bottle, Medicine, Save The Horse Spavin Remedy 4.00
Bottle, Medicine, Seven Aids Indian Relief Tonic, Blob Top, Cork, Label 8.50
Bottle, Medicine, Shiloh's Consumption Cure .... *Illus* 7.50
Bottle, Medicine, Shirley Universal Renovator, Embossed, Open Pontil 60.00
Bottle, Medicine, Siegel Curative Syrup, 5 In.High .... *Illus* 25.00
Bottle, Medicine, Simmon's Liver Regulator 4.50
Bottle, Medicine, Sims' Tonic Elixir Of Pyrophosphate Of Iron, Amber 8.75
Bottle, Medicine, Spohn's Distemper Cure 4.00
Bottle, Medicine, Stella Vitae Mother's Cordial 5.00
Bottle, Medicine, Swaim's Panacea, Light Emerald Green 40.00
Bottle, Medicine, Tilden & Co., New Lebanon, Embossed, Iron Pontil, Green 100.00
Bottle, Medicine, True Elixir Worm Expeller, Auburn, Me. 1.50
Bottle, Medicine, Udolpho Wolfe's Aromatic Schnapps, Square, Amber 8.50
Bottle, Medicine, Warner's Log Cabin Liver Pills 12.00
Bottle, Medicine, Warner's Nervine, Embossed Safe Remedies Co., Label 35.00
Bottle, Medicine, Warner's Safe Cure, Broken Bubble 16.50
Bottle, Medicine, Warner's Safe Kidney & Liver Cure 10.00
Bottle, Medicine, Warner's Safe Kidney & Liver Cure, Amber 12.00
Bottle, Medicine, Warner's Safe Kidney & Liver Cure, Rochester, N.Y., Amber 20.00
Bottle, Medicine, Warner's Safe Kidney & Liver Remedy 20.00
Bottle, Medicine, Warner's Safe Remedies Co., Amber, 12 1/2 Oz. .... 16.00 To 20.00
Bottle, Medicine, Warner's Safe Remedies, Clear, 6 Oz. 20.00
Bottle, Medicine, Wigwam Indian Herb Tonic 7.50
Bottle, Medicine, Wyeth's Granular Lithium & Potassium Carbonates, Cobalt 8.00
Bottle, Medicine, Yankee Worm Killer, Full, Box 5.50
Bottle, Milk, Horlick's Malted, Embossed, Metal Screw Cap, Aqua, 6 3/4 In. 5.00
Bottle, Milk, Hot & Co., Potsdam, N.Y., Clear, 8 1/2 In. .... *Illus* 55.00
Bottle, Milk, Missouri Pacific 2.00
Bottle, Milk, New York Condensed Milk Co., Hutch Top, Round, Embossed, Clear 12.00
Bottle, Milk, Round Twist Cream Separator Top, Square, Pair 12.00
Bottle, Milk, Van Hornesville Dairy, Ribbed Neck, Cecil C.Harrad, N.Y. 2.50
Bottle, Moses, Green, Screw Top, 10 In.High 2.50
Bottle, National Corn Bitters, Amber 225.00
Bottle, No.1 Shaker Syrup, Canterbury, N.H., Aqua, 7 3/4 In.High 18.00
Bottle, Nursing, Acme Bladder 10.00
Bottle, Nursing, Advertising, Borden 6.50
Bottle, Nursing, Cat & Kittens, Embossed 6.50
Bottle, Nursing, Clapp's, Embossed, Amber 2.50
Bottle, Nursing, Dog, Embossed 6.50
Bottle, Nursing, Elephant, Embossed 8.50
Bottle, Nursing, Even-Flo, Nipple, Miniature 1.00
Bottle, Nursing, Happy Baby, Embossed 5.50
Bottle, Nursing, Kidney Shape, Ounce Scale, 6 1/4 In. 13.00
Bottle, Nursing, Rabbits 5.00
Bottle, Nursing, Screw Top, Nipple, 2 1/2 In.High 4.00
Bottle, Nursing, Sonny Boy, Embossed 8.50
Bottle, Nursing, The Graduated Nurser, Embossed 5.00
Bottle, Nursing, The Soothem Nurser, Turtle Style, Embossed 14.00
Bottle, Nursing, Vitafle, Embossed 3.00
Bottle, Oil, Shell 15.00
Bottle, Oil, Thomas A Edison Battery Oil, Signature, Clear, 4 1/4 In.High 1.50
Bottle, Old Pine Oil, Cork Top, 5 1/2 In.High 5.00
Bottle, Olive Oil, French Label, Aqua, Slender 15.00
Bottle, One Minute Cough Cure 3.50
Bottle, Pepper Sauce, Cathedral, Rough Pontil, Blown In The Mold, Stain 29.00

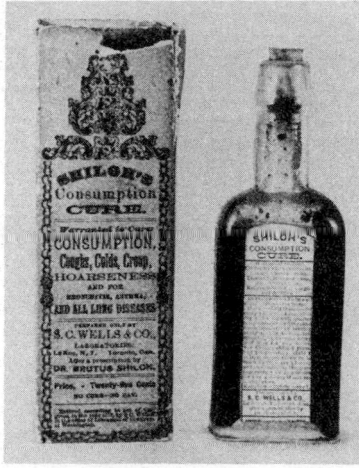

Bottle, Medicine, Shiloh's Consumption Cure
See Page 56

Bottle, Medicine,
Siegel Curative Syrup,
5 In.High
See Page 56

Bottle, Milk,
Hot & Co., Potsdam, N.Y.,
Clear, 8 1/2 In.
See Page 56

Bottle, Pepper Sauce, Diamonds, Spirals, & Arched Panels, Aqua	29.00
Bottle, Pepper Sauce, Fluted, Open Pontil, Aqua	17.50
Bottle, Pepper Sauce, Mills Western Spice, Cathedral, 4 Sided, Embossed, Aqua	35.00
Bottle, Perfume, Amber, Stopper, 6 In., Pair	10.00
Bottle, Perfume, Amethyst Glass, Ribbed, Marked France, 4 In.High	10.00
Bottle, Perfume, Atomizer, Devilbiss, Orange, Gold, Tall	10.00
Bottle, Perfume, Baccarat, Cone Shape, Stopper, 4 1/2 In.High, Pair	15.00
Bottle, Perfume, Cameo Glass, Brown Floral Design On Cream, Signed Ciarama	137.00
Bottle, Perfume, Clear, Scrollwork, Ground Pontil, Blown, Circa 1800	7.50
Bottle, Perfume, Cobalt Blue, Ormolu, Black Onyx Medallions, Floral, France	95.00
Bottle, Perfume, Crystal, Bulbous, Silver Deposit, 2 5/8 In.Tall	15.00
Bottle, Perfume, Crystal, Silver Deposit Neck, Rim, Stopper, 4 1/2 In.	30.00
Bottle, Perfume, Cut Design Base, Blue, Stopper, Made In Czechoslovakia	17.50
Bottle, Perfume, Etched Top	12.50
Bottle, Perfume, Fiddle, Opening In Bottom, Amber	125.00
Bottle, Perfume, Floral Decoration, Gold Outline, Gold Beaded Trim	38.00
Bottle, Perfume, French, Blue & White Twisted Ribbons, 7 Sided, Star Cut	160.00
Bottle, Perfume, Frosted, Rose, Butterfly Stopper, Made In France	12.50
Bottle, Perfume, Gold Design, Cobalt Blue Case, Candlestick Top	25.00
Bottle, Perfume, Green, Sterling Overlay, Chrysanthemums, Bird Medallion	135.00
Bottle, Perfume, Larkin Co., American Beauty, Boxed	3.50
Bottle, Perfume, Liberty Bell, 1926	10.00
Bottle, Perfume, Palmer Red Clover, Blob Stopper, Clear	4.00
Bottle, Perfume, Palmer, Green	8.00
Bottle, Perfume, Panels, Clear, Amethyst, Marked Cristal Nancy, France, 4 In.	8.00
Bottle, Perfume, Paperweight Type, Bird Stopper, Clear, 6 In.High	8.00
Bottle, Perfume, Paperweight, Multicolored Flowers, White Ground	130.00
Bottle, Perfume, Purse, Daisy & Button, Clear, Tin Screw On Cap, 7 In.Long	25.00
Bottle, Perfume, Seely Perfumer, Detroit, Michigan, Boxed	10.00
Bottle, Perfume, Silver Overlay, Silver Overlay Stopper	75.00
Bottle, Perfume, Sterling Silver Overlay, 3 In.	11.00
Bottle, Perfume, Vaseline, Stopper, Powder Box	19.50
Bottle, Pickle, Bunker Hill, Honey Color	18.00
Bottle, Pickle, Bunker Hill, 5 1/4 In.High	5.00
Bottle, Pickle, Cathedral, Aqua, Gallon	50.00
Bottle, Pickle, Cathedral, Iron Pontil, Dark Green, 2 Quart	180.00
Bottle, Pickle, Cathedral, 4 Panels, Iron Pontil, Stain, Aqua, 1 1/2 Quart	40.00
Bottle, Pickle, Cathedral, 6-Sided, Aqua	45.00
Bottle, Pickle, Skillton Foote, Bunker Hill, Pint	35.00
Bottle, Poison, Embossed, Label, Stopper, Blue	8.00
Bottle, Poison, Iodine, Skull & Crossbones, Brown	6.00

Bottle, Poison, Owl Drug Co., Cobalt Blue, Tricornered 12.50
Bottle, Polar Star Cough Cure 4.25
Bottle, Powder, Milk Glass, 4 7/8 In.High 5.95
Bottle, Rickett's, Embossed, Patent, Blue 25.00
Bottle, Sarsaparilla, Dr.Thomson's, Great English Remedy 35.00
Bottle, Sarsaparilla, Dr.Townsend's, Iron Pontil, Black Glass 95.00
Bottle, Sarsaparilla, Guysott's, Oval, Spotty Cloud, Bluish Aqua 70.00
Bottle, Sarsaparilla, Hood's, Embossed, Label, Screw Cap, 1929, Clear 3.50
Bottle, Sarsaparilla, Rush's, Stain 8.00
Bottle, Scent, Finger Type, Dutch Girls, Windmill, Brass Cap, Chain, Ring 22.00
Bottle, Scent, Ivory, Garden Scene, Oriental Figures, Script 25.00
Bottle, Scent, Pale Amethyst, Sandwich, Pewter Top 50.00
Bottle, Scent, Seagull's Head Form, Webb Type, White To Lemon, Silver 625.00
Bottle, Scent, White, Gilt, Raised Floral Gardens, Russia, Popov, 7 In.High 95.00
Bottle, Scott's Emulsion Cod Liver Oil With Lime & Soda 3.25
Bottle, Scott's Emulsion Cod Liver Oil, Raised Design, Fisherman, Aqua 2.95
Bottle, Seltzer, Cobalt, Whitehall, N.Y., Marked Czechoslovakia On Bottom 12.00
Bottle, Seltzer, Etched Indian On Front, Aetna Bottling, Blue, Pewter Top 25.00
Bottle, Seltzer, One Blue, One Clear, Original Hardware, Pair 23.50
Bottle, Seltzer, Penn Bottling, Reading, Penn.Etched, Clear 12.50
Bottle, Shaker Digestive Cordial, A.J.White, N.Y., Aqua, 8 3/4 In.High 16.00
Bottle, Shaker Fluid Extract Valerian, Aqua, 3 1/2 In. 15.00
Bottle, Sitting Bear, Black Milk Glass 37.00
Bottle, Smith's White Root, Patent July 17, 1866, Pottery, 10 In.High 35.00
Bottle, Snuff Jug, Flowers, Leaves, Crockery Pebbled, Wire Handle, Blue, 6 In. 21.00
Bottle, Snuff, Agate Like, Red, Gray, Green Veins, Peking Glass, Jade Stopper 55.00
Bottle, Snuff, Black Agate, White & Brown Pebble Profusion, Agate Stopper 45.00
Bottle, Snuff, Boy Riding On Carp, Spoon In Mouth, Ivory 95.00
Bottle, Snuff, Bulbous, Dyed Blue Stone, Carved Ogre Mask, Ring Handles 50.00
Bottle, Snuff, Bulbous, Gray Agate, Carved Monkey, Peach, Horse, 1780-1880 ..... 140.00
Bottle, Snuff, Carved Ivory 20.00
Bottle, Snuff, Carved Lapis Lazuli 110.00
Bottle, Snuff, Carved Woman, Bridge, Coral Stopper .... Illus 625.00
Bottle, Snuff, Carved, Orange Overlay, Inside Painted, Chinese 28.00
Bottle, Snuff, Cherry Amber, Carved Panels, Etched Floral, Ivory Spoon 65.00
Bottle, Snuff, Cinnabar, Carved, Floral, Leaves, Carved Stopper, Ivory Dipper 65.00
Bottle, Snuff, Cinnabar, Carved, Spoon 32.00
Bottle, Snuff, Cylindrical, Blue & White, Peachbloom, Men, Boat, C.1850 .... 60.00
Bottle, Snuff, Cylindrical, Iron & Gold On White, Dragon, Ch'len Lung 70.00
Bottle, Snuff, Cylindrical, Porcelain, White On Black, Dragons, Coral, C.1850 ..... 130.00
Bottle, Snuff, Double Gourd, Green Gray Jade, Carved Branches, Bat, Stopper 40.00
Bottle, Snuff, Double Gourd, Rock Crystal, Carved Branches & Gourds, Stopper 70.00
Bottle, Snuff, Drum Shape Flask, Fei-Ts'Ui Jade, Carved Medallion, Figures 225.00
Bottle, Snuff, Embossed Floral, Triangle, Ball Feet, Sterling, Coral Top 45.00
Bottle, Snuff, Enameled Glass, Peking 70.00
Bottle, Snuff, Enameled Glass, Peking .... Illus 135.00
Bottle, Snuff, Figural Bearded Sage, Porcelain, Brass Lid, 3 In.High 190.00
Bottle, Snuff, Fish Form, Smoke Crystal, Carved Carp, Stopper 50.00
Bottle, Snuff, Flask, Gray & Brown Agate, Carved Horse, Glass Stopper 60.00
Bottle, Snuff, Flask, Gray Jade, Mottled, Fei-Ts'Ui Jade Stopper 40.00
Bottle, Snuff, Flask, Gray Striped Agate, Coral Stopper 60.00

Bottle, Snuff, Carved Woman,
Bridge, Coral Stopper

Bottle, Snuff, Enameled Glass, Peking

Bottle, Snuff, Flat Ovoid, Oriental Figures, Lion Handles, Porcelain, C.1920 .... 18.00
Bottle, Snuff, Flattened Flask, Brown Agate, Carved Horses, 1780-1800 .... 625.00
Bottle, Snuff, Flattened Flask, Brown Quartz, Mottled, Coral Stopper 30.00
Bottle, Snuff, Flattened Flask, Fei-Ts'Ui Jade, White, Mottlings, Stopper 60.00
Bottle, Snuff, Flattened Flask, Turquoise, Matrix, Fei-Ts'Ui Jade Stopper 90.00
Bottle, Snuff, Flattened Flask, White Jade, Coral Stopper 30.00
Bottle, Snuff, Flattened Heart Shape, Blue Sodalite, Aventurine Stopper 30.00
Bottle, Snuff, Flattened Ovate, Fei-Ts'Ui Jade, Gray, Brown, & Lavender 225.00
Bottle, Snuff, Flattened Ovate, Gray Agate, Carved Peonies, Insects 60.00
Bottle, Snuff, Flattened Ovate, Green Quartz, White & Black Mottlings 50.00
Bottle, Snuff, Flattened Ovate, Hair Crystal, Black Tourmaline Needle, 1800 .... 150.00
Bottle, Snuff, Flattened Ovate, White Calcite, Carved Ogre Mask, Handles 30.00
Bottle, Snuff, Flattened Quadrangular Shield Shape, Mutton Fat Jade, Carved 40.00
Bottle, Snuff, Flattened Shield Shape, Amethystine Quarts, Carved Birds 60.00
Bottle, Snuff, Flattened Shield Shape, Fei-Ts'Ui Jade, Lavender & Green 100.00
Bottle, Snuff, Flattened Shield Shape, Hair Crystal, Black Tourmaline 50.00
Bottle, Snuff, Flattened Shield Shape, Lacque-Burgaute, Mother-Of-Pearl 90.00
Bottle, Snuff, Flattened Shield Shape, Spinach Green Jade, Gold Decoration 120.00
Bottle, Snuff, Flattened Shield Shape, White & Brown Jade, Mottlings 40.00
Bottle, Snuff, Flattened, Hair Crystal, Black Tourmaline Needles, 1800-1900 .... 125.00
Bottle, Snuff, Flattened, White Jade, Brown Mottlings, Incised, Stopper 60.00
Bottle, Snuff, Flattened, White Jade, Mottlings, Carved Elephant, Stopper 160.00
Bottle, Snuff, Flattened, White, Carved, Ogre Mask & Ring Handles, Stopper 20.00
Bottle, Snuff, Form Of Robed Woman On Elephant, Coral, Head Forms Stopper 300.00
Bottle, Snuff, Group Of Cranes, Dated Autumn 1971, Signed Shin Mao Kit 250.00
Bottle, Snuff, Hair Crystal, Dragons, Gold Reptile, C.1880 .... 180.00
Bottle, Snuff, Interior Painted, Turquoise Stopper, Signed 35.00
Bottle, Snuff, Ivory Inset, Hand Carved Panels, Bronze, 5 In.Tall 118.00
Bottle, Snuff, Ivory, Bronze, Jewels, Stopper, China 100.00
Bottle, Snuff, Ivory, Carved .... 28.50 To 32.50
Bottle, Snuff, Ivory, Carved, Hand-Painted Scenes, Dippers, Pair 135.00
Bottle, Snuff, Ivory, Etched, 2 1/2 In. 45.00
Bottle, Snuff, Ivory, Wooden Base, 3 1/2 In. 25.00
Bottle, Snuff, Lacquer, Burguate, Meip'Ling Shape, Miniature, Teak Stand 155.00
Bottle, Snuff, Lady's, Mottled Green & White Jade, Carnelian Stopper 145.00
Bottle, Snuff, Lapis Lazuli, Allover Carving, Flowers, Animals 270.00
Bottle, Snuff, Malachite, Carved Fruits & Vines 110.00
Bottle, Snuff, Marshall's, Quart 4.25
Bottle, Snuff, Melon Form, Carnelian Agate, Carved Dragonfly, Stopper 100.00
Bottle, Snuff, Melon Shape, White Jade, Carved Blossoms, Coral Stopper, 1850 .... 125.00
Bottle, Snuff, Milk White, Ovate, Famille Rose Enamels, Ku Yueh Hsuan, 1850 .... 450.00
Bottle, Snuff, Molded Porcelain, Immortals, Peking Glass Stopper, China 95.00
Bottle, Snuff, Mother-Of-Pearl, Sectioned, Shell Carving In Center 165.00
Bottle, Snuff, Muttonfat Jade, White, Rounded Bottom, Carved, Green Stopper 165.00
Bottle, Snuff, Nut Form, Gray & Brown Agate, Carved, Jade Stopper, 1780-1880 .... 100.00
Bottle, Snuff, Opaque White, Cameo Blue Floral, Insects, Carnelian Stopper 85.00
Bottle, Snuff, Ovate, Red & Opaque Yellow, Carved Fu Lions, C.1850 .... 120.00
Bottle, Snuff, Ovate, Red & Opaque Yellow, Coral Stopper, C.1850 .... 50.00
Bottle, Snuff, Oviform, Brown Quartz, Mottled, Red Glass Stopper 20.00
Bottle, Snuff, Oviform, Lapis Blue Porcelain, Dragon & Phoenix, Chia Ch'Ing 125.00
Bottle, Snuff, Oviform, Rock Crystal, Carved Basketry Design, Jade Stopper 70.00
Bottle, Snuff, Oviform, Rock Crystal, Carved Toad, Green Stopper, C.1800 .... 60.00
Bottle, Snuff, Oviform, White & Brown Jade, Carved Dragons, Metal Stopper 100.00
Bottle, Snuff, Oviform, White Jade, Carved Dragons, Pursuit Of Jewel 125.00
Bottle, Snuff, P.Lorillard, Amber 9.00
Bottle, Snuff, Painted Floral & Bird Inside, Aqua, Ivory Dipper, China 45.00
Bottle, Snuff, Painted Inside, Figures In Garden, Amber, 19th Century 38.00
Bottle, Snuff, Painted Inside, Figures, Grasshoppers, Cabbages, Beets, Stopper 37.50
Bottle, Snuff, Painted Interior, Boy On Water Buffalo, Yeh Chung-San 250.00
Bottle, Snuff, Pebble Form, Gray Brown Agate, Carved Boys, Holding Box 40.00
Bottle, Snuff, Pebble Shape, White Jade, Matrix, Coral Stopper, Wooden Spoon 125.00
Bottle, Snuff, Peking, Blue, Snowflake Glass, C.1800-1860 .... *Illus* 100.00
Bottle, Snuff, Peking, Green, White Glass, C.1800-1860 .... *Illus* 1900.00
Bottle, Snuff, Peking, Inside Painting 35.00
Bottle, Snuff, Peking, Multicolored, Glass, C.1850-1900 .... *Illus* 375.00
Bottle, Snuff, Peking, Red, Snowflake Glass, C.1800-1860 .... *Illus* 125.00

Bottle, Snuff, Peking, Red, Snowflake Glass, C.1800-1860 .... *Illus* 150.00
Bottle, Snuff, Peking, White, Glass, C.1800-1860 .... *Illus* 70.00
Bottle, Snuff, Porcelain, Baluster, Green, Bamboo Trellis, Jade Stopper, 1850 .... 250.00
Bottle, Snuff, Porcelain, Blue, Gray, Red, Two Poems, Signed, 1800-1900 .... 140.00
Bottle, Snuff, Porcelain, Flask, Iron & Green On White, Shou Figures, 1850 .... 60.00
Bottle, Snuff, Porcelain, Flattened Pear, Lime Green, Landscape, C.1850 .... 180.00
Bottle, Snuff, Porcelain, Flattened Quadrangular, Iron & White, Yung Cheng 40.00
Bottle, Snuff, Porcelain, Form Of Liu Han With Toad, Blue Gray, Stopper 40.00
Bottle, Snuff, Porcelain, Hand-Painted, Jade Stopper 13.00
Bottle, Snuff, Porcelain, Ju-I Shape Flask, Floral Medallion, White, C.1850 .... 150.00

 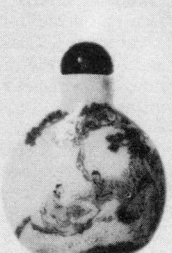  

| Bottle, Snuff, Snowflake Glass, Peking, Blue, C.1800-1860 *See Page 59* | Bottle, Snuff, White Glass, Peking, Green C.1850-1860 *See Page 59* | Bottle, Snuff, Glass, Peking, Multicolored, C.1850-1900 *See Page 59* | Bottle, Snuff, Snowflake Glass, Peking, Red, C.1800-1860 *See Page 59* |

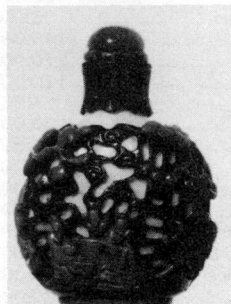   

| Bottle, Snuff, Snowflake Glass, Peking, Red, C.1800-1860 | Bottle, Snuff, Glass, Peking, White, C.1800-1860 | Bottle, Snuff, White Glass, Enameled, C.1850-1900 *See Page 61* | Bottle, Snuff, White Glass, Enameled, Tourmaline Stopper *See Page 61* |

Bottle, Snuff, Porcelain, Oviform, Ch'len Lung, C.1850 .... 275.00
Bottle, Snuff, Porcelain, Round, Lemon Yellow, Fu Lions, C.1890 .... 70.00
Bottle, Snuff, Porcelain, Stopper, 3 In.High 12.95
Bottle, Snuff, Porcelain, Twin, Cylindrical, Iron Red Dragons, C.1850 .... 40.00
Bottle, Snuff, Quadrangular, Smoke Crystal, Carved Blossoms, Bird, Stopper 60.00
Bottle, Snuff, Red Landscape, Blue & White Touches, Carnelian Top, Stand 95.00
Bottle, Snuff, Round, Porcelain, Sepia Dragons On Yellow, Ch'len Lung, 1850 .... 80.00
Bottle, Snuff, Ruby Glass, Silver Flakes, 19th Century, German 110.00
Bottle, Snuff, Shield Shape, Gray & Brown Agate, Carved Ogre Masks, 1780 .... 50.00
Bottle, Snuff, Smoky Crystal, Carnelian & Metal Stopper 85.00
Bottle, Snuff, Swimming Goldfish Form, Carnelian Agate, Carved, Stopper 80.00
Bottle, Snuff, Tapering Flask, Rock Crystal, Carved Ogre Mask, C.1800 .... 60.00

Bottle, Snuff, Tapering, Gray Agate, Chalcedony, Carved, Coral Stopper 180.00
Bottle, Snuff, Tapering, Oval Section, Gray Agate, Carved Ogre Mask Handles 30.00
Bottle, Snuff, Toad Form, Malachite, Carved, Coral Stalk Stopper 60.00
Bottle, Snuff, Toad Form, Mottled Green Jade, Carved, Coral Stalk Stopper 45.00
Bottle, Snuff, Tortoise Form, Gray Agate, Carved, Green Glass Stopper 50.00
Bottle, Snuff, Turquoise, Flattened Tapering, Carved Women, Twin Genii 210.00
Bottle, Snuff, Twin, Flattened Flask, Rock Crystal, Carved Peonies, Stoppers 60.00
Bottle, Snuff, Urn Shape, Baby Design, Cloisonne, 20th Century, 3 In. .... Illus 90.00
Bottle, Snuff, White Glass, Enameled, C.1850-1900 .... Illus 140.00
Bottle, Snuff, White Glass, Enameled, Tourmaline Stopper .... Illus 400.00
Bottle, Snuff, White Jade, Feitsui Jade Top 65.00
Bottle, Snuff, White Jade, Green Jade Stopper, Teak Stand, Uncarved 135.00
Bottle, Soda Water, Rounded Base, 12 In. 2.98
Bottle, Soda, Blob Top, Embossed, Yellow 7.00
Bottle, Soda, Blob Top, Round Bottom 2.00
Bottle, Soda, Blob Top, Torpedo Shape, Wintle & Sons 3.75
Bottle, Soda, Canada Dry, Carnival Glass, Marigold .... 10.00 To 15.00
Bottle, Soda, Carnation, Embossed Flower 2.00
Bottle, Soda, Cherry Smash, 5 Cents, Always Cherry, Black Lettering, 12 In. 75.00
Bottle, Soda, Clicquot Club Celebrated, Made In America, Clear, 10 In.High 3.00
Bottle, Soda, Clicquot Club, Millis, Mass., Teal Blue 6.00
Bottle, Soda, Coffee, Etched, Clear Swirling, Ground Bottom 65.00
Bottle, Soda, Donald Duck 35.00
Bottle, Soda, Douglass Pineapple, Black Lettering, 12 In.High 50.00
Bottle, Soda, Dr.Pepper, Inverted Letters, Grenville, Tx, Green 3.50
Bottle, Soda, Elk Head, Embossed 2.00
Bottle, Soda, English, Screw In Stopper, Embossed Brand Name 4.50
Bottle, Soda, Fowler's Cherry Smash, Decal Label, Red, 12 In.High 50.00
Bottle, Soda, Ginger, English Stoneware, Screw In Stopper 4.00
Bottle, Soda, H.Wetter, St.Louis, Blob Top, Light Green 15.00
Bottle, Soda, Hippo, Embossed 4.00
Bottle, Soda, Independent Bottling Works, Chicago, Blob Top, Blue Green 2.00
Bottle, Soda, J.Moran, Burlington, Round, Embossed Flag With 13 Stars, Aqua 45.00
Bottle, Soda, Moxie, Embossed Licensed Only For Serving 12.00
Bottle, Soda, Moxie, Label, Contents 15.00
Bottle, Soda, Moxie, Porcelain, Wire Cap, Green, 11 3/4 In.High 12.50
Bottle, Soda, Owen Casey Eagle Soda Works, Blue 25.00
Bottle, Soda, Pepsi-Cola, Amber 35.00
Bottle, Soda, Raspberry, Etched, Cruet Shape, 7 In.High 12.00
Bottle, Soda, Root Beer, Etched 35.00
Bottle, Soda, Round Bottom, Green 7.50
Bottle, Soda, Sherbet, Jade, Recessed Label, Metal Top, Red, 12 In.High 35.00
Bottle, Soda, Sprite, Miniature, Hobnail, Emblem, Filled & Capped, Green .... .50
Bottle, Soda, Trayder's Belfast, Blob Top, Squat, Puce Amber 13.50
Bottle, Soda, Western, Deer's Head 4.50
Bottle, Souvenir, New York World's Fair, 1939, Opaque White Glass, 9 In. 9.75
Bottle, Spirits, Four Bottles In One, Applied Glass Collar 29.00
Bottle, Spirits, Four Part, 11 In.High 35.00
Bottle, Spring Water, Clark & White, N.Y., Pint 20.00
Bottle, Sprite, Miniature, Hobnail, Emblem, Filled & Capped, Green .... .50
Bottle, Stoneware, Pig, John Gaubotz, St.Louis, Mo., Incised Railroad Routes 400.00
Bottle, Swirl, Cobalt Blue, Pontil Mark, 7 In.High 40.00
Bottle, The Pure Oil Company, Clear, Quart 25.00
Bottle, Three Mold, Castor, Diamond Sunburst & Rib Pattern 30.00
Bottle, Toilet Water, Contents, 1906 .... 5.00
Bottle, Toilet Water, Three Sections, Leaf & Vine, Blown, Stopper 23.00
Bottle, Toilet Water, Twelve Flat Panels, Rough Pontil, Mold Blown, 6 In. 38.00
Bottle, Townsend's Sarsaparilla, Light Green, Graphite Pontil 62.50
Bottle, Turn Mold, Silver Overlay, CEP Monogram Engraved, Amber, Quart 35.00
Bottle, Two Sections, Green, Blown, Nozzle Top 7.00
Bottle, Water, Ball Shape Base, Removable Top, Silver Collar, Pattern 18.00
Bottle, Water, General Electric, Embossed Refrigerator 9.50
Bottle, Water, Hanbury Smith Vichy Water 30.00
Bottle, Water, Mineral, Clarke & White, Large C, New York, Dark Green, Quart 34.50
Bottle, Water, Mineral, Clarke & White, N.Y., Bubbly, Dark Olive Green 26.00
Bottle, Water, Mineral, Clarke & White, N.Y., Olive Green, Pint 25.00

Bottle, **Water**, Mineral, Clarke & White, New York, Dark Olive Amber, Quart	22.50
Bottle, **Water**, Mineral, Clarke & White, Whittled, Dark Green	29.00
Bottle, **Water**, Mineral, Congress & Empire, Amber, Quart	45.00
Bottle, **Water**, Mineral, Congress & Empire, Large C, Saratoga, Green, Pint	19.50
Bottle, **Water**, Mineral, Gettysburg Katalysine, Green, Quart	45.00
Bottle, **Water**, Mineral, Guilford Mineral Spring Water, Vt., Emerald, Quart	32.00
Bottle, **Water**, Mineral, J.Cosgrove & Son, Charleston, Blob Top, Cobalt	39.00
Bottle, **Water**, Mineral, John Ryan, Iron Pontil, Cobalt	3.00
Bottle, **Water**, Mineral, Middletown Healing Springs, Amber, Quart	25.00
Bottle, **Water**, Mineral, Saratoga Star Spring, Green, Quart	39.00
Bottle, **Water**, Mineral, Ypsilanti Mineral Springs, Blob Top, Amber	32.50
Bottle, **Water**, Pink Satin, Quilted, Silver Top	125.00
Bottle, **Wheaton Commemorative**, Apollo II	45.00
Bottle, **Wheaton Commemorative**, Apollo, 13	4.95
Bottle, **Wheaton Commemorative**, General Eisenhower	3.95
Bottle, **Wheaton Commemorative**, Helen Keller .... *Illus*	5.00
Bottle, **Wheaton Commemorative**, Jean Harlow	4.95
Bottle, **Wheaton Commemorative**, Political, Humphrey-Muskie, 1968	3.95
Bottle, **Wheaton Commemorative**, Political, Nixon-Agnew, 1968	3.95
Bottle, **Wheaton Commemorative**, Presidential, Eisenhower	3.95
Bottle, **Wheaton Commemorative**, Presidential, John F.Kennedy .... 25.00 To 45.00
Bottle, **Wheaton Commemorative**, Presidential, Lincoln	3.95
Bottle, **Wheaton Commemorative**, Presidential, Roosevelt	3.95
Bottle, **Wheaton Commemorative**, Presidential, Washington	3.95
Bottle, **Wheaton Commemorative**, Robert Kennedy	4.95
Bottle, **Wheaton Commemorative**, Thomas Jefferson .... *Illus*	5.00
Bottle, **Whiskey**, Barvells, Greeleys Bourbon, B.Heis, Amber	115.00
Bottle, **Whiskey**, Binninger, Puce, Square	60.00
Bottle, **Whiskey**, Bourbon, M.Bininger & Co., N.Y., 1848 .... *Illus*	80.00
Bottle, **Whiskey**, Cabin Still, Hillbilly, 1939	150.00
Bottle, **Whiskey**, Chestnut Grove Whiskey CW, Jug, Handled, Amber	176.00
Bottle, **Whiskey**, Congress Hall, Maryland Rye, Embossed	15.00
Bottle, **Whiskey**, Cottage Brand Embossed, Cabin Shape, Aqua	95.00
Bottle, **Whiskey**, Cut Glass, Embossed Spring Park, 11 1/2 In.High	25.00
Bottle, **Whiskey**, Duffy's Malt	4.00
Bottle, **Whiskey**, Duffy's Malt, Round, Bottom Dated 1886, Amber	4.50
Bottle, **Whiskey**, Dyottville Glass Works, Phila., Iron Pontil, Olive Amber	32.50
Bottle, **Whiskey**, Flask, Swirl Ribbed Pattern Lower Half, Clear, 7 1/2 In.	6.00
Bottle, **Whiskey**, Flora Temple Harness Trot	160.00
Bottle, **Whiskey**, Four Roses, Paul Jones, Embossed, Honey Amber	30.00
Bottle, **Whiskey**, Green River, Label	7.00
Bottle, **Whiskey**, Hayner's, Amber	9.00
Bottle, **Whiskey**, Hayner's, Clear	12.00
Bottle, **Whiskey**, Highland Whiskey, Embossed Ship At Sea, Amber, 7 In.	15.00
Bottle, **Whiskey**, Hollywood, Amber	5.00
Bottle, **Whiskey**, I.W.Harper's, Straw Basket, Recessed Paper Label, Amber	25.00
Bottle, **Whiskey**, Jesse Moore, Old Bourbon, Horns	12.00
Bottle, **Whiskey**, John Wyeth & Bro., Phila., Malt, Amber, 9 In.High	4.50
Bottle, **Whiskey**, Jug, Applied Handle, Deep Amber, 3/4 Pint	18.00
Bottle, **Whiskey**, Kellerstrass Distilling, Clear	60.00
Bottle, **Whiskey**, Kellerstrass Distilling Co., St.Louis, Sun Color Amethyst	7.00
Bottle, **Whiskey**, Kellogg's Wilmerding, Loewe, San Francisco, Inside Thread	25.00
Bottle, **Whiskey**, Lady's, Leg, Knee, Amber	12.50
Bottle, **Whiskey**, M.A.Ingalls, Liquor Dealer, Herkimer, N.Y., 5 Gallon	60.00
Bottle, **Whiskey**, O.Blake Bourbon, Barrel, Clear	8.00
Bottle, **Whiskey**, O.Blake Rye, Barrel, Clear	8.00
Bottle, **Whiskey**, Old Times, 1st Prize, World's Fair 1893, Clear	10.00
Bottle, **Whiskey**, Olive Green, Bubbles, Dyottville Glass Works	15.00
Bottle, **Whiskey**, Paul Jones, Blob Seal, Amber	10.00
Bottle, **Whiskey**, Perkins Stern & Co.Three Mold, Amber	10.50
Bottle, **Whiskey**, Personal Service, Sherman Hotel, Chicago, 1870s, Etched, 5	50.00
Bottle, **Whiskey**, Rey Del Rey, Clear	6.00
Bottle, **Whiskey**, The Old Bush Hill's Distilling Co., Aqua	10.00
Bottle, **Whiskey**, Turner Brothers, New York, Amber	125.00
Bottle, **Whiskey**, Week's & Potter Boston, Three Mold, Threads, Amber	12.50
Bottle, **Whiskey**, White Horse, Three Mold	7.00

Bottle, Whiskey, Wilmerding, Loewe, San Francisco, Kellogg's Co., Amber	30.00
Bottle, White Bear, Hubelin	28.00
Bottle, Wild Rose Perfume Oil, 1964, Full & Boxed	4.99
Bottle, Wild Rose Powder Sachet, 1953	7.00
Bottle, Wine, Black, Sandman, Royal Doulton	55.00
Bottle, Wine, Grape Design, Amber, Pewter Trim, Pewter Stopper, 10 In.High	22.50
Bottle, Wine, Jug, Porcelain, Man's Face, Brown Nightcap	85.00
Bottle, Wine, Onion Shape, Onion Rib, Green	37.50
Bottle, Wishing Duette Set	9.95
Bottle, Zanesville, Globular, 24 Rib Swirls, Dark Amber	200.00
Bottle, Zanesville, 24 Ribbed, Amber	275.00

Boxes of all kinds are collected. They were made of thin strips of inlaid wood, metal, tortoiseshell, embroidery, or other material.

Box, see also Porcelain, Store, Tin

Box, Band, Wallpaper, Mass., C.1830, 11 In.High	*Illus*	160.00
Box, Battersea, see Battersea, Box		
Box, Bible, Charles I, Oak, Rectangular, Carved, C.1650		180.00

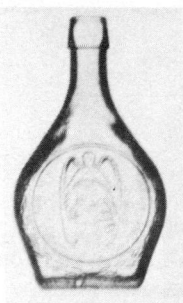

Bottle,
Wheaton Commemorative,
Thomas Jefferson
See Page 62

Bottle, Wheaton Commemorative,
Helen Keller
See Page 62

Bottle, Whiskey, Bourbon,
M.Bininger & Co., N.Y.,
1848
See Page 62

Box, Band, Wallpaper, Mass., C.1830,
11 In.High

Box, Bible, Oak, Circular Chip Carving On Face & Sides, C.1650	500.00
Box, Bible, Oak, Cleated Lid, Strap Hinges, 17th Century	90.00
Box, Bible, Oak, Floral Motifs Carved On Face, Demilune Arches, C.1650	225.00
Box, Bible, Oak, Slant Lid, Flute Carved Face, 17th Century	190.00
Box, Bible, Oak, 2 Carved Scrolled Panels & Rosette On Face, C.1650	225.00
Box, Bible, Pine, Reverse Molded Cleats At Top, 17th Century	80.00
Box, Bible, Pine, Snipe Hinges, Lock	90.00

Box, **Blue Band**, Crossed Blue Arrow, Scene Of Lovers, Domed Lid, Octagon 65.00
Box, **Bonbonniere**, Bird Form, Enameled, Silver Gilt Mounts, Round, C.1850 .... 240.00
Box, **Bonbonniere**, Malachite, French, Gold & Enamel Mounts, Oval 275.00
Box, **Carved Walnut**, Hinged Lid, Ball Feet, Footed, Presentation, Brass Mounts 90.00
Box, **Casket**, Carnelian, Panels Of Red & White Striated, Gilt Metal, 4 Feet 130.00
Box, **Casket**, Table, Italian, Renaissance Style, Gilt Metal, Benson & Hedges 325.00
Box, **Celluloid**, Harbor Scene & Lighthouse, Clasp 8.50
Box, **Celluloid**, Ivory, Raised Flowers, Acorns & Leaves, Lined 4.50
Box, **Chinese**, Enamel On Copper, Hinged, Four Tiny Copper Feet 43.00
Box, **Cigarette**, Malachite, Italian, Silver Hinge, White Onyx Interior 130.00
Box, **Cigarette**, Portrait Of Girl On Cover, Dated 1901, Ornate Hinges, Label 15.00
Box, **Covered**, Chinese Lacquer, Round, Flowers, Gold On Red, C.1850 .... 175.00
Box, **Cowhide Cover**, 9 X 4 In. .... *Illus*   35.00
Box, **Deed**, Mini Rose Stencil, Blue, Japanned, 3 1/2 X 2 X 2 1/4 In. 35.00
Box, **Dresser**, Mirrored, Tooled Leather Sides, Floral Still Life On Cover 50.00
Box, **Enamel On Copper**, Turquoise, Floral, People, Red Seal Mark, China 20.00
Box, **Enamel Over Copper**, Bird On Limb Inside Lid, China 40.00
Box, **Enamel**, German Silver Mounted, Rectangular, Design On White, C.1750 .... 180.00
Box, **Fan**, Lacquered, Black, Gold Design, China 12.50
Box, **Glass**, Hinged Lid, Hand-Painted Porcelain Medallion, Woman, French 55.00

Box, Cowhide Cover, 9 X 4 In.

Box, **Gloria Swanson Painted On Lid**, Round, Tin, 4 In.Diameter 5.00
Box, **Glove**, Burned Wood, Girl With Flowing Hair, Pink Silk Lined 9.00
Box, **Glove**, Celluloid, Picture Of Young Girl, Red Rose, Green Ground, Lined 4.50
Box, **Glove**, Pyrography, Brass Hinges & Catch, Irises 6.00
Box, **Glove**, Rosewood, Brass & Mother-Of-Pearl Inlay, Key 38.00
Box, **Gold Mounted**, Lacquer, Cylindrical, Enamel Plaque En Grisaille, C.1800 .... 300.00
Box, **Handkerchief**, Celluloid, Turquoise, Embossed Flowers, Lined 7.50
Box, **Hinged**, Round, Lime Green Glass, Enameled Lavender Violets & Green 40.00
Box, **Jewel**, Art Nouveau, Girls' Heads With Flowing Hair On Cover & Sides 9.75
Box, **Jewel**, Austria, Like Small Trunk, Jewels On Cover, Wood Lined, Dome 12.00
Box, **Jewel**, Enamel Design, White, Brass Hinge, Green Glass, Cover 22.00
Box, **Jewel**, Victorian, Footed, Hinged, Raised Acorns, Leaves 16.50
Box, **Jewel**, Victorian, Hinged Lid, Art Nouveau 15.00
Box, **Jewelry**, Green Glass, Hinged, Hand-Painted Enamel Flower On Top 38.00
Box, **Jewelry**, Musical, Black Lacquer, Oriental Scene, Mother-Of-Pearl Inlay 29.00
Box, **Jewelry**, Wooden, Hand-Carved, Birds & Floral 15.00
Box, **Knife**, Mahogany, Inlaid Shell Pattern, Sloping Lid, C.1750 .... 90.00
Box, **Knife**, Mahogany, Scrimshaw, One Drawer, Carved Knob & Ring 175.00
Box, **Lacquer**, Black, Gold Trim, 3 In.Diameter 15.00
Box, **Leather Covered**, Brass Studded, Papered Interior, 16 In.Long, Key 25.00
Box, **Light Blue**, Floral, Whie Cartouches, Porcelain, Gardner, Russia, 4 In. 95.00
Box, **Mahogany**, Openwork Hand Carving 12.00
Box, **Malachite**, Russian, Rectangular, Hinged, 1850 .... 325.00
Box, **Match Holder**, Ashtray, Golfer, Metal 65.00
Box, **Match**, Dull Metal, Cherub, Oblong, Footed, Striker Plate Inside Cover 12.00
Box, **Music**, Two Dolls Dance, Dressed As Cossacks, Wind, Black Lacquer, French 225.00
Box, **Painted Picture Of Gloria Swanson**, Signature, Tin, 4 In.Diameter 6.00
Box, **Paper**, Dutch, Hinge, Shadow Box Top, Portrait Of Lady, Valentine In Base 15.00
Box, **Patch**, Figure By Urn, Lavender Ground, Accept This Trifle, France, 1860 .... 105.00
Box, **Patch**, Openwork Silver, Moss Agate Lid & Base, Mask Catch 48.00

Box, **Perfume**, Black Lacquer, Oriental, 2 Hand Blown Bottles, 1920 .... 10.00
Box, **Photograph**, Victorian, Bird's-Eye Maple, Brass Trim, 2 Compartments 19.00
Box, **Pine**, Snipe Hinges, Shoe Feet, Dovetailed, 18th Century 70.00
Box, **Pine**, 18th Century, 21 1/2 X 15 In. 100.00
Box, **Ping Pong**, Wooden, Dovetailed, Label, Victorian Couple 35.00
Box, **Playing Card**, Queen Of Hearts Shape, Top Lifts Off At Waist, Heubach 35.00
Box, **Poite A Mouches**, Louis XVI, Gold Mounted, Guilloche Ground, 1780 .... 450.00
Box, **Porcelain**, Six Panels, Green, Red, Chicken Decor, China 35.00
Box, **Powder**, Blue Glass, Hinged Lid, White Enamel Lilies Of The Valley 30.00
Box, **Powder**, French Smoky Crystal, Footed, Covered, Kneeling Nude On Cover 35.00
Box, **Powder**, Glass, Brass, Gold Painting Of Deer, Hinged Lid 35.00
Box, **Powder**, Louis XVI, Gold & Enamel, Round, Oval Miniature, J.L.D., 1780 .... 2600.00
Box, **Powder**, Louis XVI, Gold, Enamel, Round, Miniature Of Girl, Beckers, 1779 .... 1300.00
Box, **Powder**, Yellow, Nosegay, Scene On Lid, Man & Woman In Woods, Porcelain 30.00
Box, **Quillwork**, 18th Century, 5 In. .... *Illus* 340.00
Box, **Round**, Ivory, Miniature French Lady Painting, Scene 165.00
Box, **Sailor's**, Walnut, Inlaid Portrait Of British Ship, C.1850 .... 145.00
Box, **Salt**, Porcelain, Blue Trim, Hinged Wooden Cover, Germany 29.00
Box, **Salt**, Rainbow Luster, Child's Head, Wooden Cover, Hole To Hang, Germany 15.00
Box, **Salt**, Wall, Two Compartments, Cover, Wooden 45.00
Box, **Sandalwood**, Carved Medallions Of Oriental Figures, Household Scenes 45.00
Box, **Seal**, Wooden, Hand-Carved, Purple Ribbon, Wax 12.00
Box, **Sewing**, Ivory Inlay, 8 In. .... *Illus* 65.00
Box, **Shaving**, Wooden, Traveling, Key & Mirror 10.00

Box, Quillwork, 18th Century, 5 In.

Box, Sewing, Ivory Inlay, 8 In.

Box, **Silver**, Hinged, Tortoiseshell Inlaid, Garland Top, Hallmarked 20.00
Box, **Snuff**, Bird, Foliage, Dragonfly, Clover Leaf, Gold Trim, Porcelain 65.00
Box, **Snuff**, Horn, Wooden Cover, Oval 11.00
Box, **Snuff**, Shell Shape, Burled Wood, Lead Lined, Mirror Under Lid 45.00
Box, **Snuff**, Shell Shape, Goldstone On Base, Set In Sterling 125.00
Box, **Stamp**, Miniature Replica Of Shakespeare's School Desk, Silver, 5 In. 48.00
Box, **Strong**, Dutch, Mahogany, Iron & Copper Strapwork 60.00
Box, **Strong**, Wooden, Hinged, Iron Straps, Lock, C.1650 .... 145.00
Box, **Sugar**, Yellow & Red Basket Flowers, Stencil, Twist Off Cover, 12 In. 125.00
    Box, **Tea Caddy, see also Furniture, Tea Caddy**
Box, **Three Compartments**, Carved White Jade Inset In Top, Wooden, 4 X 7 In. 75.00
Box, **Trinket**, Courtier Bending Over His Lady Reclining On Sofa 30.00
Box, **Trinket**, Dog Lying On Pink Pillow 26.00
Box, **Trinket**, Hen, Rooster, & 3 New Chicks On Gate, Footed 45.00
Box, **Trinket**, Kauffmann Type Portrait On Lid, Cobalt, Gold, Porcelain, German 17.50
Box, **Trinket**, Winged, Footed, Brass Ormulu Base, Hand-Painted Scene 110.00
Box, **Walnut**, Hinged Cover, 7 1/4 X 4 1/2 X 2 3/4 In. 4.75
Box, **Wooden**, Curved Lid, Buildings, Trees, Etc. 50.00
Box, **Wooden**, Leather Covered, Brass Lid, Carved Lion, England, 5 1/2 X 3 In. 15.00

Brass has been used for decorative pieces and useful tablewares since ancient times. It is an alloy of copper, zinc, and other metals.
Brass, see also Bells, Bronze, Miniature, Tools, Trivet, etc.
Brass & Copper, Bed Warmer, Pierced Top, Wrought Handle 42.50

Brass, **Ashtray**, Engraved Floral, Handled Holder, Marked China, Set Of 3 .... 10.00
Brass, **Ashtray**, Mounted Cigar Cutter, Ship's Wheel Operates, Striker, German 65.00
Brass, **Basket**, Soap, Hand On Tub 7.50
Brass, **Basket**, 9 In.High 7.50
Brass, **Bed Knob**, 3 3/4 In.Long, Pair 7.50
Brass, **Bed Warmer**, Finely Engraved 95.00
Brass, **Bed Warmer**, Pierced Top 110.00
Brass, **Bed Warmer**, Round, Long Wooden Handle 47.50
Brass, **Bell**, School, Stippled Design, Wooden Handle 35.00
Brass, **Bell**, Table, Embossed Sailing Ship Handle, 7 In.High 12.50
Brass, **Belt Plate**, British Cross, Volunteer Unit, Copper Design 57.50
Brass, **Belt Plate**, British Royal Marine Officer's, Cross, C.1850 .... 97.50
Brass, **Belt Plate**, Cold Stream Guards Officer's, Cross, C.1840 .... 125.00
Brass, **Bill Clip**, Horseshoe, Jockey Cap, Advertising Spencerian Pens 6.50
Brass, **Birdcage**, Stand 20.00
Brass, **Birdcage**, Dome Top, 15 In.High 15.00
Brass, **Blowtorch**, Max Sievert, Sweden, 5 1/2 In.High 12.00
Brass, **Bookends**, The Angelus, Pair 12.00
Brass, **Bookends**, White Jade Carving, 6 1/2 In.Tall, Pair 147.00
Brass, **Bowl**, Double Dragon Design, Marked China, 9 In.Diameter 9.75
Brass, **Bowl**, Incised Dragon, Pedestal, China, 10 In. 11.00
Brass, **Bowl**, Marked China, Incised Dragons, Teakwood Stand, 9 In. 7.50
Brass, **Bowl**, Popcorn, Allover Design, 4 3/4 In.Diameter, Set Of 6 .... 16.50
Brass, **Bowl**, Russian, 7 1/2 In. 25.00
Brass, **Bowl**, Teak Stand, China, 9 In.Diameter 25.00
Brass, **Box**, Allover Dragons, Wood Lined, China 40.00
Brass, **Box**, Cigarette, Etched Design, Cedar Lined, Hinged Cover, Marked China 8.75
Brass, **Box**, Engraved Flowers, Dragons, Enamel Oval On Cover, China .... · 18.50
Brass, **Box**, Letter, Slot In Back For Letters, 12 In.High, 10 In.Long 52.50
Brass, **Box**, Match, Applied Sickle & Wheat Design On Lid, Hinged, Russian 35.00
Brass, **Box**, Match, Elephant, Raised Trunk, Austrian, Cover 25.00
Brass, **Box**, Match, Frog Design, Cover 15.00
Brass, **Box**, Match, Hinged, Bradley, Hubbard Co. 5.00
Brass, **Box**, Queen's Christmas Gift To Her Soldiers, 1914 .... 22.00
Brass, **Box**, Stamp, Birds In Flight 17.50
Brass, **Box**, Stamp, Marked China, 1 1/2 X 2 In. 18.00
Brass, **Box**, Stamp, Paperweight, Bradley & Hubbard 15.00
Brass, **Box**, Stamp, Raised Enamel Decoration, Three Sections, Marked China 10.50
Brass, **Bucket**, Sap, Iron Bale Handle, 13 In.Diameter 30.00
Brass, **Buckle**, Belt, British, Pierced Royal Seal, C.1870 .... 14.50
Brass, **Buckle**, Belt, G.A.R., Rectangular 4.25
Brass, **Buckle**, Belt, Military, Salesman's Sample, C.1870 .... 19.50
Brass, **Cabinet**, Brush, Mirror Edging, Engraved, Center Mirror, Two Brushes 135.00
Brass, **Calendar**, Desk, Russian, Centered By Tazza, Rectangular Top, C.1850 .... 170.00
Brass, **Can**, Handy Grip, Round, Colgate Co., Dated 1917 .... 5.00
Brass, **Candelabrum**, Adjustable, 3 Branch, 14 1/2 In., Pair 40.00
Brass, **Candelabrum**, Center Holder, Four Branches, Ornate, 14 X 14 In. 50.00
Brass, **Candelabrum**, Table, Dutch, 4 Pierced Scrolled Arms, C.1890, Pair 200.00
Brass, **Candelabrum**, 5 Branch, Pair 50.00
Brass, **Candle Lighter & Extinguisher**, Long 22.00
Brass, **Candleholder**, Push-Up, Saucer, Hand Hold 45.00
Brass, **Candleholder**, Ring Handle, Saucer Base, Thumb Rest, Push-Up, 5 In.High 16.00
Brass, **Candleholder**, Saucer Type, Germany 15.00
Brass, **Candleholder**, Stick Type, Screw Connection, C.1880, 5 In., Pair 55.00
Brass, **Candlesnuffer**, Figure Of Animal Top, Marked China, 7 3/4 In.Long 4.75
Brass, **Candlesnuffer**, Pipe Shape, Twisted Handle, Marked China 4.00
Brass, **Candlesnuffer**, Scissor Type, Chain For Hanging .... 17.00 To 19.00
Brass, **Candlesnuffer**, Scissors, Box 28.00
Brass, **Candlestick**, Altar, IHS On Base, Triangular, 30 1/2 In.High, Pair 85.00
Brass, **Candlestick**, Beehive, Screw Connection, C.1880, 9 In., Pair 55.00
Brass, **Candlestick**, Beehive, 5 In. 19.50
Brass, **Candlestick**, Bulbous Turning, Footed, 18 In.High, Pair 65.00
Brass, **Candlestick**, Capstan, Engraved 75.00
Brass, **Candlestick**, Carved Figures, Cherub, Leaf, C.1910, 28 1/2 In.Tall, Pair 125.00
Brass, **Candlestick**, Chamber, Ring Handle, Thumbrest, Marked China 4.75
Brass, **Candlestick**, Classic Shape, Square Base, 8 In.High, Pair 25.00

Brass, Candlestick, Dome Base 100.00
Brass, Candlestick, English, Weighs 3 Lbs., 8 In.High, Pair 85.00
Brass, Candlestick, Engraved Floral, Leaves, Marked China, 2 1/2 In., Pair 4.75
Brass, Candlestick, Figural Boy & Dog On Marble Base, Dietz Bros. 35.00
Brass, Candlestick, Footed, 20 1/2 In.Tall, Pair 65.00
Brass, Candlestick, For Tavern, Bell In Stem, Wheel & Chain For Ringing 75.00
Brass, Candlestick, Hand Tooled, 11 1/2 In., Pair 90.00
Brass, Candlestick, Hogscraper, Wedding Band, Signed Shaw, 7 1/2 In.High 90.00
Brass, Candlestick, Incised Design, Sacred Heart, 16 1/2 In.Tall, Pair 35.00
Brass, Candlestick, Incised Design, 25 In.Tall 100.00
Brass, Candlestick, Mid Drip Pan 190.00
Brass, Candlestick, Oriental Design, Footed, 11 In.High, Pair 45.00
Brass, Candlestick, Push-Up, Pair 50.00
Brass, Candlestick, Push-Up, 6 3/4 In.High 8.50
Brass, Candlestick, Push-Up, 8 In.High, Pair .... 30.00 To 32.00
Brass, Candlestick, Pusher, Pair 45.00
Brass, Candlestick, Rectangular Base, 6 1/4 In.High, Pair 20.00
Brass, Candlestick, Saucer Type, Ring Handle, Marked China 3.95
Brass, Candlestick, Saucer, Folding, 8 In., Pair 120.00
Brass, Candlestick, Scroll Design, Victorian, Square Base, 6 1/2 In., Pair 48.00
Brass, Candlestick, Spiral Columns, Amber & Clear Prisms, 9 1/2 In., Pair 35.00
Brass, Candlestick, Turned Baluster Stem, Tapered Cup, 11 1/2 In., Pair 98.00
Brass, Candlestick, Wide Threads, 5 In.High, Pair 30.00
Brass, Candlestick, 18th Century, 8 1/2 In.High, Pair 125.00
Brass, Case For Three Cigars, Embossed Flowers 7.00
Brass, Chamberstick, Dutch Boy Stands At Base 47.50
Brass, Chamberstick, Ring Handle 15.00
Brass, Chamberstick, Saucer Type, Clipper Ship Handle, Says Revenge 12.50
Brass, Chandelier, Continental, 10-Light, Female Terms, Cherub's Heads 325.00
Brass, Chandelier, 12-Light, Continental, 2 Tiers Of Arms, C.1750 .... 800.00
Brass, Club, Billy, Policeman's, Presentation, June 14, 1887, N.Y. 145.00
Brass, Coffee Server, Engraved, Turkish 11.50
Brass, Compass & Sundial, B.Pike & Son, N.Y., C.1830, Mahogany Box 97.00
Brass, Compass, Surveying, Sight Attachments, Maker Wm.Davenport, Phila. 225.00
Brass, Corkscrew, Embossed Cherubs On Sides Of Handles, 7 In. 12.00
Brass, Crumb Scoop, Gargoyle Handle 3.00
Brass, Cup & Saucer, Footed Base, Russia, Circa 1775, Cup 12 In.High 69.00
Brass, Cup, Nickel Plated, Collapsible, Marked R.Germany 3.75
Brass, Cuspidor, 10 In.Diameter 27.50
Brass, Decanter, Anchor & Wheel Cutouts, Musical, Sweden 18.50
Brass, Decanter, Lantern, Musical 16.50
Brass, Dish, Chafing, Alcohol Burner, Two Top Pans, Ebony Handles 49.50
Brass, Dish, Marked Russia, 5 5/8 In.Diameter 6.75
Brass, Dish, Soap, Traveling 2.00
Brass, Door Knocker, Hand With Apple 45.00
Brass, Door Knocker, Lion's Head, Ring In Mouth, Dated 1880, 5 3/4 In.High 37.50
Brass, Doorstop, Basket 30.00
Brass, Doorstop, Hare, Stretched Out 20.00
Brass, Eagle, American, Head To Left, Spread Wings, Repousse, Chinese, C.1850 .... 450.00
Brass, Ear Trumpet, Cone Shape, Painted Black, Tiemann 15.00
Brass, Elephant, Howdah Holds & Dispenses Cigarettes 15.00
Brass, Ewer, Hammered, Swan Neck Spout, Imprinted Eagle On Bottom, Russia 32.00
Brass, Ewer, Russian, Signed With Double Eagle, 10 In.High 50.00
Brass, Fernery, Claw Feet, 6 In.Diameter 8.00
Brass, Figurine, Buddha, 4 1/4 In.High 37.50
Brass, Figurine, Clown, Taking Bow, Jacquard Suit, Baton In Hand, China 22.50
Brass, Figurine, Lady Dancer, Wooden Base, C.1900, 4 In.Tall 25.00
Brass, Figurine, Massasolt, C.Dalin, 11 In. 600.00
Brass, Figurine, Old Man, Carrying Book, Hat, Wood Base, C.1905, 2 3/4 In.Tall 25.00
Brass, Figurine, Parrot, Enameled Tail, 6 In. 50.00
Brass, Figurine, Policeman, Beard, Potbelly, 5 3/4 In.Tall 28.00
Brass, Figurine, Tiger, Oriental, 17 1/2 In.Long, 9 1/2 In.High 165.00
Brass, Figurine, Woman's Head, Crown, 6 In.Tall 35.00
Brass, Flask, Perfume, Flat, 1 1/2 X 2 1/4 In. 6.50
Brass, Flask, Powder, Deer Standing, Embossed, 6 1/2 In.Long, 3 1/4 In.Wide 25.00
Brass, Frame, Easel, Ornate, Victorian, 11 1/2 X 9 1/2 In. 35.00

Brass, Frame, For Holy Picture, Cross & Crown Of Thorns, Cranberry Light	15.00
Brass, Frame, Hanging, Lacy, Gothic Top, Takes 3 1/2 X 6 1/2 In.Picture	16.00
Brass, Goblet, Doll's House	3.00
Brass, Hanger, Hat, Screws On Wall	40.00
Brass, Helmet, European, Oval Plate, Engraved, Lobster Tail Back	34.50
Brass, Helmet, Turkish-Persian, Battle, Engraved, Mythological Scenes	64.50
Brass, Holder, Bouquet, Ornate, Ring For Finger	15.00
Brass, Holder, Flower, Grid For Inserting Flowers, 7 In.Diameter	10.00
Brass, Holder, Letter, Hand, Victorian	8.00
Brass, Holder, Letter, Lacy, Ornate, Two Cherubs' Heads	12.50
Brass, Holder, Matchbox, Safety	2.00
Brass, Holder, Tumbler & Toothbrush, Wall, Holds 4 Toothbrushes	8.50
Brass, Holder, Tumbler, For Wall, Slots For Toothbrushes, Burnished	12.00
Brass, Hook, Ceiling, Dolphin, Screw In Type, 11 1/4 In.Long	3.75
Brass, Hook, Coat, Elephant, India, Pair	3.00
Brass, Horn, Coach, France	135.00
Brass, Hourglass, Glass Filled With Sand, 1930, 9 In.High	29.00
Brass, Humidor, Cigar	12.50
Brass, Humidor, Russian, Rectangular, Hinged, Repousse, Imperial Eagle, 1850	170.00
Brass, Humidor, Tobacco, Silver Pipe Decoration, 9 1/2 In.	15.00
Brass, Hydrometer, English, Silver Finish, Velvet Lined Wood Case	19.50
Brass, Incense Burner, Open Scrollwork, Foo Dog Handles, Finial, China	55.00
Brass, Ink Blotter, Rocker Type, Engraved Floral & Leaves	12.00
Brass, Inkstand, Openwork, Scallops, Beveled Glass Inkwell, England	30.00
Brass, Inkwell & Pen Holder, Traveling, 9 In.Long	57.50
Brass, Inkwell, Berries, Leaves	20.00
Brass, Inkwell, Engraved Cupids, Victorian Head, Scrolling	115.00
Brass, Inkwell, Filigree, Pink Art Glass Insert	55.00
Brass, Inkwell, Form Of Lizard, Red Glass Eyes, Tail Winds Around Well	75.00
Brass, Inkwell, Hinged Cover, Embossed, Cobalt Insert, 3 Stepped Base	35.00
Brass, Inkwell, Owl, Glass Insert, Glass Eyes	45.00
Brass, Inkwell, Porcelain Insert	8.00
Brass, Inkwell, Sliding Top For Lady's Writing Desk, Flower Garlands	35.00
Brass, Insignia, Hat, Royal Canadian Mounted Police	9.00
Brass, Insignia, Hat, U.S.Infantry, Gilt, C.1870	1.50
Brass, Insignia, Hat, U.S.Infantry, Gilt, Openwork Center, C.1870	1.75
Brass, Jardiniere, Hammered, Three Ball Feet, Two Lion Head Handles, Rings	35.00
Brass, Jardiniere, Rose Border Around Top, 12 In.Diameter	35.00
Brass, Kettle, Bail, Marked H.W.Hayden's Ansonia Brass Co., Pat.1851	24.75
Brass, Kettle, Forged Rattail Bail, Base, 18 In.	70.00
Brass, Kettle, Forged Rattail Bail, Stand, 17 In.	60.00
Brass, Kettle, Jam, Movable Iron Handle, 8 X 12 In.Diameter	25.00
Brass, Kettle, Jelly, 14 In.Diameter	25.00
Brass, Kettle, Marked C.G.Huss & Co., Pittsburgh, Iron Bail, 11 In.Diameter	22.50
Brass, Kettle, Rattail Bail, Iron Footed Stand, E.Miller & Co., 1868, 21 In.	80.00
Brass, Kettle, 14 3/4 In.Diameter, 8 1/2 In.High	35.00
Brass, Knocker, Door, Burnished, 8 In.	14.00
Brass, Ladle, Brass Handle, Size 2, England	38.00
Brass, Ladle, Copper Mountings, Iron Handle, 20 In.Long	25.00
Brass, Ladle, Engraved, Wrought Iron Handle	70.00
Brass, Ladle, Slotted Handle	70.00
Brass, Ladle, Wrought Iron Handle	25.00
Brass, Lamp, Brass Shade, 15 In.High	35.00
Brass, Lamp, Hangs, Wick Comes Out Of Spout, Claw Type Handle, Three Chains	85.00
Brass, Lamp, Scenic, Scrollwork, Electric, China, 20 In., Pair	150.00
Brass, Letter Opener, Horseshoe Handle, Says Good Luck, England, 6 In.Long	2.75
Brass, Letter Opener, Metropolitan Life Insurance Co.	2.75
Brass, Letter Opener, Shape Of Swordfish	5.95
Brass, Lock & Key, Marked China, Key Folds, 5 1/2 In.Long, 2 In.Wide	15.00
Brass, Lock, Chair, & Key, Marked Lancaster	17.50
Brass, Lock, Patent WR	9.00
Brass, Lock, Trunk, Key	4.00
Brass, Match Holder, Banjo, 2 Compartments	25.00
Brass, Match Holder, Book Shape, 'Gott Mit Uns, ' German Matches	7.50
Brass, Match Holder, Shoe, Copper Toe	7.00
Brass, Match Safe, Soldier	30.00

Brass, **Match Safe**, 1 In.Wide 15.00
Brass, **Measure**, Hat Gauge, Oval, Gauge In Center, Carved Handles 12.50
Brass, **Mirror**, Easel, 12 X 16 In. 27.50
Brass, **Mirror**, Lady's, Embossed Frame, Handle, 5 In.Diameter 8.00
Brass, **Mirror**, 15 In.High 75.00
Brass, **Model**, Dardanelles Breech-Loading Cannon, Scale Model, C.1860 .... 165.00
Brass, **Mortar & Pestle**, Twin Handles, 2 In.High Mortar 9.50
Brass, **Mortar & Pestle**, 17th Century, 4 In.Tall & 5 1/2 In.Tall 50.00
Brass, **Mortar & Pestle**, 2 In.High 12.00
Brass, **Nut Cup**, Chinese 2.00
Brass, **Nutcracker**, Eagle Head Shape, 6 In.Long 12.50
Brass, **Nutcracker**, Embossed Fleur-De-Lis, Italy 7.50
Brass, **Nutcracker**, Figural, Alligator, Burnished, 14 In.Long 35.00
Brass, **Nutcracker**, Parrot, 6 In.Long 16.50
Brass, **Nutcracker**, Rooster, Two Handles .... 12.00 To 30.00
Brass, **Nutcracker**, Shakespeare Reliefs 9.50
Brass, **Opener**, Letter, Jade Handle Carved, 9 3/4 In.Long 22.00
Brass, **Opener**, Letter, Patent Atorney, O'Brien 4.50
Brass, **Ornament**, Chimney, Victorian, Flat Back, Form Of High Top Shoes, Pair 19.50
Brass, **Pan**, Jelly 35.00
Brass, **Pan**, Spun, Ansonia Brass Co., H.N.Hayden, Dated, 7 1/2 In.High 25.00
Brass, **Paper Clip**, Duck's Head 12.00
Brass, **Paper Clip**, Figural, Frog On Leaf, Marked China 17.00
Brass, **Paper Clip**, Frog On Lily Pad 12.00
Brass, **Paper Clip**, Horseshoe 12.00
Brass, **Paperweight & Spindle File**, Dragon, Attached To Base With Screws 25.00
Brass, **Pen Wiper**, Pig 45.00
Brass, **Pipe Rack** 25.00
Brass, **Pipe**, Opium, Incised Decoration, China, 10 In.High 50.00
Brass, **Pitcher**, English, Embossed Parlor Scene, 8 1/2 In.High 6.00
Brass, **Planter**, Rectangular, 23 X 8 X 6 In. 50.00
Brass, **Planter**, Three Lion's Paw Feet, Marked Russia, 4 In.Diameter 7.95
Brass, **Plaque**, Flight Of Mohammed Over The Mountains 100.00
Brass, **Plaque**, Lincoln's Head, Calverly, 1898, 10 1/2 In.Diameter 60.00
Brass, **Plaque**, Raised Figure Of Washington, Progressive Brass, Kansas City 12.00
Brass, **Plaque**, Seminude Woman, Rose Border, C.1710, 22 X 9 In. 250.00
Brass, **Plaque**, Soldier's Farewell, 'Breaking Home Ties In 1898' 34.50
Brass, **Plaque**, Tavern Scene, 1i In.Oval 5.00
Brass, **Plate**, Helmet, British Lancer, C.1900, Royal Lancers 17.50
Brass, **Plate**, White House, Flowers, 4 1/4 In.Diameter 18.00
Brass, **Rack**, Letter, Fan Shape, 2 Compartment, Pierced Edges, Etched Floral 24.00
Brass, **Rack**, Letter, Two Compartments, Ornate, 8 In.Wide X 8 1/2 In.High 40.00
Brass, **Rack**, Towel, 3 Arm, 15 In.Long 5.00
Brass, **Samovar, see Samovar**
Brass, **Sander**, For Letters, 2 In.High 45.00
Brass, **Scale**, Reams Of Paper & Weight Of Letter Sheets, Union Selling Co. 22.50
Brass, **Scuttle**, Coal, Raised Floral & Leaf Pattern, Shovel, Wooden Handle 100.00
Brass, **Sealer**, American Express-Preston, Idaho, Nickel Plated Handle 11.00
Brass, **Shell Case**, U.S.Artillery, 75 Mm.Engraved, Birdgeport Brass Co., 1941 .... 17.50
Brass, **Ship**, Holds 2 Blown Decanters, White To Pink, Flowers 165.00
Brass, **Snuffbox**, Round, Mosaic Top 10.00
Brass, **Spectacles**, Feather Decoration On Sides 50.00
Brass, **Spigot For Barrel**, Marked Strater & Sons, Boston, 8 1/2 In.Long 5.95
Brass, **Spigot**, For Barrel, 7 1/2 In.Long 4.50
Brass, **Spindle File & Paperweight**, Dragon Form, 4 1/2 In.High 22.00
Brass, **Spit**, Bird, Arched Rack, Adjustable, Cabriole Legs, C.1790 .... 190.00
Brass, **Spittoon**, Flares Out To 7 1/2 In., 4 1/4 In.High 14.00
Brass, **Spittoon**, Two Handle, Copper Bottom, 16 In.Diameter 45.00
Brass, **Spoon**, Round, Monkeys On Handle 2.25
Brass, **Spoon**, Tea Caddy, Dewey's Head On Handle 7.00
Brass, **Stenciling Device**, Patent Dated, 1868-1871, Alphabet & Numerals 11.50
Brass, **Stirrup**, Ornate, Shoe Type, Horse's Head, Pair 45.00
Brass, **Strainer**, Tea, German 2.50
Brass, **Sundial**, Handmade, Octagon, 'Amyddst Ye Flowres-I Tell Ye Houres' 74.50
Brass, **Tankard**, Three Handles, Russian, Double Eagle Mark 115.00
Brass, **Tea Caddy**, Souvenir, Lipton, British Empire Exhibition 1925 .... 17.50

Brass, **Tea Caddy**, 5 In.High To Top Of Finial 15.00
Brass, **Teakettle**, Acorns, Raised Leaves, Stand, Burner 55.00
Brass, **Teakettle**, Hammered Around Sides & Spout, Burnished 30.00
Brass, **Teakettle**, Squat & Wide, Marked China 20.00
Brass, **Teapot & Box**, Pewter Lined Pot, Medallions, Jade Inlay, Chinese 45.00
Brass, **Teapot**, Gooseneck Spout, Flowers & Birds, Copper Bottom, 1880-90 .... 25.00
Brass, **Teapot**, Gooseneck Spout, Hinged Lid, Russia 45.00
Brass, **Teapot**, Tapered Pouring Spout, Hinged Cover, Russia 30.00
Brass, **Telescope**, Leather Binding, G.W.C.Emille, Extends To 46 1/2 In. 275.00
Brass, **Telescope**, Miniature, 3 Sections, Opens To 6 In. 9.50
Brass, **Telescope**, Opens To 23 In., 4 Sections, Lens Cover 24.50
Brass, **Telescope**, Signed Hawkeye, Made In France, Opens To 16 In. 35.00
Brass, **Telescope**, 45 In.Open, 13 In.Closed, Cowhide Case 150.00
Brass, **Tieback**, American Eagle, Gilt, French, C.1815, Pair 375.00
Brass, **Tray**, Basket Weave, Footed, 12 X 8 X 2 In. 25.00
Brass, **Tray**, Cigar Holder, Cigarette Holder, Match Holder, Enameled 23.00
Brass, **Tray**, Dresser, Double Glassed For Doily Encasing, Marked Apollo 18.00
Brass, **Tray**, Dresser, Double Glassed For Doily, Marked France, Footed 25.00
Brass, **Tray**, Dutch Scenes, People, Boats, Handles, Handmade, 17 X 12 In. 11.00
Brass, **Tray**, Handles, Marked Russian, 11 1/2 In.Diameter 14.75
Brass, **Tray**, Handles, Russian, 15 1/2 In.Oval 25.00
Brass, **Tray**, India, Peacock, Round, 11 1/2 In. 7.50
Brass, **Tray**, Russian Writing, Double Eagle Touchmark, 7 3/4 X 3 1/2 In. 27.50
Brass, **Tray**, Russian, Signed, Round, Handles, 17 In. 30.00
Brass, **Tray**, Scale, 18 In.Long 15.00
Brass, **Trivet**, Ball Feet, Marked China, 5 In.Square 6.00
Brass, **Trivet**, Circa 1830 .... 45.00
Brass, **Trivet**, Openwork Center Design, Footed, Marked China 4.75
Brass, **Tumbler**, Grape & Leaf Design, Marked Belgium, 3 3/4 In.High 12.00
Brass, **Tumbler**, Russian, Marked 18.00
Brass, **U.S.Post Office Box Front**, Combination Lock 5.00
Brass, **Vase**, Bud, Marked China, 5 In.High, Pair 3.75
Brass, **Vase**, Carved, Oriental, 5 In., Pair 10.00
Brass, **Vase**, Ormolu, Oriental, 5 1/8 In. 20.00
Brass, **Vase**, Trumpet, Engraved, 9 In. 7.00
Brass, **Watch Stand**, Cobbler On Bench, Drinks Ale, England 40.00
Brass, **Wax Seal**, Wrist & Hand 55.00
Brass, **Whistle**, From Lake Boat, Marked Crain 45.00
Brass, **Whistle**, Steamboat, 7 1/2 Pounds 100.00

*Brides' Baskets of glass were usually one-of-a-kind novelties made in
American and European glass factories. They were especially popular about
1880 when the decorated basket was often given as a wedding gift. Cut-glass
baskets were popular after 1890. All Brides' Baskets lost favor about
1905.*

Bride's Basket, Amber Glass, Enamel Floral, Silver Plate Frame, Cattails 95.00
Bride's Basket, Amethyst, Swirls, Green Rim, E.P.N.S.Stand, Footed, Handle 85.00
Bride's Basket, Aqua Satin Glass, Pleated, Scalloped, Silver Holder 135.00
Bride's Basket, Blue Shell & Tassel Pattern, Silver Holder 75.00
Bride's Basket, Bristol Glass Insert, Pink, Ruffled 30.00
Bride's Basket, Clear Pressed Glass, Bowl, Silver Plate Frame 42.00
Bride's Basket, Clear To Cranberry, Ruffles, Pleats, Silver Plate Basket 195.00
Bride's Basket, Cranberry Bowl, Pink Overlay, Footed Frame 95.00
Bride's Basket, Cranberry, Ruffled, Silver Holder, Grapes, Vines, Fish, Dogs 195.00
Bride's Basket, Hobnail, Clear, Silver Plate Ornate Holder 42.00
Bride's Basket, Martinsville Peachblow, Ruffles, Pleats, Silver Basket 150.00
Bride's Basket, Pink Mother-Of-Pearl, Herringbone, Enamel, Brass Stand 785.00
Bride's Basket, Pink To Yellow, Ruffled & Scalloped, Silver Holder 85.00
Bride's Basket, Purple To Lilac To Opalescent Clear, Floral, Brass Frame 87.50
Bride's Basket, Quilted, Amber To Rose, Ornate Silver Holder 285.00
Bride's Basket, Raspberry To Pink, Fluted, Enamel Floral, Resilvered Frame 160.00
Bride's Basket, Rose & White Cased Ruffled Dish, Silver Plate Frame 64.50
Bride's Basket, Salmon To Yellow, Hobnail Dots, Wilcox Silver Holder 90.00
Bride's Basket, Sandwich Overshot, Emerald Green, Footed, Silver Holder 125.00
Bride's Basket, Satin Glass, Amethyst, Ruffled, Pleated, Silver Plate Holder 72.00
Bride's Basket, White Outside, Apricot Inside, Clear Casing, Silver Frame 75.00

Bride's Bowl, Blue & White End Of Day, Amber Applied Rim, Crimped 80.00
Bride's Bowl, Blue, White, Crimped, Amber Rim, 12 1/2 In. 85.00
Bride's Bowl, Cranberry To Pink To Lighter Overlay, Ruffle, Embossed, Angel 67.00
Bride's Bowl, Cranberry To White, White Cased, Clear Edge, Ruffled, Crimped 40.00
Bride's Bowl, Enamel Forget-Me-Nots, Gold Designs, White Cased, Red Inside 135.00
Bride's Bowl, Frosted Puff Panels, Cut Thumbprints, Ivy, Silver Plate Frame 175.00
Bride's Bowl, Mother-Of-Pearl, Pink To Deep Rose, Raindrop Pattern, Ruffles 85.00
Bride's Bowl, Pink To White Bottom, White Cased, Ground Off Pontil 95.00
Bride's Bowl, Rose To White Bristol Glass, Ruffled, Silver Plate Pedestal 75.00
Bride's Bowl, Ruby Swirl Overlay, Footed Holder, Acorns & Leaves 150.00
Bride's Bowl, Shaded Cranberry, Opal Lined, Crimped, Ruffled, 10 In.Diameter 53.00
Bride's Bowl, Shaded Green, Overlay, Ruffled, Enamel Lavender Violets, Birds 60.00
Bride's Bowl, Spanish Lace, Blue, Ruffled, Shadowy Mums, Silver Holder 71.50
Bride's Bowl, Tan Sheen, Enameled Blue Flowers, Gold Scrolls 24.00
Bridle, Bit & Reins, Nickel Plate, Braided Leather Thongs 7.50
Bridle, Bit, U.S.Cavalry .... 6.00 To 35.00
Bridle, Button, Flowers On Yellow, Brass Mounting, Pair 9.50
Bridle, Hame, Acorn, Brass, Pair 40.00
Bridle, Hame, Brass, Polished, Pair 24.00
Bridle, Rosette, Head Of Horse Under Glass 2.50
Bridle, Rosette, Raised Motif, Brass, Pair 4.00

Bristol Glass was made in Bristol, England, after the 1700s. The
Bristol Glass most often seen today is a Victorian, lightweight opaque
glass that is often blue. Some of the glass was decorated with enamels.
Bristol, Basket, Melon Rib, Ruffled, Thorn Handle, Hand Blown 140.00
Bristol, Bottle, Cologne, Lime Green Satin, Enameled & Gilt 35.00
Bristol, Bowl, Lily Design, Ruffled, Blue 30.00
Bristol, Box, Scene On Lid, Two Ladies, Cherub, Hinged Lid 27.50
Bristol, Cologne, White, 11 In. 22.00
Bristol, Creamer, Flowers & Leaves, Applied Handle 45.00
Bristol, Dresser Set, Child's, Two Cologne Bottles, Powder Jar, Hand-Painted 50.00
Bristol, Ewer, Green, Floral, Butterflies, Ruffled Top 42.50
Bristol, Jar, Cracker, Hand-Painted Trim, Silver Lid & Bail, 8 In.High 85.00
Bristol, Jar, Powder, Blue Jay, Leaf & Flower Design, 6 3/4 In. High 19.50
Bristol, Jar, Sweetmeat, Metal Rim & Handle, Sanded Flowers 8.50
Bristol, Lamp, Blue, Hand-Painted Floral, Handle, Clear Chimney, Brass, 9 In. 46.50
Bristol, Lamp, Gone With The Wind, Three Section, Yellow, 32 1/2 In.Tall 165.00
Bristol, Lamp, Hanging, Black Iron Frame, Copper Font 275.00
Bristol, Lamp, Oil, Allover Enamel, Brass Collar, 11 In. 45.00
Bristol, Mug, Blue, Think Of Me, Applied Handle, Blown 25.00
Bristol, Mug, Child's, Louisa, White, Gold 25.00
Bristol, Mug, Remember Me, Painted Pastels 34.00
Bristol, Perfume, Blue Jay, Leaf & Flowers, Opaque White, 9 In.High 27.50
Bristol, Plaque, Floral, Bisque, Oval, Concave, Roses & Floral, C.1780 .... 200.00
Bristol, Rose Bowl, Egg Shape, Light To Dark Blue, Pinch Pleats, White Cased 15.00
Bristol, Rose Bowl, Matsunake Design, Custard, 6 In.High, 7 In.Wide 65.00
Bristol, Salt & Pepper, Relief Flower & Leaf, Brass Lids 18.50
Bristol, Smoke Bell, Cranberry Ruffled Edge, 8 1/2 In.Across 12.00
Bristol, Stand, Teapot, Octagonal, Pink Rose Center, Garlands, Gilt, C.1775 .... 160.00
Bristol, Sugar & Creamer, Blown, Applied Handle, Footed, Fiery 90.00
Bristol, Sugar & Creamer, Blown, Pedestal Sugar 25.00
Bristol, Vase, Acorn Design, Cream, Amber, Cranberry, 6 1/2 In.Tall, Pair 190.00
Bristol, Vase, Birds, Flowers, Brown, Green, Gold, Yellow Trim, 7 In.Tall, Pair 50.00
Bristol, Vase, Blue, Enamel Butterfly & Flowers, 10 In.High 35.00
Bristol, Vase, Blue, Enamel Pattern, Scalloped, Pink, Green, White Pontil 35.00
Bristol, Vase, Blue, Flowers, 6 3/4 In. 25.00
Bristol, Vase, Blue, Yellow Flowers, Funnel Shape, 6 3/4 In. 25.00
Bristol, Vase, Bluebirds, Pair 95.00
Bristol, Vase, Brown To Cream, Orange Floral, Gold Enamel, 11 1/2 In. 37.50
Bristol, Vase, Brown Top, Cream Base, Enamel Floral, 6 In., Pair 35.00
Bristol, Vase, Bud, Blue, Enamel Lilies Of The Valley, Open Pontil, 6 1/4 In. 7.50
Bristol, Vase, Bud, Blue, Lacy Silver Stand, Victorian 85.00
Bristol, Vase, Cream Ground, Bird In Floral Setting, Hand Decorated 65.00
Bristol, Vase, Cream Ground, Enameled Branch & Floral, English, 10 In. 25.00
Bristol, Vase, Daisy, Butterflies, Pink, Hand-Painted, 9 1/2 In.Tall, Pair 145.00

Bristol, Vase, Ewer Shape, Green, Swallows, Floral, Applied Handle, Pair 38.00
Bristol, Vase, Flower Design, Enamel, Blue, 8 1/2 In.High, Pair 55.00
Bristol, Vase, Flowers, Branches, White, Pink, Ruffled Top, 8 In.Tall 24.50
Bristol, Vase, Framed Portrait, Child, Hand-Painted, 14 1/2 In., Pair 180.00
Bristol, Vase, Frosted, Floral, 8 In.High, Pair 30.00
Bristol, Vase, Green Ground, Hand-Painted Floral, Leaves, 17 1/2 In., Pair 150.00
Bristol, Vase, Green, Yellow, White & Orange Floral, Ruffled, 7 3/4 In., Pair 55.00
Bristol, Vase, Hand Holds Vase, Hand-Painted Flowers, 5 In. 40.00
Bristol, Vase, Hand, Enamel Flowers, Opalescent, 5 1/2 In. 37.50
Bristol, Vase, Light Blue To Cream, Enameled Floral, Yellow Bird, Blue Wings 48.00
Bristol, Vase, Mary Gregory Type Enamel Of Lady, Smoky, Ruffled Top 30.00
Bristol, Vase, Overlay, White, Pink & Yellow Floral, Pink Lining, Crimped Top 38.00
Bristol, Vase, Pink Cased, Enamel 75.00
Bristol, Vase, Pink Orchid, Hand-Painted White, Yellow Flowers, 13 1/2 In. 35.00
Bristol, Vase, Pink, Cased, Hand-Painted Birds On Tree Branch, 12 In., Pair 115.00
Bristol, Vase, Pink, Enamel Butterflies & Floral, 14 In.High, Pair 110.00
Bristol, Vase, Portrait, Burnt Orange Ground, Squat, 11 In., Pair 125.00
Bristol, Vase, Portrait, Turquoise, White, 8 1/2 In., Pair 32.50
Bristol, Vase, Red, Brown, Green, Cream, Hand-Painted, 11 1/2 In.Tall, Pair 68.50
Bristol, Vase, Roses, Bluebells, Ruffle Top, 15 In.Tall 36.00
Bristol, Vase, Stick, Rose To Gray Blue, Cased, White Lining, Gold Floral 48.50
Bristol, Vase, Strawberries, Blossoms, White, Red, Green, 8 3/4 In.High 13.00
Bristol, Vase, White, Blown, Cone Shape, Pedestal, Hand-Painted Flowers 20.00
Bristol, Vase, White, Blue & Red Design, 7 1/2 In.High 8.50
Bristol, Vase, White, Rose Buds, Lily Of The Valley, Gold Trim, 10 In. 30.00
Bristol, Vase, Yellow Fan, Signed 80.00
Bristol, Vase, Yellow Ground, Flowers, Enameled Red Bands On Top & Bottom 18.00
Bristol, Whiskey Set, Blue, Silver Deposit, 5 Piece 47.00
Bronze, Ashtray & Incense Burner, Lizards, Tiered Marble Base 195.00
Bronze, Bookend, Fish, Copyright I.Bartoli, 1930, 7 1/2 In.High, Pair 25.00
Bronze, Bookend, Pointing Setter, Amour Launton, 7 In.Long, Pair 30.00
Bronze, Bookend, Tiger, Standing, Oriental, 8 In., Pair 250.00
Bronze, Bowl, Bulb, Bats At Each End, Wings Form Bowl, Japan 75.00
Bronze, Bowl, Footed, Signed Cain, 13 In.Diameter 145.00
Bronze, Bowl, Japanese, Bat Design, Signed, 7 In. 85.00
Bronze, Brazier, Flared Cylindrical Shape, Insert Holds Fuel, Circa 1800 .... 75.00
Bronze, Buckle, British Military, Robin Hood Rifles-Nottingham, C.1850 .... 34.50
Bronze, Buddha, Black Patina, Signed, 6 In.High 55.00
Bronze, Bust Of Napoleon, Signed Bertoz, 7 In.Wide, 12 In.High 235.00
Bronze, Bust, Head Of A Youth, French, Smiling, C.1750 .... 800.00
Bronze, Bust, Woman, Hat, 'HNL Godet Medle D'Or Salon 1893, ' 8 3/4 In. 150.00
Bronze, Candelabrum, Female Figurine, Signed Roman Bronze Works, 12 In., Pair 175.00
Bronze, Candlestick, Applied Sterling Decoration, 10 In.High, Pair 18.00
Bronze, Cannon, Temple, Japanese, Leaf Motifs, Dolphin Handles 145.00
Bronze, Compote, Three Muses Sitting Around Base 375.00
Bronze, Door Knocker, Figural, Perched Bird, Dark Patina, 5 In.Long 35.00
Bronze, Ewer, Cherub Handles, Rams' Heads, Pedestal, Pair 185.00
Bronze, Figurine, Apollo, Standing, 24 In.High 300.00
Bronze, Figurine, Arab On Camel, Polychrome, Vienna, 7 X 7 In.High 150.00
Bronze, Figurine, Armed Tribesman On Horse, Leads Cow, Gretcho Fabb, Russia 1000.00
Bronze, Figurine, Bear, Austrian, Polychromed, 5 1/2 X 3 1/2 In. 125.00
Bronze, Figurine, Bird Picking Bug Off Ground, Signed E.Delabrierre, 10 In. 160.00
Bronze, Figurine, Bird, Butterfly, Signed J.Moigniez 155.00
Bronze, Figurine, Bird, On Mound Of Rock Crystal, Signed J.Moigniez 185.00
Bronze, Figurine, Bird, Royal Vienna, Marked Geschutz, 5 In.High 95.00
Bronze, Figurine, Bird, Standing, Signed Dubucand, 5 In.High 195.00
Bronze, Figurine, Bird, Vienna, 3 1/2 In.High 42.00
Bronze, Figurine, Bodhisattva, Seates In Virasana, C.1750, 8 3/4 In.High 275.00
Bronze, Figurine, Boxer, Signed Fraisse, 13 In. .... *Illus* 345.00
Bronze, Figurine, Boy Saying 'shame' With Fingers, Signed Kauba, 7 1/2 In. 225.00
Bronze, Figurine, Boy Standing, Bare Feet, Marble Base, Signed, Dated 1889 .... 185.00
Bronze, Figurine, Buddha Seated On Lotus Base, China, Circa 1820, 10 In.High 175.00
Bronze, Figurine, Buddha, Hands In Lap, Fitted Stand, 3 1/2 In.High 50.00
Bronze, Figurine, Buddha, Sitting, Northern India, 15 1/2 In.High 420.00
Bronze, Figurine, Buffalo, Pan-American Exposition, 1901, 2 In.High 29.00
Bronze, Figurine, Bust Of Abraham Lincoln, George E.Bissell, 1898, 7 In.High 155.00

Bronze, Figurine, Boxer, Signed Fraisse, 13 In
See Page 72

Bronze, Figurine, Cat, Long Tail, Gray, Vienna	24.00
Bronze, Figurine, Cat, Pearl Gray, Back Hunched, Vienna, 1 In.	24.00
Bronze, Figurine, Cat, Playing, 2 In.High	8.00
Bronze, Figurine, Cat, Sitting, Signed Fremiet, 4 X 4 In.	155.00
Bronze, Figurine, Cat, Striped Gray, Hunched Back, Vienna	24.00
Bronze, Figurine, Cat, Vienna, Arched Back, Kitten In Mouth	32.00
Bronze, Figurine, Cavalier, Titan, 30 In.High	95.00
Bronze, Figurine, Ceremonial Elephant, Rooster Sitting On Top, 18 In.Tall	1800.00
Bronze, Figurine, Chamois, Jumping, Mene, 5 X 7 In.	195.00
Bronze, Figurine, Chamois, Signed P.J.Mene, 5 In.Long	250.00
Bronze, Figurine, Chick In Branches, Vienna, Marked Geschutz, 5 In.	165.00
Bronze, Figurine, Chicks, Signed Ch.Virion, 1 Standing, 1 Sitting	290.00
Bronze, Figurine, Classical Female Figure, Seated, Dore, Directoire, Pair	350.00
Bronze, Figurine, Classical Female, Signed Pouret, Seated, 10 In.	250.00
Bronze, Figurine, Classical Nude, Runner Carrying Baton, Green Marble Base	175.00
Bronze, Figurine, Crane, Standing On A Turtle, Barye, Barbedienne Foundry	95.00
Bronze, Figurine, Cupid Next To Tree, Prancing Goat, Pedestal, 10 X 9 In.	275.00
Bronze, Figurine, Dachshund, Named Erdmann, Standing, Artist R.Duje	95.00
Bronze, Figurine, Deer, Antlers, Signed P.J.Mene, 3 In.Long	150.00
Bronze, Figurine, Deer, Signed Barye, Miniature, Head Turned	150.00
Bronze, Figurine, Devil, Austria, Enameled, On Roulette Wheel, Jug On Head	45.00
Bronze, Figurine, Devil, Austria, Enameled, Wearing 1 Boot, Polishing Other	45.00
Bronze, Figurine, Dog, Irish Setter, French, Signed Dubucand, Pedestal Base	145.00
Bronze, Figurine, Dog, Russian Wolfhound, Signed J.B.No.2907, 10 In.High	75.00
Bronze, Figurine, Dog, Scottie, E.B.Parsons, American, 5 In.High	250.00
Bronze, Figurine, Dog, Setter, Signed Mene, 5 1/2 X 3 In.	190.00
Bronze, Figurine, Dog, Signed I.Rochard, Seated, Guarding Dead Rabbit, 12 In.	250.00
Bronze, Figurine, Dog, Signed Mene, 5 In.Long, 2 3/4 In.High	225.00
Bronze, Figurine, Dog, Signed Paul Herzel, 8 1/2 In.High	225.00
Bronze, Figurine, Donkey, Vienna, Signed Geschutz, Insert For Quills	85.00
Bronze, Figurine, Dying Gaul, 12 X 6 In.	125.00
Bronze, Figurine, Eagle On Rock, Bayre, Barbedianne Founders	850.00
Bronze, Figurine, Eagle, Perched On Metal Stump, 20 In.Wingspread, 15 In.	225.00
Bronze, Figurine, Eagle, Spread Wings, Holds Clock In Mouth, Paste Jeweled	650.00
Bronze, Figurine, Egyptian Dancer, Enameled Costume, Marble Base, Chiparus	645.00
Bronze, Figurine, Elephant, Austrian, Signed, Standing On Bronze Base, Pair	80.00
Bronze, Figurine, Elephant, Running, Signed Barye, 14 X 9 In.	600.00
Bronze, Figurine, Father Bird Watches Mother Feed Baby Birds, E.Cana	750.00
Bronze, Figurine, Female Nude, Signed Kutschke, Standing On One Foot, Marble	75.00
Bronze, Figurine, Field Worker, Scythe Over Shoulder, Marble Step Base	50.00
Bronze, Figurine, Foo Dog	55.00
Bronze, Figurine, Fox Preying On Pheasant, Unsigned	250.00
Bronze, Figurine, Fox With Paw Caught In Trap, Vienna	38.00
Bronze, Figurine, Gazelle, Signed A.Leonard, 6 1/2 X 6 In.	150.00
Bronze, Figurine, Girl & Lamb, M.Courbier, C.1930, Kneeling	300.00
Bronze, Figurine, Golfer, Hat, Tie, Shirt, Long Pants, Laced Shoes, Teeing Off	45.00

Bronze, Figurine, Greyhound, Signed Bayre 375.00
Bronze, Figurine, Group Of Two Birds, Signed J.Moigniez 175.00
Bronze, Figurine, Horse, Rearing, Slave Holds Reign, Signed Couston 210.00
Bronze, Figurine, Horse, Rearing, Soldier Holds Reign, Signed C.Kauba, 3 In. 95.00
Bronze, Figurine, Horse, Rider Beside, 12 In.Wide, 16 In.Tall, Pair 139.50
Bronze, Figurine, Horse, Sculptured Base, P.J.Mene, 7 X 5 1/2 In. 180.00
Bronze, Figurine, Icarus, Lauchhammer, Budguss, C.1930, Marble Base 375.00
Bronze, Figurine, Indian Sentry, Carl Kauba, 4 X 2 1/2 In. 160.00
Bronze, Figurine, Indian Tracker With Rifle, Carl Kauba, 4 X 2 1/2 In. 175.00
Bronze, Figurine, Irish Setter, Rectangular Base, Unsigned, 15 1/2 In. 150.00
Bronze, Figurine, Irish Setter, Signed Dubucand, French, 5 In.Tall 145.00
Bronze, Figurine, Isadora Duncan, J.Lormier, C.1925, Marble Base 425.00
Bronze, Figurine, Joan Of Arc Carrying Banner, Gaudez, 30 In.High 395.00
Bronze, Figurine, Joan Of Arc, Signed A.Gaudez, 32 In.High 375.00
Bronze, Figurine, Knight In Armor Kneeling, Angel, 14 1/2 In.High 875.00
Bronze, Figurine, La Prairie, Signed A.Moreau, Winged Female Figures, 8 In. 150.00
Bronze, Figurine, La Reconnaissance, Medaille D'Honneur Au Salon 700.00
Bronze, Figurine, La Source, Signed A.Moreau, Winged Female Figures, 8 In. 150.00
Bronze, Figurine, Lady, Dove, Bare Chest, Robe Draped, Unsigned, 18 1/2 In. 425.00
Bronze, Figurine, Leda & The Swan, 7 1/2 In.High X 10 In.Long 650.00
Bronze, Figurine, Lion & Lioness, Signed A.Geo.Troy, 1889, 22 X 13 In. 600.00
Bronze, Figurine, Lion & Serpent, Dark Green Finish, Signed Barye 247.00
Bronze, Figurine, Lion, Signed Barye, Walking .... *Illus* 425.00
Bronze, Figurine, Lion, Stalking Pose, 4 1/4 In.Long 30.00
Bronze, Figurine, Little Girl Clown, Signed Chipparus 195.00
Bronze, Figurine, Little Girl Of The 20s, Signed Chipparus 195.00
Bronze, Figurine, Little Girl, 3 3/4 In.Tall 32.50
Bronze, Figurine, Madonna & Child, Green Onyx Plinth, 5 In.High 175.00
Bronze, Figurine, Man & Bear, Russian, Evgenie Lanceray, Standing, C.1870 .... 1050.00
Bronze, Figurine, Man Sculpting Head Of Girl, Black Base, 5 In.High 150.00
Bronze, Figurine, Mother Hen, Chicks, Signed Fremlet, 2 1/2 In. 95.00
Bronze, Figurine, Mountain Goat, Onyx Base, Signed Salat, 8 In.High 75.00
Bronze, Figurine, Mouse, Vienna, 3 In.Long 30.00
Bronze, Figurine, Mouse, Vienna, 3/4 In.Long 23.00
Bronze, Figurine, Napoleon, Marble Base, Signed 150.00
Bronze, Figurine, Nathan Hale, Frederic Macmonnies, N.Y., C.1890, 27 1/4 In. 4000.00
Bronze, Figurine, Nude Baby On Stomach, Signed Fonderia Giorgio Sommers 65.00
Bronze, Figurine, Nude Oriental Female Dancer, Allman Clark, Marble Base 450.00
Bronze, Figurine, Nude With Tambourine, Child, Marble Base, 10 In.High 325.00
Bronze, Figurine, Nude, Discus Thrower, Black, 6 1/2 In. 48.00
Bronze, Figurine, Nude, Male, Seated, Black, 4 X 4 In. 59.00
Bronze, Figurine, Nude, Signed B.Grundmann, French, Arms Outstretched, 14 In. 110.00
Bronze, Figurine, Nude, Warrior, Signed La Pointe, 1904, Loincloth, Sword 145.00
Bronze, Figurine, Oriental Character Astride A Carp, 6 X 6 In. 65.00
Bronze, Figurine, Oriental Man Seated Beneath Gnarled Tree, Mountain 325.00
Bronze, Figurine, Owl, Tiered Marble Base, Vienna, 5 In.High 185.00
Bronze, Figurine, Panther, Coiled Snake Around Tree, Turtle, Cain 175.00
Bronze, Figurine, Panther, Fangs Showing, Signed T.Cartier, France, 5 In.Tall 95.00
Bronze, Figurine, Parakeet, Vienna, 3 1/2 In.High 75.00
Bronze, Figurine, Peacock With Spread Tail, Vienna, 3 In.High 65.00
Bronze, Figurine, Peasant Maid, Signed Pierre Oge, Carrying Book & Flowers 290.00
Bronze, Figurine, Pheasant With Four Baby Pheasants, Signed E.Cana 750.00
Bronze, Figurine, Pheasant, Signed J.Moigniez, 21 In.Long, 11 In.High 475.00
Bronze, Figurine, Polynesian Goddess, Gilded, 6 1/2 In. 45.00
Bronze, Figurine, Premier Triomphe, French, Signed Angles, Young Man, Lyre 190.00
Bronze, Figurine, Rabbit, French, 2 1/8 In.Long 27.00
Bronze, Figurine, Romulus & Remus, Square Base, 2 1/4 In.High 28.50
Bronze, Figurine, Rooster, Crowing, Onyx & Ormulu Base, Barye 575.00
Bronze, Figurine, Running Buffalo, C.Kauba, 6 1/2 X 3 1/2 In. 165.00
Bronze, Figurine, Russian Wolfhound, Signed J.B., 16 1/2 In. 175.00
Bronze, Figurine, Russian Wolfhound, Signed Joseph Heu, 16 In.Long 400.00
Bronze, Figurine, Seated Female Bather, Godard, C.1930, Onyx Base 300.00
Bronze, Figurine, Setter Stands Over Leaves Concealing Rabbit, Moigniez 400.00
Bronze, Figurine, Setter, Signed P.J.Mene, 9 1/2 In.Long 325.00
Bronze, Figurine, Sheep, Signed I.Bonheur, Brown Patina, 10 X 7 1/2 In. 425.00
Bronze, Figurine, Sheep, Signed I.Bonheur, Gold Patina, 10 X 7 1/2 In. 425.00

Bronze, Figurine, Shepherd, Staff, Red Marble Base, O.Gladenbeck, 13 In.High 190.00
Bronze, Figurine, Stag & Doe, P.J.Mene, 7 X 5 In. 275.00
Bronze, Figurine, Stag, Barye, 7 1/4 In.High .... *Illus* 550.00
Bronze, Figurine, Standing Female, Pants, Marble Plinth, 16 In. 125.00
Bronze, Figurine, Tailor On Bench With Thread & Scissors, Vienna 105.00
Bronze, Figurine, Terrier, P.J.Mene, 5 1/4 In.Base 199.00
Bronze, Figurine, Three Dogs Looking Under Rock For Quarry, P.J.Mene 975.00
Bronze, Figurine, Tiger, Roaring, Signed, Wooden Base, 25 In.Long, 14 In.Tall 350.00
Bronze, Figurine, Tiger, Signed Barye, Walking .... *Illus* 475.00

Bronze, Figurine, Tiger, Signed Barye, Walking   Bronze, Figurine, Lion, Signed Barye, Walking
See Page 74

Bronze, Figurine, Stag, Barye, 7 1/4 In.High

Bronze, Figurine, Troika, Russian, Signed, Cyrillic Letters, 19 In.Long 1200.00
Bronze, Figurine, Trotting Horse, Signed Geo.Malissard, 15 In.Long 950.00
Bronze, Figurine, Two Bulldogs Snuggled Together, Cartier, 8 In.Long 250.00
Bronze, Figurine, Two Children, Gilt, Green Marble Base, 7 1/4 X 8 In.High 325.00
Bronze, Figurine, Two Dogs Peering Down A Hole, Signed Moigniez 225.00
Bronze, Figurine, Two Rabbits, One Scratches Ear, Gray Marble Base, Cain 165.00
Bronze, Figurine, Whippet, Lying On Iron Base, 5 3/4 In.Long 140.00
Bronze, Figurine, Wild Boar, Austrian, Polychromed, 4 1/2 X 3 In. 110.00
Bronze, Figurine, Wild Boar, 1 In.High 8.00
Bronze, Figurine, Wolves Attack Troika, Lanceray, 1873, Russia, 19 In.Long 2250.00
Bronze, Figurine, Woman, Flowing Robes, Holds Garlands, Premiere Rose, Moreau 150.00
Bronze, Figurine, Woman, Signed Dorval, Ivory Face, 8 In.Tall 450.00
Bronze, Figurine, Woodland Nymph, Signed Pouret, Action Pose, Renaissance 250.00
Bronze, Figurine, Young Man, Muscular, Brown Patina, Signed A.Bofill, 26 In. 375.00
Bronze, Footlight Cover, Radiating Sunbeam Form, 13 1/2 In.High, Pair 125.00
Bronze, Fox Peeking At Rabbit Under Eock, Signed Masson, 4 1/4 In.High 185.00
Bronze, Frame, Deep Floral Relief, Stems, Art Nouveau, Stand-Up, 8 1/2 In. 30.00
Bronze, Frame, Easel, Art Nouveau, Semidraped Women, Flowers, 14 X 12 In. 46.00
Bronze, Group, Equestrian, Russian, E.Naps, Rider Is 18th Century Boyar, 1850 .... 800.00

Bronze, Group, Equestrian, Russian, Eugenie Lanceray, Tartar Soldier, C.1850 .... 900.00
Bronze, Group, Equestrian, Russian, P.Gratchev, Cossack Soldier, C.1850 .... 900.00
Bronze, Group, Horses, Sleigh, & Driver, Russian, P.Gratchev, C.1850 .... 1000.00
Bronze, Group, Polynesian Family, Mythological, 5 In. 48.00
Bronze, Group, Two Men On Horses Charging A Third, Marble Base, 4 In.Long 32.50
Bronze, Head, Kuan Yin, C.1650, 8 1/2 In.High, Pair 175.00
Bronze, Incense Burner, Animal Finial, Four Legs, Oriental 89.00
Bronze, Incense Burner, Dragon Handles, Animal Finial, Embossed, Legs, 8 In. 110.00
Bronze, Incense Burner, Foo Dog Finial, China 80.00
Bronze, Incense Burner, Foo Dog Handles & Finial, 18 In.High 350.00
Bronze, Incense Burner, Foo Dog Tops Each Leg, Foo Dog Finial, Japan 85.00
Bronze, Incense Burner, Foo Dog, 9 In.High 110.00
Bronze, Incense Burner, Japanese, Buddha, Green & Red Lacquer, Kamakura 50.00
Bronze, Incense Burner, Kinko Seated On Carp, 6 In.High 115.00
Bronze, Incense Burner, Oriental, 18th Century 65.00
Bronze, Incense Burner, Reclining Heron, Legs Folded, 8 X 10 In. 145.00
Bronze, Incense Burner, Shape Of Reclining Heron, 10 In.Long 165.00
Bronze, Incense Burner, Silver Inlay, Pierced Silver Lid 45.00
Bronze, Letter Opener, Signed P.Teneysizuk, 9 In.Long 25.00
Bronze, Match Container, Shape Of Fly, Wings Lift Up 19.75
Bronze, Match Holder, With Figure Of Dog 29.50
Bronze, Mold, Pewter Spoons 195.00
Bronze, Mold, Spoon, For Spelter Spoon 195.00
Bronze, Nutcracker, Dog, 12 In.Long 30.00
Bronze, Nutcracker, Rooster, 5 3/4 In.Long 35.00
Bronze, Plaque, Bonaparte, Signed David, 7 1/2 In. .... *Illus* 450.00

Bronze, Plaque, Bonaparte, Signed David, 7 1/2 In.

Bronze, Plaque, Depicting Two Oxen, Signed I.Bonheur, 7 X 9 1/2 In. 140.00
Bronze, Plaque, Horse, Dan Patch, Attached To Wooden Shield Back, Pair 95.00
Bronze, Plaque, Nazi, Hitler & Goering, Relief Profile Bust, Pair 19.50
Bronze, Plaque, Richard Wagner, Bust, Frame, 8 X 9 In. 40.00
Bronze, Plaque, Theodore Roosevelt, James Earle Fraser, Dated 1920 .... 49.50
Bronze, Polyptych, Russian, Instruments Of The Passion, Enamel, C.1850 .... 225.00
Bronze, Pot, Wine, Raised Leaf Design, Elongated Spout, Tripod Legs, 1820 .... 65.00
Bronze, Sconce, Dore, Wall, Lyre Back, 3 Light, Diamond Prisms, 4 .... 1000.00
Bronze, Sculpture, Bonsai Tree, Copper Needles, Mounted On Rock 225.00
Bronze, Statue, French Gentleman, 19th Century, Signed Leger, Marble Base 75.00
Bronze, Sundial, W.Flud, 1605 .... 175.00
Bronze, Tray, Cat's Face, Cast 4.00
Bronze, Tray, Pin, Reclining Nude, Art Nouveau, 7 In.Long 25.00
Bronze, Tsuba, 2 Kissing Dolphins In Relief, Openwork, 18th Century 75.00
Bronze, Urn, China, 3 1/2 In.High 25.00
Bronze, Vase, Apple Blossom Limb & Blossoms, Oriental Mark, 7 In., Pair 22.50
Bronze, Vase, Black Dragon, Floral, Geometric Trim, Signed Japan 55.00
Bronze, Vase, Bud, Grecian Key, Scalloped Shell & Circle, Lyre Handles, 5 In. 25.00
Bronze, Vase, Carp Swimming, Reeds, Tree Stumps, High Relief, 12 In., Pair 225.00
Bronze, Vase, Four Bacchus Heads In Relief, Pedestal, 14 In. 135.00
Bronze, Vase, Grapes, Vines, Leaves, Tendrils, Bold Relief, 6 In.High 75.00
Bronze, Vase, Pear Shape, Elongated Neck, Branches, Leaves, Twig Handles 105.00
Bronze, Vase, Petal Shape, Slender Elongated Neck, 1 In. 85.00
Bronze, Vase, Signed Baubien, Pyriform, Enameled Female's Head, Chased, Pair 100.00

Bronze, Vase, Sterling Flowers, Leaves, Vines, Dated 1912	20.00
Bronze, Watch Holder, Moorish Shape	35.00
Brouwer, Vase, Pink, Purple, Luster Glaze, 3 1/2 In.High	70.00
Brownie, Quilt, Marked Palmer Cox, Pat.1895, Cotton, 79 X 80 In.	45.00
Brownie, Spoon, Heart Shape, Twisted Handle, Enameled Brownie On Handle	12.75
Brownie, Toothpick, One Brownie Caught By Foot By A Crab, One Skipping	45.00
Buck Rogers, Book, Big Big Book, 1934, 316 Pages	25.00
Buck Rogers, Book, Pain, 1935, Whitman, 96 Pages	75.00
Buck Rogers, Coloring Set	3.50
Buck Rogers, Game, Card, Complete	100.00
Buck Rogers, Gun, Rubber Band, 1940, Colored	20.00
Buck Rogers, Pistol, Water	50.00
Buck Rogers, Ring, Magic Code Ring Of Saturn	39.00
Buck Rogers, Spaceship	6.00 To 20.00

Buffalo Pottery was made in Buffalo, New York, after 1902. The
company was established by the Larkin Company, famous manufacturers of soap.
The wares are marked with a picture of a buffalo and the date of manufacture.
Deldare ware is the most famous pottery made at the factory. It is a
khaki-colored transfer-decorated ware.

Buffalo Pottery, see also Blue Willow

Buffalo Pottery, Bowl, Semivitreous, Warranted Underglaze, 1907	25.00
Buffalo Pottery, Chamber Pot, Roses, Red, White, Cover	12.00
Buffalo Pottery, Creamer, Blue & White	7.50
Buffalo Pottery, Creamer, Roosevelt Bears, Landing By Balloon In Chicago	57.50
Buffalo Pottery, Cup & Saucer, Master's, Blue Willow, Take Ye A Cuppe	24.50
Buffalo Pottery, Deldare, Bowl, Dr.Syntax Reading His Tours	265.00 To 280.00
Buffalo Pottery, Deldare, Bowl, Fallowfield Hunt, 9 In.Diameter	125.00
Buffalo Pottery, Deldare, Bowl, Fruit, Dr.Syntax Reading His Tour, Signed	310.00
Buffalo Pottery, Deldare, Bowl, Ye Village Street, Signed L.Anna	110.00
Buffalo Pottery, Deldare, Bowl, Ye Village Tavern, Caird, 1908	135.00 To 195.00
Buffalo Pottery, Deldare, Candlestick, Signed R.Simpson, 1909	108.00
Buffalo Pottery, Deldare, Creamer, Ye Olden Days, L.Newman, 1909, Hexagonal	75.00
Buffalo Pottery, Deldare, Creamer, Ye Olden Days, Signed H.S., Dated 1908	75.00
Buffalo Pottery, Deldare, Cup & Saucer, The Fallowfield Hunt, Dated 1909	80.00
Buffalo Pottery, Deldare, Cup & Saucer, Ye Olden Days, Dated 1909	75.00
Buffalo Pottery, Deldare, Cup & Saucer, Ye Olden Times	155.00
Buffalo Pottery, Deldare, Hair Receiver, Ye Village Street	85.00
Buffalo Pottery, Deldare, Humidor, There Was An Old Sailor, 8 In.	300.00
Buffalo Pottery, Deldare, Mug, Fallowfield Hunt, 1909, Salesman's Sample	165.00
Buffalo Pottery, Deldare, Mug, Ye Lion Inn, 1908, Signed	120.00 To 125.00
Buffalo Pottery, Deldare, Mug, Ye Lion Inn, 1909	165.00
Buffalo Pottery, Deldare, Pitcher, Advise In Whisper, 1909	150.00 To 165.00
Buffalo Pottery, Deldare, Pitcher, Breaking Cover, Signed	95.00
Buffalo Pottery, Deldare, Pitcher, The Hunt Supper, Signed, 12 1/2 In.	295.00
Buffalo Pottery, Deldare, Pitcher, With A Cane Superior Air, W.Foster, 9 In.	195.00
Buffalo Pottery, Deldare, Plaque, Dr.Syntax, Emerald	275.00
Buffalo Pottery, Deldare, Plaque, Fallowfield Hunt	225.00
Buffalo Pottery, Deldare, Plate, At Ye Lion Inn, 1908, 6 1/4 In.	35.00 To 86.50
Buffalo Pottery, Deldare, Plate, Chop, An Evening At Ye Lion Inn, 1908	180.00
Buffalo Pottery, Deldare, Plate, Dr.Syntax Disputing His Bill, Blue	100.00
Buffalo Pottery, Deldare, Plate, Dr.Syntax Making A Discovery	190.00 To 200.00
Buffalo Pottery, Deldare, Plate, Dr.Syntax Presenting Bouquet, Emerald	110.00
Buffalo Pottery, Deldare, Plate, Dr.Syntax Soliloquizing, Emerald, 7 1/4 In.	115.00
Buffalo Pottery, Deldare, Plate, Emerald, Dr.Syntax Loses His Wig, 9 1/2 In.	185.00
Buffalo Pottery, Deldare, Plate, Fallowfield Hunt, Breaking Cover, Sheehan	80.00
Buffalo Pottery, Deldare, Plate, Fallowfield Hunt, The Death, 8 1/2 In.	75.00
Buffalo Pottery, Deldare, Plate, Fallowfield Hunt, The Start, 1908	90.00
Buffalo Pottery, Deldare, Plate, Village Gossips, J.Gerhardt, 1908, 10 In.	115.00
Buffalo Pottery, Deldare, Plate, Ye Town Crier, 8 1/4 In.	65.00 To 70.00
Buffalo Pottery, Deldare, Plate, Ye Village Street, 7 1/4 In.	75.00
Buffalo Pottery, Deldare, Saucer, Fallowfield Hunt, Dated 1908	45.00
Buffalo Pottery, Deldare, Sugar & Creamer, Ye Village Scenes	200.00
Buffalo Pottery, Deldare, Sugar, Covered, Artist-Signed, 1908	125.00 To 135.00
Buffalo Pottery, Deldare, Sugar, Open, Breaking Cover, Dated 1908, Hexagonal	78.00
Buffalo Pottery, Deldare, Tankard, English Scene, 12 1/2 In.High	195.00

Buffalo Pottery, Deldare, Tea Tile, Traveling In Ye Olden Days, Dated 1908 .... 105.00
Buffalo Pottery, Deldare, Tea Tile, Ye Olden Days, G.Eaton, 1908 .... 100.00
Buffalo Pottery, Deldare, Tea Tile, Ye Olden Days, Signed K.S., 1924 .... 100.00
Buffalo Pottery, Deldare, Teapot, Artist-Signed, 1908 .... 125.00
Buffalo Pottery, Deldare, Teapot, Fallowfield Hunt, Dated 1908, Signed Vogt 145.00
Buffalo Pottery, Deldare, Tray, Artist Ball, 12 X 10 1/2 In. 275.00
Buffalo Pottery, Deldare, Tray, Card, Dr.Syntax Robbed 175.00
Buffalo Pottery, Deldare, Tray, Card, Ye Lion Inn, E.Dowman 65.00
Buffalo Pottery, Deldare, Tray, Dancing Ye Minuet, Signed W.Foster, 1909 .... 170.00
Buffalo Pottery, Deldare, Tray, Dresser, Dr.Syntax Mistakes House For Inn 330.00
Buffalo Pottery, Deldare, Tray, Fallowfield Hunt, Signed H.Ford, Dated 1909 .... 100.00
Buffalo Pottery, Dish, Child's, Campbell Kids, Boy And Girl 35.00
Buffalo Pottery, Dish, Feeding, Campbell Kids .... 20.00 To 37.00
Buffalo Pottery, Jug, Geranium, Allover Blue & White, 6 1/2 In. 75.00
Buffalo Pottery, Jug, Triumph 60.00
Buffalo Pottery, Jug, Washington 135.00
Buffalo Pottery, Jug, Whaling City, New Bedford 130.00
Buffalo Pottery, Pitcher, Chrysanthemum, 7 In.High 20.00
Buffalo Pottery, Pitcher, George Washington, Mt.Vernon, Signature, Date 1907 .... 135.00
Buffalo Pottery, Pitcher, John Paul Jones, Blue & White, Dated 1907 .... 90.00
Buffalo Pottery, Pitcher, Milk, Bluebirds, 7 In.High 16.00
Buffalo Pottery, Pitcher, Milk, Cinderella, Dated 1906, 6 In.High 160.00
Buffalo Pottery, Pitcher, Small, Tea Rose 40.00
Buffalo Pottery, Pitcher, Tankard, Figure Scene, White, Marked, 12 In.Tall 125.00
Buffalo Pottery, Pitcher, Washstand, Chrysanthemum Design 35.00
Buffalo Pottery, Pitcher, Washstand, Gold Trim, Roses In Spout 22.00
Buffalo Pottery, Pitcher, Washstand, Yellow & Purple Roses, Signed 17.50
Buffalo Pottery, Pitcher, Whirl Of The Town, 1907 .... 100.00
Buffalo Pottery, Plate, Bangor Pattern, Allover Pink Floral, Dated 1906 .... 20.00
Buffalo Pottery, Plate, Brown, White, Country Garden, 11 In. 15.00
Buffalo Pottery, Plate, Commemorates Wanamaker's Anniversary, 1911 .... 12.50
Buffalo Pottery, Plate, Game, Dusky Grouse, Green, Gold Rim, 1908 .... 27.50 To 32.00
Buffalo Pottery, Plate, Gates Circle, Buffalo, N.Y., 7 1/2 In.Diameter 13.00
Buffalo Pottery, Plate, George Washington, Made For Railroad 100.00
Buffalo Pottery, Plate, Mt.Vernon, Blue, 10 In. 15.00
Buffalo Pottery, Plate, Mt.Vernon, Washington's Home, 7 1/2 In.Diameter 13.00
Buffalo Pottery, Plate, Mt.Vernon, 10 1/2 In.Diameter 22.50
Buffalo Pottery, Plate, Niagara Falls, Blue, Green, 7 1/2 In. 17.50
Buffalo Pottery, Plate, Niagara Falls, Blue, 10 1/4 In. 17.00
Buffalo Pottery, Plate, Train Across Center, New Haven R.R. 38.50
Buffalo Pottery, Plate, United States Capitol, 7 1/2 In.Diameter 13.00
Buffalo Pottery, Plate, Washington's Home At Mt.Vernon, 10 1/4 In. 27.50
Buffalo Pottery, Plate, White House, 7 1/2 In.Diameter 13.00
Buffalo Pottery, Teapot, Argyle Pattern 18.00
Buffalo Pottery, Teapot, Blue, White, Argyle, Strainer Hangs From Cover, 1914 .... 48.50
Buffalo Pottery, Teapot, Poppy Design In Canton Blue, 8 In.High 125.00
Buffalo Pottery, Teapot, White, Blue Roses, Rose Trees, Strainer, Chain, 1914 .... 48.50
Buffalo Pottery, Tile, Traveling In Ye Olden Days, Signed M.F.Crooker, 1908 .... 110.00
Buffalo Pottery, Tureen, Bonrea 7.50
Buffalo Pottery, Vase, Apple Blossoms, Bluebirds, Signed R.Stuart, 11 In. 125.00
Buffalo Pottery, Vase, Green, Clematis Spray, Rococo, 1905, 10 1/4 In.High 175.00
Buffalo Pottery, Washstand Set, Mug, Blue Chrysanthemums, Signed 50.00
Buggy, Amish 300.00
Buggy, Steel Rim Wheels, Topless, Date 1889 .... 250.00
Buggy, U.S.Mail, 75 Years Old 200.00
Buggy, 2 Passenger, Rubber Tires, Harness & Shafts, Date 1895 .... 450.00
Burgues, Figurine, Chickadee On Pink Dogwood, No.460 .... 925.00
Burgues, Figurine, Yellow Warbler, No.475 .... 700.00

Burmese Glass was developed by Frederick Shirley at the Mt.
Washington Glass Works in New Bedford, Massachusetts, in 1885. It
is a two-tone glass, shading from peach to yellow. Some have a pattern mold
design. A few Burmese pieces were decorated with pictures or applied glass
flowers of colored Burmese Glass.

Burmese, Bottle, Cologne, Ball Shaped, Hallmarked Silver Top, 5 1/2 In., Pair 280.00
Burmese, Bowl, Decorated, 4 In. .... *Illus* 395.00

Burmese, Bowl, Fluted Edge, Pink Stripe On Yellow Base, 4 1/2 In.High 600.00
Burmese, Bowl, Peach To Lemon Yellow, Turned In Scalloped Top, 4 3/4 In. 275.00
Burmese, Bowl, Rose, Yellow & Pink Edge Extends Halfway Down, 2 1/2 In.High 260.00
Burmese, Bowl, Triangular Section, Overlay Of Daisies & Leaves 140.00
Burmese, Bowl, Tricorner, Stripes, Yellow Edge, Acid Finish, 5 1/8 In. 345.00
Burmese, Candlestick, Brass Fittings, 8 1/4 In., Pair .... *Illus* 525.00

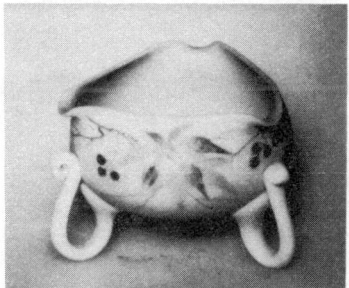

Burmese, Bowl, Decorated, 4 In.
See Page 78

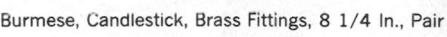

Burmese, Candlestick, Brass Fittings, 8 1/4 In., Pair

Burmese, Celery, Scalloped Top, Mt.Washington 325.00
Burmese, Creamer, Salmon Pink, Applied Yellow Handle, Mt.Washington 350.00
Burmese, Creamer, Salmon, Yellow Handle & Rim, Mt.Washington .... 375.00 To 475.00
Burmese, Cruet, Ribbed Body & Matching Stopper, Acid Finish 400.00
Burmese, Ewer, Allover Queen's Decor, Mt.Washington, 1o In.High 875.00
Burmese, Jar, Cracker, Silver Bail & Top, Mt.Washington 425.00
Burmese, Lamp, Fairy, Enameled Decoration, Marked 160.00
Burmese, Lamp, Fairy, Flower Form Base, Marked Clarke 450.00
Burmese, Lamp, Fairy, Signed Clarke Base 225.00
Burmese, Lamp, Fairy, Three On Oval Mirror, Clarke Cups, Circa 1890 .... 850.00
Burmese Muffineer, Queen's Design, Enamel Decoration, 1889, Pewter Top 365.00
Burmese, Pitcher, Water, Mt.Washington 550.00
Burmese, Pitcher, Water, Salmon Pink, Yellow Handle, Mt.Washington 750.00
Burmese, Rose Bowl, Floral Decor, Hexagon Throat 350.00
Burmese, Rose Bowl, Gunderson, Crimped Top, 3 X 4 In. 95.00
Burmese, Salt & Pepper, Mt.Washington 185.00
Burmese, Salt & Pepper, Ribbed, Mt.Washington 225.00
Burmese, Salt & Pepper, Straight Ribbed 250.00
Burmese, Saltshaker, Ribbed 85.00
Burmese, Toothpick, Acid Finish, Hand Decorated Flowers, 2 In. 298.00
Burmese, Toothpick, Acid Finish, Hand-Painted Flowers, Tricornered, 2 In. 350.00
Burmese, Toothpick, Acid Finish, Mt.Washington 275.00
Burmese, Toothpick, Diamond Optic, Mt.Washington 250.00
Burmese, Toothpick, Diamond-Quilted, Satin Finish, Tricornered 195.00
Burmese, Toothpick, Diamond-Quilted, Tricornered, Glossy Finish 250.00
Burmese, Toothpick, Diamond-Quilted, Tricornered, Mt.Washington 325.00
Burmese, Toothpick, Diamond-Quilted, Tricornered, Satin Finish .... 150.00 To 195.00
Burmese, Toothpick, Diamond-Quilted, Tricornered, 2 In. .... 250.00 To 300.00
Burmese, Toothpick, Enameled White Daisies & Foliage 235.00
Burmese, Toothpick, Five Petal Rose, 2 1/2 In.High 225.00
Burmese, Toothpick, Hand Decorated Flowers, Acid Finish, Tricornered, 2 In. 350.00
Burmese, Toothpick, Mt.Washington .... 170.00 To 225.00
Burmese, Toothpick, Yellow To Deep Pink, Ruffled, Footed 350.00
Burmese, Tumbler, Glossy Finish 180.00
Burmese, Tumbler, Mt.Washington 275.00
Burmese, Tumbler, Queen's Design 525.00
Burmese, Tumbler, Salmon Pink, Mt.Washington 185.00
Burmese, Vase, Enameled, Poem By Thomas Hood, 8 In. .... *Illus* 450.00

Burmese, Vase, Enameled, 12 1/2 In.High .... *Illus* 300.00
Burmese, Vase, Encrusted Enamel Decoration, Mt.Washington .... 750.00 To 995.00
Burmese, Vase, Floral Decoration, Mt.Washington .... 485.00 To 550.00
Burmese, Vase, Flower Form, Glossy, Unmarked, 6 In. 265.00
Burmese, Vase, Fluted Top, 3 In.High 110.00
Burmese, Vase, Gourd Shape, Pink, Salmon, Amber, White Lined, Unsigned Webb 325.00
Burmese, Vase, Ivy Leaves In Greens & Browns, Mt.Washington 400.00
Burmese, Vase, Lily, Salmon Pink To Yellow, Acid, Mt.Washington, 10 In.High 275.00
Burmese, Vase, Lily, Salmon Pink To Yellow, Yellow Edging, Mt.Washington 335.00
Burmese, Vase, Matte Finish, 2 3/4 In.High 120.00
Burmese, Vase, Peach To Yellow, Ovoid Shape, Wafer Foot, Mt.Washington 345.00
Burmese, Vase, Ribbed, Decorated, Small Pedestal Foot 395.00

Burmese, Vase, Enameled,
Poem By Thomas Hood, 8 In.
See Page 79

Burmese, Vase, Enameled,
12 1/2 In.High

Burmese, Vase, Ribbed, Small Size 495.00
Burmese, Vase, Ribs, Floral, Pedestal Base, 5 1/2 In.High 495.00
Burmese, Vase, Ruffled Rim & Base, 4 1/2 In.High 275.00
Burmese, Vase, Trumpet, Everted Lip, Irregular Edge, Bronze Base 140.00
Burmese, Vase, Trumpet, Irregular Rim, 18 1/2 In.High 140.00
Burmese, Vase, Yellow To Pink, Two Handles, 6 1/2 In.High 595.00
  Burmese, Webb, see Webb
Buster Brown, Bank, Long Stockings, Cardboard, Label 7.50
Buster Brown, Bank, Tige, Iron 50.00
Buster Brown, Button, Pinback, Buster & Tige, Celluloid 5.00
Buster Brown, Camera, No.2c, Wooden Inside 10.00
Buster Brown, Candy Container, With Tige, Shaker Cap 14.50
Buster Brown, Creamer, Tige, Buster Balancing Teakettle On Nose 45.00
Buster Brown, Hatchet 15.00
Buster Brown, Knife, 3 1/2 In. 20.00
Buster Brown, Pitcher, Milk, Serving Tea To A Friend 20.00
Buster Brown, Plate, Brown Center, Girl Drinking Tea, 6 In. 24.00
Buster Brown, Plate, Cookie, Buster Brown & Tige 14.00
Buster Brown, Playing Cards, Copyright 1906, By U.S.Playing Card Co., Case 18.00
Buster Brown, Poster, In Person, C.1910, 10 X 16 In. 5.00
Buster Brown, Ring, Radio, Ornate, C.1930 .... 29.00
Buster Brown, Rug, Buster & Tige, Advertises Shoes, 26 X 36 In. 50.00
Buster Brown, Valentine, Signed Outcault, Large 7.50

    Butter Chips, or Butter Pats, were small individual dishes for butter.
    They were in the height of fashion from 1880 to 1910. Earlier as well as
    later examples are known.
Butter Chip, Marked Karlsbad, Austria, Embossed, Violets 1.50
Butter Chip, White, Gold Rim, Porcelain, Set Of 9 .... 13.50
  Buttermilk Glass, see Custard Glass

    Buttons have been known through the centuries, and there are millions of
    styles. Only a few of the most common types are listed for comparison.
Button, Advertising, Humble Gasoline, Orange Marble Color, 2 1/2 In. 4.50

Button, Brass, American Diplomat's Dress, Gilt, U.S.A., C.1837, 6 .... 29.50
Button, Brass, Bust Of George Washington, Gold Finish, Ridabock Co., N.Y., 4 .... 3.95
Button, Brass, Lighthouse, Masted Ship, 1 5/8 In. 6.50
Button, Center Raised Castle Scene, Ornate Edge, 1 1/2 In. 2.00
Button, Embossed Cross Reads U.S.A.Cuba Puerto Rico, Philippines, 5/8 In. 2.00
Button, Enameled Brass, Floral Blooms, Rococo Scroll Border, Set Of 7 .... 35.00
Button, Gold & Pewter, Gold Flower Profusion, Gold Star In Center, France 20.00
Button, Paperweight, Green Glass, Flowers, Gold, Set Of 5 .... 30.00
Button, Picture, Bee In Ornate Silver Openwork, Pair 16.00
Button, Picture, Three Children, Goat, Fence, Brass, Set Of 6 .... 36.00
Button, Porcelain, Hand-Painted, Ladies & Gents In Court Type Dress, 9 .... 25.00
Button, Railroad Union, Pair 1.00
Button, U.S.Artillery Corps, Circa 1810, Brass 19.50
Button, Venetian Peacock-Eye, Orange Center, Blue Rim, Brass Shank, 12 .... 20.00
Button, Wells Fargo, Brass 1.25
    Buttonhook, see Store, Buttonhook
    Calcite, see Steuben

    Calendar Plates were very popular in the United States from 1906 to
    1929. Since then plates have been made every year. A calendar, the name of a
    store, a picture of flowers, a girl, or a scene was featured on the plate.
Calendar Plate, 1907, Santa & Sleigh, 8 3/4 In. 35.00
Calendar Plate, 1907, Santa, Reindeer, Sleigh 37.50
Calendar Plate, 1908, Center Niagara Falls 15.00
Calendar Plate, 1908, Rose Decoration, Dresden 22.00
Calendar Plate, 1908, Woman In Green, Signed G.Bonfits, 9 1/4 In. 16.00
Calendar Plate, 1909, Blue Forget-Me-Nots, Mountain Scene, Water, Sailboats 18.00
Calendar Plate, 1909, Brunette Wearing Green Chiffon, 9 In. 15.00
Calendar Plate, 1909, Christy, Compliments Of F.M.Altland 20.00
Calendar Plate, 1909, D & M Zimmerman, Glidden, Wis. 16.50
Calendar Plate, 1909, Fruit 12.00
Calendar Plate, 1909, Full Length Gibson Girl 35.00
Calendar Plate, 1909, Holly Border, Fruit Center 16.00
Calendar Plate, 1909, Mountain Scene 12.00
Calendar Plate, 1909, Multifruit Center, 9 In. 14.00
Calendar Plate, 1909, Portrait Of Young Lady, 9 1/2 In. 14.00
Calendar Plate, 1909, Portrait, Artist Frost, Holly Sprays, Berries 28.00
Calendar Plate, 1909, River, Stone Bridge, Man On Horse, Man Fishing, House 22.00
Calendar Plate, 1909, Rope Decoration, 9 1/2 In. 12.00
Calendar Plate, 1909, Rose Design 17.50
Calendar Plate, 1909, Strawberries 14.00
Calendar Plate, 1909, Terrier's Head, 9 1/2 In.Diameter 14.00
Calendar Plate, 1910, Advertising, Old Rose Distilling Co., 9 In. 25.00
Calendar Plate, 1910, Angel Holds Flowers, Cloud Background 17.00
Calendar Plate, 1910, Angels Ringing Bell, Souvenir Of Warren, Maine 12.00
Calendar Plate, 1910, Betsy Ross & Flag, 8 1/4 In. 16.00
Calendar Plate, 1910, Betsy Ross Making First Flag, 9 1/2 In. .... 15.00 To 18.50
Calendar Plate, 1910, Cherubs, Flowers, Gold, Pastel Glaze 25.00
Calendar Plate, 1910, Dogs .... 12.00 To 14.00
Calendar Plate, 1910, Dog In Center, Yellow Luster Border 17.00
Calendar Plate, 1910, Dog With Calendars In Mouth 16.00
Calendar Plate, 1910, Four Cupids In A Bird's Nest, 9 1/2 In. 15.00
Calendar Plate, 1910, Fruit Center, Compliments Of Myser China & Glass 17.00
Calendar Plate, 1910, Girl, Fur Hat, Muff 16.00
Calendar Plate, 1910, Horseshoe, Dog Peering Out, Gibson Girl 18.00
Calendar Plate, 1910, Indian Head, 7 1/2 In. 20.00
Calendar Plate, 1910, Lady With Feathered Hat, 7 3/8 In. 7.00
Calendar Plate, 1910, Large Florals, Advertising 14.00
Calendar Plate, 1910, Large Rose 12.00
Calendar Plate, 1910, Medallion Scene, Old Swimming Hole, Holly, Berries 35.00
Calendar Plate, 1910, Months In Book Form, Ivy Leaves, Gold Border 12.50
Calendar Plate, 1910, Old Rose Distilling, Chicago, Pink Roses 22.00
Calendar Plate, 1910, Poppies 12.00
Calendar Plate, 1910, Poppy Sprays, Embossed Lavender Border 16.00
Calendar Plate, 1910, Portrait Center, Queen Louise 20.00
Calendar Plate, 1910, Rose & Violet Center, Landscape Scenes Around Edge 15.00

Calendar Plate, 1910, Rose, Undertaker Advertising, 9 1/2 In.	15.00
Calendar Plate, 1910, Roses, Souvenir, 8 1/4 In.	14.00
Calendar Plate, 1910, Violets, Banner	18.00
Calendar Plate, 1910, Washington's Home At Mt.Vernon	18.00
Calendar Plate, 1910, White Ground, Holly Sprays	12.50
Calendar Plate, 1910, White, Miner, Pick, Wishbone Arch, Good Luck	12.50
Calendar Plate, 1911, Clocks Set At Midnight U.S.A.In 20 Cities Of World	18.00
Calendar Plate, 1911, Cupid Seated On Book	14.00
Calendar Plate, 1911, Floral Rim, Center Angel Lighting Candle	15.00
Calendar Plate, 1911, Gibson Girl, Plumed Hat, Cherubs	14.00
Calendar Plate, 1911, Lady, Brown Hair, Cherub Border	12.00
Calendar Plate, 1911, Seascape, Roses, 8 3/8 In.	16.00
Calendar Plate, 1911, Swan In Lake	16.00
Calendar Plate, 1911, Two Horses' Heads Inside Horseshoe	15.50
Calendar Plate, 1911-1912, Double Calendar, Rural Scene	23.00
Calendar Plate, 1911-1912, Double Calendar, Tuskind Bros., Davenport, N.D.	21.00
Calendar Plate, 1912, Balloonists	18.00
Calendar Plate, 1912, Blue Plums, Hand-Painted, Scalloped Edge	22.00
Calendar Plate, 1912, Center Apple Medallion, Floral Edge, Advertising	12.00
Calendar Plate, 1912, Early Aircraft Center, Floral, Fruit, Months Border	22.00
Calendar Plate, 1912, Fruit	10.00
Calendar Plate, 1912, Girl In Pink Dress By Lakeshore, Apple Blossom	20.00
Calendar Plate, 1912, Girl, Middy Dress, Boat	15.00
Calendar Plate, 1912, Multicolor Fruit, Scalloped Edge	17.00
Calendar Plate, 1912, Multifruit, Scalloped Edge, 7 1/8 In.	17.00
Calendar Plate, 1912, Owl Sits On Calendar Book	15.00
Calendar Plate, 1912, Owl, Open Book, Woodland Scene, 7 3/4 In.	16.50
Calendar Plate, 1912, Panama Canal, Flow Blue Edge, 8 In.	15.00
Calendar Plate, 1912, Plums, Medallion, Leaves, Hand-Painted, 9 1/4 In.	18.00
Calendar Plate, 1912, Portrait Of Young Boy	12.00
Calendar Plate, 1912, Portrait, Sports Equipment Mixed With Calendars	25.00
Calendar Plate, 1912, Quail, Gun, Hunter	18.00
Calendar Plate, 1913, Girl On Rock, Gazing Into River	14.00
Calendar Plate, 1913, Green Holly, Red Berries, Cottage Scene Center	18.00
Calendar Plate, 1913, Yosemite Valley, Holly	20.00
Calendar Plate, 1914, Fox Hunt Scene, Month Border, Dolan's Wine Store	14.50
Calendar Plate, 1914, Valley Forge Scene, Flower Border, 8 1/2 In.Diameter	18.50
Calendar Plate, 1915, Black Man Eating Melon	22.00
Calendar Plate, 1915, Boy, Waves, Father Time	15.00
Calendar Plate, 1915, Panama Canal Scene, 7 1/8 In. 12.00 To	18.00
Calendar Plate, 1915, Panama Canal, Advertising, 7 1/2 In.	15.00
Calendar Plate, 1915, Panama Canal, Flag	15.00
Calendar Plate, 1915, Panama Canal, Souvenir Burkett Bakery, Camden, Maine	18.00
Calendar Plate, 1915, Panama Canal, 8 1/2 In.	14.00
Calendar Plate, 1917, American Flag	18.00
Calendar Plate, 1917, Battleship Flusser Center, Flags & Calendars Rim	27.00
Calendar Plate, 1917, France & England, Flags, Signed	15.00
Calendar Plate, 1917, 5 U.S.Flags, Biplane, Battleships	25.00
Calendar Plate, 1919, Peace With Honor, Dove, Flags, 9 In.	35.00
Calendar Plate, 1920, Peace, Flags	20.00
Calendar Plate, 1920, The Great World War, Peace, Flag, Doves 18.00 To	20.00
Calendar Plate, 1920, The Great World War, 7 1/8 In.	22.00
Calendar Plate, 1920, Wild Turkey, Bluebird Border, Christmas	25.00
Calendar Plate, 1920, World War Victory Peace Dove, Flags, World Globe	25.00
Calendar Plate, 1929, Tile For Teapot, N.H., Advertising, Round, Pink Roses	35.00
Calendar Plate, 1955, Mantel Clock Design, Green	6.00
Calendar Plate, 1955, Tin 2.00 To	5.00
Calendar Plate, 1964, Lincoln's Home, God Bless This House	8.00

*Cambridge Art Pottery was made in Cambridge, Ohio, from about 1895
until World War I. The factory made brown glazed decorated wares marked
with a variety of marks including an acorn, the name Cambridge, the name
Oakwood, or the name Terrhea.*

Cambridge Pottery, Ewer, Bulbous, Oakwood, 7 3/4 In.High, 6 1/2 In.Diameter	85.00
Cambridge Pottery, Mug, High Glaze, Brown, Berries	87.50
Cambridge Pottery, Vase, Dark Brown, Bamboo Leaves, Mark 205	21.00

Cambridge Pottery, Vase, Pear Shape, Cream To Brown Glaze, Marked Oakwood 45.00

The Cambridge Glass Company made Pressed Glass in Cambridge, Ohio. It was marked with a C in a triangle about 1902. The words near-cut were used after 1906.

Cambridge, Ashtray, Crown Tuscan	16.00
Cambridge, Ashtray, Green, Signed	6.50
Cambridge, Ashtray, Individual, Caprice, Moonlight Blue, Triangular	5.00
Cambridge, Bowl, Amber, 6 In.Square	8.00
Cambridge, Bowl, Console, Pink, Chrysanthemums	7.50
Cambridge, Bowl, Farber, Handled, Green Insert, 5 In.Diameter	17.00
Cambridge, Bowl, Flying Lady, Crown Tuscan	95.00
Cambridge, Bowl, Flying Lady, Pink, Crown Tuscan	105.00
Cambridge, Bowl, Fruit, Rosepoint, 12 In.	31.00
Cambridge, Bowl, Gadroon, Amethyst	17.50
Cambridge, Bowl, Green, Flared, Footed, Green Girl Flower Holder, 8 In.	40.00
Cambridge, Bowl, Heron, Flower Frog, Clear, 10 In.	25.00
Cambridge, Bowl, Ivy, Cobalt Blue Top, Nude Stem	39.00
Cambridge, Bowl, Jade Green, Footed, 8 1/2 In.	15.00
Cambridge, Bowl, Opaque Yellow Green, 11 In.	36.00
Cambridge, Bowl, Oval, Seashell, Crown Tuscan, 9 In.	40.00
Cambridge, Bowl, Pink, Etched, Open Handles, Signed, 12 1/2 In.	12.00
Cambridge, Bowl, Portia Pattern, Two Handles, Amber	30.00
Cambridge, Bowl, Primrose, Community Pattern	25.00
Cambridge, Bowl, Ram's Head, Doric Candlesticks, Heliotrope	350.00
Cambridge, Bowl, Ram's Head, Helio, Pair Candlesticks, Silver Gilt	375.00
Cambridge, Bowl, Rosepoint Pattern, Crown Tuscan, 9 In.	75.00
Cambridge, Bowl, Sectioned, Gold Etched Rosepoint, 5 1/2 In.Diameter	18.00
Cambridge, Box, Candy, Covered, Primrose, 2 Pounds	40.00
Cambridge, Box, Covered, Dolphin Feet, Crown Tuscan	35.00
Cambridge, Bucket, Ice, Yellow, Etched Floral, Scalloped Top, Bail	15.00
Cambridge, Candleholder, Caprice, Clear, Shell Base, Prisms, Pair	18.00
Cambridge, Candlestick, Caprice, Moonlight Blue, Prism, 7 In.High	22.00
Cambridge, Candlestick, Doric Column, Helio, Pair	95.00
Cambridge, Candlestick, Doric Column, Jade, Pair	95.00
Cambridge, Candlestick, Doric Column, Opaque, Helio, Pair	95.00
Cambridge, Candlestick, Doric Column, Opaque, Jade, Pair	95.00
Cambridge, Candlestick, Jade, Twist Stem, 10 1/2 In.Pair	45.00
Cambridge, Candlestick, Nude, Enamel Floral Decoration, Crown Tuscan	75.00
Cambridge, Candlestick, Pink, Nude Lady, Crown Tuscan, Pair	95.00
Cambridge, Carafe, Pressed Feather Pattern	18.00
Cambridge, Celery, Green, Signed	8.00
Cambridge, Champagne, Crystal Nude Lady, Amethyst Bowl	32.00
Cambridge, Champagne, Nude Lady, Amber	50.00
Cambridge, Compote, Candy, Amber, Base & Holder Marked Farberware	38.00
Cambridge, Compote, Candy, Clear Nude, Ruby Bowl	65.00
Cambridge, Compote, Custard Shell, Signed	45.00
Cambridge, Compote, Diamond Optic, Amethyst, 5 In.High, 8 1/4 In.Diameter	19.00
Cambridge, Compote, Ebony With Heavy Gold Encrustation	25.00
Cambridge, Compote, Farber Nude, Amber Glass	28.00
Cambridge, Compote, Fiery Pink Ruffled Top Edge, Crown Tuscan	35.00
Cambridge, Compote, Flying Lady, Crown Tuscan	85.00
Cambridge, Compote, Jade, Opaque, 8 3/4 In.High	60.00
Cambridge, Compote, Nude Lady, Royal Blue	45.00
Cambridge, Compote, Nude, Flared, Crown Tuscan	40.00
Cambridge, Compote, Pink, Cut Log, Flared Foot, Crown Tuscan	15.00
Cambridge, Compote, Shell, Nude, Red Roses Center	95.00
Cambridge, Compote, Shell, Three Roses, Nude Lady Stem, Crown Tuscan	110.00
Cambridge, Compote, Silver Flowers, Two Handles, Caprice, 3 In.High	10.00
Cambridge, Compote, Strawberry Pattern, Open, 10 In.High	40.00
Cambridge, Compote, Sweetmeat, Amberina, Cover, 10 In.Tall	50.00
Cambridge, Compote, Tomato Shape, 7 In.Diameter	60.00
Cambridge, Compote, Yellow, Signed, Small	15.00
Cambridge, Console Set, Blue, Caprice Pattern, Prisms On Candlesticks	18.00
Cambridge, Console Set, Ebony, Ram's Head Footed Bowl, Doric Candlesticks	235.00
Cambridge, Console Set, Jade	70.00

Cambridge, Console Set, Shell Shape Bowl, Nude Candleholders, Crown Tuscan 150.00
Cambridge, Console Set, Shell, Nude, Crown Tuscan 275.00
Cambridge, Cordial Set, Chrome Holder, Lady In Center, 7 Piece 18.00
Cambridge, Cornucopia, On Shell Base, Crown Tuscan, 3 In. 15.00
Cambridge, Cornucopia, Seashell, Crown Tuscan, 9 1/2 In. 45.00
Cambridge, Cruet, Green, Signed, Pair 14.00
Cambridge, Cruet, Pink, Etched, Pair, Tray, Handles, Signed 22.50
Cambridge, Cruet, Two Attached, Oil, Vinegar, One Handle, Clear, Stoppers 15.00
Cambridge, Decanter, Wine, Amethyst, Six Tumblers, Chrome Holders 65.00
Cambridge, Dish, Candy, Deep Blue, Black Knob & Base, Satin 20.00
Cambridge, Dish, Candy, Etched Portia, Gold, 3 Section, Covered, Crown Tuscan 40.00
Cambridge, Dish, Candy, Tomato Cover 125.00
Cambridge, Dish, Lemon, Blue, Caprice Pattern, Square 5.00
Cambridge, Figurine, Swan, Crystal, 7 In. 20.00
Cambridge, Flower Frog, Lady, Crystal, 6 1/2 In. 15.00
Cambridge, Flower Frog, Nude Girl 20.00
Cambridge, Flower Holder, Nude Child, Deer, Amber, 9 In. 35.00
Cambridge, Flower Holder, Nude Woman, Stooping, Crystal, 6 1/4 In. 25.00
Cambridge, Flower Holder, Sea Gull 22.00
Cambridge, Goblet, Caprice Pattern, Crystal, 8 In. 5.00
Cambridge, Goblet, Etched Portia Pattern, Gold Encrusted, Crystal, 7 In. 10.00
Cambridge, Goblet, Rosepoint 9.00
Cambridge, Goblet, Water, Carmen Red Top, Crystal Nude Stem 35.00
Cambridge, Holder, Cigarette, Caprice, Moonlight Blue, Triangular 15.00
Cambridge, Ice Bucket, Amber, Unsigned 24.00
Cambridge, Ice Tub, Cobalt, Chrome Handle, 6 In. 19.50
Cambridge, Iced Tea, Mt.Vernon Pattern 4.00
Cambridge, Ivy Ball, Crystal & Amethyst 17.50
Cambridge, Ivy Ball, Ribbed Optic, Cobalt Blue, Footed, 8 1/2 In. 28.00
Cambridge, Jug, Royal Blue, Crystal Handle, Ice Lip, 4 Tumblers 50.00
Cambridge, Juice, Mt.Vernon Pattern 3.00
Cambridge, Perfume, Helio, Marked De Vilbiss Atomizer 35.00
Cambridge, Pitcher, Water, Inverted Strawberry, Near Cut, Signed 25.00
Cambridge, Plate, Cake, Handled, Amber, Marked 12.50
Cambridge, Plate, Caprice, Moonlight Blue, Handled, 6 In. 7.50
Cambridge, Plate, Etched Candlelight Pattern, Gold Encrusted, Handled 22.00
Cambridge, Plate, Grapes, Leaves, Etched, Signed, 10 Sided, Amber 3.00
Cambridge, Plate, Helio, Ground Bottom, 8 In., Set Of 8 .... 75.00
Cambridge, Plate, Pink, Etched Scroll Border, 8 In. 8.50
Cambridge, Plate, Salad, Enameled Roses, Crown Tuscan, 7 In. 25.00
Cambridge, Plate, Sandwich, Center Handle, Pink, Gold Band 7.50
Cambridge, Platter, Cake, Pale Blue, Handles, Marked C In Triangle 15.00
Cambridge, Rose Bowl, Japonica, Flared Top, Satin Finish, Marked 35.00
Cambridge, Salt & Pepper, Etched Candlelight Pattern 10.00
Cambridge, Salt Dip, Etruscan Shell, Pink, Signed, 3 In.Diameter 18.50
Cambridge, Salt Dip, Swan, Cobalt Blue, Signed 22.50
Cambridge, Salt, Mt.Vernon Pattern, Pair 15.00
Cambridge, Salt, Swan, Pink, Signed 15.00
Cambridge, Shell, Crown Tuscan, Signed 75.00
Cambridge, Sugar & Creamer, Amber, Signed 15.00
Cambridge, Sugar & Creamer, Caprice Pattern, Crystal 10.00
Cambridge, Sugar & Creamer, Caprice, Moonlight Blue 16.00
Cambridge, Sugar & Creamer, Pink, Marked 7.50
Cambridge, Sugar, Creamer, & Candy, Pink, Etched Flowers, Leaves, Drape 12.50
Cambridge, Swan, Clear, Signed, 4 1/2 In. 22.50
Cambridge, Swan, Clear, Twisted Neck, Marked, 6 In. 25.00
Cambridge, Swan, Crystal, 6 1/2 In. 20.00
Cambridge, Sweetmeat, Etched Design, Gold, Amber, Cover 10.00
Cambridge, Tray, Sandwich, Pink, Handle, Gold Encrusted Band 7.50
Cambridge, Tumbler, Inverted Strawberry Variant, Red Flash Top, Set Of 6 .... 60.00
Cambridge, Tumbler, Inverted Thistle, Marked Near Cut 12.50
Cambridge, Vase, Boy Holding Up Kid, Green, Frosted, 8 1/2 In.Tall 24.00
Cambridge, Vase, Bud, Crown Tuscan, 10 In. 25.00
Cambridge, Vase, Bud, Rosepoint, Pair 35.00
Cambridge, Vase, Caprice, Moonlight Blue, Bulbous, Silver Collar & Top 22.00
Cambridge, Vase, Carmen, Crystal Foot, 10 In. 32.00

Cambridge, Vase, Cornucopia, Seashell Base, Crown Tuscan, 9 1/2 In., Pair 200.00
Cambridge, Vase, Diane, Crown Tuscan, 11 In. .... *Illus* 185.00
Cambridge, Vase, Etched Rose Pattern, Globe, Crown Tuscan, 5 1/2 In.High 42.50
Cambridge, Vase, Flower Design, Gold, Squatty, 4 3/4 In.High 30.00
Cambridge, Vase, Pistachio, Gold Rim, Blue Base 25.00
Cambridge, Vase, Rosepoint, 9 In., High X 9 1/2 In., Across Top 45.00
Cambridge, Vase, Royal Blue, Crystal Foot, 10 In. 32.00
Cambridge, Vase, Seashell, Crown Tuscan, 7 1/2 In.High 42.00

*Cameo Glass was made in layers in much the same manner as a cameo in
jewelry. Part of the top layer of glass was cut away to reveal a different
colored glass beneath. The most famous cameo glass was made during the
nineteenth century.*

Cameo, see also De Vez, Galle, Le Verre Francais
Cameo, Bottle, Perfume, Flowers, Green, Gold, Signed V & S, Stopper, 6 1/2 In. 95.00
Cameo, Bowl, Animals, Floral, Berries, White Ground, Peking, 4 1/2 In.Diameter 185.00
Cameo, Bowl, Frosted Ground, Purple Wisteria, Signed Moda 75.00
Cameo, Bowl, Reynaud, 5 X 5 In. 175.00
Cameo, Box, Raised Flower Lid, Petal Sides, Signed Rousseau, 4 1/2 In. 450.00
Cameo, Box, Sunset Scene, Boats, Mountain, Water, Trees, Signed Richard, France 225.00
Cameo, Chandelier, French, Signed Degue, Red Carving Of Birds & Leaves 295.00
Cameo, Compote, Swans, Spread Wing, Signed Rousseau, 6 In.Diameter, 4 In.High 375.00
Cameo, Flask, Scent, Webb Type, Heart Shape, Roses & Butterflies On Red 225.00
Cameo, Lamp, French, Geef-Lyons, Four Seasons, Enameled Porcelain Base 695.00
Cameo, Perfume, Citron Ground, White Zinnia, Butterfly, Silver Lid, England 395.00
Cameo, Perfume, English, Lay Down, White Carved Flowers On Citron 350.00
Cameo, Perfume, Green Florals, Cut To Opaque White Ground, Stopper, Pekin 95.00
Cameo, Perfume, Lay Down, Citron Ground, English .... 275.00 To 295.00
Cameo, Plate, Purple, Lavender Colors, Signed Charder 125.00
Cameo, Rose Bowl, Marked St.Denis, Frosted Ground, Acid Cut Floral, Gold 144.00
Cameo, Rose Bowl, Yellow, Three Layer, 3 1/8 In.High 597.00
Cameo, Vase, Amberina, Gray & Amber Overlay, Artist G.Raspiller, France 300.00
Cameo, Vase, Amphora, Moorish Pattern, 7 1/4 In.High .... *Illus* 550.00

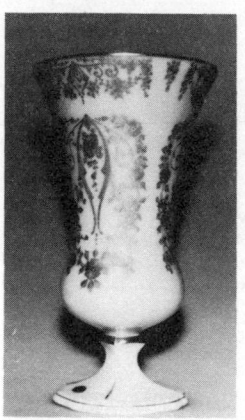

Cambridge, Vase, Diane,
Crown Tuscan, 11 In.

Cameo, Vase, Amphora,
Moorish Pattern, 7 1/4 In.High

Cameo, Vase, Broken Egg Shape, Signed R.H. 195.00
Cameo, Vase, Carved Flowers, Frosted Ground, Orange, Green, Lovanka, France 220.00
Cameo, Vase, Carved Green Lilies, Crystal Ground, Gold Rim, Eriebach 50.00
Cameo, Vase, Castle Scene, Short Neck, Signed T.Michel, 13 In.Tall 335.00
Cameo, Vase, Cranberry Floral, Gold Centers, St.Louis 225.00
Cameo, Vase, Cut Iris, Cranberry, Green Stippled Ground, Gold, French 65.00
Cameo, Vase, Floral & Spider Web Acid Ground, Red Enamel Mums, French, 5 In. 75.00
Cameo, Vase, Flowers, Vines, Cranberry, Clear, Signed St.Louis, 7 In.Tall 275.00
Cameo, Vase, French, Bowling Pin Shape, Autumn Scene, Signed Lamartine 165.00
Cameo, Vase, French, Pink Floral On Clear, Signed, 3 3/4 In.High 125.00
Cameo, Vase, French, Purple At Bottom To Blue, Lily-Of-The-Valley Branches 225.00
Cameo, Vase, French, Shaped Like Bowling Pin, Signed Lamartine 165.00

Cameo, Vase, Green Leaves & Vines, Signed Arsall, 12 In.High 225.00
Cameo, Vase, Honesdale, Yellow On White Frosted Ground, Carnation Pattern 67.00
Cameo, Vase, Hunting Dog 185.00
Cameo, Vase, Michel, Cut, 7 In. 295.00
Cameo, Vase, Nicholas, 6 In. .... *Illus* 245.00
Cameo, Vase, Pantin, Red Floral, Iridescent, Pearlized Ground, 6 1/4 In. 225.00
Cameo, Vase, Purple Grecian Figures, Frosted Glass, Purple & Clear Panels 130.00
Cameo, Vase, Russet & Amber, Pea Pods, Leaves, 12 In.High 195.00
Cameo, Vase, Shades Of Purple, Blue, Green, & Yellow, G.Argy Rousseau 495.00
Cameo, Vase, Stag Decor, Pineaud, France 225.00
Cameo, Vase, Stick, Blue, Cut White To Blue 492.00
Cameo, Vase, Three Layers, Cranberry, Carved Roses, Bellflowers, Leaves, 5 In. 625.00
Cameo, Vase, Webb Type, Pestle Shape, Apple Blossoms & Raspberries On Ocher 2200.00
Cameo, Vase, White On Aquamarine & Ocher, 9 1/8 In. .... *Illus* 1500.00
Cameo, Vase, 6 5/8 In.High .... *Illus* 2200.00

Cameo, Vase,
Nicholas, 6 In.

Cameo, Vase,
White On
Aquamarine & Ocher,
9 1/8 In.

Cameo, Vase,
6 5/8 In.High

Cameo, Webb, see Webb
Cameo, Wine, Cut Flowers, Apricot, Signed Vessiere, French 110.00
Cameo, Wine, Cut Flowers, Green, Signed Vessiere, French 110.00
Cameo, Wine, French, Signed Vessiere, Nancy, Apricot 115.00
Cameo, Wine, French, Signed Vessiere, Nancy, Green 115.00
Campaign, see Political Campaign

*Camphor Glass is a cloudy white glass that has been blown or pressed. It
was made by many factories in the midwest during the mid-nineteenth century.*
Camphor Glass, Basket, Clear Handle, 6 In. 8.50
Camphor Glass, Bottle, Cut Design, 6 In.High 30.00
Camphor Glass, Box, Pink, Heart Shape, 1 1/2 X 4 1/2 In. 10.00
Camphor Glass, Butter, Duck Cover, Etchings On Inside 85.00
Camphor Glass, Cologne, Bulbous, Tall Neck, Flaring Top, Gold Trim, Stopper 20.00
Camphor Glass, Dish, Candy, Shaped Like Open Rose Petals 12.00
Camphor Glass, Dish, Swan 14.50
Camphor Glass, Figurine, Cat, Reclining, Siamese 17.50
Camphor Glass, Hen On Nest, 6 In. 22.50
Camphor Glass, Jar, Powder, Gold Base, Gold Decoration On Lid 25.00
Camphor Glass, Jar, Powder, Lovebirds 10.00
Camphor Glass, Jar, Powder, Pink, Art Nouveau Lady Lid, Signed Toussant 15.00
Camphor Glass, Jar, Powder, Pink, Molded Elephant For Lid Finial 18.50
Camphor Glass, Jar, Powder, Two Lovebirds 20.00
Camphor Glass, Match Holder, Wall, Man's Comical Smiling Face 9.50
Camphor Glass, Muffineer, Covered, Cut, Etched & Engraved Flowers, Bulbous 48.00
Camphor Glass, Mug, Embossed Red Rose & 16 Star American Flag 19.00
Camphor Glass, Perfume, Amber Top, Celluloid Removable Base 15.00
Camphor Glass, Salt & Pepper, Melon Rib, Daisies, Pewter Rims & Tops 35.00
Camphor Glass, Salt, Master, Swan 15.00
Camphor Glass, Toothpick, Jolly Man's Head, Green 10.50

Camphor Glass, Tray, Dresser, Gold Rim, 8 1/2 In.Long, 6 In.Wide	7.50
Camphor Glass, Vase, Blown Out Poppies & Leaves, Ormolu Collar & Feet	35.00
Camphor Glass, Vase, Centennial, 1876, Hand Figural	17.50
Camphor Glass, Vase, Grapes, Leaves, Ribbed, Marked, White, 8 In.Tall	24.00
Camphor Glass, Vase, Green, Silver Overlay, Signed Rockwell, 8 In.	65.00
Camphor Glass, Vase, Iris Design, Pink, White, 10 1/2 In.Tall	30.00
Camphor Glass, Vase, Silver Deposit, Lilies-Of-The-Valley, 6 In.	25.00
Canary Glass, see Vaseline Glass	
Candelabra, Empire, Bronze & Ormolu, Lady Support, 3-Light, C.1850, Pair	375.00
Candelabra, Gilt Metal & Rock Crystal, Urn Form, 2 Arms, Pair	400.00
Candelabra, Ormolu & Bronze, 3 Candle Arms, C.1850, Pair	800.00
Candelabra, Restauration, Ormolu & Bronze, 3 Candle Arms, C.1850, Pair	800.00
Candelabra, Venetian Style, Table, Gilt Metal & Cut Glass, Pair	350.00
Candelabra, Wall, Gilt Wood, Carved Wheat Sheaves, Fruit, 4 Arms, Pair	225.00
Candelabra, Wall, Mirror Panels, 2 Scrolling Drop Hung Branches, Pair	120.00
Candelabra, 2 Branch, Victorian, Brass & Enamel, Blue Glass, Prisms, Pair	90.00
Candelabra, 3 Branch, Lions Rampant, 11 In.High, Pair	45.00
Candelabra, 3 Branch, Ornate Silver, Pair	195.00
Candelabra, 4 Branch, Crystal, Pear Shape Prisms, Metal Bobeches, Pair	600.00
Candelabra, 5 Branch, Waterford, Diamond Point, Ball Column, 28 In.High	850.00
Candelabrum, Cambridge Crystal, Dolphin, Prisms, 10 In.High	40.00
Candelabrum, Ruby To Clear, Three Branches, Bobeches, Prisms, Floral, Pair	525.00
Candleholder, Fastens Over Chair Back, Wood Base, Iron Top, Spiral Raiser	180.00
Candleholder, 'stickin Tommy, 'Two Pronged, Galvanized	17.50
Candleholder, Wood Case, 2 Candle, Hand Tooled Tin Sconce	170.00
Candlestick, see also Brass, Candleholder, Pewter, Pressed Glass	
Candlestick, Brass, Griffin Stem, Green Diamond Point Candleholder	17.50
Candlestick, Brass, Onyx Stem, 30 In., Pair	79.00
Candlestick, Brass, 5 In. *Illus*	45.00
Candlestick, Continental, Silver Medal, Baluster Stem, Square Base, Pair	40.00
Candlestick, George & Martha Washington, French Bisque & Porcelain, Pair	265.00
Candlestick, Georgian, Mahogany, Fluted Standard, Brass Socket, C.1750, Pair	190.00
Candlestick, Glass, Clear, Twisted, 7 1/2 In.Tall, 4 1/2 In.Round Base, Pair	22.00
Candlestick, Glass, Clear, Twisted, 9 1/2 In.Tall, 4 1/2 In.Round Base, Pair	24.00
Candlestick, Hogscraper, Push-Up, Signed Shaw	25.00
Candlestick, Hogscraper, 9 In.Tall	35.00
Candlestick, Hollow Blown, Applied Trim, Amber, Blue, 8 1/2 In.Tall, Pair	45.00
Candlestick, Italian, Chancel, Parcel Gilt, Fluted, C.1750, 42 In.High	70.00
Candlestick, Italian, Gilt Wood, Carved Acanthus Base, C.1750, Pair	50.00
Candlestick, Italian, Painted, Triple Scroll Support, C.1750, Pair	60.00
Candlestick, Louis Philippe, Bronze, Ormolu, & Cut Glass, C.1890, 4	475.00
Candlestick, Paperweight, Yellow Floral, Applied Handle, Pair	27.50
Candlestick, Petticoat, Dolphin, Clear To Opalescent	45.00
Candlestick, Russian, Gold Wash, 12 In., Pair *Illus*	155.00

Candlestick, Brass, 5 In.

Candlestick, Russian,
Gold Wash, 12 In., Pair

Candlestick,
Sheffield, 8 1/2 In., Pair
See Page 88

Candlestick, Sapphire Blue, Etched Base, 3 1/4 In.High, Pair	14.50
Candlestick, Sheffield, 8 1/2 In., Pair .... *Illus*	225.00
Candlestick, Spiral Top, Wood Base, 17th Century, Pair	85.00
Candlestick, Wood & Wrought Iron, Spiral Twist Pusher & Hanger	165.00
Candlestick, Wooden, Traveling, Pair	60.00
Candlestick, Yellow Floral, Clear Handle, Pair	25.00

Candy Containers, especially those made of glass, were popular during the late Victorian era.

Candy Container, Advertising, Bond Electric Co., Globe, Tin Top & Bottom	20.00
Candy Container, Aeroplane, Spirit Of Good Will, Closure, Paint, Propellor	32.00
Candy Container, Airplane, Army Bomber 15 P 7	10.00
Candy Container, Airplane, Contents	15.00
Candy Container, Amos & Andy In Fresh Air Taxi	135.00
Candy Container, Army Car	12.00
Candy Container, Auto	7.00
Candy Container, Auto, Glass	10.00
Candy Container, Auto, Streamlined, Contents	6.00
Candy Container, Auto, 1937, Red Paint	15.00
Candy Container, Baseball, Tin Closure	10.00
Candy Container, Battleship .... 3.00 To 12.00
Candy Container, Battleship, Contents, Victory Glass Co.	7.50
Candy Container, Battleship, 5 1/2 In.	18.00
Candy Container, Bear, Driving Car	27.50
Candy Container, Bear, Reading Book, Metal Lid	18.00
Candy Container, Boat	9.00
Candy Container, Boat, Clear, 2 1/2 In.	3.00
Candy Container, Boat, Frosted, 3 In.	5.00
Candy Container, Bomber	15.00
Candy Container, Boot	8.00
Candy Container, Bottle, Nursing, Flat Type, Rubber Nipple, Contents, 3 In. ...	5.00
Candy Container, Brass, Pressed Glass Liner, Cover, 3 1/4 In.Tall	15.00
Candy Container, Bulldog	6.50
Candy Container, Bulldog, Screw Opening In Base	20.00
Candy Container, Car, Electric, Vail Bros., Paper Label	45.00
Candy Container, Charlie Chaplin .... 30.00 To 40.00
Candy Container, Charlie Chaplin, Paint	55.00
Candy Container, Chicken On Nest .... 4.00 To 15.00
Candy Container, Clarinet, Really Plays, Screw Top, Says Musical Toy	15.00
Candy Container, Cornucopia, Closure	22.50
Candy Container, Cruiser	10.50
Candy Container, Dog, Metal Bell On Head, 'Kiddies Breakfast Bell, '4 In. ...	7.00
Candy Container, Dog, Metal Collar, Painted	6.00
Candy Container, Dog, Painted, Souvenir Of Reno, Nevada, 3 In.	15.00
Candy Container, Dog, Sad, Sitting, Holes For Salt In Lid, 3 1/2 In.	5.00
Candy Container, Dog, Scotty	6.00
Candy Container, Dog, Sitting .... 5.00 To 9.00
Candy Container, Dog, Sitting, Cobalt	6.00
Candy Container, Electric Coupe, 1913	16.00
Candy Container, Elephant, Tin Lid	20.00
Candy Container, Fire Engine	12.50
Candy Container, Fire Engine, Contents, Label On Bottom, Victory Glass Co. ..	7.50
Candy Container, Fire Engine, Contents, Victory Glass Co.	7.50
Candy Container, Fire Engine, Metal Wheels, Patent Nov.24-14, 5 1/8 In.Long .	20.00
Candy Container, Fire Engine, Train	8.00
Candy Container, Fire Truck .... 10.00 To 12.50
Candy Container, Fire Truck, 5 In.	15.00
Candy Container, Goose Girl, Large .... •	15.00
Candy Container, Gun, Cork Stopper Muzzle, Glass, 10 In.Long	9.00
Candy Container, Gun, Metal Screw Cap	10.00
Candy Container, Gun, No Closure, 7 In.	6.50
Candy Container, Gun, Whistle Toy, Contents, 4 1/2 In.	8.00
Candy Container, Hansom Cab, Embossed, West Bros.Co., Greatville, Pa.,Glass .	20.00
Candy Container, Hat, Band Master's, Glass	12.00
Candy Container, Hen On Nest .... 6.50 To 17.00
Candy Container, Humpty Dumpty On Egg, Tin	9.00

Candy Container, Iron	15.00
Candy Container, Jack-O'-Lantern, Straight Eyes, Painted	35.00
Candy Container, Jeep	6.00
Candy Container, Jeep, Willy, No Closure, Fully Signed	15.00
Candy Container, Lady Holding Child	75.00
Candy Container, Lantern	4.00 To 10.00
Candy Container, Lantern, Clear, Tin, Top	10.00
Candy Container, Lantern, Contents	8.50
Candy Container, Lantern, Dated Dec., '04	10.00
Candy Container, Lantern, Glass	7.50
Candy Container, Lantern, Plamate Bond Electric Co., N.J.	16.00
Candy Container, Lantern, Railroad, Battery Can Be Installed, 6 1/2 In.	15.00
Candy Container, Lantern, Railroad, Clear Glass, Tin Top & Bail	8.50
Candy Container, Lantern, Red Top & Bail	4.00
Candy Container, Lantern, Ribbed Glass Globe, Wire Bail, Marked	14.00
Candy Container, Lantern, Tin Cover, Marked Jeanette Glass Co.	8.00
Candy Container, Lantern, Tin Top, 6 In.	12.00
Candy Container, Lantern, Tin, Red, Clear Glass, Marked Jeanette, Pa.	7.00
Candy Container, Lantern, Twins On An Anchor	18.00
Candy Container, Lantern, 4 1/2 In.	10.00
Candy Container, Liberty Bell, Blue	30.00
Candy Container, Liberty Bell, Tin Bottom Closure, Glass, Contents	15.00
Candy Container, Locomotive	12.50 To 15.00
Candy Container, Locomotive 888	12.50
Candy Container, Locomotive, Engineer In Cab, Screw Cap On Back	18.00
Candy Container, Locomotive, 5 In. ... Illus	8.00

Candy Container, Locomotive, 5 In.

Candy Container, Military Hat, U.S.A., Full	12.00
Candy Container, Milk Glass, Suitcase, Brown Paint	25.00
Candy Container, Moon Mullins, Shaker Cap	14.50
Candy Container, Opera Glasses, Closure	28.00
Candy Container, P.T.Boat	9.50
Candy Container, Phone, Upright, Dial	12.50
Candy Container, Phone, Upright, Ribbed, Wood Receiver, Label, T.H.Stough Co.	19.00
Candy Container, Pipe, Amber Stem	39.50
Candy Container, Pistol	12.50
Candy Container, Pistol, Large Size	8.00
Candy Container, Pistol, Metal Cap, 7 1/2 In.	18.00
Candy Container, Pistol, Small Size	4.50
Candy Container, Pistol, Tin Lid, Small Size	6.00
Candy Container, Plane	7.00
Candy Container, Puppy, Sitting, Clear Glass	2.95
Candy Container, Rabbit Eating Carrot	11.00
Candy Container, Rabbit In Egg	25.00
Candy Container, Rabbit With Basket, Tin Closure	32.00
Candy Container, Rabbit, Easter	8.00
Candy Container, Rabbit, No Closure, 7 X 4 In.	10.00
Candy Container, Rabbit, Reclining On Rectangular Base, Painted	27.50
Candy Container, Rabbit, Sitting, Brown, Papier-Mache, 9 In.	12.00
Candy Container, Rabbit, Sitting, 4 1/2 In.Tall	12.00
Candy Container, Rabbit, 6 1/4 In.	15.00
Candy Container, Revolver, Closure	12.50
Candy Container, Revolver, No Cap	10.00
Candy Container, Revolver, Tin Screw Cap On Muzzle, 7 1/2 In.Long	12.00
Candy Container, Revolver, 8 In.Long	16.00
Candy Container, Santa	8.50 To 25.00

Candy Container, Santa, Papier-Mache, 9 In.	8.00
Candy Container, Santa, Standing, Celluloid Head	20.00
Candy Container, Santa, 5 In.	16.50
Candy Container, Santa's Boot	4.50
Candy Container, Santa's Boot, Sticker, Contents	10.00
Candy Container, Scottie Dog, 3 In.High	9.00 To 14.00
Candy Container, Seated Rabbit, Original Candy, 6 1/2 In.High	9.00
Candy Container, Sedan	25.00
Candy Container, Sitting Rabbit, 6 1/2 In.Tall	18.00
Candy Container, Six Paneled Chamber, 7 In.Long	15.00
Candy Container, Spark Plug	42.00
Candy Container, Speedboat	5.00
Candy Container, Stick, Policeman's, Amber, Closure	27.50
Candy Container, Suitcase, Glass	12.50
Candy Container, Suitcase, Large Size	12.50
Candy Container, Tank, 4 In.	9.00 To 13.00
Candy Container, Telephone	4.00
Candy Container, Telephone, Child's, Plastic	20.00
Candy Container, Telephone, French, Metal Receiver, Closure, Contents, Clear	4.00
Candy Container, Telephone, French, Metal Receiver, Contents, 2 In.	5.00
Candy Container, Telephone, Lynne Type, Contents	10.00
Candy Container, Telephone, Stick, Contents, Victory Glass Co.	7.50
Candy Container, Telephone, Tin Bottom	11.00
Candy Container, Telephone, Upright, Metal Closure, Label	20.00
Candy Container, Telephone, Upright, No Closure	15.00
Candy Container, Telephone, Upright, Red Mouthpiece, Wooden Receiver, 4 In.	8.00
Candy Container, Telephone, Wooden Receiver	12.00
Candy Container, Train Engine	16.00
Candy Container, Train Engine, Whistle	5.25
Candy Container, Trunk, Round Top	22.50
Candy Container, Turkey	20.00
Candy Container, Turkey, Tin Bottom	35.00
Candy Container, Twin Lanterns On Anchor	12.50 To 18.00
Candy Container, Upright Telephone, Clear	8.75
Candy Container, Van With Driver	12.50
Candy Container, Wagon	10.00
Candy Container, War Tank, Closure, Contents	10.00
Cane, Carved Ivory Handle, Fruit, Leaves, Oriental Design On Bamboo Stick	45.00
Cane, Ebony, Gold Knob, Circa 1900	49.00
Cane, Embossed Gold Top	35.00
Cane, Flask, Footed Tumbler	55.00
Cane, Glass, Hollow, Swirl, Knob End, 53 In.	35.00
Cane, Gold Head, Chased Design, Dated 1886	40.00
Cane, Gold Top	45.00
Cane, Handle, Man's, Gold Filled, Embossed	32.00
Cane, Pewter Handle, Embossed, G.A.R.Flags, Soldiers	40.00
Cane, Stag Handle, Hickory	12.00
Cane, Sterling Silver Handle, Tiffany, Dated 1884	40.00
Cane, Tortoise Shell, Snuff Box Concealed In Handle	55.00
Cane, Walking, Hallmarked Silver Top With Liquor Holder	50.00
Cane, Walking, Lead Handle, Marked G.A.R., Eagle & Flag Design	15.00
Cane, Walnut, Ivory Head	8.00
Cane, Wooden, Sterling Head, Bone Tip	10.00

Canton China is a blue-and-white ware made near Canton, China, from about 1785 to 1895. It has hand-decorated chinese scenes.

Canton, Basket, Blue & White, Oval, C.1815, 10 In.Long	130.00
Canton, Bouillon, Tray, Cover	75.00
Canton, Bowl, Blue & White, Rectangular, Oriental Scene, C.1850	100.00
Canton, Bowl, Blue, Early 1800's, 10 In.Diameter	85.00
Canton, Bowl, Covered, Octagon	140.00
Canton, Bowl, Fish Shape, Turned Up Tail, Sauce Dip	26.00
Canton, Bowl, Kidney Shape, Famille Rose, C.1820 *Illus*	95.00
Canton, Bowl, Rice, Early 19th Century, 2 1/8 In.High, 4 7/8 In.Diameter	45.00
Canton, Bowl, Scalloped Edge, China, 8 In.	150.00
Canton, Bowl, Shell Shape, Famille Rose Enamels, C.1820 *Illus*	160.00

Canton, Bowl, Turquoise Enamel Inside, Blue Figures 50.00
Canton, Bowl, Vegetable, Covered, Rectangular, C.1825, Pair .... 375.00 To 425.00
Canton, Chocolate Pot, Ladies In Garden, Blue & White 60.00
Canton, Creamer, Extended Lip 65.00
Canton, Creamer, Fish Shape, Gold 50.00
Canton, Creamer, 3 1/2 In. .... *Illus* 85.00
Canton, Cup & Saucer, Blue 28.00
Canton, Cup & Saucer, Blue & White 30.00
Canton, Cup & Saucer, Butterflies 40.00
Canton, Cup & Saucer, Demitasse, Foliage, Chinese Elders, Blue On White 35.00
Canton, Cup & Saucer, Plate, Red Flowers, Fowl In Center, Marked 45.00
Canton, Jar, Blue & White, Cover 98.00
Canton, Jar, Bulbous, Wood Top & Stand, 6 In.Diameter, 8 In.Tall 135.00
Canton, Jar, Ginger, Blue & White, Lid 60.00
Canton, Jar, Ginger, Blue With White, 18th Century 63.00
Canton, Jar, Ginger, White Prunus Blossoms On Dark Blue, 4 1/2 In. 28.00
Canton, Jar, Ginger, White Prunus Blossoms On Dark Blue, 6 In. 34.00
Canton, Plate, Blue & White Design, 12 1/4 In.Diameter 45.00
Canton, Plate, Blue, 7 In. 16.00
Canton, Plate, Famille Rose, Court Scenes Center, Gilt Crest, C.1825, Pair 150.00
Canton, Plate, Famille Rose, Oriental Figures, Buddhist Trophies, C.1825 .... 40.00
Canton, Plate, Medallions Of Birds Encircle Center Bird, Floral, C.1810 .... 57.50
Canton, Platter, Blue, Unmarked, 15 1/2 X 12 1/2 In. 110.00
Canton, Platter, Blue, Wood & Sons, England, 8 1/4 X 11 In. 15.00
Canton, Platter, Well & Tree, Oblong, Cut Corners, 14 X 11 1/4 In. 150.00
Canton, Sauce, Hand-Painted, Artist-Signed 17.00
Canton, Seat, Garden, C.1840, Pair .... *Illus* 1200.00
Canton, Teabowl & Saucer, Willow Pattern, C.1840 .... *Illus* 55.00
Canton, Teapot, Bird Of China Figural, Glazed Gray Bisque, Marked 35.00

Canton, Bowl, Kidney Shape,
Famille Rose, C.1820
See Page 90

Canton, Creamer, 3 1/2 In.

Canton, Bowl, Shell Shape,
Famille Rose Enamels, C.1820
See Page 90

Canton, Seat,
Garden, C.1840, Pair

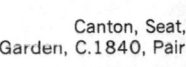

Canton, Teabowl & Saucer,
Willow Pattern, C.1840
See Page 91

Canton, **Teapot**, Blue, White, Branch Handle, 6 In.Tall, 4 1/2 In.Diameter	95.00
Canton, **Teapot**, Blue, White, Raised Base, Dome Top	135.00
Canton, **Teapot**, Rose, People, Birds, Panel, 6 1/2 In.Tall	75.00
Canton, **Tureen**, Boar Handles, 12 In.	450.00
Canton, **Tureen**, Covered, Oval, Famille Rose, White Ground, Figures, C.1825	775.00
Canton, **Vase**, Blue, Oriental Lady & Boy	20.00
Canton, **Vase**, Rose, Foo Dog Handle, 5 In.Tall	25.00
Canton, **Vegetable**, Diamond Shape, Cover	110.00

Capo-Di-Monte Porcelain was first made in Naples, Italy, from 1743 to 1759. The factory moved near Madrid, Spain, and reopened in 1771 and worked to 1834. Since that time the Doccia factory of Italy acquired the molds and style, even using the N and crown mark, which was made famous by the factory.

N

Capo-Di-Monte, **Bell**, Dinner, Raised Cherubs, Blue Crown Mark	29.50
Capo-Di-Monte, **Box**, Cherubs On Top And On Sides, Crown & N, 6 In.Long	235.00
Capo-Di-Monte, **Box**, Children Playing Instruments, Oval, Hinged Lid, Old Mark	90.00
Capo-Di-Monte, **Box**, Covered, Classical Figure, C.1850, 4 In.Long	250.00
Capo-Di-Monte, **Box**, Hinged Lid, Allover Children & Women, Heavy Gold Trim	350.00
Capo-Di-Monte, **Box**, Hinged, Greek Ladies & Children, Brass Bound, Marked	145.00
Capo-Di-Monte, **Box**, Hunting Scenes, Pastoral Scene On Lid, 3 X 4 In.	165.00
Capo-Di-Monte, **Box**, Jewel, Multicolor Mythical Figures, Footed, Signed	45.00
Capo-Di-Monte, **Box**, Lid, Classical Figure, 4 In.Long, 3 In.Tall	250.00
Capo-Di-Monte, **Box**, Ornate Design, Colors, Hinged Cover	250.00
Capo-Di-Monte, **Clock**, Cherubs, Flowers, New Works, Crown & N Mark, 5 1/2 In.	70.00
Capo-Di-Monte, **Compote**, Garden Scene, Classical Nudes, Cherubs, 11 In.High	30.00
Capo-Di-Monte, **Compote**, Multicolor Mythical Figures, Lid, 11 1/4 In.High	55.00
Capo-Di-Monte, **Compote**, Musketeer, Grotesque, 4 In.	85.00
Capo-Di-Monte, **Cup & Saucer**	35.00
Capo-Di-Monte, **Figurine**, Dancing Pair, Man Plays String Instrument, Stand	1000.00
Capo-Di-Monte, **Figurine**, Elephant, Decorated Trappings, Blue, Red, Gold, White	55.00
Capo-Di-Monte, **Figurine**, Lady In Bonnet, Man In Top Hat, Crown With N, Pair	70.00
Capo-Di-Monte, **Figurine**, Man, Woman, Colorful Decoration, Pair	160.00
Capo-Di-Monte, **Figurine**, Two Women, Base, Circa 1890, 10 X 7 In.	250.00
Capo-Di-Monte, **Garniture**, Muses, Reticulated Basket, Marked, 9 Piece	875.00
Capo-Di-Monte, **Inkwell**, Double, Cherubs & Floral, Blue Crown N Mark	65.00
Capo-Di-Monte, **Jar**, Candy, Multicolor Mythical Figures, Lid, Signed	45.00
Capo-Di-Monte, **Lamp**, Women, Babies, Relief, Brass Base, New Silk Shade	275.00
Capo-Di-Monte, **Plaque**, Circa 1820, Black Frame, 4 X 6 In.	198.00
Capo-Di-Monte, **Plaque**, Tiger's Head, Oval, 10 In.High	60.00 To 65.00
Capo-Di-Monte, **Stein**, Boar On Lid, 8 1/2 In.High	305.00
Capo-Di-Monte, **Stein**, Cupid On Hinged Lid	400.00
Capo-Di-Monte, **Stein**, Helmet & Feathers On Lid, Hinged	400.00
Capo-Di-Monte, **Stein**, Hinged Lid	400.00
Capo-Di-Monte, **Stein**, Pouring, Bacchanale, 1/2 Liter, Unsigned	250.00
Capo-Di-Monte, **Stein**, Set On Lid, Early 18th Century, 10 In.High	380.00
Capo-Di-Monte, **Stein**, 1/2 Liter, Lion & Shield Lid Finial, Circa 1900	200.00
Capo-Di-Monte, **Sugar & Creamer**, Raised Figures Of Nude Children, Gold	50.00
Capo-Di-Monte, **Urn**, Covered, Oriental Scroll Handles, Figures, Gilt, Pair	500.00
Capo-Di-Monte, **Urn**, Double Handled, Ovoid, Allegorical Figures, Pair	800.00
Capo-Di-Monte, **Vase**, White, Angels, Embossed Palm Leaves On Pedestal, Gold	45.00

Captain Midnight, Book, Big Little Book, 1946	6.00
Captain Midnight, Book, Secret Manual, 1949	30.00
Captain Midnight, Book, Trick & Riddle, 1939 Skelly Premium	10.00
Caramel Slag, see Slag	
Card, see also Postcard	
Card, Advertising, Ayer's Sarsaparilla	2.00
Card, Advertising, Burdock Blood Bitters	2.00
Card, Advertising, Jayne's Expectorant	2.00
Card, Advertising, Lydia Pinkham's	2.00
Card, Advertising, Mrs.Winslow's Soothing Syrup	2.00
Card, Game, Game Of Flags, 1896	9.00
Card, Greeting, Christmas, Calendar, Woman In Red & Furs, 1910	1.00
Card, Greeting, Christmas, Pre-1915, Set Of 6	3.00
Card, Greeting, Christmas, Santa, Embossed, Tinseled	15.00
Card, Greeting, Christmas, Stage Coach Mounted In Raised Gold, Cellophane	2.00
Card, Greeting, Christmas, Velvet, Roses & Birds	2.00
Card, Greeting, Embossed Children's Toys & Santa	1.00
Card, Greeting, Santa Claus, Pre-1915, Set Of 6	5.00
Card, Greeting, Santa In Tin Lizzie Car Filled With Toys	2.00
Card, Greeting, Santa In Velvet Car	2.00
Card, Greeting, Tuck	15.00
Card, Greeting, Tuck, Shakespearian Character, Perforated Border Is Frame	3.60
Card, Komical Konversation Kards, Parker Bros., 1893, Lithograph	12.00
Card, Negro, Children, Seals Of State In Gold	2.00
Card, Playing, Blue, White, Gift Of American Red Cross, 1943, 52	2.50
Card, Playing, Confederate, Questions & Answers, C.1870	19.50
Card, Playing, Congress, Woman Riding Horse, Marked Moon Fairy	25.00
Card, Playing, Dogs, Miniature	3.50
Card, Playing, English, Player's Cigarettes, Waddington, 52	1.70
Card, Playing, English, Player's Tobacco, Waddington, 52	1.60
Card, Playing, Fauntleroy, Miniature	3.00
Card, Playing, Floral, Portraits Of Royalty Or Notables, Frankfort, 52	10.00
Card, Playing, French, Gala De La Publicite, 1960, 1 Day Gala, 52	15.00
Card, Playing, French, Printed In Lyons In 1650, Reprint, Scolar Press, 52	3.25
Card, Playing, French, St.Michel Cigarettes, Says Tabakken Gosset, 32	1.25
Card, Playing, German, Joan Of Arc, Reprint, 1805, 52	16.60
Card, Playing, German, Yost Amman's 1588, Reprint, 52	10.77
Card, Playing, Lewandos, Cleaners & Dyers, U.S.A., 52	3.80
Card, Playing, Pan-American Exposition, 1901	25.00
Card, Playing, Railroad, Great Northern Black Foot Indian Series, Deck	10.00
Card, Playing, Red & White Ground, Advertises Grand Order Cigar 5 Cents, 52	3.00
Card, Playing, Rook, Parker Bros., 1910	4.50
Card, Playing, Scenes, Niagara Falls, Buffalo, N.Y., 52	8.00
Card, Playing, Union Pacific Railroad, 52	2.50
Card, Valentine, Aquatint, C.1830, 8 X 10 In.	35.00 To 45.00
Card, Valentine, Cutout, Verse, Dated 1830, Frame	55.00
Card, Valentine, Dated 1880, In Frame, 15 1/4 X 11 1/4 In.	15.00
Card, Valentine, Lacy Border, Pasted Flowers, Bird, Dated 1845, Frame	45.00
Card, Valentine, Sailor's, American, C.1850, 9 In.High	*Illus* 350.00
Card, Valentine, Tuck, Girl, Hat, Verse, Easel Back, 7 In.	13.00
Card, Valentine, Whitney	20.00
Carder, see Steuben, Aurene	

Carlsbad, Germany, is a mark found on china made by several factories in Germany. Most of the pieces available today were made after 1891.

Carlsbad, Basket, Hand-Painted Pink & Green Floral, Scalloped, Marked	30.00
Carlsbad, Bottle, Cobalt, Bust Of Napoleon, Marked Victoria, Austria	42.50
Carlsbad, Bowl, Curved Rim, Hand-Painted Sky, Mountains, Floral	18.00
Carlsbad, Bowl, Platter, Quinces, Leaves, C.Ahrenfeldt Factory, Germany, 1886	52.50
Carlsbad, Cup & Saucer, Demitasse, Bittersweet & Gold Decor	6.75
Carlsbad, Dish, Celery, Green, Floral, 14 1/4 In.	22.50
Carlsbad, Fish Set, Pink Border, Gold Decor, Gold Scales On Fish, 15 Pieces	165.00
Carlsbad, Gravy Boat, Attached Underplate, Flowers, Gold, Marked Austria	8.00
Carlsbad, Jar, Tobacco, Orange Devil, Victoria	40.00
Carlsbad, Pitcher, Green, Cucumber Shape, Cucumber Flower Spout, Gold Handle	38.00
Carlsbad, Plate, Portrait, Classical Woman & Man, Green & Gold Border	32.00

Card, Valentine, Sailor's, American,
C.1850, 9 In.High
See Page 93

Carlsbad, Plate, Portrait, Green Border, Gold Trim, Gold Handles 35.00
Carlsbad, Plate, Quinces, Leaves, C.Ahrenfeldt Factory, Germany, 1886 .... 17.50
Carlsbad, Plate, Violets, Double Open Handles 6.00
Carlsbad, Ring Tree, Floral, Gold Trim, Marked Victoria, Austria 15.00
Carlsbad, Tea Caddy, White, Pale Gold Flowers 15.00
Carlsbad, Tea Caddy, White, Portrait Of Lady, Marked Austria 22.00
Carlsbad, Tray, Dresser, Butterfly Shape, Floral Center, Pink & Gold Edge 14.00
Carlsbad, Vase, Bud, Light Blue, Enameled Butterflies & Daisies, 7 1/2 In. 165.00

Carnival, or Taffeta, Glass was an inexpensive, pressed, iridescent glass
made from about 1900 to 1920. Carnival Glass is currently being reproduced.
Over 200 different patterns are known.
Carnival Glass, see also Northwood
Carnival Glass, Ashtray, Cleveland, Amethyst 1250.00
Carnival Glass, Ashtray, Polo Player, Marigold 45.00
Carnival Glass, Atomizer, Marigold 17.50
Carnival Glass, Banana Boat, Cherry Wreathed, Purple 125.00
Carnival Glass, Banana Boat, Cherry Wreathed, Purple, Miniature 45.00
Carnival Glass, Banana Boat, Fenton's Thistle, Blue, Footed, Oval 125.00
Carnival Glass, Banana Boat, Grape & Cable, Green, 13 1/4 X 7 In. 175.00
Carnival Glass, Banana Boat, Grape And Cable, Purple 250.00
Carnival Glass, Banana Boat, Pear & Peach, Amethyst 105.00
Carnival Glass, Banana Boat, Thistle, Amethyst, Fenton, Footed 210.00
Carnival Glass, Banana Boat, Wreathed Cherry, White 250.00
Carnival Glass, Bank, Be Wise, Pastel Marigold, 7 In.Tall 25.00
Carnival Glass, Bank, Owl, Be Wise, Marigold 14.75
Carnival Glass, Bank, Owl, Marigold 28.50
Carnival Glass, Base, Ripple, Purple, 8 In.Tall 25.00
Carnival Glass, Basket, Basket Weave, Marigold 25.00
Carnival Glass, Basket, Beaded Hearts, Marigold, Maple Leaf In Bottom 67.50
Carnival Glass, Basket, Beaded, Marigold, 2 Handled 27.50
Carnival Glass, Basket, Bushel, Blue 75.00
Carnival Glass, Basket, Bushel, Purple, Marked N 45.00
Carnival Glass, Basket, Bushel, White, Northwood 75.00
Carnival Glass, Basket, Fenton, Blue 32.50
Carnival Glass, Basket, Fenton, Red 125.00
Carnival Glass, Basket, Open Edged, Amber, Fenton 55.00
Carnival Glass, Basket, Waffle Block, Marigold 14.00
Carnival Glass, Bell, Daisy Cut, Marigold 375.00
Carnival Glass, Bell, Daisy Cut, Ruffled, Marigold 800.00
Carnival Glass, Berry Bowl, Maple Leaf, Purple 40.00
Carnival Glass, Berry Dish, Peacock At The Fountain, Ice Blue 45.00
Carnival Glass, Berry Set, Butterfly & Berry, Marigold, 7 Piece 215.00
Carnival Glass, Berry Set, Diamond Lace, Marigold 75.00
Carnival Glass, Berry Set, Grape & Cable With Thumbprint, Purple, 7 Piece 165.00
Carnival Glass, Berry Set, Grape & Cable, Marigold, Marked N, 6 Piece 85.00
Carnival Glass, Berry Set, Grape & Cable, Purple, N Mark, 6 Piece 235.00

Carnival Glass, Berry Set, Grape & Cable, Purple, Ruffled, N Mark, 7 Piece	300.00
Carnival Glass, Blackberry, Red, Hat Shape, 5 1/2 In.	125.00
Carnival Glass, Boat, Banana, Peaches & Pears, Marigold	65.00
Carnival Glass, Bonbon, Birds & Bough, Blue, Two Handles	75.00
Carnival Glass, Bonbon, Birds And Cherries, Green	25.00
Carnival Glass, Bonbon, Birds On Bough, Green	58.00
Carnival Glass, Bonbon, Butterfly & Rays, Purple, Two Handles	50.00
Carnival Glass, Bonbon, Butterfly, Amethyst And Purple, Marked Horlacker	60.00
Carnival Glass, Bonbon, Butterfly, Marigold, Millersburg, Two Handles	45.00
Carnival Glass, Bonbon, Butterfly, Purple, Handle, Marked N	35.00
Carnival Glass, Bonbon, Figural Swan, Purple	63.00
Carnival Glass, Bonbon, Grape & Cable, Purple, Handle, Marked N	47.50
Carnival Glass, Bonbon, Persian Medallion, 2 Handles, Green, 7 1/2 In.	50.00
Carnival Glass, Bonbon, Pond Lily, Green	35.00
Carnival Glass, Bonbon, Question Mark, Purple, 2 Handles	25.00
Carnival Glass, Bonbon, Stemmed, Three Fruits, Green, 7 1/2 In.	27.50
Carnival Glass, Bonbon, Strawberry, Ice Green, Two Handles, Ruffled Edge	46.00
Carnival Glass, Bonbon, Strawberry, Purple, Ruffled, 2 Handles	24.00
Carnival Glass, Bonbon, Three Fruits, Blue	75.00
Carnival Glass, Bonbon, Vintage, Amethyst, Two Handles	40.00
Carnival Glass, Bottle, Canada Dry, Marigold	12.50
Carnival Glass, Bottle, Captain's, Purple	125.00
Carnival Glass, Bottle, Cleopatra, Marigold	715.00
Carnival Glass, Bottle, Cologne, Grape & Cable, Purple	175.00
Carnival Glass, Bottle, Corn, Smoky Lavender	165.00
Carnival Glass, Bottle, Crown Perfume, Marigold	12.50
Carnival Glass, Bottle, Golden Wedding, Marigold, Large	17.50
Carnival Glass, Bottle, Golden Wedding, Marigold, Medium	15.00
Carnival Glass, Bottle, Horn Of Plenty, Marigold	45.00
Carnival Glass, Bottle, Jackman Whiskey, Marigold, Large	45.00
Carnival Glass, Bottle, Jackman Whiskey, Marigold, Small	60.00
Carnival Glass, Bottle, Perfume, Purple, With Dabber	90.00
Carnival Glass, Bottle, Stag & Holly, Blue, Footed	95.00
Carnival Glass, Bottle, Whiskey, Continental, Marigold	55.00
Carnival Glass, Bottle, Whiskey, Golden Wedding, Marigold, Salesman's Sample	45.00
Carnival Glass, Bowl, Acanthus, Smoky	35.00
Carnival Glass, Bowl, Acorn Pattern, Marigold, 7 1/2 In.Diameter	12.75
Carnival Glass, Bowl, Acorn, Collar Based, Green, 7 1/2 In.	27.50
Carnival Glass, Bowl, Acorn, Green, 8 In.	38.00
Carnival Glass, Bowl, Acorn, Marigold, 7 1/2 In.	20.00
Carnival Glass, Bowl, Age Herald, Amethyst	1050.00
Carnival Glass, Bowl, Apple Candy, Marigold	15.00
Carnival Glass, Bowl, Autumn Acorns, Green, Collar Base, 8 In.	49.00
Carnival Glass, Bowl, Banana, Grape & Cable, Marigold	65.00
Carnival Glass, Bowl, Banana, Grape & Cable, Marigold, 3 Footed	225.00
Carnival Glass, Bowl, Banana, Thistle, Marigold, Fenton	95.00
Carnival Glass, Bowl, Banana, Two Fruits, Marigold	45.00
Carnival Glass, Bowl, Banana, Two Fruits, Purple, 12 1/2 In.Long	135.00
Carnival Glass, Bowl, Banana, Wreathed Cherry, Purple	100.00
Carnival Glass, Bowl, Basket Weave, Ice Blue	150.00
Carnival Glass, Bowl, Basket Weave, Purple, Strawberry Inside, Marked N, Low	65.00
Carnival Glass, Bowl, Basket Weave, Red, 5 3/4 In.Diameter	100.00
Carnival Glass, Bowl, Basket Weave, White, Flat, Fenton, 8 1/2 In.	125.00
Carnival Glass, Bowl, Battenburg Lace, White, Ruffled, 8 In.	75.00
Carnival Glass, Bowl, Beaded Cable Rose, Blue	100.00
Carnival Glass, Bowl, Beaded Stars, Marigold, Dome Base	16.50
Carnival Glass, Bowl, Beads, Green, N Mark	21.00
Carnival Glass, Bowl, Bearded Berry, Green, Orange Tree Inside, 9 In.	55.00
Carnival Glass, Bowl, Berry, Dahlia, Marigold	22.50
Carnival Glass, Bowl, Berry, Dahlia, Purple	45.00
Carnival Glass, Bowl, Berry, Flute, Purple	12.00
Carnival Glass, Bowl, Berry, Grape & Cable, Purple, N Mark, Set Of 5	95.00
Carnival Glass, Bowl, Berry, Grape & Thumbprint, Purple	95.00
Carnival Glass, Bowl, Berry, Inverted Strawberry, Amethyst, Near Cut	40.00
Carnival Glass, Bowl, Berry, Master, Acorn Burr, Purple	150.00
Carnival Glass, Bowl, Berry, Orange Tree, Clambroth, Wreathed Cherry Inside	40.00

Carnival Glass, Bowl, Berry, Panther, Marigold, Footed .... 29.00 To 85.00
Carnival Glass, Bowl, Berry, Peacock At Fountain, Ice Blue, Signed N 45.00
Carnival Glass, Bowl, Berry, Sailboat, Red 145.00
Carnival Glass, Bowl, Berry, Singing Birds, Green, 4 1/2 In. 35.00
Carnival Glass, Bowl, Blackberries, Green 25.00
Carnival Glass, Bowl, Blackberry Wreath, Amethyst, Millersburg 80.00
Carnival Glass, Bowl, Blackberry Wreath, Marigold, Millersburg 45.00
Carnival Glass, Bowl, Blackberry, Red, 6 1/2 In.Diameter 150.00
Carnival Glass, Bowl, Blackberry, Red, 6 3/4 In. 140.00
Carnival Glass, Bowl, Brooklyn Bridge, Marigold 180.00
Carnival Glass, Bowl, Butterfly & Tulip, Marigold, Footed 295.00
Carnival Glass, Bowl, Butterfly And Berry, Blue, 3 Footed, 9 3/4 In. 70.00
Carnival Glass, Bowl, Captive Rose, Green, 8 1/2 In. 75.00
Carnival Glass, Bowl, Carnival Hobstar, Marigold, Large Size 25.00
Carnival Glass, Bowl, Carnival Holly, Amber, 8 1/2 In. 75.00
Carnival Glass, Bowl, Carnival Holly, Blue, 8 1/4 In. 45.00
Carnival Glass, Bowl, Carnival Holly, White, Flared, 9 In. 135.00
Carnival Glass, Bowl, Caroline, Peach, Knife Pleated 35.00
Carnival Glass, Bowl, Cereal, Kittens, Blue 58.50
Carnival Glass, Bowl, Checkers, Marigold, Cover 23.00
Carnival Glass, Bowl, Cherries, Marigold, Ruffled, 3 Footed, 8 1/2 In. 27.00
Carnival Glass, Bowl, Cherry, Amethyst, Millersburg 250.00
Carnival Glass, Bowl, Cherry, Marigold, Two Handles 35.00
Carnival Glass, Bowl, Coin Dot, Amethyst 45.00
Carnival Glass, Bowl, Coin Dot, Green, 7 In. 23.00
Carnival Glass, Bowl, Coin Dot, Green, 9 In. 18.00
Carnival Glass, Bowl, Colonial, Purple, Large 135.00
Carnival Glass, Bowl, Cosmos, Cobalt, 9 In. 42.00
Carnival Glass, Bowl, Cosmos, Marigold, Ruffled 25.00
Carnival Glass, Bowl, Court House, Amethyst, Millersburg 325.00
Carnival Glass, Bowl, Court House, Amethyst, Ruffled, Millersburg 295.00
Carnival Glass, Bowl, Daisy & Plume, Amethyst, Footed, Marked N, 5 In.High 69.50
Carnival Glass, Bowl, Daisy Wreath, Peach, Low, 8 1/2 In. 37.50
Carnival Glass, Bowl, Diamond Ring, Smoky, 9 In. 40.00
Carnival Glass, Bowl, Diamond Rings, Smoky, Fluted 30.00
Carnival Glass, Bowl, Diving Dolphin, Marigold, Square 150.00
Carnival Glass, Bowl, Dogwood Sprays, Purple, Dome Foot, Fluted 30.00
Carnival Glass, Bowl, Double Stemmed Rose, Marigold, Footed, 9 In.Across 32.00
Carnival Glass, Bowl, Double Stemmed Rose, Purple, Pedestal 48.00
Carnival Glass, Bowl, Dragon & Lotus, Blue, 2 In.High, 8 In.Diameter 40.00
Carnival Glass, Bowl, Dragon & Lotus, Blue, 8 1/2 In. 35.00
Carnival Glass, Bowl, Dragon & Lotus, Cobalt, Ruffle, Collar Base, 9 In. 40.00
Carnival Glass, Bowl, Dragon & Lotus, Green, 8 In. 65.00
Carnival Glass, Bowl, Dragon & Lotus, Marigold, Footed, 7 In. 30.00
Carnival Glass, Bowl, Dragon & Lotus, Marigold, Turned In Top, 8 1/2 In. 27.00
Carnival Glass, Bowl, Dragon & Lotus, Marigold, 9 In.Diameter .... 30.00 To 65.00
Carnival Glass, Bowl, Dragon & Lotus, Purple, Ruffled Edge 45.00
Carnival Glass, Bowl, Dragon & Lotus, Red 295.00
Carnival Glass, Bowl, Dragon & Lotus, Violet, Orange Iridescence, Footed 35.00
Carnival Glass, Bowl, Dragon & Strawberry, Green 350.00
Carnival Glass, Bowl, Dragon & Strawberry, Marigold, Footed 325.00
Carnival Glass, Bowl, Dragon And Lotus, Green, 8 In. 65.00
Carnival Glass, Bowl, Dragon And Lotus, Red 295.00
Carnival Glass, Bowl, Dragon And Strawberry, Green 350.00
Carnival Glass, Bowl, Drapery Rose, Purple, N Mark 45.00
Carnival Glass, Bowl, Dutch Windmill, Green, 5 In. 22.50
Carnival Glass, Bowl, Elks, Green, Detroit 1910 .... 550.00
Carnival Glass, Bowl, Embossed Scroll, White, 7 1/4 In. 60.00
Carnival Glass, Bowl, Farm Yard, Amethyst 2250.00
Carnival Glass, Bowl, Feather Scroll, Marigold, Grape Arbor Inside, Footed 105.00
Carnival Glass, Bowl, Feathered Serpent, Green, 9 In. 45.00
Carnival Glass, Bowl, Fenton Lion, Marigold, 7 In.Diameter 95.00
Carnival Glass, Bowl, Fenton's Heavy Grape, Purple, Scalloped, 7 In. 38.00
Carnival Glass, Bowl, Field & Flowers, Marigold, 8 In. 25.00
Carnival Glass, Bowl, File, Marigold, 9 In.Diameter 25.00
Carnival Glass, Bowl, Fine Rib, Green, Flared, N Marked, 13 In. 47.50

Carnival Glass, Bowl, Fish, Green, Ruffled 185.00
Carnival Glass, Bowl, Fleur-De-Lis, Purple, Ribbon Edge, Millersburg 175.00
Carnival Glass, Bowl, Flowering Almond, Marigold, Ruffled, 7 1/2 In. 18.50
Carnival Glass, Bowl, Flutes, Smoky, 9 1/4 In. 27.50
Carnival Glass, Bowl, Four Flowers, Deep Purple, 9 1/2 In. 85.00
Carnival Glass, Bowl, Four Flowers, Purple, 9 In. 35.00
Carnival Glass, Bowl, Frosty Block, White, 8 In.Square 45.00
Carnival Glass, Bowl, Fruit, Octagon, Blue, 9 In. 42.50
Carnival Glass, Bowl, Fruit, Round-Up, White, 9 In. 65.00
Carnival Glass, Bowl, Garden Path, Marigold, 8 In.Diameter 42.50
Carnival Glass, Bowl, Goddess Of Harvest, Blue, Ribbon Edge 4250.00
Carnival Glass, Bowl, Good Luck, Amethyst, Marked N, 8 In.Across 105.00
Carnival Glass, Bowl, Good Luck, Ice Green, Opalescent 130.00
Carnival Glass, Bowl, Good Luck, Marigold ....40.00 To 105.00
Carnival Glass, Bowl, Good Luck, Marigold, Basket Weave Outside, Marked N 52.00
Carnival Glass, Bowl, Good Luck, Marigold, 8 3/4 In. 65.00
Carnival Glass, Bowl, Good Luck, Orange, 9 In. 47.00
Carnival Glass, Bowl, Good Luck, Purple 175.00
Carnival Glass, Bowl, Grape & Cable Out, Persian Medallion In, Marigold 65.00
Carnival Glass, Bowl, Grape & Cable, Amber, Hat Shape, N Mark 35.00
Carnival Glass, Bowl, Grape & Cable, Amethyst, Ruffled ....50.00 To 125.00
Carnival Glass, Bowl, Grape & Cable, Amethyst, 8 X 3 1/2 In. 32.50
Carnival Glass, Bowl, Grape & Cable, Blue, Footed, 7 1/2 In.Diameter 40.00
Carnival Glass, Bowl, Grape & Cable, Green, Collar Base, Fenton, 7 1/2 In. 65.00
Carnival Glass, Bowl, Grape & Cable, Green, Collar Base, 8 In. 45.00
Carnival Glass, Bowl, Grape & Cable, Green, Marked N, 7 In. 39.00
Carnival Glass, Bowl, Grape & Cable, Green, Marked N, 8 1/2 In. 95.00
Carnival Glass, Bowl, Grape & Cable, Green, 3 Footed, Fenton, 8 In. 75.00
Carnival Glass, Bowl, Grape & Cable, Ice Green, Ruffled, Footed, 8 1/2 In. 95.00
Carnival Glass, Bowl, Grape & Cable, Marigold, Footed, 8 In. .... 23.00 To 45.00
Carnival Glass, Bowl, Grape & Cable, Marigold, Ruffled Edge, Marked N 25.00
Carnival Glass, Bowl, Grape & Cable, Purple Blue, Footed 90.00
Carnival Glass, Bowl, Grape & Cable, Purple, Footed, 8 In. .... 55.00 To 95.00
Carnival Glass, Bowl, Grape & Cable, Purple, Marked N, 9 3/4 In. 75.00
Carnival Glass, Bowl, Grape & Cable, Purple, Shallow 135.00
Carnival Glass, Bowl, Grape & Cable, Red 195.00
Carnival Glass, Bowl, Grape & Fruit, Purple, Marked N 95.00
Carnival Glass, Bowl, Grape & Gothic Arches, Cobalt Blue, 6 In. 15.00
Carnival Glass, Bowl, Grape & Leaves, Amethyst, Marked N, 8 In.Across 69.50
Carnival Glass, Bowl, Grape & Lotus, Green, Footed, 6 In. 37.50
Carnival Glass, Bowl, Grape, Green, 8 In.Diameter 23.00
Carnival Glass, Bowl, Grape, Marigold, Three Splayed Feet, Northwood, 8 In. 35.00
Carnival Glass, Bowl, Grape, Marigold, 10 In. 28.00
Carnival Glass, Bowl, Greek Key, Sunflower, Footed, N Mark 25.00
Carnival Glass, Bowl, Hattie, Marigold, 8 In.Across, 4 In.Deep 28.00
Carnival Glass, Bowl, Heart & Vine, Amethyst 55.00
Carnival Glass, Bowl, Heart & Vine, Cobalt Blue, Ruffled, Green Highlights 45.00
Carnival Glass, Bowl, Heart & Vine, Green, 7 1/2 In.Diameter 35.00
Carnival Glass, Bowl, Hearts & Flowers, Ice Blue, 9 In. 85.00
Carnival Glass, Bowl, Hearts & Flowers, Ice Green, Low, 8 3/4 In. 95.00
Carnival Glass, Bowl, Heavy Grape, Amber, Fenton, 10 1/4 In. 75.00
Carnival Glass, Bowl, Hello, Grape Imperial, Green, 7 In. 25.00
Carnival Glass, Bowl, Hobstars & Arches, Marigold, Fluted 16.00
Carnival Glass, Bowl, Holly & Berry, Amethyst, 9 In. 38.00
Carnival Glass, Bowl, Holly & Berry, Red, 6 In.Diameter 95.00
Carnival Glass, Bowl, Holly & Berry, Red, 8 3/4 In.Diameter 195.00
Carnival Glass, Bowl, Holly Ribbon, Blue, 9 In. 45.00
Carnival Glass, Bowl, Holly Whirl, Millersburg, Green, 9 1/2 In. 47.50
Carnival Glass, Bowl, Holly Wreath, Marigold, 10 In. 35.00
Carnival Glass, Bowl, Holly, Blue 75.00
Carnival Glass, Bowl, Holly, Marigold, 9 In.Diameter 27.00
Carnival Glass, Bowl, Holly, White, Ruffled Edge, 9 1/2 In.Diameter 65.00
Carnival Glass, Bowl, Holly, White, 9 1/4 In.Diameter .... 43.00 To 95.00
Carnival Glass, Bowl, Horses' Heads Medallion, Amber, 7 1/2 In. 55.00
Carnival Glass, Bowl, Horses' Heads Medallion, Blue, Three Footed 135.00
Carnival Glass, Bowl, Horses' Heads Medallion, Green .... 85.00 To 115.00

Carnival Glass, Bowl, Horses' Heads Medallion, Marigold, Footed 95.00
Carnival Glass, Bowl, Horses' Heads, Red, Three Footed 475.00
Carnival Glass, Bowl, Ice Cream, Grape & Cable, Marigold, Stemmed, Marked N 25.00
Carnival Glass, Bowl, Ice Cream, Grape & Cable, Purple 225.00
Carnival Glass, Bowl, Ice Cream, Peacock At Fountain, Frosty White 195.00
Carnival Glass, Bowl, Ice Cream, Peacock At The Urn, White, Large, Signed N 195.00
Carnival Glass, Bowl, Ice Cream, Persian Garden, White 125.00
Carnival Glass, Bowl, Imperial Grape, Amber 27.50
Carnival Glass, Bowl, Imperial Grape, Purple, Large 85.00
Carnival Glass, Bowl, Imperial Jewels, Ice Green, Footed, 8 In. 28.00
Carnival Glass, Bowl, Imperial Jewels, Pink, Footed, 5 In.High 48.00
Carnival Glass, Bowl, Imperial Jewels, Smoky, 9 1/2 In. 35.00
Carnival Glass, Bowl, Imperial Jewels, White, Stemmed, 10 In. 75.00
Carnival Glass, Bowl, Inverted Strawberry, Green, Marked Near-Cut, Cambridge 35.00
Carnival Glass, Bowl, Kingfish, Marigold, 9 In. 85.00
Carnival Glass, Bowl, Kittens, Marigold 55.00
Carnival Glass, Bowl, Kittens, Marigold, Fluted 35.00
Carnival Glass, Bowl, Kittens, Marigold, Ruffled .... 50.00 To 90.00
Carnival Glass, Bowl, Kittens, Marigold, 4 3/8 In.Diameter 45.00
Carnival Glass, Bowl, La Bella Rose, Purple, 9 In. 45.00
Carnival Glass, Bowl, Large Roses, Marigold, Footed, 10 In.Diameter 65.00
Carnival Glass, Bowl, Leaf & Beads, Blue, Marked N, Footed 75.00
Carnival Glass, Bowl, Leaf Chain, Blue Amethyst, 7 In. 60.00
Carnival Glass, Bowl, Leaf Chain, Cobalt, 7 In. 25.00
Carnival Glass, Bowl, Leaf Chain, Red, 7 In.Diameter 145.00
Carnival Glass, Bowl, Leaf Chain, White, 8 1/2 In. 49.50
Carnival Glass, Bowl, Leaf Chain, White, 9 In. Flat 97.50
Carnival Glass, Bowl, Lion & Tulip, Marigold, Grapes Outside 50.00
Carnival Glass, Bowl, Lion, Marigold 95.00
Carnival Glass, Bowl, Little Fishes, Blue, 10 In.Diameter 165.00
Carnival Glass, Bowl, Little Flowers, Amethyst, Millersburg 125.00
Carnival Glass, Bowl, Little Flowers, Amethyst, 5 In.Diameter 25.00
Carnival Glass, Bowl, Little Flowers, Green 35.00
Carnival Glass, Bowl, Little Flowers, Marigold, 10 X 2 In. 30.00
Carnival Glass, Bowl, Low, Ruffled Rib, Green, 9 1/2 In. 35.00
Carnival Glass, Bowl, Luster Rose, White, 3 Footed, 11 In. 50.00
Carnival Glass, Bowl, Magpie, Marigold, Australian 85.00
Carnival Glass, Bowl, Magpie, Purple, Australian 110.00
Carnival Glass, Bowl, Many Stars, Blue 125.00
Carnival Glass, Bowl, Many Stars, Green, Ruffled 125.00
Carnival Glass, Bowl, Many Stars, Marigold, Millersburg 165.00
Carnival Glass, Bowl, Many Stars, Marigold, 9 1/2 In.Diameter 60.00
Carnival Glass, Bowl, Many Stars, Purple, 10 In.Diameter 85.00
Carnival Glass, Bowl, Millersburg Holly Whirl, Amethyst, 10 In. 105.00
Carnival Glass, Bowl, Millersburg Holly, Purple, Nearcut On Back, 9 In. 45.00
Carnival Glass, Bowl, Millersburg Mayan, Green, 8 In. 25.00
Carnival Glass, Bowl, Nesting Swan, Amethyst, Millersburg 225.00
Carnival Glass, Bowl, Nesting Swan, Emerald, Millersburg, Piecrust Edge 295.00
Carnival Glass, Bowl, Nesting Swan, Green 120.00
Carnival Glass, Bowl, Nesting Swan, Marigold, Millersburg .... 100.00 To 175.00
Carnival Glass, Bowl, Nesting Swan, Pastel Marigold, 9 1/2 In. 175.00
Carnival Glass, Bowl, Northwood Beads, Green 27.50
Carnival Glass, Bowl, Northwood's Poppy, Marigold, Marked N 9.00
Carnival Glass, Bowl, Nut, Grape, Red, Footed 85.00
Carnival Glass, Bowl, Nut, Heavy Grape, Marigold, Fenton 9.50
Carnival Glass, Bowl, Nut, Imperial Grape, Cobalt Blue, 3 Legged 75.00
Carnival Glass, Bowl, Nut, Vintage, Blue, Footed, Fenton 57.50
Carnival Glass, Bowl, Nut, Vintage, Purple, Footed .... 45.00 To 75.00
Carnival Glass, Bowl, Oak Leaves, Marigold, Ruffled 37.50
Carnival Glass, Bowl, Octagon, Clear, Rainbow Highlights, Near Cut 16.00
Carnival Glass, Bowl, Open Rose Pedestal, Purple 48.00
Carnival Glass, Bowl, Open Rose, Smoky, 11 In. 75.00
Carnival Glass, Bowl, Orange Tree, Marigold, Bearded Berry Out, 8 1/2 In 28.00
Carnival Glass, Bowl, Orange Tree, Marigold, Footed 65.00
Carnival Glass, Bowl, Orange Tree, White, Ruffled, 8 1/2 In. 62.50
Carnival Glass, Bowl, Orange Tree, White, 8 3/4 In.Diameter 32.00

Carnival Glass, Bowl, Orange, Grape & Cable, Blue, Footed 175.00
Carnival Glass, Bowl, Orange, Grape & Cable, Purple, Marked N 110.00
Carnival Glass, Bowl, Orange, Luster Rose, Marigold, Footed 19.50
Carnival Glass, Bowl, Orange, Luster Rose, Red 650.00
Carnival Glass, Bowl, Orange, Stag & Holly, Marigold, 9 In.Diameter 70.00
Carnival Glass, Bowl, Pansy Spray, Green, 8 1/2 In.Diameter 25.00
Carnival Glass, Bowl, Panther & Grape, Marigold, Ruffled 35.00
Carnival Glass, Bowl, Panther, Marigold, Footed 115.00
Carnival Glass, Bowl, Panther, Marigold, Violet Iridescence, 3 Ball Feet 75.00
Carnival Glass, Bowl, Peacock & Grape, Amethyst & Purple, 9 In. 65.00
Carnival Glass, Bowl, Peacock & Grape, Amethyst, 9 In. 75.00
Carnival Glass, Bowl, Peacock & Grape, Blue, 9 In. 65.00
Carnival Glass, Bowl, Peacock & Grape, Green, Collar Base, 9 In. 60.00
Carnival Glass, Bowl, Peacock & Grape, Green, 3 Footed, 8 In. 59.00
Carnival Glass, Bowl, Peacock & Grape, Purple, Footed 38.00
Carnival Glass, Bowl, Peacock & Urn, Blue 65.00
Carnival Glass, Bowl, Peacock & Urn, Blue, With Bee 82.00
Carnival Glass, Bowl, Peacock & Urn, Cobalt, 9 In.Diameter 48.00
Carnival Glass, Bowl, Peacock At Fountain, Cobalt Blue, N Mark 20.00
Carnival Glass, Bowl, Peacock At Fountain, Marigold, 8 1/2 In. 65.00
Carnival Glass, Bowl, Peacock At Fountain, Purple, Marked N, Footed 250.00
Carnival Glass, Bowl, Peacock At Fountain, Purple, 9 X 4 In. 175.00
Carnival Glass, Bowl, Peacock At Urn, Amethyst, Ruffled 135.00
Carnival Glass, Bowl, Peacock At Urn, Blue, Bearded Berry Out, Fenton 75.00
Carnival Glass, Bowl, Peacock At Urn, Blue, Fenton, Ruffled, 9 In. 125.00
Carnival Glass, Bowl, Peacock At Urn, Marigold, Blackberry Out 45.00
Carnival Glass, Bowl, Peacock At Urn, Marigold, Fenton, Ruffled, 9 In. 65.00
Carnival Glass, Bowl, Peacock At Urn, Marigold, 9 In.Diameter .... 30.00 To 40.00
Carnival Glass, Bowl, Peacock At Urn, Purple 85.00
Carnival Glass, Bowl, Peacock At Urn, White, Fenton 95.00
Carnival Glass, Bowl, Peacock On Fence, Aqua 125.00
Carnival Glass, Bowl, Peacock On Fence, Green Opal 235.00
Carnival Glass, Bowl, Peacock On Fence, Marigold, 9 In.Diameter 45.00
Carnival Glass, Bowl, Peacock On Fence, Purple 85.00
Carnival Glass, Bowl, Peacock Tail, Green, Flared, 6 In. .... 25.00 To 45.00
Carnival Glass, Bowl, Peacock Tail, Purple, Basket Weave Out 35.00
Carnival Glass, Bowl, Persian Garden, Marigold, 10 1/4 X 4 In. 75.00
Carnival Glass, Bowl, Persian Medallion, Green, Ribbon Edge, 9 In. 65.00
Carnival Glass, Bowl, Petal And Fan, Peach 55.00
Carnival Glass, Bowl, Peter Rabbit, Blue 1050.00
Carnival Glass, Bowl, Pine Cones, Amethyst, 7 In.Diameter 38.00
Carnival Glass, Bowl, Pineapple, Marigold, Millersburg 27.50
Carnival Glass, Bowl, Pony Head, Amethyst 150.00
Carnival Glass, Bowl, Pony Head, Gold Horse Head, Amethyst 175.00
Carnival Glass, Bowl, Pony Head, Marigold .... 55.00 To 95.00
Carnival Glass, Bowl, Poppy Show, Green, Ruffled 260.00
Carnival Glass, Bowl, Poppy Show, Ice Blue 260.00
Carnival Glass, Bowl, Poppy, Purple, Northwood 27.50
Carnival Glass, Bowl, Primrose, Amethyst, 10 In. 45.00
Carnival Glass, Bowl, Primrose, Purple, Millersburg, 10 In. 85.00
Carnival Glass, Bowl, Punch, Fashion, Marigold, Base 95.00
Carnival Glass, Bowl, Punch, Grape & Cable, Marigold, Medium Size 395.00
Carnival Glass, Bowl, Punch, Grape & Cable, Marigold, On Base 900.00
Carnival Glass, Bowl, Punch, Grape & Cable, Purple, Banquet 1150.00
Carnival Glass, Bowl, Punch, Grape & Cable, Purple, Base, Nine Cups, Hangers 875.00
Carnival Glass, Bowl, Punch, Grape & Cable, Purple, Base, 11 1/2 In. 425.00
Carnival Glass, Bowl, Punch, Imperial Grape, Green 125.00
Carnival Glass, Bowl, Punch, Many Fruits, White, On Base 850.00
Carnival Glass, Bowl, Punch, Orange Tree, Blue, Base 170.00
Carnival Glass, Bowl, Punch, Orange Tree, Purple, Six Cups 275.00
Carnival Glass, Bowl, Punch, Peacock At Fountain, Marigold, Stand, Mark N 125.00
Carnival Glass, Bowl, Rainbow Luster, Purple, Mark N 35.00
Carnival Glass, Bowl, Rays, Purple, Ruffled, 7 In. 11.00
Carnival Glass, Bowl, Roses, Marigold, Footed, 10 In.Diameter 35.00
Carnival Glass, Bowl, Roundup, Blue Amethyst 60.00
Carnival Glass, Bowl, Rose Show, Green Opal, Ruffled 260.00

Carnival Glass, Bowl, Rose Show, Ice Blue 260.00
Carnival Glass, Bowl, Rose Show, Orange, Iridescent 98.00
Carnival Glass, Bowl, Roundup, Peach, 8 1/2 In. 45.00
Carnival Glass, Bowl, Ruffled Rib, Amethyst, 9 In.Diameter 17.50
Carnival Glass, Bowl, Sailboat, Marigold, Ruffled 22.50
Carnival Glass, Bowl, Sailboat, Red 225.00
Carnival Glass, Bowl, Salad, Bouquet & Lattice, Marigold 1.95
Carnival Glass, Bowl, Scales, Amethyst, Saucer 45.00
Carnival Glass, Bowl, Scalloped, White 65.00
Carnival Glass, Bowl, Scroll Embossed, Amethyst 52.50
Carnival Glass, Bowl, Scroll Embossed, Green, 7 In. 40.00
Carnival Glass, Bowl, Scroll Embossed, Green, 8 1/2 In.Diameter 20.00
Carnival Glass, Bowl, Sea Gull, Amethyst 75.00
Carnival Glass, Bowl, Shallow, Grape And Cable, Red, 9 In. 195.00
Carnival Glass, Bowl, Shell & Sand, Marigold, Dark, 7 In. 15.00
Carnival Glass, Bowl, Ski Star, Peach Opalescent, Dome Foot, 8 3/4 In. 40.00
Carnival Glass, Bowl, Ski Star, Peach, Rolled Edge 32.00
Carnival Glass, Bowl, Ski Star, Purple, Gold, Green, Pink Iridescent, Fluted 85.00
Carnival Glass, Bowl, Ski Star, Purple, Large Size 115.00
Carnival Glass, Bowl, Square, Star And File, White, 6 In. 30.00
Carnival Glass, Bowl, Stag & Holly, Amethyst, Footed, 8 In. 85.00
Carnival Glass, Bowl, Stag & Holly, Blue, Spatula Footed, 8 In. 70.00
Carnival Glass, Bowl, Stag & Holly, Blue, 8 In. 100.00
Carnival Glass, Bowl, Stag & Holly, Marigold, Footed, Deep, Large Size 85.00
Carnival Glass, Bowl, Stag & Holly, Marigold, Footed, 7 1/4 In. 49.50
Carnival Glass, Bowl, Stag & Holly, Marigold, Footed, 7 1/2 In. 55.00
Carnival Glass, Bowl, Stag & Holly, Marigold, Footed, 8 In.Diameter 45.00
Carnival Glass, Bowl, Stag & Holly, Marigold, Scalloped, Spatula Footed 45.00
Carnival Glass, Bowl, Stag & Holly, Marigold, 10 In. .... 80.00 To 85.00
Carnival Glass, Bowl, Stag & Holly, Purple, Three Footed, Large Size 145.00
Carnival Glass, Bowl, Stag & Holly, Purple, 8 In. 58.00
Carnival Glass, Bowl, Star & File, White, 6 In.Square 30.00
Carnival Glass, Bowl, Star Medallion, White, 7 1/2 In. 30.00
Carnival Glass, Bowl, Star Of David And Bows, Green, 8 In. 50.00
Carnival Glass, Bowl, Star Of David, Purple, N Mark, 7 1/2 In. 60.00
Carnival Glass, Bowl, Star Of David, Purple, Ruffled 85.00
Carnival Glass, Bowl, Star Of David, Purple, 9 In.Diameter 55.00
Carnival Glass, Bowl, Stippled Grape & Cable, Ice Blue, N Mark 75.00
Carnival Glass, Bowl, Stippled Rays, Amethyst & Purple, Marked N 65.00
Carnival Glass, Bowl, Stippled Rays, Amethyst, Fluted, N Mark 22.00
Carnival Glass, Bowl, Stippled Rays, Amethyst, Straw & N Mark, 9 In.Diameter 35.00
Carnival Glass, Bowl, Stippled Rays, Purple, Fluted, N Mark, 8 1/2 In. 22.00
Carnival Glass, Bowl, Stippled Rays, Purple, N Mark 35.00
Carnival Glass, Bowl, Stippled Strawberry, Green Pastel, Basket Weave Back 75.00
Carnival Glass, Bowl, Stippled Strawberry, Green, N Mark, Flat 65.00
Carnival Glass, Bowl, Strawberry, Amethyst, Piecrust Edge 95.00
Carnival Glass, Bowl, Strawberry, Amethyst, Stippled Ground, Piecrust Edge 95.00
Carnival Glass, Bowl, Strawberry, Amethyst, 8 In., Marked N 65.00
Carnival Glass, Bowl, Strawberry, Green, N Mark, 8 1/2 In. 49.00
Carnival Glass, Bowl, Strawberry, Green, 8 1/2 In.Diameter 32.00
Carnival Glass, Bowl, Strawberry, Purple, N Mark, 9 In.Diameter 45.00
Carnival Glass, Bowl, Strawberry, Purple, N Mark, 10 In. 59.00
Carnival Glass, Bowl, Stretch Type, Blue, 2 1/4 In.High 8.00
Carnival Glass, Bowl, Sunflower, Amethyst, Ruffled Top, Footed, 8 In. 42.50
Carnival Glass, Bowl, Sunflower, Green, 7 3/4 In. 25.00
Carnival Glass, Bowl, Sunflower, Marigold, 7 3/4 In. 24.00
Carnival Glass, Bowl, Swan, Purple, Australian .... 110.00 To 195.00
Carnival Glass, Bowl, Ten Mums, Amethyst, Candy Ribbon Edge 175.00
Carnival Glass, Bowl, Ten Mums, Amethyst, 9 In. 85.00
Carnival Glass, Bowl, Thistle, Green, 8 In. 39.00
Carnival Glass, Bowl, Thistle, Marigold 95.00
Carnival Glass, Bowl, Three Fruits, Amethyst, Marked N, 7 In.Across 69.50
Carnival Glass, Bowl, Three Fruits, Aqua, Opalescent 90.00
Carnival Glass, Bowl, Three Fruits, Marigold, , 9 In. 28.00
Carnival Glass, Bowl, Three Fruits, Marigold, 9 In. 28.00
Carnival Glass, Bowl, Three Fruits, Purple, Footed 95.00

Carnival Glass, Bowl, Three Fruits, Purple, Green Base, Marked N 40.00
Carnival Glass, Bowl, Three Fruits, Purple, 9 In.Diameter 60.00
Carnival Glass, Bowl, Twin Fruit, Marigold, On Stand 55.00
Carnival Glass, Bowl, Twins, Smoky, Fluted, 6 In. 25.00
Carnival Glass, Bowl, Two Flowers, Blue, Footed, 7 1/2 In. 55.00
Carnival Glass, Bowl, Vintage, Amethyst, 6 1/2 In.Diameter, 2 In.High 25.00
Carnival Glass, Bowl, Vintage, Blue, Footed, 5 1/2 In. 35.00
Carnival Glass, Bowl, Vintage, Blue, 9 3/4 X 2 1/2 In. 55.00
Carnival Glass, Bowl, Vintage, Green, 7 In. 37.00
Carnival Glass, Bowl, Vintage, Green, 8 1/2 In. 45.00
Carnival Glass, Bowl, Vintage, Green, 8 1/2 X 3 In. 38.50
Carnival Glass, Bowl, Vintage, Marigold, 7 1/2 In.Diameter 14.50
Carnival Glass, Bowl, Vintage, Purple, 6 In.Diameter 16.00
Carnival Glass, Bowl, Water Lily, Red, Footed, 6 In. 100.00
Carnival Glass, Bowl, Wild Rose, Amethyst, Footed, Marked N, 3 1/2 In.High 82.50
Carnival Glass, Bowl, Wild Rose, Green, Footed, Signed N 50.00
Carnival Glass, Bowl, Windflower, Purple, Ruffled, 8 3/4 In. 30.00
Carnival Glass, Bowl, Windmill And Chrysanthemum, Marigold, 3 Feet 40.00
Carnival Glass, Bowl, Windmill, Marigold, Footed 36.00
Carnival Glass, Bowl, Windmill, Purple, Footed 65.00
Carnival Glass, Bowl, Windmill, White, 8 In. 50.00
Carnival Glass, Bowl, Wishbone Variant, Dark Blue, Marked N, 9 In.Across 69.50
Carnival Glass, Bowl, Wishbone, Amethyst, Footed 95.00
Carnival Glass, Bowl, Wishbone, Amethyst, Footed, 8 In. 95.00
Carnival Glass, Bowl, Wreathed Cherry, Amethyst, Oval 20.00
Carnival Glass, Bowl, Wreathed Cherry, Purple, Oval, Large Size 140.00
Carnival Glass, Bowl, Wreathed Cherry, Purple, Oval, Small Size 32.50
Carnival Glass, Box, Powder, Orange Tree, Marigold, Covered 32.50
Carnival Glass, Bushel Basket, Amethyst 100.00
Carnival Glass, Bushel Basket, Ice Green 100.00
Carnival Glass, Bushel Basket, Marigold 45.00
Carnival Glass, Bushel Basket, Purple 100.00
Carnival Glass, Bushel Basket, White 100.00
Carnival Glass, Butter, Butterfly & Berry, Cobalt 135.00
Carnival Glass, Butter, Cherry, Marigold, Cover, Millersburg 65.00
Carnival Glass, Butter, Grape & Cable, Purple, Marked N .... 145.00 To 150.00
Carnival Glass, Butter, Grape & Thumbprint, Green, N Mark, Cover 125.00
Carnival Glass, Butter, Inverted Strawberry, Amethyst 175.00
Carnival Glass, Button, Owl, Ice Blue, Large 150.00
Carnival Glass, Candle Lamps, Grape And Cable, Green, Complete 775.00
Carnival Glass, Candleholder, Marigold, Pair 35.00
Carnival Glass, Candlestick, Cornucopia, White, Pair 135.00
Carnival Glass, Candlestick, Grape & Cable, Marigold 125.00
Carnival Glass, Celery, Cathedral, Marigold, 6 1/2 In. 30.00
Carnival Glass, Chalice, Colonial N, Green 115.00
Carnival Glass, Cologne, Grape & Cable, Marigold 120.00
Carnival Glass, Cologne, Grape & Cable, Purple 165.00
Carnival Glass, Compote, Blackberry Bramble, Amethyst 25.00
Carnival Glass, Compote, Blackberry Wreath, Marigold, Millersburg 40.00
Carnival Glass, Compote, Blackberry, Blue, Miniature 75.00
Carnival Glass, Compote, Boutonniere, Marigold, Millersburg 25.00
Carnival Glass, Compote, Cherry, Marigold 48.00
Carnival Glass, Compote, Christmas, Purple 3000.00
Carnival Glass, Compote, Curved Star, Blue, 5 3/4 X 4 3/4 In. 35.00
Carnival Glass, Compote, Diving Dolphins, Green 425.00
Carnival Glass, Compote, Dolphin, Amethyst 450.00
Carnival Glass, Compote, Double Dolphin, Amber 47.50
Carnival Glass, Compote, Five Hearts, Marigold 75.00
Carnival Glass, Compote, Floral & Wheat, Purple 65.00
Carnival Glass, Compote, Floral & Wheat, White, 2 Handles 72.50
Carnival Glass, Compote, Frosty Block, White, 5 X 4 3/4 In. 37.50
Carnival Glass, Compote, Fruit & Flower, Basket Weave, Blue 30.00
Carnival Glass, Compote, Fruits & Flowers, Basket Weave, Green, Handles 30.00
Carnival Glass, Compote, Grape & Cable, Green, Open 450.00
Carnival Glass, Compote, Grape & Cable, Purple, Cover 475.00
Carnival Glass, Compote, Grape And Cable, Purple 275.00

Carnival Glass, Compote, Headdress, Ruffled Top 21.00
Carnival Glass, Compote, Hearts And Flowers, White 85.00
Carnival Glass, Compote, Holly, Marigold, Footed 16.50
Carnival Glass, Compote, Jelly, Blossom Time, Green, 5 1/4 In.Tall 25.50
Carnival Glass, Compote, Jelly, Grape, Blue, 6 In.Tall 22.50
Carnival Glass, Compote, Little Beads, Peach 12.00
Carnival Glass, Compote, Maple Leaf, Purple, Large 150.00
Carnival Glass, Compote, Mikado, Marigold, Footed 105.00
Carnival Glass, Compote, Orange Tree, Blue 35.00
Carnival Glass, Compote, Peacock & Urn, Blue, Footed 32.50
Carnival Glass, Compote, Peacock & Urn, Blue, 5 In. 25.00
Carnival Glass, Compote, Peacock & Urn, Marigold, 6 In. 40.00
Carnival Glass, Compote, Peacock At Fountain, Purple, Open 265.00
Carnival Glass, Compote, Peacock At Urn, Green 45.00
Carnival Glass, Compote, Peacock At Urn, Marigold 35.00
Carnival Glass, Compote, Peacock At Urn, Marigold & Green 45.00
Carnival Glass, Compote, Peacock At Urn, Purple 27.50
Carnival Glass, Compote, Peacock Tail, Amethyst 55.00
Carnival Glass, Compote, Primrose, Marigold, N Mark 25.00
Carnival Glass, Compote, Rayed, Green 32.50
Carnival Glass, Compote, Rose Panel, Marigold, Large 60.00
Carnival Glass, Compote, Rose Spray Whimsy, White, Stemmed 45.00
Carnival Glass, Compote, Rose Wreaths, Green, Fluted, Two Handles 30.00
Carnival Glass, Compote, Star Of David & Bows, Amethyst, 8 1/4 In. 85.00
Carnival Glass, Compote, Stippled Rays, Marigold, 6 In.High 9.50
Carnival Glass, Compote, Sweetmeat, Grape & Cable, Purple 155.00
Carnival Glass, Compote, Sweetmeat, Grape & Cable, Purple, Marked N 175.00
Carnival Glass, Compote, Thin Rib, Marigold, N Mark, 5 3/4 In.High 7.50
Carnival Glass, Compote, Three Fruit, Purple, Basket Weave Out, 2 Handles, N 75.00
Carnival Glass, Compote, Three Fruit, Purple, 4 In.Tall 45.00
Carnival Glass, Creamer, Acorn Burr, Green 75.00
Carnival Glass, Creamer, Acorn Burr, Purple .... 75.00 To 89.00
Carnival Glass, Creamer, Dahlia, White 85.00
Carnival Glass, Creamer, Dahlia, White, Footed 48.00
Carnival Glass, Creamer, Drapery, Blue, Opalescent, Mark N 35.00
Carnival Glass, Creamer, Grape & Cable, Purple, Marked N 50.00
Carnival Glass, Creamer, Inverted Strawberry, Marigold, Marked Near-Cut 110.00
Carnival Glass, Creamer, Maple Leaf, Purple .... 49.00 To 85.00
Carnival Glass, Creamer, Singing Birds, Marigold, N Mark 39.00
Carnival Glass, Creamer, Strutting Peacock, Purple 45.00
Carnival Glass, Creamer, Thistle And Thorn, Marigold 31.00
Carnival Glass, Creamer, Thumbprint & Spear, Marigold 9.00
Carnival Glass, Cruet, Buzz Saw, Green 375.00
Carnival Glass, Cup & Saucer, Imperial Grape, Green 85.00
Carnival Glass, Cup, Kittens, Marigold .... 50.00 To 95.00
Carnival Glass, Cup, Loving, Orange Tree, Blue 110.00
Carnival Glass, Cup, Loving, Orange Tree, Purple 145.00
Carnival Glass, Cup, Loving, Orange Tree, Purple, Fenton, 2 Handles 145.00
Carnival Glass, Cup, Punch, Acorn & Burr, Cobalt, N Mark 25.00
Carnival Glass, Cup, Punch, Fashion, Marigold 11.00
Carnival Glass, Cup, Punch, Grape & Cable, Green, Marked N 15.00
Carnival Glass, Cup, Punch, Grape & Cable, Purple 35.00
Carnival Glass, Cup, Punch, Many Fruits, Purple 9.00
Carnival Glass, Cup, Punch, Orange Tree, Blue .... 12.50 To 35.00
Carnival Glass, Cup, Punch, Orange Tree, Marigold 12.00
Carnival Glass, Cup, Punch, S-Repeat, Purple .... 25.00 To 27.50
Carnival Glass, Cup, Punch, Stork & Rushes, Amethyst 12.00
Carnival Glass, Cup, Punch, Stork & Rushes, Marigold 9.00
Carnival Glass, Cup, Punch, Vintage, Marigold 8.50
Carnival Glass, Cuspidor, Lady's, Hobnail, Amethyst 350.00
Carnival Glass, Cuspidor, Lady's, Hobnail, Marigold 175.00
Carnival Glass, Decanter, Grape And Cable, Purple 750.00
Carnival Glass, Decanter, Grape, Marigold, Matching Round Stopper 60.00
Carnival Glass, Decanter, Imperial Grape, Green, Lid 90.00
Carnival Glass, Decanter, Imperial Grape, Purple, No Stopper 75.00
Carnival Glass, Decanter, Vintage, Marigold, Stopper, 6 Wines 275.00

Carnival Glass, Decanter, Whiskey, Grape & Cable, Purple 550.00
Carnival Glass, Decanter, Wine, Grape, Purple, Mushroom Stop 250.00
Carnival Glass, Dish, Candy, Arcs, Circles, Zipper, Purple, Ruffled 28.00
Carnival Glass, Dish, Candy, Beaded Panel, Marigold, Cover 25.00
Carnival Glass, Dish, Candy, Captive Rose, Purple 50.00
Carnival Glass, Dish, Candy, Dill Hat Shape, Marigold, Ribbon Edge 18.00
Carnival Glass, Dish, Candy, Drapery, Ice Blue, Tricornered 45.00
Carnival Glass, Dish, Candy, Drapery, White, Tricornered 75.00
Carnival Glass, Dish, Candy, Fine Cut & Roses, Purple, Footed, Marked N 48.00
Carnival Glass, Dish, Candy, Leaf & Bead, Green, N Mark 30.00
Carnival Glass, Dish, Candy, Persian Medallion, Purple, 2 Handle 35.00
Carnival Glass, Dish, Candy, Stippled Rays, Amethyst, Two Handles 25.00
Carnival Glass, Dish, Candy, Stippled Rays, Green, Two Handles 20.00
Carnival Glass, Dish, Candy, Stippled Rays, Marigold 15.00
Carnival Glass, Dish, Duck Cover, Marigold 25.00
Carnival Glass, Dish, Pickle, Melon Rib, Smoky, 6 1/2 In. 25.00
Carnival Glass, Dish, Powder, Bambi, Marigold 10.00
Carnival Glass, Dish, Powder, Swan On Cover, Marigold, 4 1/2 In. 6.00
Carnival Glass, Dresser Set, Grape & Cable, 7 Piece 795.00
Carnival Glass, Epergne, Fishnet, Peach 165.00
Carnival Glass, Epergne, Single Lily, Peach, Ribbon Candy Edge Bowl 250.00
Carnival Glass, Epergne, Vintage, Blue 85.00
Carnival Glass, Epergne, Vintage, Blue, Small Single Lily 195.00
Carnival Glass, Fernery, Vintage, Blue 70.00
Carnival Glass, Fernery, Vintage, Purple, Footed 38.00
Carnival Glass, Fish Bowl, Amethyst 185.00
Carnival Glass, Goblet, Apple Tree, Marigold 15.00
Carnival Glass, Goblet, Imperial Grape, Marigold .... 27.50 To 35.00
Carnival Glass, Goblet, Imperial Grape, Purple .... 60.00 To 95.00
Carnival Glass, Goblet, Octagon, Marigold 32.50
Carnival Glass, Hair Receiver, Persian Medallion, Marigold, Square Opening 47.50
Carnival Glass, Hat, Blackberry Spray, Blue 37.50
Carnival Glass, Hat, Blackberry, Marigold, Flared 16.50
Carnival Glass, Hat, Blue To Pink 18.00
Carnival Glass, Hat, Fern Panel, Red, 6 In.Wide, 4 In.High 110.00
Carnival Glass, Hat, Grape & Cable, Marigold, Ruffled, Marked N 39.50
Carnival Glass, Hat, Holly, Green 27.50
Carnival Glass, Hat, Jeweled, Pink And Blue Pastel 28.00
Carnival Glass, Hat, Rainbow Luster, Green, Pink, 7 In.High, 5 In.Across 65.00
Carnival Glass, Hat, Waffle & Band, Marigold, N Mark 35.00
Carnival Glass, Hatpin Holder, Grape And Cable, Green 195.00
Carnival Glass, Hatpin Holder, Grape And Cable, Marigold 140.00
Carnival Glass, Hatpin Holder, Grape And Cable, Purple .... 75.00 To 185.00
Carnival Glass, Hatpin Holder, Grape And Cable, White And Yellow 375.00
Carnival Glass, Hatpin Holder, Orange Tree, Blue 150.00
Carnival Glass, Hatpin Holder, Orange Tree, Marigold .... 59.00 To 125.00
Carnival Glass, Hatpin Holder, Orange Tree, Red 95.00
Carnival Glass, Hatpin, Bat And Stars, Purple 125.00
Carnival Glass, Hatpin, Belle, Purple 19.00
Carnival Glass, Hatpin, Bumblebees, Purple 13.00
Carnival Glass, Hatpin, Butterfly, Purple 60.00
Carnival Glass, Hatpin, Cattails, Purple 60.00
Carnival Glass, Hatpin, Dragonfly, Purple 60.00
Carnival Glass, Hatpin, Owl, Purple 450.00
Carnival Glass, Hatpin, Prism, Purple 60.00
Carnival Glass, Hatpin, Rooster, Amethyst 40.00
Carnival Glass, Hatpin, Top Of Morning, Purple 21.00
Carnival Glass, Hatpin, Triad, Purple 40.00
Carnival Glass, Humidor, Grape & Cable, Marigold, Marked N 295.00
Carnival Glass, Inkwell, Purple 150.00
Carnival Glass, Jar, Cookie, Grape & Cable, Purple, Covered 350.00
Carnival Glass, Jar, Covered, Daisy, Marigold, Illinois 50.00
Carnival Glass, Jar, Cracker, Grape & Cable, Purple, Cover 495.00
Carnival Glass, Jar, Cracker, Grape & Cable, Purple, Marked N 300.00
Carnival Glass, Jar, Cracker, Hobstar, Marigold, Top 27.00
Carnival Glass, Jar, Dresser, Orange Tree, Cobalt 10.00

Carnival Glass, Jar, Pickle, Golden Flowers, Marigold 35.00
Carnival Glass, Jar, Powder, Bambi, Marigold 12.50
Carnival Glass, Jar, Powder, French Poodle, Orange, Lid 7.50
Carnival Glass, Jar, Powder, Grape & Cable, Purple, Marked N 75.00
Carnival Glass, Jar, Powder, Poodle, Marigold 12.50
Carnival Glass, Jar, Powder, Scottie, Marigold 12.50
Carnival Glass, Jar, Swirl, Smoky, 7 1/4 In. High 36.00
Carnival Glass, Ladies Cuspidor, Inverted Strawberry, Green 750.00
Carnival Glass, Ladies Cuspidor, Inverted Strawberry, Marigold 550.00
Carnival Glass, Lamp Shade, Floral Border, Marigold, Pair 12.00
Carnival Glass, Lamp, Gone With The Wind, Hollyhock, Clambroth 3200.00
Carnival Glass, Lamp, Zippered Loop, Marigold .... 135.00 To 195.00
Carnival Glass, Lamp, Zippered Loop, Marigold, 11 1/4 In.High 108.00
Carnival Glass, Lamp, Zippered Loop, Smoky 295.00
Carnival Glass, Large Bowl, Millersburg And Hobnail, Marigold 135.00
Carnival Glass, Light Fixture, Star, Marigold, 4 In.Diameter, Pair 47.50
Carnival Glass, Loving Cup, Orange Tree, Marigold 125.00
Carnival Glass, Loving Cup, Orange Tree, White 185.00
Carnival Glass, Mug, Beaded Shell, Purple 45.00
Carnival Glass, Mug, Bopeep, Marigold 32.00
Carnival Glass, Mug, Cincinnati, Amber, 1971 .... 14.00
Carnival Glass, Mug, Dayton, Green, 1968 .... 14.00
Carnival Glass, Mug, Fisherman, Marigold, With Red Fish 125.00
Carnival Glass, Mug, Fisherman, Purple .... 42.00 To 75.00
Carnival Glass, Mug, Fisherman, Purple, Silver Iridescence 58.00
Carnival Glass, Mug, Los Angeles, Blue, 1969 .... 14.00
Carnival Glass, Mug, Orange Tree, Blue 25.00
Carnival Glass, Mug, Orange Tree, Cobalt Blue 23.00
Carnival Glass, Mug, Orange Tree, Cobalt, Silver Iridescent Outside 50.00
Carnival Glass, Mug, Orange Tree, Marigold 12.50
Carnival Glass, Mug, Orange Tree, Purple 45.00
Carnival Glass, Mug, Orange Tree, Red .... 85.00 To 225.00
Carnival Glass, Mug, Robin, Marigold .... 30.00 To 75.00
Carnival Glass, Mug, Singing Bird, Blue, N Mark 49.00
Carnival Glass, Mug, Singing Bird, Marigold 35.00
Carnival Glass, Mug, Singing Bird, Purple 45.00
Carnival Glass, Mug, Stork In Rushes, Orange 16.00
Carnival Glass, Mug, Washington, Red, 1967, Souvenir 50.00
Carnival Glass, Mustard Barrel, Green 50.00
Carnival Glass, Nappy, Butterfly, Amethyst, 2 Handles 30.00
Carnival Glass, Nappy, Heavy Grape, Marigold, Fenton, 1 Handle 18.00
Carnival Glass, Nappy, Heavy Grape, Purple, Fenton 27.50
Carnival Glass, Nappy, Leaf Rays, Amethyst 20.00
Carnival Glass, Nappy, Leaf Rays, Amethyst, Handle 30.00
Carnival Glass, Nappy, Leaf Rays, Peach And Opalescent 23.00
Carnival Glass, Nappy, Leaf Rays, White, Handle 40.00
Carnival Glass, Nappy, Leaf Rays, White, 7 In. 55.00
Carnival Glass, Nappy, Pansy Spray, Marigold 16.50
Carnival Glass, Nappy, Rays, Purple, 2 Handles, Marked N 28.00
Carnival Glass, Nappy, Stippled Holly & Berry, Peach 35.00
Carnival Glass, Nappy, Strawberry Spray, Marigold, Two Handles 14.00
Carnival Glass, Nappy, Three Fruit, Blue 85.00
Carnival Glass, Nappy, Three Fruits, Amethyst 57.50
Carnival Glass, Perfume, Grape & Cable, Marigold 475.00
Carnival Glass, Pickle Jar, Golden Flowers, Marigold 35.00
Carnival Glass, Pin Tray, Seacoast, Amethyst 375.00
Carnival Glass, Pin Tray, Seacoast, Green 250.00
Carnival Glass, Pin Tray, Seacoast, Marigold 575.00
Carnival Glass, Pin Tray, Sunflower, Green 375.00
Carnival Glass, Pitcher, Apple Tree, Marigold 45.00
Carnival Glass, Pitcher, Cherubs, Parian 75.00
Carnival Glass, Pitcher, Dandelion, Purple, Northwood, 3 Tumblers 900.00
Carnival Glass, Pitcher, Field Flower, Amber 65.00
Carnival Glass, Pitcher, Floral & Grape, Blue 150.00
Carnival Glass, Pitcher, Frosty Block, White, 6 In. 50.00
Carnival Glass, Pitcher, Grape & Lattice, Marigold, Tankard 125.00

Carnival Glass, Pitcher, Heavy Iris, Marigold 345.00
Carnival Glass, Pitcher, Milk, Four-Seventy-Four, Green 175.00
Carnival Glass, Pitcher, Milk, Four-Seventy-Four, Purple 450.00
Carnival Glass, Pitcher, Milk, Poinsettia, Green 350.00
Carnival Glass, Pitcher, Milk, Poinsettia, Marigold 60.00
Carnival Glass, Pitcher, Milk, Raspberry, Dark Marigold 49.00
Carnival Glass, Pitcher, Milk, Star Medallion, Marigold .... 14.75 To 35.00
Carnival Glass, Pitcher, Peacock At Fountain, Marigold, Marked N 75.00
Carnival Glass, Pitcher, Split Diamond, Marigold, Miniature 27.50
Carnival Glass, Pitcher, Stippled Panel, Marigold 14.00
Carnival Glass, Pitcher, Thistle, Purple, 5 Tumblers 2250.00
Carnival Glass, Pitcher, Water, Amethyst, Perfection 850.00
Carnival Glass, Pitcher, Water, Apple Tree, Marigold 125.00
Carnival Glass, Pitcher, Water, Floral & Grape, Marigold .... 65.00 To 75.00
Carnival Glass, Pitcher, Water, Fluffy Bird, Amethyst 575.00
Carnival Glass, Pitcher, Water, Flute, Purple 550.00
Carnival Glass, Pitcher, Water, Grape & Cable, Purple 225.00
Carnival Glass, Pitcher, Water, Hand Painted, Ice Green, 10 In. 125.00
Carnival Glass, Pitcher, Water, Lacy Daisy, Pearl 127.50
Carnival Glass, Pitcher, Water, Luster Rose, Amber 135.00
Carnival Glass, Pitcher, Water, Open Rose, Marigold 45.00
Carnival Glass, Pitcher, Water, Rambler Rose, Marigold, Bulbous 85.00
Carnival Glass, Pitcher, Water, Raspberry, White, Marked N 225.00
Carnival Glass, Pitcher, Water, Singing Birds, Amethyst 450.00
Carnival Glass, Pitcher, Water, Singing Birds, Purple 325.00
Carnival Glass, Pitcher, Water, Swirl, Marigold To Clear, Tankard .. 125.00
Carnival Glass, Pitcher, Water, Tiger Lily, Green 150.00
Carnival Glass, Plate, Acanthus, Marigold, 10 In. 125.00
Carnival Glass, Plate, Acanthus, Smoky, 10 In. 150.00
Carnival Glass, Plate, Apple Blossom Twig, Marigold 55.00
Carnival Glass, Plate, Apple Blossom, Blue, Ruffled, 9 In. 125.00
Carnival Glass, Plate, Brooklyn Bridge, Marigold .... 225.00 To 285.00
Carnival Glass, Plate, Captive Rose, Green 90.00
Carnival Glass, Plate, Carnival Holly, Blue 89.50
Carnival Glass, Plate, Carnival Holly, Clambroth 75.00
Carnival Glass, Plate, Carnival Holly, Marigold, 9 In. 59.50
Carnival Glass, Plate, Carnival Holly, White 99.50
Carnival Glass, Plate, Cherry Chain, Blue, Flat, 6 1/4 In. 65.00
Carnival Glass, Plate, Chop, Heavy Grape, Marigold 145.00
Carnival Glass, Plate, Chop, Heavy Grape, Marigold, Fenton, 11 In. .. 175.00
Carnival Glass, Plate, Chrysanthemum, Amethyst, Nuart 1500.00
Carnival Glass, Plate, Columbus, Marigold 27.50
Carnival Glass, Plate, Cosmos Variant, Marigold, 9 In. 145.00
Carnival Glass, Plate, Court House, Amethyst, Millersburg, Unlettered .. 495.00
Carnival Glass, Plate, Daisy Wreath, Peach 75.00
Carnival Glass, Plate, Double Stem Rose, White, Footed 85.00
Carnival Glass, Plate, Dutch, Marigold 26.00
Carnival Glass, Plate, Embossed Scroll, Amethyst 77.50
Carnival Glass, Plate, Fanciful, Cobalt Blue, Flat 125.00
Carnival Glass, Plate, Fanciful, White, Flat 150.00
Carnival Glass, Plate, Four Flowers, Purple, Ruffled, 9 1/4 In. 125.00
Carnival Glass, Plate, Frosty Block, White 50.00
Carnival Glass, Plate, Garden Path, Purple 1800.00
Carnival Glass, Plate, Good Luck, Green 295.00
Carnival Glass, Plate, Good Luck, Purple 295.00
Carnival Glass, Plate, Grape & Cable, Amethyst, Footed 145.00
Carnival Glass, Plate, Grape & Cable, Aqua, Stippled, 9 In.Diameter .. 250.00
Carnival Glass, Plate, Grape & Cable, Green 195.00
Carnival Glass, Plate, Grape & Cable, Green, 9 In. 69.50
Carnival Glass, Plate, Grape & Cable, Marigold, Basket Weave Back, 9 In. .. 69.00
Carnival Glass, Plate, Grape & Cable, Purple, 9 1/2 In.Diameter 65.00
Carnival Glass, Plate, Grape, Purple, Fenton 135.00
Carnival Glass, Plate, Heart & Horseshoe, Marigold, Ruffled 500.00
Carnival Glass, Plate, Heart And Vine, Marigold 250.00
Carnival Glass, Plate, Heavy Grape, Green, Fenton, Flat 115.00
Carnival Glass, Plate, Heavy Grape, Marigold, Fenton, Flat 85.00

Carnival Glass, Plate, Horse Medallion, Red, 7 In.Diameter 175.00
Carnival Glass, Plate, Imperial Grape, Amethyst, 6 In. 28.00
Carnival Glass, Plate, Imperial Grape, Green, Flat, 6 1/2 In. 37.50
Carnival Glass, Plate, Imperial Grape, White, 9 In. 75.00
Carnival Glass, Plate, Imperial Jewels, Orange 2.50
Carnival Glass, Plate, Leaf Chain, Emerald Green, Fenton, Flat, 9 1/2 In. 125.00
Carnival Glass, Plate, Leaf Chain, Marigold 85.00
Carnival Glass, Plate, Little Stars, Purple 50.00
Carnival Glass, Plate, Luster And Clear, White, 6 In. 22.00
Carnival Glass, Plate, Luster Rose, Marigold 75.00
Carnival Glass, Plate, Luster Rose, White, 9 In. 75.00
Carnival Glass, Plate, Millersburg Vintage, Amethyst, Flat, 9 1/2 In. 85.00
Carnival Glass, Plate, Old Homestead, Amethyst, Nuart 900.00
Carnival Glass, Plate, Old Homestead, Green, Nuart 1000.00
Carnival Glass, Plate, Old Homestead, Green, Silver Luster, Signed Nuart 750.00
Carnival Glass, Plate, Orange Tree, Clambroth 75.00
Carnival Glass, Plate, Orange Tree, White, 9 1/4 In. 100.00
Carnival Glass, Plate, Pansy, Amber, Ruffled, 9 In. 75.00
Carnival Glass, Plate, Peacock & Grape, Purple, Footed 175.00
Carnival Glass, Plate, Peacock At Urn, Blue, Fenton 225.00
Carnival Glass, Plate, Peacock At Urn, Cobalt Blue 250.00
Carnival Glass, Plate, Peacock At Urn, Marigold 195.00
Carnival Glass, Plate, Peacock At Urn, Marigold, Fenton, Flat, 9 In. 125.00
Carnival Glass, Plate, Peacock At Urn, White 135.00
Carnival Glass, Plate, Peacock On Fence, Ice Green .... 195.00 To 285.00
Carnival Glass, Plate, Peacock On Fence, Ice Green, N Mark, 9 In.Diameter 125.00
Carnival Glass, Plate, Peacock On Fence, Marigold 135.00
Carnival Glass, Plate, Peacock On Fence, Purple 250.00
Carnival Glass, Plate, Peacock On Fence, White, N Mark, 9 In.Diameter 165.00
Carnival Glass, Plate, Persian Garden, White, 7 In.Diameter .... 65.00 To 75.00
Carnival Glass, Plate, Persian Medallion, Cobalt Blue, 9 In.Diameter 65.00
Carnival Glass, Plate, Peter Rabbit, Marigold 1050.00
Carnival Glass, Plate, Pinecone, Marigold, Small Size 25.00
Carnival Glass, Plate, Pinecone, Marigold, 6 In.Diameter 30.00
Carnival Glass, Plate, Poppy Show, Deep Blue 360.00
Carnival Glass, Plate, Poppy Show, Marigold .... 250.00 To 260.00
Carnival Glass, Plate, Rose Show, Blue 360.00
Carnival Glass, Plate, Rose Show, Marigold 225.00
Carnival Glass, Plate, Rose Show, White .... 285.00 To 295.00
Carnival Glass, Plate, Roundup, Amethyst 195.00
Carnival Glass, Plate, Sailboat, Blue 65.00
Carnival Glass, Plate, Soda Gold, Marigold 12.00
Carnival Glass, Plate, Soldiers And Sailors, Blue 750.00
Carnival Glass, Plate, Soutache, Peach 75.00
Carnival Glass, Plate, Star & File, Pastel Marigold, Flat, 9 3/4 In. 45.00
Carnival Glass, Plate, Star Medallion, Marigold, 9 In.Diameter 35.00
Carnival Glass, Plate, Strawberry, Green, Stippled 125.00
Carnival Glass, Plate, Strawberry, Marigold, 9 In. 59.50
Carnival Glass, Plate, Strawberry, Purple, Basket Weave Back, Marked N 85.00
Carnival Glass, Plate, Strawberry, Stippled, Green 125.00
Carnival Glass, Plate, Stretch Glass, Marigold 25.00
Carnival Glass, Plate, Three Fruit, Amethyst 125.00
Carnival Glass, Plate, Three Fruit, Amethyst & Purple, 9 In. 125.00
Carnival Glass, Plate, Three Fruit, Marigold 55.00
Carnival Glass, Plate, Three Fruit, Marigold, Stippled 60.00
Carnival Glass, Plate, Three Fruit, Purple, Stippled Ground 125.00
Carnival Glass, Plate, Town Pump, Grape & Cable, Purple 400.00
Carnival Glass, Plate, Windflower, Blue 125.00
Carnival Glass, Plate, Windflower, Blue, Flat, 9 1/4 In. 150.00
Carnival Glass, Plate, Wreathed Cherry, Marigold, Small Size 25.00
Carnival Glass, Platter, Bouquet & Lattice, Marigold, 12 In.Long 3.95
Carnival Glass, Powder Jar, Vintage, White, Covered 100.00
Carnival Glass, Punch Set, Broken Arches, Purple, 6 Piece 350.00
Carnival Glass, Punch Set, Four-Seventy-Four, Marigold, 8 Piece 250.00
Carnival Glass, Punch Set, Hobstars, Marigold, Pedestal, 13 Piece 185.00
Carnival Glass, Punch Set, Little Giant, Purple, N Mark, 14 Piece 1500.00

Carnival Glass, Punch Set, Many Fruits, Blue, 8 Piece	750.00
Carnival Glass, Punch Set, Memphis, Marigold, Marked N, 8 Piece	325.00
Carnival Glass, Punch Set, Orange Tree, Marigold, 12 In. Bowl, 8 Cups	250.00
Carnival Glass, Relish, Quilted, Amber, Pansy Inside	37.50
Carnival Glass, Relish, Quilted, Green, Pansy Inside	37.50
Carnival Glass, Relish, Quilted, Marigold, Pansy Inside	27.50
Carnival Glass, Relish, Quilted, Purple, Pansy Inside	37.50
Carnival Glass, Relish, Windmill, Green	22.00
Carnival Glass, Rose Bowl, Beaded Cable, Amethyst	55.00 To 75.00
Carnival Glass, Rose Bowl, Beaded Cable, Dark Green	55.00
Carnival Glass, Rose Bowl, Beaded Cable, Opal Green	75.00
Carnival Glass, Rose Bowl, Coin Dot, Green	38.50
Carnival Glass, Rose Bowl, Daisy & Plume, Green, Footed, Marked N	55.00
Carnival Glass, Rose Bowl, Daisy & Plume, Marigold, Pedestal Foot, Marked N	37.50
Carnival Glass, Rose Bowl, Fenton's Flower, Cobalt Blue	47.50
Carnival Glass, Rose Bowl, Fine Cut & Roses, Ice Blue	59.00
Carnival Glass, Rose Bowl, Fine Cut & Roses, Purple	45.00 To 75.00
Carnival Glass, Rose Bowl, Fine Cut & Roses, Purple, Marked N	50.00
Carnival Glass, Rose Bowl, Floral Diamond Point, Green	75.00
Carnival Glass, Rose Bowl, Flowers, Marigold, Fenton	35.00
Carnival Glass, Rose Bowl, Flowers, Purple, Fenton's	55.00
Carnival Glass, Rose Bowl, Frosty Block, White	55.00 To 60.00
Carnival Glass, Rose Bowl, Garland Rose, Marigold	37.50
Carnival Glass, Rose Bowl, Grape & Cable, Cobalt & Copper, Scalloped Edge	35.00
Carnival Glass, Rose Bowl, Grape Delight, Purple	85.00
Carnival Glass, Rose Bowl, Grape Delight, White	70.00 To 75.00
Carnival Glass, Rose Bowl, Greek, Mythology, Marigold	600.00
Carnival Glass, Rose Bowl, Hob & Feather, Purple	850.00
Carnival Glass, Rose Bowl, Hobnail, Marigold	100.00
Carnival Glass, Rose Bowl, Leaf & Beads, Amethyst, Footed	55.00
Carnival Glass, Rose Bowl, Leaf & Beads, Blue, Circled N	65.00 To 70.00
Carnival Glass, Rose Bowl, Leaf & Beads, Dark Green, Footed	55.00
Carnival Glass, Rose Bowl, Leaf & Beads, Green, Souvenir Milwaukee, 1909	105.00
Carnival Glass, Rose Bowl, Leaf & Beads, Marigold, Northwood	35.00 To 39.00
Carnival Glass, Rose Bowl, Leaf And Beads, Green	75.00
Carnival Glass, Rose Bowl, Louisa, Green, 3 Footed	45.00
Carnival Glass, Rose Bowl, Louisa, Orchid	85.00
Carnival Glass, Rose Bowl, Orange Tree Variant, Green, Flared	75.00
Carnival Glass, Rose Bowl, Orange Tree, Apricot, Footed	27.50
Carnival Glass, Rose Bowl, Roses & Fine Cut, Ice Blue	125.00
Carnival Glass, Rose Bowl, Ruffled, Blue	260.00
Carnival Glass, Rose Bowl, Stag & Holly, Marigold	195.00 To 250.00
Carnival Glass, Rose Bowl, Thistle & Thorn, Marigold, Footed	45.00
Carnival Glass, Rose Bowl, Venetian, Green	950.00
Carnival Glass, Rose Bowl, Vintage Grape, Blue, Footed	75.00
Carnival Glass, Rose Bowl, Vintage, White, 6 Footed	100.00
Carnival Glass, Rose Bowl, Wreath Of Roses, Marigold	27.00
Carnival Glass, Salt And Pepper, Tree Of Life, Smoky	275.00
Carnival Glass, Salt Dip, Swan, Blue	16.00
Carnival Glass, Salt Dip, Swan, Green	16.00
Carnival Glass, Salt Shaker, Octagon, Marigold	110.00
Carnival Glass, Salt, Footed, Ice Blue	75.00
Carnival Glass, Salt, Footed, Marigold	60.00
Carnival Glass, Salt, Master, Swan, Amethyst	35.00
Carnival Glass, Salt, Master, Swan, Green	35.00
Carnival Glass, Salt, Master, Swan, Ice Blue	40.00
Carnival Glass, Salt, Master, Swan, Ice Green, Pair	45.00
Carnival Glass, Salt, Master, Swan, Marigold	45.00
Carnival Glass, Salt, Master, Swan, Pastel Green	25.00
Carnival Glass, Salt, Master, Swan, Purple	135.00
Carnival Glass, Salt, Paneled, Ice Blue, N Mark, Pedestal	70.00
Carnival Glass, Sauce, Bouquet & Lattice, Marigold	1.95
Carnival Glass, Sauce, Butterfly & Berry, Marigold, 4 1/2 In.Diameter	14.00
Carnival Glass, Sauce, Diamond Ring, Smoky	16.50
Carnival Glass, Sauce, Grape & Cable, Purple	35.00
Carnival Glass, Sauce, Little Fish, Marigold, Ruffled, Footed	60.00

Carnival Glass, Sauce, Maple Leaf, Purple, Stemmed 14.00
Carnival Glass, Sauce, Petal & Fan, Peach, Ruffled 19.50
Carnival Glass, Sauce, Pine Cone, Blue 20.00
Carnival Glass, Sauce, Snow Fancy, Purple 27.50
Carnival Glass, Sauce, Stippled Rays, Red 185.00
Carnival Glass, Sauce, Stork & Rushes, Amethyst 10.00
Carnival Glass, Sauce, Vintage, Marigold 12.50
Carnival Glass, Sauceboat, Holly Whirl, Peach, Millersburg, Footed, Handle 45.00
Carnival Glass, Saucer, Kittens, Marigold, Sides Turned Up 75.00
Carnival Glass, Shade, Lamp, Paneled, Marigold, Green Edge, 5 1/2 In.High 30.00
Carnival Glass, Shade, Painted Winter Scene, Marigold, 2 1/4 In.Fitter, Pair 50.00
Carnival Glass, Shade, Primrose Panels, Marigold, 2 1/4 In.Fitter 25.00
Carnival Glass, Shade, Starlyte, Green, 2 In.Fitter 25.00
Carnival Glass, Shade, Starlyte, Marigold, 2 In.Fitter 25.00
Carnival Glass, Sherbet, Bouquet & Lattice, Marigold, Footed 1.95
Carnival Glass, Shot Glass, Grape And Cable, Marigold 55.00
Carnival Glass, Shot Glass, Grape And Cable, Purple 200.00
Carnival Glass, Smoky Soda, Gold 47.00
Carnival Glass, Spooner, Beaded Shell, Marigold 35.00
Carnival Glass, Spooner, Cherry, Purple, Millersburg .... 40.00 To 47.50
Carnival Glass, Spooner, Drapery, Blue, Opalescent, Mark N 28.00
Carnival Glass, Spooner, Grape & Cable, Purple 80.00
Carnival Glass, Spooner, Kittens, Blue 135.00
Carnival Glass, Spooner, Kittens, Marigold .... 52.50 To 95.00
Carnival Glass, Spooner, Millersburg Cherry, Purple 47.50
Carnival Glass, Spooner, Peacock At Fountain, Marigold 55.00
Carnival Glass, Spooner, Peacock At Fountain, Purple 110.00
Carnival Glass, Sugar & Creamer, Flute, Purple 95.00
Carnival Glass, Sugar & Creamer, Lea, Marigold 56.50
Carnival Glass, Sugar & Creamer, Orange Tree, White 175.00
Carnival Glass, Sugar & Creamer, Snow, Marigold 49.00
Carnival Glass, Sugar & Creamer, Strutting Peacock, Purple 42.00
Carnival Glass, Sugar Bowl, Thistle And Thorn, Marigold 31.00
Carnival Glass, Sugar, Acorn Burr, Marigold, N Mark, Cover 60.00
Carnival Glass, Sugar, Apple Panel, Marigold, Open 15.00
Carnival Glass, Sugar, Creamer, & Spooner, Carnival Hobstar, Marigold 60.00
Carnival Glass, Sugar, Drapery, Blue, Opalescent, Cover, Mark N 40.00
Carnival Glass, Sugar, Estate, Marigold 38.00
Carnival Glass, Sugar, Honeycomb, Marigold, Dark 12.50
Carnival Glass, Sugar, Lea, Marigold 20.00
Carnival Glass, Sugar, Maple Leaf, Purple, Covered, Blue Finial 95.00
Carnival Glass, Sugar, Orange Tree, Cobalt, Footed, Cover 44.00
Carnival Glass, Sugar, Orange Tree, White, Handle 35.00
Carnival Glass, Sugar, Orange Tree, White, Open 35.00
Carnival Glass, Sugar, Peacock At Fountain, Marigold, N Mark, Cover 70.00
Carnival Glass, Sugar, Shell & Jewel, Marigold, Cover 25.00
Carnival Glass, Sugar, Shell, Marigold 17.50
Carnival Glass, Sugar, Strutting Peacock, Purple, Open 48.00
Carnival Glass, Swan, Covered, Amethyst 100.00
Carnival Glass, Swan, Nesting, Purple, Millersburg 145.00
Carnival Glass, Swan, Pastel Amethyst 95.00
Carnival Glass, Swan, Pastel Green .... 15.00 To 18.00
Carnival Glass, Swan, Pastel White 30.00
Carnival Glass, Sweetmeat, Grape & Cable, Amethyst, Open 375.00
Carnival Glass, Sweetmeat, Grape & Cable, Purple, Covered, N .... 165.00 To 175.00
Carnival Glass, Sweetmeat, Grape & Cable, Purple, Marked N 137.00
Carnival Glass, Swirl, Green, N Mark 27.00
Carnival Glass, Tankard, Grape Arbor, White 285.00
Carnival Glass, Tie Pin, Beetle, Green, Pair 20.00
 Carnival Glass, Toothpick Holder, see also Toothpick
Carnival Glass, Toothpick, Flute, Green 55.00
Carnival Glass, Toothpick, Flute, Marigold 49.50
Carnival Glass, Toothpick, Flute, Purple ....65.00 To 100.00
Carnival Glass, Toothpick, Hat, Daisy And Button, Marigold 45.00
Carnival Glass, Toothpick, Hat, Marigold, Rim Turns Up & Down, Blown 19.50
Carnival Glass, Toothpick, Indian Head, Cobalt, Marked St.Clair 6.00

Carnival Glass, **Toothpick**, Octagon, Amethyst 110.00
Carnival Glass, **Toothpick**, Stork & Rushes, Cobalt Blue, Fish At Bottom 10.00
Carnival Glass, **Town Pump**, Northwood, Green 1250.00
Carnival Glass, **Town Pump**, Northwood, Marigold 900.00
Carnival Glass, **Town Pump**, Northwood, Purple 450.00
Carnival Glass, **Tray**, Dresser, Grape & Cable, Purple .... 150.00 To 175.00
Carnival Glass, **Tray**, Ice Cream, Grape & Cable, White, 10 1/2 In. 195.00
Carnival Glass, **Tray**, Pin, Grape & Cable, Purple 150.00
Carnival Glass, **Tray**, Pin, Seacoast, Amethyst 375.00
Carnival Glass, **Tray**, Sandwich, Vintage, Pastel Marigold, Center Handle 45.00
Carnival Glass, **Tumbler**, Acorn Burrs, Purple 40.00
Carnival Glass, **Tumbler**, Apple Tree, Marigold .... 15.00 To 20.00
Carnival Glass, **Tumbler**, Beaded Shell, Deep Amethyst 45.00
Carnival Glass, **Tumbler**, Beaded Shell, Purple 30.00
Carnival Glass, **Tumbler**, Blackberry Block, Deep Amethyst 45.00
Carnival Glass, **Tumbler**, Blackberry Block, Purple 35.00
Carnival Glass, **Tumbler**, Blueberry, Blue 60.00
Carnival Glass, **Tumbler**, Blueberry, Marigold 45.00
Carnival Glass, **Tumbler**, Bouquet, Marigold, Dark 15.00
Carnival Glass, **Tumbler**, Butterfly & Berry, Blue .... 25.00 To 32.50
Carnival Glass, **Tumbler**, Butterfly & Berry, Marigold 14.50
Carnival Glass, **Tumbler**, Butterfly & Berry, Purple 23.00
Carnival Glass, **Tumbler**, Butterfly & Fern, Green 35.00
Carnival Glass, **Tumbler**, Butterfly And Plume, Amethyst 40.00
Carnival Glass, **Tumbler**, Chatelaine, Purple 165.00
Carnival Glass, **Tumbler**, Cosmos & Cane, Marigold 12.00
Carnival Glass, **Tumbler**, Crabclaw, Marigold 23.00
Carnival Glass, **Tumbler**, Crackle, Marigold 6.50
Carnival Glass, **Tumbler**, Daisy & Diamond, Marigold 25.00
Carnival Glass, **Tumbler**, Diamond Lace, Purple 28.00
Carnival Glass, **Tumbler**, Enamel Floral, Marigold, Marked N & E, Set Of 4 .... 50.00
Carnival Glass, **Tumbler**, Fentonia Variant, Cobalt 23.00
Carnival Glass, **Tumbler**, Field Flower, Marigold 12.00
Carnival Glass, **Tumbler**, Fleur-De-Lis, Blue 8.50
Carnival Glass, **Tumbler**, Floral & Grape, Amber 20.00
Carnival Glass, **Tumbler**, Floral & Grape, Blue 35.00
Carnival Glass, **Tumbler**, Floral & Grape, Green 22.00
Carnival Glass, **Tumbler**, Floral & Grape, Marigold 15.00
Carnival Glass, **Tumbler**, Flower, Blue, Enameled 15.00
Carnival Glass, **Tumbler**, Flowers & Leaves, Marigold 16.00
Carnival Glass, **Tumbler**, God And Home, Blue 195.00
Carnival Glass, **Tumbler**, Grape & Cable, Marigold 22.50
Carnival Glass, **Tumbler**, Grape & Cable, Purple .... 20.00 To 23.50
Carnival Glass, **Tumbler**, Grape & Cable, Purple, N Mark 30.00
Carnival Glass, **Tumbler**, Grape & Cable, Purple, Signed N 22.00
Carnival Glass, **Tumbler**, Grape & Gothic Arches, Marigold 11.00
Carnival Glass, **Tumbler**, Grape & Lattice, Marigold .... 12.00 To 20.00
Carnival Glass, **Tumbler**, Grape Arbor, Marigold 30.00
Carnival Glass, **Tumbler**, Grape Arbor, Purple 75.00
Carnival Glass, **Tumbler**, Grapevine Lattice, Marigold 12.00
Carnival Glass, **Tumbler**, Harvest Flower, Marigold 22.00
Carnival Glass, **Tumbler**, Heart & Feather, Amethyst 25.00
Carnival Glass, **Tumbler**, Hobstar Band, Honey Color 25.00
Carnival Glass, **Tumbler**, Imperial Grape, Marigold .... 12.00 To 15.00
Carnival Glass, **Tumbler**, Imperial Grape, Purple 30.00
Carnival Glass, **Tumbler**, Iris, White 75.00
Carnival Glass, **Tumbler**, Jeweled Heart, Marigold 65.00
Carnival Glass, **Tumbler**, Lattice & Daisy, Marigold 12.00
Carnival Glass, **Tumbler**, Lattice & Grape, Blue 35.00
Carnival Glass, **Tumbler**, Lattice & Grape, Marigold 12.00
Carnival Glass, **Tumbler**, Lattice, Marigold 20.00
Carnival Glass, **Tumbler**, Luster Rose, Marigold 9.00
Carnival Glass, **Tumbler**, Maple Leaf, Marigold, Northwood 20.00
Carnival Glass, **Tumbler**, Morning Glory, Amethyst 29.00
Carnival Glass, **Tumbler**, Oriental Poppy, Deep Purple 45.00
Carnival Glass, **Tumbler**, Oriental Poppy, Ice Blue, N Mark 55.00

Carnival Glass, Tumbler, Oriental Poppy, Purple .... 26.00 To 55.00
Carnival Glass, Tumbler, Paneled Dandelion, Blue 35.00
Carnival Glass, Tumbler, Peacock At Fountain, Blue 19.00
Carnival Glass, Tumbler, Peacock At Fountain, Dark Blue 20.00
Carnival Glass, Tumbler, Peacock At Fountain, Marigold, Circle Mark 15.00
Carnival Glass, Tumbler, Peacock At Fountain, Purple .... *Illus* 30.00
Carnival Glass, Tumbler, Raspberry, Green 20.00

Carnival Glass, Tumbler, Peacock At Fountain, Purple

Carnival Glass, Tumbler, Raspberry, Marigold, Marked N 17.00
Carnival Glass, Tumbler, Singing Birds, Purple, Signed N 26.00
Carnival Glass, Tumbler, Star Medallion, Marigold 17.50
Carnival Glass, Tumbler, Stork And Rushes, Blue 35.00
Carnival Glass, Tumbler, Stork In Rushes, Marigold, XXX Band 60.00
Carnival Glass, Tumbler, Strawberry Scroll, Marigold 75.00
Carnival Glass, Tumbler, Swirl, Marigold, Mark N 20.00
Carnival Glass, Tumbler, Ten Mums, Blue 60.00
Carnival Glass, Tumbler, Tiger Lily, Green 22.00
Carnival Glass, Tumbler, Water Lily, Marigold 15.00
Carnival Glass, Tumbler, Wild Rose, Marigold 30.00
Carnival Glass, Tumbler, Windmill, Purple .... 29.50 To 40.00
Carnival Glass, Tumbler, Wreathed Cherry, Purple 28.00
Carnival Glass, Vase, Butterfly & Berry, Green, 11 In.High 47.00
Carnival Glass, Vase, Butterfly & Berry, Marigold, 8 In., Pair 55.00
Carnival Glass, Vase, Car, Daisylike Flowers, Marigold 19.50
Carnival Glass, Vase, Car, Tree Of Life, Marigold 15.00
Carnival Glass, Vase, Corn, Amethyst 225.00
Carnival Glass, Vase, Corn, Green 300.00
Carnival Glass, Vase, Corn, Ice Green 225.00
Carnival Glass, Vase, Corn, Marigold 375.00
Carnival Glass, Vase, Corn, White 100.00
Carnival Glass, Vase, Cornucopia, Marigold 9.00
Carnival Glass, Vase, Daisy And Drape, Ice Blue 150.00
Carnival Glass, Vase, Dance Of The Veils, Marigold 1250.00
Carnival Glass, Vase, Diamond & Rib, Amethyst, 11 In. 28.75
Carnival Glass, Vase, Diamond & Rib, Green, 10 1/2 In. 25.00
Carnival Glass, Vase, Diamond & Rib, Green, 11 In. 28.75
Carnival Glass, Vase, Diamond & Rib, Marigold, 11 In. 19.75
Carnival Glass, Vase, Diamond Point, Blue, Marked N, 9 1/2 In. 37.50
Carnival Glass, Vase, Diamond Rib, Green, 10 3/4 In. 15.00
Carnival Glass, Vase, Diamond, Purple, N Mark, 10 In.High 32.00
Carnival Glass, Vase, Fan, Dolphin, Pastel Pink, Dolphin Handles 53.00
Carnival Glass, Vase, Fan, Imperial Jewels, Green, Gold Iridescence, Stretch 25.00
Carnival Glass, Vase, Flute, Marigold, Signed N 45.00
Carnival Glass, Vase, Horizontal Rib, Fluted, Purple, 11 1/2 In.High, Pair 50.00
Carnival Glass, Vase, Imperial, Marigold, 9 In.High 42.00
Carnival Glass, Vase, Knotted Beads, Blue, Crimped Top, 8 3/4 In. 25.00
Carnival Glass, Vase, Large Roses, Purple, Two Handles, 4 In.High 60.00
Carnival Glass, Vase, Paneled, Green, Large Size 85.00
Carnival Glass, Vase, Plume Panels, Green, 10 In. 37.50
Carnival Glass, Vase, Pulled Loop, Green, 10 In. 27.50
Carnival Glass, Vase, Rib Swirl, Peach, Opalescent, 8 In.High 17.50

Carnival Glass, Vase, Rib Swirl, Peach, Opalescent, 9 In.High 17.50
Carnival Glass, Vase, Rib, Green, Flared Top, 11 1/2 In., Pair 59.00
Carnival Glass, Vase, Ribbed, Purple, N Mark, 10 1/2 In.High 32.00
Carnival Glass, Vase, Ribbed, Red, 10 1/2 In.Tall 80.00
Carnival Glass, Vase, Ribbed, Red, 11 1/2 In.Tall 100.00
Carnival Glass, Vase, Ripple, Amber, 14 In.High, 8 1/4 In.Wide 95.00
Carnival Glass, Vase, Ripple, Marigold 17.50
Carnival Glass, Vase, Ripple, Purple, 9 In.High 17.00
Carnival Glass, Vase, Ripple, Purple, 10 In.High, 6 In.Flare 35.00
Carnival Glass, Vase, Ripple, Smoky 37.50
Carnival Glass, Vase, Rose, Buds, Fern, Marigold, Painted, Pink, Green, & White 18.50
Carnival Glass, Vase, Rustic, Cobalt Blue, 17 In.High 48.00
Carnival Glass, Vase, Stork, Marigold 12.00
Carnival Glass, Vase, Striated, Greenish Amber, Footed, 5 In.High 40.00
Carnival Glass, Vase, Sweet Pea, Tree Trunk, Purple, 6 In. 37.50
Carnival Glass, Vase, Tadpoles, Purple 125.00
Carnival Glass, Vase, Thin Rib, Red, 10 In. 85.00
Carnival Glass, Vase, Three Cornered Flaring, Ice Green 55.00
Carnival Glass, Vase, Thumbprint, Green, 11 In.High 20.00
Carnival Glass, Vase, Tornado, Purple, Ribbed 138.00
Carnival Glass, Vase, Tree Bark, Green, Marked N, 10 In. 20.00
Carnival Glass, Vase, Tree Bark, Marigold, 7 1/4 In.High, Pair 30.00
Carnival Glass, Vase, Tree Bark, Purple, 7 3/4 In. 25.00
Carnival Glass, Vase, Tree Of Life, Marigold 15.00
Carnival Glass, Vase, Tree Trunk, Marigold 65.00
Carnival Glass, Vase, Tree Trunk, Purple 95.00
Carnival Glass, Vase, Two Handled, Roses, Purple, 4 In.High 30.00
Carnival Glass, Vase, Wall, Cockatoo, Marigold 45.00
Carnival Glass, Vase, Wheat, Purple Blue, N Mark, 10 In. 22.00
Carnival Glass, Water Pitcher, Chatelaine, Purple 1250.00
Carnival Glass, Water Pitcher, Fashion, Purple 800.00
Carnival Glass, Water Pitcher, Grape Arbor, Amethyst 650.00
Carnival Glass, Water Pitcher, Heavy Iris, Marigold 200.00
Carnival Glass, Water Pitcher, Octagon, Purple 650.00
Carnival Glass, Water Pitcher, Peacock At The Fountain, White 750.00
Carnival Glass, Water Pitcher, Star Flower, Purple 1250.00
Carnival Glass, Water Set, Acorn Burr, Purple, Marked N, 7 Piece 575.00
Carnival Glass, Water Set, Apple Tree, Marigold 295.00
Carnival Glass, Water Set, Butterfly & Berry, Marigold 225.00
Carnival Glass, Water Set, Butterfly & Fern, Marigold 200.00
Carnival Glass, Water Set, Crackle, Marigold, Lid On Pitcher, 7 Piece 125.00
Carnival Glass, Water Set, Diamond Lace, Purple, 7 Piece .... 450.00 To 495.00
Carnival Glass, Water Set, Enameled Flowers, Marigold, Bulbous, 6 Piece 45.00
Carnival Glass, Water Set, Fashion, Smoky, 7 Piece 595.00
Carnival Glass, Water Set, Floral & Grape, Amethyst, 7 Piece 250.00
Carnival Glass, Water Set, Floral & Grape, Blue, 7 Piece 279.00
Carnival Glass, Water Set, Grape & Cable, Purple .... 350.00 To 395.00
Carnival Glass, Water Set, Grape & Cable, Purple, Marked N, 5 Piece 285.00
Carnival Glass, Water Set, Grape & Cable, Purple, N, 7 Piece .... 495.00 To 550.00
Carnival Glass, Water Set, Greek Key, Marigold, 7 Piece 900.00
Carnival Glass, Water Set, Imperial Grape, Marigold 75.00
Carnival Glass, Water Set, Iris & Herringbone, Marigold, Pitcher, 6 Tumbler 30.00
Carnival Glass, Water Set, Lattice & Grape, Marigold 195.00
Carnival Glass, Water Set, Luster Rose, Marigold, 7 Piece 95.00
Carnival Glass, Water Set, Maple Leaf, Purple, 7 Piece 550.00
Carnival Glass, Water Set, Peacock At Fountain, Blue, N Mark, 7 Piece 545.00
Carnival Glass, Water Set, Raspberry, Green, Northwood, 7 Piece 435.00
Carnival Glass, Water Set, Raspberry, Purple, 5 Piece 360.00
Carnival Glass, Water, Tiger Lily, Marigold, 7 Piece 170.00
Carnival Glass, Wine Set, Octagon, Marigold, 7 Piece 275.00
Carnival Glass, Wine, Pillow & Sunburst, Marigold 24.50
Carnival Glass, Wine, Ship & Sails, Blue 32.00
Carnival Glass, Wine, Windmill, Marigold 35.00
Carnival, Bowl, Vintage, Amethyst, 7 In. 25.00
Carousel Horse, Allan Herschell, C.1925, 48 X 28 In. 200.00
Carousel Horse, American, Wooden, Carved, C.1850 .... Illus 325.00

Carousel Horse,
American, Wooden,
Carved, C.1850
See Page 111

Castor, Pickle, Blue Liner,
Gold Plated, 11 In.
See Page 113

Carousel Horse, Carved, By Herschel Spilman, Wooden, 36 X 60 In.	250.00
Carousel Horse, Hand-Carved, Hair Tail, Glass Eyes	200.00
Carousel Horse, Loop, Lion Head On Saddle, 52 X 36 In.	300.00
Carousel, British Centaur, 80 X 48 In.	1200.00
Carousel, Camel, Carved In U.S., C.1885, 72 X 48 In.	950.00

Cased Glass is made with one thin layer of glass over another layer or layers of colored glass. Many types of art glass were cased. Cased Glass is usually a well-made piece by a reputable factory.

Cased Glass, Basket, Blue Opaque To Opalescent Blue, Threaded Pattern	45.00
Cased Glass, Bowl, Pink Inside, Raised Diamond Pattern, Foot Rim, Blown	85.00
Cased Glass, Pitcher & Tumbler, Pink & Yellow, Swirl	225.00
Cased Glass, Vase, Amber, White Overlay, Floral, 17 In.High, Pair	175.00
Cased Glass, Vase, White Lining, Pink Case, Cut Panels, Enamel Floral, Gold	95.00
Cased Glass, Vase, Yellow Cased, Wheeling, West Virginia	35.00

Castor Sets have been known as early as 1705. Most of those that have been found today date from Victorian times. A castor set usually consists of a silver-plated frame that holds three to seven condiment bottles. The Pickle Castor was a single glass jar about six inches high and held in a silver frame. A cover and tongs were kept with the jar. They were popular from 1890 to 1900.

Castor Set, Two Bottles, Ladder Cut Glass, Resilvered, Reliefs, Cutouts	125.00
Castor Set, Two Bottles, Miniature, Metal Holder With Handle	12.50
Castor Set, Three Bottles, Clear Glass, Elephants' Heads Base	110.00
Castor Set, Three Bottles, Etched, Pewter Frame	35.00
Castor Set, Three Bottles, Pressed Glass, Pewter Frame	43.00
Castor Set, Four Bottles, Crystal, Silver Plate Stand, 1890 Mark	35.00
Castor Set, Four Bottles, Cut & Etched, Silver Plate Frame	35.00
Castor Set, Four Bottles, Cut & Etched, Square Footed Frame	75.00
Castor Set, Four Bottles, Cut Glass, Ornate Sterling Lids & Holder	175.00
Castor Set, Four Bottles, Diamond & Fan, Vinegar, Mustard, & Salt	110.00
Castor Set, Four Bottles, Etched Ferns, Boat Shape Silver Holder, Footed	32.50
Castor Set, Four Bottles, Etched, Silver Holder, Meriden	39.00
Castor Set, Four Bottles, Etched, Silver Holder, Tall Handle	39.00
Castor Set, Four Bottles, Miniature, Pewter	50.00
Castor Set, Four Bottles, Miniature, Pewter Holder, Revolves	60.00
Castor Set, Four Bottles, Opalescent Stripe, 1 Vaseline, 1 Blue, 2 Flint	65.00
Castor Set, Four Bottles, Painted Red Apples, Iron Holder, Tall Handle	16.50
Castor Set, Four Bottles, Paneled, Fine Cut, Amber	75.00
Castor Set, Five Bottles, Bell Top, Silver Frame	85.00
Castor Set, Five Bottles, Cobalt, Cut To Clear, Resilvered & Lacquer Frame	100.00
Castor Set, Five Bottles, Gothic Pattern, Pewter Frame	50.00
Castor Set, Five Bottles, Reed & Barton Silver Plate Frame	65.00

Castor Set, Five Bottles, Revolving Stand, Stoppers, Glass 115.00
Castor Set, Five Bottles, Silver Frame, Center Handle 69.50
Castor Set, Six Bottles, Amber, Scenic, Silver Holder 45.00
Castor Set, Six Bottles, Bell On Top, Victorian 85.00
Castor Set, Six Bottles, Brass Frame, English 37.50
Castor Set, Six Bottles, Cut & Etched Bottles, Reed & Barton Frame 60.00
Castor Set, Six Bottles, Frosted Vine, Pedestal Base 45.00
Castor Set, Seven Bottles, Silver, Bailey & Kitchen, Phila., 1833-1848 .... 875.00
Castor Set, Seven Bottles, Waterford, England 130.00
Castor, Frame, Five Hole, Open Handle, Meriden Silver Co. 15.00
Castor, Pickle, Amber Daisy & Button Insert, Silver Plate Holder 85.00
Castor, Pickle, Amber Insert, Silver 95.00
Castor, Pickle, Amber, Inverted Thumbprint, Enameled Liner, Resilvered Frame 89.50
Castor, Pickle, Amber, Quilted, Silver Holder, New Tongs 125.00
Castor, Pickle, Beaded Columns, 11 In.High, Tongs 45.00
Castor, Pickle, Belted Icicle, Clear Insert 35.00
Castor, Pickle, Block & Fan, Tongs 65.00
Castor, Pickle, Block Pattern, Silver, Fork 32.00
Castor, Pickle, Blue & White Mother-Of-Pearl Insert, Lovebirds On Frame 275.00
Castor, Pickle, Blue Insert, Daisy & Button, Silver Holder 100.00
Castor, Pickle, Blue Insert, On Legs 95.00
Castor, Pickle, Blue Liner, Gold Plated, 11 In. .... *Illus* 225.00
Castor, Pickle, Blue Star Insert, Tongs 85.00
Castor, Pickle, Blue, Daisy & Button Insert, Silver Frame, Cover, Tongs 68.50
Castor, Pickle, Blue, Daisy & Button, Resilvered Holder & Tongs 65.00
Castor, Pickle, Blue, Pressed Glass, Webster Silver Plate Holder, Tongs 95.00
Castor, Pickle, Caneware Pattern, Blue, Silver Holder 75.00
Castor, Pickle, Clear Zipper Insert, Footed Frame, Dog On Lid 125.00
Castor, Pickle, Cranberry, Diamond-Quilted, Silver Holder & Tongs 75.00
Castor, Pickle, Cranberry, Enameled Decoration, Meriden Holder 100.00
Castor, Pickle, Cranberry, Enameled Flowers, Silver Plated Holder 225.00
Castor, Pickle, Cranberry, Inverted Thumbprint, Enameled Magnolias, Silver 135.00
Castor, Pickle, Cranberry, Inverted Thumbprint, Frame 115.00
Castor, Pickle, Cranberry, Inverted Thumbprint, James Tufts Plate Frame 95.00
Castor, Pickle, Cranberry, Inverted Thumbprint, Rogers-Smith Holder 125.00
Castor, Pickle, Cranberry, Inverted Thumbprint, Silver Frame & Tongs 150.00
Castor, Pickle, Cranberry, Paneled, Metal Lid 55.00
Castor, Pickle, Cranberry, Quilted, Resilvered Holder & Tongs 65.00
Castor, Pickle, Cranberry, Thumbprint, Silver Plate Lid, Bail, Tongs 60.00
Castor, Pickle, Cupid & Venus, Tongs 70.00
Castor, Pickle, Cut Bottle, Lid, Silver Stand, Fork Rests In Glass Container 50.00
Castor, Pickle, Cut Jar, Resilvered Holder & Tongs 55.00
Castor, Pickle, Diamond-Quilted, Blue, Silver Plated Holder & Tongs 105.00
Castor, Pickle, Double, Cranberry, 2 Quilted Jars, Floral Engraved Holder 155.00
Castor, Pickle, Double, Swirl, Clear, Tongs 110.00
Castor, Pickle, Elk Medallion Insert 45.00
Castor, Pickle, Frosted, Birds, Floral, Butterflies, Silver Plate Holder, Fork 75.00
Castor, Pickle, Glass Insert, Silver, Tongs 50.00
Castor, Pickle, Harvard Pattern, Silver Holder, Etched Base, Cover, Tongs 37.50
Castor, Pickle, Hobnail & Etched Glass, Embossed Silver Holder & Tongs 39.00
Castor, Pickle, Hobstar, Silver Holder, Floral, Ornate Handles, Footed, Tongs 41.50
Castor, Pickle, Pink Satin, Shell & Seaweed, Silver Holder & Tongs 150.00
Castor, Pickle, Pink, Scene In The Glass, Silver Stand 100.00
Castor, Pickle, Pressed Glass, Silver Holder, Handle, Cover, Tongs 50.00
Castor, Pickle, Pressed Glass, Silver Plate 28.00
Castor, Pickle, Prismatic Jar, Engraved & Embossed Silver, Signed Webster 43.00
Castor, Pickle, Ribbed, Notched, Clear, 11 In., Tongs 75.00
Castor, Pickle, Ruby, Cut Pattern, Silver Stand, Pull Handle, Lid Comes Off 70.00
Castor, Pickle, Silver Frame, Portland Pattern Liner, Tongs 45.00
Castor, Pickle, Silver Plate, Green Tree Of Life Glass Bowl, Tongs 60.00
Castor, Pickle, Vaseline Insert, Cane Pattern, Silver Plate Frame 40.00
Castor, Pickle, Vaseline Insert, Daisy & Button, Silver Plate, Holder, Tongs 75.00

Cauldon is an English pottery factory working after 1905.

Cauldon, Eggcup, White, Pink Roses, Gold Bands, England 6.00
Cauldon, Plate, Basket Of Flowers Center, Gold Edge, Rose Color Border 1.25
Cauldon, Plate, White, Gold Band, Three Leaf Clover, 10 In. 12.00
Cauldon, Ramekin & Saucer, Gold Embossed Rim 1.50
Cauldon, Relish, Flow Blue, Sculptured Cucumber In The Bottom, 15 In.Long 45.00

Celadon is a Chinese porcelain having a velvet-textured green-gray glaze.
Japanese and Korean factories also made a celadon-colored glaze.
Celadon, Bottle, Figure Of Dragon Around Neck, Incised, K'Ang Hsi Period 4250.00
Celadon, Bowl, Sugar, Lid 20.00
Celadon, Box, Decorated, 5 1/2 X 3 1/4 X 3 1/2 In.High 75.00
Celadon, Charger, Sculptured, 14 In. 225.00
Celadon, Cup & Saucer, Florals 14.50
Celadon, Dish, Fish & Seaweed, 4 1/2 In. 18.00
Celadon, Dish, Octagonal, Ring Foot, Green Glaze, Brown Crackle, C.1750 .... 60.00
Celadon, Figurine, Duck, 10 In.High, Pair 145.00
Celadon, Figurine, Monkey, Seated, In Monk's Robe, Korea, Circa 1822 .... 225.00
Celadon, Jar, Ginger, Birds & Flowers, Signed 28.00
Celadon, Jug, Glazed, John Bell, Waynesboro, 8 In.High 175.00
Celadon, Plate, Birds & Butterflies, Fruit, 8 1/2 In. 30.00
Celadon, Sugar & Creamer, Raised Flowers 15.00
Celadon, Urn, Green Ground, Blue Decoration, 23 In.High 325.00
Celadon, Vase, Green Ground, Dark Green, Brown & White Allover Design 40.00
Celadon, Vase, Peonies, Butterfly, Raised Pattern Under Glaze, Pale Green 65.00
Celadon, Vase, Raised Pink & White Flowers, Hexagon, 12 In.High 150.00
Celadon, Vase, Red Underglaze Splash At Shoulder, Nabeshima, Circa 1850 .... 145.00
Celadon, Vase, Wall, 13 1/2 In.Long 25.00
Celluloid, Album, Photo, Blue Forget-Me-Nots, Green Leaves 25.00
Celluloid, Album, Photo, Picture Of Blue Boy, Velvet Backing, Clasp 25.00
Celluloid, Album, Photo, Simulated Wood, Says 'Photographs, ' Embossed Metal 25.00
Celluloid, Box, Glove, Portrait On Lid, 12 In.Long 10.50
Celluloid, Box, Makeup, Circa 1930 .... 3.50
Celluloid, Box, Scene, Two Little Girls, Kitten, 4 3/8 X 3 1/4 In. 10.00
Celluloid, Comb, Hair, Lady's Leg 3.50
Celluloid, Dresser Set, Hand-Painted Flowers, 8 Piece 35.00
Celluloid, Dresser Set, 5 Piece 18.00
Celluloid, Hair Receiver 2.00
Celluloid, Hair Receiver, Brush, Tray, Powder Box 8.00
Celluloid, Syrup, Aunt Jemima 4.00
Celluloid, Tatting Shuttle 2.00
Celluloid, Tray, Dresser, Gold & Amber Streaked, 6 1/2 X 13 In. 2.50
Celluloid, Whistle, Bird 7.50

Chalkware is really plaster of paris decorated with watercolors. The
pieces were molded from known Staffordshire and other porcelain models and
painted and sold as inexpensive decorations. Most of this type of Chalkware
was made from about 1820 to 1870.
Chalkware, Bust, Indian Chief, Full Headdress, Paint 58.00
Chalkware, Bust, Longfellow, 9 In.High 25.00
Chalkware, Bust, Oriental Girl, 9 1/2 In.High 25.00
Chalkware, Figurine, Cat, Tabby, Blue Ribbon 15.00
Chalkware, Figurine, Frog On Lily Pad, 5 1/2 In.High 14.50
Chalkware, Figurine, Monkey, Top Hat, Shirt, Tie, Jacket, Paris, 8 In.High 55.00
Chalkware, Figurine, Owl, Glass Eyes, Signed Cipir, Czechoslovakia, 1892 .... 135.00
Chalkware, Figurine, Santa, Painted, Place For Candle, 9 1/2 In. 11.00
Chalkware, Fruit With Leaves On Pedestal 125.00
Chalkware, Pig, Pennsylvania Dutch, Butcher Shop Advertisement 100.00
Chalkware, Rabbit, Decorated 115.00
Chalkware, Rooster, Decorated 170.00
Chantilly, Plate, Blue, White, Blue Floral, Basket Weave Border, Circa 1760 .... 125.00
Charder, Vase, Ovoid, Purple On Frosted Blue, Cut, Signed Le Verre Francais 550.00
Charder, Vase, Tapering, Lavender Acid Cut Floral On Frosted, Signed 175.00
Charlie Chaplin, Candy Container, Beside Barrel 29.50
Charlie Chaplin, Candy Container, Painted 32.00
Charlie McCarthy, Doll, Composition, Monocle 22.00
Charlie McCarthy, Doll, Composition, Original Dress, 1930s, Marked K.& S. 150.00

Charlie McCarthy, Doll, Ventriloquist's, Dressed 50.00
Charlie McCarthy, Spoon, Duchess Silver Plate 6.00
Charlie McCarthy, Spoon, Silver 3.00
Charlie McCarthy, Teaspoon 5.00
Charlie McCarthy, Teaspoon, Silver Plate 4.00

Chelsea Grape Pattern was made before 1840, probably at the Coalport
Factory in England and at other firms. A small bunch of grapes in a
raised design, colored with purple or blue luster, is on the border of the white
plate. Most of the pieces are unmarked. The pattern is sometimes called
Aynsley or Grandmother.
Chelsea Grape, Cup & Saucer, Violet Luster Grapes .... 18.50 To 32.50
Chelsea Grape, Plate, Cake 15.00
Chelsea Grape, Plate, Lavender Luster Spray, 7 In. 8.00
Chelsea Grape, Plate, 4 In. 3.00
Chelsea Grape, Ramekin, Blue Trim, Marked Aderley, England 12.50
Chelsea Grape, Sauce, Blue Trim, Marked Aderley, England 4.25
Chelsea Grape, Sugar, Open, Luster 22.50

Chelsea Porcelain was made in the Chelsea area of London from about
1745 to 1784. Recent copies of this work have been made from the original
molds.
Chelsea, Cup & Saucer, Embossed, Blue Vine & Acorns, Gold Flowers 4.50
Chelsea, Eggcup, Blue Trim, Grape & Leaf Decor, Marked Aderley, England 4.00
Chelsea, Figurine, Boy, Bare Feet, Carries Sheaf Of Wheat, 3 In. 75.00
Chelsea, Jug, Apostle, Lavender Luster Apostles On Gothic Panels 75.00
Chelsea, Pitcher, Floral Decorations, 8 In.High 22.50
Chelsea, Plate, Bouquet & Floral Sprigs, Brown Wavy Edge, Red Anchor, 1760 .... 600.00
Chelsea, Plate, Brown Rim, Green Leaves, Puce Veins, Red Anchor Mark, 1775 .... 1140.00
Chelsea, Plate, Floral, Brown Wavy Edge, 12 Indentations, Red Anchor, 1755 .... 875.00
Chesapeake, Plate, Faience, Embossed Black Raspberries, Marked Avalon, 1882 .... 35.00

Chinese Export Porcelain is all the many kinds of porcelain made in
China for export to America and Europe in the 18th and 19th centuries.
Included in the category are Nanking, Canton, Chinese Lowestoft,
Armorial, Jesuit, and other types of the ware.
Chinese Export, see also Canton, Nanking
Chinese Export, Beaker, Baluster, Famille Verte, Ladies, Boys, Fu Lion 350.00
Chinese Export, Beaker, Famille Verte, Bird & Flower, K'Ang Hsi, Pair 2400.00
Chinese Export, Blue On Gray Crackle, Two Fishermen, Signed 95.00
Chinese Export, Bottle, Gourd, Famille Verte, Gold On Blue, K'Ang Hsi 900.00
Chinese Export, Bottle, Snuff, Cylindrical, Famille Rose Enamels, Sages, 1850 .... 50.00
Chinese Export, Bottle, Snuff, Famille Rose Enamels .... 170.00 To 325.00
Chinese Export, Bottle, Snuff, Flask, Famille Rose Enamels, C.1850 .... 150.00
Chinese Export, Bottle, Snuff, Flattened Flask, Famille Rose Enamels, C.1850 .... 425.00
Chinese Export, Bottle, Snuff, Flattened Flask, Famille Rose, Ch'len Lung 60.00
Chinese Export, Bottle, Snuff, Flattened Ovate, Famille Rose Enamels, 1850 .... 30.00
Chinese Export, Bottle, Snuff, Ovate Flask, Famille Rose .... 275.00 To 325.00
Chinese Export, Bottle, Snuff, Ovate, Famille Rose, Dragon, Chia Ch'Ing 275.00
Chinese Export, Bottle, Snuff, Oviform, Famille Rose Enamels, Tao Kuang 120.00
Chinese Export, Bottle, Snuff, Oviform, Famille Rose, Riverscape, K'Ang Hsi 400.00
Chinese Export, Bottle, Snuff, Quadrangular, Famille Rose, Gods, Chia Ch'Ing 50.00
Chinese Export, Bowl & Stand, Fitted, Pierced, Floral Medallions, C.1800 .... 275.00
Chinese Export, Bowl, American Dressed In Roman Attire, Eagle, Lion & Flags 250.00
Chinese Export, Bowl, Armorial, Bouquets In Puce, Yellow, & Iron, C.1765 .... 130.00
Chinese Export, Bowl, Armorial, Circa 1820, Pair 175.00
Chinese Export, Bowl, Blue & Rose Decoration, 7 1/2 In.Diameter 55.00
Chinese Export, Bowl, Famille Rose, Calligraphy, Sages, C.1850, Pair 130.00
Chinese Export, Bowl, Famille Rose, Red & Gilt Dragons, Kuang-Hsu, Pair 200.00
Chinese Export, Bowl, Fish, Famille Verte, Boating Festival, K'Ang Hsi 4500.00
Chinese Export, Bowl, Famille Verte, Butterflies On White, K'Ang Hsi, Pair 3600.00
Chinese Export, Bowl, Punch, Pink & Iron Blossoms, Bouquet Inside, C.1785 .... 1150.00
Chinese Export, Bowl, Rose & Blue Decoration, 6 1/2 In.Diameter 85.00
Chinese Export, Bowl, Rouge, Lid, Famille Rose 37.50
Chinese Export, Bowl, Sand, Women In Garden, Calligraphy On Ends, Footed 55.00
Chinese Export, Bowl, Small Flowers, 3 In.Deep, 6 1/3 In.Diameter 37.50

Chinese Export, Box, Flower & Insect Design, Brass Trim, 5 In.Long 50.00
Chinese Export, Box, Snuff, Horn & Bone 30.00
Chinese Export, Box, Woman & Man At Scholar's Table, Brass Trim 45.00
Chinese Export, Box, 1000 Butterfly Design, Orange Peel Glaze, Circa 1800 .... 185.00
Chinese Export, Brushpot, Peach Form, Pierced, Turquoise Inside, C.1850 .... 100.00
Chinese Export, Caddy, Tea, Ovoid, Famille Rose Bouquets, Footed, C.1775 .... 50.00
Chinese Export, Can, Coffee, Mandarin Pattern 65.00
Chinese Export, Candlestick, Elephant, C.1815, Pair .... *Illus* 1400.00
Chinese Export, Chocolate Pot, SVL In Shield, Crabstock Spout, C.1790 .... 350.00
Chinese Export, Coffeepot, Lighthouse, Cup & Saucer, Love Birds, White, Blue 600.00
Chinese Export, Coffeepot, Lighthouse, Cup, Saucer, White, Blue, Lovebirds 500.00
Chinese Export, Coffeepot, Pear Shape, Famille Rose, Gilt, Reserve, C.1775 .... 250.00
Chinese Export, Coupe, Form Of Kneeling Woman, Famille Rose Enamel, C.1850 .... 525.00
Chinese Export, Creamer, Black Decoration, Flowers 90.00
Chinese Export, Creamer, Helmet, Rose Design 90.00
Chinese Export, Cup & Saucer, Coffee, Double Ogee, Famille Rose, C.1775, Pair 100.00
Chinese Export, Cup & Saucer, Gray White, Cartouches Of Pink Roses, Gold 40.00
Chinese Export, Cup & Saucer, Gray White, Pink Flowers, Lavender Edge 25.00
Chinese Export, Cup & Saucer, Single Rose & Wavy Line Decoration 20.00
Chinese Export, Cup, Gold Monogram In Oval, Green & Gold Leaf, Vine At Rim 8.75
Chinese Export, Dish, Crested, Famille Rose, C.1740, 9 7/8 In.Diameter 250.00
Chinese Export, Dish, Diamond Shape, Flat, Bamboo Sides, Flowers, Pair 400.00
Chinese Export, Dish, Famille Rose, Peonies, C.1745, 8 7/8 In.Diameter 130.00
Chinese Export, Dish, Hot Water, Court Scene, C.1785, Pair 650.00
Chinese Export, Dish, Hot Water, EEP In Shield, Lion & Snake Crest, C.1790 .... 200.00
Chinese Export, Dish, Hot Water, Oval, Shield, Gilt Stars On Blue, C.1790 .... 375.00
Chinese Export, Dish, Hot Water, Rockefeller Pattern, Scale, C.1785, Pair 625.00
Chinese Export, Dish, Hot Water, WPL In Shield, Lion Crest, C.1790 .... 225.00
Chinese Export, Dish, Lozenge Form, Famille Rose Court Figures, C.1850, Pair 150.00
Chinese Export, Dish, Meat, Covered, Oval, Potted, Famille Rose Floral, C.1780 .... 100.00
Chinese Export, Dish, Meat, Covered, Oval, Potted, Famille Rose, C.1770 .... 80.00
Chinese Export, Dish, Meat, Covered, Stand, Oval, Potted, Feathered Rim, C.1790 .... 200.00
Chinese Export, Dish, Off-White, Orchid Check Border, Floral Spray 13.50
Chinese Export, Dish, Vegetable, Covered, Blue & White, Oval, Pavilion, C.1790 .... 300.00
Chinese Export, Dish, Vegetable, Covered, Famille Rose, C.1830, 9 In.Long 225.00
Chinese Export, Figurine, Elephant, Standing, Flesh Tone, Yellow, C.1820 .... 325.00
Chinese Export, Figurine, Horse, Running, Hand Carved, Wood Base, 6 X 9 In. 130.00
Chinese Export, Figurine, Hotel, God Of Happiness, Five Children, Signed 145.00
Chinese Export, Figurine, Kylin, Seated, Ferocious Expression, C.1850, Pair 800.00
Chinese Export, Figurine, Magpie Birds On Branches, Plum Blossoms, 14 In. 250.00
Chinese Export, Figurine, Wise Man, Beard, Robe, Colored Glaze, 9 In. 45.00
Chinese Export, Holder, Brush, Turquoise, Branches, K'Ang Hsi 350.00
Chinese Export, Jar, Cookie, Water, Pagoda, Boat, Tree, Cobalt Blue, Ball Shape 45.00
Chinese Export, Jar, Ginger, Famille Noire, 8 Buddhist Emblems On Black 275.00
Chinese Export, Jar, Ginger, Wooden Top, Ovoid, Birds & Peonies, Pair 130.00
Chinese Export, Jar, Rectangular, White, Birds, Flowers, & Fowl, Pair 400.00
Chinese Export, Jardiniere, Double, Bat Shape, Famille Rose, C.1820, Pair 850.00
Chinese Export, Jardiniere, Kidney Shape, Famille Rose Insects, C.1850, Pair 250.00
Chinese Export, Jardiniere, Rectangular, Famille Rose, Footed, C.1800 .... 125.00
Chinese Export, Jug, Covered, Barrel Shape, WR In Shield, Blue, Gilt, C.1790 .... 200.00
Chinese Export, Jug, Hot Milk, Blue & White, Covered, Pear Shape, C.1800 .... 200.00
Chinese Export, Jug, Milk, Armorial, Famille Rose Bouquets, C.1750 .... 90.00
Chinese Export, Jug, Milk, Armorial, Wills Impaling Wakebridge, C.1750 .... 210.00
Chinese Export, Jug, Milk, Blue & White, Pyriform, Pavilions, Boats, C.1790 .... 80.00
Chinese Export, Jug, Milk, Pear Shape, Meissen Style, Harbor Scene, C.1750 .... 110.00
Chinese Export, Lamp, Gray, White, Dragon, Bird, Flowers, 12 In.High 475.00
Chinese Export, Lamp, Hexagonal Baluster, Famille Rose Floral, C.1780, Pair 250.00
Chinese Export, Lamp, Vase, Cylindrical, White, Garden Scene, Pair 650.00
Chinese Export, Mug, Barrel Shape, Husks & Dentil Motifs In Green, C.1785 .... 160.00
Chinese Export, Mug, Blue & White, Strap Handle, Pavilions, Figures, C.1780 .... 140.00
Chinese Export, Mug, Blue Scale, Famille Rose Harbor Scene, Floral, C.1780 .... 200.00
Chinese Export, Mug, Famille Rose Floral & Insects, Strap Handle, C.1770 .... 260.00
Chinese Export, Mug, Famille Rose Lotus, Peonies, & Insects, C.1770 .... 160.00
Chinese Export, Mug, Helmet Shape, Blue & White, Pavilions, Boats, C.1780 .... 80.00
Chinese Export, Mug, Puce, Iron, & Gilt Bouquets, Strap Handle, C.1785 .... 150.00
Chinese Export, Pillow, Cock, Blue & White, 5 X 6 In. 75.00

Chinese Export, **Pillow**, Etched Floral, Figures, Famille Rose, 19th Century 72.00
Chinese Export, **Plaque**, Sherman & Taft, C.1910, Pair .... *Illus* 450.00
Chinese Export, **Plate**, Allegorical, En Grisaille, Jupiter In Chariot, C.1790 .... 250.00
Chinese Export, **Plate**, Armorial, Cutler, Palm Fronds, C.1790, Pair 190.00
Chinese Export, **Plate**, Armorial, Gibson Impaling Green, Floral, C.1760, Pair 325.00
Chinese Export, **Plate**, Armorial, Herzeele Family, Peacocks, C.1740, Pair 300.00
Chinese Export, **Plate**, Armorial, Octagonal, C.1775, 9 1/2 In.Diameter 150.00
Chinese Export, **Plate**, Blue & White, Armorial, Order Of Bath, C.1790, Pair 175.00
Chinese Export, **Plate**, Blue Fitzhugh, Beale Crest 125.00
Chinese Export, **Plate**, Famille Rose Bird On Peony Tree, 1 Flying, C.1775 .... 50.00
Chinese Export, **Plate**, Fitzhugh, Green, 8 1/2 In.Diameter 17.50
Chinese Export, **Plate**, Floral Sprigs, Scattered Floral Border, C.1770 .... 42.00
Chinese Export, **Plate**, Fruit, Pierced Edge, Circa 1790, 7 1/2 In., Pair 70.00
Chinese Export, **Plate**, Octagonal, Shield, Crest, Doves, Gilt, Blue, C.1790 .... 37.50
Chinese Export, **Plate**, Soup, Armorial, Morgan, Palm Fronds, C.1795 .... 125.00
Chinese Export, **Plate**, Soup, Octagonal, Famille Rose Peacock, Peonies, C.1760 .... 60.00
Chinese Export, **Platter**, Blue Fitzhugh On White, Initials W.M.B., C.1760 .... 250.00

Chinese Export, Candlestick,
Elephant, C.1815, Pair
See Page 116

Chinese Export, Plaque,
Sherman & Taft, C.1910, Pair

Chinese Export, **Platter**, Central Bouquet, Floral Panels, Pink, Puce, C.1775 .... 150.00
Chinese Export, **Platter**, Famille Rose Brown Cornucopia, Octagonal, C.1775 .... 250.00
Chinese Export, **Platter**, Gray White, Monogram In Oval, Gold, Blue Bands 40.00
Chinese Export, **Platter**, Scalloped Edge, 15 In.Long 200.00
Chinese Export, **Sauceboat**, Pseudo-Tobacco Leaf, C.1745 .... *Illus* 150.00
Chinese Export, **Sauceboat**, Quatrefoil Shape, Buddhas On Lotus, C.1850, Pair 75.00
Chinese Export, **Saucer**, Doccia Decorated, Gold & Iron Scrolls, Scene, C.1755 .... 275.00
Chinese Export, **Saucer**, Grisaille Decorated, Scene, Scrolls, C.1760, Pair 125.00
Chinese Export, **Saucer**, Iron Lion Rampant Crest, Gilt Scrolls, C.1760, Pair 100.00
Chinese Export, **Saucer**, Monogram JSL In Cartouche, Iron Scrolls, C.1790 .... 29.50
Chinese Export, **Saucer**, White, Gold Band Edge, Scroll 5.00
Chinese Export, **Spoon**, Rice, Famille Rose Coloring Floral, Marked, Pair 12.50
Chinese Export, **Stand**, Oval, Pierced Basket Rim, Blue Floral, C.1785, Pair 400.00
Chinese Export, **Stand**, Quatrefoil, Brown Cornucopia, Pink Scale, C.1785 .... 90.00
Chinese Export, **Stand**, Teapot, Famille Rose Bouquets, Hexagonal Rim, C.1765 .... 130.00
Chinese Export, **Stand**, Tobacco Leaf, Leaf Shape, Bouquets, C.1750 .... 850.00

Chinese Export, **Stool**, Garden, Blue & White, Octagonal Barrel, Pair	250.00
Chinese Export, **Stool**, Garden, Famille Verte, Barrel, Pierced, C.1850	450.00
Chinese Export, **Sucrier**, Covered, Double Handled, Pavilions, Boats, C.1780	160.00
Chinese Export, **Sugar**, Covered, Pomegranate Finial, C.1790, 5 1/2 In.High	140.00
Chinese Export, **Tea Caddy**, Amorous Decoration, C.1775 *Illus*	350.00
Chinese Export, **Tea Caddy**, Covered, Armorial, Wood Family, Rectangle, C.1790	250.00
Chinese Export, **Tea Caddy**, Jesuit, Ovoid, Juno Seated In Clouds, C.1750	160.00
Chinese Export, **Tea Caddy**, Rectangular, Famille Rose Bouquets, C.1775	80.00
Chinese Export, **Teabowl & Saucer**, Famille Rose, Pink Scale, C.1770, Pair	70.00
Chinese Export, **Teabowl & Saucer**, White Relief Garlands Of Floral, C.1750	60.00
Chinese Export, **Teapot**, Armorial, European, Famille Rose Scenes, C.1775	250.00

Chinese Export, Sauceboat,
Pseudo-Tobacco Leaf, C.1745
See Page 117

Chinese Export, Tea Caddy,
Amorous Decoration, C.1775

Chinese Export, **Teapot**, Covered, Globular, Famille Rose Bouquets, C.1785	225.00
Chinese Export, **Teapot**, Cylindrical, Blue & White, Pavilions, Boats, C.1790	175.00
Chinese Export, **Teapot**, Decorated After Engraving By Bernard Picart	345.00
Chinese Export, **Teapot**, Floral, Circa 1790	185.00
Chinese Export, **Teapot**, Globular, Famille Rose Blossoms, Gilt, C.1760	160.00
Chinese Export, **Teapot**, Globular, Famille Rose Bouquets, Gilt, C.1770	225.00
Chinese Export, **Teapot**, Oval, FJS In Shields, Lion Rampant Crest, C.1790	150.00
Chinese Export, **Teapot**, Pseudo-Tobacco Leaf, C.1780 *Illus*	375.00
Chinese Export, **Teapot**, Straight Spout, Strap Handle, C.1790, 6 In.High	175.00
Chinese Export, **Tray**, Dragon Design, Brass, Handle, 5 1/2 In.	25.00
Chinese Export, **Tureen**, C.1790, 7 3/4 In.Long, Pair *Illus*	775.00
Chinese Export, **Tureen**, Covered, Stand, Blue & White, Octagonal, Scene, C.1780	650.00
Chinese Export, **Tureen**, Sauce, Stand, Oblong Octagonal, Famille Rose, C.1770	180.00
Chinese Export, **Tureen**, Stand, C.1790, 14 In.Long *Illus*	1500.00
Chinese Export, **Urn**, Figures, Characters, Lid, Ching Dynasty, 11 1/2 In.High	275.00
Chinese Export, **Vase**, Blue & White, Baluster, Landscape, C.1800, Pair	275.00
Chinese Export, **Vase**, Bulb, Blue, White, Circa 1790, 11 In.High	245.00
Chinese Export, **Vase**, Club Shape, Famille Verte, Combat Scene, K'Ang Hsi	850.00
Chinese Export, **Vase**, Family Scenes, Floral Panels, C.1780, Pair	1100.00
Chinese Export, **Vase**, Gray Crackle Glaze, Baluster Shape, 18th Century, Pair	250.00
Chinese Export, **Vase**, Miniature, Ovoid, Dragon Handles, C.1780, 6 In., Pair	450.00
Chinese Export, **Vase**, Red, Sang De Boeuf, White Rim, 18th Century, 10 In.	220.00
Chinese Export, **Vase**, Salmon, Polychrome & Gold Figures, Ormolu Stand, Pair	300.00
Chinese Export, **Vase**, Sepia Vignettes, Polychrome Scenes, Mandarin, Cover	450.00
Chinese Export, **Vase**, Shield Shape, C.1785, Pair *Illus*	6000.00
Chinese Export, **Vase**, Wall, Baluster, Y Pattern On Coral, Scene, C.1785	125.00
Chinese Export, **Vase**, White, Floral In Gold & Orange, Pair	50.00
Chocolate Glass, see Slag, Caramel	
Christmas Ornament, Light, Diamond Pattern, Emerald Green, Pressed Glass	12.00
Christmas Plate, see Collector Plate	
Christmas Tree Candleholder, Prong Type, Tin, Candles, Lot Of 14	14.75
Christmas Tree Ornament, Amberina, Scalloped Top, Footed, Baccarat	45.00
Christmas Tree Ornament, Ball, Green, Flat Brass Top, 4 1/2 In., Pair	20.00
Christmas Tree Ornament, Ball, Mercury Glass, 5 In.	15.00
Christmas Tree Ornament, Ball, Mercury Glass, 8 In.	75.00
Christmas Tree Ornament, Light, Blue Milk Glass, Diamond Grill, 3 5/8 In.	10.00
Christmas Tree Ornament, Light, Pressed Glass, Pair	5.50

Bennington pottery Toby pitcher, c. 1850.

Decorated earthenware jug made by Hubbell & Chesebro, Geddes, New York, 1868.

American pottery stein modeled after German stein.

Covered jar of tulip and leaf design made in southeastern Pennsylvania, c. 1830.

New York pottery flowerpot with ruffled flange and drip pan, mid-19th century.

Pennsylvania earthenware "Dove" plate, c. 1800.

American chalkware fruit centerpiece, 19th century.

Pennsylvania earthenware plate, "Deer's Chase," made by David Spinner, c. 1800.

Ceramic eagle mantel decoration, mid-19th century.

American Gothic-type shelf clock, made by Birge and Fuller, c. 1845.

Mantel clock with flat pediment and carved pilasters, mid-19th century.

American mahogany tall case clock with rounded hood, c. 1780–95.

Printed cast-iron mirror frame topped by an eagle, c. 1862.

Shaker perforated-tin paneled cupboard, made in Kentucky, 19th century.

Oakwood and gumwood kas with monochrome painting of fruit and flowers, late 17th-century American.

18th-century painted Pennsylvania dowry chest.

American Directory-style sofa with acanthus leaf decorated legs, c. 1810–25.

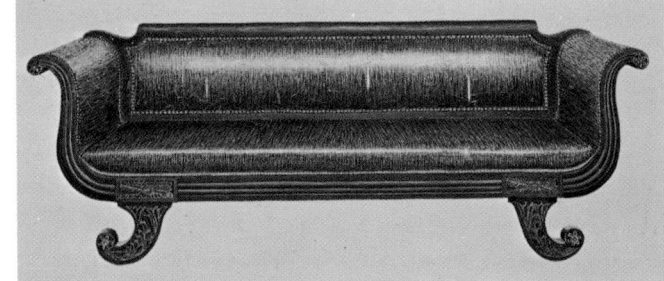

Ohio Shaker four-poster bed, mid-19th century.

American Sheraton-style inlaid writing desk, c. 1795–1800.

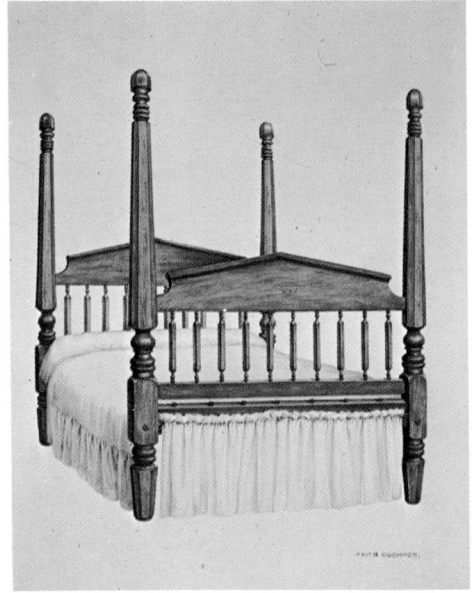

Mahogany lowboy with cabriole legs, made by William Savery, Philadelphia, c. 1760–75.

Card table with pineapple saw-tooth columns, American, c. 1820–40.

Late 18th-century American blockfront kneehole dressing table of solid mahogany.

Curly maple highboy, made in Pennsylvania, c. 1750.

American Hepplewhite-style bowfront chest of drawers, c. 1793–1803.

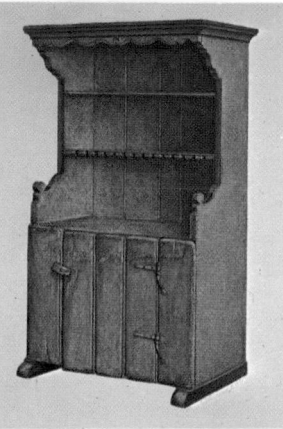

Pennsylvania open kitchen dresser, early 19th century.

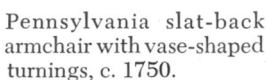

Pennsylvania slat-back armchair with vase-shaped turnings, c. 1750.

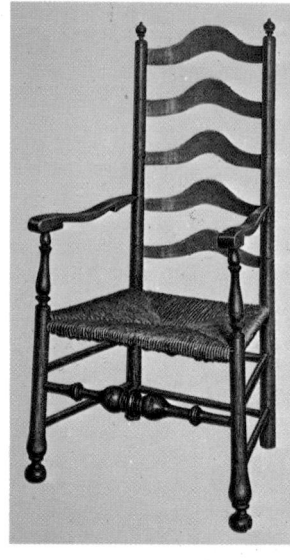

18th-century (American) Chippendale-style side chair.

Low-backed firehouse Windsor chair, American, c. 1840–65.

American Sheraton-style "drawing book chair," c. 1795–1810.

Late Victorian open-back chair with high seat and turned forelegs.

Cane-seated Hitchcock chair with fruit basket and leaf decoration, mid-19th century.

Ruby flashed tumbler with fluted sides and beading, 19th century.

Enameled Stiegel flip glass or runner, 18th century.

Eight-sided goblet with enamel decoration, early 19th century.

Heavy six-sided tumbler with arch design, 19th-century.

Striped glass molasses or syrup jar with silver-plated copper top, c. 1850.

Covered butter dish of red enamel over clear pressed glass, Pittsburgh, c. 1890.

Eagle flask made by Lancaster Glassworks, c. 1850–60.

Pattern glass sugar bowl with swirl finial, late 18th century.

Flint glass wine carafe in grape and vine motif, with overlay stopper, c. 1870.

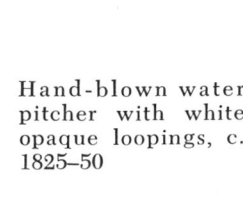

Hand-blown water pitcher with white opaque loopings, c. 1825–50

Chinese Export, Teapot,
Pseudo-Tobacco Leaf, C.1780
See Page 118

Chinese Export, Tureen, Stand,
C.1790, 14 In.Long
See Page 118

Chinese Export,
Tureen, C.1790,
7 3/4 In.Long, Pair
See Page 118

Chinese Export, Vase, Shield Shape, C.1785, Pair
See Page 118

Cinnabar, Cigarette Box, 3 In.
See Page 120

Christmas Tree Ornament, Light, Santa, Blown Glass, Circa 1935	4.00
Christmas Tree Ornament, Santa, Cloth, 4 1/2 & 2 1/2 In., 2	4.25
Christmas Tree Ornament, Santa, Japan, 6 In.	5.00
Christmas Tree Ornament, Square Diamond Pattern, Cobalt & Amber	6.50

*Cinnabar is a vermilion or red lacquer. Some pieces are made with hundreds
of thicknesses of the lacquer that is later carved.*

Cinnabar, Bottle, Snuff, Flattened Flask, Lacquer, Carved Woman, Ch'len Lung	60.00
Cinnabar, Bottle, Snuff, Flattened Shield Shape, Lacquer, Carved, Ch'len Lung	80.00
Cinnabar, Bottle, Snuff, Heart Shape, Lacquer, Carved Deer, Ch'len Lung, 1850	70.00
Cinnabar, Box, Carved, Dragon, White, Cover, China	35.00
Cinnabar, Box, Carved, People, Trees, Mountains, Mutton Fat Jade On Lid, China	145.00
Cinnabar, Box, Cigarette, Carved Foliage, Mountains, Trees, People	24.00
Cinnabar, Box, Cigarette, Match Cover, Bowl, Turquoise Lining, China	25.00

Cinnabar, Box, Covered, Lacquer, Round, Shu Character, Dragons, Gold 200.00
Cinnabar, Box, Garden Scene, Man, Woman, Marked China 10.00
Cinnabar, Box, Jewel, Cartouche, Lacquer, Carved Floral Vases, Ch'len Lung 1800.00
Cinnabar, Box, Marked China, 6 1/2 X 4 1/2 In. 27.50
Cinnabar, Box,. Mutton Fat Jade Medallion, Oriental Figures, Cover 175.00
Cinnabar, Box, Oriental Scene, Marked China, Round 12.00
Cinnabar, Box, Ornately Carved, Reign Of Ch'len Lung, 1736-1795 .... 50.00
Cinnabar, Box, Pin, Carved, Red, Oriental, Cover, 3 5/8 In.Long 15.00
Cinnabar, Box, Red, Garden Scene, Two Figures, Tree, Cover 30.00
Cinnabar, Box, White Jade Cover, Carved, 3 X 4 1/4 X 1 5/8 In. 49.00
Cinnabar, Button, Silver Mounting 12.00
Cinnabar, Cigarette Box, 3 In.   *Illus*   40.00
Cinnabar, Jar, Ginger, Covered, 10 In.High 245.00
Cinnabar, Panel, Stand, Lacquer, Double Sided, Lake Scene 200.00
Cinnabar, Urn, Oriental Scenes, Carved, Acorn Finial, Wood Base, 10 In., Pair 185.00
Cinnabar, Vase, Carved Figures In Landscape Design, 7 1/2 In. 75.00
Cinnabar, Vase, Carved Flowers & Scenes Of People, C.1750, 9 In.High 98.00
Cinnabar, Vase, Carved Foliage, People, Mountains, Trees, 6 1/4 In., Pair 50.00
Cinnabar, Vase, Carved, Paper Sticker, China, 8 1/2 In.High 85.00
Cinnabar, Vase, Carved, 20 In. X 12 In.High 185.00
Cinnabar, Vase, Figures, Tree, Mountain, 14 1/2 In.Tall, 7 In.Diameter, Pair 360.00
Cinnabar, Vase, Garden Scene, Carved Stand, Marked China, 6 1/2 In.High 75.00
Cinnabar, Vase, Mountain Scene, Teak Stand, 14 1/2 In.High, Pair 360.00
Cinnabar, Vase, 5 In., Teak Stand 65.00

Civil War Mementos are important collectors' items. Most of the pieces
are military items used from 1861 to 1865.
Civil War, Boots, Black Leather, Child's Size, 13 In.High, Pair 29.50
Civil War, Boots, Cavalry, Russet Leather, 17 In.High, Pair 37.50
Civil War, Boots, Officer's, Gray Suede Leather, Lined, Hip Length, Pair 69.50
Civil War, Boots, U.S.Cavalry, Black Leather, C.1870, Pair 34.50
Civil War, Box, Stamp, Crossed Rifles, Army Cap, Says Stamps, Silver Plate 65.00
Civil War, Box, Stamp, Hinged, Scrolls, Engraved, Quadruple Plate 65.00
Civil War, Button, Confederate 17.50
Civil War, Carbine, Sharp's 250.00
Civil War, Curry Comb, U.S.Cavalry Issue, Leather Block, Iron Combs 5.95
Civil War, Curry Comb, U.S.Cavalry, 8 1/2 In.Long 8.50
Civil War, Diary, 1864 .... 15.00
Civil War, Flag, Battle, Union, Framed, National Colors Of Infantry Regiment 275.00
Civil War, Fork & Spoon Combination, Slides Together With A Knife, 1861 .... 15.00
Civil War, Frog, Belt, U.S.Navy, For M1860 Cutlass, Black Leather 5.50
Civil War, Hat, American, Black Fur, Busby, Leather Visor 39.50
Civil War, Hobble, U.S.Cavalry, Leather Straps, Iron Chain 9.50
Civil War, Insignia, Infantry, Embroidered, For Slouch Hat 18.00
Civil War, Picture, Engraving, The Depot At Culpeper, Va., Frame 45.00
Civil War, Picture, The Battle Of Pittsburg Landing, 1862, Wood Engraving 15.00
Civil War, Pistol, Tower, Engraved, 17th Lancers 225.00
Civil War, Record, Lyon's Scouts, 127th Illinois Regiment, 98 Names 23.00
Civil War, Revolver, Moore, Engraved Frame, Silver On Brass, 7 Shot 175.00
Civil War, Saber, Light Cavalry, Sheath, Brass & Steel, U.S.1865 .... 80.00
Civil War, Saddle, Brown Leather Over Rawhide, McClellan 95.00
Civil War, Shaving Mug, Tin 12.50
Civil War, Shoes, Infantryman's, Wooden Soles, Leather, 1865, Pair 185.00
Civil War, Song, Tombigbic River, 1863, Hand Written 12.00
Civil War, Sword & Scabbard, Pommel, Washington's Head, Eagle 60.00
Civil War, Sword, Cavalry 100.00
Civil War, Valise, Saddle, Round Leather Box, Brass Plaque, C.1840 .... 19.50

Clambroth Glass, popular in the Victorian era, is a grayish color and is
semiopaque like the soup.
Clambroth, Bottle, Barber, Witch Hazel, Pewter Spout 10.00
Clambroth, Box, Trinket, Floral, Souvenir Of Kankakee, Ill. 37.50
Clambroth, Candlestick, Dolphin, Pair 525.00
Clambroth, Coal Hod, Souvenir, Bennington, Vermont 7.75
Clambroth, Cruet, Applied Blue Rope, Clear Faceted Stopper 65.00
Clambroth, Dish,. Double Hands With Grapes, Atterbury 27.50

Clambroth, Goblet, Button Arches, Gold Band	25.00
Clambroth, Incense Burner, Cameo Black Koro Design, Coral Inset Top	65.00
Clambroth, Lamp, Hand, Whale Oil, Waisted Loop	165.00
Clambroth, Pitcher, Water, Flute, Carnival Glass	70.00
Clambroth, Salt, Lacy, Sandwich Glass	75.00
Clambroth, Vase, Cameo, Blue Leaves & Stems, England, 5 1/4 In., Pair	175.00
Clambroth, Vase, Opalescent, Silver Color Decoration, Blown, 5 In.	20.00

*Clews Pottery was made by George Clews & Co. of Brownhills
Pottery, Tunstall, England, from 1906 to 1961.*

Clews, see also Flow Blue

Clews, Bowl, Soup, Historical Blue, States, 10 1/2 In.	70.00
Clews, Cup & Saucer, Handleless, Deep Blue, Urn Of Flowers	30.00
Clews, Cup & Saucer, Neptune, Dark Blue, Staffordshire	110.00
Clews, Plate, Don Quixote & Sancho Panza, Blue, 9 In.Diameter	88.00
Clews, Plate, Don Quixote Series, Sancho Panza At Boar Hunt, Staffordshire	95.00
Clews, Plate, Dr.Syntax Disputing Bill, 10 1/2 In.Diameter	80.00
Clews, Plate, Dr.Syntax Takes Possession Of His Lodging, 10 1/2 In.	90.00
Clews, Plate, Hudson R., Sandy Hill, Blue, Signed, 7 3/4 In.Diameter	45.00
Clews, Plate, Landing Of Lafayette, Blue, 10 In.Diameter	140.00 To 190.00
Clews, Plate, Picturesque Views Bakers Falls, Hudson River, Blue	125.00
Clews, Plate, States, Blue, 8 3/4 In.Diameter	150.00
Clews, Plate, States, Signed, 8 1/2 In.	140.00
Clews, Plate, Winter Scene, Pittsfield, 8 In.	115.00
Clews, Platter, Landing Of Lafayette, Castle Garden, Marked, 19 In.Wide	425.00
Clews, Tureen, Landing Of Lafayette, 5 1/2 In.	270.00
Clifton, Vase, Indian Ware, Terra-Cotta With Hand-Painted Black Designs	45.00
Clock, Alarm, Bell On Top, Junghan	15.00
Clock, Alarm, Circa 1910, Lot Of 6	36.00
Clock, Alarm, Dark Face With Moving Eyes, Green Bowtie, Coat	110.00
Clock, Alarm, Thirty Hour, Miniature, Seth Thomas	245.00
Clock, Ansonia, Brass, Glass, Porcelain Face, Strike, Pendulum, 17 In.High	175.00
Clock, Ansonia, Cast Iron, Mantel, Gold Trim On Black, 8 Day, Striker	75.00
Clock, Ansonia, Cottage, 8 Day	48.00
Clock, Ansonia, Crystal Palace, No Dome	260.00
Clock, Ansonia, Gingerbread, Kitchen, Oak, 8 Day, Striker, 22 In.High	70.00
Clock, Ansonia, Mantel, Black Japanned & Gold Gilded	115.00
Clock, Ansonia, Mantel, Iron, Black Finish, Gold, Scroll Base, Key Wind	35.00
Clock, Ansonia, Outside Escapement, Bevel Glass, Ornate French Case, Metal	200.00
Clock, Ansonia, Pink Porcelain	140.00
Clock, Ansonia, Regulator, Crystal, 11 In.High	145.00
Clock, Ansonia, Roses, Forget-Me-Nots, Porcelain Face, Time, Chime, 11 In.High	138.00
Clock, Ansonia, Royal Bonn Porcelain With Violets, Shell At Top	135.00
Clock, Ansonia, School, Calendar Hand, Brass Bezel, Glass Door, Pendulum	145.00
Clock, Ansonia, School, Long Drop, Striking	155.00
Clock, Arched Top, Inlaid, Mahogany, New Haven, 9 1/2 In.High	47.00
Clock, Art Nouveau, Cupid Pulling Bell Cords, Porcelain Face, Brass, 1902	31.00
Clock, Austrian, Wall, Weight Driven, Schloss Jugmundar, Painted Dial, C.1850	70.00
Clock, Banjo, Ansonia, 8 Day, Crystal, Crown, Porcelain Dial, Mercury Pendulum	175.00
Clock, Banjo, Ansonia, 8 Day, Crystal, Porcelain Dial, Mercury Pendulum, Brass	140.00
Clock, Banjo, Bigelow, Kenard, 8 Day, Crystal, Porcelain Dial	130.00
Clock, Banjo, Chinnocks Patent, Iron Front, 8 Day, Pin Type Movement, Strike	65.00
Clock, Banjo, Eight Day, Bim Bam Strike, Sessions, 35 In.	110.00
Clock, Banjo, Federal, Mahogany & Parcel Gilt, Drum, Acorn Finial, N.E., 1825	625.00
Clock, Banjo, Federal, Mahogany & Parcel Gilt, Drum, Eagle Finial, N.E., 1825	900.00
Clock, Banjo, Ingraham, Nyanaza, 8 Day, Reverse Black & Gold	125.00
Clock, Banjo, Ingraham, 8 Day, Treasure Isle Pirates, Brass Side Rails	140.00
Clock, Banjo, Inlaid Mahogany, Drum, Brass Eagle Finial, Eglomise, N.E., 1825	600.00
Clock, Banjo, Mahogany, New England, C.1820 *Illus*	775.00
Clock, Banjo, New England, Mahogany & Gilded Frame, C.1830	300.00
Clock, Banjo, New Haven, 8 Day, Crystal, Porcelain Dial, Mercury Pendulum	190.00
Clock, Banjo, New Haven, 8 Day, Reverse Ships At Sea, Brass Side Rails	140.00
Clock, Banjo, New Haven, 8 Day, Westminster Chime Glasses In Reverse, Brass	140.00
Clock, Banjo, New Haven, 8 Day, Whitney Picture Of Ships, Brass Side Rails	75.00
Clock, Banjo, Sessions, Somerset, 8 Day, Green Paint, Brass Side Rails	60.00
Clock, Banjo, Sessions, 8 Day, Reverse Lighthouse & Ship, Wood Side Rails	130.00

Clock, Banjo, Mahogany, New England, C.1820
See Page 121

Clock, **Banjo**, Seth Thomas, Clipper Ship, Anchors, Eagle, Electric 30.00
Clock, **Baroque**, Dore Bronze, 22k Gold Wash, Male, Female, Angel, Starr & Frost 1500.00
Clock, **Berry & Whitmore Co.**, Mahogany, Balloon, Bracket, Striking, C.1890 .... 50.00
Clock, **Boudoir**, Dore Bronze, Overall Figural Flower Forms, Beveled Crystal 24.00
Clock, **Boudoir**, Viennese, Gilt Metal & Enamel, Cartouche Shape Case, C.1890 .... 400.00
Clock, **Bracket**, Brass, Beveled Glass Sides, Porcelain Face, R.Schulz, 9 In. 185.00
Clock, **Brass Ship's Clock**, 6 In.Diameter 50.00
Clock, **Brass**, Skeleton, Pierced, Fretwork, Striking, Anchor Escapement, C.1850 .... 250.00
Clock, **Calendar**, Gingerbread, Oak, Ingraham 100.00
Clock, **Calendar**, Regulator, Oak, 36 In.Long 95.00
Clock, **Carriage**, Brass, French 120.00
Clock, **Carriage**, Brass, Repeating, Striking, Alarm, Lever Escapement 800.00
Clock, **Carriage**, Brass, White Enamel Dial, Hinged Bail Handle 90.00
Clock, **Carriage**, French, Brass Case, Hinged Bail Handle, White Enamel Dial 140.00
Clock, **Carriage**, French, Brass, Striking, Alarm, Lever Movement, White Dial 225.00
Clock, **Carriage**, Gold Plate Case, Cherubs, Bevel Glass, France 265.00
Clock, **Carriage**, Musical, Two Tunes, German 89.50
Clock, **Carriage**, Repeater, Waterbury, Brass 35.00
Clock, **Carriage**, Swiss, Silver & Enamel, Miniature, 15 Jewel Lever Movement 225.00
Clock, **Carriage**, Victor Fleury, French, Brass, Grande Sonnerie, Alarm 450.00
Clock, **Case**, Victorian, Carved Pointed Top, 5 Shelves 55.00
Clock, **Ceramic**, Double Handled, Arabic Scene, Marked Made In England 20.00
Clock, **Cherub On Top Of Clock**, Man With Bundle Of Wheat, France, 16 In.High 350.00
Clock, **China**, Erotic Scene 95.00
Clock, **China**, Porcelain Face, Aqua, Pink, Green, 13 In.Tall, 10 In.Wide 95.00
Clock, **Coalbrookdale**, Encrusted Floral, Scrolls, Spring Driven, C.1835 .... 100.00
Clock, **Composition Front**, Moving Bird, Wind, Keebler 15.00
Clock, **Continental**, Lantern, Brass, Alarm, 2 Graduated Bells, C.1690 .... 750.00
Clock, **Crystal Regulator**, Model Peer, Gold Visible Escapement 175.00
Clock, **Crystal Regulator**, Model Symbol, Ansonia 250.00
Clock, **Cuckoo**, Black Forest, Quail & Cuckoo, Carved Eagle & Oak Leaves 125.00
Clock, **Cut Glass**, Boudoir, Harvard Pattern 95.00
Clock, **Cylinder**, Silver Gilt & Enamel, Urn Shape, Onyx Base, C.1900 .... 550.00
Clock, **Davy Crockett**, Haddon, Electric, Illuminated, Animated, 1950s 115.00
Clock, **Desk**, Bronze, 7 In.Wide, 3 1/2 In.Tall 12.50
Clock, **Desk**, Crystal Ball Paperweight, Brass Works, France 125.00
Clock, **Devereux Bonly**, London, George Iii, Mahogany, Long Case, Brass, C.1750 .... 850.00
Clock, **Directoire**, Balthazar A Paris, Mantel, Ormolu, Hive Shape, C.1850 .... 225.00
Clock, **Dish**, Porcelain, Pendulum, American 12.00
Clock, **Double Dial**, Calendar, Oak, New Haven, 47 X 17 In. 325.00
Clock, **Draped Woman Holds Clock**, Pendulum, Painted Metal, Ch.Rucbot, 14 In. 127.50
Clock, **Dresden**, Rococo Style, Girl, Boy, & Floral, Crossed Swords, C.1850 .... 500.00
Clock, **Dutch**, Long Case, Burr Walnut, H.Il Ratsma, Jr., Harlingen, 1750 .... 2300.00

Clock, Dutch, Stoelklok, Strikes, C.1780 .... 1150.00
Clock, Edward K.Jones, Conn., Shelf, Mahogany, Stenciled, Spread Eagle, C.1830 .... 170.00
Clock, Eight Day, Green, Flowers, Porcelain Dial, Strike, Gilbert 100.00
Clock, Eight Day, Spindle Work On Top & Base, Waterbury 125.00
Clock, Elbe, New Haven, Walnut, Kitchen, Alarm, Cathedral Gong, 8 Day 150.00
Clock, Electric, Pluto, Animated, Allied Manufacturing Co., 1946 .... 90.00
Clock, Eli Terry & Sons, Shelf, Inlaid Mahogany, Pillar & Scroll, C.1825 .... 725.00
Clock, Empire Case, Tablet, Eight Day, Birge & Fuller 165.00
Clock, Fashion Model No.4 .... 800.00
Clock, Federal, Inlaid Birch & Cherry, Tall Case, E.Mallard, Maine, C.1800 .... 1650.00
Clock, Federal, Inlaid Mahogany, Shelf, Kidney Dial, Nathaniel Munroe, C.1810 .... 5000.00
Clock, Federal, Inlaid Mahogany, Tall Case, Simon Willard, Mass., C.1800 .... 1100.00
Clock, Federal, Mahogany, Tall Case, Shelf, Joshua Wilder, Mass., C.1790 .... 8500.00
Clock, Federal, Pine & Maple, Tall Case, Joshua Wilder, Mass., C.1800 .... 4500.00
Clock, Female Figure, Bronze, Onyx, Pair Urns, La Fontaine Aux Mesanges 325.00
Clock, Figure Of Scotsman, Dead Game, Fruit, N.Muller, N.Y., 1858, Metal Face 150.00
Clock, Fire, German, 16th Century, Globe Filled With Oil Which Burned Down 1275.00
Clock, Francis Stampfer, Red Lacquer, Dwarf, Long Case, Engraved, Cherub Mask 2100.00
Clock, French, Man With Wheat Bundle, Cherub With Legs Crossed 350.00
Clock, French, Silver Gilt & Enamel, Inkstand, E.Dreyfous, C.1900 .... 1150.00
Clock, George III Style, Miniature, Mahogany, Long Case, Brass Dial, Chimes 900.00
Clock, George III, John Yeile, Grove, Red Lacquer, Long Case, Scenes, C.1750 ...... 1000.00
Clock, Gilbert, Banjo, Windup, 23 In. 35.00
Clock, Gilbert, Boudoir, Gold Metal Case, Cupids, Dated 1904 .... 34.00
Clock, Gilbert, China, 8 Day 100.00
Clock, Gilbert, Concord, Victorian, Kitchen, Gingerbread, Oak, 8 Day, Strike 55.00
Clock, Gingerbread, Eight Day, New Haven 55.00
Clock, Grandfather, Thomas Logan, Dial Signed, Second & Calendar Dials 325.00
Clock, Grandfather, Visible Weights & Pendulum, Gustav Becker, 6 1/2 Ft. 300.00
Clock, Herchedehall, Grand Prize, Mantel 19.95
Clock, Hopalong Cassidy, Alarm 85.00
Clock, Hourglass, 18th Century 150.00
Clock, Iceman, Electric 10.00
Clock, Ingraham & Co., Shelf, Pine & Maple, Eglomise Panel, C.1880 .... 130.00
Clock, Ingraham, Calendar, Wall, Round Drop 165.00
Clock, Ingraham, Dew Drop, Calendar, Wall 150.00
Clock, Ingraham, Dew Drop, Rosewood Case, 8 Day 130.00
Clock, Ingraham, Figure Eight Door, C.1858 .... 85.00
Clock, Ingraham, Store Regulator, 15 X 32 In. 75.00
Clock, Ionic, Eight Day, Rosewood & Walnut Case, Ingraham 140.00
Clock, Ithaca, Calendar, Octagon Top 350.00
Clock, Ithaca, D.D.Kildare, Mantel 150.00
Clock, J.C.Brown, Ripple Front, Beehive 295.00
Clock, Jerome Gilbert & Grant, O.G.Label, 30 Hour 85.00
Clock, Jerome, Alarm, Miniature Steeple 65.00
Clock, Jerome, 8 Day, 2 Door 95.00
Clock, John Martin, London, Silver Mounted, Ebony Veneer, Bracket, C.1750 .... 3500.00
Clock, Kitchen, Blue & White Porcelain, Ships, Windmills, 30 Hour 48.50
Clock, Kitchen, Strike, Oak, C.1920, Ingraham 45.00
Clock, Kitchen, Wall, Frying Pan, 30-Hour, Handmade 7.50
Clock, Kreuber, Flowers, Porcelain, Pink, Green 125.00
Clock, La Roux, Paris, Rhinestone Pendulum Outside Of Face 1500.00
Clock, Lantern, Brass, French Striking Movement, Engraved, Spring Driven 170.00
Clock, Liberty Of London, Pewter, Blue Green Enamel Face, Art Nouveau Lines 200.00
Clock, Louis XVI, Japy Freres Movement, Brass & Pink Marble, Pair Urns 375.00
Clock, Lux, U.S.A., Cuckoo, Oak Leaves, Roman Numerals 28.00
Clock, Magnetic, Battery Operated, Labeled Bulle 45.00
Clock, Mantel, Art Nouveau, Gilt Metal, Female Figure, Scroll Legs 200.00
Clock, Mantel, Austrian, Carl Wurn In Wein, Ormolu Mounted Mahogany, C.1850 ..... 350.00
Clock, Mantel, Black, Copper Trim, Porcelain Face, Seth Thomas 40.00
Clock, Mantel, Black, Eight Half Columns, Ornate Face, Sessions 45.00
Clock, Mantel, Bronze Figurine, Porcelain Dial, New Haven, 20 X 15 In. 175.00
Clock, Mantel, Bronze, Marble, Figure Of Mercury, 1884, Ansonia 300.00
Clock, Mantel, Carved, Pillars, Eight Day Vista Strike, Chime, 1882, Ansonia 100.00
Clock, Mantel, Charles X, Leroy A Paris, Ormolu, White Enamel Dial, C.1890 .... 250.00
Clock, Mantel, Charles X, Ormolu Patinated Bronze, Painted Tole, C.1850 .... 200.00

Clock, Mantel, Crystal Regulator, Brass Case, Seth Thomas 100.00
Clock, Mantel, Empire, Ormolu, White Enamel Dial, Female Figure, C.1850 .... 325.00
Clock, Mantel, French, Gilt, Bronze, C.1805 .... *Illus* 6250.00
Clock, Mantel, Hand-Painted Face, Art Nouveau, 15 In.High 55.00
Clock, Mantel, Louis XV-XVI Style, Ormolu & Black Marble 250.00
Clock, Mantel, Louis XVI Style, Alabaster & Ormolu Mounted, Striking 175.00
Clock, Mantel, Louis XVI, Marble, Ormolu, Bronze, C.1755 .... *Illus* 750.00
Clock, Mantel, Mahogany, Musical, Canterbury & Westminster Chimes 150.00
Clock, Mantel, Marble 28.00
Clock, Mantel, Marble Inlay, Ansonia 65.00
Clock, Mantel, Oval Top, Strike, Mahogany, Seth Thomas 25.00
Clock, Mantel, Porcelain, Two Seminude Ladies, Two Cherubs 75.00
Clock, Mantel, Sessions, Electric, Mahogany, C.1938 .... 14.00
Clock, Mantel, Seth Thomas, Black, Simulated Marble Top, Columns, Gold Face 30.00
Clock, Mantel, Vaseline Glass, Daisy & Button, 14 In.Long, 6 In.High 140.00
Clock, Mantel, Walnut, Round Dial, Roman Numerals, Carved, Huntsman, C.1850 .... 200.00
Clock, Mantel, Walnut, Seth Thomas, Chimes 55.00
Clock, Mantel, Starr & Frost, Marble, Bronze Figures, Gold Washed 2500.00
Clock, Mantel, Westminster Chime, Eight Day, Seth Thomas 55.00
Clock, Mantel, 8 Day, Pristine, Walnut 69.00
Clock, Marble Base, Brass Eagle, Brass Inset At Base, 9 In.Wide Spread 145.00
Clock, Marble, Brass Face & Trim, White, Gold Trim, Square Base, 14 In.High 195.00
Clock, Meat, For Fireplace, Wheel, Hooks, Brass 150.00
Clock, Mission Style, Oak, Brass Pendulum, 17 In.High 56.00
Clock, Musical, Desk, Alarm, Cream Enamel Over Brass, Brass Feet 19.00
Clock, New Haven, Banjo, Eagle On Top, Brass Rails, 8 Day 125.00
Clock, New Haven, Banjo, Pendulum, Pictures Ship, 8 Day 85.00
Clock, New Haven, Pendulum, Pictures Blair House, 8 Day, Time Strike 10.00
Clock, New Haven, Pendulum, Pictures Ships, 8 Day, Time Strike 100.00
Clock, New Haven, 30 Hour, Original Tablet 75.00
Clock, Noah Pomeroy Iron, Cherubs On Case, 8 Day, Time Strike 125.00
Clock, Octagon, Drop Regulator, Seth Thomas 135.00
Clock, Office, Self Winding, Refinished 21 In.Case, C.1898, Oak 55.00
Clock, Office, Walnut, 30 Day, Seth Thomas, 19 In.Square 110.00
Clock, Pillar & Scroll, Chauncey Ives, C.1825 .... *Illus* 425.00
Clock, Porcelain Dial, Visible Escapement, Pansies, Floral, Ansonia 115.00
Clock, Porcelain, Cherubs, Gold Trim, 9 In.High, 5 1/2 In.Wide 125.00
Clock, Porcelain, Flowers, Cupid On Top, Blue, White, 19th Century, Germany 60.00
Clock, Porcelain, Ivory Color, Gold Tracery, C.A.W., Germany, 12 1/2 In.High 24.00
Clock, Porcelain, Violets, Beveled Glass Over Face, Seth Thomas, 5 1/2 In. 43.00
Clock, Porcelain, White, Lavender Pansies, Gold Border, Wreath Around Face 85.00
Clock, Railroad, Chronometer Co., Chicago, Embossed Oak, 21 In.Square 85.00
Clock, Rancoulet, Signed, Printemps, Gold Scroll Feet, Green Onyx, Pendulum 195.00
Clock, Regency, Mantle, Mahogany, White Enamel Dial, Brass Feet, C.1890 .... 100.00
Clock, Regulator, Bevel Glass On Four Sides, Bronze Frame, Wattles & Sons 75.00
Clock, Regulator, Calendar, Oak 145.00
Clock, Roy Rogers, Trigger On Face, Animated, Alarm Sounds Like Gun Shots 35.00
Clock, Russian, Malachite, Roman Numerals, C.1850, 10 1/2 In.High 950.00
Clock, Sarreguemines Face, 12 In.High 275.00
Clock, School, Chain Driven Fusee, Circa 1825, John Kerry 235.00
Clock, School, Glass Door, Pendulum, Eight Day, 19 In.Long 150.00
Clock, School, Glass In Door, Oak Case, Admiral 135.00
Clock, School, Time & Strike, Long Drop, Ornate, Germany, 25 In.High 125.00
Clock, Schoolhouse, Calendar, Eight Day, Oak, Waterbury 140.00
Clock, Schoolhouse, Eight Day, Oak, Sessions 100.00
Clock, Schoolhouse, New Haven, Regulator, Embossed Oak, Octagon 185.00
Clock, Schoolhouse, Regulator, Wall, Ingraham 125.00
Clock, Sessions, Cottage, Pennsylvania Pine, 8 Day, Key Wind, Tolls Hour 55.00
Clock, Sessions, Gingerbread, Kitchen, Calendar, Oak, 8 Day, Striker 110.00
Clock, Sessions, Mantel, Mahogany Finish, 8 Day 18.00
Clock, Sessions, School 125.00
Clock, Set, French, Cloisonne, Candlesticks, 11 In. .... *Illus* 2200.00
Clock, Seth Thomas, Alarm, White Metal, Stem Wind 28.50
Clock, Seth Thomas, Shelf, Inlaid Mahogany & Curly Maple, Eglomise Panel 160.00
Clock, Seth Thomas, Shelf, Stenciled, Crest Of Spread Eagle, C.1825 .... 475.00
Clock, Seth Thomas, Steeple, Walnut 85.00

Clock, Mantel,
French, Gilt,
Bronze, C.1805
See Page 124

Clock, Pillar & Scroll,
Chauncey Ives, C.1825
See Page 124

Clock, Mantel, Louis XVI, Marble,
Ormolu, Bronze, C.1755
See Page 124

Clock, Set, French,
Cloisonne, Candlesticks, 11 In.
See Page 124

Clock, **Seth Thomas**, Wall, Flat Weight Behind Board Which Lifts Up 285.00
Clock, **Shelf**, Carved Black Wood Case, Brass Bezel Door, C.1895, England 45.00
Clock, **Shelf**, Inlaid Rosewood, Coved Cornice, Eglomise Panel, American, 1850 .... 150.00
Clock, **Shelf**, Riley Whiting, Acanthus Leaf, Wood Works, 30 Hr., Mahogany, 1813 .... 275.00
·Clock, **Shelf**, Walnut Gingerbread Case, Strike, 30 Hour, Wm.L.Gilbert 68.00
Clock, **Ship's**, Brass, 6 In.Diameter 50.00
Clock, **Signed Cachard Sucr.De Ch.Le Roy**, Ormolu & Marble, Mantel, C.1850 .... 500.00
Clock, **Signed Louelsa Weller**, Brown Glaze, Floral, Art Nouveau 225.00
Clock, **Signed Pr.Le Roy A Paris**, Louis XVI, Ormolu, Cartel, C.1750 .... 575.00
Clock, **Signed Vor.Alex Rehm**, Louis XVI, Ormolu, Mantel, Female Masks, 1750 .... 4000.00
Clock, **Silas Hoadley**, Franklin Case, Upside Down Wooden Works 325.00
Clock, **Simon Willard**, Tall Case, Chippendale Federal, Inlaid Mahogany, 1766 .... 6000.00
Clock, **Smith's English**, Ltd., 'London 1945', 8 Day, 16 In.Diameter 35.00
Clock, **Smith's**, 8 Day, Marked London 1952, 15 In.Diameter 30.00
Clock, **St.Bernard Figure**, Metal 35.00
Clock, **Steeple**, Ansonia Brass & Copper Co., Reverse Eagle Painting 110.00
Clock, **Steeple**, Eight Day, Jerome & Co., New Haven, Conn. 165.00
Clock, **Steeple**, Floral On Lower Glass, E.N.Welch, Rosewood, 14 1/2 In.Tall 85.00
Clock, **Store**, Mayo's Tobacco, Baird Clock Co., N.Y., Registered 1878 .... 450.00
Clock, **Store**, Ward's Orange Crush, Reverse Paint, Always Time For Ward's 400.00
Clock, **Sundial**, Slate, American, 18th Century .... *Illus* 220.00
Clock, **Swiss**, Silver Gilt & Enamel, Upright Rectangular, C.1850 .... 175.00
Clock, **Syntex Time**, Electric, 31 In.High 50.00
Clock, **Table**, Brass, Alarm, Verge Movement, Pierced & Engraved Monarchs 525.00
Clock, **Table**, Brass, Verge Movement & Fusee, Drum Shape Case, Handle 300.00
Clock, **Table**, Zacharias Moller, Dantzig, Hexagonal, Gilt Metal, Alarm, C.1680 .... 3000.00
Clock, **Tall Case**, Chippendale, Cherry, Brass Finials, American, C.1770 .... 1000.00
Clock, **Tall Case**, Federal, Cherry, New England, C.1820 .... *Illus* 850.00

Clock, Tall Case, Federal, Inlaid Mahogany, C.1800 .... *Illus*	2500.00
Clock, Teardrop, Eight Day, Strike, Walnut Case, Gilbert	125.00
Clock, Tiffany & Co., Gilt Metal, Mantel, Striking, White Enamel Dial	180.00
Clock, Travel, Brass & Glass, French, Visible Works, 6 1/2 In.Tall	175.00
Clock, Victorian, Bracket, Oak, Silvered Metal, Gilt, Lion's Paw Feet, C.1850	325.00
Clock, Viennese, Gilt Metal & Enamel, Screen, Court Figures, C.1850	300.00
Clock, Viennese, Regulator, Cathedral Gong, Walnut, New Haven	185.00
Clock, Viennese, Regulator, Spring Driven, Porcelain Face, Walnut, 21 Day	120.00
Clock, Viennese, Regulator, 2 Weights, Porcelain Face, Walnut, Striker	200.00
Clock, Visible Escapement, Bronze, Porcelain Dial, Iron Base, New Haven	125.00
Clock, W.S.Conant, N.Y., Shelf, Inlaid Mahogany, Eglomise Panel, C.1825	80.00
Clock, Wall, Free Swinger, Germany	85.00
Clock, Wall, French, Pearl Inlay, Signed, 18 X 15 In.	85.00
Clock, Wall, German, Decorated Porcelain Dial, 56 X 17 In.	245.00
Clock, Wall, Sessions, Painted Scene, Eagle Finial, Brass Trim	75.00
Clock, Wall, Waterbury, 30 Day, Cherry Case, Second Hand, Time Only, 66 In.	450.00
Clock, Walt Disney, Pluto, Made In France	25.00
Clock, Waterbury, Carriage Type, Miniature, Porcelain Face, Patent 1905	18.50
Clock, Waterbury, Carriage, Brass, Beveled Glass, Hour Repeater	150.00

Clock, Sundial, Slate,
American, 18th Century
See Page 125

Clock, Tall Case, Federal, Cherry,
New England, C.1820
See Page 125

Clock, Tall Case, Federal, Inlaid Mahogany, C.1800

Clock, Waterbury, Doric, Painted Dial, 8 Day, Time Strike	60.00
Clock, Waterbury, Gallery, 26 In.	185.00
Clock, Waterbury, Mantel, Sears 1902 Catalogue	65.00
Clock, Waterbury, Ogee, 2 Weight, 30 Hour, Alarm, Dark Wood, Striker	75.00
Clock, Waterbury, Ornate Gold Dore, Chimes, Art Nouveau	150.00
Clock, Waterbury, Shelf, Inlaid Rosewood & Pine, Eglomise Panel, C.1870	90.00
Clock, Weight Driven, Gray & Pink Mouse Head On Top, Germany	10.00
Clock, Wells Forbes, N.H., Shelf, Mahogany, Scrolled Crest, Eglomise, 1842	150.00
Clock, Western Union Naval Observatory, Round, Battery Operated	49.65
Clock, Western Union Naval Observatory, Square, Battery Operated	49.65
Clock, Westminster, Wall, Chimes	250.00
Clock, White, Flowers, Eight Day, Strike, Kroeber, Porcelain	110.00
Clock, Will Rogers Figurine, Spelter, Lux	16.00
Clock, William & Mary Style, Miniature, Lantern, Brass, Turned Feet, C.1850	140.00
Clock, Willam L.Gilbert Clock Co., Conn., Shelf, Inlaid Rosewood, C.1825	110.00
Clock, Woman With Wings, Holds Wreath, Gilt Bronze, France, 9 3/4 In.	310.00

Clock, Wooden, Carved, Chimes 1/2 Hour & Hour, 14 In.High 265.00
Clock, Yellow Marble Base & Frame, Brass Eagle, 8 In.Wing Spread, 8 Day 135.00

*Cloisonne Enamel was developed during the nineteenth century. A glass
enamel was applied between small ribbon-like pieces of metal on a metal base.
Most Cloisonne is Japanese.*

Cloisonne, Ashtray, Red, Green, Leaves, Flowers, Marked China 12.00
Cloisonne, Bird, 10 In., Pair .... *Illus* 250.00
Cloisonne, Bottle, Snuff, Butterflies & Flowers 100.00
Cloisonne, Bottle, Snuff, Flask, Farmer & Buffalo On White, Ch'len Lung 60.00
Cloisonne, Bottle, Snuff, Flask, Still Life Reserves On Blue, Ch'len Lung 50.00

Cloisonne, Bird, 10 In., Pair

Cloisonne, Bottle, Snuff, Flowering Trees On Dark Ground, Tan 75.00
Cloisonne, Bottle, Snuff, Flowers, Yellow Butterflies On Light Ground 75.00
Cloisonne, Bottle, Snuff, Multicolored Dragon On Dark Ground, Brass Band 120.00
Cloisonne, Bottle, Snuff, Multicolors On White Ground 75.00
Cloisonne, Bottle, Snuff, Panda Bears On Bamboo & Blue Sky Ground 100.00
Cloisonne, Bottle, Snuff, Pear Shape, Lotus Blossoms On Turquoise, Stopper 50.00
Cloisonne, Bottle, Snuff, Stag & Doe On Trees & Flowers Ground 120.00
Cloisonne, Bowl, Black, White & Turquoise Floral, Goldstone, Footed, 7 In. 95.00
Cloisonne, Bowl, Blue Green Ground, Multicolor Flowers, China Stamp 22.00
Cloisonne, Bowl, Cover, Signed Kinkozan, 6 In.Diameter, 4 In.High 175.00
Cloisonne, Bowl, Flower Design, Black, Green, Pink, 4 1/2 In.Diameter 10.00
Cloisonne, Bowl, Miniature, Lid, Footed 48.00
Cloisonne, Bowl, Nut, Green, Red, Blue, Yellow Flowers, Signed 25.00
Cloisonne, Bowl, Pale Blue Tones, 5 In., Pair 5 In.Candlesticks 125.00
Cloisonne, Bowl, Red Ground, Blue & Pink Floral, Turquoise Lining, 4 1/2 In. 18.00
Cloisonne, Bowl, Rose, Black Ground, Panels, Birds, Flowers, Cover 125.00
Cloisonne, Box, Alligator Ground, Flying Bird, Leaves, Cover 135.00
Cloisonne, Box, Aqua Ground, Multicolor Flowers, Hinged Lid 18.50
Cloisonne, Box, Black, Blue Dragons, Cylinder Shape, 3 X 2 1/8 In.High 55.00
Cloisonne, Box, Blue, Floral, Marked China, 3 1/2 In. 25.00
Cloisonne, Box, Blue, Lamb On Lid, Oval 575.00
Cloisonne, Box, Blue, White Floral, Green Enamel Lining, Foo Dog Finial 45.00
Cloisonne, Box, Cigarette, Lid, Royal Blue, White, Red, Blue Flowers, Signed 35.00
Cloisonne, Box, Compartments, Floral On Yellow, 6 In.Long 18.50
Cloisonne, Box, Fish Scale Pattern, Double Tops For Cigarettes 42.00
Cloisonne, Box, Floral, Goldstone, Birds On Lid, 2 3/4 In.Diameter 45.00
Cloisonne, Box, Floral, Multicolor Ground, Blue Inside 48.00
Cloisonne, Box, Goldstone, Iris, Green Interior, Cover 45.00
Cloisonne, Box, Green, Cream Colored Flowers, Hinged Lid, Footed 30.00
Cloisonne, Box, Match, Allover Floral, Blue Ground 22.00
Cloisonne, Box, Patch, Flower Design, Gold Trim, 2 1/2 In.Diameter 22.00
Cloisonne, Box, Pill, Yellow, Multicolored Floral, Hinged Lid 22.00
Cloisonne, Box, Powder, Green, Bright Flowers, Marked China 27.00
Cloisonne, Box, Rectangular, White Carved Jade, Pastor Scene, Turquoise 375.00
Cloisonne, Box, Rouge, Black Ground, Multicolor Motif, Cover 85.00
Cloisonne, Box, Stamp, Blue, Pink Floral, Marked China 10.50
Cloisonne, Box, Stamp, Brass, Marked China, 1 X 1 1/2 In. 14.00

Cloisonne, Box, Turquoise, Flowers, Cover, 2 In. 20.00
Cloisonne, Box, Water Buffalo Reclines On Lid, Blue, 8 3/4 In.Long 1000.00
Cloisonne, Box, Yellow Ground, Chrysanthemum, Enamel Inside, Cover, Footed 27.50
Cloisonne, Buckle For Belt, Lady's, Butterfly Shape 65.00
Cloisonne, Candleholder, Blue Panda, Gold Plate Bear On Lid On Back 950.00
Cloisonne, Candlestick, Pricket, Buddhist Emblems, Ch'len Lung, Pair 925.00
Cloisonne, Clock & Candelabra Set, Dragon Handles, Elephant's Heads 800.00
Cloisonne, Dish, Candy, Floral On Black, 3 Compartments, Foo Dog Handle 97.50
Cloisonne, Dish, Candy, Lid, Royal Blue, White, Red, Blue Flowers, Signed 46.00
Cloisonne, Dish, Green Ground, White Floral, 1 In.Deep, 4 1/2 In.Diameter 18.50
Cloisonne, Ewer, 6 In.Tall 87.50
Cloisonne, Figurine, Bird On Mountain, Red, Blue, Pink, 7 In.High 150.00
Cloisonne, Figurine, Bird, Perched On Top Of Mountain, Red, Blue, Pink, 7 In. 150.00
Cloisonne, Figurine, Carp Swimming, Jointed Sections, 8 In.Long 75.00
Cloisonne, Figurine, Crane, Standing, Candleholder In Beak, C.1850, Pair 1900.00
Cloisonne, Figurine, Fish, Swimming Carp In Jointed Sections, Black, Orange 80.00
Cloisonne, Figurine, Mule, Carries Two Water Caskets, 6 X 7 In. 250.00
Cloisonne, Holder, Cigarette, Silver Gilt, Horn Shape Terminal, C.1900 .... 130.00
Cloisonne, Holder, Match Box, Yellow Ground, Blue & Green Floral 12.00
Cloisonne, Incense Burner, Tripod, Imperial, Gilded Bronze, Chia Ch'Ing 3600.00
Cloisonne, Incense Container, Blue Horse, Hollow Body 495.00
Cloisonne, Jar, Cigarette, Aqua, Chinese Emblem 40.00
Cloisonne, Jar, Ginger, Black Ground, Floral, Gold Outlines, 7 1/2 In.High 65.00
Cloisonne, Jar, Ginger, Blue Green, Pastel Decoration, Lid, Pair 85.00
Cloisonne, Jar, Ginger, Yellow Ground, Blue, White, Pink, Red Floral 65.00
Cloisonne, Jar, Ginger, Yellow, Green Leaves, Pink & Blue Flowers 75.00
Cloisonne, Jar, Rose, White, Scrolls, Blue Green Lining, Marked China 28.50
Cloisonne, Jar, Swirl Effect, Floral, Goldstone, Mushroom Shape Lid 59.50
Cloisonne, Jardiniere, Light Green Ground, Shaded Floral, Marked China 85.00
Cloisonne, Jardiniere, Tree Plant, Carved Jade Flowers, Leaves, 28 In.High 650.00
Cloisonne, Lamp, Brass And Teakwood Base, Flowers And Butterlies 95.00
Cloisonne, Lamp, White Ground, Black Floral, 9 In. 52.00
Cloisonne, Mirror, Hand, Hair Brush, Floral, Ormolu Handles, Art Nouveau 84.00
Cloisonne, Napkin Holder, Blue, Dragon 8.50
Cloisonne, Napkin Ring, Black Ground, Finely Woven Web Of Cloisonnes 11.00
Cloisonne, Napkin Ring, Maroon, Gold Floral 10.00
Cloisonne, Napkin Ring, Turquoise Ground, Red & Yellow Floral 20.00
Cloisonne, Napkin Ring, White Ground, Cobalt Dragon, Blue Lined 12.00
Cloisonne, Napkin Ring, White, Blue Dragon 18.00
Cloisonne, Napkin Ring, Yellow Ground, Black Flower & Leaves, Aqua Lining 12.50
Cloisonne, Plaque, Blue Ground, Fans, Floral, 11 In.Diameter 95.00
Cloisonne, Plaque, Goldstone & Black Ground, Green, Red, White Dragon 170.00
Cloisonne, Plaque, Green Ground, Allover Pink Roses, Birds, Geometric Border 85.00
Cloisonne, Plaque, Roses, Leaves, Birds, Green, Pink, 11 1/2 In.Diameter 85.00
Cloisonne, Plaque, Three Quail, Floral, Blue Ground, 18 In.Diameter 200.00
Cloisonne, Plate, Blue Cranes Mounted On Gilt Base Of Elephant Heads 175.00
Cloisonne, Plate, Blue Fan, Flowers, Open Book, Scenic, House, Tree, 12 In. 135.00
Cloisonne, Plate, Floral, Bird, Japanese, 8 1/2 In.Diameter 90.00
Cloisonne, Plate, Flower Design, Iris, Unsigned, 9 1/2 In.Diameter 79.00
Cloisonne, Plate, Landscape, Floral, Butterfly, Heron, Goldstone, 12 In. 135.00
Cloisonne, Plate, Pink, White, Yellow Floral & Geometric Designs, 12 In. 75.00
Cloisonne, Plate, Watergarden Scene, Unsigned, Blue, 9 3/4 In.Diameter 78.00
Cloisonne, Pot, Saki, Blue Ground, Green & White Floral, 19th Century, Japan 100.00
Cloisonne, Pot, Wine, Blue & Green, Japanese, 4 In.High 90.00
Cloisonne, Rose Bowl, Lid, Black Ground, Geometrics 77.00
Cloisonne, Salt & Pepper, Green, Floral, Marked China 16.00
Cloisonne, Salt, Open, Pepper Shaker, Turquoise, Red & Yellow Floral 22.00
Cloisonne, Teapot, Blue Ground, Butterflies, Floral, Miniature, 2 1/4 In. 45.00
Cloisonne, Teapot, Inlaid With Butterflies, 6 In.High 25.00
Cloisonne, Teapot, Miniature, Gold Stone, Overall Flower Decor 97.50
Cloisonne, Teapot, Sugar, Creamer, Pair Cups & Saucers, Black, Gold, Dragons 265.00
Cloisonne, Teapot, White Ground, Allover Multicolor Floral 195.00
Cloisonne, Teapot, White, Floral 195.00
Cloisonne, Tile, Tree, Flowers, Bird, Floral Border, 6 In.Square 37.50
Cloisonne, Tray, Black Ground, Yellow & White Dragons, C.1820 .... 84.00
Cloisonne, Tray, Brush, Footed, Floral On Blue 45.00

Cloisonne, Tray, Ducks, Fans, Butterflies, Shells, Floral, Brass Handles, Rim 125.00
Cloisonne, Tray, Says Made In China In Gold In Panel, 10 X 7 In. 53.00
Cloisonne, Urn, Ormolu Mounted, Young Lovers, Pomegranate Finial, Pair 230.00
Cloisonne, Urn, Ritual, White Ground, 9 Colors, C.1780, Pair 2500.00
Cloisonne, Urn, Temple, Cover, Black, Colorful Dragons, 7 In. 65.00
Cloisonne, Urn, Yellow, Pink & Red Floral, Cover, China, 10 1/2 In., Pair 185.00
Cloisonne, Vase, Beige, Colorful Floral, 7 1/2 In., Pair 90.00
Cloisonne, Vase, Birds, Butterflies, Floral, Three Panels, Japan, 6 In., Pair 240.00
Cloisonne, Vase, Black With Dragon 40.00
Cloisonne, Vase, Blue Floral Ground, American & Chinese Flags, 8 In. 240.00
Cloisonne, Vase, Blue Green Ground, Multicolor Flowers, China Stamp, 6 In. 45.00
Cloisonne, Vase, Blue Ground, Floral, Foliage, Scrollwork, 9 1/2 In.High 65.00
Cloisonne, Vase, Blue Ground, Floral, Japan, 6 1/2 In., Pair 85.00
Cloisonne, Vase, Blue Ground, Flying Eagle, Swallow Among Pines, Snow 165.00
Cloisonne, Vase, Blue Ground, Lilies, Pink Daisies, 6 1/2 In., Pair 95.00
Cloisonne, Vase, Blue Ground, Pink Floral, Incised China 18.00
Cloisonne, Vase, Blue, Black On Copper, 9 In.Tall, Pair 95.00
Cloisonne, Vase, Blue, Overall Floral, Butterflies, Gold Mica In Base, 5 In. 37.50
Cloisonne, Vase, Blue, Scenes, House, Lake, Mountains, Silver Base, 1880, Pair 175.00
Cloisonne, Vase, Brown Tones, Turquoise, Rust, Green, Bird & Butterfly, 7 In. 50.00
Cloisonne, Vase, Chinese Tree Limb, White, Pink And Blue, 10 1/2 In.High 155.00
Cloisonne, Vase, Club Shape, Rouleau, Shrubs Of Seasons, C.1850, Pair 200.00
Cloisonne, Vase, Dark Gray & Silver, Pair 37.50
Cloisonne, Vase, Dragon Design, Black Ground, Yellow Decoration, 9 In., Pair 110.00
Cloisonne, Vase, Dragon, Phoenix, Goldstone, Multicolor, Circa 1890, 9 In. 95.00
Cloisonne, Vase, Dragons, Clouds, 9 In., Pair 600.00
Cloisonne, Vase, Dragons, Stand, Pair 100.00
Cloisonne, Vase, Dragons, 9 In.High, Pair 600.00
Cloisonne, Vase, Enamel, Gilt, Man, Woman, Gray Base, White Lined, Pair 87.50
Cloisonne, Vase, Fishscale, Green Ground, Red & Pink Floral, 4 In., Pair 60.00
Cloisonne, Vase, Fishscale, Roses, Bamboo Stalks, Japan, 6 3/4 In. 55.00
Cloisonne, Vase, Fishscale, 2 In.High 20.00
Cloisonne, Vase, Flag Of China Crossed By 41 Star U.S.Flag On Floral 200.00
Cloisonne, Vase, Flowers, Butterfly, Blue, Enamel, French, 6 3/4 In. 75.00
Cloisonne, Vase, Flowers, Leaves, Green, Rust, 12 1/2 In.Tall, Pair 185.00
Cloisonne, Vase, Flowers, Swirled, Blue, Black, Green, 6 1/2 In.Tall, Pair 125.00
Cloisonne, Vase, Four Blue & Green Panels, Butterflies, Cherry Blossoms 24.00
Cloisonne, Vase, Gold Ground, Red Flowers, Green Leaves, 5 1/4 In., Pair 75.00
Cloisonne, Vase, Gourd Shape, Aqua, Red, Yellow, & Green, 6 In.High 15.00
Cloisonne, Vase, Green, Purple Snakes, Varicolored Birds 65.00
Cloisonne, Vase, Lavender Stone Ground, Butterflies, Floral, 9 In. 60.00
Cloisonne, Vase, Oriental Scene, Black, Gold, Signed, 7 In.Tall 59.00
Cloisonne, Vase, Purple Enamel, Blue & White Dragon, 5 1/2 In.High 65.00
Cloisonne, Vase, Royal Blue, Multicolored Flowers, 12 In. 75.00
Cloisonne, Vase, Rust Ground, China, 6 In.High 18.50
Cloisonne, Vase, Silver Base & Wires, Black Ground, Flying Cranes, 1880 .... 150.00
Cloisonne, Vase, Stick, Black, Diamond-Quilted Stems, Floral, 7 In., Pair 150.00
Cloisonne, Vase, Tan With Flowers, 3 In. 28.00
Cloisonne, Vase, Tan, Brown, Turquoise, Butterflies, Birds, Flowers, Panels 75.00
Cloisonne, Vase, White Design, Pigeon Blood 25.00
Cloisonne, Vase, White Fish Scale With Purple Iris, 3 5/8 In.High 20.00
Cloisonne, Vase, White Ground, Brown, Pink & Blue Dragon, 4 In.High 35.00
Cloisonne, Vase, Wood Stand, 7 1/2 In.High, Pair 75.00
Cloisonne, Vase, Yellow, Multicolor Phoenix Decoration, Japan, 8 1/2 In. 185.00

Cluthra Glass is a two-layered glass with small air pockets that form white spots. The Steuben Glass Works of Corning, New York, made it after 1903. Kimball Glass Company of Vineland, New Jersey, made Cluthra from about 1925.

Cluthra, see also Steuben
Cluthra, Bowl, White, Green Band At Top, Steuben 250.00
Cluthra, Vase, Amethyst, Steuben, 10 In.High 450.00
Cluthra, Vase, Blue & White, Shaded, Signed, 8 1/2 In.High 345.00
Cluthra, Vase, Blue To White At Bottom, Signed Two Places, 8 1/4 In.High 385.00
Cluthra, Vase, Blue, Kimball, Signed, 12 In.High 250.00
Cluthra, Vase, Fleur-De-Lis Design, Blue, Signed, Bulbous, 9 In.Tall 695.00

Cluthra, Vase, Green Jade, Flared Top, 6 In.Tall	70.00
Cluthra, Vase, Green Jade, Flared, England	88.00
Cluthra, Vase, Green, White, Signed Monart, 10 In.	60.00
Cluthra, Vase, Kimball, Tortoiseshell Mottle, Green Shading, 6 1/2 In.	165.00
Cluthra, Vase, Planter Shape, Shaded White To Green, Signed	265.00
Cluthra, Vase, Red On Clear Glass, Footed, 5 1/2 In.High	175.00
Cluthra, Vase, Strawberries, Alabaster Handles, Urn Shape, Signed	595.00
Cluthra, Vase, Violet Color	45.00
Cluthra, Vase, White, Unsigned, 10 In.High	450.00

Coalbrookdale was made by the Coalport porcelain factory of England during the Victorian period. The pieces are heavily decorated with floral encrustations.

Coalbrookdale, Taperstick, Snuffer, Leaf Shape Drip Pan, Floral, C.1820	40.00
Coalbrookdale, Teapot, Ovoid, Squat, Flower Encrusted, Shells, C.1820	100.00

Coalport Ware has been made by the Coalport Porcelain Works of England from 1795 to the present time.

Coalport, Coffe Can, White & Gold, C.1880, 6 In.High	75.00
Coalport, Cornucopia, Dolphin, Pair	55.00
Coalport, Cup & Saucer, Blue Ground, Birds, Gold, C.1850, Hand-Painted	85.00
Coalport, Cup & Saucer, Cobalt, Floral Masses, Circa 1835	72.00
Coalport, Cup & Saucer, Demitasse, Allover Blue Floral, Signed	10.00
Coalport, Cup & Saucer, Mustache, Ribbed, Gold Handle, Circa 1891	35.00
Coalport, Cup & Saucer, Pink, Panels Of Flowers, Circa 1840	60.00
Coalport, Inkstand, Double, Rectangular, Shell Handles, Floral, C.1830	60.00
Coalport, Inkwell, Shell Shape, Flower Encrusted, Pierced, C.1835	80.00
Coalport, Pitcher, Baskets Of Flowers In Relief, Roses & Floral, 9 1/2 In.	45.00
Coalport, Plate, Hand-Painted Flowers, Circa 1840, 9 In.	41.00
Coalport, Soup, Indian Tree	13.00
Coalport, Tea Set, Indian Tree, 20 Piece	125.00
Coalport, Tea Set, White, Flower Groups, Gold Trim, Crown Mark, 3 Piece	95.00
Coalport, Teapot, Miniature, Globular, C-Scrolls, Gilt, Turquoise, C.1820	190.00
Coalport, Tray, Tree Of Life, Scalloped Edge, England, 12 In.	25.00
Coalport, Urn, Raised Floral, Two Handles, Cover, Circa 1820, 11 In.High	235.00
Coalport, Vase, Aqua Ground, Red, White, Gold Beading, Jeweled, 3 1/2 In.	85.00
Coalport, Vase, Jeweled, Gold Neck, Blue Ground, Signed, 3 1/8 In.High	110.00
Coalport, Vase, Rose Pompadour, Covered, Gilt Scrolls, Birds, C.1871, Pair	800.00

Cobalt Blue Glass was made using oxide of cobalt. The characteristic bright dark blue identifies it for the collector. Most Cobalt Glass found today was made after the Civil War.

Cobalt Blue, see also Shirley Temple

Cobalt Blue, Bell, 10 In.High	135.00
Cobalt Blue, Bottle, Bar, Cut Panels At Base & Neck, 10 1/2 In.High	40.00
Cobalt Blue, Bottle, Bar, Eight Broad Panels	40.00
Cobalt Blue, Bottle, Pewter Screw On Lid, 2 1/2 In.High	20.00
Cobalt Blue, Bottle, Rectangular, 4 1/4 In.High	3.50
Cobalt Blue, Bowl, Console, Pairpoint, 12 In.Diameter	65.00
Cobalt Blue, Bowl, Expanded Glass, Iridescent, Black Glass Footed Base	35.00
Cobalt Blue, Bowl, Finger, Blown, Heavy Swirl	40.00
Cobalt Blue, Bowl, Footed, Narrow White Rim, 4 1/2 In.Diameter	55.00
Cobalt Blue, Bowl, Wide & Narrow Alternating Panels, Scalloped Edge, Flint	50.00
Cobalt Blue, Box, Flowers, Beading, Enamel, Hinged, 2 1/2 X 2 1/2 In.	37.00
Cobalt Blue, Box, Glass, Round And Hinged, Four Fancy Ormolu Feet	95.00
Cobalt Blue, Box, Hinged, Brass Feet, Round, Shamrocks In White & Pink	98.00
Cobalt Blue, Box, Jewelry, Allover Gold Decor, Hinged, 5 1/2 X 3 1/2 In.	65.00
Cobalt Blue, Candelabrum, Three Candle, Scrolls On Arms & Stem, 6 1/2 In.	22.00
Cobalt Blue, Candlestick, Pin Dots, Pairpoint, 10 1/2 In.High, Pair	65.00
Cobalt Blue, Candlestick, Wide Base, 9 In.High, Pair	25.00
Cobalt Blue, Carafe, Overlay, Cut, Clear, 7 In.High	27.50
Cobalt Blue, Compote, Clear Threaded Glass Stem, Scalloped Base	20.00
Cobalt Blue, Compote, White Edge, Rough Pontil, Blown	47.50
Cobalt Blue, Console Set, Flower Design, Enamel, Cover	185.00
Cobalt Blue, Creamer, Blown, Applied Curled Handle, 4 In.High	140.00

Cobalt Blue, Creamer, Sterling Silver Deposit, Art Nouveau Flowers	8.00
Cobalt Blue, Cruet, Thumbprint	15.00
Cobalt Blue, Cup, Dose, Wyeth	4.00
Cobalt Blue, Cup, Spit, Lady's, Pairpoint, 3 1/4 In.High	27.00
Cobalt Blue, Decanter, White Spiral Stripes, Pair	160.00
Cobalt Blue, Finger Bowl, Underplate, Corning	55.00
Cobalt Blue, Goblet, Clear Squatty Stem	5.00
Cobalt Blue, Goblet, Greek Key, Dated 1877	31.50
Cobalt Blue, Hair Receiver, Flower Design, Gold Trim	18.00
Cobalt Blue, Hat, Three Mold, Diamond & Checker	210.00
Cobalt Blue, Hen, Large	37.50
Cobalt Blue, Lemonade Set, Hand-Painted Enamel Flowers, 13 Piece	145.00
Cobalt Blue, Lemonade Set, Silver Trim, Pitcher & 12 Glasses	45.00
Cobalt Blue, Letter Holder, Gold Trim, Germany	18.00
Cobalt Blue, Mug, Enamel, Blown, Applied Handle	48.00
Cobalt Blue, Mustard, Round, Pewter Top & Bottom	15.00
Cobalt Blue, Ornament, Christmas, Bunch Of Grapes, Hanger, 6 In.Long	35.00
Cobalt Blue, Pitcher, Lemonade, Applied Handle, Lid, 9 In.	40.00
Cobalt Blue, Pitcher, Sailboat Design	12.00
Cobalt Blue, Pitcher, Swirled Rib, Applied Handle, 3 1/2 In.High	7.50
Cobalt Blue, Pitcher, Water, Enamel Decoration, Gold Trim, Fluted, Ruffled	25.00
Cobalt Blue, Pitcher, Water, Royal Lace	47.50
Cobalt Blue, Rose Bowl, White Decoration, Satin Glass	50.00
Cobalt Blue, Salt, Lafayette	50.00
Cobalt Blue, Salt, Metal Holder	6.50
Cobalt Blue, Salt, Open, Pedestal, Hexagonal, Blown	6.00
Cobalt Blue, Salt, Openwork, Sterling Silver Holder, Open	12.00 To 15.00
Cobalt Blue, Salt, Pittsburgh, Anchor On Bottom	230.00
Cobalt Blue, Sherbet, 3 3/4 X 4 In.High	12.00
Cobalt Blue, Shoe	10.00
Cobalt Blue, Shoe, Lady's, Blue, White Coralene Trim, Germany	30.00
Cobalt Blue, Shoe, White Cameo On Front, Gold Trim, Marked Germany	12.00
Cobalt Blue, Slipper, Lady's High Heel	7.50
Cobalt Blue, Slipper, Souvenir, Mohawk Trail	4.75
Cobalt Blue, Sugar, Blown, Expanded Pattern, Applied Twisted Finial	65.00
Cobalt Blue, Sugar, Covered, Folded Rim On Cover, 10 In.High	500.00
Cobalt Blue, Sugar, Covered, Footed, Swirled To Left, Broad Swirl On Lid	340.00
Cobalt Blue, Table Set, Sawtooth Pattern, 4 Piece	240.00
Cobalt Blue, Teapot, Gold Ferns Allover, 7 In.High	45.00
Cobalt Blue, Toothpick, Cube	7.50
Cobalt Blue, Tray, Flowers, Leaves, Scrolling, Handle, Marked, 13 In.Across	35.00
Cobalt Blue, Tumbler, Enameling	18.00
Cobalt Blue, Tumbler, Overlay, Cut To Clear, 3 3/4 In.High	12.50
Cobalt Blue, Vase, Bud, Urn Shape, 8 In., Pair	13.00
Cobalt Blue, Vase, Flip, Pairpoint, 8 In.High	55.00
Cobalt Blue, Vase, Gold Band Around Edge, Flares At Top, 7 In.High	45.00
Cobalt Blue, Vase, Gold Hummingbird & Leaves, 4 1/2 In.	6.00
Cobalt Blue, Vase, Scalloped Flared Rim, Blown	14.00
Cobalt Blue, Vase, Silver Design On Top, 10 In.High, Pair	15.00
Cobalt Blue, Vase, Sterling Floral & Leaf Overlay, 8 In.High	35.00
Cobalt Blue, Vase, Tall, Pair	5.00
Cobalt Blue, Wine Set, Hand Cut Overlay, Handle & Stopper, Stemmed, 7 Piece	60.00
Cobalt Blue, Wine, Blue, Pedestal, Pair	39.00
Cobalt Blue, Wine, Metal Base, Signed Chase, U.S.A.	3.25

Coca-Cola Advertising Items have become a special field for collectors.

Coca-Cola, Ad, 1905, 4 Passengers In Car Being Served Coke, Black & White	5.00
Coca-Cola, Ad, 1937, Full Page, Color	3.25
Coca-Cola, Ad, 1938, Full Page, Color	3.25
Coca-Cola, Badge, Tin, 'Refreshing, ' Red, Gold Border, 9 In.Diameter	30.00
Coca-Cola, Barrel, With Stand, Label	45.00
Coca-Cola, Billfold, Man's, 1950s, Original Coke Box	10.00
Coca-Cola, Blotter, Boy Scout Holds Bottle	5.00
Coca-Cola, Blotter, Red Lettering On White, 1920s	2.50
Coca-Cola, Booklet, Know Your Planes, 1943	10.00
Coca-Cola, Bottle Opener, Wall Style	5.00

Coca-Cola, **Bottle**, Amber	9.00 To 12.00
Coca-Cola, **Bottle**, Amber, 7 Oz.	15.00
Coca-Cola, **Bottle**, Christmas, Dated Dec.25, 1923	3.50
Coca-Cola, **Bottle**, Dated Nov.1915	3.75
Coca-Cola, **Bottle**, Dated 1923, Mold Error Shows 3 Backward	8.00
Coca-Cola, **Bottle**, Dug, Amber	9.75 To 14.75
Coca-Cola, **Bottle**, Embossed Indian Head Profile, Casco, Pat.12/29/25, Aqua	50.00
Coca-Cola, **Bottle**, Embossed Property Of Coca-Cola Bottling Co., 1923, Aqua	3.50
Coca-Cola, **Bottle**, Gold, 7 In.	10.00
Coca-Cola, **Bottle**, Miniature, Marked Coca-Cola On 2 Sides, Metal Cap, 3 In.	.75
Coca-Cola, **Bottle**, Miniature, Marked, Capped, 3 In.High	.75
Coca-Cola, **Bottle**, Miniature, 2 1/2 In.	7.00
Coca-Cola, **Bottle**, Miniature, 24 In Case	7.50
Coca-Cola, **Bottle**, Seltzer, Etched Name, Blue	45.00
Coca-Cola, **Bottle**, Seltzer, Etched, Uniontown, Green	45.00
Coca-Cola, **Bottle**, Square	3.50
Coca-Cola, **Bottle**, Straight Sided, Script Writing, C.1905	3.50
Coca-Cola, **Bowl**, Ice, Aluminum, Bottle Legs, Dated 1935	30.00
Coca-Cola, **Bowl**, Pretzel, Metal	42.50
Coca-Cola, **Bowl**, Pretzel, Three Bottle Legs	25.00
Coca-Cola, **Calendar**, Lady In White Tennis Outfit, Umbrella, Framed	100.00
Coca-Cola, **Calendar**, Miss June Caprice Drinking Coke, 1900s	12.00
Coca-Cola, **Calendar**, 1915	400.00
Coca-Cola, **Calendar**, 1921, 12 X 32 In.	60.00
Coca-Cola, **Cards**, Playing, Picnic Design	1.75
Coca-Cola, **Case**, Display, Miniature, Holds 24 Bottles, 6 1/2 X 4 1/4 In.	1.00
Coca-Cola, **Chronometer**, Coke Bottle, Metal	15.00
Coca-Cola, **Clock**, Brass Base, Etched Name On Reverse Glass, Stand Up	45.00
Coca-Cola, **Clock**, Glass Front, Two Lights Inside, Electric, 16 In.Square	30.00
Coca-Cola, **Clock**, Oak Finish, Electric, 14 In.Square	50.00
Coca-Cola, **Clock**, Paper Face, Key Wind, Pendulum, Oak Case, 12 In.Square	65.00
Coca-Cola, **Clock**, Round Face, Metal, Electric, Circa 1942	42.00
Coca-Cola, **Clock**, Store, Oak Case	100.00
Coca-Cola, **Clock**, Wall	225.00
Coca-Cola, **Door Handle**, Pull Is Coca-Cola Bottle, 1940s	40.00
Coca-Cola, **Glass**, C.1920	12.50
Coca-Cola, **Holder**, Bottle, Aluminum, 12 Bottle	12.00
Coca-Cola, **Holder**, Bottle, Bentwood, 6 Bottle	30.00
Coca-Cola, **Holder**, Bottle, Wooden, Red, 6 Bottle	25.00
Coca-Cola, **Ice Pick**	5.00
Coca-Cola, **Ice Pick**, C.1945	2.50
Coca-Cola, **Key Chain**, Gold	.75
Coca-Cola, **Key Chain**, Round, Advertising	2.75
Coca-Cola, **Key Chain**, Square, Advertising	2.50
Coca-Cola, **Knife With Keychain**	4.00
Coca-Cola, **Knife**, 5 Cents	2.00
Coca-Cola, **Lamp**, Name & Five Cents On Shade, 9 1/2 X 12 1/2 In.High	1200.00
Coca-Cola, **Lighter**, Bottle Shape	1.50
Coca-Cola, **Lighter**, Cigarette, Miniature, Bottle	6.00
Coca-Cola, **Lighter**, Shape Of Bottle, 2 1/2 In.High	3.00
Coca-Cola, **Mirror**, Reverse, Five Cents, C.1900	50.00
Coca-Cola, **Opener**, Bottle, Wall, Drink Coca-Cola	2.00
Coca-Cola, **Opener**, Bottle, Wall, Metal	8.00
Coca-Cola, **Opener**, Wall	5.00
Coca-Cola, **Paperweight**, Coke Is Coca-Cola	18.00
Coca-Cola, **Paperweight**, Flying Goose	11.00
Coca-Cola, **Paperweight**, Red Base, Clear Bubbles, Made By J.Gentile, 1943	40.00
Coca-Cola, **Paperweight**, Topless Girl	25.00
Coca-Cola, **Pen**, Everite	2.00
Coca-Cola, **Pencil Box**, Blotter, Pencil, Given To Chilren In 1920	15.00
Coca-Cola, **Pencil Sharpener**, Bottle Shape, Metal	6.00
Coca-Cola, **Pencil Sharpener**, Shape Of Bottle, Iron	12.00
Coca-Cola, **Pencil**, Dated 1959	1.00
Coca-Cola, **Plate**, 'Refresh Yourself, Drink Coca-Cola, ' China, 1930s	45.00
Coca-Cola, **Playing Cards**, Boy & Girl With Dog	7.00
Coca-Cola, **Playing Cards**, Red Haired Girl	7.00

Coca-Cola, Poster, Woman, Drink Coke, 1911, 9 X 13 In. 12.00
Coca-Cola, Print, Girls, Brown Paper, 9 X 14 In., Set Of 5 .... 5.00
Coca-Cola, Radio, Cooler Type, Restored 59.00
Coca-Cola, Ruler, 'Do Unto Others As You-, ' Novelty Co., Ohio 12.00
Coca-Cola, Ruler, Drink Coca-Cola, 5 Cents, Wooden 1.50
Coca-Cola, Shade, Tiffany Type, Leaded, Round, White With Red & Green 2800.00
Coca-Cola, Sign, Bottle, Red, Tin, 9 In.Diameter 15.00
Coca-Cola, Sign, Girl Bowling, C.1940, Frame 45.00
Coca-Cola, Sign, New Betty Girl, Blue Dress, Signing Into Microphone, Tin 35.00
Coca-Cola, Sign, Please Pay When Served, Electric 20.00
Coca-Cola, Sign, Thermometer 12.50
Coca-Cola, Sign, 'Tired-Coca-Cola Relieves Fatigue, 'Man, Syrup Bottle, 1906 .... 100.00
Coca-Cola, Sign, Trademark Reg'T, Porcelain On Tin, Red & White 75.00
Coca-Cola, Sign, 1917, Calendar Girl Top, Orange, Bottle, Tin, Walnut Frame 100.00
Coca-Cola, Sign, 1922, Girl, Blue Tam, Sitting In Garden, Tin, 13 X 28 In. 100.00
Coca-Cola, Straight Side, C.1905-1910 .... 3.75
Coca-Cola, Tacker, Bottle, Companion Piece To Thermometer, 16 In. 7.50
Coca-Cola, Thermometer, Bottle Shape, 30 In. 26.50
Coca-Cola, Thermometer, Centigrade Scale, 7 In.Gold Bottle 2.50
Coca-Cola, Thermometer, Fahrenheit Scale, 16 In.Natural .... Color 6.00
Coca-Cola, Thermometer, Oval, Metal, 30 In. 18.00
Coca-Cola, Thermometer, Shape Of Bottle, 16 1/2 In. 16.50
Coca-Cola, Thermometer, White On Red, Convex Glass, Circa 1927, 12 In. 35.00
Coca-Cola, Thermometer, 17 In.Bottle 7.50
Coca-Cola, Thermometer, 1950s, 15 In.High 10.00
Coca-Cola, Thimble .... 1.00 To 12.00
Coca-Cola, Thimble, Yellow Plastic, Red Coke, Circa 1955 .... 1.10
Coca-Cola, Token, Brass, Good For One 5 Cent Drink, Langley Mills, 1930s 5.00
Coca-Cola, Tote Bag 10.00
Coca-Cola, Toy, Truck, Two Cartons Cokes, Rubber Tires, Buddy L, 15 In.Long 30.00
Coca-Cola, Tray, Bottle, Trademark, Round, Tin, 13 In. 2.00
Coca-Cola, Tray, Change, Elaine 37.00
Coca-Cola, Tray, Change, Girl, World War I 57.00
Coca-Cola, Tray, Change, Scene, Mexico City Main Plaza, Tin 32.50
Coca-Cola, Tray, Change, 1905 .... 110.00
Coca-Cola, Tray, Change, 1909 .... 125.00
Coca-Cola, Tray, Change, 1912 .... 47.00 To 95.00
Coca-Cola, Tray, Change, 1914 .... 60.00
Coca-Cola, Tray, Change, 1918 .... 40.00
Coca-Cola, Tray, Change, 1918, Betty, Oval 85.00
Coca-Cola, Tray, Change, 1920, Garden, Girl 125.00
Coca-Cola, Tray, Girl With Beret Holds Bottle 9.50
Coca-Cola, Tray, Girl With Chin Resting On Hand, Coke In Other Hand 14.00
Coca-Cola, Tray, Girl With Menu 6.00
Coca-Cola, Tray, Hand Pouring Bottle 3.50
Coca-Cola, Tray, Hand Pouring Coke In Glass, Flowers Around Glass 10.00
Coca-Cola, Tray, Pansy Design 7.00
Coca-Cola, Tray, Thirst Knows No Season, Girl, Menu 9.50
Coca-Cola, Tray, 1912, Brunette Flapper Girl .... 20.00 To 28.00
Coca-Cola, Tray, 1914 .... 85.00
Coca-Cola, Tray, 1917 .... 90.00
Coca-Cola, Tray, 1920, Oval 256.00
Coca-Cola, Tray, 1923 .... 57.00
Coca-Cola, Tray, 1924 .... 57.00
Coca-Cola, Tray, 1925, Beveled & Rolled Rim, Lady 27.75
Coca-Cola, Tray, 1926, Golfers 40.00
Coca-Cola, Tray, 1930, Bathing Beauty 35.00
Coca-Cola, Tray, 1937, Girl .... 12.00 To 19.00
Coca-Cola, Tray, 1938, Girl In Yellow Dress, Signed Crandall .... 14.00 To 18.00
Coca-Cola, Tray, 1939, Bathing Beauty .... 14.00 To 18.00
Coca-Cola, Tray, 1940, Girl Sailing .... 14.00 To 25.00
Coca-Cola, Tray, 1940, 'Thirst Knows No Season, ' 13 In. 15.00
Coca-Cola, Tray, 1942, Girls In Auto, 10 1/2 X 13 In. .... 12.50 To 20.00
Coca-Cola, Tray, 1943, Redhead 10.00
Coca-Cola, Tray, 1950, Girl Holding Menu 10.00
Coca-Cola, Tray, 1950, Have A Coke 16.00

Coca-Cola, Tray, 1950, Redhead	10.00
Coca-Cola, Tray, 1956, Red, Harvest Table, Vegetables, Violin, Jar	12.00
Coca-Cola, Tray, 1961, Pansy Garden	5.50
Coca-Cola, Tray, 1961, Thanksgiving	4.50
Coca-Cola, Truck, 1950s, Yellow	15.00
Coca-Cola, Tumbler, Etched, Glass	1.90
Coca-Cola, Tumbler, Star Bottom, 6 Oz.	2.00
Coca-Cola, Wallet, Bottle & Gold Lettering Inside	15.00
Coca-Cola, Wallet, Leather, Bottle On Front, Gold Lettering, 1915	20.00

Coffee Grinders, home size, were first made about 1894. They lost favor by the 1930s.

Coffee Grinder, Brass, Handmade, Square, German Plaque, H.T.-Armin	75.00
Coffee Grinder, Counter Top, Original Paint, Iron	79.00
Coffee Grinder, Drawer In Base, Handle At Side, Black Metal, 8 1/2 In.High	23.50
Coffee Grinder, French, Red Wood, Drawer	10.00
Coffee Grinder, Grecian Women In Each Corner, Footed, Brass	150.00
Coffee Grinder, Iron, Red Paint, One Wheel, 8 3/4 In.High	45.00
Coffee Grinder, Label, Dated '05, Tin	22.00
Coffee Grinder, Miniature, Cast Iron, 9 In.High	48.50
Coffee Grinder, Parker No.50, Tin	20.00
Coffee Grinder, Swift Mill Lane Bros., Millbrook, N.Y., Double Wheel	450.00
Coffee Grinder, Swift Mill Lane Bros., Pat.1876, 9 In.Diameter Wheel, Iron	85.00
Coffee Grinder, Tin, France	25.00
Coffee Grinder, Two Wheels, 17 In.	140.00
Coffee Grinder, Wall, Blue & White Landscape, Glass Measure, Iron, Germany	31.00
Coffee Grinder, Wall, Small, Charles Parker, Meriden, Conn.	16.00
Coffee Grinder, Wooden Ends, Tin Front & Back, Wooden Drawer, 8 In.High	42.50
Coffee Grinder, 7 In.Wheel With Crank, Drawer In Base, Iron, 9 In.High	55.00

Christmas Plates were made by several firms. The most famous were made by The Bing & Grondahl Factory of Denmark, after 1895, and the Royal Copenhagen Factory, after 1908. Each of these plates has a blue-and-white glaze with a scene in the center, the date, and the word jule.

Collector, Bell, Berlin, Christmas, 1972	10.00
Collector, Bell, Fischer, Christmas, 1972, Crystal	10.00
Collector, Bell, Hammersly, Christmas, 1971	35.00
Collector, Bell, Hammersly, Christmas, 1972	25.00
Collector, Bell, Hummel, Schmid, 1972	13.50
Collector, Bell, Lincoln Mint, Dali, Sterling	200.00
Collector, Bell, Noritake, Christmas, 1972	12.50 To 15.00
Collector, Cup & Saucer, Haviland, Lincoln	80.00
Collector, Cup, Hummel, Schmid, Child's, 1973	8.50 To 10.00
Collector, Dish, Wedgwood, Mayflower, 1970	7.50
Collector, Egg, KPM, Easter, 1972	42.50
Collector, Egg, Noritake, Easter, 1971, 1st Issue	40.00 To 48.00
Collector, Egg, Noritake, Easter, 1972	10.00 To 22.00
Collector, Egg, Noritake, Easter, 1973	10.00
Collector, Egg, Royale, Easter, 1972	60.00
Collector, Figurine, American Crystal, Whooping Crane, 1972	45.00
Collector, Figurine, Gorham, Four Seasons, Rockwell, Set Of 4	250.00
Collector, Figurine, Hutschenreuther, 1972, Pair	150.00
Collector, Figurine, Royale, Easter, 1971, Rabbit	20.00
Collector, Figurine, Royale, Easter, 1972, Rabbit	15.00 To 16.00
Collector, Fork, Michelsen, Christmas, 1971	25.00
Collector, Glass, Noritake, Father's Day, 1972	42.00
Collector, Greeting Card, Franklin Mint, Christmas, 1972, Adoration Of Magi	2.50
Collector, Greeting Card, Franklin Mint, Christmas, 1972, Dove Of Peace	2.50
Collector, Greeting Card, Franklin Mint, Christmas, 1972, Festival Of Lights	2.50
Collector, Greeting Card, Franklin Mint, Christmas, 1972, Home For Christmas	2.50
Collector, Ingot, Franklin Mint, Christmas, 1971, Sterling	12.00 To 12.50
Collector, Ingot, Franklin Mint, Christmas, 1972	12.00
Collector, Ingot, Franklin Mint, Father's Day, 1972	18.00
Collector, Ingot, Lincoln Mint, Mother's Day, 1972, Silver	26.00 To 35.00
Collector, Medal, Franklin Mint, Children's Fund, 1971, Silver	15.00 To 22.50
Collector, Medal, Franklin Mint, Nixon, Peace Journey, 1972, Gold	22.50 To 30.00

Collector, Medallion, Wellings Mint, Mother's Day, 1972 .... 9.00
Collector, Mug, Blue Delft, Father's Day, 1971 .... 9.00
Collector, Mug, Bygdo, Christmas, 1969, Hans Christian Andersen 10.50
Collector, Mug, Bygdo, Christmas, 1970, Hans Christian Andersen .... 6.00 To 9.00
Collector, Mug, Bygdo, Christmas, 1971, Hans Christian Andersen 10.00
Collector, Mug, Porsgrund, Christmas, 1970, 1st Issue .... 13.50 To 15.00
Collector, Mug, Porsgrund, Christmas, 1971 .... 14.50 To 15.00
Collector, Mug, Porsgrund, Christmas, 1972, Deluxe 20.00
Collector, Mug, Porsgrund, Father's Day, 1972 .... 11.00
Collector, Mug, Royal Copenhagen, Christmas, 1969, Large Size 27.50
Collector, Mug, Royal Copenhagen, Christmas, 1970, Large Size .... 25.00 To 30.00
Collector, Mug, Royal Copenhagen, Christmas, 1970, Small Size 8.50
Collector, Mug, Royal Copenhagen, Christmas, 1971, Large Size 28.50
Collector, Mug, Royal Copenhagen, Christmas, 1971, Small Size 10.50
Collector, Mug, Wedgwood, Christmas, 1971, 1st Issue .... 17.50 To 20.00
Collector, Ornament, Franklin Mint, Christmas, 1971, 1st Issue, Sterling 30.00
Collector, Ornament, Franklin Mint, Christmas, 1972 .... 30.00
Collector, Ornament, Gorham, Christmas, 1970 .... 30.00
Collector, Ornament, Gorham, Christmas, 1971, Sterling .... 10.00 To 15.00
Collector, Ornament, Gorham, Christmas, 1972, Snowflake, Silver 10.00
Collector, Ornament, Haviland, Christmas, 1971, 1st Issue, Angels .... 7.50 To 13.00
Collector, Ornament, Haviland, Christmas, 1972, Horse 9.95
Collector, Ornament, Noritake, Valentine's Day, 1973, Heart .... 15.00 To 20.00
Collector, Paperweight, Royale Crystal, 1970 .... 180.00
Collector, Paperweight, Royale Crystal, 1972 .... 270.00
Collector, Paperweight, St.Clair, Sitting Bull, Sioux, 1971 .... 20.00
Collector, Paperweight, St.Clair, Yellow Hand, Cheyenne, 1971 .... 20.00
Collector, Pendant, Franklin Mint, U.N.Children's Fund, 1971, Bronze, Chain 8.00
Collector, Plaque, Marmot, 1971, Stag 120.00
Collector, Plaque, Royale, Bird, 1972 .... 200.00
Collector, Plate, America House, Landing Of Columbus, 1972, Bronze 100.00
Collector, Plate, America House, Landing Of Columbus, 1972, Silver 250.00
Collector, Plate, American Crystal, Annual, 1971 .... 50.00 To 100.00
Collector, Plate, American Crystal, Astronaut, 1969 .... 40.00
Collector, Plate, American Crystal, Christmas, 1970, 1st Issue .... 35.00 To 60.00
Collector, Plate, American Crystal, Christmas, 1971 .... 15.00 To 30.00
Collector, Plate, American Crystal, Christmas, 1972 .... 30.00
Collector, Plate, American Crystal, Mother's Day, 1971 .... 15.00 To 55.00
Collector, Plate, American Crystal, Sixth Summer, 1972, Iceberg 65.00
Collector, Plate, Andrew Wyeth, Christmas, 1971, 1st Issue .... 38.00 To 50.00
Collector, Plate, Anri, Christmas, 1971, 1st Issue, Wood .... 40.00 To 45.00
Collector, Plate, Anri, Christmas, 1972 .... 34.50 To 45.00
Collector, Plate, Anri, Christmas, 1973 .... 45.00
Collector, Plate, Anri, Father's Day, 1972, 1st Issue .... 17.50 To 35.00
Collector, Plate, Anri, Mother's Day, 1972, 1st Issue .... 17.50 To 35.00
Collector, Plate, Antique Trader, Christmas, 1970 .... 11.00
Collector, Plate, Arlington Mint, Hands In Prayer, 1972 .... 125.00
Collector, Plate, August Wendell Forge, Columbus, 1972, Pewter .... 30.00 To 35.00
Collector, Plate, August Wendell Forge, Kennedy, 1972, Pewter .... 30.00 To 35.00
Collector, Plate, August Wendell Forge, Pilgrims, 1972, Pewter .... 35.00 To 40.00
Collector, Plate, August Wendell Forge, Ships, 1971, Pewter 40.00
Collector, Plate, Bareuther, Christmas, 1967, 1st Issue .... 60.00 To 75.00
Collector, Plate, Bareuther, Christmas, 1968 .... 15.00 To 28.00
Collector, Plate, Bareuther, Christmas, 1969 .... 8.00 To 15.00
Collector, Plate, Bareuther, Christmas, 1970 .... 6.00 To 13.50
Collector, Plate, Bareuther, Christmas, 1971 .... 10.00 To 12.50
Collector, Plate, Bareuther, Christmas, 1972 .... 10.00 To 14.50
Collector, Plate, Bareuther, Father's Day, 1969 .... 25.00 To 50.00
Collector, Plate, Bareuther, Father's Day, 1970 .... 5.00 To 14.00
Collector, Plate, Bareuther, Father's Day, 1971 .... 7.95 To 12.75
Collector, Plate, Bareuther, Father's Day, 1972 .... 10.00 To 14.50
Collector, Plate, Bareuther, Father's Day, 1973 .... 11.50
Collector, Plate, Bareuther, Mother's Day, 1969, 1st Issue .... 25.00 To 50.00
Collector, Plate, Bareuther, Mother's Day, 1970 .... 5.00 To 13.00
Collector, Plate, Bareuther, Mother's Day, 1971 .... 7.95 To 12.75
Collector, Plate, Bareuther, Mother's Day, 1972 .... 10.00 To 14.50

Collector, Plate, Bareuther, Mother's Day, 1973 .... 11.50
Collector, Plate, Bareuther, Thanksgiving, 1971, 1st Issue .... 11.50 To 13.50
Collector, Plate, Bareuther, Thanksgiving, 1972 .... 15.00
Collector, Plate, Belleek, Christmas, 1970, 1st Issue .... 62.50 To 100.00
Collector, Plate, Belleek, Christmas, 1971 .... 25.00 To 42.00
Collector, Plate, Berlin, Christmas, 1971 .... 5.00 To 14.50
Collector, Plate, Berlin, Christmas, 1972 .... 10.00 To 15.00
Collector, Plate, Berlin, Father's Day, 1971, 1st Issue .... 5.00 To 15.00
Collector, Plate, Berlin, Father's Day, 1972 .... 7.50 To 13.00
Collector, Plate, Berlin, Mother's Day, 1971, 1st Issue .... 10.00 To 25.00
Collector, Plate, Berlin, Mother's Day, 1972 .... 15.00
Collector, Plate, Berlin, Mother's Day, 1973 .... 15.00 To 16.50
Collector, Plate, Bing & Grondahl, Christmas, 1895 .... 2500.00
Collector, Plate, Bing & Grondahl, Christmas, 1896 .... 1300.00
Collector, Plate, Bing & Grondahl, Christmas, 1897 .... 850.00
Collector, Plate, Bing & Grondahl, Christmas, 1898 .... 400.00
Collector, Plate, Bing & Grondahl, Christmas, 1899 .... 795.00
Collector, Plate, Bing & Grondahl, Christmas, 1900 .... 600.00
Collector, Plate, Bing & Grondahl, Christmas, 1901 .... 225.00
Collector, Plate, Bing & Grondahl, Christmas, 1902 .... 165.00
Collector, Plate, Bing & Grondahl, Christmas, 1903 .... 155.00
Collector, Plate, Bing & Grondahl, Christmas, 1904 .... 90.00
Collector, Plate, Bing & Grondahl, Christmas, 1905 .... 90.00
Collector, Plate, Bing & Grondahl, Christmas, 1906 .... 65.00
Collector, Plate, Bing & Grondahl, Christmas, 1907 .... 100.00
Collector, Plate, Bing & Grondahl, Christmas, 1908 .... 50.00
Collector, Plate, Bing & Grondahl, Christmas, 1909 .... 70.00
Collector, Plate, Bing & Grondahl, Christmas, 1910 .... 65.00
Collector, Plate, Bing & Grondahl, Christmas, 1911 .... 65.00
Collector, Plate, Bing & Grondahl, Christmas, 1912 .... 65.00
Collector, Plate, Bing & Grondahl, Christmas, 1913 .... 65.00
Collector, Plate, Bing & Grondahl, Christmas, 1914 .... 50.00
Collector, Plate, Bing & Grondahl, Christmas, 1915 .... 90.00
Collector, Plate, Bing & Grondahl, Christmas, 1916 .... 54.00
Collector, Plate, Bing & Grondahl, Christmas, 1917 .... 54.00
Collector, Plate, Bing & Grondahl, Christmas, 1918 .... 54.00
Collector, Plate, Bing & Grondahl, Christmas, 1919 .... 54.00
Collector, Plate, Bing & Grondahl, Christmas, 1920 .... 43.00 To 50.00
Collector, Plate, Bing & Grondahl, Christmas, 1921 .... 43.00
Collector, Plate, Bing & Grondahl, Christmas, 1922 .... 35.00 To 50.00
Collector, Plate, Bing & Grondahl, Christmas, 1923 .... 35.00 To 43.00
Collector, Plate, Bing & Grondahl, Christmas, 1924 .... 35.00 To 50.00
Collector, Plate, Bing & Grondahl, Christmas, 1925 .... 35.00 To 50.00
Collector, Plate, Bing & Grondahl, Christmas, 1926 .... 43.00 To 50.00
Collector, Plate, Bing & Grondahl, Christmas, 1927 .... 60.00
Collector, Plate, Bing & Grondahl, Christmas, 1928 .... 35.00 To 50.00
Collector, Plate, Bing & Grondahl, Christmas, 1929 .... 60.00
Collector, Plate, Bing & Grondahl, Christmas, 1930 .... 70.00
Collector, Plate, Bing & Grondahl, Christmas, 1931 .... 43.00 To 50.00
Collector, Plate, Bing & Grondahl, Christmas, 1932 .... 54.00
Collector, Plate, Bing & Grondahl, Christmas, 1933 .... 43.00 To 50.00
Collector, Plate, Bing & Grondahl, Christmas, 1934 .... 43.00 To 50.00
Collector, Plate, Bing & Grondahl, Christmas, 1935 .... 43.00 To 50.00
Collector, Plate, Bing & Grondahl, Christmas, 1936 .... 43.00 To 50.00
Collector, Plate, Bing & Grondahl, Christmas, 1937 .... 60.00
Collector, Plate, Bing & Grondahl, Christmas, 1938 .... 62.50 To 90.00
Collector, Plate, Bing & Grondahl, Christmas, 1939 .... 85.00 To 125.00
Collector, Plate, Bing & Grondahl, Christmas, 1940 .... 125.00
Collector, Plate, Bing & Grondahl, Christmas, 1941 .... 240.00
Collector, Plate, Bing & Grondahl, Christmas, 1942 .... 120.00
Collector, Plate, Bing & Grondahl, Christmas, 1943 .... 77.50 To 120.00
Collector, Plate, Bing & Grondahl, Christmas, 1944 .... 65.00
Collector, Plate, Bing & Grondahl, Christmas, 1945 .... 90.00
Collector, Plate, Bing & Grondahl, Christmas, 1946 .... 52.50
Collector, Plate, Bing & Grondahl, Christmas, 1947 .... 55.00 To 65.00
Collector, Plate, Bing & Grondahl, Christmas, 1948 .... 43.00 To 50.00

Collector, Plate, Bing & Grondahl, Christmas, 1949 .... 43.00 To 50.00
Collector, Plate, Bing & Grondahl, Christmas, 1950 .... 60.00
Collector, Plate, Bing & Grondahl, Christmas, 1951 .... 55.00
Collector, Plate, Bing & Grondahl, Christmas, 1952 .... 55.00
Collector, Plate, Bing & Grondahl, Christmas, 1953 .... 50.00
Collector, Plate, Bing & Grondahl, Christmas, 1954 .... 60.00
Collector, Plate, Bing & Grondahl, Christmas, 1955 .... 65.00
Collector, Plate, Bing & Grondahl, Christmas, 1956 .... 77.50 To 82.50
Collector, Plate, Bing & Grondahl, Christmas, 1957 .... 77.50 To 85.00
Collector, Plate, Bing & Grondahl, Christmas, 1958 .... 60.00 To 70.00
Collector, Plate, Bing & Grondahl, Christmas, 1959 .... 110.00
Collector, Plate, Bing & Grondahl, Christmas, 1960 ....77.50 To 125.00
Collector, Plate, Bing & Grondahl, Christmas, 1961 .... 56.00
Collector, Plate, Bing & Grondahl, Christmas, 1962 .... 32.50
Collector, Plate, Bing & Grondahl, Christmas, 1963 .... 72.50 To 82.50
Collector, Plate, Bing & Grondahl, Christmas, 1964 .... 25.00 To 27.50
Collector, Plate, Bing & Grondahl, Christmas, 1965 .... 25.00 To 26.50
Collector, Plate, Bing & Grondahl, Christmas, 1966 .... 20.00 To 22.50
Collector, Plate, Bing & Grondahl, Christmas, 1967 .... 15.00 To 27.00
Collector, Plate, Bing & Grondahl, Christmas, 1968 .... 12.00 To 24.00
Collector, Plate, Bing & Grondahl, Christmas, 1969 .... 7.50 To 21.00
Collector, Plate, Bing & Grondahl, Christmas, 1970 .... 7.50 To 15.00
Collector, Plate, Bing & Grondahl, Christmas, 1971 .... 7.50 To 15.00
Collector, Plate, Bing & Grondahl, Christmas, 1972 .... 10.00 To 16.50
Collector, Plate, Bing & Grondahl, Jubilee, 1915, 1st Issue 100.00
Collector, Plate, Bing & Grondahl, Jubilee, 1920 .... 80.00
Collector, Plate, Bing & Grondahl, Jubilee, 1925 .... 100.00
Collector, Plate, Bing & Grondahl, Jubilee, 1930 .... 200.00
Collector, Plate, Bing & Grondahl, Jubilee, 1935 .... 500.00
Collector, Plate, Bing & Grondahl, Jubilee, 1940 .... 1200.00
Collector, Plate, Bing & Grondahl, Jubilee, 1945 .... 200.00
Collector, Plate, Bing & Grondahl, Jubilee, 1950 .... 130.00
Collector, Plate, Bing & Grondahl, Jubilee, 1955 .... 125.00
Collector, Plate, Bing & Grondahl, Jubilee, 1960 .... 110.00
Collector, Plate, Bing & Grondahl, Jubilee, 1965 .... 75.00
Collector, Plate, Bing & Grondahl, Jubilee, 1970 .... 15.00 To 25.00
Collector, Plate, Bing & Grondahl, Mother's Day, 1969, 1st Issue .... 125.00 To 180.00
Collector, Plate, Bing & Grondahl, Mother's Day, 1970 .... 11.00 To 25.00
Collector, Plate, Bing & Grondahl, Mother's Day, 1971 .... 7.00 To 22.00
Collector, Plate, Bing & Grondahl, Mother's Day, 1972 .... 8.50 To 15.00
Collector, Plate, Bing & Grondahl, Mother's Day, 1973 .... 9.00 To 13.00
Collector, Plate, Bing & Grondahl, Olympic, 1972 .... 11.50 To 17.50
Collector, Plate, Blue Delft, Christmas, 1970, 1st Issue .... 11.00 To 14.00
Collector, Plate, Blue Delft, Christmas, 1971 .... 10.00 To 14.00
Collector, Plate, Blue Delft, Father's Day, 1971, 1st Issue .... 8.00 To 11.00
Collector, Plate, Blue Delft, Mother's Day, 1971, 1st Issue .... 8.00 To 11.00
Collector, Plate, Boehm, Bird Of Peace .... 445.00 To 675.00
Collector, Plate, Bonita, Mother's Day, 1972, Sterling, 1st Issue ....75.00 To 125.00
Collector, Plate, Bygdo, Christmas, 1969, Hans Christian Andersen......... 6.00 To 10.50
Collector, Plate, Bygdo, Christmas, 1970, Hans Christian Andersen......... 6.00 To 9.00
Collector, Plate, Bygdo, Christmas, 1971, Hans Christian Andersen......... 6.00 To 10.00
Collector, Plate, Caritas, Rose Kennedy, 1973 .... 30.00
Collector, Plate, Carlo Monti, Mother's Day, 1973, 1st Issue 35.00
Collector, Plate, Cartier, Cathedral, 1972, 1st Issue .... 45.00 To 50.00
Collector, Plate, Churchill Mint, Hour Of Decision, Proof Plate 550.00
Collector, Plate, Churchill Mint, Hour Of Decision, Sterling 150.00
Collector, Plate, Creative World, Chief Wapello 15.00
Collector, Plate, Cristal D'Albret, Astronauts 80.00
Collector, Plate, Cristal D'Albret, Christmas, 1972 .... 125.00 To 150.00
Collector, Plate, Cristal D'Albret, Summer .... 300.00 To 550.00
Collector, Plate, Crown Delft, Christmas, 1969, 1st Issue .... 10.00 To 19.00
Collector, Plate, Crown Delft, Christmas, 1970 .... 6.00
Collector, Plate, Crown Delft, Father's Day, 1970, 1st Issue 6.00
Collector, Plate, Danbury Mint, Winter, 1972 .... 125.00 To 150.00
Collector, Plate, Danish Church, Christmas, 1968, 1st Issue .... 7.00 To 18.00
Collector, Plate, Danish Church, Christmas, 1969 .... 7.00 To 12.00

Collector, Plate, Danish Church, Christmas, 1970 .... 7.00 To 9.75
Collector, Plate, Daum, Dali, 1971, Pair 400.00
Collector, Plate, Daum, Famous Musicians, Bach 60.00
Collector, Plate, Daum, Famous Musicians, Beethoven 60.00
Collector, Plate, Daum, Famous Musicians, Gershwin 60.00
Collector, Plate, Daum, Famous Musicians, Mozart 60.00
Collector, Plate, Daum, Famous Musicians, Wagner 60.00
Collector, Plate, Daum, Four Seasons, 1971, Set Of 4 .... 600.00
Collector, Plate, Doughty, 1972, Bird, 1st Issue .... 400.00 To 650.00
Collector, Plate, Dresden, Christmas, 1971, 1st Issue .... 30.00 To 60.00
Collector, Plate, Dresden, Christmas, 1972 .... 13.00 To 28.00
Collector, Plate, Dresden, Mother's Day, 1972, 1st Issue .... 11.00 To 25.00
Collector, Plate, Dresden, Mother's Day, 1973 .... 15.00 To 16.00
Collector, Plate, Egermann, Christmas, 1972, Crystal, 1st Issue .... 40.00 To 60.00
Collector, Plate, Eschenbach, Christmas, 1971, 1st Issue .... 5.00 To 14.00
Collector, Plate, Fenton, Christmas, 1970, Carnival, 1st Issue .... 10.00 To 12.50
Collector, Plate, Fenton, Christmas, 1970, Marble, 1st Issue .... 9.00 To 12.50
Collector, Plate, Fenton, Christmas, 1971 .... *Illus* 12.50

Collector, Plate, Fenton, Christmas, 1971

Collector, Plate, Fenton, Christmas, 1971, Carnival .... 10.00 To 12.50
Collector, Plate, Fenton, Christmas, 1971, Marble .... 10.00 To 12.50
Collector, Plate, Fenton, Christmas, 1972, Carnival 12.00
Collector, Plate, Fenton, Christmas, 1972, Marble 12.00
Collector, Plate, Fenton, Christmas, 1972, Satin 12.00
Collector, Plate, Fenton, Mother's Day, 1971, Carnival, 1st Issue .... 12.50 To 15.00
Collector, Plate, Fenton, Mother's Day, 1971, Marble, 1st Issue 12.50
Collector, Plate, Fenton, Mother's Day, 1972, Carnival .... 7.50 To 12.50
Collector, Plate, Fenton, Trades, Glassblower 10.00
Collector, Plate, Fenton, Trades, Printer .... 7.00 To 15.00
Collector, Plate, Fenton, Valentine's Day, 1972, Carnival, 1st Issue 15.00
Collector, Plate, Fenton, Valentine's Day, 1972, Marble, 1st Issue 15.00
Collector, Plate, Fontana, Christmas, 1972, 1st Issue .... 40.00 To 69.00
Collector, Plate, Fontana, Mother's Day, 1973, 1st Issue .... 30.00 To 35.00
Collector, Plate, Fostoria, Annual, 1971, The Flag, 1st Issue .... 12.00 To 14.00
Collector, Plate, Fostoria, State, 1971, California 12.50
Collector, Plate, Fostoria, State, 1971, New York 12.50
Collector, Plate, Fostoria, State, 1971, Ohio 12.50
Collector, Plate, Fostoria, State, 1972, Florida 12.50
Collector, Plate, Fostoria, State, 1972, Hawaii 12.50
Collector, Plate, Fostoria, State, 1972, Massachusetts 12.50
Collector, Plate, Fostoria, State, 1972, Pennsylvania 12.50
Collector, Plate, Fostoria, State, 1972, Texas 12.50
Collector, Plate, Franklin Mint, Bobwhite, 1972 .... 125.00
Collector, Plate, Franklin Mint, Brandywine, 1972, Sterling 125.00
Collector, Plate, Franklin Mint, Cardinal, 1972, Sterling .... 125.00 To 175.00
Collector, Plate, Franklin Mint, Christmas, 1970, 1st Issue .... 350.00 To 600.00
Collector, Plate, Franklin Mint, Christmas, 1971, Rockwell .... 125.00 To 200.00
Collector, Plate, Franklin Mint, Christmas, 1972, Rockwell 125.00

Collector, Plate, Franklin Mint, George Washington, Sterling 150.00
Collector, Plate, Franklin Mint, Horizon West, 1972 .... 150.00
Collector, Plate, Franklin Mint, John Adams, Silver 150.00
Collector, Plate, Franklin Mint, Mallards, Silver 125.00
Collector, Plate, Franklin Mint, Mother's Day, 1972, 1st Issue .... 125.00 To 165.00
Collector, Plate, Franklin Mint, Mountain Man, Sterling 150.00
Collector, Plate, Franklin Mint, Mountain Man, 22K Gold 2200.00
Collector, Plate, Franklin Mint, Thanksgiving, 1972 .... 125.00
Collector, Plate, Franklin Mint, Thomas Jefferson, Sterling 150.00
Collector, Plate, Frankoma, Annual, 1969 .... 7.00
Collector, Plate, Frankoma, Annual, 1970 .... 7.00
Collector, Plate, Frankoma, Bicentennial, 1972 .... 5.00
Collector, Plate, Frankoma, Christmas, 1965, 1st Issue .... 150.00 To 175.00
Collector, Plate, Frankoma, Christmas, 1966 .... 50.00 To 60.00
Collector, Plate, Frankoma, Christmas, 1967 .... 35.00 To 50.00
Collector, Plate, Frankoma, Christmas, 1968 .... 4.00 To 15.00
Collector, Plate, Frankoma, Christmas, 1969 .... 4.00 To 7.00
Collector, Plate, Frankoma, Christmas, 1970 .... 6.00
Collector, Plate, Frankoma, Christmas, 1971 .... 5.00
Collector, Plate, Frankoma, Christmas, 1972 .... 5.00
Collector, Plate, Fuerstenberg, Christmas, 1971, 1st Issue .... 10.00 To 14.00
Collector, Plate, Fuerstenberg, Christmas, 1971, Deluxe, 1st Issue .... 50.00 To 95.00
Collector, Plate, Fuerstenberg, Christmas, 1972 .... 10.00 To 16.00
Collector, Plate, Fuerstenberg, Christmas, 1972, Deluxe .... 35.00 To 45.00
Collector, Plate, Fuerstenberg, Easter, 1971, 1st Issue .... 20.00 To 32.50
Collector, Plate, Fuerstenberg, Easter, 1972 .... 10.00 To 15.00
Collector, Plate, Fuerstenberg, Father's Day, 1972 .... 10.00 To 15.00
Collector, Plate, Fuerstenberg, Mother's Day, 1972 .... 10.00 To 15.00
Collector, Plate, Fuerstenberg, Olympic, 1972 .... 20.00
Collector, Plate, George Washington Mint, N.C.Wyeth, July 4th, 1972 .... 150.00
Collector, Plate, George Washington Mint, Picasso, 1972, Sterling 125.00
Collector, Plate, George Washington Mint, Whistler's Mother .... 125.00 To 150.00
Collector, Plate, Gorham, Christmas, 1971, Rembrandt, 1st Issue 50.00
Collector, Plate, Gorham, Christmas, 1972, Rembrandt .... 40.00 To 50.00
Collector, Plate, Gorham, Four Seasons, 1971, Rockwell, 4 .... 73.00 To 95.00
Collector, Plate, Gorham, Four Seasons, 1972, Rockwell, 4 .... 55.00 To 60.00
Collector, Plate, Gorham, Gainsborough Portrait, 1973 .... 50.00
Collector, Plate, Gorham, Mother's Day, 1973, Moppets .... 12.50 To 15.00
Collector, Plate, Grandma Moses, 1972, Set Of 8 .... 160.00
Collector, Plate, Granget, 1972, American .... 50.00 To 95.00
Collector, Plate, Granget, 1972, European .... 25.00 To 30.00
Collector, Plate, Hamilton Mint, Picasso, Le Gourmet, Silver, 1st Issue 125.00
Collector, Plate, Hamilton Mint, Picasso, The Lovers 125.00
Collector, Plate, Hamilton Mint, Picasso, The Tragedy .... 125.00 To 185.00
Collector, Plate, Haviland & Parlon, Unicorn, 1971 ....75.00 To 100.00
Collector, Plate, Haviland & Parlon, Unicorn, 1972 .... 35.00
Collector, Plate, Haviland, Burning Of The Gaspee, 1972 .... 30.00 To 40.00
Collector, Plate, Haviland, Christmas, 1970, 1st Issue ....60.00 To 120.00
Collector, Plate, Haviland, Christmas, 1971 .... 21.00 To 35.00
Collector, Plate, Haviland, Christmas, 1972 .... 24.00 To 35.00
Collector, Plate, Haviland, Christmas, 1973 .... 22.00 To 25.00
Collector, Plate, Haviland, Mother's Day, 1973 .... 26.00 To 29.00
Collector, Plate, Haviland, Presidential, Grant 100.00
Collector, Plate, Haviland, Presidential, Hayes 110.00
Collector, Plate, Haviland, Presidential, Lincoln 60.00
Collector, Plate, Haviland, Presidential, Washington .... 50.00 To 75.00
Collector, Plate, Hummel, Goebel, Annual, 1971 .... 35.00 To 60.00
Collector, Plate, Hummel, Goebel, Annual, 1972 .... 25.00 To 30.00
Collector, Plate, Hummel, Geobel, Annual, 1973 .... 32.00
Collector, Plate, Hummel, Goebel, Christmas, 1971, 1st Issue .... 25.00 To 56.00
Collector, Plate, Hummel, Goebel, Christmas, 1972 .... 28.00 To 35.00
Collector, Plate, Hummel, Goebel, Olympic, 1972 .... 13.50 To 16.00
Collector, Plate, Hummel, Schmid, Christmas, 1971, 1st Issue .... 13.50 To 25.00
Collector, Plate, Hummel, Schmid, Christmas, 1972 .... 12.50 To 15.00
Collector, Plate, Hummel, Schmid, Mother's Day, 1972 .... 13.50 To 15.00
Collector, Plate, Hummel, Schmid, Mother's Day, 1973 .... 15.00

Collector, Plate, Hutschenreuther, Songbirds, 1972, Ruthven, 2 ....90.00 To 150.00
Collector, Plate, Imperial, Christmas, 1970, Blue, 1st Issue 6.50
Collector, Plate, Imperial, Christmas, 1970, Carnival, 1st Issue .... 11.50 To 13.00
Collector, Plate, Imperial, Christmas, 1971, Blue 12.00
Collector, Plate, Imperial, Christmas, 1971, Carnival .... 11.00 To 13.00
Collector, Plate, Imperial, Christmas, 1971, Crystal 15.50
Collector, Plate, Imperial, Christmas, 1971, White Satin 12.50
Collector, Plate, Imperial, Christmas, 1972, Carnival .... 12.00 To 12.50
Collector, Plate, Imperial, Christmas, 1972, Crystal 16.50
Collector, Plate, Imperial, Coin, 1971 .... 15.00 To 16.50
Collector, Plate, Imperial, Coin, 1972 .... 14.00 To 15.00
Collector, Plate, Israel, Annual, 1967 .... 7.00
Collector, Plate, Israel, Annual, 1968 .... 7.00
Collector, Plate, Israel, Annual, 1969 .... 7.00 To 10.00
Collector, Plate, Israel, Annual, 1970 .... 7.00 To 7.50
Collector, Plate, Israel, Annual, 1971 .... 7.50
Collector, Plate, Jensen, Georg, Chagall, The Lovers 40.00
Collector, Plate, Jensen, Georg, Christmas, 1972, 1st Issue 15.00
Collector, Plate, Jensen, Svend, Christmas, 1970, 1st Issue 15.00
Collector, Plate, Jensen, Svend, Christmas, 1971 .... 12.00 To 15.00
Collector, Plate, Jensen, Svend, Christmas, 1972 .... 11.00 To 16.50
Collector, Plate, Jensen, Svend, Mother's Day, 1970, 1st Issue .... 8.75 To 15.00
Collector, Plate, Jensen, Svend, Mother's Day, 1971 .... 10.00 To 15.00
Collector, Plate, Jensen, Svend, Mother's Day, 1972 .... 12.00 To 15.00
Collector, Plate, Jensen, Svend, Mother's Day, 1973 .... 14.50
Collector, Plate, Kaiser, Anniversary, 1972 .... 13.50 To 14.00
Collector, Plate, Kaiser, Christmas, 1970, 1st Issue .... 18.00 To 25.00
Collector, Plate, Kaiser, Christmas, 1971 ....10.00 13.50
Collector, Plate, Kaiser, Christmas, 1972 .... 12.00 To 16.50
Collector, Plate, Kaiser, Mother's Day, 1971, 1st Issue .... 11.00 To 25.00
Collector, Plate, Kaiser, Mother's Day, 1972 .... 12.00 To 16.50
Collector, Plate, Kaiser, Mother's Day, 1973 .... 13.50 To 16.50
Collector, Plate, Kaiser, Thanksgiving, 1972, 1st Issue 16.50
Collector, Plate, Kera, Christmas, 1967, 1st Issue 24.00
Collector, Plate, Kera, Christmas, 1968 .... 20.00
Collector, Plate, Kera, Christmas, 1969 .... 18.00
Collector, Plate, Kera, Christmas, 1970 .... 16.00
Collector, Plate, Kirk, Bicentennial, 1972, Sterling 75.00
Collector, Plate, Kirk, Christmas, 1972, Sterling, 1st Issue, With Book 150.00
Collector, Plate, Kirk, Mother's Day, 1972, Sterling, 1st Issue .... 115.00 To 135.00
Collector, Plate, Kirk, Thanksgiving, 1972, Sterling, 1st Issue ....80.00 To 150.00
Collector, Plate, Kosta, Annual, 1971, Sweden .... 10.00 To 19.00
Collector, Plate, Kosta, Christmas, 1971 .... 29.00 To 30.00
Collector, Plate, Kosta, Christmas, 1972 .... 29.50
Collector, Plate, Lalique, Annual, 1965, 1st Issue .... 925.00 To 1100.00
Collector, Plate, Lalique, Annual, 1966 .... 180.00 To 250.00
Collector, Plate, Lalique, Annual, 1967 .... 110.00 To 190.00
Collector, Plate, Lalique, Annual, 1968 ....70.00 To 100.00
Collector, Plate, Lalique, Annual, 1969 ....60.00 To 85.00
Collector, Plate, Lalique, Annual, 1970 ....50.00 To 70.00
Collector, Plate, Lalique, Annual, 1971 ....40.00 To 65.00
Collector, Plate, Lalique, Annual, 1972 .... 50.00
Collector, Plate, Laurel & Hardy, 1971 .... 20.00
Collector, Plate, Lenox, Boehm, Bird Of Peace, 1972 .... 675.00 To 750.00
Collector, Plate, Lenox, Boehm Bird, 1970, Woodthrushes, 1st Issue .... 195.00 To 240.00
Collector, Plate, Lenox, Boehm Bird, 1971, Goldfinches ....90.00 To 125.00
Collector, Plate, Lenox, Boehm Bird, 1972, Bluebirds ....55.00 To 75.00
Collector, Plate, Lihs Lindner, Christmas, 1972 .... 22.50 To 40.00
Collector, Plate, Lihs Lindner, Easter, 1973 ....30.00 To 37.50
Collector, Plate, Lihs Lindner, Mother's Day, 1972, 1st Issue ....62.00 To 100.00
Collector, Plate, Lihs Lindner, Mother's Day, 1973 .... 25.00
Collector, Plate, Limoges, Carte A Jouer, Dali, The Royal Flush, Set Of 5 .... 300.00
Collector, Plate, Limoges, Christmas, 1972, 1st Issue 25.00
Collector, Plate, Lincoln Mint, Annual, 1971 .... *Illus* 100.00
Collector, Plate, Lincoln Mint, Annual, 1972, Dionysos, Dali, Gold 2000.00
Collector, Plate, Lincoln Mint, Annual, 1972, Dionysos, Sterling .... 100.00 To 125.00

Collector, Plate, Lincoln Mint, Annual, 1971
See Page 140

Collector, Plate, Lincoln Mint, Annual, 1972, Dionysos, Vermeil .... 150.00 To 175.00
Collector, Plate, Lincoln Mint, Easter, 1972, Dali, Gold Overlay .... 200.00 To 225.00
Collector, Plate, Lincoln Mint, Easter, 1972, Dali, Sterling .... 100.00 To 165.00
Collector, Plate, Lincoln Mint, Madonna, Sterling 125.00
Collector, Plate, Lincoln Mint, Mother's Day, 1972, 1st Issue .... 100.00 To 185.00
Collector, Plate, Lladro, Christmas, 1971, 1st Issue .... 18.00 To 35.00
Collector, Plate, Lladro, Christmas, 1972 .... 27.50 To 32.00
Collector, Plate, Lladro, Mother's Day, 1971, 1st Issue ....60.00 To 100.00
Collector, Plate, Lladro, Mother's Day, 1972 .... 18.00 To 35.00
Collector, Plate, Lourioux, Christmas, 1971, 1st Issue .... 12.50 To 15.00
Collector, Plate, Lund & Clausen, Astronaut, 1969, Moon Landing .... 7.95 To 13.50
Collector, Plate, Lund & Clausen, Christmas, 1971, 1st Issue .... 9.50 To 13.00
Collector, Plate, Lund & Clausen, Mother's Day, 1970, 1st Issue .... 14.50 To 35.00
Collector, Plate, Lund & Clausen, Mother's Day, 1971 .... 14.50 To 30.00
Collector, Plate, Lund & Clausen, Mother's Day, 1972 .... 14.50
Collector, Plate, Mallek, Christmas, 1971, 1st Issue, Navajo 15.00
Collector, Plate, Marmot, Christmas, 1970, 1st Issue .... 9.50 To 18.00
Collector, Plate, Marmot, Christmas, 1971 .... 8.00 To 12.00
Collector, Plate, Marmot, Christmas, 1972 .... 12.00 To 16.00
Collector, Plate, Marmot, Father's Day, 1970, 1st Issue .... 9.00 To 22.50
Collector, Plate, Marmot, Father's Day, 1971 .... 9.00 To 18.00
Collector, Plate, Marmot, Father's Day, 1972 .... 13.50
Collector, Plate, Marmot, Mother's Day, 1972 .... 10.00 To 16.00
Collector, Plate, Marmot, President, 1971, Washington, 1st Issue .... 10.00 To 25.00
Collector, Plate, Marmot, President, 1972, Jefferson 25.00
Collector, Plate, Moser, Annual, 1970, 1st Issue .... 300.00 To 400.00
Collector, Plate, Moser, Annual, 1971 .... 65.00 To 75.00
Collector, Plate, Moser, Annual, 1972 .... 75.00 To 85.00
Collector, Plate, Moser, Christmas, 1970, 1st Issue, Crystal .... 425.00 To 450.00
Collector, Plate, Moser, Christmas, 1971, Crystal ....60.00 To 100.00
Collector, Plate, Moser, Christmas, 1972 .... 85.00
Collector, Plate, Moser, Mother's Day, 1971, 1st Issue, Crystal .... 225.00 To 350.00
Collector, Plate, Moser, Mother's Day, 1972, Crystal .... 75.00 To 85.00
Collector, Plate, Mueller, Christmas, 1971, 1st Issue .... 7.50 To 13.00
Collector, Plate, Nidaros, Annual, 1970, Aluminum, Red 15.00
Collector, Plate, Nidaros, Annual, 1971, Aluminum, Blue 15.00
Collector, Plate, Orrefors, Annual, 1970 .... 50.00
Collector, Plate, Orrefors, Annual, 1971 .... 50.00
Collector, Plate, Orrefors, Annual, 1972 .... 29.50 To 50.00
Collector, Plate, Orrefors, Christmas, 1970, Cathedral, 1st Issue 50.00
Collector, Plate, Orrefors, Christmas, 1971 .... 45.00 To 50.00
Collector, Plate, Orrefors, Mother's Day, 1971, 1st Issue 39.50
Collector, Plate, Orrefors, Mother's Day, 1972 .... 45.00
Collector, Plate, Orrefors, Mother's Day, 1973 .... 30.00
Collector, Plate, Peanuts, Christmas, 1972, Schmid, 1st Issue 10.00
Collector, Plate, Peanuts, Mother's Day, 1972, Schmid, 1st Issue 10.00
Collector, Plate, Peanuts, Mother's Day, 1973, Schmid 10.00
Collector, Plate, Pearl Buck, 1972, Veneto Flair, 1st Issue 35.00
Collector, Plate, Pickard, Presidential, 1971, Truman .... 30.00 To 35.00

Collector, Plate, Poillerat, Summer, 1972 .... 200.00
Collector, Plate, Poole, Medieval Calendar, January, 1972 .... 80.00 To 100.00
Collector, Plate, Porcelana Granada, Annual, 1971, 1st Issue 12.00
Collector, Plate, Porsgrund, Christmas, 1968, 1st Issue .... 37.50 To 65.00
Collector, Plate, Porsgrund, Christmas, 1969 .... 9.00 To 13.00
Collector, Plate, Porsgrund, Christmas, 1970 .... 8.00 To 12.00
Collector, Plate, Porsgrund, Christmas, 1970, Deluxe, 1st Issue .... 35.00 To 50.00
Collector, Plate, Porsgrund, Christmas, 1971 .... 8.00 To 12.00
Collector, Plate, Porsgrund, Christmas, 1971, Deluxe .... 35.00 To 50.00
Collector, Plate, Porsgrund, Christmas, 1972 .... 9.75 To 12.00
Collector, Plate, Porsgrund, Christmas, 1972, Deluxe 50.00
Collector, Plate, Porsgrund, Easter, 1972, 1st Issue .... 10.00 To 20.00
Collector, Plate, Porsgrund, Father's Day, 1971, 1st Issue .... 4.00 To 7.50
Collector, Plate, Porsgrund, Father's Day, 1972 .... 4.00 To 8.00
Collector, Plate, Porsgrund, Father's Day, 1973 .... 6.50 To 8.00
Collector, Plate, Porsgrund, Jubilee, 1970, 1st Issue .... 14.00 To 25.00
Collector, Plate, Porsgrund, Mother's Day, 1970, 1st Issue .... 6.00 To 17.50
Collector, Plate, Porsgrund, Mother's Day, 1971 .... 3.50 To 7.50
Collector, Plate, Porsgrund, Mother's Day, 1972 .... 4.00 To 8.00
Collector, Plate, Porsgrund, Mother's Day, 1973 .... 5.00 To 8.00
Collector, Plate, Portmerion, Mother's Day, 1971, 1st Issue .... 8.00 To 15.00
Collector, Plate, Reed & Barton, Audubon Bird, 1970, Pine Sisken .... 55.00 To 95.00
Collector, Plate, Reed & Barton, Audubon Bird, 1971, Red Hawk .... 60.00 To 65.00
Collector, Plate, Reed & Barton, Audubon Bird, 1972, Sandpiper 65.00
Collector, Plate, Reed & Barton, Christmas, 1970, 1st Issue 175.00
Collector, Plate, Reed & Barton, Christmas, 1971 .... 60.00 To 72.50
Collector, Plate, Rorstrand, Christmas, 1968, 1st Issue .... 85.00 To 100.00
Collector, Plate, Rorstrand, Christmas, 1969 .... 8.00 To 18.00
Collector, Plate, Rorstrand, Christmas, 1970 .... 8.00 To 14.50
Collector, Plate, Rorstrand, Christmas, 1971 .... 8.00 To 17.50
Collector, Plate, Rorstrand, Christmas, 1972 .... 11.50 To 16.00
Collector, Plate, Rorstrand, Father's Day, 1971, 1st Issue .... 7.50 To 13.50
Collector, Plate, Rorstrand, Father's Day, 1972 .... 10.00 To 15.00
Collector, Plate, Rorstrand, Mother's Day, 1971, 1st Issue .... 7.50 To 13.50
Collector, Plate, Rorstrand, Mother's Day, 1972 .... 10.00 To 15.00
Collector, Plate, Rosenthal, Christmas, 1910 Through 1967, Each 65.00
Collector, Plate, Rosenthal, Christmas, 1968 .... 65.00
Collector, Plate, Rosenthal, Christmas, 1969 .... 35.00 To 65.00
Collector, Plate, Rosenthal, Christmas, 1970 .... 32.50 To 65.00
Collector, Plate, Rosenthal, Christmas, 1971 .... 32.50 To 50.00
Collector, Plate, Rosenthal, Christmas, 1971, Deluxe, 1st Issue .... 95.00 To 120.00
Collector, Plate, Rosenthal, Christmas, 1972, Deluxe .... 95.00 To 100.00
Collector, Plate, Roskilde, Christmas, 1968, 1st Issue 12.50
Collector, Plate, Roskilde, Christmas, 1969 .... 5.00
Collector, Plate, Roskilde, Christmas, 1970 .... 4.00
Collector, Plate, Roskilde, Christmas, 1971 .... 8.50 To 16.00
Collector, Plate, Roskilde, Christmas, 1972 .... 11.00 To 16.00
Collector, Plate, Royal Bayreuth, Christmas, 1972, 1st Issue 15.00
Collector, Plate, Royal Copenhagen, Annual, Mermaid 20.00
Collector, Plate, Royal Copenhagen, Annual, Statue Of Liberty 23.50
Collector, Plate, Royal Copenhagen, Christmas, 1908, 1st Issue 1000.00
Collector, Plate, Royal Copenhagen, Christmas, 1909 .... 100.00
Collector, Plate, Royal Copenhagen, Christmas, 1910 .... 67.50 To 90.00
Collector, Plate, Royal Copenhagen, Christmas, 1911 .... 67.50 To 110.00
Collector, Plate, Royal Copenhagen, Christmas, 1912 .... 67.50 To 100.00
Collector, Plate, Royal Copenhagen, Christmas, 1913 .... 67.50 To 105.00
Collector, Plate, Royal Copenhagen, Christmas, 1914 .... 67.50 To 90.00
Collector, Plate, Royal Copenhagen, Christmas, 1915 .... 67.50 To 90.00
Collector, Plate, Royal Copenhagen, Christmas, 1916 .... 47.50 To 65.00
Collector, Plate, Royal Copenhagen, Christmas, 1917 .... 65.00
Collector, Plate, Royal Copenhagen, Christmas, 1918 .... 65.00
Collector, Plate, Royal Copenhagen, Christmas, 1919 .... 65.00
Collector, Plate, Royal Copenhagen, Christmas, 1920 .... 55.00
Collector, Plate, Royal Copenhagen, Christmas, 1921 .... 50.00
Collector, Plate, Royal Copenhagen, Christmas, 1922 .... 50.00
Collector, Plate, Royal Copenhagen, Christmas, 1923 .... 38.50 To 60.00

Collector, Plate, Royal Copenhagen, Christmas, 1924 .... 60.00
Collector, Plate, Royal Copenhagen, Christmas, 1925 .... 55.00
Collector, Plate, Royal Copenhagen, Christmas, 1926 .... 55.00
Collector, Plate, Royal Copenhagen, Christmas, 1927 .... 80.00
Collector, Plate, Royal Copenhagen, Christmas, 1928 .... 55.00
Collector, Plate, Royal Copenhagen, Christmas, 1929 .... 60.00
Collector, Plate, Royal Copenhagen, Christmas, 1930 .... 60.00
Collector, Plate, Royal Copenhagen, Christmas, 1931 .... 65.00
Collector, Plate, Royal Copenhagen, Christmas, 1932 .... 65.00
Collector, Plate, Royal Copenhagen, Christmas, 1933 .... 80.00
Collector, Plate, Royal Copenhagen, Christmas, 1934 .... 80.00
Collector, Plate, Royal Copenhagen, Christmas, 1935 .... 85.00
Collector, Plate, Royal Copenhagen, Christmas, 1936 .... 100.00
Collector, Plate, Royal Copenhagen, Christmas, 1937 .... 100.00
Collector, Plate, Royal Copenhagen, Christmas, 1938 .... 190.00
Collector, Plate, Royal Copenhagen, Christmas, 1939 .... 200.00
Collector, Plate, Royal Copenhagen, Christmas, 1940 .... 300.00
Collector, Plate, Royal Copenhagen, Christmas, 1941 .... 225.00
Collector, Plate, Royal Copenhagen, Christmas, 1942 .... 300.00
Collector, Plate, Royal Copenhagen, Christmas, 1943 .... 375.00
Collector, Plate, Royal Copenhagen, Christmas, 1944 .... 105.00
Collector, Plate, Royal Copenhagen, Christmas, 1945 .... 300.00
Collector, Plate, Royal Copenhagen, Christmas, 1946 .... 100.00
Collector, Plate, Royal Copenhagen, Christmas, 1947 .... 135.00
Collector, Plate, Royal Copenhagen, Christmas, 1948 ....70.00 To 137.50
Collector, Plate, Royal Copenhagen, Christmas, 1949 ....85.00 To 105.00
Collector, Plate, Royal Copenhagen, Christmas, 1950 .... 110.00
Collector, Plate, Royal Copenhagen, Christmas, 1951 .... 220.00
Collector, Plate, Royal Copenhagen, Christmas, 1952 .... 70.00
Collector, Plate, Royal Copenhagen, Christmas, 1953 .... 70.00
Collector, Plate, Royal Copenhagen, Christmas, 1954 .... 100.00
Collector, Plate, Royal Copenhagen, Christmas, 1955 .... 140.00
Collector, Plate, Royal Copenhagen, Christmas, 1956 .... 95.00
Collector, Plate, Royal Copenhagen, Christmas, 1957 .... 75.00
Collector, Plate, Royal Copenhagen, Christmas, 1958 .... 80.00
Collector, Plate, Royal Copenhagen, Christmas, 1959 .... 100.00
Collector, Plate, Royal Copenhagen, Christmas, 1960 ....61.00 To 100.00
Collector, Plate, Royal Copenhagen, Christmas, 1961 .... 60.00 To 80.00
Collector, Plate, Royal Copenhagen, Christmas, 1962 ....92.00 To 108.00
Collector, Plate, Royal Copenhagen, Christmas, 1963 .... 32.50 To 41.00
Collector, Plate, Royal Copenhagen, Christmas, 1964 .... 20.00 To 36.00
Collector, Plate, Royal Copenhagen, Christmas, 1965 .... 25.00 To 45.00
Collector, Plate, Royal Copenhagen, Christmas, 1966 .... 18.00 To 26.00
Collector, Plate, Royal Copenhagen, Christmas, 1967 .... 15.00 To 27.00
Collector, Plate, Royal Copenhagen, Christmas, 1968 .... 12.50 To 24.00
Collector, Plate, Royal Copenhagen, Christmas, 1969 .... 11.50 To 21.00
Collector, Plate, Royal Copenhagen, Christmas, 1970 .... 10.00 To 18.00
Collector, Plate, Royal Copenhagen, Christmas, 1971 .... 9.50 To 15.00
Collector, Plate, Royal Copenhagen, Christmas, 1972 .... 10.75 To 16.00
Collector, Plate, Royal Copenhagen, Moon, 1969 .... 10.00 To 16.50
Collector, Plate, Royal Copenhagen, Mother's Day, 1971, 1st Issue....................40.00 To 110.00
Collector, Plate, Royal Copenhagen, Mother's Day, 1972 .... 10.00 To 13.00
Collector, Plate, Royal Copenhagen, Olympic, 1972 .... 22.50 To 26.50
Collector, Plate, Royal Delft, Apollo, 1969 .... 17.50
Collector, Plate, Royal Delft, Christmas, 1972, 7 In. 40.00
Collector, Plate, Royal Delft, Christmas, 1972, 9 In. 70.00
Collector, Plate, Royal Delft, Easter, 1973, 9 In. 75.00
Collector, Plate, Royal Delft, Father's Day, 1973, 7 In. 50.00
Collector, Plate, Royal Delft, Mother's Day, 1972, 7 In. .... 30.00 To 40.00
Collector, Plate, Royal Delft, Mother's Day, 1973, 7 In. 50.00
Collector, Plate, Royal Delft, Valentine's Day, 1973, 1st Issue .... 60.00 To 75.00
Collector, Plate, Royal Doulton, Christmas, 1972, 1st Issue .... 29.50 To 35.00
Collector, Plate, Royal Limoges, Christmas, 1972, 1st Issue .... 22.50 To 25.00
Collector, Plate, Royal Rockwood, Christmas, 1970, 1st Issue .... 22.00 To 45.00
Collector, Plate, Royal Rockwood, Christmas, 1971 .... 12.50 To 16.00
Collector, Plate, Royal Rockwood, Christmas, 1972 .... 15.00

Collector, Plate, Royal Rockwood, Father's Day, 1970, 1st Issue .... 15.00 To 38.00
Collector, Plate, Royal Rockwood, Father's Day, 1971 .... 15.00 To 25.00
Collector, Plate, Royal Rockwood, Father's Day, 1972 .... 15.00
Collector, Plate, Royal Tettau, Papal, 1971, Paul VI, 1st Issue .... 70.00 To 100.00
Collector, Plate, Royal Worcester, Bicentennial, 1972, Pewter 45.00
Collector, Plate, Royale, Annual, 1970, Crystal, 1st Issue .... 370.00 To 490.00
Collector, Plate, Royale, Annual, 1971, Crystal .... 150.00 To 200.00
Collector, Plate, Royale, Annual, 1972, Crystal .... 190.00 To 250.00
Collector, Plate, Royale, Astronaut, 1969 .... 65.00 To 85.00
Collector, Plate, Royale, Christmas, 1969, Porcelain, 1st Issue .... 40.00 To 60.00
Collector, Plate, Royale, Christmas, 1970, Crystal, 1st Issue .... 285.00 To 445.00
Collector, Plate, Royale, Christmas, 1970, Porcelain .... 5.00 To 17.00
Collector, Plate, Royale, Christmas, 1971, Porcelain .... 10.00 To 15.00
Collector, Plate, Royale, Christmas, 1972, Porcelain .... 12.00 To 16.00
Collector, Plate, Royale, Father's Day, 1970, 1st Issue .... 10.00 To 36.00
Collector, Plate, Royale, Father's Day, 1971 .... 8.00 To 14.00
Collector, Plate, Royale, Father's Day, 1972 .... 10.00 To 16.00
Collector, Plate, Royale, Game, 1972 .... 180.00
Collector, Plate, Royale, Mother's Day, 1970, Porcelain, 1st Issue .... 20.00 To 40.00
Collector, Plate, Royale, Mother's Day, 1971, Crystal, 1st Issue .... 225.00 To 350.00
Collector, Plate, Royale, Mother's Day, 1971, Porcelain .... 8.00 To 16.00
Collector, Plate, Royale, Mother's Day, 1972, Crystal .... 140.00 To 180.00
Collector, Plate, Royale, Mother's Day, 1972, Porcelain .... 10.00 To 16.00
Collector, Plate, Sabino, Annual, 1971 .... 62.50
Collector, Plate, Santa Clara, Christmas, 1970, 1st Issue .... 10.00 To 15.00
Collector, Plate, Santa Clara, Christmas, 1971 .... 12.00 To 15.00
Collector, Plate, Santa Clara, Christmas, 1972 .... 12.00 To 15.00
Collector, Plate, Santa Clara, Mother's Day, 1971, 1st Issue .... 8.00 To 16.00
Collector, Plate, Santa Clara, Mother's Day, 1972 .... 12.00 To 15.00
Collector, Plate, Schumann, Christmas, 1971, 1st Issue .... 8.00 To 12.00
Collector, Plate, Schumann, Composers, Beethoven .... 10.00 To 13.00
Collector, Plate, Sebring, Mother's Day, 1971 .... 5.00
Collector, Plate, Selandia, Christmas, 1972, Pewter, 1st Issue .... 20.00 To 30.00
Collector, Plate, Seven Seas, Christmas, 1970, 1st Issue, Carol .... 8.00 To 14.50
Collector, Plate, Seven Seas, Christmas, 1971, Carol .... 7.95 To 14.50
Collector, Plate, Seven Seas, Church, 1969, Marble, 1st Issue 7.95
Collector, Plate, Seven Seas, Church, 1970, Marble 7.95
Collector, Plate, Seven Seas, History, 1969, Landing With Flag, 1st Issue 15.00
Collector, Plate, Seven Seas, History, 1969, Landing Without Flag, 1st Issue 33.00
Collector, Plate, Seven Seas, History, 1970, Year Of Crisis, 1st Issue 14.50
Collector, Plate, Seven Seas, Mother's Day, 1970, 1st Issue .... 15.00 To 18.00
Collector, Plate, Seven Seas, Mother's Day, 1971 .... 14.50
Collector, Plate, Seven Seas, New World, 1970, 1st Issue .... 10.00 To 14.50
Collector, Plate, Seven Seas, New World, 1971 .... 14.50
Collector, Plate, Seven Seas, Passion Play, 1970 .... 9.95 To 12.00
Collector, Plate, Silver City, Christmas, 1971 .... 17.50
Collector, Plate, Smith Glass, Christmas, 1971, 1st Issue .... 8.50 To 10.00
Collector, Plate, Smith Glass, Coin, 1971, Silver Dollar 10.00
Collector, Plate, Smith Glass, Famous Americans, 1971, Kennedy, 1st Issue 22.00
Collector, Plate, Smith Glass, Famous Americans, 1971, Lincoln, 1st Issue 22.00
Collector, Plate, Spode, Christmas, 1970, 1st Issue .... 17.50 To 35.00
Collector, Plate, Spode, Christmas, 1971 .... 17.00 To 45.00
Collector, Plate, Spode, Dickens .... 50.00 To 60.00
Collector, Plate, Spode, Imperial Plate Of Persia, 1971 .... 85.00 To 98.00
Collector, Plate, Spode, Lowestoft, 1970 .... 25.00
Collector, Plate, St.Amand, Christmas, 1970, 1st Issue .... 4.50 To 8.50
Collector, Plate, St.Amand, Christmas, 1971 .... 7.00 To 7.50
Collector, Plate, Sterling America, Christmas, 1970, Partridge, 1st Issue 25.00
Collector, Plate, Sterling America, Christmas, 1970, Yule Log, 1st Issue 25.00
Collector, Plate, Sterling America, Christmas, 1971, Holland 20.00
Collector, Plate, Sterling America, Christmas, 1971, Two Turtle Doves 18.00
Collector, Plate, Sterling America, Christmas, 1972, Norway 18.00
Collector, Plate, Sterling America, Christmas, 1972, Three French Hens 18.00
Collector, Plate, Sterling America, Mother's Day, 1971, 1st Issue .... 18.00 To 25.00
Collector, Plate, Sterling America, Mother's Day, 1972 .... 18.00
Collector, Plate, Stumar, Christmas, 1970, 1st Issue .... 6.00 To 10.00

Collector, Plate, Stumar, Christmas, 1971 .... 8.00 To 8.50
Collector, Plate, Stumar, Mother's Day, 1971, 1st Issue 8.00
Collector, Plate, Stumar, Mother's Day, 1972 .... 8.00
Collector, Plate, Tirschenreuth, Christmas, 1969, 1st Issue 20.00
Collector, Plate, Tirschenreuth, Christmas, 1970 .... 8.00 To 13.00
Collector, Plate, Tirschenreuth, Christmas, 1971 .... 8.00 To 12.00
Collector, Plate, Tirschenreuth, Christmas, 1972 .... 12.00
Collector, Plate, Ulmer, Christmas, 1971, 1st Issue 15.00
Collector, Plate, Val St.Lambert, Annual, 1968, Pair, 1st Issue .... 55.00 To 95.00
Collector, Plate, Val St.Lambert, Annual, 1969, Pair 50.00
Collector, Plate, Val St.Lambert, Annual, 1970, Pair 50.00
Collector, Plate, Val St.Lambert, Annual, 1971, Pair .... 45.00 To 50.00
Collector, Plate, Val St.Lambert, Old Masters, 1968, Pair, 1st Issue 50.00
Collector, Plate, Val St.Lambert, Old Masters, 1969, Pair 42.50
Collector, Plate, Val St.Lambert, Old Masters, 1970, Pair .... 37.50 To 50.00
Collector, Plate, Val St.Lambert, Rembrandt, 1970 .... 20.00 To 23.00
Collector, Plate, Val St.Lambert, Thanksgiving, 1970 .... 25.00
Collector, Plate, Veneto Flair, Bird, 1972, Owl, 1st Issue ....85.00 To 175.00
Collector, Plate, Veneto Flair, Bird, 1973, Falcon 88.00
Collector, Plate, Veneto Flair, Christmas, 1971, 1st Issue .... 100.00 To 225.00
Collector, Plate, Veneto Flair, Christmas, 1972 ....,,70.00 To 100.00
Collector, Plate, Veneto Flair, Christmas, 1972, Silver .... 125.00 To 275.00
Collector, Plate, Veneto Flair, Dog, 1972, Shepherd, 1st Issue ....80.00 To 130.00
Collector, Plate, Veneto Flair, Dog, 1973, Poodle 88.00
Collector, Plate, Veneto Flair, Easter, 1973, 1st Issue .... 75.00 To 88.00
Collector, Plate, Veneto Flair, Four Seasons, 1972, Fall 125.00
Collector, Plate, Veneto Flair, Last Supper ....80.00 To 100.00
Collector, Plate, Veneto Flair, Madonna, 1970 .... 500.00 To 750.00
Collector, Plate, Veneto Flair, Mother's Day, 1972 .... 155.00 To 350.00
Collector, Plate, Veneto Flair, Mother's Day, 1973 .... 70.00 To 88.00
Collector, Plate, Veneto Flair, Valentine's Day, 1973, Silver 135.00
Collector, Plate, Veneto Flair, Wildlife, 1970, Stag, 1st Issue .... 450.00 To 550.00
Collector, Plate, Veneto Flair, Wildlife, 1971, Elephant .... 200.00 To 260.00
Collector, Plate, Veneto Flair, Wildlife, 1972, Puma ....75.00 To 150.00
Collector, Plate, Veneto Flair, Wildlife, 1973, Tiger 88.00
Collector, Plate, Vernonware, Christmas, 1971, 1st Issue .... 15.00 To 30.00
Collector, Plate, Vernonware, Christmas, 1972 .... 17.00 To 17.50
Collector, Plate, Washington Mint, Last Supper, 1972, 1st Issue 125.00
Collector, Plate, Wedgwood, Apollo, 1969 .... 10.00 To 25.00
Collector, Plate, Wedgwood, Bicentennial, 1972, Tea Party, 1st .... 25.00 To 30.00
Collector, Plate, Wedgwood, Child's Day, 1971, 1st Issue .... 5.00 To 11.00
Collector, Plate, Wedgwood, Child's Day, 1972 .... 8.95
Collector, Plate, Wedgwood, Christmas, 1969, 1st Issue ....65.00 To 110.00
Collector, Plate, Wedgwood, Christmas, 1970 .... 13.75 To 25.00
Collector, Plate, Wedgwood, Christmas, 1971 .... 16.50 To 30.00
Collector, Plate, Wedgwood, Christmas, 1972 .... 24.50 To 35.00
Collector, Plate, Wedgwood, Commonwealth, Virgina, 1972 .... 18.00 To 20.00
Collector, Plate, Wedgwood, Mother's Day, 1971, 1st Issue .... 14.50 To 25.00
Collector, Plate, Wedgwood, Mother's Day, 1972 .... 12.50 To 22.50
Collector, Plate, Wedgwood, Mother's Day, 1973 .... 16.50 To 18.00
Collector, Plate, Wedgwood, Olympia, 1972 .... 25.00
Collector, Plate, Wedgwood, Windsor Castle, 1969 .... 85.00
Collector, Plate, Wellings Mint, Christmas, 1971, 1st Issue ....60.00 To 120.00
Collector, Plate, Wellings Mint, Mother's Day, 1972, 1st Issue ....60.00 To 100.00
Collector, Spoon, Kirk, Christmas, 1972 .... 12.50
Collector, Spoon, Michelsen, Christmas, 1910 ....60.00 To 110.00
Collector, Spoon, Michelsen, Christmas, 1911 ....60.00 To 110.00
Collector, Spoon, Michelsen, Christmas, 1912 ....60.00 To 110.00
Collector, Spoon, Michelsen, Christmas, 1913 ....60.00 To 110.00
Collector, Spoon, Michelsen, Christmas, 1914 ....60.00 To 110.00
Collector, Spoon, Michelsen, Christmas, 1915 ....60.00 To 110.00
Collector, Spoon, Michelsen, Christmas, 1916 ....60.00 To 110.00
Collector, Spoon, Michelsen, Christmas, 1917 ....60.00 To 110.00
Collector, Spoon, Michelsen, Christmas, 1918 ....60.00 To 110.00
Collector, Spoon, Michelsen, Christmas, 1919 ....60.00 To 110.00
Collector, Spoon, Michelsen, Christmas, 1920 .... 36.00 To 52.00

Collector, Spoon, Michelsen, Christmas, 1921 .... 36.00 To 52.00
Collector, Spoon, Michelsen, Christmas, 1922 .... 36.00 To 52.00
Collector, Spoon, Michelsen, Christmas, 1923 .... 36.00 To 52.00
Collector, Spoon, Michelsen, Christmas, 1924 .... 36.00 To 52.00
Collector, Spoon, Michelsen, Christmas, 1925 .... 36.00 To 52.00
Collector, Spoon, Michelsen, Christmas, 1926 .... 36.00 To 52.00
Collector, Spoon, Michelsen, Christmas, 1927 .... 36.00 To 52.00
Collector, Spoon, Michelsen, Christmas, 1928 .... 36.00 To 52.00
Collector, Spoon, Michelsen, Christmas, 1929 .... 36.00 To 52.00
Collector, Spoon, Michelsen, Christmas, 1930 .... 25.00 To 46.00
Collector, Spoon, Michelsen, Christmas, 1931 .... 25.00 To 46.00
Collector, Spoon, Michelsen, Christmas, 1932 .... 25.00 To 46.00
Collector, Spoon, Michelsen, Christmas, 1933 .... 25.00 To 46.00
Collector, Spoon, Michelsen, Christmas, 1934 .... 25.00 To 46.00
Collector, Spoon, Michelsen, Christmas, 1935 .... 25.00 To 46.00
Collector, Spoon, Michelsen, Christmas, 1936 .... 25.00 To 46.00
Collector, Spoon, Michelsen, Christmas, 1937 .... 25.00 To 46.00
Collector, Spoon, Michelsen, Christmas, 1938 .... 25.00 To 46.00
Collector, Spoon, Michelsen, Christmas, 1939 .... 25.00 To 46.00
Collector, Spoon, Michelsen, Christmas, 1940 .... 25.00 To 38.00
Collector, Spoon, Michelsen, Christmas, 1941 .... 25.00 To 38.00
Collector, Spoon, Michelsen, Christmas, 1942 .... 25.00 To 38.00
Collector, Spoon, Michelsen, Christmas, 1943 .... 25.00 To 38.00
Collector, Spoon, Michelsen, Christmas, 1944 .... 25.00 To 38.00
Collector, Spoon, Michelsen, Christmas, 1945 .... 25.00 To 38.00
Collector, Spoon, Michelsen, Christmas, 1946 .... 25.00 To 38.00
Collector, Spoon, Michelsen, Christmas, 1947 .... 25.00 To 38.00
Collector, Spoon, Michelsen, Christmas, 1948 .... 25.00 To 38.00
Collector, Spoon, Michelsen, Christmas, 1949 .... 25.00 To 38.00
Collector, Spoon, Michelsen, Christmas, 1950 ....   32.00
Collector, Spoon, Michelsen, Christmas, 1951 ....   32.00
Collector, Spoon, Michelsen, Christmas, 1952 ....   32.00
Collector, Spoon, Michelsen, Christmas, 1953 ....   32.00
Collector, Spoon, Michelsen, Christmas, 1954 ....   32.00
Collector, Spoon, Michelsen, Christmas, 1955 ....   32.00
Collector, Spoon, Michelsen, Christmas, 1956 ....   32.00
Collector, Spoon, Michelsen, Christmas, 1957 ....   32.00
Collector, Spoon, Michelsen, Christmas, 1958 ....   32.00
Collector, Spoon, Michelsen, Christmas, 1959 ....   32.00
Collector, Spoon, Michelsen, Christmas, 1960 ....   30.00
Collector, Spoon, Michelsen, Christmas, 1961 ....   30.00
Collector, Spoon, Michelsen, Christmas, 1962 ....   30.00
Collector, Spoon, Michelsen, Christmas, 1963 ....   30.00
Collector, Spoon, Michelsen, Christmas, 1964 ....   30.00
Collector, Spoon, Michelsen, Christmas, 1965 ....   30.00
Collector, Spoon, Michelsen, Christmas, 1966 ....   30.00
Collector, Spoon, Michelsen, Christmas, 1967 ....   30.00
Collector, Spoon, Michelsen, Christmas, 1968 ....   30.00
Collector, Spoon, Michelsen, Christmas, 1969 ....   30.00
Collector, Spoon, Michelsen, Christmas, 1970 ....   30.00
Collector, Spoon, Michelsen, Christmas, 1971 ....   27.00
Collector, Spoon, Michelsen, Christmas, 1972 ....   27.00
Collector, Stein, Berlin, Christmas, 1971, 1st Issue 40.00
Collector, Stein, Falstaff, Christmas, 1971 ....   16.75
Collector, Tankard, Royal Doulton, Christmas, 1971, 1st Issue .... 35.00 To 49.00
Collector, Tankard, Royal Doulton, Christmas, 1972 ....   37.50
Collector, Tankard, Stromberg, Christmas, 1970, 1st Issue 50.00
Collector, Tankard, Stromberg, Christmas, 1971 ....   20.00
Collector, Tankard, Stromberg, Christmas, 1972 ....   25.00
Collector, Tile, Blue, Delft, Christmas, 1967, 1st Issue 20.00
Collector, Tile, Blue Delft, Christmas, 1968 .... 10.00 To 12.00
Collector, Tile, Blue Delft, Christmas, 1969 ....   8.00
Collector, Tile, Blue Delft, Christmas, 1970 ....   6.00
Collector, Tile, Blue Delft, Christmas, 1971 ....   4.50
Collector, Vase, Lihs Lindner, Christmas, 1972 .... 75.00 To 85.00
Collector, Vase, Mark Peiser, 1972 ....   100.00

Collector, Vase, Royal Haeger, 1971 .... 10.00

Commemoration items have been made to honor members of Royalty and those of
great national fame. World's Fairs and important historical events are also
remembered with commemoration pieces.
Commemoration, see also Coronation
Commemoration, Bell, Pope Leo 25.00
Commemoration, Bottle, Head Of Washington, 1732-1932, Clear, Embossed 5.98
Commemoration, Bowl, Victoria, 1897, Stoneware 15.00
Commemoration, Box, Edward VII & Alexandra, Dated 1902, Tin 30.00
Commemoration, Button, Harry S.Truman, In Memoriam .... .75
Commemoration, Cup & Saucer, Demitasse, Martha Washington, 1776-1876, Motto .. 20.00
Commemoration, Eggcup, George V & Mary, Pair 25.00
Commemoration, Goblet, Edward VIII, 1937, Brown Pottery 10.00
Commemoration, Match Box Holder, King George V, Jubilee 1935, Nickel Plated 6.50
Commemoration, Medal, Pope Paul VI, On Easel, Bronze 15.00
Commemoration, Mug, Coronation Of King Edward VII, 1902, Portraits, Flags 15.00
Commemoration, Mug, Edward VII, 1902 .... 16.00
Commemoration, Mug, Elizabeth II, 1953 .... 9.00
Commemoration, Mug, George V, 1911, God Save The King 25.00
Commemoration, Mug, George VI, 1937 .... 9.00
Commemoration, Mug, Juliana & Bernhard, Netherlands, 25th Anniversary 12.00
Commemoration, Mug, Shaving, '1904 World's Fair, 'Floral And Scenes 27.50
Commemoration, Mug, Spanish-American War, Battleship Maine, Cream Ground 12.50
Commemoration, Mug, Victoria, Diamond Reign, 1837-1867, Porcelain 15.00
Commemoration, Mustache Cup & Saucer, Victoria's 60 Year Reign 38.00
Commemoration, Newspaper, Charles Lindbergh, Dated 1927 .... 14.50
Commemoration, Pitcher, Elizabeth II, 1953 .... 12.50
Commemoration, Pitcher, George VI, 1939 .... 11.00
Commemoration, Plate, Eisenhower, Dated 10/14/53, 10 3/4 In.Diameter 50.00
Commemoration, Plate, Elizabeth II, Visit To Australia, 1954, White, Blue 17.50
Commemoration, Plate, George V & Mary, Crowned June 22, 1911, 7 In. 5.00
Commemoration, Plate, King George's Visit To U.S., Mulberry Transfer 3.50
Commemoration, Plate, Napoleon, Carlsbad, Austria, 6 In. 10.00
Commemoration, Plate, Victoria's Jubilee, Amber, 10 In. 25.00
Commemoration, Plate, Victoria's Jubilee, Clear Glass, 9 1/2 In. 15.00
Commemoration, Plate, Victoria's Jubilee, 10 1/2 In. 18.00
Commemoration, Plate, 200th Anniversary Of The U.S., Double Eagle 125.00
Commemoration, Ribbon, In Memoriam, President Garfield, Silk, 6 In.Long 4.00
Commemoration, Saucer, Victoria, Golden Reign, 1837-1887 .... 7.00
Commemoration, Silk Square, Louisiana Purchase, 1904 Exposition, Eagles 20.00
Commemoration, Tumbler, St.Louis Expedition, 1904, Clear, 5 In.High 15.00
Commemoration, Tray, McKinley, Aluminum 7.00
Compass, Ship's, Brass, Floating, Glass Door On Front, U.S.Navy 25.00
Compass, Surveyor's, Brass, W. & L.E.Gurley, Troy, N.Y., 1845, Box 175.00
Compass, Surveyor's, G.R.Whitehouse, Farmington, N.H., Pine Box 165.00

W.T.Copeland & Sons, Ltd., ran the Spode Works in Staffordshire,
England, from 1847 to the present. Copeland & Garrett was the firm
name from 1833 to 1847.
Copeland, see also Spode
Copeland Spode, Bowl, Peacock, Enameled, Square, C.1850, 9 In. 75.00
Copeland Spode, Bowl, Serving, Blue, Center Scene, Floral Border, 9 1/2 In. 12.50
Copeland Spode, Cake Set, Green Shamrocks, Marked, 19 1/2 In.Plate, 7 Piece 35.00
Copeland Spode, Cup & Saucer, Blue Tower 8.50
Copeland Spode, Cup & Saucer, Demitasse, Blue Willow 18.50
Copeland Spode, Cup & Saucer, Demitasse, English Hunt Scene 12.50
Copeland Spode, Dish, Vegetable, Blue 15.00
Copeland Spode, Jug, Grape Vines, Village Drinking Scene, Vine Handle 55.00
Copeland Spode, Pitcher, Blue, White, Men On Horses On Fox Chase, 8 1/4 In. 75.00
Copeland Spode, Pitcher, Cider, Deep Blue, White Enamel, Drinking Scenes 59.00
Copeland Spode, Pitcher, Hunting Scene, Horses, Dogs, Deer, England, 7 In. 65.00
Copeland Spode, Pitcher, Jasper, Blue, White Figures, Hops & Men Drinking 75.00
Copeland Spode, Plate, Castle Ruins, Flow Blue, 1845 .... 14.00
Copeland Spode, Plate, English Hunt Scene, 8 In. 18.50
Copeland Spode, Plate, Portland Vase, Red Roses In Vase, Blue Border, Pair 25.00

Copeland Spode, Plate, Scene Of Island, Bird, & Butterfly, Dated Nov.1879	6.00
Copeland Spode, Plate, Swags Of Blue Flowers, Gold Scallops, 1890	10.00
Copeland Spode, Platter, Fluted, Scalloped, Signed Spode, Lorraine, England	22.00
Copeland Spode, Soup, English Hunt Scene, 9 In.	22.50
Copeland Spode, Teapot, Blue & White	32.00
Copeland Spode, Teapot, Sugar, Creamer, Green Ground, White Grecian Ladies	50.00
Copeland, Cup & Saucer, Miniature, 1833 Mark	25.00
Copeland, Cup & Saucer, Pale Blue & White	10.00
Copeland, Cup & Saucer, 'We'Ll Take A Cup O' Kindness, 'spode	18.00
Copeland, Dish, Cheese, Blue & White	60.00
Copeland, Jar, Biscuit, Jasper, Blue Ground, White Figures, Hunters	45.00
Copeland, Pitcher, Blue & White Transfer, Tower Pattern, Circa 1835, 5 In.	38.00
Copeland, Pitcher, Blue With White Classical Figures, 4 In.	30.00
Copeland, Pitcher, Blue, Flowers, Gold Design	5.50
Copeland, Pitcher, Brown, Green & White Figures Of Children, 5 1/2 In.	35.00
Copeland, Pitcher, Gray Ground, White Classic Borders, Hunter, Dogs, Horses	38.00
Copeland, Pitcher, Jasper, Brown, White Figures, Hunters, 8 In.	78.00
Copeland, Pitcher, Jasper, Hunting Scene, C.1847-1868, 8 In.	95.00
Copeland, Plaque, Underglaze Sepia Painting, Signed W.Yale, Circa 1857	125.00
Copeland, Plate, Fighting Warriors, Greek Key Bands, Fluted Rim, Circa 1880	18.00
Copeland, Plate, June, Framed Cherubs	90.00
Copeland, Plate, Leaf & Acorn, 5 In.	14.00
Copeland, Plate, Sepia Castle, Acorn Rim, Circa 1885, 8 7/8 In.	14.00
Copeland, Plate, Turkey, Blue, Spode, England, Set Of 12	200.00
Copeland, Plate, Willow Pattern, Gold Border, Signed	18.00
Copeland, Platter, Fleur-De-Lis Border	30.00
Copeland, Teapot, Blue Jasper, Dancing Maidens	44.00
Copeland, Vase, Cherubs On Base, Hold Trumpet Vase, Grapes, Leaves, Pair	140.00
Copeland, Vase, Lady In White Dress, Enameled Jewels, Gold, Artist S.Alcock	200.00
Copeland, Vase, Trumpet Shape, Three Cherubs On Base, Foliage, Grapes, Pair	140.00
Copper & Brass, Teakettle, Brass Handle Covered With Bamboo, Oriental	17.50
Copper, Badge, American Slave Identification, Charleston, Dated 1846	185.00
Copper, Beaker, Russian, Coronation Of Czar Nicholas II, 1896, Enameled	140.00
Copper, Bed Warmer, Brass Stopper, 8 1/2 In.Diameter	17.00
Copper, Bed Warmer, Long Wooden Handle, England	85.00
Copper, Bottle, Hot Water, Copper, Brass Neck & Stopper, C.1820, 11 In.Long	25.00
Copper, Bottle, Hot Water, Flat, Brass Screw, 10 In.Diameter	24.50
Copper, Bottle, Hot Water, Loaf Shape, England, 10 In.Long	24.00
Copper, Bowl, Fruit, Cutout Trim, Stem, 8 In.High, 10 In.Diameter	18.50
Copper, Bowl, Ring For Hanging, Signed J.H.& M.Co., 10 1/2 In.Diameter	45.00
Copper, Box, Jewelry, Cupids On Top In Heavy Relief, Claw Feet	48.00
Copper, Box, Snuff, Silver Wire Inlaid Design	32.50
Copper, Can, Measuring, Pint	6.00
Copper, Chocolate Pot, 2 Brass Bands, Plunger With Brass Finial, 11 In.High	39.50
Copper, Coal Hod, Helmet Type, England	75.00
Copper, Coffeepot, Chuck Wagon, 2 Gallon	50.00
Copper, Dish, Chafing, Child's, Wooden Handle & Knob, 5 In.High	25.00
Copper, Dish, Chafing, Pat.Nov.8, 1904	37.50
Copper, Eagle On Ball, Mounted On Wood Pedestal, Flagpole Figure	55.00
Copper, Foot Warmer, Railway, Bottle Shape, 11 In.High	25.00
Copper, Grater, Handmade	20.00
Copper, Helmet, Diving	500.00
Copper, Helmet, Parade, Gilt Finish, Italian, Bare Breasted Angel, C.1750	185.00
Copper, Horn, Coaching, Circa 1845	80.00
Copper, Humidor, Leather Covered	4.00
Copper, Jug, Wine, English, Crown Mark, Gallon	65.00
Copper, Kettle, Apple Butter, Iron Bail, 12 In.Deep, 18 In.Top Diameter	77.50
Copper, Kettle, England, Brass Handle, 7 1/2 In.High	27.50
Copper, Kettle, Gooseneck Spout, Flat Handle, Copper, Brass Knob, 5 Qt.	35.00
Copper, Kettle, Tea, C.1900, 20 In.High	90.00
Copper, Kettle, Wash, Lid	25.00
Copper, Kettle, Wrought Iron Bail, 30 In.Diameter, 18 In.High	85.00
Copper, Kettle, 10 In.	10.00
Copper, Lightning Rod, Blue Moon & Star Pattern, Glass Ball, 4 In.	27.50
Copper, Measure, Circa 1810, 2 Gallon	90.00
Copper, Measure, Circa 1840, 2 Gallon	90.00

Copper, Measure, Circa 1840, 2 Gallon 118.00
Copper, Measure, Strap Handle, Dated 1757, Pennsylvania Dutch Style, 6 Quart 85.00
Copper, Mold, Jello, Design On Top 25.00
Copper, Napkin Ring, Says Copper Taken From Ship Success Built 1790 .... 7.00
Copper, Pail, Bail 12.49
Copper, Pan, Egg, Polished 11.75
Copper, Pitcher, Blue Porcelain Lined, Brass Handle & Hinged Top, China 27.50
Copper, Pot & Lid, Iron Handle, Pierced For Hanging, 5 In., Pair 65.00
Copper, Pot, Candy, 2 Iron Loop Handles, Round Bottom, 13 In.Diameter 65.00
Copper, Pot, Miniature, Tripod Stand, Handmade, 1 1/4 In.Tall 15.00
Copper, Skillet, Zinc Clad Interior, Handmade, S.Bolzini, N.Y., Signed 55.00
Copper, Teakettle, Brass Trim 38.00
Copper, Teakettle, Gooseneck, Dovetail, Large 135.00
Copper, Teakettle, Gooseneck, French Hallmarked, 3 1/2 Quarts 32.00
Copper, Teakettle, Iron Handle, 4 1/2 In. .... *Illus* 30.00
Copper, Teakettle, Lid, Gooseneck Spout, Strap Handle 80.00
Copper, Teakettle, Onyx Handle, Hinged Cover, 9 In.Tall 18.00
Copper, Teakettle, Penna., C.1850, 15 1/2 In.High .... *Illus* 350.00
Copper, Teakettle, Wooden Handles, Polished .... *Illus* 19.00
Copper, Teakettle, 17 In.High .... *Illus* 190.00

Copper, Teakettle, Penna.,
C.1850, 15 1/2 In.High

Copper, Teakettle, 17 In.High

Copper, Teakettle
Iron Handle, 4 1/2 In.

Copper, Teapot, Brass Stand, Tray 135.00
Copper, Teapot, Pewter Finial, Ebony Handle, Burnished, 8 3/4 In.Tall 18.00
Copper, Teapot, Tin Lined, Brass Handle, Wooden Insulator, Stand, Burner, 1892 .... 65.00
Copper, Teapot, Trivet, & Tray 47.50
Copper, Tray, North African, Gadrooned Border, Etched Geometric Designs 300.00
Copper, Tray, Round, 10 In. 10.00
Copper, Urn, Brass Spigot, 14 In.High, 8 1/2 In.Across 125.00
Copper, Urn, Coffee, Hand Hammered, Square Base, Open Handles, Engraved 50.00
Copper, Vase, Chinese Scene, Black Finish, Pedestal Base, Pair 15.00
Copper, Wash Boiler, Cover, Polished 40.00

*Coralene Glass was made by firing many small colored beads on the outside
of glassware. It was made in many patterns in the United States and
Europe in the 1880s. Reproductions are made today.*

Coralene, Bottle, Crystal Ground, Blue, Coralene Decoration, Stopper, 6 In. 195.00
Coralene, Creamer, Green To Blue, White Coralene Bird, Gold, Japan, 1909 .... 85.00
Coralene, Glass, Juice, Geometric Design, Paneled, Amber 70.00
Coralene, Jar, Blue, Mother-Of-Pearl, Gold Stars, Bulbous, 4 3/4 In. 425.00
Coralene, Jar, Cracker, Blue & White 85.00
Coralene, Juice Glass, Amber, Yellow Beading 75.00
Coralene, Juice Glass, Geometric, Yellow Beading, Ribbed Amber Ground 70.00
Coralene, Sugar Sifter, Heavy Orange Beading, Frosted Ground 165.00
Coralene, Vase, Applied Glass Beads Representing Bird On Branch, 6 In. 150.00
Coralene, Vase, Aqua, Mother-Of-Pearl, Gold Beading 375.00

Coralene, Vase, Blue, Water Lily Decoration, Ruffled Top, 5 In. 50.00
Coralene, Vase, Carnation Design, Pink, Green, Yellow, Beaded, 10 1/2 In. 90.00
Coralene, Vase, Gourd Shape, Three Color Satin Glass, Coralene Beading 185.00
Coralene, Vase, Mother-Of-Pearl, Puffed, 7 In. 140.00
Coralene, Vase, Mother-Of-Pearl, Satin, Pink, Pair .... *Illus* 425.00

Coralene, Vase, Mother-Of-Pearl, Satin, Pink, Pair

Coralene, Vase, Wheat Pattern 85.00
Corona Ware, Dresser Set, Blue Floral, Gold, White, Tray, Candlesticks & Box 25.00

Coronation Cups have been made since the 1800s. Pieces of pottery or
glass with a picture of the monarch and the date have been made as souvenirs
for many coronations.

Coronation, see also Commemoration
Coronation, Ashtray, Edward XIII, 4 1/4 In.Diameter, Pair 9.00
Coronation, Ashtray, George VI, 1937 .... 5.00
Coronation, Basket, King George VI, 1937 .... 15.00
Coronation, Beaker, Edward VIII, 1937 .... 12.50
Coronation, Beaker, George VI, 1937 .... 11.00
Coronation, Bowl, Queen Elizabeth, 1953, Crown Shape, Clear Glass 35.00
Coronation, Cup & Saucer, Demitasse, George V, 1935 .... 12.00
Coronation, Cup & Saucer, Elizabeth II, 1953, Bone Porcelain .... 7.95 To 12.50
Coronation, Cup & Saucer, George V, 1911, Hand-Painted 15.00
Coronation, Cup & Saucer, George VI, 1937 .... 10.00
Coronation, Cup, Edward VIII, May, 12, 1937, 4 1/4 In. .... 5.00 To 13.00
Coronation, Cup, Loving, George VI, Gold Handles, 5 In.High 18.00
Coronation, Cup, Loving, George VI, May, 1937, Royal Doulton, Signed Noke 98.00
Coronation, Cup, Presentation, King Edward III, Royal Doulton 17.50
Coronation, Dish, Queen Elizabeth II, 1953, 4 3/4 In. 4.95
Coronation, Fan, Carlton Hotel, 1902 .... 14.50
Coronation, Jar, Cover, Elizabeth, Duke Of Edinburgh, 1953, Wedgwood 30.00
Coronation, Mug, Edward VII, 1902 .... 15.00
Coronation, Mug, Edward VII, 1902, Royal Doulton 35.00
Coronation, Mug, Edward VIII, 1937, By Dame Laura Knight .... 18.00 To 20.00
Coronation, Mug, Edward VIII, 1937, 3 1/2 In.High .... 12.00 To 22.50
Coronation, Mug, Elizabeth II, 1953, Embossed, Pottery, England 9.50
Coronation, Mug, Elizabeth II, 1953, 4 1/4 In. 4.95
Coronation, Mug, George & Mary, Dated 1911, 'God Save The King' 19.00
Coronation, Mug, George & Mary, June 22, 1911 .... 7.95
Coronation, Mug, George & Mary, Portraits, Flags 12.50
Coronation, Mug, George V, 1935 .... 13.00
Coronation, Mug, George VI 12.50
Coronation, Pitcher, Edward VII, Pictures, Pink Luster, 1902 .... 35.00
Coronation, Pitcher, Edward VII, 1902, Glass, 4 1/2 In. 17.50
Coronation, Pitcher, Edward VIII, Wadeheath Ware, England 20.00
Coronation, Pitcher, Elizabeth II, Mask Spout, Worcester Bone China 25.00
Coronation, Pitcher, Elizabeth II, Portrait, Mask Spout, 5 1/2 In. 22.00
Coronation, Pitcher, George V, 1935, 5 In. 18.00

Coronation, Plaque, Elizabeth II, 1953, English Bone China, 3 1/2 In.High 4.95
Coronation, Plate, Edward VIII, Profile, Blue, Ceramic 5.00
Coronation, Plate, Edward VIII, 1935, 6 In. 8.50
Coronation, Plate, Edward VIII, 1937, 8 3/4 In. 12.00
Coronation, Plate, Elizabeth II, 1953, 6 1/2 In. 7.50
Coronation, Plate, Elizabeth II, 1953, 9 In. .... 9.00 To 14.00
Coronation, Plate, George & Mary, Stoke On Trent, 10 In. 12.00
Coronation, Plate, George VI, Clear, 10 In. 12.00
Coronation, Plate, George VI, 1937, Glass, Gold, Red, Green 12.50
Coronation, Plate, George VI, 1937, 6 In. 8.00
Coronation, Plate, Victoria, 1897, 8 In. 18.00
Coronation, Ribbon, Elizabeth II, 1953, Silk, White, Purple, Portrait, Legend 6.00
Coronation, Spoon, Anointing, Replica, George & Elizabeth, Sterling 17.50
Coronation, Spoon, Edward, Alexandra, 1902, Portraits, Coin Silver, Demitasse 8.50
Coronation, Teapot, Blue Jasper, Wedgwood, 1953 .... 45.00
Coronation, Tin, Biscuit, Elizabeth & Philip, 1953, England 7.50
Coronation, Tin, Candy, George VI, Gray Photograph Design, 6 In. 7.00
Coronation, Tin, Elizabeth II, 1953, Lid, 5 In.Diameter 4.75
Coronation, Wine, Elizabeth II, 3 In. 7.50

Cosmos Pattern Glass is a pattern of pressed milk glass with colored
flowers.
Cosmos, Bowl, Peach, 10 In. 18.00
Cosmos, Butter, Covered, Pink Band .... 135.00 To 140.00
Cosmos, Butter, Covered, Yellow Band 95.00
Cosmos, Butter, Frosted, Clear 27.50
Cosmos, Butter, Milk Glass 126.50
Cosmos, Butter, Pastel Floral, Translucent, 8 In.Diameter 160.00
Cosmos, Castor Set, 3 Bottles 185.00
Cosmos, Lamp Base 65.00
Cosmos, Lamp Base, Pink Band, 7 In.High 42.00
Cosmos, Lamp, Miniature, Clear 25.00
Cosmos, Pitcher 150.00
Cosmos, Pitcher, Water, Pink Band, Six Tumblers 400.00
Cosmos, Spoon Holder, Milk Glass 50.00
Cosmos, Spooner, Pink Band 52.00
Cosmos, Sugar, Covered, 6 1/2 In.High 120.00
Cosmos, Syrup, Lid 110.00
Cosmos, Syrup, Three Colored Flowers, Pink Band, Spring Lid 115.00
Cosmos, Tumbler 41.00
Country Store, see Store

Cowan Pottery was made in Cleveland, Ohio, from 1913 to 1920. Most
pieces of the art pottery were marked with the name of the firm in various
ways.
Cowan, Candlestick, Pair 15.00
Cowan, Vase, Classic Design, Marked, Orchid Color, 6 1/2 In.High 22.00
Cowan, Vase, Ground Hog Decoration, Green 65.00

Crackle Glass was originally made by the Venetians, but most of the ware
found today dates from the 1800s. The glass was heated, cooled, and refired so
that many small lines appeared inside the glass. It was made in many
factories in the United States and Europe.
Crackle Glass, Cruet, Red, Blown, Applied Clear Handle & Stopper 12.50
Crackle Glass, Pitcher, Water, Cranberry, Reeded Handle, Not Overshot 52.00
Crackle Glass, Rose Bowl, Rubena, Applied Flowers, Green & End-Of-Day 100.00
Crackle Glass, Vase, Lion Head Medallions Each Side, Green, 9 In.High 45.00

Cranberry Glass is an almost transparent yellow red glass. It resembles
the color of cranberry juice.
Cranberry Glass, see also Cruet, Toothpick, Rubena Verde, etc.
Cranberry Glass, Basket, Applied Flowers, Clear Foot 37.50
Cranberry Glass, Basket, Bride's, Meriden Holder 95.00
Cranberry Glass, Basket, Clear Handle, Fluted & Ruffled, 4 X 6 In. 60.00
Cranberry Glass, Basket, Crimped & Fluted Edge 65.00
Cranberry Glass, Basket, Crystal Handle & Trim, 5 In. 62.00

Cranberry Glass, Basket, Fluting, Handle, 5 1/2 X 5 In. 65.00
Cranberry Glass, Basket, Jam, Clear Scallops, Heart On Handle, Silver Holder 45.00
Cranberry Glass, Basket, Jam, Vaseline Scallops, Two In Silver Plate Holder 90.00
Cranberry Glass, Basket, Quilted, Crystal Handle 75.00
Cranberry Glass, Basket, Ribbon Crimped, Ruffled, Flared, Polished Pontil 245.00
Cranberry Glass, Basket, Ruffled, Fluted, Clear Crystal Handle 55.00
Cranberry Glass, Basket, Ruffled, Silver Frame & Handle 78.00
Cranberry Glass, Basket, Sandwich Overshot, Clear Looped Handle 68.00
Cranberry Glass, Basket, Swirl, Art Glass, Thorn Handle 59.00
Cranberry Glass, Basket, Thumbprint, Crystal Feet & Handle 65.00
Cranberry Glass, Bell, Clear Handle, Blown Clapper, 10 In.High 85.00
Cranberry Glass, Bell, White Porcelain Handle And Clapper 85.00
Cranberry Glass, Bobeche, Threaded, Fluted, 4 In., Set Of 4 .... 55.00
Cranberry Glass, Bottle Vase, Shaped Neck & Top 55.00
Cranberry Glass, Bottle, Scent, Crystal & Gilt 75.00
Cranberry Glass, Bowl & Underplate, Finger, Hand Threaded, J.Northwood, 1820 .... 65.00
Cranberry Glass, Bowl, Bubbly, 6 In.Diameter, 2 1/4 In.Deep 24.50
Cranberry Glass, Bowl, Finger, Baby Thumbprint 20.00
Cranberry Glass, Bowl, Finger, Clear Base, Set Of 3 .... 36.00
Cranberry Glass, Bowl, Finger, Gold Filigree, Enamel Decoration 45.00
Cranberry Glass, Bowl, Finger, Swirl Inverted Rib 25.00
Cranberry Glass, Bowl, Finger, Swirls 35.00
Cranberry Glass, Bowl, Finger, Underplate, Hand Threaded, J.Northwood, C.1820 .... 65.00
Cranberry Glass, Bowl, Fluted, Clear Pedestal 25.00
Cranberry Glass, Bowl, Gold Threads, Fluted Rim, 5 1/4 In. 40.00
Cranberry Glass, Bowl, Hand Cut, Scalloped Edge, Signed Hawkes 35.00
Cranberry Glass, Bowl, Nut, Ribbed Sides, 4 In. 14.50
Cranberry Glass, Bowl, Opalescent, Ruffled Top, 7 In. 22.50
Cranberry Glass, Bowl, Punch, Lid, Tray, Ribbon Faceted 275.00
Cranberry Glass, Bowl, Salad, Lacy Silver Holder, Ornate Curved Feet 59.00
Cranberry Glass, Bowl, Shell Design, Clear, 5 1/4 In.Diameter, 3 1/2 In.High 37.00
Cranberry Glass, Bowl, Wide Ruffled Rim, 8 In. 55.00
Cranberry Glass, Bowl, 5 1/8 In.Diameter 17.50
Cranberry Glass, Box, Cigarette, Etched Castle On Lid 16.50
Cranberry Glass, Box, Jewelry, Hinged Clear Lid, 2 1/2 In.Diameter 30.00
Cranberry Glass, Bride's Basket, Crimped, Silver Plate Holder, Footed 195.00
Cranberry Glass, Bride's Basket, Spanish Lace, Piecrust Edge, Silver Holder 85.00
Cranberry Glass, Bride's Basket, Thumbprint, Holder 85.00
Cranberry Glass, Bride's Bowl, Crimped, Ruffled Rim, Opalescent Lined 53.00
Cranberry Glass, Butter, Enamel Daisy & Beads, Dome Lid, Tree Branch Finial 70.00
Cranberry Glass, Butter, Melon Ribbed, Swirls, Frosted & Clear Leaf Finial 150.00
Cranberry Glass, Candle Cup, Leaf Design 40.00
Cranberry Glass, Candlestick, Flowers On Bottom, Pisces Fish Handle, 4 In. 60.00
Cranberry Glass, Candlestick, White Enamel Flowers, Brass, Bobeches, Pair 150.00
Cranberry Glass, Castor, Pickle, Diamond-Quilted, Ornate Silver Holder 120.00
Cranberry Glass, Castor, Pickle, Forget-Me-Nots, Wide Out Frame, Over Handle 250.00
Cranberry Glass, Castor, Pickle, Inverted Thumbprint, Enamel Floral, Holder 135.00
Cranberry Glass, Castor, Pickle, Inverted Thumbprint, Enamel, Silver Lid 65.00
Cranberry Glass, Castor, Pickle, Inverted Thumbprint, Silver Plate Holder 95.00
Cranberry Glass, Celery Vase, Ruffled, Applied Clear Feet 47.50
Cranberry Glass, Celery, Clear Footed, 7 3/4 In.High 49.00
Cranberry Glass, Cherries, 53 In A Bunch 65.00
Cranberry Glass, Compote, Crystal Hollow Blown Stem 45.00
Cranberry Glass, Compote, Flashed, Clear Foot 28.00
Cranberry Glass, Compote, Gold Encrustation, 6 1/2 In.Diameter 65.00
Cranberry Glass, Cordial, Clear Ball Stem & Foot 8.50
Cranberry Glass, Cruet, Allover Graduated Cut Loopings, Crystal Stopper 50.00
Cranberry Glass, Cruet, Cut Loopings On Body, Crystal Stopper, 6 In.High 66.00
Cranberry Glass, Cruet, Enameled Floral, Clear Stopper, Ribbed Handle 75.00
Cranberry Glass, Cruet, Flat Sides, Ripple Top, Acid Etched Stopper 130.00
Cranberry Glass, Cruet, Gold Decoration, Rope Handle, Cut Stopper 95.00
Cranberry Glass, Cruet, Gold, Twisted Rope Handle, Cut Stopper, 7 In. 95.00
Cranberry Glass, Cruet, Hobnail .... 12.50 To 15.00
Cranberry Glass, Cruet, Inverted Thumbprint, Blown, Clear Handle & Stopper 49.00
Cranberry Glass, Cruet, Inverted Thumbprint, Enamel Daisies, Forget-Me-Nots 75.00
Cranberry Glass, Cruet, Inverted Thumbprint, Enameled Cones & Wild Flowers 65.00

Cranberry Glass, Cruet, Opalescent, Coin Spot, Clear Handle, Cut Stopper 125.00
Cranberry Glass, Cruet, Overlay 40.00
Cranberry Glass, Cruet, Quilted, Clear Rigaree Base 18.50
Cranberry Glass, Cruet, Swirled Ribs, Clear Handle & Stopper 26.00
Cranberry Glass, Cruet, Vine Pattern, Fluted, Stopper 35.00
Cranberry Glass, Cruet, Wine, Trefoil Top, Clear Applied Handle & Stopper 70.00
Cranberry Glass, Cup & Saucer, Demitasse, Gold Encrusted 50.00
Cranberry Glass, Cup & Saucer, Hand-Painted Pink & White Floral, Gold, 6 .... 250.00
Cranberry Glass, Cuspidor 95.00
Cranberry Glass, Decanter, Blown Stopper 60.00
Cranberry Glass, Decanter, Blown Stopper, Pair 125.00
Cranberry Glass, Decanter, Clear, Facet Stopper, 9 In.High 40.00
Cranberry Glass, Decanter, Crystal Applied Handle, Cut Stopper 100.00
Cranberry Glass, Decanter, Crystal Blown Stopper, Applied Handle, 9 In. 60.00
Cranberry Glass, Decanter, Fluted Top, Applied Handle, Clear Stopper, 10 In. 55.00
Cranberry Glass, Decanter, Overlay, Pair 200.00
Cranberry Glass, Decanter, Wine, Enameled Daisies, Clear Applied Handle 40.00
Cranberry Glass, Dish, Butter, Lid 75.00
Cranberry Glass, Dish, Candy, Clear Handle, Art Glass 20.00
Cranberry Glass, Dish, Seven Clear Ribbon Feet, 5 1/2 In. 25.00
Cranberry Glass, Epergne, Center Trumpet, Crystal Swirls, Cranberry Baskets 150.00
Cranberry Glass, Epergne, Center Trumpet, Three Hanging Baskets 165.00
Cranberry Glass, Epergne, Four Horns, Glass Rigaree Decoration, 22 In.High 225.00
Cranberry Glass, Epergne, Lily Center, Ruffled Bowl, White, 16 1/2 In.Tall 95.00
Cranberry Glass, Epergne, Lily, Enamel, Silver Holder, Girl On Pedestal 65.00
Cranberry Glass, Epergne, Single Lily, Clear Ribbon, Opalescent 65.00
Cranberry Glass, Epergne, Three Lilies, Ruffled Bottom, Clear Overlay 150.00
Cranberry Glass, Epergne, Trumpet, Single, Floral, Silver Leaves & Holder 55.00
Cranberry Glass, Finger Bowl, Plate, Cut To Clear, Crystal 47.50
Cranberry Glass, Finger Bowl, Plate, Threaded, Ruffled, England 65.00
Cranberry Glass, Flower Holder, Three Sections, Rose Stems, Thorns, 6 In. 55.00
Cranberry Glass, Goblet, Wine, Crystal Stem 18.00
Cranberry Glass, Hat, Opalescent Coin Spot, Ruffled Edge 45.00
Cranberry Glass, Hat, Opalescent Coin Spot, Turned Down Ruffled Edges 50.00
Cranberry Glass, Holder, Letter, Gold Scroll Trim, Souvenir Of Oneonta, N.Y. 19.00
Cranberry Glass, Jam, Double, Applied Crystal Leaves, Silver Holder, Handle 50.00
Cranberry Glass, Jar, Allover Enamel Gold Leaves, White Blossoms, Lid 260.00
Cranberry Glass, Jar, Powder, Frosted, Gold Band Decoration 60.00
Cranberry Glass, Jug, Applied Crystal Handle, 6 In.High 43.00
Cranberry Glass, Jug, Cream, Crystal Handle 28.00
Cranberry Glass, Jug, Crystal Handle, Bulbous Base 62.00
Cranberry Glass, Jug, Ruffled Top, Applied Crystal Handle 50.00
Cranberry Glass, Jug, Whiskey, Rough Pontil, Applied Amber Handle, Blown 100.00
Cranberry Glass, Lamp, Hobnail, Black Pedestal, Ribbed, Burner, Chimney 59.50
Cranberry Glass, Lamp, Miniature, Matching Pattern In Shade & Base 165.00
Cranberry Glass, Muffineer, Beaded Leaves, Paneled, Bulbous, Clear, 3 1/2 In. 18.50
Cranberry Glass, Muffineer, Cut Glass Around Top, Silver Cover 35.00
Cranberry Glass, Muffineer, Cut Panels 95.00
Cranberry Glass, Muffineer, Flame Pattern, Open Bubble 45.00
Cranberry Glass, Muffineer, Inside Ribs, Blue & Yellow Enamel 55.00
Cranberry Glass, Muffineer, Inverted Thumbprint, Silver Plated Top 16.50
Cranberry Glass, Muffineer, Opalescent, Silver Top 57.00
Cranberry Glass, Muffineer, Ornate Brass Top 28.00
Cranberry Glass, Muffineer, Paneled .... 26.00 To 45.00
Cranberry Glass, Muffineer, Paneled, Silver Plated Top .... 27.50 To 35.00
Cranberry Glass, Muffineer, Ribbed, Opalescent Criss-Cross 65.00
Cranberry Glass, Muffineer, Silver Plated Top 35.00
Cranberry Glass, Muffineer, Silver Top 85.00
Cranberry Glass, Muffineer, Sterling Silver Top 45.00
Cranberry Glass, Perfume, Overlay, Cut Stopper, St.Louis Glass 45.00
Cranberry Glass, Perfume, Silver Overlay, Engraved Name 125.00
Cranberry Glass, Pitcher, Bulbous, Square Top, Opalescent Hobnail 225.00
Cranberry Glass, Pitcher, Crystal Handle, 5 In. 50.00
Cranberry Glass, Pitcher, Enamel Floral, Applied Clear Handle, 9 In. 85.00
Cranberry Glass, Pitcher, Gold & White Enamel, Clear Handle, 4 1/4 In. 55.00
Cranberry Glass, Pitcher, Herringbone, Indented Melon Shape, 5 In. 45.00

Cranberry Glass, Pitcher, Hobnail, Opalescent, Clear Handle, 5 1/2 In.Tall 65.00
Cranberry Glass, Pitcher, Hobnail, Square Mouth 150.00
Cranberry Glass, Pitcher, Inverted Ribbed, Clear Handle, 8 1/2 In.Tall 75.00
Cranberry Glass, Pitcher, Inverted Thumbprint To Diamond Top, Clear Handle 85.00
Cranberry Glass, Pitcher, Inverted Thumbprint, Enamel Flowers 125.00
Cranberry Glass, Pitcher, Melon Rib, Clear Applied Handle 70.00
Cranberry Glass, Pitcher, Milk, Melon Rib, Bulbous 58.00
Cranberry Glass, Pitcher, Milk, Melon Rib, Shell Handle, Stretched Top 95.00
Cranberry Glass, Pitcher, Opalescent, Applied Clear Handle, 8 1/2 In. 85.00
Cranberry Glass, Pitcher, Swirled Ribbing, Opalescent 79.00
Cranberry Glass, Pitcher, Tankard, Six Tumblers, Enameled Floral Decor 750.00
Cranberry Glass, Pitcher, Water, Blue, Gold, White Enamel, Tankard, N Mark 105.00
Cranberry Glass, Pitcher, Water, Hobnail, Six Tumblers 140.00
Cranberry Glass, Pitcher, Water, Inverted Thumbprint, Clear To Cranberry 150.00
Cranberry Glass, Pitcher, Water, Inverted Thumbprint, Enamel Floral, Crimped 125.00
Cranberry Glass, Pitcher, Water, Inverted Thumbprint, Enamel, White Daisies 85.00
Cranberry Glass, Pitcher, Water, Inverted Thumbprint, Stretched Top & Spout 95.00
Cranberry Glass, Pitcher, Water, Opalescent Hobnail 180.00
Cranberry Glass, Pitcher, Water, Opalescent, Raised Blossoms, Leaves, 10 In. 125.00
Cranberry Glass, Pitcher, Water, Panels, Applied Crystal Handle, Blown 35.00
Cranberry Glass, Pitcher, Water, Panels, Ruffled Rim, Clear Handle 55.00
Cranberry Glass, Pitcher, White Threads At Top, Footed, Clear Handle, 4 In. 25.00
Cranberry Glass, Rose Bowl, Applied Clear Feet, Miniature 30.00
Cranberry Glass, Rose Bowl, Diamond-Quilted, Clear Rigaree Around Top 58.00
Cranberry Glass, Rose Bowl, Drape Pattern, Applied Feet 65.00
Cranberry Glass, Rose Bowl, Inverted Panel, Ground Pontil 50.00
Cranberry Glass, Salt, Master, Applied Ruffled Edgings & Feet 22.50
Cranberry Glass, Sauce, Threaded, Ruffled 25.00
Cranberry Glass, Shade, Gas, Fiery, Opalescent, Hobnail, Scalloped Edge 35.00
Cranberry Glass, Shade, Gas, Swirl, For 5 In.Ring 45.00
Cranberry Glass, Shade, Hobnail, For Hanging Lamp, 14 In. 250.00
Cranberry Glass, Shade, Lamp, Diamond-Quilted, Hanging, Deep Color 150.00
Cranberry Glass, Shade, Quilted, Crimped Rim, Art Glass, C.1860, 6 In. 22.50
Cranberry Glass, Shade, Thumbprint, Ruffled 35.00
Cranberry Glass, Shaker, Salt, Silver Top 28.00
Cranberry Glass, Smoke Bell, Helical Pattern, Scalloped Rim, 5 In.Diameter 39.00
Cranberry Glass, Spittoon, Lady's, Blown, Cobalt Rim, Bubble In Bottom 45.00
Cranberry Glass, Spoon Holder, Diamond-Quilted, Barrel Shape, Bulbous 48.00
Cranberry Glass, Stein, Thumbprint, Enamel Floral, Clear Handle, Blown 90.00
Cranberry Glass, Sugar & Creamer, Open, Yellow Scrolls & Flowers, 2 In.High 40.00
Cranberry Glass, Sugar & Creamer, Ribbed, Wide Silver Rims 325.00
Cranberry Glass, Sugar Spooner, Thumbprint, Silver Holder 300.00
Cranberry Glass, Sugar, Resilvered Frame Around Bowl For 12 Spoons 115.00
Cranberry Glass, Syrup, Embossed, Dated Cover 65.00
Cranberry Glass, Syrup, Guttate Pattern, Clear Handle, Dated Apr. 1881 .... 60.00
Cranberry Glass, Syrup, Threads, Blown, Ornate Pewter Neck, Cover, Thumb Rest 60.00
Cranberry Glass, Tankard, Overshot, Frosted, Reed Handle, 8 3/4 In.High 105.00
Cranberry Glass, Toothpick, Bulging Loop, Ground Upper Rim 35.00
Cranberry Glass, Toothpick, Opalescent, Oval Bulbous Body 55.00
Cranberry Glass, Toothpick, Ruffled Top 35.00
Cranberry Glass, Toothpick, Swirled, Overshot .... 60.00 To 65.00
Cranberry Glass, Tumbler, Baby Thumbprint .... 20.00 To 28.00
Cranberry Glass, Tumbler, Diamond-Quilted .... 18.00 To 22.50
Cranberry Glass, Tumbler, Hobnail, Opalescent 65.00
Cranberry Glass, Tumbler, Inverted Baby Thumbprint 45.00
Cranberry Glass, Tumbler, Inverted Thumbprint 22.50
Cranberry Glass, Tumbler, Inverted Thumbprint, Enamel Flowers 25.00
Cranberry Glass, Tumbler, Inverted Thumbprint, Enamel Lilies Of The Valley 25.00
Cranberry Glass, Tumbler, Inverted Thumbprint, Slab Bottom 27.50
Cranberry Glass, Tumbler, Ribbed .... 7.50 To 12.50
Cranberry Glass, Tumbler, Ribbed, Enameled White & Blue Daisies & Leaves 18.00
Cranberry Glass, Tumbler, Silver Plate Holder, Victorian 50.00
Cranberry Glass, Tumbler, Spot Resist .... 30.00 To 35.00
Cranberry Glass, Tumbler, Stars & Stripes, Opalescent 27.50
Cranberry Glass, Tumbler, Ten Rows Of Hobnails 75.00
Cranberry Glass, Tumbler, Thumbprint 22.50

Cranberry Glass, **Tumbler**, Thumbprint, Floral Bouquets 28.00
Cranberry Glass, **Tumbler**, White Opalescent Stars & Stripes 22.50
Cranberry Glass, **Tumbler**, White Spatters 18.00
Cranberry Glass, **Tumbler**, Wide Margin Of Gold With Scrolls, Flowers 45.00
Cranberry Glass, **Vase**, Applied Vaseline To Pinched Center, Bulbous 40.00
Cranberry Glass, **Vase**, Bud, Applied Crystal Windings, Clear Footed Base 42.50
Cranberry Glass, **Vase**, Bud, Diamond-Quilted, Crystal Design, Applied, Marked 37.50
Cranberry Glass, **Vase**, Celery, Diamond-Quilted, 6 In. 70.00
Cranberry Glass, **Vase**, Diamond-Quilted Bottom, Flared, Fluted Top, 8 In. 55.00
Cranberry Glass, **Vase**, Diamond-Quilted, Ruffled Top, 4 3/4 In.High 32.00
Cranberry Glass, **Vase**, Dog, Boy, Tree, Applied Amber Edge 55.00
Cranberry Glass, **Vase**, Fluted Top, Metal Deer Holder 75.00
Cranberry Glass, **Vase**, Gold & Silver Flowers, 15 In.High 125.00
Cranberry Glass, **Vase**, Gold Encrusted Leaves & Scrolls, Honesdale 160.00
Cranberry Glass, **Vase**, Gold Medallion, Floral Inside, Ormolu Top & Bottom 425.00
Cranberry Glass, **Vase**, Hobnail, Opalescent, Fluted Top, Circa 1920, 4 1/2 In. 17.50
Cranberry Glass, **Vase**, Indented & Flared Neck, Vaseline Portions In Rim 45.00
Cranberry Glass, **Vase**, Inverted Ribbing, Gold, Pink, Blue & Yellow Floral 50.00
Cranberry Glass, **Vase**, Leaf Umbrella, 5 In. 85.00
Cranberry Glass, **Vase**, Light To Deep Cranberry, Rigaree, 7 In. 35.00
Cranberry Glass, **Vase**, Melon Shape, 4 In.High 45.00
Cranberry Glass, **Vase**, Openwork Silver Encased, Blown, 7 In.High 95.00
Cranberry Glass, **Vase**, Ribbed Pattern, Slender Neck, Bulbous Base 55.00
Cranberry Glass, **Vase**, Ribbed, Applied Clear Shell Festoon 45.00
Cranberry Glass, **Vase**, Rose, Uneven Shape, Applied Crystal Feet, Free Blown 40.00
Cranberry Glass, **Vase**, Silver Deposit, Fluted, 10 In. 50.00
Cranberry Glass, **Vase**, Stick, Aqua Enamel, Gold, 10 In. 48.00
Cranberry Glass, **Vase**, Swirls, Bubbles, Flecks Of Gold, Scalloped Top 75.00
Cranberry Glass, **Vase**, Swirls, Bulbous, Clear 40.00
Cranberry Glass, **Vase**, Trumpet, Knob At Base, Clear Stem, Teardrop, Foot 35.00
Cranberry Glass, **Vase**, White Enameled Gnome, Floral, 6 3/8 In.High 48.00
Cranberry Glass, **Vase**, Yellow Enamel Birds, Trees, Floral, Butterflies 75.00
Cranberry Glass, **Wash Set**, Crystal Handle, Footed, 4 In.High Jug, 2 Piece 92.00
Cranberry Glass, **Water Set**, Enamel Cross Of Lorraine, Thistles, 5 Piece 225.00
Cranberry Glass, **Wine Set**, Enamel Flowers, Gold Trim, 7 Piece 75.00
Cranberry Glass, **Wine**, Clear Stem & Foot .... 6.50 To 12.50
Cranberry Glass, **Wine**, Clear Stem, Floral & Leaf Design Bowl 5.00
Cranberry Glass, **Wine**, Clear Twisted Stem, 6 1/4 In.High 8.00
Cranberry Glass, **Wine**, Crystal Stem & Foot 18.00
Cranberry Glass, **Wine**, Cut To Clear, Clear Teardrop Stem & Base, Pair 90.00
Cranberry Glass, **Wine**, Flashed, Stemmed, Etched Flower 4.00

Creamware, or Queensware, was developed by Josiah Wedgwood about 1765.
It is a cream-colored Earthenware that has been copied by many factories.
Creamware, **Basket**, Green, Gold, Marked Wedgwood, 6 In. Long & Tall 155.00
Creamware, **Coffeepot**, Rouge De Fer & Gilt Decoration, Unsigned, Wedgwood 40.00
Creamware, **Mug**, Inscribed 'He In Glory, America In Tears, 'C.1800 .... 350.00
Creamware, **Pitcher**, Brave Soldiers & Sailors Of Crimea, D.Methven & Sons 35.00
Creamware, **Pitcher**, Embossed Holly, Fish Scale Borders, Twig Feet 10.00
Creamware, **Platter**, Pierced Basket Loop Border, Leeds, Unsigned 35.00
Creamware, **Tureen**, Covered, Ladle, Herculaneum, Oval, Transfer, C.1825 .... 150.00
Creil, **Plate**, Trompe L'Oeil, B & C, Simulated Wood, Paper Center 35.00

Croesus Glass is a special pattern of Pressed Glass made about 1897.
It was made in clear glass, emerald green, or amethyst. Each piece was
decorated with gold.
Croesus, **Green**, Bowl, Berry, Gold 115.00
Croesus, **Green**, Butter, Covered, Gold Trim .... 115.00 To 275.00
Croesus, **Green**, Creamer, 3 In. .... 60.00 To 95.00
Croesus, **Green**, Pitcher, Water, Gold 150.00
Croesus, **Green**, Relish, 10 In. 47.50
Croesus, **Green**, Salt & Pepper 69.00
Croesus, **Green**, Sauce 27.50
Croesus, **Green**, Spooner, Footed 95.00
Croesus, **Green**, Spooner, Gold .... 60.00 To 65.00

Croesus, Green, Sugar & Creamer 135.00
Croesus, Green, Sugar, Cover, Gold 85.00
Croesus, Green, Sugar, Footed 95.00
Croesus, Green, Table Set, Covered, 4 Piece 375.00
Croesus, Green, Toothpick 65.00
Croesus, Green, Toothpick, Gold .... 48.00 To 65.00
Croesus, Green, Toothpick, Gold, Four Shell Legs 85.00
Croesus, Green, Tray, Condiment 65.00
Croesus, Green, Tray, Kidney Shape, Gold, 9 In. 27.50
Croesus, Green, Tumbler, Gold .... 40.00 To 60.00
Croesus, Purple, Berry Set, 7 Piece 380.00
Croesus, Purple, Bowl, Berry, Gold 125.00
Croesus, Purple, Bowl, 9 In.Diameter, 4 In.Deep 130.00
Croesus, Purple, Butter, Gold .... 90.00 To 165.00
Croesus, Purple, Celery, Footed, 10 In. 150.00
Croesus, Purple, Compote, Gold, 4 3/4 In.High X 3 3/4 In.Across Top 65.00
Croesus, Purple, Compote, 4 X 4 1/2 In. 38.00
Croesus, Purple, Pitcher 120.00
Croesus, Purple, Pitcher, Gold, Small 60.00
Croesus, Purple, Salt & Pepper, Tray 375.00
Croesus, Purple, Sauce, Footed 55.00
Croesus, Purple, Spooner, Gold 60.00
Croesus, Purple, Sugar, Cover 110.00
Croesus, Purple, Table Set, Gold, 4 Piece 625.00
Croesus, Purple, Toothpick, Gold .... 68.00 To 70.00
Croesus, Purple, Toothpick, Spatula Feet, Gold 75.00
Croesus, Purple, Tumbler, Gold .... 45.00 To 75.00
Croesus, Toothpick, Green, Gold 58.50

*Crown Derby is the nickname given to the works of the Royal Crown
Derby factory, which began working in England in 1859. An earlier and more
famous English Derby factory existed from 1750 to 1848. The two factories
were not related. Most of the porcelain found today with the Derby mark is
the work of the later Derby factory.*
Crown Derby, see also Royal Crown Derby
Crown Derby, Candlestick, Cobalt, Floral Medallions, 10 In.High, Pair 425.00
Crown Derby, Condiment Set, Imari Pattern, 5 Bottle, Silver Caster 42.00
Crown Derby, Plate, Butterflies 22.00
Crown Derby, Plate, Flowers, Lavender, Blue, Brown, Gold Trim, C.1890, Pair 32.00
Crown Derby, Sugar & Creamer, Cobalt Blue, Gold Trim & Handle, Red Mark 45.00
Crown Derby, Tray, Six Matching Egg Cups, Tan, Pink & Blue Floral 38.00
Crown Derby, Vase, For Caldwell Of Philadelphia, Gold, Blown-Out Floral 175.00
Crown Derby, Vase, Rose Color, With Gold Decoration, 9 In.High 85.00
Crown Ducal, Plate, Colonial Times, Pink, First Thanksgiving, 10 In. 18.00
Crown Ducal, Plate, Colonial Times, Pink, Paul Revere, 9 In. 15.00
Crown Ducal, Plate, Soup, Colonial Times, Pink, Paul Revere, 9 In. 8.00
Crown Ducal, Sugar & Creamer, Colonial Times, Pink 20.00

*Crown Milano Glass was made by Frederick Shirley about 1890. It had
a plain biscuit color with a satin finish. It was decorated with flowers, and
often had large gold scrolls.*
Crown Milano, Base, Bud, Raised Gold Scrolls And Flowers 165.00
Crown Milano, Basket, Bride's, Wild Roses, Leaves, Silver Plate Holder 1500.00
Crown Milano, Bowl, Tiny Flowers, Triangular 450.00
Crown Milano, Bowl, Triangular, Pictured In Pairpoint Story, Signed 595.00
Crown Milano, Box, Powder, Swirled Ribbed Base, Embossed Floral, Blue, White 165.00
Crown Milano, Cup & Saucer, Demitasse, Signed 650.00
Crown Milano, Dish, Candy, Garden Bouquet, Gilt Outline, Lid, Signed 375.00
Crown Milano, Dish, Sweetmeat, White, Melon Rib, Roses, Blue Sprays, Lid 500.00
Crown Milano, Ewer, Bronze And Gold Decoration 1450.00
Crown Milano, Ewer, Green, Gold Scrolls, Floral, Veining, Clouds, Pairpoint 300.00
Crown Milano, Ewer, Green, Raised Gold Flowers, Scrolls, Ribbed Bottom 250.00
Crown Milano, Jar, Biscuit, Allover Puffs & Scrolls, Raised Gold Roses 350.00
Crown Milano, Jar, Biscuit, Blown-Out, Scrolls, Raised Gold Roses, Signed 375.00
Crown Milano, Jar, Biscuit, Burmese Coloring, Oak Leaf & Acorn Decoration 275.00
Crown Milano, Jar, Biscuit, Green, Gold Flowers, Hobnail, Butterfly Finial 450.00

Crown Milano, Jar, Biscuit, Pink Roses With Green Leaves 285.00
Crown Milano, Jar, Cookie, Cream With Gold, Griffin On Front, Fish On Back 475.00
Crown Milano, Jar, Cracker, Blue, Enamel Floral, Pairpoint Handles & Lid 450.00
Crown Milano, Jar, Cracker, Burmese, Oak Leaves, Acorns, Silver Lid & Handle 375.00
Crown Milano, Jardiniere, Pink, Blue Flowers, Signed 295.00
Crown Milano, Jardiniere, Pink, Gold Scrolls, Blue Cornflowers, Glossy 295.00
Crown Milano, Lamp, Peg, Mauve & Tan, Gold Traces, Gold Wash, Pairpoint Base 285.00
Crown Milano, Rose Bowl, Burmese Ground, Pansies Outlined In Gold 225.00
Crown Milano, Rose Bowl, Cream Ground, Swirls, Jewel Decoration 650.00
Crown Milano, Rose Bowl, Daisies, Mt.Washington 375.00
Crown Milano, Salt & Pepper, Melon Rib, Mt.Washington .... 60.00 To 80.00
Crown Milano, Sugar & Creamer, Reeded Handles 1500.00
Crown Milano, Tray, Card, Mum Design, Yellow, Gold Trim 100.00
Crown Milano, Tumbler, Signed With Red Enamel Wreath, Crown, Number 300.00
Crown Milano, Vase, Lusterless White Ground, Dresden Type Decor 325.00
Crown Milano, Vase, Orchids, Floral Sprays, Outlined In Gold, Handles 650.00
Crown Milano, Vase, White Matte, Enameled Rose Sprays, Daisies, Lid, Finial 525.00
    Crown Tuscan, see Cambridge

Cruets of glass or porcelain were made to hold vinegar or oil. They were especially popular during Victorian times.
    Cruet, see also other sections, Amber Glass, Pressed Glass, etc.
Cruet, Amber With Clear Beading, Applied Handle 47.50
Cruet, Blue Swirl, 8 1/2 In. 45.00
Cruet, Blue, Amber Stopper & Handle, White Enamel Floral & Leaves 45.00
Cruet, Blue, Dimpled Sides, Amber Handle & Stopper, Butterflies & Floral 55.00
Cruet, Cranberry, Thumbprint, Pair In Resilvered Holder, Cutouts, Reliefs 325.00
Cruet, Deep Purple, White Enamel Decor, Hollow Cut Stopper 45.00
Cruet, Emerald Green Glass, Applied Handle, Blue & Coral Enamel Floral 37.00
Cruet, Green Opaque, Mottling, Ruffled Top, Open Bubble, No Stopper 400.00
Cruet, Midwestern, Swirled To Right, Clear, Applied Hollow Handle 50.00
Cruet, Milk Glass On Base & Handle Graduating To Clear, Fans, Sunbursts 15.00
Cruet, Millefiori Candy Cane, Satin Finish 32.50
Cruet, Opalescent Swirl, Stopper 65.00
Cruet, Paneled, Stopper And Handle, Low Base, 7 1/2 In.Tall 40.00
Cruet, Ribbed, Flower Spray, Ivy, White, Yellow, Pink, 9 In.High 45.00
Cruet, Sapphire Blue, White Enamel Floral, Green Leaves, Bubble Stopper 45.00
Cruet, Vine Pattern, Cranberry, Clear Stopper 35.00

Cup Plates are small glass or china plates that held the cup, while a gentleman of the mid-nineteenth century drank his coffee or tea from the saucer. The most famous Cup Plates were made of glass at the Boston and Sandwich Factory located in Massachusetts.
Cup Plate, Anchor 27.50
Cup Plate, Black Transfer, 'Parental Care' 7.50
Cup Plate, Constitution 27.50
Cup Plate, Constitution, Opalescent 50.00
Cup Plate, Conventional .... 10.00 To 22.50
Cup Plate, Conventional, Amber 42.50
Cup Plate, Conventional, Opalescent .... 20.00 To 55.00
Cup Plate, Eagle .... 10.00 To 32.50
Cup Plate, Fort Pitt, Eagle, Flint 50.00
Cup Plate, Harp 20.00
Cup Plate, Heart .... 7.50 To 10.00
Cup Plate, Heart, Opalescent 15.00
Cup Plate, Henry Clay, Blue 60.00
Cup Plate, Lacy, Clear .... 7.50 To 22.50
Cup Plate, Lacy, Fort Pitt Glass Works 135.00
Cup Plate, Lacy, Green 45.00
Cup Plate, Lacy, Opalescent 22.50
Cup Plate, Lacy, Sheaf Of Wheat Border, N.E.Glass Co. 50.00
Cup Plate, Lavender Luster, Scene, Floral In Wreath 75.00
Cup Plate, Log Cabin, Fort Meigs 15.00
Cup Plate, Peacock Blue, Henry Clay 95.00
Cup Plate, Plow 100.00
Cup Plate, Roman Rosette, Opalescent, Flint 75.00

Cup Plate, Silver Blue, Lacy 125.00
Cup Plate, Sweetheart, Dark Blue, Flint 95.00
Cup Plate, Victoria .... 17.50 To 35.00

*Currier & Ives made the famous American Lithographs marked with their
name from 1857 to 1907.*
Currier & Ives, A Good Chance, Framed, 1863 .... 850.00
Currier & Ives, A Good Time Coming, Framed, 1863 .... 1000.00
Currier & Ives, A Howling Swell On The Warpath, Dated 1890, Pair 69.50
Currier & Ives, A Mountain Ramble, Frame, 16 1/4 X 12 1/4 In. 45.00
Currier & Ives, A Rising Family, Framed, 1857 .... 1100.00
Currier & Ives, Abraham's Dream, Dated 1864, Lithograph, Black & White 32.50
Currier & Ives, American Winter Scenes, Evening, Framed, 1854 ...... 1400.00
Currier & Ives, American Winter Scenes, Morning, Framed, 1854 ...... 1300.00
Currier & Ives, An Early Start, Framed, 1863 .... 1000.00
Currier & Ives, Bombardment Of Fort Henry, Tenn., 1862, 9 X 12 In. 150.00
Currier & Ives, Bowl, Fruit, Clear & Amber, 9 1/2 In.Across 50.00
Currier & Ives, Brook Trout Fishing, An Anxious Moment, Framed, 1862 ...... 1600.00
Currier & Ives, Catching A Tartar, Framed, 1861 .... 1050.00
Currier & Ives, Clara, Walnut Criss-Cross Frame, 14 X 17 In. 24.00
Currier & Ives, Darktown Wedding, The Sendoff, Dated 1892, Frame 54.00
Currier & Ives, Deer Shooting On The Shattagee, Framed, 1855 ...... 1300.00
Currier & Ives, Deer Shooting, 1865, 12 1/2 X 9 In. 175.00
Currier & Ives, Die Wacht Am Dem Rhein, Blonde Female Warrior 60.00
Currier & Ives, Dog & Rabbit Series, No.1 .... 65.00
Currier & Ives, Easter Flowers, Color 19.00
Currier & Ives, Emigrants Crossing The Plains, Framed, 1866 ...... 6000.00
Currier & Ives, For President, Franklin Pierce, William King, V.P., 1852 ...... 24.50
Currier & Ives, General Grant & Family 40.50
Currier & Ives, General U.S.Grant, President Of The U.S., 9 X 12 1/2 In. 30.00
Currier & Ives, Going For Him, J.C.Cameron 45.00
Currier & Ives, Golden Fruits Of California, Color, 20 1/2 X 14 1/2 In. 300.00
Currier & Ives, Got 'Em Both, 1882, Mat, Frame 75.00
Currier & Ives, Home Of Evangeline, In The Acadian Land, Frame, 1864 ...... 115.00
Currier & Ives, Home To Thanksgiving, Framed, 1867 .... 2900.00 To 4100.00
Currier & Ives, Homeward Bound, 1860, 10 X 13 In. 350.00
Currier & Ives, Hudson Highlands, Margins 110.00
Currier & Ives, Idlewild On The Hudson 85.00
Currier & Ives, In The Northern Wilds, 1873, 9 X 12 In. 150.00
Currier & Ives, James Polk & George Dallas, Dated 1844, Color, Lithograph .... *Color*   34.50
Currier & Ives, Just My Style, Frame 45.00
Currier & Ives, Keep Your Distance, Framed, 1853 .... 900.00
Currier & Ives, Last Ditch Of The Chivalry, 1865, Black & White 34.50
Currier & Ives, Laying Off, Framed, 1863 .... 900.00
Currier & Ives, Life In The Woods, Starting Out, 1860 .... *Illus*   300.00
Currier & Ives, Lincoln, Nation's Martyr, Medium Folio, Mat 65.00
Currier & Ives, Little Brothers, Maple Frame 45.00
Currier & Ives, Little Emmie 60.00
Currier & Ives, Little Emperor 28.50
Currier & Ives, Little Manly, Veneer Frame 28.00
Currier & Ives, Maple Sugaring, Framed, 1856 .... 2600.00
Currier & Ives, Martha Washington, Black & White 40.00
Currier & Ives, Mary Ann, Walnut Frame, 14 X 9 1/2 In. 35.00
Currier & Ives, Miniature Print In Frame, 5 3/4 X 7 In., Set Of 3 ...... 3.98
Currier & Ives, Moosehead Lake 45.00
Currier & Ives, Moosehead Lake, Small Folio, Frame 60.00
Currier & Ives, Morning In The Adirondacks, Framed, 1862 .... 1400.00
Currier & Ives, My Little Playfellow, Frame, 20 X 17 In. 35.00
Currier & Ives, My Little White Kittens Playing Dominoes 25.00
Currier & Ives, My Little White Kitties, 14 1/2 X 10 1/2 In. 38.00
Currier & Ives, Narrows, N.Y.Bay 115.00
Currier & Ives, Quail Shooting, N.Currier, 1852, 14 1/2 X 20 In. 1500.00
Currier & Ives, Returning To Camp, Framed, 1860 .... 375.00
Currier & Ives, Sarah, Red Dress, Black Curls, Holding A Rose 32.50
Currier & Ives, Snipe Shooting, On Linen, Black Frame 7.50
Currier & Ives, Some Of The Right Sort, Framed, 1856 .... 275.00

Currier & Ives, Life In The Woods, Starting Out, 1860
See Page 158

Currier & Ives, St.Patrick, Color	50.00
Currier & Ives, St.Peter, Framed	22.50
Currier & Ives, Stages Of Man's Life From Cradle To Grave, Folio, Frame	39.00
Currier & Ives, Starting Out, Framed, 1860	850.00
Currier & Ives, Staten Island & The Narrows From Ft.Hamilton	115.00
Currier & Ives, Strawberries, Color	75.00
Currier & Ives, The Body Of The Most Reverend Archbishop Hughes In State	17.50
Currier & Ives, The Cares Of A Family, Framed, 1856	1550.00
Currier & Ives, The Champion Trotting Stallion Smuggler, Framed, 1876	325.00
Currier & Ives, The Declaration Of Independence, 1847, 9 X 12 1/2 In.	150.00
Currier & Ives, The Express Train, Framed, 1870	450.00
Currier & Ives, The Farm Yard In Winter, Framed, 1861	1600.00
Currier & Ives, The Little Mechanic	60.00
Currier & Ives, The Lovers, Dated 1846, Lithograph, Color	24.50
Currier & Ives, The Morning Prayer, Frame	22.00
Currier & Ives, The Mother's Dream, Walnut Frame, 11 1/2 X 16 In.	24.00
Currier & Ives, The Playful Family	55.00
Currier & Ives, The Playful Family, Puppies	28.00
Currier & Ives, The Royal Family Of England	75.00
Currier & Ives, The Soldier's Adieu, Mahogany Frame	35.00
Currier & Ives, The Straw Yard, Winter, Framed	575.00
Currier & Ives, The Surprise, 1858, Lithograph, Color	175.00
Currier & Ives, Through To The Pacific, Frame	120.00
Currier & Ives, Tray, Water, Balky Mule	35.00
Currier & Ives, Trotting In Harness At Mystic Park, Framed, 1873	375.00
Currier & Ives, Trout Fishing On Chateaugay Lake, Framed, 1856	800.00
Currier & Ives, Up The Hudson, Frame	125.00
Currier & Ives, View On Hudson	60.00
Currier & Ives, Washington Crossing The Delaware, 1847	150.00
Currier & Ives, Washington Family, C.1850, Lithograph, Color	32.50
Currier & Ives, Westward The Course Of Empire Takes Its Way, Framed, 1868	5000.00
Currier & Ives, Wilhelm I, Black & White, Frame, 14 X 11 In.	20.00
Currier & Ives, Winter Morning, Feeding The Chickens, Framed, 1863	1900.00
Currier & Ives, Winter Morning, Framed, 1861	500.00
Currier, American Country Life, Summer's Evening, Palmer, 1855, Lithograph	200.00
Currier, Death Of General Andrew Jackson, Frame	28.00

Currier, Perry's Victory On Lake Erie, 1845 .... 325.00
Currier, Presidents Of The United States, 1844 .... 185.00
Currier, Print, Mary, Framed 32.00
Currier, Star Of Love, Framed 32.00
Currier, Surrender Of Cornwallis, 1845 .... 150.00
Currier, The Battle Of Bunker Hill, 1850 .... 125.00
Currier, Woodcock Shooting, 1852 .... 1250.00

Custard Glass is an opaque glass sometimes known as Buttermilk Glass.
It was first made after 1886 at the La Belle Glass Works,
Bridgeport, Ohio.
Custard Glass, Banana Boat, Blue, Chrysanthemum Sprig, Northwood 395.00
Custard Glass, Banana Boat, Chrysanthemum Sprig, Northwood .... 125.00 To 150.00
Custard Glass, Banana Boat, Grape & Cable, Nutmeg Trim, Iridescent 275.00
Custard Glass, Banana Boat, Louis XV, Footed 110.00
Custard Glass, Bell, Daisy & Button Pattern 12.50
Custard Glass, Berry Set, Inverted Fan & Feather, Pink, Gold, 7 Piece 875.00
Custard Glass, Bowl, Argonaut Shell, Seaweed, Gold Edged, Northwood 200.00
Custard Glass, Bowl, Banana, Chrysanthemum Sprig, Gold Feet 125.00
Custard Glass, Bowl, Banana, Geneva 150.00
Custard Glass, Bowl, Berry, Argonaut Shell, Oval, Gold 225.00
Custard Glass, Bowl, Berry, Beaded Circle, Footed .... 32.50 To 35.00
Custard Glass, Bowl, Berry, Chrysanthemum, Blue, Northwood 325.00
Custard Glass, Bowl, Berry, Fan, Footed, Gold, Northwood 65.00
Custard Glass, Bowl, Berry, Intaglio, Pedestal Base, 8 1/2 In. .... 115.00 To 120.00
Custard Glass, Bowl, Berry, Inverted Fan & Feather, Four Sauces 375.00
Custard Glass, Bowl, Berry, Little Gem, Gold Bands & Legs 85.00
Custard Glass, Bowl, Berry, Louis XII 35.00
Custard Glass, Bowl, Berry, Louis XV, Gold, Footed .... 38.00 To 58.00
Custard Glass, Bowl, Berry, Louis XV, Pedestal 55.00
Custard Glass, Bowl, Blackberry Pattern, Three Mold, 6 In.Diameter 28.00
Custard Glass, Bowl, Centerpiece, Chrysanthemum Sprig, Flower Band, N 250.00
Custard Glass, Bowl, Centerpiece, Inverted Fan & Feather, Gold & Pink Trim 195.00
Custard Glass, Bowl, Chrysanthemum Sprig, Footed, 8 X 11 In. 125.00
Custard Glass, Bowl, Fruit, Beaded Circle, Enamel, 8 1/2 X 5 In. 125.00
Custard Glass, Bowl, Fruit, Chrysanthemum Sprig, Oval, Footed 135.00
Custard Glass, Bowl, Fruit, Grape & Leaves, 3 Footed, Signed N 225.00
Custard Glass, Bowl, Grape & Cable, Basket Weave Exterior, Marked N 27.00
Custard Glass, Bowl, Grape & Cable, Footed, Marked N 35.00
Custard Glass, Bowl, Grape & Thumbprint, Brown Ground, N Mark, 9 3/8 In. 150.00
Custard Glass, Bowl, Ice Cream, Peacock In Center, Marked N, 10 In. 100.00
Custard Glass, Bowl, Jelly, Chrysanthemum Sprig 75.00
Custard Glass, Bowl, Miniature, Argonaut Shell, Gold, 3 In.High 75.00
Custard Glass, Bowl, Orange, Inverted Fan & Feather, Pink, Gold .... 175.00 To 195.00
Custard Glass, Bowl, Peacock & Dahlia, Berry & Leaf Exterior, Green Traces 45.00
Custard Glass, Bowl, Swan & Cattails, Oval, Footed, Stourbridge Mark 35.00
Custard Glass, Box, Powder, Winged Scrolls, Red Roses, Gold, Cover 65.00
Custard Glass, Box, Souvenir, Alta Vista, Kansas, Painted Rose On Lid 48.50
Custard Glass, Butter, Argonaut Shell, Covered, Gold 185.00
Custard Glass, Butter, Chrysanthemum Sprig, Gold 125.00
Custard Glass, Butter, Everglades, Gold 145.00
Custard Glass, Butter, Geneva, Covered .... 53.00 To 115.00
Custard Glass, Butter, Intaglio, Covered, Green Trim, Gold .... 125.00 To 135.00
Custard Glass, Butter, Inverted Fan & Feather, Covered, Gold .... 170.00 To 185.00
Custard Glass, Butter, Louis XV .... 110.00 To 125.00
Custard Glass, Candlestick, Holly Band, Pair 16.00
Custard Glass, Compote, Blue, Octagon Base, Scalloped Rim, Florals 40.00
Custard Glass, Compote, Chrysanthemum Sprig 60.00
Custard Glass, Compote, Intaglio, 6 In.High, 8 1/2 In.Diameter 125.00
Custard Glass, Compote, Jelly, Argonaut Shell .... 60.00 To 125.00
Custard Glass, Compote, Jelly, Chrysanthemum Sprig, Gold .... 35.00 To 45.00
Custard Glass, Compote, Jelly, Intaglio, Green Scrolls 100.00
Custard Glass, Creamer, Argonaut Shell .... 72.00 To 85.00
Custard Glass, Creamer, Cherry Spray, 4 1/2 In.High 50.00
Custard Glass, Creamer, Chrysanthemum Sprig, Northwood .... 65.00 To 75.00
Custard Glass, Creamer, Chrysanthemum Sprig, Northwood Script .... 75.00 To 105.00

Custard Glass, Creamer, Conneaut Lake, 4 1/2 In., High	35.00
Custard Glass, Creamer, Fluted Scrolls	59.00
Custard Glass, Creamer, Green, 3 In.High	21.00
Custard Glass, Creamer, Intaglio Pattern	72.50
Custard Glass, Creamer, Louis XV	50.00
Custard Glass, Creamer, Louis XV, Gold	75.00
Custard Glass, Creamer, Louis XV, Green, Footed, Gold	42.00
Custard Glass, Creamer, Nautilus, Signed Northwood In Script	145.00
Custard Glass, Creamer, Owl Shape, Blue, Red Glass Eyes	40.00
Custard Glass, Creamer, Red Roses, Jackson, Minn.	27.50
Custard Glass, Creamer, Rose Buds, Alvord, Iowa	22.50
Custard Glass, Creamer, Souvenir	39.00
Custard Glass, Creamer, Souvenir, Casino, Hampton Beach, N.H.	20.00
Custard Glass, Creamer, Thumbprint, Rosebud Spray, Says Mother, 1912	30.00
Custard Glass, Cruet, Argonaut Shell, Original Stopper, Mint Gold	235.00
Custard Glass, Cruet, Chrysanthemum Sprig, Original Stopper, Gold	180.00
Custard Glass, Cruet, Louis XV, Custard Stopper	135.00
Custard Glass, Cup, Hobnail, Blue, Star Base	75.00
Custard Glass, Cup, Punch, Blue Stained Leaves, Delaware	35.00
Custard Glass, Cup, Red Rose, Souvenir Horton, Kansas	17.50
Custard Glass, Dish, Candy, Intaglio, Pedestal Base	65.00
Custard Glass, Goblet, Grape, Arches, Opaque	35.00
Custard Glass, Goblet, Souvenir, Osage City, Kansas	45.00
Custard Glass, Jar, Powder, Little Gem, Covered, Footed	29.00
Custard Glass, Jar, Powder, Little Gem, Covered, Roses, Souvenir	35.00
Custard Glass, Jigger, Souvenir, Dodge City, Kansas, High School	18.50
Custard Glass, Juicer, Marked Sunkist	22.00
Custard Glass, Mug, Diamond & Peg, Miniature	25.00
Custard Glass, Mug, Diamond Peg, Huron, South Dakota	40.00
Custard Glass, Mug, Johnsonburg, Pa.	15.00
Custard Glass, Mug, Punty Band, Phillips Academy, New Rockford, N.D.	25.00
Custard Glass, Mug, Singing Bird, Mark N	45.00
Custard Glass, Mug, Souvenir, Boone, Iowa	12.00 To 25.00
Custard Glass, Mug, Souvenir, Cedar Falls, Iowa State Normal, Red Lettering	14.00
Custard Glass, Mug, St.Augustine, Miniature, 2 1/2 In.High	12.00
Custard Glass, Mug, Two Fisherman, Yellow	45.00
Custard Glass, Nappy, Heisey's Winged Scroll, Gold	50.00
Custard Glass, Nappy, Honeycomb, Flower Rim, Center Handle	23.50
Custard Glass, Paperweight, Souvenir	16.50
Custard Glass, Pitcher, Chrysanthemum Sprig, Signed	135.00
Custard Glass, Pitcher, Flanderfall, S.D., 4 In.High	28.00
Custard Glass, Pitcher, Red Rose, 6 In.Tall	26.00
Custard Glass, Pitcher, Water, Argonaut Shell, 4 Tumblers, Signed Northwood	400.00
Custard Glass, Pitcher, Water, Chrysanthemum Sprig, No Gold	125.00
Custard Glass, Pitcher, Water, Chrysanthemum Sprig, 6 Tumblers	300.00
Custard Glass, Pitcher, Water, Fluted Scroll	150.00
Custard Glass, Pitcher, Water, Inverted Fan & Feather, Gold & Pink Trim	275.00
Custard Glass, Plate, Winged Scroll, 5 1/2 In.	35.00
Custard Glass, Potty, Miniature	20.00
Custard Glass, Relish, Poppy	25.00
Custard Glass, Rose Bowl, Beaded Circle, Footed, N Mark, 3 1/2 In.Tall	85.00
Custard Glass, Rose Bowl, Persian Medallion, Green	65.00
Custard Glass, Salt & Pepper, Louis XV	120.00
Custard Glass, Salt Shaker, Panelled Sea Shell, Green	8.50
Custard Glass, Salt, Creased Waist, Pewter Top, Pair	82.50
Custard Glass, Sauce, Corn Sprays, Gold Scalloped, Green, Dubuque, Iowa	28.00
Custard Glass, Sauce, Geneva, Green & Red Paint, Footed	25.00 To 28.00
Custard Glass, Sauce, Inverted Fan & Feather	45.00
Custard Glass, Sauce, Inverted Fan & Fern, Footed, Set Of 5	195.00
Custard Glass, Sauce, Little Gem, Gold Trim	35.00
Custard Glass, Sauce, Nautilus, Boat Shape, Signed Northwood In Script	75.00
Custard Glass, Sauce, Winged Scroll	20.00 To 29.00
Custard Glass, Shaker, Salt, Blue, Scroll & Dot Pattern	22.00
Custard Glass, Shaker, Salt, Holly Band	9.00
Custard Glass, Shaker, Salt, Mormon Temple Face, Pewter Cover	25.00

Custard Glass, Sherbet, Blackberry Band, Signed Mckee 15.00
Custard Glass, Shot Glass, Pastel Enameled Flowers 16.50
Custard Glass, Spooner, Argonaut Shell 75.00
Custard Glass, Spooner, Chrysanthemum Sprig, Gold .... 55.00 To 70.00
Custard Glass, Spooner, Chrysanthemum Sprig, Northwood Script .... 49.50 To 60.00
Custard Glass, Spooner, Covered Sugar, Covered Butter, Rose Design 130.00
Custard Glass, Spooner, Inverted Fan & Feather 85.00
Custard Glass, Spooner, Inverted Fan & Feather, Gold 95.00
Custard Glass, Spooner, Louis XV, Gold .... 40.00 To 75.00
Custard Glass, Spooner, Maple Leaf 60.00
Custard Glass, Spooner, Maple Leaf, Gold, 3 Loop Handles, Northwood 95.00
Custard Glass, Spooner, Pleated Drape, Pink Rose 36.50
Custard Glass, Spooner, Winged Scroll 65.00
Custard Glass, Sugar & Creamer, Green To Cream Top, Gold Beading, Souvenir 32.00
Custard Glass, Sugar, Chrysanthemum Sprig, Covered, Gold, N .... 80.00 To 89.50
Custard Glass, Sugar, Creamer, Spooner, & Covered Butter, Green, Gold Beaded 250.00
Custard Glass, Sugar, Grape & Cable, Burnt Umber Shades, Handles, N Mark 60.00
Custard Glass, Sugar, Inverted Fan & Feather, Covered 140.00
Custard Glass, Sugar, Louis XV .... 48.00 To 75.00
Custard Glass, Sugar, Nautilus, Gold, Signed Northwood In Script 125.00
Custard Glass, Sugar, Open, Beaded, Flared Top, Souvenir, Green 26.00
Custard Glass, Sugar, Roses, Gold Scallops, Individual, Amery, Wis. 25.00
Custard Glass, Table Set, Louis XV, Covered, 3 Piece 300.00
Custard Glass, Toothpick, Chrysanthemum Sprig, Gold, Northwood .... 85.00 To 135.00
Custard Glass, Toothpick, Figural, Hat, Union Glass 7.50
Custard Glass, Toothpick, Gold Beading, Scalloped Top, Wisconsin 20.00
Custard Glass, Toothpick, Harvard Pattern, Circa 1898 .... 28.00
Custard Glass, Toothpick, Ivorina Verde 90.00
Custard Glass, Toothpick, Quixote 35.00
Custard Glass, Toothpick, Raindrop, Embossed On Top 'Just A Thimblefull' 55.00
Custard Glass, Toothpick, Ring Band, Marked Heisey .... 40.00 To 45.00
Custard Glass, Toothpick, Souvenir, Butler, South Dakota 18.00
Custard Glass, Toothpick, Souvenir, Butte, Montana, Gold, Beaded Edge 19.75
Custard Glass, Toothpick, Souvenir Effingham, Illinois 12.50
Custard Glass, Toothpick, Souvenir, Enamel Floral, Beaded 17.50
Custard Glass, Toothpick, Souvenir, Little Gem, Turquoise 32.00
Custard Glass, Toothpick, Souvenir, Marengo, Illinois 25.00
Custard Glass, Toothpick, Souvenir, Newport, N.H., Etched Band Base 12.50
Custard Glass, Toothpick, Souvenir, Princeton, Illinois, Gold Edge, Signed H 24.00
Custard Glass, Toothpick, Souvenir, Revere Beach, Green 15.00
Custard Glass, Toothpick, Souvenir, Thumbprint, Floral, Marked Krystol 14.00
Custard Glass, Toothpick, Winged Scroll, Gold 55.00
Custard Glass, Toothpick, Winged Scroll, Ivorina Verde 65.00
Custard Glass, Tray, Condiment, Chrysanthemum Sprig, Signed In Script 125.00
Custard Glass, Tumbler, Chrysanthemum Sprig .... 35.00 To 39.50
Custard Glass, Tumbler, Chrysanthemum Sprig, Blue 98.50
Custard Glass, Tumbler, Chrysanthemum Sprig, Gold .... 35.00 To 45.00
Custard Glass, Tumbler, Diamond & Peg .... 25.00 To 30.00
Custard Glass, Tumbler, Diamond & Peg, Hand-Painted Enamel Rose, Krystol 35.00
Custard Glass, Tumbler, Diamond & Peg, Rose & Gold 30.00
Custard Glass, Tumbler, Everglades, Gold 35.00
Custard Glass, Tumbler, Everglades, Green, Gold Trim 39.00
Custard Glass, Tumbler, Geneva .... *Illus* 35.00
Custard Glass, Tumbler, Geneva, Red, Green Trim 39.00
Custard Glass, Tumbler, Grape & Arches 37.50
Custard Glass, Tumbler, Grape & Cable .... *Illus* 300.00
Custard Glass, Tumbler, Intaglio Pattern, Gold 40.00
Custard Glass, Tumbler, Louis XV .... *Illus* 30.00
Custard Glass, Tumbler, Souvenir Minnesota 37.50
Custard Glass, Tumbler, Three Wing Scroll 28.00
Custard Glass, Vase, Jack-In-Pulpit, Flowers, Gold, Hand-Painted, 11 In.Tall 45.00
Custard Glass, Vase, Pillar & Drape, Cinnamon Highlights, 8 1/2 In. 27.00
Custard Glass, Wine, Dew & Raindrop 7.50
Custard Glass, Wine, Gold Diamond Pegs, Hand-Painted Red Rose 24.00
Custard Glass, Wine, New Hampshire, Flared Top 8.00

Custard Glass,
Tumbler, Geneva
See Page 162

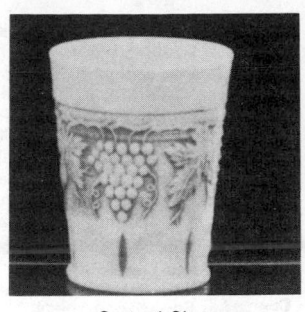

Custard Glass,
Tumbler, Grape & Cable
See Page 162

Custard Glass, Tumbler, Louis XV
See Page 162

Cut Glass has been made since ancient times, but the large majority of the pieces now for sale date from the brilliant period of glass design, 1880 to 1905. These pieces had elaborate geometric designs with a deep miter cut.

Cut Glass, see also Cruet, Toothpick, etc.

Cut Glass, Ashtray, Intaglio Rose Pattern, 7 1/2 In.	16.50
Cut Glass, Banana Boat, Allover Cut, Harvard Pattern, Brilliant, 12 In.Long	120.00
Cut Glass, Banana Boat, Harvard, Diamond & Fan, American, 11 1/2 In.Long	150.00
Cut Glass, Banana Boat, Hobnails, Starred & Diamond Point Buttons	115.00
Cut Glass, Banana Boat, Russian, Leaf & Star Shape Flower, Plain Buttons	145.00
Cut Glass, Banana Boat, Russian, Star Flower, Stem, & Leaf, 12 In.	145.00
Cut Glass, Banana Boat, Signed Hawkes, Hobstars, Single Stars & Fans	155.00
Cut Glass, Basket, Allover Cut, Rope Handle, 5 In.Tall, 7 1/2 In.Long	47.50
Cut Glass, Basket, Alternate Cane, Floral, & Intaglio, Twisted Handle	55.00
Cut Glass, Basket, Cornflower, Notched Handle, Pedestal, 11 1/2 In.High	95.00
Cut Glass, Basket, Etched & Cut, 9 1/2 In.High	24.00
Cut Glass, Basket, Hobstar, Cane, & Strawberry, 8 In.High, 5 In.Long	135.00
Cut Glass, Basket, Hobstar, Fan, & Diamond, Footed, 6 In.Diameter	110.00
Cut Glass, Basket, Hobstar, Star, & Thumbprint, Pedestal, 7 In.Diameter	110.00
Cut Glass, Basket, Leaf, Etched Flower, Design On Handle, 13 X 8 In.	42.50
Cut Glass, Basket, Pinwheel, Cane, Cross Cut Diamond, Clarke	165.00
Cut Glass, Basket, Pinwheel, Cane, Strawberry Diamond, Notched Handle, Clarke	150.00
Cut Glass, Basket, 13 1/2 In.High	95.00
Cut Glass, Bell, Brilliant Full Cut, Silver Handle	73.00
Cut Glass, Bell, Circa 1890, 4 1/2 In.High	35.00
Cut Glass, Bell, 6 In.High	16.50
Cut Glass, Bonbon, Hobstar, Cane, & Fan, Heart Shape	27.00
Cut Glass, Bonbon, Russian, Deep Cut, Heavy, 6 In.Diameter	60.00
Cut Glass, Bonbon, Teardrop, Hunt Royal, 9 In.Long	54.00
Cut Glass, Bottle, Atomizer, Green Cut To Clear, Block Pattern	45.00
Cut Glass, Bottle, Cologne, Bulbous, Sterling Stopper	45.00
Cut Glass, Bottle, Cologne, Sterling Mushroom Type Stopper, Cupid In Relief	95.00
Cut Glass, Bottle, Cordial, Hobstar, Cross Cut Diamond, Ball Stopper, 8 In.	95.00
Cut Glass, Bottle, Ink, Pewter Top With Amethyst Jewel In Center Cap	25.00

Cut Glass, Bottle, Perfume, Colonial Pattern, Pink Enamel, Sterling Stopper	25.00
Cut Glass, Bottle, Scent, Sterling Top	32.50
Cut Glass, Bottle, Signed Geo.Woodall, 6 1/2 In.High .... *Illus*	525.00
Cut Glass, Bottle, Water, Cut Base, Prismatic Neck, American	39.00
Cut Glass, Bottle, Water, Cut Flowers And Leaves	35.00
Cut Glass, Bottle, Water, Prism, Hobstar, Medallion	34.00
Cut Glass, Bottle, Water, Six Hobstars Bordered By Ridges	35.00
Cut Glass, Bottle, Whiskey, Stopper, Hobstar, Cane, Fan, Pedestal	150.00
Cut Glass, Bowl & Underplate, Finger, Intaglio, Flowers, Leaves, 1920	8.00
Cut Glass, Bowl & Underplate, Mayonnaise, Hobstars .... 65.00 To	85.00
Cut Glass, Bowl & Underplate, Mayonnaise, Iris Pattern	65.00
Cut Glass, Bowl & Underplate, Mayonnaise, Oval Shape, Harvard	145.00
Cut Glass, Bowl & Underplate, Mayonnaise, Strawberry Diamond	90.00
Cut Glass, Bowl & Underplate, Mayonnaise, 6 1/4 In.Diameter	55.00
Cut Glass, Bowl & Underplate, Signed Libbey, Engraved Daisies & Tendrils	40.00

Cut Glass, Bottle, Signed Geo.Woodall, 6 1/2 In.High

Cut Glass, Bowl & Underplate, Whipped Cream, Allover Cut	95.00
Cut Glass, Bowl, Allover Cut, Fans, Hobstars, Strawberry Diamonds, 8 1/2 In.	60.00
Cut Glass, Bowl, Allover Cut, Large, Deep, American	75.00
Cut Glass, Bowl, Allover Sharp Cut, 8 In.	87.50
Cut Glass, Bowl, American, Oval, Hobstars, Rolled Up Sides	25.00
Cut Glass, Bowl, Arcadia Pattern, 8 In.Wide, 4 In.High	55.00
Cut Glass, Bowl, Boat Shape, Hobstars, 6 1/2 In.Long	45.00
Cut Glass, Bowl, Berry, Signed Stuart, Prism Cutting, Rayed Base, England	38.00
Cut Glass, Bowl, Berry, Star, Vesica, & Strawberry, Scalloped Edge	45.00
Cut Glass, Bowl, Compartments, Chains Of Hobstars, Handle	95.00
Cut Glass, Bowl, Covered, Waterford, Serrated Edge, Oval	75.00
Cut Glass, Bowl, Finger, Etched Grape Leaves & Clusters, Star Cut Base, 6	70.00
Cut Glass, Bowl, Finger, Strawberry Diamond & Fan	27.50
Cut Glass, Bowl, Floral, Harvard, Footed	25.00
Cut Glass, Bowl, Florence Pattern, Gorham Sterling Pierced & Scalloped Rim	75.00
Cut Glass, Bowl, Harvard & Intaglio, Divided, 2 Handles, 12 In.Wide	125.00
Cut Glass, Bowl, Harvard Pattern	110.00
Cut Glass, Bowl, Hobstar & Fan, 3 In.High, 8 In.Diameter	35.00
Cut Glass, Bowl, Hobstar & Fan, 5 In.	21.00
Cut Glass, Bowl, Hobstar & Fern, Footed, Shallow, 8 1/2 In.Diameter	65.00
Cut Glass, Bowl, Hobstar, Diamond, & Fan, Bottom Hobstar, Pedestal, 9 In.	90.00
Cut Glass, Bowl, Hobstar, Fan, & Strawberry Diamond, 9 In.Diameter	60.00
Cut Glass, Bowl, Hobstar, Fan, Crosscut Diamond, & Nailhead, Sterling Rim	280.00
Cut Glass, Bowl, Hobstar, Floral, & Strawberry Diamond, Footed, Flared, 10 In.	115.00
Cut Glass, Bowl, Hobstar, Pinwheel, & Strawberry Diamond, 6 In.Diameter	25.00
Cut Glass, Bowl, Hobstar, Strawberry Diamond, Cane, & Fan, Handles, 8 In.	110.00
Cut Glass, Bowl, Hobstars, Double Thumbprint Handles	55.00
Cut Glass, Bowl, Hobstars, 4 Compartments, Handles, 10 In.Wide	95.00
Cut Glass, Bowl, Hobstars, 7 In.Diameter	37.50
Cut Glass, Bowl, Ice Cream, Hobstar & Fan, Scalloped Serrated Edge	22.50
Cut Glass, Bowl, Intaglio Rose & Hobstar, Crosshatched Rim, Low Pedestal	125.00
Cut Glass, Bowl, Maple Leaf Shape, Strawberry Diamond & Fan, 10 1/4 In.	70.00
Cut Glass, Bowl, Mayonnaise, Leaves, Fleur-De-Lis, Round	23.50

Cut Glass, Bowl, Mayonnaise, Signed Hawkes, Flowers, Birds, & Branch In Color 60.00
Cut Glass, Bowl, Orange, Allover Cut, Fan, Hobstar, & Strawberry Diamond 125.00
Cut Glass, Bowl, Orange, Harvard, Crescent Shape 120.00
Cut Glass, Bowl, Orange, Hobstars, Allover Cut 75.00
Cut Glass, Bowl, Orange, Signed Hoare, Nailhead & Diamond Point, Star Base 160.00
Cut Glass, Bowl, Pairpoint, Daisies & Butterflies, 48 Point Star Base 70.00
Cut Glass, Bowl, Panels Of Brilliant & Intaglio Cutting, Tuthill 100.00
Cut Glass, Bowl, Panels, Alternate Flower, Star & Crosscut, 8 In.Diameter 50.00
Cut Glass, Bowl, Pedestal, 9 1/2 In.Diameter 75.00
Cut Glass, Bowl, Pinched Sides, 10 1/2 In.Diameter 95.00
Cut Glass, Bowl, Pineapple & Fan, Shallow, 9 In. 40.00
Cut Glass, Bowl, Pinwheel & Fan 61.00
Cut Glass, Bowl, Pinwheel & Fan, 3 1/2 In.Deep 65.00
Cut Glass, Bowl, Punch, Covered, Faceted Finial, Hobstar, Fan, & Prism 275.00
Cut Glass, Bowl, Punch, Crosshatching, Sawtooth, Scalloped Edge, 2 Part 185.00
Cut Glass, Bowl, Punch, Hobstar, Fan, & Crosshatching, 2 Piece 395.00
Cut Glass, Bowl, Punch, Hobstar, Pinwheel, Cane, & Fan, 2 Piece 550.00
Cut Glass, Bowl, Punch, Hobstar, Prism, & Fan, Serrated & Scalloped 385.00
Cut Glass, Bowl, Punch, Hobstars, Panels, 8 1/2 In.Diameter, 6 In.High 39.00
Cut Glass, Bowl, Punch, Signed Clarke, Hobstar & Diamond, 2 Piece 975.00
Cut Glass, Bowl, Punch, Signed Hoare, Hobstar, Cane, Vesica, Prism, & Fan 1150.00
Cut Glass, Bowl, Punch, Strawberry Diamond & Star, 14 1/2 In. 400.00
Cut Glass, Bowl, Russian Variant With Fans, 10 In.Wide 150.00
Cut Glass, Bowl, Russian Variant, 8 In.Diameter 100.00
Cut Glass, Bowl, Russian, Persian Pattern, Starred Center 55.00
Cut Glass, Bowl, Russian, Vesicas Alternating With 16 Point Hobstars 42.50
Cut Glass, Bowl, Russian, Persian Pattern, Starred Center 55.00
Cut Glass, Bowl, Shallow, Divided, Hobstars, Two Handles 85.00
Cut Glass, Bowl, Shaped Sides, 9 In.Diameter 45.00
Cut Glass, Bowl, Signed Hawkes, Engraved Roses, Ferns, Thumbprints, Gravic 195.00
Cut Glass, Bowl, Signed Hawkes, Hobstar, Diamond Point, & Pineapple, Scallops 43.00
Cut Glass, Bowl, Signed Hawkes, Square, Variation Pattern, Notched Handles 70.00
Cut Glass, Bowl, Signed Hoare, Floral Center, Allover Brilliant Cut 65.00
Cut Glass, Bowl, Signed Irving, Scalloped & Fluted, 4 X 8 In. 45.00
Cut Glass, Bowl, Signed Libbey, Hobstar & Strawberry Diamond, 10 1/2 In. 135.00
Cut Glass, Bowl, Signed Libbey, Hobstar, Notched Prism, & Fan 75.00
Cut Glass, Bowl, Signed Libbey, Holly & Berry Garland Around Center, Flared 75.00
Cut Glass, Bowl, Signed Libbey, Ribbon Star Pattern, 8 1/2 In. 75.00
Cut Glass, Bowl, Signed Sinclaire, Violet, Deep Intaglio Asters 65.00
Cut Glass, Bowl, Signed Stuart, Diamond Pattern, Indented Thumb Holders 55.00
Cut Glass, Bowl, Six Flowers, Hobstars, 10 In. 75.00
Cut Glass, Bowl, Star, Strawberry, & Vesica, Scalloped Rim 15.00
Cut Glass, Bowl, Sterling Rim, Notched Prism, 32 Point Hobstar Base 135.00
Cut Glass, Bowl, Strawberry Diamond, 8 1/2 In.Diameter 48.00
Cut Glass, Bowl, Strawberry, Leaves, Ground Pontil, 9 1/2 In.Diameter 28.00
Cut Glass, Bowl, Waterford, Strawberry Diamond, Sheffield Stand, C.1810 .... 350.00
Cut Glass, Bowl, Waterford, Strawberry Diamond, 32 Point Star Base 130.00
Cut Glass, Bowl, 4 Sprays Of Feathered Flowers, Applied Blue Center Handle 60.00
Cut Glass, Bowl, 8 1/4 In.Diameter 50.00
Cut Glass, Box, Covered, Hinged, Intaglio 165.00
Cut Glass, Box, Fan, Butterfly, & Frosted Cut Floral, Silver Bands 97.50
Cut Glass, Box, Glove, Harvard, Floral 200.00
Cut Glass, Box, Glove, Hinged Cover, 11 In.Long 425.00
Cut Glass, Box, Handkerchief, Hinged, Intaglio Flowers, Star Base, Silver 225.00
Cut Glass, Box, Heart Shape, Diamond & Block, Rayed Bottom, Sterling Lid 22.50
Cut Glass, Box, Hinged Cover, Hobstar Chains Top & Bottom, 8 Sided 225.00
Cut Glass, Box, Hinged, 8 Sided, 7 1/2 In.Diameter 250.00
Cut Glass, Box, Jewel, Signed Hawkes, Hobstars, Hinged, 6 In.Diameter 150.00
Cut Glass, Box, Powder, Cut Top, 2 1/2 In.High 35.00
Cut Glass, Box, Powder, Hobstar & Fan, Sterling Top, Monogram 35.00
Cut Glass, Box, Powder, Intaglio Cut Flowers, Hinged Lid 147.00
Cut Glass, Box, Signed Hawkes, Diamond Cut Pattern, Sterling Knob On Lid 148.50
Cut Glass, Box, Signed Sinclaire, Medallion & Diamond, Sterling Lid 95.00
Cut Glass, Box, Signed Tuthill, Hobstar & Intaglio Motif, Star Bottom 300.00
Cut Glass, Box, Silver Lid, 1 1/2 In.Diameter 9.00
Cut Glass, Box, Vanity, Hinged Cover, Round 175.00

Cut Glass, Bucket & Underplate, Ice, Dorflinger, Strawberry Diamond & Fan	245.00
Cut Glass, Bucket, Ice, Allover Cut, Pinwheel Bottom, Star Cut Tabs	95.00
Cut Glass, Bucket, Ice, Double Lozenge Pattern, 5 In.High, 6 In.Wide	49.00
Cut Glass, Bucket, Ice, Harvard, Fan, Shield, & Diamond, 2 Tabs	65.00
Cut Glass, Bucket, Ice, Hobstar, Strawberry Diamond, & Fan, Star Bottom	165.00
Cut Glass, Bucket, Ice, Tabs, 5 1/2 In.Diameter	75.00
Cut Glass, Bun Warmer, X Vesica, Beading, Hobstar, Strawberry Diamond, & Fan	135.00
Cut Glass, Butter Pat, Allover Cut, Brilliant	18.50
Cut Glass, Butter Pat, Fans, 8 Point Hobstar Base	12.50
Cut Glass, Butter Pat, Hobstar & Notched Prism, Star Base, Set Of 6	125.00
Cut Glass, Butter Pat, Russian Pattern, Clear Buttons, Pair	35.00
Cut Glass, Butter Pat, 16 Point Hobstars Separated By Fine Cut Bands, 4	6.50
Cut Glass, Butter Tub, Hobstar In Diamond Shape Band, Fans, Step Cut	80.00
Cut Glass, Butter Tub, Hobstar, Strawberry Diamond Band, Star, & Fan	90.00
Cut Glass, Butter, Covered, Allover Cut, Domed	250.00
Cut Glass, Butter, Covered, Allover Harvard, Scalloped	55.00
Cut Glass, Butter, Covered, Hobstar, Cane, & Vesica, Pair	200.00
Cut Glass, Butter, Covered, Hobstar, Star, & Fan, Cut Knob	150.00
Cut Glass, Butter, Covered, Hobstar, Strawberry Diamond, & Fan, Domed, Square	215.00
Cut Glass, Butter, Covered, Liberty Bell Pattern, Domed	250.00
Cut Glass, Butter, Covered, Meriden's Plymouth Pattern, Domed	250.00
Cut Glass, Butter, Harvard, Intaglio Cut, Brilliant	150.00
Cut Glass, Butter, Hobstar Chain & Daisy, Strawberry Diamond Border	- 85.00
Cut Glass, Butter, Hobstar, Strawberry Diamond, & Fan	150.00
Cut Glass, Butter, Hobstars	125.00
Cut Glass, Cake Stand, Gallery, Hobstar & Fan, 12 In.Diameter	225.00
Cut Glass, Cake Stand, Harvard Border, Triangle Of Intaglio Flowers	125.00
Cut Glass, Cake Stand, Intaglio Flowers, Trefoil Legs, 9 In.Diameter	125.00
Cut Glass, Candelabra, Drop Hung Drip Pans, Octagonal Base, 3 Arms, Pair	130.00
Cut Glass, Candelabra, George III, Drops, 5 Scrolling Arms, C.1800, Pair	550.00
Cut Glass, Candleholder, Signed Libbey, Gravic, 12 In.	65.00
Cut Glass, Candlestick, Brass Reliefs With Dance Of The Hours, Pair	38.00
Cut Glass, Candlestick, Etched Flowers, 7 1/2 In.High, Pair	12.50
Cut Glass, Candlestick, Floral & Cane, Teardrop Center, 8 1/4 In., Pair	185.00
Cut Glass, Candlestick, Flowers & Leaves, 7 1/2 In.High, Pair	20.00
Cut Glass, Candlestick, Hobstar Base, Mitered Leaves, Teardrop Stem, Pair	95.00
Cut Glass, Candlestick, Saucer Base, Notched Prism, Bobeche, Silver, Pair	125.00
Cut Glass, Candlestick, Signed Hawkes, Green Threads, Copper Wheel Engraved	60.00
Cut Glass, Candlestick, Signed Hawkes, Teardrop, Notched, Hobstars, Pair	190.00
Cut Glass, Candlestick, Signed Libbey, Carnations, Flared Top, 10 In., Pair	150.00
Cut Glass, Candlestick, William IV, Bronze, Ormolu, Anthemion, 1890, Pair	250.00
Cut Glass, Candy, Footed, Flowers, 6 In.Diameter	25.00
Cut Glass, Canoe, Deep Cut, Brilliant, 12 In.	55.00
Cut Glass, Canoe, Harvard Band, Cosmos Flower & Leaf, Sawtooth Rim	45.00
Cut Glass, Canoe, Harvard, 8 In.Long	80.00
Cut Glass, Canoe, Hobstar, Star, & Crosscut Diamond, 11 1/2 In.Long	115.00
Cut Glass, Carafe, Diamond & Fan, Star Base	28.00
Cut Glass, Carafe, Fan & Diamond, 12 1/2 In.High	65.00
Cut Glass, Carafe, Hobstar & Diamond, 8 In.	69.00
Cut Glass, Carafe, Hobstar, Crosshatching, & Fan	50.00
Cut Glass, Carafe, Hobstar, Squatty, 7 In.High & Diameter	32.00
Cut Glass, Carafe, Lotus Pattern	65.00
Cut Glass, Carafe, Notched Prisms Ending In Diamonds	38.00
Cut Glass, Carafe, Water, Hobstar, Buzz, & Fan, Step Cut Neck	45.00
Cut Glass, Carafe, Water, Hobstar, Diamond Point & Fan, Star Base	43.00
Cut Glass, Carafe, Water, Notched Prisms Ending In Diamonds	38.00
Cut Glass, Carafe, Water, Russian Pattern	88.00
Cut Glass, Carafe, Water, Strawberry Diamond & Intaglio Floral, Ring Neck	60.00
Cut Glass, Castor, Pickle, Diamond Cut, Gorham Silver Holder, Embossed	150.00
Cut Glass, Castor, Pickle, Wheel Cut, Mushroom Lid, Silver Plate Holder	27.50
Cut Glass, Celery, Allover Cut, Hobstar & Strawberry Diamond	65.00
Cut Glass, Celery, Allover Hobstar Clusters & Crosscut Diamond	45.00
Cut Glass, Celery, Heart & Hobstar	295.00
Cut Glass, Celery, Hobstar & Fan	24.00
Cut Glass, Celery, Hobstar, Cane, & Strawberry Diamond, 12 X 5 In.	45.00
Cut Glass, Celery, Hobstar, Diamond Point, & Fan, 10 3/4 In.Long	65.00

Cut Glass, Celery, Hobstar, Pinwheel, & Fan, 9 1/2 In.High	165.00
Cut Glass, Celery, Hobstar, Strawberry Diamond, & Fan	85.00
Cut Glass, Celery, Intaglio Leaves, Sides Turn In	55.00
Cut Glass, Celery, Notched Prism & Hobstar, 11 In.Long	50.00
Cut Glass, Celery, Signed Clarke	87.00
Cut Glass, Celery, Signed Clarke, Allover Cane & Buzz	90.00
Cut Glass, Celery, Signed Clarke, Flat, 12 In.Long	75.00
Cut Glass, Celery, Signed Hawkes, Hobstars, Blaze On Sides, Star Bottom	95.00
Cut Glass, Celery, Signed Hawkes, Star Chain & Hobstar	95.00
Cut Glass, Celery, Signed Libbey, Imperial	85.00
Cut Glass, Celery, Signed P & B, Serrated Rim, Allover Cutting	55.00
Cut Glass, Celery, Signed Sinclaire	150.00
Cut Glass, Celery, 10 1/2 X 4 1/2 In.	30.00
Cut Glass, Champagne, American, Cobalt, Flute Cut, C.1840	22.50
Cut Glass, Champagne, Arcadia, Hobstar Base	25.00
Cut Glass, Champagne, Hobnail, Teardrop Stem, Star Base	20.00
Cut Glass, Champagne, Hobstar, Single Star	20.00
Cut Glass, Champagne, Russian, Honeycomb, Clear Button, Rayed Bottom	75.00
Cut Glass, Champagne, Signed Libbey, Crosscut Diamond & Fan, Hollow Stem	37.50
Cut Glass, Champagne, Signed Libbey, Hobstar, Star, Crosscutting, & Fan, 4	175.00
Cut Glass, Champagne, Signed Libbey, Stemmed	10.00
Cut Glass, Clock, Helmet Shape	110.00
Cut Glass, Coffeepot, Etched Flowers, St.Louis Cutting On Handle	395.00
Cut Glass, Cologne, Ball Shape	38.00
Cut Glass, Cologne, Czechoslovakia, Green, Stopper, Signed	35.00
Cut Glass, Cologne, Signed Hawkes, Hobstar & Fine Diamond	55.00
Cut Glass, Compote, Allover Complex Cutting, Brilliant, Cut Thumbprint Stem	98.00
Cut Glass, Compote, Allover Sharp Cutting, Scalloped Base	85.00
Cut Glass, Compote, Faceted Knob On Stem, Rayed Base, 7 X 5 1/4 In.High	85.00
Cut Glass, Compote, Flower Form, Brilliant Period	150.00
Cut Glass, Compote, Footed, 5 In.High, 5 In.Diameter	30.00
Cut Glass, Compote, Funnel Shape, Lotus Pattern, Pedestal Base, 8 In.High	95.00
Cut Glass, Compote, Harvard & Floral	22.00
Cut Glass, Compote, Hobstar & Cane, Variant, Notched Stem, Rayed Bottom, 4 In	55.00
Cut Glass, Compote, Hobstar & Pinwheel, Notched Stem, 5 1/2 In.High	62.00
Cut Glass, Compote, Hobstar Border At Top, Teardrop Stem, 6 Petal Flowers	65.00
Cut Glass, Compote, Hobstar Rosettes, Strawberry, Hobnail & Fan	55.00 To 75.00
Cut Glass, Compote, Hobstar, Cane, Fan, & Diamond Point, 8 In.High, 6 In.Wide	95.00
Cut Glass, Compote, Hobstar, Strawberry Diamond, & Cane, 11 1/2 In.High	175.00
Cut Glass, Compote, Hobstar, Strawberry Diamond, & Crosshatching	85.00
Cut Glass, Compote, Hobstar, Strawberry Diamond, & Fan, Teardrop Stem	75.00
Cut Glass, Compote, Hobstar, Strawberry Diamond, Nailhead, & Fan	95.00
Cut Glass, Compote, Hobstars, Teardrop Stem	85.00
Cut Glass, Compote, Hobstars, Teardrop Stem, 7 1/2 In.High	75.00
Cut Glass, Compote, Hollow Stem, Brilliant	150.00
Cut Glass, Compote, Jelly, Arcadia Pattern, On Standard	110.00
Cut Glass, Compote, Jelly, Footed, 4 1/2 In.High	42.00
Cut Glass, Compote, Jelly, Hobstar, Crosscut Diamond, & Cane, Boat Shape	135.00
Cut Glass, Compote, Jelly, Sterling Cover & Spoon, Initial	26.00
Cut Glass, Compote, Jelly, 8 In.Tall, Fan And Small Diamond, Notched Stem	65.00
Cut Glass, Compote, Leaf, Intaglio Cut Floral, Notched Stem	45.00
Cut Glass, Compote, Leaves, Frosted Flowers With Crossbar Centers, Rayed	29.00
Cut Glass, Compote, Mayonnaise, Cosmos Flowers, Star Bottom, Ladle	50.00
Cut Glass, Compote, Overall Hobstars	76.00
Cut Glass, Compote, Pinwheel & Fan, Starred Bottom, Notched Stem, 5 In.High	35.00
Cut Glass, Compote, Salesman's Sample	75.00
Cut Glass, Compote, Serrated & Notched Stem, 24 Point Star In Foot	95.00
Cut Glass, Compote, Signed Clarke, Floral, Leaves, & Bull's-Eye, Notched Edge	75.00
Cut Glass, Compote, Signed Floyd F.Cary For Pairpoint, Urn With Flame	32.00
Cut Glass, Compote, Signed Hawkes, 5 1/2 In.High	40.00
Cut Glass, Compote, Signed Hoare, Intaglio Daisy, Leaf, Cane, Prism, & Fan	145.00
Cut Glass, Compote, Signed Tuthill, Engraved Flowers & Leaves	125.00
Cut Glass, Compote, Silver Framed	48.50
Cut Glass, Compote, Swirled Ribs, Sawtooth, Ruffled Edge, Pedestal Base	19.00
Cut Glass, Compote, Twisted Stem, 9 In.High	110.00
Cut Glass, Compote, Two Color, Knobbed Teardrop Stem	125.00

Cut Glass, Compote, Variation Of Corinthian Pattern, 8 1/2 In.High 75.00
Cut Glass, Condiment Set, Four Bottles, Silver Plated Holder & Spoon 58.00
Cut Glass, Console Set, Signed Sinclaire, Amber, Intaglio Grape, 3 Piece 495.00
Cut Glass, Creamer, Cut Base & Handle, American 21.00
Cut Glass, Creamer, Hobstars 18.00
Cut Glass, Creamer, Log, Scalloped Top, 3 In.Tall 8.00
Cut Glass, Creamer, Pinwheel Pattern 35.00
Cut Glass, Creamer, Pinwheels, Hobstar Base 35.00
Cut Glass, Cruet, Bull's-Eye & Hobstar, Triple Lip, Teardrop Stopper 35.00
Cut Glass, Cruet, Captain's, Brilliant Period 65.00
Cut Glass, Cruet, Clover Lip 30.00
Cut Glass, Cruet, Crosscut Diamond & Fan 28.00
Cut Glass, Cruet, Fan & Diamond, Bulbous, Stopper, 7 In.High 22.00
Cut Glass, Cruet, Hobstar & Pinwheel 32.00
Cut Glass, Cruet, Pedestal, Hobstar, Rosettes, & Fan, Diamond Cut Stopper 50.00
Cut Glass, Cruet, Pinwheel, Fan, & Crosshatching, Notched Handle, Stopper 50.00
Cut Glass, Cruet, Pinwheels, 7 1/2 In.High 48.00
Cut Glass, Cruet, Signed Hawkes 70.00
Cut Glass, Cruet, Signed Hawkes, Oil & Vinegar, Double Lip 45.00
Cut Glass, Cruet, Signed Hawkes, 9 In.High .... *Illus* 95.00

Cut Glass, Cruet, Signed Hawkes, 9 In.High

Cut Glass, Cruet, Signed Tuthill, Fan, Crosshatching, & Hobstar, 9 In. 60.00
Cut Glass, Cruet, Snowflake & Fan, 5 1/2 In.High 45.00
Cut Glass, Cruet, Vertical Design, Sharp Cut, Bulbous, 6 1/2 In.Tall 22.00
Cut Glass, Cruet, Vinegar, Brilliant Period, Stopper 36.50
Cut Glass, Cruet, Vinegar, Rose Design 45.00
Cut Glass, Cruet, Wheel Pattern, 5 1/2 In.High 49.00
Cut Glass, Cup, Punch, Allover Cutting, Plain Applied Handle 22.50
Cut Glass, Cup, Punch, Signed Hawkes 27.00
Cut Glass, Cup, Punch, Starburst, Hobstar, & Fan, Star Bottom 7.00
Cut Glass, Cuspidor, Lady's, Intaglio Flower & Leaf, Ruffled Edge, 10 In. 185.00
Cut Glass, Decanter, Bakewell, Pedestal, 4 Rings Around Neck, Stopper 125.00
Cut Glass, Decanter, Hobstar & Fan, Bulbous, S Shape Double Notched Handle 275.00
Cut Glass, Decanter, Hobstar & Fan, S Shape Handle, Faceted Stopper 225.00
Cut Glass, Decanter, Hobstar & Fan, Star Base, Diamond Stopper 75.00
Cut Glass, Decanter, Hobstar, Buzz, & Fan, Teardrop Stopper, 12 In.High 135.00
Cut Glass, Decanter, Hobstar, Fan, Crosshatching, & Strawberry Diamond 165.00
Cut Glass, Decanter, Hobstar, Star, Diamond, Crosscut Diamond, & Fan, 12 In. 95.00
Cut Glass, Decanter, Hobstar, Strawberry Diamond, & Crosscut Fan, Stopper 125.00
Cut Glass, Decanter, Hobstar, Strawberry Diamond, Notched Prism, & Fan 65.00
Cut Glass, Decanter, Hobstars, Notched Prism Cut Stopper, Brilliant, 11 In. 125.00
Cut Glass, Decanter, Hobstars, Two Pouring Spouts, Handleless, Brilliant 125.00
Cut Glass, Decanter, Intaglio Flowers, Swirled Panels, Star Base, Teardrop 75.00
Cut Glass, Decanter, Intaglio On Sides, Clear & Amber 100.00
Cut Glass, Decanter, Notched Prism, Triple Notched Handle, Lapidary Stopper 115.00
Cut Glass, Decanter, Pyramid, Hobstar, Cane Vesica, & Strawberry Diamond 135.00
Cut Glass, Decanter, Sharp Nailhead, Stopper, 13 3/4 In.High 100.00
Cut Glass, Decanter, Signed Hawkes, Handle, Middlesex, Facet Cut Stopper 135.00
Cut Glass, Decanter, Signed Libbey, Allover Cut, 12 1/4 In. 160.00
Cut Glass, Decanter, Square, Currier & Ives Cut Cane, 3 1/2 X 8 In. 45.00

Cut Glass, Decanter, Vertical Panel Cutting, Honeycomb Stopper, 13 1/2 In. 45.00
Cut Glass, Decanter, Whiskey, Allover Harvard, Square Shape, Ball Stopper 77.50
Cut Glass, Decanter, Whiskey, Honeycomb, Steeple Stopper, Pair 300.00
Cut Glass, Decanter, With Stopper, 13 In.High 125.00
Cut Glass, Dish & Saucer, Cheese, Hobtar & Fan, Hobstarred Knob 200.00
Cut Glass, Dish & Underplate, Cheese, Covered, Harvard, Shield & Fan 275.00
Cut Glass, Dish & Underplate, Cheese, Covered, Hobstar, Cane, Buzz, & Diamond 295.00
Cut Glass, Dish & Underplate, Cheese, Panels Of Hobstar & Pinwheel Hobs 95.00
Cut Glass, Dish & Underplate, Mayonnaise, Hobstars 85.00
Cut Glass, Dish, American, Oval, Hobstars, Rolled Up Sides 25.00
Cut Glass, Dish, Banana, Leaves, Star Shape Flowers, Plain Buttons, Russia 145.00
Cut Glass, Dish, Boat Shape, Hobstars, 6 1/2 In.Long 45.00
Cut Glass, Dish, Bonbon, Deep Cut, Heavy, Russian, 6 In.Diameter 60.00
Cut Glass, Dish, Candy, Four Sections, Cut Handles, Hobstar, Arc, & Prism 73.00
Cut Glass, Dish, Candy, Rectangular, Hobstar, Strawberry Diamond, & Fan 55.00
Cut Glass, Dish, Candy, Swan Shape, Curved Neck, 6 In.Long, 3 In.High 20.00
Cut Glass, Dish, Cheese, Covered, American Shield, Harvard, Brilliant 275.00
Cut Glass, Dish, Cheese, Covered, Hobstar & Cane, Domed, 9 In.Diameter 285.00
Cut Glass, Dish, Cheese, Covered, Signed Clarke 400.00
Cut Glass, Dish, Cheese, Covered, Signed Clarke, Hobstars, Variant 325.00
Cut Glass, Dish, Cheese, Harvard, Fan, Shield, & Diamond 265.00
Cut Glass, Dish, Cheese, Hobstar Rosette, Fan, & Crosscut Diamond 245.00
Cut Glass, Dish, Cheese, Signed Clarke, Pair 795.00
Cut Glass, Dish, Dresser, Florals, Rayed Base, Cut Top 30.00
Cut Glass, Dish, Nut, Harvard, Canoe Shape 21.00
Cut Glass, Dish, Powder, 4 In.Diameter 25.00
Cut Glass, Dish, Sundae, Canoe Shape, Buttons, 6 Point Star, Sawtooth Edge 45.00
Cut Glass, Dome, Lamp, Pinwheels 200.00
Cut Glass, Fernery, Allover Sharp Cut, Three Feet, 8 In. 45.00
Cut Glass, Fernery, Footed 85.00
Cut Glass, Fernery, Harvard Cut, Legs, American 85.00
Cut Glass, Fernery, Harvard, Diamond Point, & Fan, Serrated Edge, Three Legs 110.00
Cut Glass, Fernery, Hobstar & Fan, Footed, Brilliant 46.50
Cut Glass, Fernery, Hobstar, Pinwheel, & Strawberry Diamond, Star Base 55.00
Cut Glass, Flower Center, Cut Top, Side Notching, Flowers, Rayed Bottom 110.00
Cut Glass, Flower Center, Hobstar, Vesica, Diamond, & Fan 150.00
Cut Glass, Flower Center, Signed Clarke, Hobstar, Strawberry Diamond 360.00
Cut Glass, Frame, Signed Hawkes, Strawberry Diamonds, Velvet Back 100.00
Cut Glass, Goblet, Dorflinger's Middlesex, Set Of 6 .... 265.00
Cut Glass, Goblet, Double Lozenge Pattern, Set Of 6 .... 275.00
Cut Glass, Goblet, Russian, Engraved Imperial Eagle, Military Trophy, 1762 .... 225.00
Cut Glass, Goblet, Signed Corning & Hoare, 1853 .... 26.50
Cut Glass, Goblet, Signed Libbey, Hobstars 65.00
Cut Glass, Goblet, Signed Libbey, Hobstars, Set Of 6 .... 65.00
Cut Glass, Goblet, Signed Libbey, Tear Drop Stem, Set Of 4 .... 220.00
Cut Glass, Goblet, Water, Strawberry Diamond & Fan, Star Base, Set Of 10 .... 150.00
Cut Glass, Hair Receiver, Floral, Rayed Base, Cut Glass Top 25.00
Cut Glass, Hair Receiver, Florals, Rayed Base 25.00
Cut Glass, Hair Receiver, Sterling Silver Art Nouveau Lid, 8 In.Round 135.00
Cut Glass, Holder, Cigarette, Geometric Diamond Design, 1920, Pair 9.00
Cut Glass, Holder, Spoon, Intaglio Pattern, Octagon Shape, 5 In.Tall 27.50
Cut Glass, Humidor, Hobstar & Cane, Star Bottom, Sterling Art Nouveau Lid 175.00
Cut Glass, Humidor, Queen's Pattern Variant, 16 Point Hobstar Bottom 200.00
Cut Glass, Humidor, Queen's Pattern, 16 Point Hobstar Bottom, 7 1/2 In.High 200.00
Cut Glass, Iced Tea, Hobstar & Fan 22.00
Cut Glass, Inkstand, Boat Shape, Gilt Metal Mounts, Reeded Handles, 9 1/2 In 120.00
Cut Glass, Inkwell, Cut Top, Concave Sides, Brass Hinged Collar, Square 49.00
Cut Glass, Jar, Biscuit, Hand-Cut Lead Crystal, Allover Cut, Brilliant 49.00
Cut Glass, Jar, Biscuit, Harvard, Silver Plate Handle, Rim, & Lid 225.00
Cut Glass, Jar, Covered, Bull's-Eye & Star, 10 1/2 In.Diameter, 6 In.High 48.00
Cut Glass, Jar, Cracker, Pinwheel Design, Cover 36.50
Cut Glass, Jar, Cracker, Signed Hawkes, Intaglio Flower & Miter Leaf 165.00
Cut Glass, Jar, Hobstar, Crosscutting, & Fan, Star Base, Hobstar Stopper 85.00
Cut Glass, Jar, Horseradish, Hobstars, Hollow Top, 4 In. 25.00
Cut Glass, Jar, Horseradish, Rounded Oval, Wafer Top, Cut Stopper 36.00
Cut Glass, Jar, Mustard, Allover Cut, Silver Plated Lid & Handle 16.00

Cut Glass, Jar, Mustard, Covered, Cut Base & Lid, American 24.00
Cut Glass, Jar, Mustard, Covered, Faceted Knob 10.00
Cut Glass, Jar, Mustard, Covered, Thumbprint & Step Cut Panel, Star Base 12.00
Cut Glass, Jar, Mustard, Notched Prisms, Silver Plated Lid 12.00
Cut Glass, Jar, Mustard, Punty & Raised Diamond, Sterling Silver Lid 45.00
Cut Glass, Jar, Panel Cut, Sterling Top, 1 1/4 In.Tall 6.50
Cut Glass, Jar, Powder, Art Nouveau Sterling Cover 38.00
Cut Glass, Jar, Powder, Covered, Hobstars, Heavy Cut 50.00
Cut Glass, Jar, Powder, Crisscross & Fan, Sterling Cover 18.00
Cut Glass, Jar, Powder, Elongated Thumbprint & Notched Vesica, Sterling Lid 39.00
Cut Glass, Jar, Powder, Floral Embossed Sterling Cover 20.00
Cut Glass, Jar, Powder, Harvard, Hobstars, Silver Plate Cover 60.00
Cut Glass, Jar, Powder, Sterling Silver Lid 22.00
Cut Glass, Jar, Sachet, Hinged Sterling Cover Marked Theodore B.Starr 55.00
Cut Glass, Jar, Signed J.Hoare, Harvard, Fan, & Geometric, Star Base 90.00
Cut Glass, Jar, Silver Rim, Gold Wash Cover, Embossed Floral Spray 25.00
Cut Glass, Jar, Sterling Repousse Cover, Star Base 37.50
Cut Glass, Jar, Strawberry Diamond & Fan, Sterling Silver Top 18.00
Cut Glass, Jar, Tobacco, Hobstar, Fan, & Diamond Point, Cut Lid 125.00
Cut Glass, Jug, Whiskey, Signed Hoare, Hobstar, Fan, & Prism, Cut Stopper 225.00
Cut Glass, Juice Set, Dorflinger's Middlesex, Flared Top Pitcher, 7 Piece 265.00
Cut Glass, Juice, Hobstar, Fan, Diamond, & Notched Prism, Rayed Bottom 20.00
Cut Glass, Juice, Hobstar, Strawberry Diamond, & Fan 15.00
Cut Glass, Juice, Pineapple, Pair 22.00
Cut Glass, Knife Rest, Ball Shape Ends With Lapidary Cut 28.00
Cut Glass, Knife Rest, Brilliant, Ball Ends 18.00
Cut Glass, Knife Rest, Diamond Pattern With Cross In Each Diamond 14.00
Cut Glass, Knife Rest, Dumbbell Ends 16.50
Cut Glass, Knife Rest, English Strawberry Diamond, Hobstar, & Fan 17.50
Cut Glass, Knife Rest, Fluted, Notched, Star In Ends 27.50
Cut Glass, Knife Rest, Hobnail In Diamond & Prism .... 17.50 To 20.00
Cut Glass, Knife Rest, Lapidary Ball Ends, 5 1/2 In.Long 22.00
Cut Glass, Knife Rest, Prism Cut Ends, 6 In.Long 25.00
Cut Glass, Knife Rest, Strawberry Diamond & Fan, Brass Box, Set Of 12 .... 75.00
Cut Glass, Lamp Base, Florence Pattern 200.00
Cut Glass, Lamp, Allover Cut, Hanging Prisms, 17 X 10 In.Diameter Shade 675.00
Cut Glass, Lamp, Flower, Butterfly, & Prism, 15 In.High 275.00
Cut Glass, Lamp, Hanging Prisms, 10 In.Diameter Shade .... 575.00 To 750.00
Cut Glass, Lamp, Harvard Cut Flowers, 19 Prisms, 2 Lights, 29 In.High 1750.00
Cut Glass, Lamp, Harvard, Floral, 12 In.Diameter Shade, 22 In.High, 2 Light 675.00
Cut Glass, Lamp, Hobstar, Buzz, Diamond, & Fan, Hanging Prisms, 10 In.Shade 650.00
Cut Glass, Lamp, Mushroom Shade, Butterfly & Flower, 26 Prisms, Electric 255.00
Cut Glass, Lamp, Mushroom Shade, C.1920, 9 In.Across, 19 In.High 250.00
Cut Glass, Lamp, Mushroom Shade, Hobstar, Diamond, & Buzz, 17 In.High 550.00
Cut Glass, Lamp, Prisms, 12 In.High 250.00
Cut Glass, Liqueur Set, French, Gilt Metal, Paw Feet On Tray, 1850, 12 Piece 250.00
Cut Glass, Match Holder, Signed Hawkes 55.00
Cut Glass, Muffineer, Allover Cut, Quadrangular, Silver Scroll Top 26.00
Cut Glass, Muffineer, Cane Pattern 45.00
Cut Glass, Muffineer, Diamond Cut, Pewter Top, 5 In. 18.00
Cut Glass, Muffineer, Moss Rose Pattern, Sterling Top 59.00
Cut Glass, Muffineer, Signed Stuart, England 28.00
Cut Glass, Napkin Ring, Allover Harvard 65.00
Cut Glass, Napkin Ring, Crosshatching, Flat Crystal Base 10.00
Cut Glass, Napkin Ring, Harvard 55.00
Cut Glass, Napkin Ring, Middlesex Pattern 45.00
Cut Glass, Napkin Ring, Panel & Star, 2 In. Long 11.00
Cut Glass, Nappy, Brilliant Cut, 6 In. 39.50
Cut Glass, Nappy, Clover Shape, Step Cut Handle, Middlesex Variant 35.00
Cut Glass, Nappy, Double Handled, 11 In. 60.00
Cut Glass, Nappy, Fan, Hobstar, & Strawberry Diamond, 7 In.Diameter 35.00
Cut Glass, Nappy, Flattened Diamond Cutting, Rayed Base 12.50
Cut Glass, Nappy, Floral, Handle 26.00
Cut Glass, Nappy, Geometric, Star, & Fan, Sawtooth Edge, Ring Handle 22.00
Cut Glass, Nappy, Hobstar & Fan, Paneled, Four Sections, 7 In.Diameter 75.00
Cut Glass, Nappy, Hobstar & Strawberry Diamond, 6 In.Diameter 30.00

Cut Glass, Nappy, Hobstar Pattern, 2 Handles, 8 In.Across 55.00
Cut Glass, Nappy, Hobstars, 2 Notched Handles, Salesman's Sample 35.00
Cut Glass, Nappy, Hunt's Royal Pattern, Handle, 7 In. 75.00
Cut Glass, Nappy, Pinwheel & Fan, Strawberry Diamond Base, 6 In.Diameter 22.50
Cut Glass, Nappy, Ring Hole, 6 In. 22.50
Cut Glass, Nappy, Russian Pattern, Notched Handle 35.00
Cut Glass, Nappy, Side Handle, Allover Cut 48.00
Cut Glass, Nappy, Signed Hawkes, Fan & Strawberry Diamond, Star Base 90.00
Cut Glass, Nappy, Signed Hawkes, Handle 40.00
Cut Glass, Nappy, Trellis Ruffled, Serrated, Looped Handle, American 23.00
Cut Glass, Nappy, Two Handles, Salesman's Sample 65.00
Cut Glass, Paperweight, Faceted 25.00
Cut Glass, Parfait, Wild Roses, Leaves, Copperwheel, Signed Tuthill 32.50
Cut Glass, Perfume, Atomizer, Allover Cut, Pedestal Base, Sterling Top, 8 In. 34.50
Cut Glass, Perfume, Ball Shape, Silver Top, Marked W.& H., Dated 1898 .... 50.00
Cut Glass, Perfume, Bulbous, Cut Stopper, Pair 48.00
Cut Glass, Perfume, Diamond Point & Fan, Lapidary Cut Stopper 27.50
Cut Glass, Perfume, Diamond Sides & Front, Cut Stopper, 5 1/2 In.High 15.00
Cut Glass, Perfume, Diamond, Star, Ball Shape, Cork, Screw Cap 10.00
Cut Glass, Perfume, Faceted Stopper, 2 In Leather Casket, Brass Trim 67.50
Cut Glass, Perfume, Flower & Leaf Design, Facet Stopper, 5 1/4 In.High 23.00
Cut Glass, Perfume, Hobstars Separated By Notched Prisms, Star Base 40.00
Cut Glass, Perfume, Horn Shaped, Hinged Sterling Lid, 5 In.Long 15.00
Cut Glass, Perfume, Intaglio, Rose, & Fuchsia, 6 1/2 In.High 30.00
Cut Glass, Perfume, Purse, Stopper, Hinged Sterling Top 20.00
Cut Glass, Perfume, Square Star Cut Base, Stopper, 8 In.High, Pair 25.00
Cut Glass, Perfume, Sterling Engraved Stopper, Pair 75.00
Cut Glass, Perfume, Strawberry Diamond & Fan, Stopper, 5 In.High 45.00
Cut Glass, Perfume, Thumbprint, Pear Shape, Hinged Top 22.00
Cut Glass, Pitcher & Tumble-Up, Intaglio Flowers With Hobstar Centers 150.00
Cut Glass, Pitcher, Allover Cut Cornflowers 135.00
Cut Glass, Pitcher, Allover Harvard, Cut Handle, 8 1/4 In.High 225.00
Cut Glass, Pitcher, Barrel Shape, Flowers 39.50
Cut Glass, Pitcher, Barrel Shape, Hobstar & Fine Checkering, Cut Handle 75.00
Cut Glass, Pitcher, Brilliant Cut, Notched Handle, 10 In.High 75.00
Cut Glass, Pitcher, Bulbous, Panel Cut At Top & Bottom, Star Base 35.00
Cut Glass, Pitcher, Buttermilk, Notched Prisms, Hobstar Top, 7 In.High 110.00
Cut Glass, Pitcher, Cider, Barrel Shape, Notched Prisms 175.00
Cut Glass, Pitcher, Cider, Signed Hoare, Brilliant 110.00
Cut Glass, Pitcher, Cider, Squatty, Deep Cut 55.00
Cut Glass, Pitcher, Claret, Hobstar Chains, Beading, Cut Handle 150.00
Cut Glass, Pitcher, Cranberry Base, 9 1/4 In. 70.00
Cut Glass, Pitcher, Heart Panel, Hobstar, & Star, 8 1/2 In.High 130.00
Cut Glass, Pitcher, Hobstars, Beading, Triple Cut Handle, Claret, 12 In. 150.00
Cut Glass, Pitcher, Hobstar, Strawberry Diamond, Notched Prism, & Fan 85.00
Cut Glass, Pitcher, Intaglio Scotch Thistle, Triple Notched Handle 125.00
Cut Glass, Pitcher, Milk, Hobnails, Cut Handle 60.00
Cut Glass, Pitcher, Milk, Vintage, Triple Notched Handle, 4 1/2 In.High 75.00
Cut Glass, Pitcher, On Standard, Honeycomb, Thumbprint, Silver Plate Collar 110.00
Cut Glass, Pitcher, Ornate Sterling Silver Top, 11 3/4 In. 125.00
Cut Glass, Pitcher, Panels Of 4 Way Fans, Stars, Vertical Ribs 65.00
Cut Glass, Pitcher, Pinwheel, Fan, & Strawberry Diamond, Starred Bottom 70.00
Cut Glass, Pitcher, Pinwheel, Hobstar, Fan, & Cane, Star Base, 8 In.High 40.00
Cut Glass, Pitcher, Pinwheels, Double Bull's-Eye Handle, Hobstar Base, 11 In 68.50
Cut Glass, Pitcher, Pinwheels, Double Bull's-Eye Handle, 11 In.High 65.00
Cut Glass, Pitcher, Russian, Bulbous, Star Buttons, Triple Notched Handle 350.00
Cut Glass, Pitcher, Signed Eggington 200.00
Cut Glass, Pitcher, Signed Hawkes, Brilliant 250.00
Cut Glass, Pitcher, Signed Libbey, Barrel Shape, Hobstar, Fan, & Strawberry 155.00
Cut Glass, Pitcher, Signed Libbey, Barrel Shape, 8 In.High 170.00
Cut Glass, Pitcher, Solid Harvard Pattern, Brilliant Cut, 9 1/2 In. 125.00
Cut Glass, Pitcher, Strawberry Diamond, Fan, Notched Prism, & Crosshatching 125.00
Cut Glass, Pitcher, Strawberry Diamonds, Cut Handle, 6 In.High 60.00
Cut Glass, Pitcher, Sunburst Pattern, Double Thumbprint Handle, Star Bottom 120.00
Cut Glass, Pitcher, Water, Allover Cut Flowers, Barrel Shape 39.50
Cut Glass, Pitcher, Water, Covered, Signed Hawkes, Flowers At Middle & Cover 65.00

Cut Glass, Pitcher, Water, Heavily Patterned, Double Notched Handle, 9 In. 85.00
Cut Glass, Pitcher, Water, Hobstar & Diamond Panel, 10 3/4 In.High 59.50
Cut Glass, Pitcher, Water, Hobstar, Starburst, & Notched Prism 75.00
Cut Glass, Pitcher, Water, Rose & Foliage 18.50
Cut Glass, Pitcher, Water, Russian Pattern, Cut Buttons, 6 1/4 In.High 325.00
Cut Glass, Pitcher, Water, Signed Hawkes, 32 Point Star Base 95.00
Cut Glass, Pitcher, Water, Signed Libbey 115.00
Cut Glass, Pitcher, Water, Strawberry Diamond Pattern 85.00
Cut Glass, Pitcher, Water, Thistle Pattern 37.00
Cut Glass, Pitcher, Waterford, Applied Handle, Etched 38.00
Cut Glass, Planter, Hobstar Rosettes Separated By Fans, Silver, Star Base 80.00
Cut Glass, Plate, Allover Cutting, Brilliant, 1/4 In.Thick, 11 In.Diameter 200.00
Cut Glass, Plate, Alternating Panels Of Pinwheel & Hobstar, Central Star 75.00
Cut Glass, Plate, Arcadia Pattern, 7 In.Diameter 26.00
Cut Glass, Plate, Cake, Signed Bergen, Chain Of Hobstar & Fan, Pinwheel 110.00
Cut Glass, Plate, Copper Wheel Engraved Thistle Type Floral & Leaf, 9 In. 45.00
Cut Glass, Plate, Hobstar & Strawberry Diamond, Allover Cut, Brilliant 95.00
Cut Glass, Plate, Hobstar, Cane, & Vesica, Brilliant, 10 1/2 In. 110.00
Cut Glass, Plate, Hobstar, Fan, & Prism, Sawtooth, Scalloped Edge, 10 In. 40.00
Cut Glass, Plate, Hobstars, Scalloped Edge, Harvard Center, 7 In.Diameter 18.00
Cut Glass, Plate, Ribbed, Floral, Bud, & Swirling Leaf, 6 1/2 In. 10.00
Cut Glass, Plate, Russian Pattern, 7 1/4 In.Diameter 45.00
Cut Glass, Plate, Scalloped Edge, 9 1/2 In.Diameter 50.00
Cut Glass, Plate, Signed Fry, 11 1/2 In.Diameter 125.00
Cut Glass, Plate, Signed Hawkes, 4 Medallions With Engraved Birds 30.00
Cut Glass, Plate, Signed Libbey, Kimberly, 7 In. 55.00
Cut Glass, Plate, Signed Libbey, Santa Maria, Copyright 1893 By A.E.Smith 225.00
Cut Glass, Plate, Signed Libbey, Trademark & Sword, Advertising, 8 In 575.00
Cut Glass, Platter, Signed Clarke, Hobstar & Diamond, 7 X 14 In. 145.00
Cut Glass, Punch Set, Signed Pairpoint On Ladle, 3/4 In.Thick, 2 Piece 750.00
Cut Glass, Relish, Allover Cut, Scalloped, Sawtooth Rim, 3 Sections 36.00
Cut Glass, Relish, Boat Shape, Allover Cut, 7 In. 30.00
Cut Glass, Relish, Buzz, Star, & Strawberry Diamond 50.00
Cut Glass, Relish, Harvard & Floral, 2 Handle, 4 Section 45.00
Cut Glass, Relish, Harvard Cut, Scalloped, Serrated Edge 55.00
Cut Glass, Relish, Signed Hawkes, Hobstar, Geometric, & Star 35.00
Cut Glass, Relish, Signed Libbey, Buzz & Hobstar, 4 Sections, 7 In.Wide 115.00
Cut Glass, Relish, Star Of David 26.00
Cut Glass, Rose Bowl, American, Geometric Top, Vertical Panel & Flower 47.00
Cut Glass, Rose Bowl, Canes, England 45.00
Cut Glass, Rose Bowl, Diagonal Fluting 16.00
Cut Glass, Rose Bowl, Harvard At Edge, Hobstar & Petaled Flower 59.00
Cut Glass, Rose Bowl, Intaglio & Floral, Star Base, Oval 30.00
Cut Glass, Rose Bowl, Pedestaled, 6 In.High 95.00
Cut Glass, Rose Bowl, Russian, Hobstars, 6 In. 285.00
Cut Glass, Rose Bowl, Signed Clarke, Hobstar & Star Diamond, 6 In.High 250.00
Cut Glass, Rose Bowl, Signed L.Straus, Acid Etched Star In Circle 325.00
Cut Glass, Rose Bowl, Thistle Pattern 45.00
Cut Glass, Salt & Pepper 7.50
Cut Glass, Salt & Pepper, German Silver Screw Cap, 2 X 2 In. 12.00
Cut Glass, Salt & Pepper, Signed Hawkes, Sunburst, Sterling Top 75.00
Cut Glass, Salt & Pepper, Square Geometrics 14.00
Cut Glass, Salt Dip, Signed Hoare 32.50
Cut Glass, Salt Dip, Swan, 2 In.Tall 6.50
Cut Glass, Salt Dip, Zipper Cut, Set Of 8 .... 33.00
Cut Glass, Salt, Diamond & Fan, Star Bottom, Toothed Scalloped Top 4.00
Cut Glass, Salt, Diamond, Block, & Fan, Scalloped Top, Pair 21.00
Cut Glass, Salt, Individual, Open, Notched Prisms, Set Of 8 ... . 48.00
Cut Glass, Salt, Individual, Ribbed, Clear, Round 5.00
Cut Glass, Salt, Master & Individual, Signed Stuart, Flattened Diamond 25.00
Cut Glass, Salt, Master, Cane Pattern 35.00
Cut Glass, Salt, Master, Diamond, Round 10.00
Cut Glass, Salt, Master, Signed Walsh, Diamond Cut, Footed, Pair 57.50
Cut Glass, Salt, Master, Signed Waterford, Diamond Cut Bowl, Turned Down Rim 25.00
Cut Glass, Salt, Master, Signed Waterford, Flared Top 15.00
Cut Glass, Salt, Signed Dorflinger 5.00

Cut Glass, Sauce, Russian Inside, Hobstar On Edges, 5 In.Diameter 50.00
Cut Glass, Shade, Mushroom, Intaglio Daisies, 10 1/2 In.Diameter 115.00
Cut Glass, Shaker, Cocktail, Signed Hawkes, Silver Top, Etched Leaves 29.75
Cut Glass, Sherbet, Feather Cutting, Set Of 4 .... 45.00
Cut Glass, Sherbet, Signed Hawkes, Greek Key 30.00
Cut Glass, Sherbet, Signed Hawkes, Square Base 16.75
Cut Glass, Sherry, Hobnail, Teardrop Stem, Star Base, 4 3/4 X 2 1/4 In. 17.00
Cut Glass, Shot Glass, Pedestal Base, Smoky Color, Set Of 5 .... 16.00
Cut Glass, Shot Glass, Strawberry Diamond & Fan, Set Of 4 .... 60.00
Cut Glass, Spire, Tapered, Thumb Cut Edges, Silver Metal Base, Pair 110.00
Cut Glass, Spooner, Allover Cut 65.00
Cut Glass, Spooner, Alternate Vertical Hobstar & Notched Prism 65.00
Cut Glass, Spooner, Buzz & Fan, Star Bottom, Notched Handles 39.00
Cut Glass, Spooner, Buzz, Star Of David Bottom, Two Handles 39.00
Cut Glass, Spooner, Cane Pattern, 2 Handles 65.00
Cut Glass, Spooner, Harvard Deep Cut, 4 1/2 In.High 45.00
Cut Glass, Spooner, Hobstar, Cane, Diamond Point, & Fan, 2 Handles 75.00
Cut Glass, Spooner, Hobstar, Cane, Strawberry Diamond, & Fan 65.00
Cut Glass, Spooner, Hobstars, Two Handles 85.00
Cut Glass, Spooner, Pinwheels, Star Center Bottom, 4 3/4 In.High 85.00
Cut Glass, Spooner, Vesica, Fan, & Diamond, Cut Handles, Brilliant 85.00
Cut Glass, Stein, Etched, Pewter Cover 45.00
Cut Glass, Sugar & Creamer, Allover Cut, Three Column Cut Handles 58.00
Cut Glass, Sugar & Creamer, Allover Geometrics 95.00
Cut Glass, Sugar & Creamer, Clear Ribs, Shaggy Flowers, Thumbprint Handles 35.00
Cut Glass, Sugar & Creamer, Diamond, Crosshatching, & Thumbprint 95.00
Cut Glass, Sugar & Creamer, Double X Vesica, Hobstar, & Strawberry Diamond 50.00
Cut Glass, Sugar & Creamer, Harvard Cut .... 65.00 To 110.00
Cut Glass, Sugar & Creamer, Harvard, Notched Handles, Brilliant 125.00
Cut Glass, Sugar & Creamer, Hobstar & Diamond Point, Hobstar In Bottoms 55.00
Cut Glass, Sugar & Creamer, Hobstar & Diamond Point, 2 1/2 In.High 65.00
Cut Glass, Sugar & Creamer, Hobstar & Fan, Star Bottoms, Notched Teeth 55.00
Cut Glass, Sugar & Creamer, Hobstar & Fan, 3 In.High 40.00
Cut Glass, Sugar & Creamer, Hobstar & Vesica Blaze, Rayed Bases 90.00
Cut Glass, Sugar & Creamer, Hobstar & Vesicas Of Crosscut Diamond 90.00
Cut Glass, Sugar & Creamer, Hobstar & Zipper, Star Bottoms 50.00
Cut Glass, Sugar & Creamer, Hobstar, Cane, Crosscut Diamond, Star, & Fan 55.00
Cut Glass, Sugar & Creamer, Hobstar, Cane, Fan, & Hobnail, Notched Handles 75.00
Cut Glass, Sugar & Creamer, Hobstar, Fan, & Bull's-Eye, Small 50.00
Cut Glass, Sugar & Creamer, Hobstar, Fan, & Star, Thumbprint Handle, 2 3/4 In 54.00
Cut Glass, Sugar & Creamer, Hobstars, Notched Handles 125.00
Cut Glass, Sugar & Creamer, Hobstars, Notched Handles, Rayed Bottoms 59.00
Cut Glass, Sugar & Creamer, Hobstars, Pedestaled, Brilliant 225.00
Cut Glass, Sugar & Creamer, Large Hobstar, Diamond, & Fan, Brilliant Cut 55.00
Cut Glass, Sugar & Creamer, Pinwheels 37.00
Cut Glass, Sugar & Creamer, Signed Clarke 135.00
Cut Glass, Sugar & Creamer, Signed Libbey 135.00
Cut Glass, Sugar & Creamer, Wedding, Frosted 65.00
Cut Glass, Sugar, Double Handled 20.00
Cut Glass, Sugar, Flower & Leaf, 2 Handles, 4 In.Diameter, 3 In.High 17.50
Cut Glass, Sugar, Hobstars, Florence Pattern, Pedestal 39.00
Cut Glass, Sugar, Pinwheels 10.00
Cut Glass, Syrup & Underplate, Chocolate 185.00
Cut Glass, Syrup, Ball Shape, Silver Collar, Swivel Top With Lift, Handle 31.00
Cut Glass, Syrup, Block Pattern, Applied Silver Handle & Cover 38.00
Cut Glass, Syrup, Fine Cut & Fan, Silver Plated Top & Handle 22.00
Cut Glass, Syrup, Strawberry Diamond & Fan, Sterling Silver Top & Handle 55.00
Cut Glass, Syrup, Twisted Handle, Silver Top, England 125.00
Cut Glass, Tankard, Checkerboard Of Stars & Xs, Star Base, 12 In.High 125.00
Cut Glass, Tankard, Hobstar & Fan, Double Notched Handle, Star Base 85.00
Cut Glass, Tankard, Hobstar, Strawberry Diamond, Pinwheel, & Fan 95.00
Cut Glass, Tankard, Pinwheel & Hobstar, Brilliant Cut 69.00
Cut Glass, Tankard, Pinwheel & Hobstar, Cut Edge, American, Brilliant Period 65.00
Cut Glass, Tankard, Water, Hobstar, Diamond Point, & Fan 65.00
Cut Glass, Tea Caddy, Signed Waterford, Starburst & Hatching, C.1810, Pair 90.00
Cut Glass, Teapot, Cornflower 50.00

Cut Glass, Toothpick, Geometrics	8.50
Cut Glass, Toothpick, Notched Rib Cut	16.00
Cut Glass, Toothpick, Ribbed, Notched, 2 In.Tall	10.00
Cut Glass, Toothpick, Serrated Columns	10.00
Cut Glass, Toothpick, Zipper	14.00
Cut Glass, Toothpick, Zipper, Scalloped Top & Bottom	12.50
Cut Glass, Toothpick, 8 Point Star	14.00
Cut Glass, Tray, Champion, 14 In.Long	145.00
Cut Glass, Tray, Cheese & Cracker, Signed Clarke, Intaglio Thistle, 2 Tier	95.00
Cut Glass, Tray, Dorflinger's Strawberry Diamond & Fan, 14 1/2 X 8 In.	225.00
Cut Glass, Tray, Dresser, Signed Hawkes, Kohinoor Pattern, Rose & Leaf	115.00
Cut Glass, Tray, Harvard, Diamond Shape, Brilliant	245.00
Cut Glass, Tray, Ice Cream, Hobstar, Notched Prism, Hobnail, & Crosscutting	85.00
Cut Glass, Tray, Ice Cream, Hobstars, 7 1/2 X 14 In.	82.00
Cut Glass, Tray, Ice Cream, Russian & Floral, Pontoon Shape, 14 In.Long	245.00
Cut Glass, Tray, Ice Cream, Square Panels, Floral & Bands Of Cane	85.00
Cut Glass, Tray, Ice Cream, Sunburst, Double X Vesica, Hobstar, & Diamond	135.00
Cut Glass, Tray, Ice Cream, 14 In.	75.00
Cut Glass, Tray, Leaves, Pears, Miter Cut, 10 1/4 In.Diameter, Tuthill	225.00
Cut Glass, Tray, Rectangular, Pinwheel & Hobstar, Raised Edge, 12 X 8 In.	98.00
Cut Glass, Tray, Sandwich, Hobstar, Notched Prism, Diamond Point, & Fan	130.00
Cut Glass, Tray, Signed Hawkes, Miniature, Round, Etched, Nickel Handle	12.50
Cut Glass, Tray, Signed Libbey, Imperial Pattern, 7 1/2 In.Wide	125.00
Cut Glass, Tray, Signed Libbey, Raised Rim In Center, 2 Handles	125.00
Cut Glass, Tray, Signed Sinclaire, Engraved Roses, 2 Part	275.00
Cut Glass, Tray, Sugar Loaf, Thumb Handle, 6 1/2 X 2 1/2 In.	15.00
Cut Glass, Tumble-Up, Strawberry Diamond & Fan, Flute Cut Neck	30.00
Cut Glass, Tumbler, Butterfly & Thistle, Set Of 6	72.50
Cut Glass, Tumbler, Buzz & Fan, Star Bottom	12.50
Cut Glass, Tumbler, Empire Period, 1830	20.00
Cut Glass, Tumbler, Harvard Lower Half, Floral Intaglio Upper, Set Of 5	50.00
Cut Glass, Tumbler, Harvard, Intaglio Flowers	12.00
Cut Glass, Tumbler, Hobstar, Notched Strawberry, & Fan, Rayed Bottom	25.00
Cut Glass, Tumbler, Hobstar, Strawberry Diamond, Crosscut Diamond & Fan, 5	75.00
Cut Glass, Tumbler, Hobstars	10.00
Cut Glass, Tumbler, Hobstars, Allover Cut	15.00
Cut Glass, Tumbler, Intaglio, Daisy, & Harvard Band, 1 In., Set Of 4	40.00
Cut Glass, Tumbler, Pineapple & Fan, Brilliant	12.00
Cut Glass, Tumbler, Pinwheel, Fan, & Crosshatching	16.00
Cut Glass, Tumbler, Pinwheel, Fan, & Star, Star Base	12.50
Cut Glass, Tumbler, Signed Hawkes	28.00
Cut Glass, Tumbler, Signed Hawkes, Hobstars	23.00
Cut Glass, Tumbler, Signed Hoare	25.00
Cut Glass, Tumbler, Signed Tuthill, Hobstar, Fan, & Crosshatching	28.00
Cut Glass, Tumbler, Strawberry & Fan, Star Cut Base, Set Of 6	72.50
Cut Glass, Tumbler, Water, Florence Pattern, Set Of 6	120.00
Cut Glass, Tumbler, Whiskey, Signed Sinclaire, Hobstars, Set Of 3	60.00
Cut Glass, Vase, Allover Cut, Corset Center, Scalloped & Notched Top, 6 In.	85.00
Cut Glass, Vase, Allover Floral & Leaf, Notched Rim, 16 Point Star Base	42.50
Cut Glass, Vase, Blank, Floral Cutting, Pedestal, 12 In.High, Tuthill	175.00
Cut Glass, Vase, Blue Overlay, 8 1/4 In.High	32.50
Cut Glass, Vase, Bud, Allover Multipattern, 9 1/2 In.High	20.00
Cut Glass, Vase, Bud, Diamonds, Sawtooth Rim, 6 1/2 In.High	50.00
Cut Glass, Vase, Bud, Silver Rim, 7 In.	13.50
Cut Glass, Vase, Butterfly & Rose, 10 In.High	65.00
Cut Glass, Vase, Corset Shape, Notched Prism & Hobstar, 7 1/2 In.High	37.50
Cut Glass, Vase, Cylindrical, 8 In.High	45.00
Cut Glass, Vase, Daisy & Thistle, Cylinder Shape	225.00
Cut Glass, Vase, Fan, Signed Sinclair	35.00
Cut Glass, Vase, Fish Decor, Ground Pontil, 6 In.High	12.00
Cut Glass, Vase, Floral & Leaf, Scalloped Rim, Star Base, 10 In.High	12.00
Cut Glass, Vase, Harvard & Floral, 12 In. High	58.00
Cut Glass, Vase, Harvard, Intaglio, & Primrose, 12 In.High	110.00
Cut Glass, Vase, Hobstars, Etched, 11 In.High	45.00
Cut Glass, Vase, Hobstars, 14 In.High	44.00
Cut Glass, Vase, Intaglio Cut, Etched, Sawtooth Top Rim, 8 In.	37.50

Cut Glass, Vase, Iris & Leaf, Signed, 10 In.High 145.00
Cut Glass, Vase, Leaf & Floral, 10 In. 26.00
Cut Glass, Vase, Notched Rim, Crosscut Diamond Band, Daisy, Leaf, & Vine 95.00
Cut Glass, Vase, Pedestal, Salesman's Sample, 5 In.High 65.00
Cut Glass, Vase, Pinwheel & Star, Chalice Type, Notched Stem, Star Base 185.00
Cut Glass, Vase, Pinwheel & Star, Notched Edge, 4 1/2 In.Diameter 32.50
Cut Glass, Vase, Prism & Bull's-Eye With Chain Of Hobstars, Scalloped 85.00
Cut Glass, Vase, Rose Bush & Frosted Rose, Scalloped Top, Square Base 37.00
Cut Glass, Vase, Serrated & Scalloped Rim, 9 1/2 In.High 85.00
Cut Glass, Vase, Signed Clarke, Pinwheel, Hobstar, & Crosscut Diamond 85.00
Cut Glass, Vase, Signed Clarke, Pinwheel, Hobstar, & Strawberry Diamond 75.00
Cut Glass, Vase, Signed Clarke, Triple Square Pattern, 11 3/4 In.High 115.00
Cut Glass, Vase, Signed Hawkes, Etched Floral & Checkerboard Panel, 8 In. 44.00
Cut Glass, Vase, Signed Hawkes, Gravic, 10 1/4 In.High 195.00
Cut Glass, Vase, Signed Hawkes, Queen's Pattern, 11 1/2 In.High 125.00
Cut Glass, Vase, Signed J.Hoare 225.00
Cut Glass, Vase, Signed Libbey, Gravic Flowers, Polished Leaves, Pedestal 115.00
Cut Glass, Vase, Signed Libbey, Intaglio Cut Morning Glories, Footed 85.00
Cut Glass, Vase, Signed Libbey, Intaglio Cut Poppies, 8 In.High 82.50
Cut Glass, Vase, Signed Libbey, Paneled, Rose, Leaf, & Cut Channels 110.00
Cut Glass, Vase, Signed Libbey, 12 X 4 1/2 In. 150.00
Cut Glass, Vase, Signed P & B, 8 In.High 45.00
Cut Glass, Vase, Signed Sinclaire, Hobstars, Engraved, 12 1/2 In.High 185.00
Cut Glass, Vase, Strawberry Diamond & Fan, Oval For Initial 85.00
Cut Glass, Vase, Sunburst Cutting, 12 1/4 In.High 250.00
Cut Glass, Vase, Trumpet, Banded Flute Around Pedestal Base, Fan & Check 30.00
Cut Glass, Vase, Trumpet, Hobstar & Fan, Star Base, 9 1/2 In.High 18.00
Cut Glass, Vase, Trumpet, Notched Prism, Hobstar, & Strawberry Diamond 225.00
Cut Glass, Vase, Trumpet, Signed Hawkes, Brunswick Pattern, 12 In.High 110.00
Cut Glass, Vase, Trumpet, Star & Fan, Allover Cut, Star Cut Base, Scalloped 35.00
Cut Glass, Vase, Trumpet, Triangular Ormolu Stand, 10 In. 19.50
Cut Glass, Vase, Tulip, Frosted Panels, 11 In. 65.00
Cut Glass, Water Set, Brilliant Cut Pinwheels, 7 Piece 110.00
Cut Glass, Water Set, Brilliant Period, Signed Tuthill, 7 Piece 325.00
Cut Glass, Water Set, Checkering & Bull's-Eye, Signed, 6 Piece 108.00
Cut Glass, Water Set, Flower & Thumbprint, 5 Piece 150.00
Cut Glass, Water Set, Heart & Hobstar, 11 1/2 In.High, 7 Piece 600.00
Cut Glass, Water Set, Intaglio, Star Bottom, 5 Piece 60.00
Cut Glass, Water Set, Tankard Type Pitcher, Harvard, Hobstar Base, 6 Piece 325.00
Cut Glass, Whiskey Set, Honeycomb Pattern, 7 Piece 295.00
Cut Glass, Wine & Underplate, Signed Hawkes, Cut Stem, Engraved 25.00
Cut Glass, Wine Set, Rhine, Six Pieces 65.00
Cut Glass, Wine, Ashburton, Applied Knob Stem & Foot, Ground Pontil 25.00
Cut Glass, Wine, Diamond & Fan, 3 5/8 In.High 8.50
Cut Glass, Wine, Hobnail, Teardrop Stem, Star Base, 5 1/4 X 2 7/8 In. 20.00
Cut Glass, Wine, Pairpoint, Vintage Grape & Intaglio, Amber, 4 1/4 In. 15.00
Cut Glass, Wine, Signed Hawkes, Bell Shape, Set Of 8 .... 150.00
Cut Glass, Wine, Signed Tuthill, Hobstar, Crosscut Diamond, & Fan, 4 1/2 In. 40.00
Cut Glass, Wine, Strawberry Diamond & Fan, Star Base, Set Of 6 .... 90.00
Cut Glass, Wine, Zipper Cut Stem, 4 1/2 In.Tall 20.00

*Cut Velvet is a special type of Art Glass made with two layers of
Blown Glass, which shows a raised pattern. It usually had an acid finish
or velvetlike texture. It was made by many glass factories during the late
Victorian years.*

Cut Velvet, Creamer, Butterscotch, White Lining, Amber Reed Handle 155.00
Cut Velvet, Ewer, Rose To White, Diamond-Quilted, Applied Handle, 11 In. 225.00
Cut Velvet, Pitcher, Butterscotch, 8 In., Six Tumblers 550.00
Cut Velvet, Tumbler, Yellow Cut To White, Rose Lining 75.00
Cut Velvet, Vase, Apple Green, 9 In.High 165.00
Cut Velvet, Vase, Blue, Diamond-Quilted, Ball Shape, Long Thin Neck 88.00
Cut Velvet, Vase, Pink Overlay, 5 3/4 In. 85.00
Cut Velvet, Vase, Stick Neck, Bulbous Body, Yellow, Blown, 6 1/2 In.High 65.00
Cut Velvet, Vase, Stick, Diamond-Quilted, Apple Green Over White, 8 In. 85.00
Cybis, Figurine, Calla Lily 850.00
Cybis, Figurine, Conductor's Hands 575.00

Cybis, Figurine, Dahlia, Yellow 1100.00
Cybis, Figurine, Dogwood & Chickadees 1100.00
Cybis, Figurine, Eleanor Of Aquitaine 875.00
Cybis, Figurine, Great White Heron 1850.00
Cybis, Figurine, Guinevere 850.00
Cybis, Figurine, Hamlet .... 875.00 To 1100.00
Cybis, Figurine, Horse's Head 1000.00
Cybis, Figurine, Infant Of Prague 145.00
Cybis, Figurine, Kwan Yin 1250.00
Cybis, Figurine, Little Blue Heron 1200.00
Cybis, Figurine, Little Bunny 20.00
Cybis, Figurine, Little Duckling 50.00
Cybis, Figurine, Pansies 275.00
Cybis, Figurine, Peter Pan .... 150.00 To 175.00
Cybis, Figurine, Peter Pan, Signed 150.00
Cybis, Figurine, Sandpipers 1100.00
Cybis, Figurine, Squirrel 145.00
Cybis, Figurine, Stallion, Brown 550.00
Cybis, Figurine, Thoroughbred 1000.00
Cybis, Figurine, Unicorn 1250.00
Cybis, Figurine, Wendy 50.00
Cybis, Pinto Colt 150.00
    Daguerreotype, see Album, Photo, Photography, Daguerreotype
    D'Albret, Paperweight, see Paperweight, D'Albret
    Danish Christmas Plates, see Christmas Plates
    Dant, see Bottle, Dant

    D'Argental was a French cameo glassmaker of the late Victorian period.
D'Argental, Atomizer, Cameo, Green, Red Brown Floral, French, 4 In.High 99.00
D'Argental, Bowl, Floral Design On Pale Yellow, Green Base, Flowers 250.00
D'Argental, Bowl, Trees, Mountains, Gold, Apricot, Chestnut Brown, 2 7/8 In. 225.00
D'Argental, Box, Cameo, Ice Blue Ground, Butterflies, Irises, Finial On Lid 395.00
D'Argental, Box, Covered, Ice Blue Ground, Purple Butterflies On Cover 395.00
D'Argental, Vase, Acid Cut Tulips, Blue & Maroon, 10 1/2 In. 270.00
D'Argental, Vase, Berries Leaves, Purple, Signed, 5 In.Tall 125.00
D'Argental, Vase, Brown, Orange, & Beige Floral, Cameo, Signed, 7 In.High 195.00
D'Argental, Vase, Cameo, Blue Purple Leaves & Flowers, Frosted, France 160.00
D'Argental, Vase, Cameo, Brown Berries & Leaves, Bulbous, 6 In. 225.00
D'Argental, Vase, Cameo, Brown, Orange, Beige Floral, 7 In., Signed 195.00
D'Argental, Vase, Cameo, Cranberry Over White, Cherry Pattern, 4 1/2 In. 135.00
D'Argental, Vase, Cameo, Smoked Gray Ground, Gray Floral, Pedestal Base 400.00
D'Argental, Vase, Caramel Ground, Cut Amethyst Bearded Iris Design 350.00
D'Argental, Vase, Citron Ground, Dark Blue Cameo Floral, 4 X 2 1/2 In.High 195.00
D'Argental, Vase, Lemon Ground, Black Cherries & Foliage, 4 1/2 In. 235.00
D'Argental, Vase, Three Color, Deep Cut, Burgundy Leaf Spray, Pear Shape 285.00

    Daum Nancy is the mark used by Auguste and Antonin Daum on pieces of
    French Cameo Glass made after 1875.
    Daum Nancy, see also Cameo Glass
Daum Nancy, Bowl, Acid Burgundy Floral, Leaves, Frosted Ground, Quadrilobe 190.00
Daum Nancy, Bowl, Autumn Landscape Scene, Signed, 4 In.High 180.00
Daum Nancy, Bowl, Autumn Scene, 3 Dimensional Effect 350.00
Daum Nancy, Bowl, Boat Shape, Purple Base To Yellow To Lavender, Cut Floral 425.00
Daum Nancy, Bowl, Cameo, Acid Green, Allover Cut White Berries, Gold Leaves 125.00
Daum Nancy, Bowl, Cameo, Autumn Scene, Yellow, Chartreuse, Burnt Orange, Blue 350.00
Daum Nancy, Bowl, Cameo, Grapes, Leaves, Autumn Colors, Quartrefoil Top 185.00
Daum Nancy, Bowl, Cameo, Sweet Peas, Leaves, Vines, White, Yellow, Orange, 8 In. 265.00
Daum Nancy, Bowl, Covered, 5 Birch Trees Extend From Sides To Cover, Signed 325.00
Daum Nancy, Bowl, Frosty Mottled Green & Maroon, Raspberry Carving 245.00
Daum Nancy, Bowl, Grape, Leaves, Autumnal Color, Signed 175.00
Daum Nancy, Bowl, Multicolored Ground, Autumn Leaves, Purple Grapes, Signed 180.00
Daum Nancy, Bowl, Quadrilobed, Burgundy Floral On Frosted Yellow, Signed 150.00
Daum Nancy, Bowl, Shallow, Acid Cut, Brickwork Base, Outward Flaring Rim 100.00
Daum Nancy, Bowl, Silveria, Blue Mottle, Purple Cased, Purple Stem 95.00
Daum Nancy, Bowl, Thistles, Acid Finish, Pinched Square Shape Top 215.00
Daum Nancy, Bowl, White, Black Cameo & Enamel, Windmill, Sailboats 150.00

Daum Nancy, **Cabinet Piece**, Lavender, Gold Enameled Cut Flowers, 2 In. High 69.50
Daum Nancy, **Centerpiece**, Ovoid, Salmon & Green Floral & Vines On Milky 185.00
Daum Nancy, **Chandelier**, Autumn Shades, Signed 495.00
Daum Nancy, **Compote**, Red, Yellow, Plums Hang From Branches, Pedestal Foot 335.00
Daum Nancy, **Cordial**, Amber, Purple, Pedestal Base, Signed, 3 In.Tall 28.00
Daum Nancy, **Cordial**, Spring Scenic, Cameo, Signed, 2 In. 115.00
Daum Nancy, **Creamer**, Goose Girl & Geese, Frosted Opalescent, Pink & Black 235.00
Daum Nancy, **Decanter**, Six Stemmed Glasses, Tray, Gold Berries, Leaves, Stems 250.00
Daum Nancy, **Jardiniere**, Cameo, Four Layer, Three Color, Enamel, 8 1/4 In. 335.00
Daum Nancy, **Lamp**, Elk, Tree & Lake Scene, Signed, Iron Base 350.00
Daum Nancy, **Lamp**, Purple Leaf Design On Yellow Orange, Lighted Base, Signed 795.00
Daum Nancy, **Lamp**, The First Snow, Cameo 550.00
Daum, Nancy, **Liqueur Glass**, Bubbly Amber, Purple Pedestal Base 30.00
Daum Nancy, **Liqueur Glass**, Faceted Stem, Gilt Man In Garden, Signed, Paneled 10.00
Daum Nancy, **Liqueur Set**, Intaglio, Thistles, Leaves, Decanter, Tray, 4 Glasses 175.00
Daum Nancy, **Night-Light**, Diamond Shape, Yellow Ground, Sailing Boats, Signed 350.00
Daum Nancy, **Pitcher**, Five Tumblers, Thistles, Cross Of Lorraine 135.00
Daum Nancy, **Pitcher**, Miniature, Signed, Cameo 225.00
Daum Nancy, **Rose Bowl**, Fluted, Speckled Yellow & Green With Cobalt, Signed 85.00
Daum Nancy, **Rose Bowl**, Orange & Yellow, Signed 165.00
Daum Nancy, **Salt**, Frosty Green, Gold Enamel 125.00
Daum Nancy, **Salt**, Green Ground, Gold Enameled Floral, 1 In.High 125.00
Daum Nancy, **Salt**, Miniature, Scenic, Signed, Cameo 125.00
Daum Nancy, **Tumbler**, Cameo, Frosty Blue White Ground, Mistletoe 75.00
Daum Nancy, **Tumbler**, Cameo, Mistletoe Design, Cross Of Lorraine Mark, French 115.00
Daum Nancy, **Tumbler**, Cameo, Summer Scene 225.00
Daum Nancy, **Tumbler**, Floral On Orange Yellow, Amethyst, Signed, 4 3/4 In. 175.00
Daum Nancy, **Tumbler**, Polished Orange Roses, Green Leaves, Orange Ground 155.00
Daum Nancy, **Vase**, Acid Cut Ground In Green & Rose, Fleur-De-Lis In Gold 95.00
Daum Nancy, **Vase**, Apricot, 6 1/2 In. 85.00
Daum Nancy, **Vase**, Bird Decor, Flared Rim, Stippled Ground, Signed, 14 1/2 In. 175.00
Daum Nancy, **Vase**, Blue, Gray, Water Ship Scene, Windmills, Trees, Acid Etched 220.00
Daum Nancy, **Vase**, Bowl Type, Ovoid, Red Matte, Carved Bellflowers, Signed 275.00
Daum Nancy, **Vase**, Brown, Gray, Pink Scenic, Trees, Signed, 4 In.High 295.00
Daum Nancy, **Vase**, Bud, Uncut Acid Finish, Burnt Orange, Bulbous Bottom 85.00
Daum Nancy, **Vase**, Cameo 195.00
Daum Nancy, **Vase**, Cameo Cut Flowers, Enameled In Gold, Signed, 2 In.High 69.50
Daum Nancy, **Vase**, Cameo Cut Trees, Foliage, Water, Green, Blue, 1 5/8 In. 119.00
Daum Nancy, **Vase**, Cameo, Blue, Gold Mica Flakes Blown Into Metal Frame 295.00
Daum Nancy, **Vase**, Cameo, Emerald Tree Bark, Carved Fleur-De-Lis, 7 1/2 In. 130.00
Daum Nancy, **Vase**, Cameo, Fleur-De-Lis, Gold, Green, Signed, 7 1/2 In.High 130.00
Daum Nancy, **Vase**, Cameo, Gray Blue Ground, Purple Flowers, Green Leaves 275.00
Daum Nancy, **Vase**, Cameo, Green, Tangerine, White, Morning Glories, Dated 1873 ...... 550.00
Daum Nancy, **Vase**, Cameo, I Would Die For The One I Love, Leaves, Tendrils 250.00
Daum Nancy, **Vase**, Cameo, Mottled Pink & Yellow, Purple, Floral, Leaves, Acid 135.00
Daum Nancy, **Vase**, Cameo, Opalescent Ground, Wild Roses, Stems, Wheel Cut 495.00
Daum Nancy, **Vase**, Cameo, Pink, Green, White, Iris Decoration, Metal Base 120.00
Daum Nancy, **Vase**, Cameo, Red Poppies, Gold Vines, Art Nouveau, 16 In. 190.00
Daum Nancy, **Vase**, Cameo, Rust, Yellow, Orange Ground, Orange Brown Flowers 300.00
Daum Nancy, **Vase**, Cameo, Scenic, Boats, Lake, Trees, Mountains, Three Colors 285.00
Daum Nancy, **Vase**, Cameo, Scenic, Green, White, Yellow, Lavender, Beige, Signed 140.00
Daum Nancy, **Vase**, Cameo, Stippled Orange Ground, Gold & White Floral, Label 140.00
Daum Nancy, **Vase**, Cameo, Summer Scene, Frosted Ground, 13 In.High 235.00
Daum Nancy, **Vase**, Cameo, Summer Scene, Signed, 5 In.High 210.00
Daum Nancy, **Vase**, Cameo, Summer Scene, Square, Signed 165.00
Daum Nancy, **Vase**, Cameo, Three Layer Black, Red, Yellow, Signed 185.00
Daum Nancy, **Vase**, Cameo, Winter Scene, Signed, 5 In.High .... 210.00 To 225.00
Daum Nancy, **Vase**, Cameo, Winter Scene, 9 In. 285.00
Daum Nancy, **Vase**, Carved Cerise Flowers, Cameo, Signed 205.00
Daum Nancy, **Vase**, Cranes Flying, White To Green, Signed, 19 1/2 In.Tall 375.00
Daum Nancy, **Vase**, Dark Blue Spots, Rolled Top, Polished Ribs, 13 1/2 In. 150.00
Daum Nancy, **Vase**, Faceted Everted Lip, Green & Gold Enamel On Frosted, 1925 .... 150.00
Daum Nancy, **Vase**, Flattened Diamond Shape, Green Floral On Pink, Signed 350.00
Daum Nancy, **Vase**, Floral, Greens, Browns, White, Yellow, Cameo, Signed 205.00
Daum Nancy, **Vase**, Flower Design, Bulbous, Red, Yellow, Signed, 7 In.High 250.00

Daum Nancy, Vase, Flower Design, Red, Gold, Yellow, 7 In.Tall, 6 In.Wide 250.00
Daum Nancy, Vase, Flower Design, Yellow, Orange, Signed, 4 1/2 In.High 145.00
Daum Nancy, Vase, Flowers, Butterfly, Green, Orange, Signed, 3 In.Tall 95.00
Daum Nancy, Vase, Frosted Gold Striped Ground, Thistles, Gold Trim, Signed 95.00
Daum Nancy, Vase, Frosted Yellow, Tortoise Bottom, Red Bleeding Hearts 190.00
Daum Nancy, Vase, Gold & Brown Tones, Acid Cut Leaves, Floral, 6 In. 185.00
Daum Nancy, Vase, Green Cameo, Gold, Signed, 10 3/4 In.High 325.00
Daum Nancy, Vase, Green Trees Reflected In Water, Signed, 3 3/4 In.High 275.00
Daum Nancy, Vase, Inverted Pear Shape, Pink Cherry Blossoms In Frosted 275.00
Daum Nancy, Vase, Miniature, Ovoid, Yellow, Carved Cameo Sailboats, Signed 146.00
Daum Nancy, Vase, Mottled Blues & Purples, Pedestal Base, 10 1/2 In. 300.00
Daum Nancy, Vase, Mottled Pattern, Blue, Oblong, Signed 65.00
Daum Nancy, Vase, Orange Crystal, Gold Foil Between Layers Of Glass 99.00
Daum Nancy, Vase, Pate De Verre, Flattened, Lavender Splashed Design, Signed 110.00
Daum Nancy, Vase, Peach & Yellow Ground, Cut Flowers, Pods, 11 1/2 In. 225.00
Daum Nancy, Vase, Pink Frosted Ground, Red Floral, 9 3/4 In.High 325.00
Daum Nancy, Vase, Pitcher Form, Violets On Blue To Orange, C-Scroll Handle 250.00
Daum Nancy, Vase, Pond Scene, White To Green, Signed, 19 1/2 In.High 375.00
Daum Nancy, Vase, Scenic, Orange Ground, Signed, 1i In.High 185.00
Daum Nancy, Vase, Scenic, Pine Trees, Lake, Red Sunset, White Ground, 14 In. 395.00
Daum Nancy, Vase, Square Section, Red & Brown Poppies On Yellow Frosted 120.00
Daum Nancy, Vase, Stick, Cameo, Frosted Tan, Yellow & Green Leaves, 9 1/3 In. 325.00
Daum Nancy, Vase, Sunset, Water, Tree, Burgundy Coloring, Signed, 4 In.High 275.00
Daum Nancy, Vase, Tapering, Cut Cherry Blossoms On Orange To Red Frosted 200.00
Daum Nancy, Vase, Trees, Foliage, Yellow, Orange, Green, Signed, 18 In.Tall 315.00
Daum Nancy, Vase, Trees, Water, Ships, Two Casings, Three Cuttings, Pedestal 234.00
Daum Nancy, Vase, Turquoise Hydrangea Flowers, Turquoise Ground, 4 1/2 In. 200.00
Daum Nancy, Vase, Vasiform, Maroon Frieze Of Lilies Of The Valley On Milky 375.00
Daum Nancy, Vase, Violet Mottle, Bulbous Bottom, Slender Neck, 21 In. 190.00
Daum Nancy, Vase, Winter Season, Snow In Boughs Of Trees, Unsigned, 9 In. 195.00
Daum Nancy, Vase, Yellow, Purple Grapes, Green Leaves, 4 1/2 In.High 145.00
Daum Nancy, Wine, Crystal Paneled, Knob Stem, Green Bowl, Gold Iris, Signed 95.00

Davenport Pottery and Porcelain were made at the Davenport Factory in Longport, Staffordshire, England, from 1793 to 1887. Earthenwares, Creamwares, Porcelains, Ironstone Wares, and other products were made. Most of the pieces are marked with a form of the word Davenport.

Davenport, Compote, Stylized Rust & Turquoise Pattern, Gold, Pedestal 27.00
Davenport, Creamer, Ironstone, Marked 18.00
Davenport, Cup & Saucer, White, Gold Trim, Monogram, Circa 1820, Mark 12.50
Davenport, Cup Plate, Blue Design Border & Flower Center 40.00
Davenport, Jug, Blue, Gilt, Two Panels, Enameled Floral, Scroll Handle, 1830 .... 225.00
Davenport, Lazy Susan, Blue & White, Impressed Mark, C.1820 .... 210.00
Davenport, Plate, Floral Center, Raised Gold Scroll & Floral Border, 1870 .... 17.50
Davenport, Plate, Floral Sprays, Cobalt & Gold Outline, Scrolls On Rim, Pair 45.00
Davenport, Plate, Flow Mulberry, Cypress 20.00
Davenport, Plate, Flow Mulberry, Washington Urn 20.00
Davenport, Plate, Imari Pattern, Anchor Mark, 10 In. 27.50
Davenport, Plate, Scott's Legend Of Montrose, Brown Transfer, Scenic, C.1836 .... 20.00
Davenport, Platter, Blue Floral, Circa 1820 .... 15.00
Davenport, Platter, Blue Willow, C.1810, Chinese 38.00
Davenport, Platter, Imari Pattern, Anchor Mark, 11 X 14 In. 45.00
Davenport, Platter, Pheasant & Flower Border, 9 1/2 X 12 In. 24.00
De Guy, Vase, Blue & Orange, Impressionistic Design, 5 In.High 195.00

De Vez is a name found on special pieces of French Cameo Glass made by the Cristallerie de Pantin about 1890. Monsieur de Varreux was the art director of the glassworks and he signed pieces 'De Vez.'

De Vez, Rose Bowl, Cameo, Scenic, Lake, Mountain, Forest, Citron Ground 250.00
De Vez, Vase, Cameo, Green Stems, Flowers, Leaves Cut To Frosty White 75.00
De Vez, Vase, Cameo, Pink Ground, Mountain & Forest Scenes, Pinecones 375.00
De Vez, Vase, Cameo, Scenic, Jungle Scene, Baroque Decoration, Collar 335.00
De Vez, Vase, Cameo, Venice Scene, Man In Gondola, Statue, Urns, Three Colors 195.00
De Vez, Vase, Cameo, Yellow Frosted, Blue & Rosy Scene, Castle, Island 195.00
De Vez, Vase, Miniature, Boats Scene, Cameo, Signed, 2 In.High 75.00
De Vez, Vase, Pasture Scene, White, Green, & Orange, Signed, 4 In.High 195.00

De Vez, Vase, Pink Ground, Mountain & Forest Scenes, Purple Pinecones 375.00
De Vez, Vase, Sailboats, Acid Cut, Cameo, Orange, Yellow, Signed, 10 1/2 In. 265.00
De Vilbiss, Bottle, Atomizer, Black Enamel, Gold Encrusted, Clear Band 25.00
De Vilbiss, Bottle, Atomizer, Black, Gold Decor, Marked 25.00
De Vilbiss, Bottle, Atomizer, Cut Glass, Signed 30.00
De Vilbiss, Bottle, Atomizer, Cut Glass, Stemmed, Etched Flowers, Gold Trim 15.00
De Vilbiss, Bottle, Atomizer, Medicinal, Attachment, Rubber Bulb, Sticker, Box 4.50
De Vilbiss, Bottle, Atomizer, Orange, Tall, Gold 10.00
De Vilbiss, Bottle, Perfume, Atomizer, Feather Swirl, Blue Opalescent 16.00
De Vilbiss, Bottle, Perfume, Blue Aurene, Aerator, 7 In.High 140.00
De Vilbiss, Dresser Set, Gold Covered Glass, Enameled Flowers, 4 Piece 65.00
De Vilbiss, Perfume, Atomizer, Bulbous, Cable, Gold Plated Top, Vaseline 22.00
De Vilbiss, Perfume, Atomizer, Cut Glass, Stem, Cut & Etched Floral 12.00
De Vilbiss, Perfume, Atomizer, Gold Crackle Glass 10.00
De Vilbiss, Perfume, Black Jade, Silver Scrolled Collar, Stopper, Unsigned 31.00

Decoys are carved or turned wooden copies of birds. The decoy was placed in the water to lure flying birds to the pond for hunters.

Decoy, Black Duck, Ken Anger Of Dunnsville, Ontario, Canada 70.00
Decoy, Bluebill, Wooden 25.00
Decoy, Canada Goose, Wooden, Ira Hudson, Virginia .... *Illus* 225.00
Decoy, Coot, Wooden 25.00
Decoy, Cork Body, Blue Bill, Glass Eyes, NonMovable Head 8.00
Decoy, Drake, Glass Eyes, Movable Head 8.00
Decoy, Duck, Gray, Speckled Head, Cobalt Wings, Glass Eyes 27.50
Decoy, Glass Eyes, Swivel Head, Wooden 12.00
Decoy, Hand-Painted, Wooden 45.00
Decoy, Mallard Hen, Cannas, Cork Filled, Circa 1930 .... 12.50
Decoy, Mallard Hen, Charles Perdew Of Henry, Illinois 130.00
Decoy, Mallard, Drake, Wooden, H.A.Stevens, N.Y., C.1920 .... *Illus* 120.00
Decoy, Mallard, Hand Carved, 4 X 2 1/2 In., Pair 20.00
Decoy, Mallard, Wooden 10.00
Decoy, Papier-Mache, Glass Eyes 5.00
Decoy, Red-Breasted Merganser, South Jersey, Hollow, Pair 300.00
Decoy, Red-Breasted Merganser, Wooden, Long Island .... *Illus* 60.00
Decoy, Redhead Drake, Thomas Gelston Of Quogue, Long Island, Cork Body 80.00
Decoy, Redhead, Wooden 25.00
Decoy, Wooden, Glass Eyes, Pair 55.00
Decoy, Wooden, Hand Carved, St.Lawrence River 9.50
Decoy, Wooden, Painted Eyes 8.50
Decoy, Yellow Legs 125.00

The Dedham Pottery Company of Dedham, Massachusetts, started making pottery in 1866. It was reorganized as the Chelsea Pottery Company in 1891, and became the Dedham Pottery Company in 1895. The factory was famous for its crackleware dishes, which picture blue outlines of animals, flowers, and other natural motifs.

Dedham Pottery, Bowl, Rabbits, 4 1/2 In. .... 38.00 To 85.00
Dedham Pottery, Bowl, Rabbits, 7 In. 72.00
Dedham Pottery, Bowl, Turkey, 7 1/2 In. 75.00
Dedham Pottery, Bowl, Turtles, 7 1/4 In.Diameter 125.00
Dedham Pottery, Cup & Saucer, Azalea 80.00
Dedham Pottery, Cup & Saucer, Ducks 78.00
Dedham Pottery, Cup & Saucer, Rabbit 65.00
Dedham Pottery, Jar, Jelly, Rabbit, Cover 150.00
Dedham Pottery, Pitcher, Morning & Night, Signed AR 225.00
Dedham Pottery, Pitcher, Night & Morning Pattern, 5 In. 350.00
Dedham Pottery, Plate, Azalea, 6 In. 34.00
Dedham Pottery, Plate, Azalea, 10 In. 48.00
Dedham Pottery, Plate, Bread & Butter, Rabbits, Mark, 5 1/2 In.Diameter 32.00
Dedham Pottery, Plate, Butterfly 55.00
Dedham Pottery, Plate, Cake, 10 In., 8 Matching 6 In.Plates, Varied Borders 275.00
Dedham Pottery, Plate, Dinner, Buck Border, Signed Maud Davenport, 10 In. 115.00
Dedham Pottery, Plate, Duck 57.50
Dedham Pottery, Plate, Grape Pattern, 8 In.Diameter 50.00
Dedham Pottery, Plate, Grapes, 8 1/2 In. 47.50

Decoy, Canada Goose,
Wooden, Ira Hudson,
Virginia
See Page 179

Decoy, Mallard, Drake, Wooden,
H.A.Stevens, N.Y., C.1920
See Page 179

Delatte, Vase, Enameled Glass,
Signed, 13 In.High
See Page 181

Decoy, Red-Breasted Merganser, Wooden, Long Island
See Page 179

Dedham Pottery, Plate, Grapes, 10 In.	65.00
Dedham Pottery, Plate, Horse Chestnut, 8 In.	42.00
Dedham Pottery, Plate, Iris	47.50
Dedham Pottery, Plate, Magnolia	67.50
Dedham Pottery, Plate, Mushroom	75.00
Dedham Pottery, Plate, Pond Lily, 9 In.	38.00
Dedham Pottery, Plate, Rabbit, 8 In.	32.00 To 34.50
Dedham Pottery, Plate, Rabbit, 8 1/2 In.	34.00 To 39.00
Dedham Pottery, Plate, Rabbit, 10 In.	45.00 To 50.00
Dedham Pottery, Plate, Snowtree, 6 In.	38.00
Dedham Pottery, Plate, Snowtree, 8 1/2 In.	48.00
Dedham Pottery, Plate, Swan, 10 In.	65.00
Dedham Pottery, Plate, Tiger Lily, Water Lily, Rabbit Border, 8 1/2 In.	45.00
Dedham Pottery, Plate, Turkey, 10 In.	70.00
Dedham Pottery, Teabowl, Rabbit, 12 In.High, 3 In.Diameter	56.00
Dedham Pottery, Tray, Bacon, Rabbit	75.00 To 85.00
Dedham Pottery, Vase, Volcanic, Signed H.C.R., 6 3/4 In.	190.00

*Delatte glass is a French cameo glass made by Andre Delatte. It was
first made in Nancy, France, in 1921. Lighting fixtures and opaque
glassware in imitation of Bohemian Opaline were made.*

Delatte, Rose Bowl, Pink, Signed Delatte Nancy	95.00
Delatte, Vase, Bulbous Bottom, Stick Top, France, Signed, 16 In.	85.00
Delatte, Vase, Cameo, Blue Flowers & Leaves, 10 In.	275.00

Delatte, Vase, Cameo, Pink Satin Ground, Wild Roses, Leaves 145.00
Delatte, Vase, Cameo, Yellow, Black, White, Art Deco, 6 In.Tall 115.00
Delatte, Vase, Enameled Glass, Signed, 13 In.High .... *Illus* 325.00
Delatte, Vase, Wild Roses, Thorns, Stems, Pink Liner, Wheel Cut, Nancy 170.00
Delatte, Vase, Yellow, Brown Tulips, Amethyst Base, 8 1/2 In.High 185.00
   Delaware, See Pressed Glass
   Deldare, See Buffalo Pottery

    Delft is a tin-glazed pottery that has been made since the seventeenth
    century. It is decorated with blue on white or with colored decorations.
    Most of the pieces sold today were made after 1891, and the name Holland
    appears with the Delft Factory marks.

Delft, Ashtray, Square, White & Blue, Sailboat, Signed 2.00
Delft, Bottle, Dutch Decoration, Signed Dekuypers Distilleries, Schiedam 20.00
Delft, Bottle, Shoe, Made For El Louvre Curacao, Crown Mark 20.00
Delft, Bottle, Water, Pilgrim, Blue, White, Hunting Cupid, Scenic, 18th Century 39.00
Delft, Box, Oyster Shape, Signed 25.00
Delft, Box, Salt, Hanging, White, Blue Design, Hinged Wooden Top, 'salt' 28.50
Delft, Butter, Covered, Blue, Scene, Boat, Windmill, Floral, Two Handles 18.50
Delft, Chamberstick, Blue, Crossed Pipes Mark 25.00
Delft, Charger, Dutch, Floral Medallions, C.1750, 12 In.Diameter 120.00
Delft, Charger, Peacock Pattern, C.1765, 13 1/2 In.Diameter 175.00
Delft, Charger, Peacock Pattern, C.1765, 13 5/8 In.Diameter 225.00
Delft, Charger, Windmills, Bridge, Boat, Women, Joost Thooft & Labouchere 125.00
Delft, Clock, Signed, 12 In. 100.00
Delft, Clock, Waterbury, Time, Chime, Blue & White Decoration, 9 1/2 In.High 147.00
Delft, Creamer, Cow .... 28.00 To 57.00
Delft, Cup & Saucer, Blue, Rosenthal Mark 16.50
Delft, Cup & Saucer, Demitasse, Crossed Pipes Mark, Blue 15.00
Delft, Cup & Saucer, Windmills, Cobalt Rim 10.00
Delft, Cup & Saucer, Windmills, Wide Cobalt Rims 12.00
Delft, Dish, Heart Shape, Footed, Canal Scene In Center 17.50
Delft, Dish, Polychrome, Yellow, Blue, Puce, & Iron Floral, Green, C.1750 .... 80.00
Delft, Dish, Teaplant Pattern, C.1770, 12 1/4 In.Diameter 120.00
Delft, Figurine, Dog, Polychrome, Tan, Brown, White, 15 In. X 11 In.High 59.00
Delft, Figurine, Dutch Shoe, Windmills & Ship Design, Blue, 7 In.Long 35.00
Delft, Inkwell, White, Blue Scenes, Mushroom Shape Hinged Lid, Mark 45.00
Delft, Jar, Mayonnaise, Cover, Opening For Spoon, Signed Rotterdam, Holland 21.00
Delft, Match Holder, Girl Sitting Atop Boat, Germany, 4 1/2 In. 15.00
Delft, Match Holder, 4 In.High 28.00
Delft, Plaque, Blue Boats, Windmills, T.Hooft & Labouchere, 1895 .... 15.00
Delft, Plaque, Clover Shape, Water, Ship, Scrolled Ship 22.00
Delft, Plate, Abc, Cat, Bird In Cage, Floral Border 45.00
Delft, Plate, Blue And White Woodland Scene, 15 In.Diameter 59.50
Delft, Plate, Blue, White, Floral Border, House, Lake, Boat, Windmill, Children 40.00
Delft, Plate, Chinoiserie, Bristol, C.1740, 13 1/4 In. .... *Illus* 325.00
Delft, Plate, Country Scene, Blue, Scalloped Rim, Marked Maastricht 28.00
Delft, Plate, Dutch Scene, Blue, White, Marked, 8 1/2 In. 7.50
Delft, Plate, English, C.1745, 13 1/2 In.Diameter .... *Illus* 325.00
Delft, Plate, Lambeth, 13 3/4 In.Diameter .... *Illus* 325.00
Delft, Plate, Scene, Church, Water, Boats, Women, Blue, White, 8 1/2 In. 25.00
Delft, Plate, Scene, Dock, Boats, Bridge, Buildings, White, Blue 25.00
Delft, Plate, T.Hooft & Labouchere .... *Illus* 50.00
Delft, Plate, Wall, Scenic, Windmill, Cows, Pasture, Floral Edge, Signed 59.00
Delft, Salt & Pepper, Windmills, Sailing Ships, Scrolls, Ribbed, Pairpoint 90.00
Delft, Shoe, Dutch, Blue & White, Marked, 5 In.Long 5.00
Delft, Sleigh, Blue & White, Medallions, Windmills, 4 In.Long 25.00
Delft, Stein, Windmills, Sailboats, Blue, White, 1/2 Liter 155.00
Delft, Tile, Blue & White Seascape, 6 In. 8.00
Delft, Tile, Galleon On Water, Art Nouveau, 4 1/2 In.Sq. 21.00
Delft, Tile, Pan God Assaulting Female, Wooden Frame 35.00
Delft, Toothpick, Boy Carrying Basket, German Mark 15.00
Delft, Tray & Four Coasters, Metal Bound, Windmill Scenes, Germany 35.00
Delft, Urn, Cover, Pair Vases, 10 In.High 82.00
Delft, Vase, Blue & White, BP Imprinted In Blue, Floral Scene 100.00
Delft, Vase, Center Panel, Girl & Boy At Well, Polychrome, Circa 1800 .... 135.00

Delft, Plate,
Chinoiserie, Bristol,
C.1740, 13 1/4 In.
See Page 181

Delft, Plate,
English, C.1745,
13 1/2 In.Diameter
See Page 181

Delft, Plate, Lambeth,
13 3/4 In.Diameter
See Page 181

Delft, Plate, T.Hooft & Labouchere
See Page 181

Delft, Vase, Flowers, Ship, Windmill, Blue, White, Marked	25.00
Delft, Vase, Ginger Jar, Lid, Sailing Ships, Blue & White, 7 3/4 In.High, Pair	125.00
Delft, Vase, Ribbed Top, Blue, Openwork Handles, Footed, Marked, 8 1/2 In.Tall	32.00

Depression Glass was an inexpensive glass manufactured in large quantities during the 1920s and early 1930s. It was made in many colors and patterns by dozens of factories in the United States. The name Depression Glass is a modern one.

Depression Glass, Ashtray, Open Rose, Pink, Square	2.00
Depression Glass, Berry Set, Rib Pattern Handle, 6 Smaller Bowls	18.00
Depression Glass, Bowl, American Sweetheart, Monax, Round	15.00
Depression Glass, Bowl, American Sweetheart, Monax, 6 In.	3.50
Depression Glass, Bowl, American Sweetheart, Pink, Round	5.50
Depression Glass, Bowl, American Sweetheart, Pink, 6 In.	3.00
Depression Glass, Bowl, American Sweetheart, Pink, 9 In.	6.00
Depression Glass, Bowl, Cabbage Rose, Pink, Handles, 10 In.Diameter	10.00
Depression Glass, Bowl, Cameo, Green, 3 Legs, 11 In.	20.00
Depression Glass, Bowl, Cereal, Dogwood, Pink	3.00
Depression Glass, Bowl, Cereal, Lace Edge, Pink	1.00
Depression Glass, Bowl, Cereal, No.612, Clear, 6 1/2 In.	2.50
Depression Glass, Bowl, Cherry Blossom, Pink, Footed, 10 In.	25.00
Depression Glass, Bowl, Cherry Blossom, Pink, Handled	6.00
Depression Glass, Bowl, Cherry, Delfite, Handled	11.00
Depression Glass, Bowl, Console, Madrid, Amber, 11 In.	4.00
Depression Glass, Bowl, Console, Royal Lace, Blue, Footed, Pair Candleholders	75.00
Depression Glass, Bowl, Delfite, Swirl, Blue, 9 In.Diameter	7.50

Depression Glass, Bowl, Doric, Pink, 4 1/2 In. 1.25
Depression Glass, Bowl, Floral, Green, 4 In. 1.25
Depression Glass, Bowl, Floral, Green, 9 In. 3.50
Depression Glass, Bowl, Florentine, Green, Round 3.00
Depression Glass, Bowl, Fruit, Mayfair, Green, 11 3/4 In. 12.00
Depression Glass, Bowl, Fruit, Mayfair, Pink, 5 1/2 In. 2.50
Depression Glass, Bowl, Fruit, Oyster & Pearl, Ruby, 10 1/2 In., Pair 10.50
Depression Glass, Bowl, Fruit, Sharon, Pink, 10 1/2 In. .... 4.00 To 8.00
Depression Glass, Bowl, Hat Shape, Princess, Pink 5.50
Depression Glass, Bowl, Ice, Windmill, Cobalt 5.75
Depression Glass, Bowl, Lace Edge, Pink, 9 1/2 In 4.00
Depression Glass, Bowl, Madrid, Amber, Round, 9 1/2 In. 12.00
Depression Glass, Bowl, Mayfair, Blue, Hat Shape 30.00
Depression Glass, Bowl, Mayfair, Pink, Flat, 11 3/4 In. 6.00
Depression Glass, Bowl, Mayfair, Pink, 10 In. 4.00
Depression Glass, Bowl, Miss America, Clear, Curved 22.00
Depression Glass, Bowl, Miss America, Clear, Straight Sided 13.00
Depression Glass, Bowl, Miss America, Pink, Curved Top, 8 In.Diameter 22.50
Depression Glass, Bowl, Miss America, Pink, Oval 5.50
Depression Glass, Bowl, Old Lace, Emerald 6.00
Depression Glass, Bowl, Open Lace, Pink, Deep 5.00
Depression Glass, Bowl, Oyster & Pearl, Burgundy, 6 In.Diameter 6.50
Depression Glass, Bowl, Oyster & Pearl, Ruby, Small 5.00
Depression Glass, Bowl, Paneled Cherry Blossom, Green, 8 1/2 In. 8.00
Depression Glass, Bowl, Patrician, Green, 8 1/4 In. 6.00
Depression Glass, Bowl, Petalware, Monax, 5 3/4 In. 1.75
Depression Glass, Bowl, Rose Cameo, Green, 5 In. 1.50
Depression Glass, Bowl, Royal Lace, Blue, Rolled Edge, 10 In. 24.00
Depression Glass, Bowl, Sharon, Pink, 5 In. .... 1.00 To 2.00
Depression Glass, Bowl, Sharon, Pink, 6 In. 1.25
Depression Glass, Bowl, Sharon, Pink, 10 1/2 In. 3.00
Depression Glass, Bowl, Sugar, Cameo, Green 3.00
Depression Glass, Bowl, Vegetable, Adam, Pink, Cover, 9 In.Diameter 8.50
Depression Glass, Bowl, Vegetable, Madrid, Amber, Oval, 10 In. .... 4.00 To 5.00
Depression Glass, Bowl, Vegetable, Miss America, Clear 6.50
Depression Glass, Bowl, Vegetable, Miss America, Pink 7.00
Depression Glass, Bowl, Vegetable, Royal Lace, Pink, 10 In.Diameter 5.00
Depression Glass, Bowl, Vegetable, Sharon, Pink 3.50
Depression Glass, Butter, Cameo, Green 30.00
Depression Glass, Butter, Cherry Blossom, Pink 25.00
Depression Glass, Butter, Cherry, Green 37.50
Depression Glass, Butter, Cherry, Pink 25.00
Depression Glass, Butter, Colonial, Green .... 15.00 To 18.00
Depression Glass, Butter, Columbia, Clear, Covered .... 8.00 To 10.00
Depression Glass, Butter, Floragold, Covered 10.00
Depression Glass, Butter, Florentine, Yellow 25.00
Depression Glass, Butter, Holiday, Pink 13.00
Depression Glass, Butter, Iris, Clear 10.00
Depression Glass, Butter, Madrid, Green 25.00
Depression Glass, Butter, Mayfair, Pink 22.00
Depression Glass, Butter, Patrician, Amber 30.00
Depression Glass, Butter, Princess, Green 19.50
Depression Glass, Butter, Queen Mary, Clear 8.00
Depression Glass, Butter, Sharon, Green 35.00
Depression Glass, Butter, Sharon, Pink 18.00
Depression Glass, Butter, Sharon, Pink, Covered 12.50
Depression Glass, Butter, Windsor Diamond, Pink 6.50
Depression Glass, Cake Plate, Miss America, Pink 8.00
Depression Glass, Cake Stand, Adam, Pink 7.20
Depression Glass, Candleholder, Cameo, Green, Pair 13.00
Depression Glass, Candleholder, Madrid, Amber 4.00
Depression Glass, Candleholder, Miss America, Clear, Pair 20.00
Depression Glass, Candleholder, Moonstone, Pink, Pair 4.00
Depression Glass, Candlestick, Adam, Green, Pair 15.00
Depression Glass, Candlestick, Adam, Pink, Pair 9.00
Depression Glass, Candlestick, Cameo, Green, Pair 12.50

Depression Glass, **Candlestick**, Diana, Pink, Pair 5.00
Depression Glass, **Candlestick**, Floral, Green, Pair 14.00
Depression Glass, **Candlestick**, Floral, Pink, Pair .... 12.00 To 15.00
Depression Glass, **Candlestick**, Florentine, Yellow, Pair 15.00
Depression Glass, **Candlestick**, Iris & Herringbone, Clear, Double, Pair 8.00
Depression Glass, **Candlestick**, Madrid, Amber, Pair 7.00
Depression Glass, **Candlestick**, Miss America, Green, 9 In.High, Pair 30.00
Depression Glass, **Candlestick**, Oyster & Pearl, Pink, Pair 6.00
Depression Glass, **Candlesticks**, Holiday, Pink, Pair 12.00
Depression Glass, **Candlesticks**, Two Branch, Iris, Crystal, Pair 6.50
Depression Glass, **Candy**, Cameo, Green, Covered 9.00
Depression Glass, **Candy**, Cameo, Yellow, Lid 12.00
Depression Glass, **Candy**, Doric, Blue Delfite 5.00
Depression Glass, **Candy**, Sharon, Pink, Covered 6.00
Depression Glass, **Candy**, Spiral, Green, Covered 8.50
Depression Glass, **Casserole**, Floral, Pink, Cover 9.00
Depression Glass, **Celery**, Mayfair, Pink, 10 In. 5.00
Depression Glass, **Celery**, Miss America, Clear 4.50
Depression Glass, **Cereal**, American Sweetheart, Pink 2.00
Depression Glass, **Cereal**, Miss America, Clear 2.25
Depression Glass, **Champagne**, English Hobnail, Clear 6.00
Depression Glass, **Coaster**, Cherry Blossom, Pink 1.00
Depression Glass, **Coaster**, Floral, Green 2.75
Depression Glass, **Coaster**, Princess, Green 3.50
Depression Glass, **Compote**, Dolphin, Pink 25.00
Depression Glass, **Compote**, Lace Edge, Pink, 7 In. 3.00
Depression Glass, **Compote**, Miss America, Pink 5.00
Depression Glass, **Console Set**, Royal Lace, Clear, Bowl, Candlesticks 37.50
Depression Glass, **Console Set**, Royal Lace, Cobalt, Bowl, Candlesticks 70.00
Depression Glass, **Cover**, Butter, Sharon, Pink 6.00
Depression Glass, **Cream Soup**, Royal Lace, Pink 1.50
Depression Glass, **Cream Soup**, Sharon, Pink 1.00
Depression Glass, **Creamer**, Adam, Pink 2.50
Depression Glass, **Creamer**, Cabbage Rose, Green 4.00
Depression Glass, **Creamer**, Cameo, Green, 4 1/2 In. 5.00
Depression Glass, **Creamer**, Cherry, Green 5.00
Depression Glass, **Creamer**, Cubist, Green, 3 In. 3.00
Depression Glass, **Creamer**, Doric, Green 3.50
Depression Glass, **Creamer**, Hobnail Moonstone 2.00
Depression Glass, **Creamer**, Madrid, Amber 2.50
Depression Glass, **Creamer**, Madrid, Blue .... 2.00 To 8.00
Depression Glass, **Creamer**, Mayfair, Pink 3.50
Depression Glass, **Creamer**, Miss America, Pink .... 3.00 To 5.00
Depression Glass, **Creamer**, Moderntone, Cobalt Blue .... 2.00 To 3.00
Depression Glass, **Creamer**, Poppy 2.00
Depression Glass, **Creamer**, Spiral, Green 2.00
Depression Glass, **Cup & Saucer**, American Sweetheart, Monax 7.00
Depression Glass, **Cup & Saucer**, American Sweetheart, Pink .... 3.25 To 4.00
Depression Glass, **Cup & Saucer**, Cameo, Green 4.50
Depression Glass, **Cup & Saucer**, Cameo, Yellow .... 3.90 To 5.00
Depression Glass, **Cup & Saucer**, Child's, Homespun, Clear 5.00
Depression Glass, **Cup & Saucer**, Cloverleaf, Green 3.50
Depression Glass, **Cup & Saucer**, Dogwood, Pink 5.00
Depression Glass, **Cup & Saucer**, Floral, Green 5.50
Depression Glass, **Cup & Saucer**, Florentine, Clear 3.00
Depression Glass, **Cup & Saucer**, Fruits, Green 2.50
Depression Glass, **Cup & Saucer**, Hobnail, Pink 3.00
Depression Glass, **Cup & Saucer**, Madrid, Amber 5.00
Depression Glass, **Cup & Saucer**, Madrid, Blue 8.00
Depression Glass, **Cup & Saucer**, Mayfair, Blue 27.50
Depression Glass, **Cup & Saucer**, Mayfair, Pink .... 4.00 To 6.00
Depression Glass, **Cup & Saucer**, Miss America, Crystal 5.50
Depression Glass, **Cup & Saucer**, Miss America, Pink 5.75
Depression Glass, **Cup & Saucer**, Moderntone, Cobalt 6.00
Depression Glass, **Cup & Saucer**, Patrician, Amber 5.00
Depression Glass, **Cup & Saucer**, Pink, Holiday 3.00

Depression Glass, Cup & Saucer, Princess, Green .... 2.50 To 5.00
Depression Glass, Cup & Saucer, Princess, Yellow 4.50
Depression Glass, Cup & Saucer, Rosemary, Pink 3.50
Depression Glass, Cup & Saucer, Roulette, Green 2.00
Depression Glass, Cup & Saucer, Royal Lace, Cobalt .... 13.00 To 15.00
Depression Glass, Cup & Saucer, Royal Lace, Ritz Blue 16.00
Depression Glass, Cup & Saucer, Sandwich, Clear, Anchor Hocking 2.50
Depression Glass, Cup & Saucer, Sharon, Green 7.00
Depression Glass, Cup & Saucer, Sharon, Pink 2.75
Depression Glass, Cup, Adam, Pink 2.00
Depression Glass, Cup, Cameo, Green 3.00
Depression Glass, Cup, Cherry Blossom, Pink 1.50
Depression Glass, Cup, Dogwood, Pink 1.25
Depression Glass, Cup, Floral, Green .... 2.00 To 2.50
Depression Glass, Cup, Florentine, Pink 1.25
Depression Glass, Cup, Holiday, Pink 2.00
Depression Glass, Cup, Indiana Sandwich, Clear 2.25
Depression Glass, Cup, Madrid, Amber 2.50
Depression Glass, Cup, Mayfair, Pink 3.00
Depression Glass, Cup, Moroccan, Amethyst, Set Of 5 .... 1.75
Depression Glass, Cup, Open Rose, Pink 2.50
Depression Glass, Cup, Patrician, Amber .... 2.00 To 2.50
Depression Glass, Cup, Petalware, Monax 2.50
Depression Glass, Cup, Princess, Green 3.00
Depression Glass, Cup, Sharon, Pink .... 1.25 To 3.25
Depression Glass, Cup, Spiral, Green 2.00
Depression Glass, Dish, Candy, Adam, Pink, Covered 15.00
Depression Glass, Dish, Candy, Floral, Pink, Cover 9.00
Depression Glass, Dish, Candy, Mayfair, Pink 10.00
Depression Glass, Dish, Candy, Princess, Pink, Cover 11.00
Depression Glass, Dish, Candy, Sharon, Amber, Covered 12.50
Depression Glass, Dish, Jelly, Oyster & Pearl, Pink, Heart Shape, 5 1/4 In. 1.00
Depression Glass, Dish, Olive, Old Cafe, Pink 1.00
Depression Glass, Dish, Pickle, Horseshoe, Yellow, Divided 7.00
Depression Glass, Dish, Refrigerator, Floral, Jadeite, With Cover 5.50
Depression Glass, Dish, Sweetmeat, Miss America, Pink, 11 3/4 In. 27.50
Depression Glass, Dish, Vegetable, American Sweetheart, Pink, Oval, 10 In. 6.00
Depression Glass, Dish, Vegetable, Floral, Pink, Oval 6.50
Depression Glass, Dish, Vegetable, Mayfair, Pink, Oval, 9 1/2 In. 6.00
Depression Glass, Dish, Vegetable, Sharon, Pink, Oval, 9 1/2 In. 4.00
Depression Glass, Fruit Boat, Windsor, Pink 8.00
Depression Glass, Goblet, Cameo, Green, Stemmed, 4 3/4 In. 9.00
Depression Glass, Goblet, Cameo, Green, Stemmed, 6 In. 11.00
Depression Glass, Goblet, Colonial, Clear, Stemmed, 5 In. 3.00
Depression Glass, Goblet, English Hobnail, Clear, 6 In. 5.00
Depression Glass, Goblet, Mayfair, Blue, 7 1/4 In. 45.00
Depression Glass, Goblet, Mayfair, Pink, 5 3/4 In. 15.00
Depression Glass, Goblet, Miss America, Clear, Stemmed, 5 1/2 In. 12.00
Depression Glass, Goblet, Spiral, Green, Footed, Stemmed, 7 In. 5.00
Depression Glass, Ice Bucket, Cameo, Green 30.00
Depression Glass, Ice Bucket, English Hobnail, Clear, Handles 10.00
Depression Glass, Ice Bucket, Miss America, Clear 10.00
Depression Glass, Iced Tea, Madrid, Amber, 5 1/2 In. 5.50
Depression Glass, Jar, Candy, Adam, Pink, 2 1/2 In. 10.00
Depression Glass, Jar, Candy, Block, Yellow, Covered, 2 1/4 In. 4.50
Depression Glass, Jar, Candy, Miss America, Clear, Covered 30.00
Depression Glass, Jar, Candy, Miss America, Pink, 11 3/4 In.High 35.00
Depression Glass, Jar, Cookie, Patrician, Amber, With Cover 10.00
Depression Glass, Jar, Cookie, Princess, Green, Lid .... 8.50 To 10.00
Depression Glass, Jar, Cookie, Royal Lace, Cobalt 15.00
Depression Glass, Jar, Cookie, Sandwich, Clear, Lid 10.00
Depression Glass, Jar, Cracker, Madrid, Amber, Covered 17.00
Depression Glass, Jar, Cracker, Open Rose, Pink 8.00
Depression Glass, Jar, Princess, Green, Covered 7.00
Depression Glass, Jug, Juice, Madrid, Amber, 36 Oz. 4.50
Depression Glass, Juice, Cherry Blossom, Pink, Footed 5.50

Depression Glass, **Mug**, Child's, Cherry, Green	35.00
Depression Glass, **Mustard**, Petalware, Blue, Covered	2.50
Depression Glass, **Nappy**, Bouquet & Lattice, Carnival	1.25
Depression Glass, **Nappy**, Bowknot, Green, 4 1/2 In.	1.75
Depression Glass, **Nappy**, Doric, Green, 4 1/2 In.	1.50
Depression Glass, **Nappy**, Floral, Pink, 4 In.	2.75
Depression Glass, **Nappy**, Miss America, Clear, 6 In.	3.50
Depression Glass, **Nappy**, Royal Lace, Ritz Blue, Leaf Shape	1.50
Depression Glass, **Nappy**, Sharon, Amber	4.00
Depression Glass, **Parfait**, Florentine, Yellow	5.00 To 12.50
Depression Glass, **Pitcher**, Adams, Pink, Cone Shape	11.25 To 12.50
Depression Glass, **Pitcher**, Buttermilk, Trees, Blue	15.00
Depression Glass, **Pitcher**, Cameo, Green, 8 1/2 Oz.	15.00
Depression Glass, **Pitcher**, Cherry Blossom, Pink, 7 In.Allover Pattern	15.00
Depression Glass, **Pitcher**, Cherry Blossom, Green	5.00
Depression Glass, **Pitcher**, Cherry, Green, Allover Pattern	18.00
Depression Glass, **Pitcher**, Cherry, Green, 6 1/2 In.High	22.50
Depression Glass, **Pitcher**, Dogwood, Pink	40.00
Depression Glass, **Pitcher**, Floral, Green	12.00
Depression Glass, **Pitcher**, Floral, Pink, Cone	7.50
Depression Glass, **Pitcher**, Floral, Pink, 32 Oz.	12.00
Depression Glass, **Pitcher**, Florentine, Green	12.00 To 15.00
Depression Glass, **Pitcher**, Florentine, Green, Footed	12.00
Depression Glass, **Pitcher**, Florentine, Yellow	12.50
Depression Glass, **Pitcher**, Honeycomb, Pink	12.00
Depression Glass, **Pitcher**, Horseshoe, Green	50.00
Depression Glass, **Pitcher**, Iris, Clear	8.00
Depression Glass, **Pitcher**, Juice, Mayfair, Blue	25.00
Depression Glass, **Pitcher**, Juice, Mayfair, Pink	6.50
Depression Glass, **Pitcher**, Madrid, Amber, 8 1/2 In.	10.00 To 22.50
Depression Glass, **Pitcher**, Mayfair, Blue, Medium Size	35.00
Depression Glass, **Pitcher**, Mayfair, Pink	15.00
Depression Glass, **Pitcher**, Mayfair, Pink, 8 In.High	10.00
Depression Glass, **Pitcher**, Miss America, Clear, Labeled	55.00
Depression Glass, **Pitcher**, Patrician, Amber	25.00
Depression Glass, **Pitcher**, Pink, Holiday, 7 In.	9.00
Depression Glass, **Pitcher**, Poppy, Yellow, Cone Shape	9.00
Depression Glass, **Pitcher**, Princess, Green, 8 In.	6.00 To 12.50
Depression Glass, **Pitcher**, Princess, Pink	14.00
Depression Glass, **Pitcher**, Princess, Yellow	15.00
Depression Glass, **Pitcher**, Royal Lace, Blue	45.00
Depression Glass, **Pitcher**, Royal Lace, Clear	10.00
Depression Glass, **Pitcher**, Royal Lace, Pink	35.00
Depression Glass, **Pitcher**, Royal Lace, Pink, 8 In.	13.50 To 15.00
Depression Glass, **Pitcher**, Sharon, Amber	12.00
Depression Glass, **Pitcher**, Sharon, Pink	22.00
Depression Glass, **Pitcher**, Spiral, Green, 8 In.	8.50
Depression Glass, **Pitcher**, Strawberry, Green	60.00
Depression Glass, **Pitcher**, Water, Adam, Pink	10.00
Depression Glass, **Pitcher**, Water, Sharon, Pink	23.00
Depression Glass, **Plate**, Adam, Pink, 6 In.	1.50
Depression Glass, **Plate**, Adam, Pink, 9 In.	2.00
Depression Glass, **Plate**, American Sweetheart, Monax, 10 In.	6.00
Depression Glass, **Plate**, American Sweetheart, Pink, 10 In.	2.50
Depression Glass, **Plate**, Bouquet & Lattice, Carnival, Divided, 11 In.	3.00
Depression Glass, **Plate**, Bouquet & Lattice, Carnival, 6 In.	1.50
Depression Glass, **Plate**, Bread & Butter, American Sweetheart, Monax	2.50
Depression Glass, **Plate**, Bread & Butter, American Sweetheart, Pink	1.00
Depression Glass, **Plate**, Bread & Butter, Dogwood, Green	1.00
Depression Glass, **Plate**, Bread & Butter, Petalware, Cremax	1.00
Depression Glass, **Plate**, Bread & Butter, Sharon, Pink	1.00
Depression Glass, **Plate**, Cake, Adam, Pink, 10 In.	5.00
Depression Glass, **Plate**, Cake, Cameo, Green, Footed	5.50
Depression Glass, **Plate**, Cake, Cherry Blossom, Pink	3.50
Depression Glass, **Plate**, Cake, Cherry Blossom, Pink, Open Handle	6.00
Depression Glass, **Plate**, Cake, Mayfair, Pink, Footed	4.50

Depression Glass, Plate, Cake, Mayfair, Pink, Handles, 12 In. 7.50
Depression Glass, Plate, Cake, Miss America, Clear, Footed 10.00
Depression Glass, Plate, Cake, Miss America, Pink 10.00
Depression Glass, Plate, Cake, Moderntone, Cobalt, 10 1/2 In. 3.50
Depression Glass, Plate, Cake, Princess, Green 5.00
Depression Glass, Plate, Cake, Sharon, Amber 5.00
Depression Glass, Plate, Cake, Sharon, Pink, Footed, 11 1/2 In. 6.00
Depression Glass, Plate, Cake, Sunflower, Pink, Footed 8.00
Depression Glass, Plate, Cameo, Green, Divided, 10 In. 3.00
Depression Glass, Plate, Cameo, Pink, 9 3/4 In. 8.00
Depression Glass, Plate, Chop, American Sweetheart, Monax, 11 In. 8.00
Depression Glass, Plate, Cloverleaf, Clear, 8 In. 2.50
Depression Glass, Plate, Colonial, Green, 8 1/2 In. 1.00
Depression Glass, Plate, Columbia, Crystal, 7 In. 1.25
Depression Glass, Plate, Dinner, Adam, Pink, 9 In. 2.00
Depression Glass, Plate, Dinner, American Sweetheart, Pink 3.00
Depression Glass, Plate, Dinner, Cameo, Green 2.70
Depression Glass, Plate, Dinner, Cherry Blossom, Pink 1.50
Depression Glass, Plate, Dinner, Dogwood, Pink, 9 1/4 In. .... 1.25 To 1.85
Depression Glass, Plate, Dinner, Doric, Clear 1.50
Depression Glass, Plate, Dinner, Lace Edge, Pink 1.00
Depression Glass, Plate, Dinner, Mayfair, Pink, 9 1/2 In. .... 2.50 To 14.00
Depression Glass, Plate, Dinner, Miss America, Pink 5.00
Depression Glass, Plate, Dinner, Moderntone, Cobalt 2.00
Depression Glass, Plate, Dinner, Patrician, Amber, 10 1/2 In. 2.50
Depression Glass, Plate, Dinner, Patrician, Green, 10 1/2 In. 2.50
Depression Glass, Plate, Dinner, Petalware, Cremax .... 1.25 To 8.50
Depression Glass, Plate, Dinner, Petalware, Cremax, Flowers In Center 1.25
Depression Glass, Plate, Dinner, Royal Lace, Cobalt 10.50
Depression Glass, Plate, Dinner, Royal Lace, Pink 6.00
Depression Glass, Plate, Dinner, Sharon, Pink, 9 1/4 In. 2.50
Depression Glass, Plate, Dogwood, Green, 8 In. 1.85
Depression Glass, Plate, Dogwood, Pink, 6 In. 1.50
Depression Glass, Plate, Dogwood, Pink, 8 In. 2.00
Depression Glass, Plate, Dogwood, Pink, 9 In. 2.50
Depression Glass, Plate, Doric, Pink, 9 In. 1.50
Depression Glass, Plate, Florentine, Clear, 8 1/2 In. 1.75
Depression Glass, Plate, Florentine, Green, 9 3/4 In. 1.85
Depression Glass, Plate, Florentine, Yellow, 8 1/2 In. 1.25
Depression Glass, Plate, Grill, Cameo, Green 2.00
Depression Glass, Plate, Grill, Cherry Blossom, Pink 1.50
Depression Glass, Plate, Grill, Lace Edge, Pink 1.00
Depression Glass, Plate, Grill, Madrid, Amber .... 2.00 To 2.50
Depression Glass, Plate, Grill, Madrid, Pink 3.00
Depression Glass, Plate, Grill, Miss America, Clear 4.00
Depression Glass, Plate, Grill, Miss America, Pink 5.00
Depression Glass, Plate, Grill, Old Florentine, Green 1.75
Depression Glass, Plate, Grill, Princess, Yellow, 11 1/2 In. 1.85
Depression Glass, Plate, Grill, Rosemary, Pink 2.00
Depression Glass, Plate, Luncheon, Dogwood, Pink 1.00
Depression Glass, Plate, Luncheon, Floral, Pink 1.50
Depression Glass, Plate, Luncheon, Hobnail, Pink 2.50
Depression Glass, Plate, Madrid, Amber, 6 In. 1.75
Depression Glass, Plate, Madrid, Amber, 9 In. 1.85
Depression Glass, Plate, Madrid, Amber, 11 1/2 In. 6.00
Depression Glass, Plate, Madrid, Green, 6 In. 1.75
Depression Glass, Plate, Madrid, Green, 9 In. 2.00
Depression Glass, Plate, Margery Daw, Green 21.50
Depression Glass, Plate, Mayfair, Blue, 6 In. 7.00
Depression Glass, Plate, Mayfair, Pink, Round, 6 1/2 In. 3.00
Depression Glass, Plate, Mayfair, Pink, 8 1/2 In. 3.00
Depression Glass, Plate, Miss America, Clear 3.00
Depression Glass, Plate, Miss America, Clear, Divided 3.50
Depression Glass, Plate, Miss America, Clear, 6 In. 2.50
Depression Glass, Plate, Miss America, Clear, 10 1/4 In. 4.50
Depression Glass, Plate, Miss America, Pink, 8 1/2 In. 3.00

Depression Glass, Plate, Miss America, Pink, 10 In. 4.50
Depression Glass, Plate, Moderntone, Cobalt, 9 In. 2.50
Depression Glass, Plate, Moderntone, Cobalt, 10 1/2 In. 6.00
Depression Glass, Plate, Normandie, Sunburst, 10 1/2 In. 3.50
Depression Glass, Plate, Open Rose, Pink 3.00
Depression Glass, Plate, Patrician, Amber, 6 In. 1.85
Depression Glass, Plate, Patrician, Amber, 9 In. 2.00
Depression Glass, Plate, Patrician, Green, 9 In. 1.85
Depression Glass, Plate, Petalware, Monax, 6 1/2 In. 1.25
Depression Glass, Plate, Petalware, Monax, 9 1/4 In. 2.50
Depression Glass, Plate, Pineapple And Floral, Crystal, 8 3/8 In. 1.25
Depression Glass, Plate, Princess, Green, 8 In. 2.00
Depression Glass, Plate, Princess, Pink, 6 In. 1.50
Depression Glass, Plate, Princess, Yellow 2.25
Depression Glass, Plate, Rose Cameo, Green, 7 In. 1.50
Depression Glass, Plate, Roulette, Green, 8 1/2 In. 1.50
Depression Glass, Plate, Royal Lace, Cobalt, 6 In.Diameter .... 4.50 To 5.00
Depression Glass, Plate, Salad, Floral, Pink 1.50
Depression Glass, Plate, Salad, Lace Edge, Pink 1.00
Depression Glass, Plate, Salad, Madrid, Amber 1.00
Depression Glass, Plate, Salad, Miss America, Clear 3.50
Depression Glass, Plate, Salad, Miss America, Pink 3.75
Depression Glass, Plate, Salad, Patrician, Green, 7 1/2 In. 1.85
Depression Glass, Plate, Salad, Sharon, Pink 1.00
Depression Glass, Plate, Sandwich, No.612, Green, 11 1/4 In. 3.75
Depression Glass, Plate, Sharon, Pink, 9 1/2 In. 1.50
Depression Glass, Plate, Sherbet, Cameo, Green, 6 1/2 In. 1.50
Depression Glass, Plate, Sherbet, Cameo, Yellow 1.85
Depression Glass, Plate, Sherbet, Cherry Blossom, Pink .... 1.00 To 3.00
Depression Glass, Plate, Sherbet, Mayfair, Blue, Side Ring 12.00
Depression Glass, Plate, Sherbet, Miss America, Pink 1.00
Depression Glass, Plate, Sherbet, Royal Lace, Cobalt 5.00
Depression Glass, Plate, Sherbet, Spiral, Green 1.50
Depression Glass, Plate, Spiral, Green, 8 In. 1.50
Depression Glass, Plate, Starlight, Clear, 9 1/2 In. 2.00
Depression Glass, Platter, Adam, Pink 4.50
Depression Glass, Platter, Adam, Pink, 12 In. 4.00
Depression Glass, Platter, American Sweetheart, Pink, 13 In. 4.00
Depression Glass, Platter, Bouquet & Lattice, Carnival, Oval, 12 In. 5.00
Depression Glass, Platter, Bubble, Light Blue 2.50
Depression Glass, Platter, Cameo, Green .... 4.50 To 5.00
Depression Glass, Platter, Cherry Blossom, Pink, Divided, 13 In. 4.50
Depression Glass, Platter, Cherry Blossom, Pink, Oblong 6.00
Depression Glass, Platter, Floral, Green, Oval 3.00
Depression Glass, Platter, Homespun, Pink 4.50
Depression Glass, Platter, Madrid, Amber .... 3.50 To 5.00
Depression Glass, Platter, Madrid, Blue 12.00
Depression Glass, Platter, Mayfair, Blue, 13 In. 30.00
Depression Glass, Platter, Mayfair, Pink, 12 In. .... 2.00 To 5.00
Depression Glass, Platter, Meat, Doric, Pink 4.00
Depression Glass, Platter, Meat, Patrician, Amber 6.00
Depression Glass, Platter, Meat, Princess, Green, 12 In. 5.00
Depression Glass, Platter, Meat, Royal Lace, Cobalt 18.50
Depression Glass, Platter, Miss America, Clear 7.00
Depression Glass, Platter, Sharon, Amber, 12 1/2 In. 3.00
Depression Glass, Platter, Sharon, Pink, 12 1/2 In. .... 2.25 To 5.00
Depression Glass, Relish, Cameo, Green 4.75
Depression Glass, Relish, Lace Edge, Pink, 3 Partition 2.00
Depression Glass, Relish, Lace Edge, Pink, 5 Partition 2.00
Depression Glass, Relish, Lorain, Clear 3.00
Depression Glass, Relish, Madrid, Amber 6.00
Depression Glass, Relish, Mayfair, Blue 17.50
Depression Glass, Relish, Miss America, Clear, Round 3.00
Depression Glass, Relish, Miss America, Clear, 4 Part 5.00
Depression Glass, Relish, Miss America, Crystal, 8 1/2 In. 4.00
Depression Glass, Relish, Miss America, Pink, Divided, 4 Part .... 3.00 To 4.00

Depression Glass, **Relish**, Oyster & Pearl, Pink, Divided 2.00
Depression Glass, **Salt & Pepper**, American Sweetheart, Monax 45.00
Depression Glass, **Salt & Pepper**, Cabbage Rose, Pink 8.00
Depression Glass, **Salt & Pepper**, Cameo, Green 15.00
Depression Glass, **Salt & Pepper**, Cloverleaf, Black 15.00
Depression Glass, **Salt & Pepper**, Cloverleaf, Green 6.00
Depression Glass, **Salt & Pepper**, Floral, Green 10.00
Depression Glass, **Salt & Pepper**, Florentine, Pink 8.00
Depression Glass, **Salt & Pepper**, Madrid, Amber 12.50
Depression Glass, **Salt & Pepper**, Moderntone, Blue 5.00
Depression Glass, **Salt & Pepper**, Normandie, Pink 8.00
Depression Glass, **Salt & Pepper**, Poppy, Green 12.50
Depression Glass, **Salt & Pepper**, Princess, Tall 15.00
Depression Glass, **Salt & Pepper**, Ribbon, Green, Pair 5.00
Depression Glass, **Salt & Pepper**, Royal Lace, Cobalt 60.00
Depression Glass, **Salt & Pepper**, Sharon, Pink .... 10.00 To 12.50
Depression Glass, **Saltshaker**, Mayfair, Blue 20.00
Depression Glass, **Salt Shaker**, Mayfair, Blue 20.00
Depression Glass, **Saltshaker**, Sharon, Pink 5.00
Depression Glass, **Salt**, Ribbon, Pink 2.50
Depression Glass, **Salver**, American Sweetheart, Monax, 12 In. 8.50
Depression Glass, **Sauce**, Actress, 4 1/2 In.Diameter 15.00
Depression Glass, **Sauce**, Adam, Pink 1.00
Depression Glass, **Sauce**, Floral, Green 1.25
Depression Glass, **Sauce**, Open Rose, Pink, Footed 3.00
Depression Glass, **Sauce**, Ribbed, Pink 1.00
Depression Glass, **Saucer**, Adam, Pint 1.25
Depression Glass, **Saucer**, Cameo, Green, 6 1/2 In. 1.50
Depression Glass, **Saucer**, Cherry Blossom, Pink 1.00
Depression Glass, **Saucer**, Child's, Doric & Pansy, Pink 2.00
Depression Glass, **Saucer**, Dogwood, Green 1.00
Depression Glass, **Saucer**, Dogwood, Pink 1.00
Depression Glass, **Saucer**, Madrid, Green 1.00
Depression Glass, **Saucer**, Miss America, Pink .... 1.00 To 2.00
Depression Glass, **Saucer**, Moroccan, Amethyst, Set Of 5 .... 1.00
Depression Glass, **Saucer**, Normandie, Pink 1.00
Depression Glass, **Saucer**, Petalware, Cremax 1.00
Depression Glass, **Saucer**, Rosemary, Pink 1.50
Depression Glass, **Saucer**, Sharon, Pink 1.00
Depression Glass, **Server**, Indiana Sandwich, Clear, Tiered 7.00
Depression Glass, **Server**, Mayfair, Blue, Center Handle 25.00
Depression Glass, **Shaker**, Mayfair, Blue, Clear 5.00
Depression Glass, **Shaker**, Princess, Green, 5 1/2 In.High 5.00
Depression Glass, **Sherbet**, American Sweetheart, Crystal, Metal Holder 3.50
Depression Glass, **Sherbet**, American Sweetheart, Pink 2.00
Depression Glass, **Sherbet**, Cameo, Green .... 2.00 To 3.00
Depression Glass, **Sherbet**, Cameo, Green, Set Of 12 .... 3.00
Depression Glass, **Sherbet**, Dogwood, Pink, Footed 2.00
Depression Glass, **Sherbet**, Doric, Delfite Blue 5.00
Depression Glass, **Sherbet**, Georgian, Green 1.75
Depression Glass, **Sherbet**, Madrid, Amber .... 1.00 To 3.00
Depression Glass, **Sherbet**, Madrid, Blue 5.00
Depression Glass, **Sherbet**, Madrid, Green, Footed 2.75
Depression Glass, **Sherbet**, Mayfair, Pink, Footed 3.80
Depression Glass, **Sherbet**, Mayfair, Pink, Stemmed, 4 3/4 In.High 25.00
Depression Glass, **Sherbet**, Miss America, Clear 4.00
Depression Glass, **Sherbet**, Miss America, Pink 4.00
Depression Glass, **Sherbet**, Moderntone, Cobalt Blue .... 1.50 To 2.00
Depression Glass, **Sherbet**, Parrot, Green 3.00
Depression Glass, **Sherbet**, Patrician, Amber, Footed 3.00
Depression Glass, **Sherbet**, Pink, Adam 2.00
Depression Glass, **Sherbet**, Poppy, Green 1.50
Depression Glass, **Sherbet**, Poppy, Yellow 2.50
Depression Glass, **Sherbet**, Princess, Green 2.10
Depression Glass, **Sherbet**, Rose Cameo, Green, Footed 2.00
Depression Glass, **Sherbet**, Roulette, Green 1.50

Depression Glass, Sherbet, Royal Lace, Amethyst	35.00
Depression Glass, Sherbet, Royal Lace, Cobalt, Metal Holder	15.00
Depression Glass, Sherbet, Sharon, Amber	2.50
Depression Glass, Sherbet, Sharon, Pink	1.25
Depression Glass, Sherbet, Spiral, Green	2.00
Depression Glass, Soup, Bouquet & Lattice, Carnival	2.00
Depression Glass, Soup, Cream, Petalware, Monax	2.00
Depression Glass, Soup, Sharon, Pink, 6 In.	1.50
Depression Glass, Sugar & Creamer, Actress, Amethyst, 6 In.Tall	65.00
Depression Glass, Sugar & Creamer, American Sweetheart, Pink	5.00
Depression Glass, Sugar & Creamer, Bouquet & Lattice, Sunburst	10.00
Depression Glass, Sugar & Creamer, Cabbage Rose, Pink	4.00
Depression Glass, Sugar & Creamer, Cameo, Green	8.00
Depression Glass, Sugar & Creamer, Cameo, Yellow	2.50 To 6.00
Depression Glass, Sugar & Creamer, Cherry Blossom, Pink, Covered Sugar	10.00
Depression Glass, Sugar & Creamer, Cherry, Green, Covered	2.00
Depression Glass, Sugar & Creamer, Dogwood, Pink	5.00
Depression Glass, Sugar & Creamer, Hairpin, Cobalt Blue	10.00
Depression Glass, Sugar & Creamer, Holiday, Pink, Open	4.00
Depression Glass, Sugar & Creamer, Lovebird, Green	7.00
Depression Glass, Sugar & Creamer, Madrid, Amber, Covered Sugar	8.00
Depression Glass, Sugar & Creamer, Madrid, Amber, Open Sugar	5.00
Depression Glass, Sugar & Creamer, Mayfair, Pink	6.75
Depression Glass, Sugar & Creamer, Miss America, Clear	7.00 To 8.50
Depression Glass, Sugar & Creamer, Miss America, Pink	8.00
Depression Glass, Sugar & Creamer, Moderntone, Blue	3.00
Depression Glass, Sugar & Creamer, Moderntone, Cobalt	4.50
Depression Glass, Sugar & Creamer, Patrician, Amber	6.00
Depression Glass, Sugar & Creamer, Princess, Yellow	4.00 To 7.00
Depression Glass, Sugar & Creamer, Sharon, Pink	3.00
Depression Glass, Sugar & Creamer, Sharon, Pink, Covered Sugar	4.00
Depression Glass, Sugar & Creamer, Windsor, Pink, Cover	4.00
Depression Glass, Sugar, Adam, Pink, Cover	3.50
Depression Glass, Sugar, American Sweetheart, Pink	2.50
Depression Glass, Sugar, Bouquet & Lattice, Marigold, Open	2.50
Depression Glass, Sugar, Cabbage Rose, Amber, Open, Handle	5.00
Depression Glass, Sugar, Cameo, Green, 4 1/2 In.	5.00
Depression Glass, Sugar, Cherry Delfite, Blue	20.00
Depression Glass, Sugar, Cherry, Green, Cover	6.00
Depression Glass, Sugar, Cloverleaf, Black	4.00
Depression Glass, Sugar, Floral, Green, Open	2.50
Depression Glass, Sugar, Florentine, Green	2.50
Depression Glass, Sugar, Madrid, Amber	2.00
Depression Glass, Sugar, Madrid, Blue	8.00
Depression Glass, Sugar, Mayfair, Blue	10.00
Depression Glass, Sugar, Miss America, Pink	6.00
Depression Glass, Sugar, Princess, Green, Covered	1.75 To 3.00
Depression Glass, Sugar, Sharon, Pink	3.50
Depression Glass, Sugar, Spiral, Green	2.00
Depression Glass, Tea Set, Child's, Cherry Blossom, 14 Piece	120.00
Depression Glass, Tray, Cherry Blossom, Pink, 10 1/2 In.	6.00
Depression Glass, Tray, Old Cafe, Pink	1.50
Depression Glass, Tray, Sandwich, Cherry Blossom, Pink, Handled	2.25
Depression Glass, Tumbler, Adam, Green, 4 1/2 In.	4.00
Depression Glass, Tumbler, Block, Pink, Cone Shape, Footed	4.00
Depression Glass, Tumbler, Cameo, Green, 5 In.	6.50
Depression Glass, Tumbler, Cherry, Green, 4 In.High	6.00
Depression Glass, Tumbler, Coronation, Pink, 5 In.	1.50
Depression Glass, Tumbler, Doric, Pink	6.50
Depression Glass, Tumbler, Florentine, Green, Footed, 6 Oz.	2.50 To 6.00
Depression Glass, Tumbler, Florentine, Yellow, 3 In.	3.00
Depression Glass, Tumbler, Lemonade, Floral, Green	6.00
Depression Glass, Tumbler, Lemonade, Floral, Pink	5.50
Depression Glass, Tumbler, Madrid, Amber, 4 1/2 In.	5.75
Depression Glass, Tumbler, Mayfair, Blue, Flat, 4 In.	10.00
Depression Glass, Tumbler, Mayfair, Pink, Footed, 5 1/2 In.	6.00

Depression Glass, Tumbler, Mayfair, Pink, 4 In. 6.75
Depression Glass, Tumbler, Mayfair, Pink, 5 1/4 In. 6.00
Depression Glass, Tumbler, Mayfair, Pink, 6 1/2 In. 7.00
Depression Glass, Tumbler, Miss America, Clear, 4 1/2 In. 6.50
Depression Glass, Tumbler, Miss America, Clear, 5 3/4 In. 8.00
Depression Glass, Tumbler, Miss America, Pink, 4 1/2 In. 7.00
Depression Glass, Tumbler, Open Rose, Footed 8.50
Depression Glass, Tumbler, Patrician, Amber, 4 In. 4.00
Depression Glass, Tumbler, Princess, Green, 5 In. 4.00
Depression Glass, Tumbler, Princess, Yellow, Footed, 5 1/4 In. 4.50
Depression Glass, Tumbler, Princess, Yellow, 3 1/2 In. 4.00
Depression Glass, Tumbler, Rose Cameo, Green, Footed, 5 1/2 In. 5.00
Depression Glass, Tumbler, Roulette, Green, Footed 2.50
Depression Glass, Tumbler, Royal Lace, Pink, 4 1/4 In. 5.00
Depression Glass, Tumbler, S Pattern, Crystal, 4 In. 4.00
Depression Glass, Tumbler, Sailboat, Cobalt, 8 Oz. .... 2.50 To 4.00
Depression Glass, Tumbler, Sandwich, Clear, Anchor Hocking, 5 Oz. 1.00
Depression Glass, Tumbler, Sharon, Amber, 4 In. 5.00
Depression Glass, Tumbler, Sharon, Pink 4.00
Depression Glass, Tumbler, Sharon, Pink, Cone Shape, Footed, 6 1/2 In. ... 6.00
Depression Glass, Tumbler, Spiral, Green, 3 3/4 In. 3.00
Depression Glass, Vase, Cameo, Green, 6 In. 45.00
Depression Glass, Vase, English Hobnail, Clear, 7 1/2 In. 15.00
Depression Glass, Vase, Florentine, Yellow 18.50
Depression Glass, Vase, Princess, Green, 8 In.High .... 6.50 To 7.00
Depression Glass, Vase, Quilted, Pink, Flattened Opening, Dolphin Handles ... 10.00
Depression Glass, Water Set, Adam, Pink, 7 Pieces 45.00
Depression Glass, Water Set, Royal Lace, Cobalt, Bulbous Pitcher, 6 Tumbler ... 155.50
Depression Glass, Water Set, Sailboat, Blue, 9 Piece 12.00

*Derby Porcelain was made in Derby, England, from 1756 to the present.
The factory changed names and marks several times. Chelsea Derby (1770-
1784), Crown Derby (1784-1811), and the modern Royal Crown Derby are
some of the most famous periods of the factory.*
Derby, see also Crown Derby, Royal Crown Derby, Chelsea
Derby, Biscuit Barrel, Circa 1903 .... 65.00
Derby, Cachepot, White, Lavender & Green Floral Wreath, Bloor 200.00
Derby, Cup & Saucer, Blue & Gilt Decoration, Circa 1805, Red Orange Mark ... 55.00
Derby, Cup & Saucer, White, Floral Design, Circa 1820 .... 38.00
Derby, Dish, Fish, Red, Blue, Brown, Gold, Circa 1880 .... 100.00
Derby, Figurine, Head Of Fish, English, 19th Century, Bloor, 5 1/4 In.Long ... 60.00
Derby, Mug, Allover Pattern, Cupid Panel, Gold, C.1780, Large 220.00
Derby, Plaque, Jonquils, Pink Rose, Morning Glories, Gilt Wood Frame, C.1800 ... 250.00
Derby, Tea Set, Japan Pattern, C.1820, 36 Piece 800.00
Derby, Tureen, Sauce, Covered, Stand, Japan Pattern, Oval, C.1810, Pair 500.00
Derby, Tureen, Sauce, Covered, Stand, Oval, Bombe, Gros Bleu Bands, C.1850 ... 90.00
Derby, Vase, Gros Bleu, Shield Shape, Scrolls, Foliate In Gilt, C.1815 ...... 200.00
Dick Tracy, Book, Ace Detective, 1943 .... 7.00
Dick Tracy, Book, Dick Tracy The Detective, 1938, Whitman Penny Book 4.00
Dick Tracy, Book, Hotel Murders, 1937, Big Little Book 6.00
Dick Tracy, Book, Penfield Mystery, 1934 .... 9.00
Dick Tracy, Cap Pistol, Cast Iron 8.00
Dick Tracy, Watch, New Haven Clock & Watch Co., C.1949 .... 40.00 To 50.00
Dick Tracy, Watch, Rectangular, Picture Of Dick Tracy On Dial, 1934 .... 50.00
Dionne Quintuplets, Bowl, Cereal, Raised Faces In Bottom, Names, Aluminum ... 6.50
Dionne Quintuplets, Bowl, Figures & Names Embossed, Metal, 6 In. 12.50
Dionne Quintuplets, Calendar, 1936, Picture 6.00
Dionne Quintuplets, Calendar, 1937, Picture 5.50
Dionne Quintuplets, Calendar, 1938, Picture 5.00
Dionne Quintuplets, Calendar, 1950, Riding Horseback 3.00
Dionne Quintuplets, Doll, Bisque, German, Dresses, Pins With Name 40.00
Dionne Quintuplets, Doll, Cloth Body, Composition Head, Arms, Legs, 16 In. ... 55.00
Dionne Quintuplets, Doll, Dressed, 14 In.Tall 65.00
Dionne Quintuplets, Doll, Marked, 8 In.Tall 25.00
Dionne Quintuplets, Doll, Paper, Clothes, Set 15.00
Dionne Quintuplets, Game, Marble, Goo Goo Eyes, Place Marbles In Sockets ... 5.00

Dionne Quintuplets, Scrapbook	25.00
Dionne Quintuplets, Spoon, Silver Plate	5.00
Dionne Quintuplets, Teaspoon, Silver Plate, Figure, Name, Set Of 5	25.00
Doctor, Bleeding Instrument, Trigger Action Blade, Case	65.00
Doctor, Chest, Medicine, Field, Leather Covered, Hinged, 28 Bottles, Civil War	19.50
Doctor, Kit, Surgeon's Tool, Mahogany Case, 12 Piece	35.00
Doctor, Tool, Trephine, Bores Holes *Illus*	15.00
Doll, A.I.M.251, Boy, Bisque, Kid Body, Open Mouth, Flirty Eyes, 18 In.Tall	225.00
Doll, A.M., Baby In Rompers, Sleep Eyes, 13 In.	95.00
Doll, A.M., Baby, Bald Head, Pierced Ears, Earrings, Open Mouth, 14 In.	145.00
Doll, A.M., Ball Jointed Body, Sleep Eyes, 11 In.Tall	39.00
Doll, A.M., Bisque Head, Kid Body, Marked Alma 14/0, Germany, 12 1/2 In.	62.00
Doll, A.M., Bisque Head, Stationary Eyes, Composition Body, Dressed	50.00
Doll, A.M., Bisque Head, Stick Body, Sleep Eyes, Dressed, 10 1/2 In.	35.00
Doll, A.M., Bisque, Auburn Hair, Dark Blue Eyes, 20 In.	85.00
Doll, A.M., Brown Hair & Eyes, Cloth Body, Pull String & Voice Box, 13 In.	75.00
Doll, A.M., Bulgy Eyes, Kid Body, Undressed, 18 In.	95.00
Doll, A.M., Cloth Body, Sleep Eyes, Human Hair Wig, 17 1/2 In.Tall	35.00
Doll, A.M., Dream Baby, Bisque Head, Cloth Body, Celluloid Hands, Dressed	130.00
Doll, A.M., Floradora, Auburn Hair, Fur Eyebrows, Dressed, 22 In.	167.50
Doll, A.M., Floradora, Bisque Hands, Paperweight Eyes, Open Mouth, Kid Body	75.00
Doll, A.M., Floradora, Stick Boy, Dressed, 16 In.	52.00
Doll, A.M., Girl, Cloth Body, Sleep Eyes, 17 In.Tall	35.00
Doll, A.M., Girl, Voice Box, Walker, Sleep Eyes, 29 In.	190.00
Doll, A.M., Molded Hair, Straw Stuffed Body, Closed Mouth, Composition Arms	50.00
Doll, A.M., No.210, Girl, Goo Goo, Molded Hair, Intaglio Eyes, 6 1/2 In.Tall	150.00
Doll, A.M., No.370, Girl, Human Hair Wig, Open Mouth, 17 In.Tall	55.00
Doll, A.M., No.1894, Girl, Mohair Wig, Open Mouth, 6 In.Tall	35.00
Doll, A.M., Open Mouth, Brown Eyes, Kid Arms & Legs, Dressed	55.00
Doll, A.M., Rockabye, Composition Head, 12 In.	50.00
Doll, A.M., Toddler, Breather, 14 In.	87.50
Doll, A.M., 10 In. *Illus*	50.00

Doctor, Tool, Trephine, Bores Holes

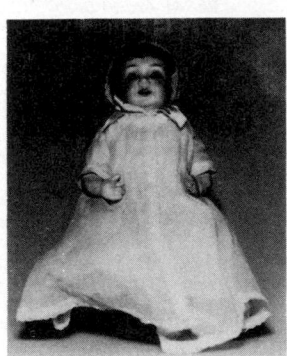

Doll, A.M., 10 In.

Doll, A.M.Dep., Bisque Shoulder Head, Turned Head, Kid Body, Bisque Arms	140.00
Doll, A.M.Germany, 34/6, Bisque Head, Composition, Glass Eyes, 18 In.Tall	125.00
Doll, A.M.370, Bisque Shoulder Head, Kid Body, Bisque Hands, Wig, 20 In.	65.00
Doll, A.M., 8/0, Dep, No.370, Kid Body, Open Mouth, Dark Hair, 13 In.Tall	55.00
Doll, ABG Germany, Flirty Eyes, Flutter Tongue, Bent Legs, Pierced Nose	150.00
Doll, ABG, Baby, Pierced Nostrils, Sleep Brown Eyes, 20 In.Tall	200.00
Doll, ABG, Boy, Sleep Eyes, Open Mouth, Teeth, Velvet Suit, 14 In.Tall	75.00
Doll, ABG, 1326, Stamped Made In Germany, Dressed, 26 In.Tall	125.00
Doll, Abraham Lincoln, Composition Molded Head, Painted Features	40.00
Doll, Alexander, Boy, Composition Head, Rubber Body, Sleeping Eyes	18.00
Doll, Alexander, Boy, Soft Body, Painted Eyes	15.00
Doll, Alexander, Cissette, Dressed	8.50
Doll, Alexander, Cissy, Dressed, C.1950	20.00 To 25.00
Doll, Alexander, Hard Plastic, 8 In.Tall	5.00
Doll, Alexander, Little Genius, 22 In.	27.00
Doll, Alexander, Little Women, 12 In.Tall, Set Of 5 In Original Box	75.00

Doll, Alexander, Princess Elizabeth, Human Hair Wig, Sleep Eyes, 13 In.	35.00
Doll, Alexander, Princess Elizabeth, 15 In.	55.00
Doll, Alexander, Pussy Cat	15.00
Doll, Alexander, Sugar Darling	15.00
Doll, Alexander, Wendy Ann, Sleep Eyes, Closed Mouth, Jointed, Dressed, 21 In.	25.00
Doll, Alvin	12.00
Doll, Amasandra, Rubber, Dressed, 9 1/2 In.Tall	15.00
Doll, Anne Shirley, Movie Star, 1935, Marked, 16 In.	35.00
Doll, Annette, Composition Head, Arms, & Legs, 14 In.Tall	10.00
Doll, Armand Marseilles, Ball Jointed, Human Hair Wig, 35 In.	240.00
Doll, Armand Marseilles, Ball Jointed, 37 In.Tall	260.00
Doll, Armand Marseilles, Bisque Head, Jointed, 16 In.Tall	85.50
Doll, Armand Marseilles, Bisque Head, Jointed Body, Pink Outfit	100.00
Doll, Armand Marseilles, Bisque Head, Shoulders, Hands, Teeth, Leather Body	110.00
Doll, Armand Marseilles, Dream Baby, 14 In.Head, Hands Repainted	175.00
Doll, Armand Marseilles, Germany, Baby, Bisque & Composition, 14 1/2 In. Tall	85.00
Doll, Armand Marseilles, Germany, Dream Baby, Composition Body, 15 In.Tall	97.00
Doll, Armand Marseilles, Kid & Cloth Body, 20 In.	75.00
Doll, Armand Marseilles, 390, Bisque Head, Sleep Eyes, 11 In.Tall	42.50
Doll, Baby Betty, Sleep Eyes, Joint Body, 13 In.	65.00
Doll, Baby Bumps, Composition, Label, Dressed, 11 In.	98.00
Doll, Baby Gloria, Sleeping Brown Eyes, 16 In.Tall	275.00
Doll, Baby Gloria, 12 1/2 In.Tall	225.00
Doll, Baby Sandy, Composition, 16 In.Tall	75.00
Doll, Baby, American Character, Rubber, Plastic Head, 16 In.Tall	12.50
Doll, Baby, Character, Bisque Head, Composition Body, Dressed, Ab1352 Mark	175.00
Doll, Baby, Closed Mouth, Molded Hair, Sleep Eyes, J.D.K.Kestner, 16 In.	200.00
Doll, Baby, Composition Body, Dream Baby, 8 In.Tall	65.00
Doll, Baby, Composition Shoulder & Head, Cloth Body, Dressed, 17 In.	27.00
Doll, Baby, Composition, Dressed, Marked Baby Petite	70.00
Doll, Baby, Composition, Jointed Limbs, Drinks, Wets, Painted Features	12.50
Doll, Baby, J.D.K.No.211, Blue Eyes, Teeth, Blond Wig, Dressed, 16 In.Tall	110.00
Doll, Baby, Kaiser, 20 In.	375.00
Doll, Baby, Pierced Nostrils, Molded Hair, Sleep Eyes, F.S.C.	150.00
Doll, Baby, Sleep Eyes, Open Mouth, Teeth, Wig, Germany, 23 In.	145.00
Doll, Baby, Tongue Works With Eyes, A.B.C., 12 1/2 In.	105.00
Doll, Bahr Proschild, Bisque Head, Sleep Eyes, Bent Limbs, 12 In.	145.00
Doll, Ball Joint Body, Bisque Head, Blonde Wig, Dressed, 29 In.	100.00
Doll, Ball Joints, Composition Body, Human Hair Wig, Dressed, Germany, 26 In.	90.00
Doll, Barney Google, Composition, 1944, 4 In.Tall	20.00
Doll, Bathing Beauty, Bisque, Hair, Silk Net Bathing Suit & Cap, Germany	50.00
Doll, Bebe Jumeau, Open Mouth, Human Hair Wig, Dressed, 22 In.	250.00
Doll, Belton, Bride, Painted Shoes & Socks, Red Lines Over Glass Eyes	65.00
Doll, Bergman-Simon Halbig, Bisque Head, Sleep Eyes, Pierced Ears	75.00
Doll, Bergman, Blonde Wig, Lavish Wine Satin Dress & Hat, 32 In.	195.00
Doll, Berman, Bisque, Pierced Ears, Sleep Eyes, 21 In.Tall	55.00
Doll, Bessie The Bashful Bride	15.00
Doll, Betsy McCall, Blonde Hair, Blue Eyes, Dressed, 29 In.Tall	37.50
Doll, Betsy McCall, Plastic, 14 1/2 In.Tall	18.50
Doll, Betsy McCall, Sunday Dress, Box	20.00
Doll, Betsy McCall, 8 In.Tall	9.50
Doll, Betty Boop, Bisque, Jointed At Shoulders, Japan, 5 In.	5.00
Doll, Betty Boop, Celluloid, Nodding Head, 7 In.Tall	60.00
Doll, Betty Boop, Jointed, Wooden, Fleisher Studios	150.00
Doll, Betty Boop, Sitting Figure, Painted, Label, Lotta-Sun-1919	25.00
Doll, Bisque Head, Baby, Blue Eyes, Marked G.B.	125.00
Doll, Bisque Head, Ball Jointed Body	79.00
Doll, Bisque Head, Blue Sleep Eyes, Brown Wig, Germany, 14 In.	75.00
Doll, Bisque Head, Closed Eyes, Squeeze Voice Box, Japan, C.1940, 5 In.	30.00
Doll, Bisque Head, Composition, Jointed, Paperweight Eyes, Voice Box, Dep.12	210.00
Doll, Bisque Head, Dressed, Marked Gerbruder Frauss, 10 In.Tall	70.00
Doll, Bisque Head, German, Baby, Colored, 9 In.Tall	85.00
Doll, Bisque Head, Jointed Body, Blue Eyes, Made In Germany	45.00
Doll, Bisque Head, Jointed Composition Body, Curls, Koppelsdorf, Germany	95.00
Doll, Bisque Head, Kid Body, Brown Hair, Dressed, 13 In.	75.00
Doll, Bisque Head, Kid Body, Marked Dep With Horseshoe, 15 In.	65.00

Doll, Bisque Head, Lashed Eyes, Wig, 390 A.6 M, 21 1/2 In. 80.00
Doll, Bisque Head, Marked C.M.Bergman, Waltershausen, 1916-9, 17 In. ....
Doll, Bisque Head, Marked L.C.In Anchor, French, Composition Body, 9 In. 84.00
Doll, Bisque Head, Marked Limoges, France, 12 In.Tall 72.00
Doll, Bisque Head, Marked Revalo, German, 16 In. 85.00
Doll, Bisque Head, Open Mouth, Kid Body, Brown Plaits Wig, Japan M.B., 20 In. 50.00
Doll, Bisque Head, Sleep Eyes, Open Mouth, Jointed, M.Germany 200.00
Doll, Bisque Head, Stationary Eyes, Marked J Anchor V France, 14 In. 96.50
Doll, Bisque Head, Textured Papier-Mache Body, Legs, Marked Dep, 18 In. 150.00
Doll, Bisque Shoulder Head, Jointed Body, Bisque Arms & Hands, Long Hair 175.00
Doll, Bisque Shoulder Head, Kid Body, Mohair Wig, Dressed, Marked Germany 75.00
Doll, Bisque Shoulder Head, Molded Collar, 5 In.Tall 50.00
Doll, Bisque Socket Head, Composition Body, Wig, Jointed, R.A. 1909 .... 65.00
Doll, Bisque Swivel Head, Composition Body, Toddler, 12 In. 15.00
Doll, Bisque Swivel Head, Composition Body, Toddler, 14 In. 17.50
Doll, Bisque, Alma, 8/0, Germany, Blonde Wig, 15 1/2 In.Tall 75.00
Doll, Bisque, Baby, Dressed, 12 In.Tall 72.50
Doll, Bisque, Bathing Beauty, Blue Eyes, Wig, Dressed, 5 1/4 In.Tall 65.00
Doll, Bisque, Boy, Girl, Painted Shoes, Stockings, Wigs, Circa 1851, 3 1/2 In. 85.00
Doll, Bisque, Character, Toddler, M.B., 17 In.Tall 73.00
Doll, Bisque, Chinese, Loose Arms And Legs, Pot Belly, 4 In. 22.50
Doll, Bisque, Closed Mouth, 11 In.Tall 99.00
Doll, Bisque, Cloth Body, Closed Mouth, Painted Eyes, 11 In. 175.00
Doll, Bisque, German, Glass Eyes, Dressed, 4 1/2 In.Tall 45.00
Doll, Bisque, Girl, Dressed, Blonde Wig, 3 In.Tall 14.00
Doll, Bisque, Girl, Molded Hair, 7 1/4 In.Tall 50.00
Doll, Bisque, Grandmother, Dressed, 5 1/4 In.Tall 45.00
Doll, Bisque, Japan, 2 In.Tall 1.50
Doll, Bisque, Jointed Arms & Legs, Painted Knee Stockings, Shoes, Undressed 175.00
Doll, Bisque, Jointed, Sleep Eyes, Open Mouth, No Wig, Germany, 23 In. 105.00
Doll, Bisque, Leather Body, Marked Dep, Germany, 12 1/2 In.Tall 65.00
Doll, Bisque, Legs Spread So It Can Stand, 3 1/4 In.Tall 22.50
Doll, Bisque, Mechanical Wind Walker, Stationary, Open Mouth, Pierced Ears 425.00
Doll, Bisque, Molded Necklace & Comb In Hair, Dresden Parian, 13 In. 335.00
Doll, Bisque, Open Dome, Marked 3939, 3 1/2 In.Tall 22.00
Doll, Bisque, Open Mouth, Ball Joint Body, Pierced Ears, 19 In.Tall 85.00
Doll, Bisque, Painted Eyes, Movable Arms & Legs, Human Hair Wig, 3 1/2 In. 35.00
Doll, Bisque, Painted Face & Shoes, Jointed, Dressed, 3 1/2 In., Pair 28.00
Doll, Bisque, Painted Socks & Shoes, Wig, Germany, 4 In. 32.00
Doll, Bisque, Paperweight Eyes, Rigid Body, Dressed, Unmarked, 18 In. 225.00
Doll, Bisque, Signed Germany, Twins, Boy & Girl, Dressed, 3 In.Tall, Pair 25.00
Doll, Bisque, Sleep Eyes, Dressed, Germany, 5 1/2 In. 60.00
Doll, Bisque, Sleep Eyes, Scant Wig, Dressed, Mark Germany, 16 In. Tall 50.00
Doll, Bisque, Strung Arms, Occupied Japan, 3 In. 6.00
Doll, Bisque, Stuffed Body, Composition, Dressed, Germany 390, A 7/om, 11 In. 38.50
Doll, Bisque, 19th Century, 18 In.Tall .... *Illus* 160.00
Doll, Bohr & Proschild, Bisque Head, Sleep Eyes, Bent Limbs, 10 1/2 In.Tall 72.00
Doll, Boy, Baby, All Bisque, Pink Romper, Sweater 50.00
Doll, Boy, Bisque Head, Glass Eyes, Original Hair & Dress 85.00
Doll, Boy, Bisque Head, Sleep Eyes, Open Mouth, Velvet Suit, Germany, 14 In. 75.00
Doll, Boy, Bisque, Indian, 8 In. 150.00
Doll, Boy, Celluloid, Glass Eyes, Blue Velvet Suit, 17 In. 45.00
Doll, Boy, Dressed, Marked Hilda, 18 In. 300.00
Doll, Boy, Grumpy, Composition Head, Velvet Suit, 12 In.Tall 32.00
Doll, Brickette 15.00
Doll, Bru, Dressed, 26 In.Tall 1350.00
Doll, Bru, Kid Body, Bisque Arms, Dressed, 15 In. 1200.00
Doll, Bruno Schmidt, Bisque Head, Composition Body, 12 In.Tall 115.00
Doll, Bubbles, Body Marked, Dressed, 14 1/2 In.Circumference 85.00
Doll, Bubbles, Dressed, Unmarked, 13 In.Circumference 50.00
Doll, Buddy Lee, Composition, Dressed, 12 1/2 In.Tall .... 45.00 To 65.00
Doll, Buddy Lee, Dressed, 13 In. 85.00
Doll, Bulgy Eyes, Closed Mouth, Dressed, Dep, France 395.00
Doll, Bye-Lo, Baby, Bisque, 4 In. 145.00
Doll, Bye-Lo, Bisque Head, Arms, Feet, Dressed, 11 In.Tall 25.00
Doll, Bye-Lo, Bisque, Painted Eyes, Jointed Limbs, Satin Lined Crib 150.00

Doll, Bye-Lo, Blue Eyes, Incised Head, 18 In.Tall 225.00
Doll, Bye-Lo, Celluloid Hands, Sleep Eyes, Cloth Body 175.00
Doll, Bye-Lo, Cloth Body, Composition, 1928, 16 In. 35.00
Doll, Bye-Lo, CPR By Grace S.Putnam, Baby, Bisque Head, Sleep Eyes 235.00
Doll, Bye-Lo, Dressed, 12 1/2 In. 215.00
Doll, Bye-Lo, Dressed, 13 In.Head Circumference 175.00
Doll, Bye-Lo, G.S.P., Rubber Head, 10 In.Tall 85.00
Doll, Bye-Lo, G.S.Putnam, Bisque, Composition Body, Sleeping Eyes, Dressed 330.00
Doll, Bye-Lo, G.S.Putnam, Bisque, 10 In.Tall 180.00
Doll, Bye-Lo, G.S.Putnam, Composition Head, Cloth Body, 14 In.Tall 105.00
Doll, Bye-Lo, G.S.Putnam, Germany, Bisque, Painted Eyes, Movable Limbs 175.00
Doll, Bye-Lo, Grace Putnam, Bisque Head, Celluloid Hands, Cloth Body 125.00
Doll, Bye-Lo, Grace Putnam, Celluloid Hands, 10 In.Head Circumference 190.00
Doll, Bye-Lo, Grace S.Putnam, Bisque Head, 13 In.Tall 150.00
Doll, Bye-Lo, Grace S.Putnam, Celluloid Hands, Cloth Body, Sleep Eyes 165.00
Doll, Bye-Lo, Grace S.Putnam, Germany, Bisque, Swivel Neck, Jointed Limbs 275.00
Doll, Bye-Lo, Signed, Bisque, Painted Eyes, 4 In.Tall 145.00
Doll, Bye-Lo, 10 In.Head, Brown Eyes 187.50
Doll, Campbell Kid, Boy, 8 In.Tall .... 5.00 To 15.00
Doll, Campbell Kid, Composition, Dressed 25.00
Doll, Campbell Kid, Girl, 8 In.Tall .... 5.00 To 15.00
Doll, Campbell Kid, Rubber, Dressed, Ideal Toy, 9 1/2 In. 14.00
Doll, Campbell Kid, Rubber, Dressed, 10 In. 14.00
Doll, Campbell Kid, Vinyl, Ideal, 7 1/2 In. 12.00
Doll, Celluloid, Child, Dressed, Marked S.& M. 8.00
Doll, Celluloid, C.1915, 4 1/2 In.Tall 4.00
Doll, Celluloid, Movable Arms, Circa 1915, 4 In.Tall 4.00
Doll, Character Baby, Bisque Head, Blue Sleep Eyes, Wig, 12 In.Tall 75.00
Doll, Character Baby, Bisque Head, Stationary Eyes, Wig 85.00
Doll, Character, Toddler, Original Clothes, Kr 121, 17 In. 150.00
Doll, Chase Baby, 20 In. 85.00
Doll, Chase Baby, 31 In. 140.00
Doll, Chatty Cathy, Dressed 18.00
Doll, China Head, Blonde, Marked G, C.1880, 6 1/2 In.Tall 50.00
Doll, China Head, Cloth Body, Kid Hands, Dressed, 7 1/2 In.Tall 195.00
Doll, China, Boy, Blonde Hair, German, Dressed, 11 1/2 In.Tall 55.00
Doll, China, Cloth Body, Blonde Molded Hair, 10 1/2 In.Tall 60.00
Doll, China, Flesh Tinted, Molded Bosom, Hair In Braided Bun, Dressed, 18 In. 795.00
Doll, China, Godey, Black Hair, China Hands & Feet, 23 In.Tall 60.00
Doll, China, Woman, Blonde Hair, Dressed, Marked, 11 1/4 In.Tall 45.00
Doll, China, 19th Century, 11 In.Tall .... *Illus* 140.00
Doll, China, 24 In.Tall .... *Illus* 190.00

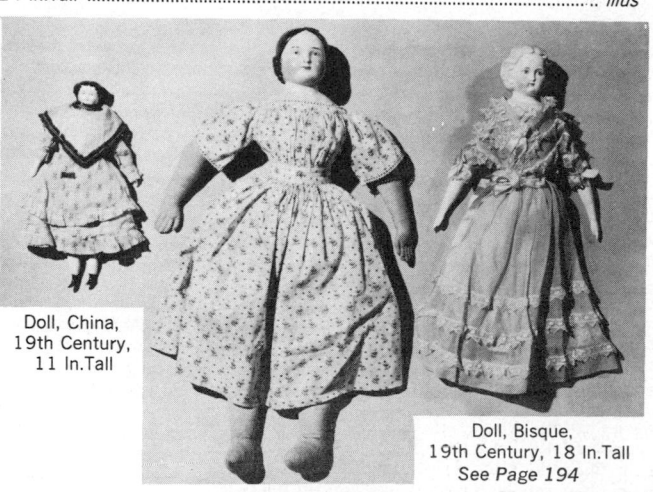

Doll, China,
19th Century,
11 In.Tall

Doll, Bisque,
19th Century, 18 In.Tall
See Page 194

Doll, China, 24 In.Tall

Doll, Chubby Chaney, Bisque, Marked Germany, Movable Head, 3 1/2 In.Tall	38.00
Doll, Chubby Chaney, Nodder Of Our Land, Marked Germany, Bisque, 3 1/2 In.	35.00
Doll, Chubby Kid, Composition, Brown Wig, Painted Features, 1920, 14 In.	37.50
Doll, Clarmaid Parian, Molded Hair, Dressed, 19 In.Tall	90.00
Doll, Cry Baby, Celluloid	7.00
Doll, Cupid, Standing, 5 In., Signed O'Neill	60.00
Doll, D.R.G.M., Shoulder Head, Kidette Body, Voice Box, 17 In.Tall	75.00
Doll, Davy Crockett	7.00
Doll, Deanna Durbin, Undressed, 25 In.	95.00
Doll, Dennis The Menace	12.00
Doll, Denunez, Colored Googly, Skin Wig, 10 In.Tall	110.00
Doll, Dolly Walker, Coleman, Wooden, 28 In.Tall	
Doll, Dopey, Composition Head, Stuffed Body, 11 In.Tall	15.00
Doll, Dotter, China Head, Marked 4 Pat.Dec.7/80, Dressed, 15 1/2 In.Tall	80.00
Doll, Dr.Doolittle	15.00
Doll, Dream Baby, Five Piece Body, Dressed, 13 In.	200.00
Doll, Dream Baby, Stationary Eyes, Dressed, 14 In.	100.00
Doll, Duchess, Open Mouth, Blue Eyes, Mohair Wig, Dressed, 18 1/2 In.Tall	72.50
Doll, Duke & Duchess Of Windsor, Composition Head, Stuffed Body, Pair	45.00
Doll, Dummy, Ventriloquist's, Juro Celebrity Dolls	26.50
Doll, E.D., Bulgy Blue Eyes, 12 In.	175.00
Doll, Eddie Munster	15.00
Doll, Eden Bebe, Ball Jointed, Human Hair Wig, Dressed In Velvet, 23 1/2 In.	425.00
Doll, Eden Bebe, Walker, Open Mouth, Paperweight Eyes, Cork Pate, Dressed	350.00
Doll, Effanbee, Baby Tinyette, Cowboy Outfit, 9 In.	25.00
Doll, Effanbee, Bubbles, 18 In.	22.00
Doll, Effanbee, Composition & Cloth Body, Googly Eyes, Dressed, 17 In.	15.00
Doll, Effanbee, Composition Head, Sleep Eyes, Human Hair Wig, 22 In.	60.00
Doll, Effanbee, Hard Plastic, Undressed, 19 In.	13.00
Doll, Effanbee, Jr., Dressed, 11 1/2 In.Tall	20.00
Doll, Effanbee, Marilee, Composition, Dressed, 21 In.Tall	25.00
Doll, Effanbee, Patsy Baby, Composition, Sleep Eyes, Dressed, 11 In.	35.00
Doll, Effanbee, Patsy Joan, Brown Sleep Eyes, Bracelet	22.50
Doll, Effanbee, Rosemary, Brown Human Hair Wig, Metal Sleep Eyes, 1918	27.50
Doll, Effanbee, Rosemary, Composition, Dressed, 21 In.Tall	25.00
Doll, Effanbee, Sweet Sue, 19 In.	40.00
Doll, Eskimo, Wooden Body, Hide & Cloth Clothing, Baby On Shoulder	200.00
Doll, Esther, China, Blonde, Dressed, 24 In.Tall	150.00
Doll, Fallen Angel	15.00
Doll, Farina, Bisque, Negro, Marked Germany, Movable Head, 3 1/2 In.Tall	38.00
Doll, Fashion, Bisque Head & Shoulder, Kid Body, Two Piece Silk Suit, Bustle	485.00
Doll, Fashion, Smiler, Kid Body, Pierced Ears, Brown Hair, Blue Eyes	425.00
Doll, Felix, Jointed, Wooden, Sullivan, Patent 1924	150.00
Doll, Felt Body, Bisque Hands, Sleep Eyes, Wig, Circa 1894, 23 In.	75.00
Doll, Flapper, Bed, Red Hair, Dressed, 26 In.Tall	25.00
Doll, Flapper, Dressed, 29 In.Tall	50.00
Doll, Floradora, A6/om, Pockethead, Handmade Lace Carrying Pouch	38.00
Doll, Floradora, Bisque Head, Kid Body, A-3-M, Made In Germany, 22 1/2 In.	78.00
Doll, Floradora, Bisque Shoulder Head, Kid Body, Germany, 22 1/2 In.Tall	85.00
Doll, Floradora, Blonde Wig, Sleep Eyes, Composition Body, 18 In.	85.00
Doll, Floradora, Made In Germany, Composition Body, Dressed, 16 In.Tall	67.50
Doll, Floradora, Marked A.M., Kid & Cloth Body, 13 In.Tall	55.00
Doll, Floradora, Sleep Blue Eyes, 31 1/2 In.	160.00
Doll, French Fashion, Kid Body, Closed Mouth, Blue Eyes, Auburn Wig	335.00
Doll, French Fashion, Kid Body, Closed Mouth, Gray Eyes, 11 1/2 In.	335.00
Doll, French Fashion, Pale Bisque, Human Hair Wig, Kid Body, 15 In.	425.00
Doll, French Fashion, Separate Shoulder, Brown Eyes, Redressed, C.1870	395.00
Doll, French, Character Baby, 14 In.Tall	125.00
Doll, French, E9D, 22 In.Tall	290.00
Doll, French, Mon Tresto Girl, Blue Eyes, Clothes, 19 In.Tall	185.00
Doll, Frozen Charlotte, Bisque, Bonnet, 2 1/2 In.	16.00
Doll, Frozen Charlotte, Black Hair, Blue Bow On Leg, Gold Shoes, 3 3/4 In.	20.00
Doll, Frozen Charlotte, Black Hair, Blue Bow On Leg, Gold Shoes, 5 In.	28.00
Doll, Frozen Charlotte, Black Hair, Bow On Leg, Gold Shoes, 4 1/2 In.	25.00
Doll, Frozen Charlotte, Black Hair, Porcelain, 4 In.Tall	30.00
Doll, Frozen Charlotte, Black Molded Hair, Porcelain, 4 1/2 In.Tall	45.00

Doll, Frozen Charlotte, Germany, Arms Extended, 2 In.Tall	12.50
Doll, Frozen Charlotte, Gold Painted Shoes, Blue Garters, Porcelain	25.00
Doll, Frozen Charlotte, Negro, 5 In.	65.00
Doll, Frozen Charlotte, Pink Luster Face, Porcelain Body, Painted Hair	495.00
Doll, Frozen Charlotte, Porcelain, 2 In.	3.00
Doll, Frozen Charlotte, Staffordshire, 2 1/8 In.	15.00
Doll, Frozen Charlotte, 3 1/8 In.	25.00
Doll, Fulper Baby, Human Hair, Open Mouth, 15 In.Tall	135.00
Doll, Fulper, Bisque Head & Hands, Cloth Body, Expressive Eyes, Teeth, 20 In.	110.00
Doll, Fulper, Girl, 17 In.	75.00
Doll, Fulper, Toddler	125.00
Doll, G.Benda Of Coburg, Red Hair, Socket Head, Silk Dress, Bustle, Lace	175.00
Doll, G.I.Joe, Dressed	2.50
Doll, Gabby, Wooden, Marked C, Paramount Pictures, Ideal, Date 1939, 10 In.	55.00
Doll, Gebruder Heubach, Character, Receding Chin, 16 In.Tall	80.00
Doll, Gebruder Heubach, Character, Sleep Eyes, 18 In.Tall	100.00
Doll, Gebruder Heubach, Germany, Character, Laughing Boy, Bisque Head, 11 In.	200.00
Doll, Geisha Girl, Bisque Head, Silk Gown, Circa 1925	35.00
Doll, Giletti, Character, Girl, Marked Depose Fabrication Francaise, 24 In.	275.00
Doll, Ginny, Vogue, Original Box	12.50
Doll, Girl Scout, Marked Gorgene On Neck, Stuffed, 13 In.Tall	5.00
Doll, Girl, Molded Hair, Blonde, Drop Earrings, Dressed, 19 In.Tall	52.00
Doll, Girl, Stationary Eyes, Ball Joint, France, 18 In.	150.00
Doll, Girl, Wax Over Papier-Mache, Glass Eyes, Cloth Body, Dressed, 16 In.	62.50
Doll, Godey, Porcelain Hands & Feet, Dressed, 13 In.	32.50
Doll, Goldilocks, Three Bears, Stuffed, Promotional, Kellogg Co., 1925	60.00
Doll, Goldwater, 6 In.Tall	3.00
Doll, Goo Goo, Bisque Head, Paperweight Sleep Eyes, Papier-Mache Body	275.00
Doll, Greiner, Papier-Mache, Cloth Body, Leather Arms, Stitched Fingers	160.00
Doll, Handwerck, Ball Jointed, Sleep Eyes, Open Mouth, Pierced Ears, 29 In.	89.50
Doll, Handwerck, Brown Eyes & Hair, Composition, Dressed, Germany, 29 In.	350.00
Doll, Handwerck, Character Face, Sleep Eyes, Blonde Wig, Dressed, 24 In.Tall	85.00
Doll, Handwerck, Oriental Baby, Brown Sleep Eyes, 17 In.Tall	95.00
Doll, Handwerck, Stationary Brown Eyes, Dressed, Pink & Blue	185.00
Doll, Happy Fat Boy, 4 In.Tall	135.00
Doll, Hebee Shebee, Japanese, Bisque, Holding Dog On Chain, 3 1/2 In.Tall	5.00
Doll, Hebee Shebee, Wooden, Jointed, 13 In.Tall	125.00
Doll, Hedda Get Better	15.00
Doll, Heubach Koppelsdorf, Baby, Composition Body, Sailor Suit, 24 In.	175.00
Doll, Heubach Koppelsdorf, Bent Legs, Open Mouth, Pierced Nostrils	65.00
Doll, Heubach Koppelsdorf, Bent Legs, Open Mouth, Wig, 14 In.Tall	65.00
Doll, Heubach Koppelsdorf, Bisque Head, Closed Eyes, Lavender Dress & Hat	125.00
Doll, Heubach Koppelsdorf, Bisque Head, Sleep Eyes, Composition Body, Dress	50.00
Doll, Heubach Koppelsdorf, Blonde Hair, Brown Eyes, 22 1/2 In.	150.00
Doll, Heubach Koppelsdorf, Brown Hair & Eyes, 27 In.Tall	125.00
Doll, Heubach Koppelsdorf, Composition Body, Sleep Eyes, Dressed, 29 In.	130.00
Doll, Heubach Koppelsdorf, Jointed Body, Mohair Wig, Dressed	85.00
Doll, Heubach Koppelsdorf, No.320, Baby, Breather, Blue Sleep Eyes, 8 In.Tall	65.00
Doll, Heubach Koppelsdorf, Sleep Eyes, Open Mouth, Dressed, 16 In.Tall	55.00
Doll, Heubach, Baby, Bald Head, Closed Mouth, Pierced Ears, 11 In.	135.00
Doll, Heubach, Bisque Head, Kid Body, Stationary Eyes, Dressed, 25 In.	140.00
Doll, Heubach, Boy, Bisque Eyes Glance To The Side, 5 In.Tall	130.00
Doll, Huebach, Boy, Intaglio Eyes, Kid Body, Velvet Suit, 22 In.Tall	235.00
Doll, Heubach, Character, Baby, Two Teeth, Dimples, 17 In.Tall	105.00
Doll, Heubach, Character, Boy, Solid Dome, 12 In.Tall	195.00
Doll, Heubach, Horseshoe Mark, Bisque Shoulder Head, 19 In.Tall	68.00
Doll, Heubach, Kid Body, Brown Stationary Eyes & Hair, 19 In.Tall	60.00
Doll, Heubach, Shoulder Head, Brown Eyes, 23 In.	97.50
Doll, Heubach, Signed With Sunburst Mark, 12 In.	225.00
Doll, Horseman, Baby, Crawling	15.00
Doll, Hummel, Girl, Rubber, Signed	75.00
Doll, Hummel, Rubber, Clothed, 11 In., Pair	45.00
Doll, Huret, Closed Mouth	800.00
Doll, Ideal, Betsy Wetsy, Composition Head, Pat.No.225207	35.00
Doll, Ideal, Composition, Flirty Eyes, Cries, Dressed, 22 In.Tall	22.00
Doll, Ideal, Marked, Flirting Eyes, Dressed	60.00

Doll, Indian Chief, Dressed, Tomahawk, Tin Face, Walks, Waves, Windup	12.00
Doll, Indian, Cloth & Buckskin, Blue, White, Red Beading, Circa 1920	30.00
Doll, Indian, Plastic, Movable Arms, Legs, & Head, Sleep Eyes, 11 In.Tall	5.00
Doll, Infant, Poured Wax, Embedded Hair, Paperweight Eyes, France, 8 In.	75.00
Doll, J.D., Paris, Closed Mouth, Bisque Head, Paperweight Eyes, Dressed	198.00
Doll, J.D.K., Baby, Bisque, Swivel Neck, Glass Sleep Eyes, 8 1/2 In.Tall	150.00
Doll, J.D.K., Character, Swivel Neck, Dome, Wiggle Tongue, 8 1/2 In.Tall	175.00
Doll, Jackie Cooper, Bisque, Marked Germany, Movable Head, 3 1/2 In.Tall	40.00
Doll, John F. Kennedy, Rocking Chair, Circa 1962, 5 In.High	3.50
Doll, Jullien, France, Girl, 15 In.Tall	225.00
Doll, Jullien, France, Open Mouth, Teeth, Pierced Ears, Human Hair Wig	425.00
Doll, Jumeau, Bebe Du Bon Marche, Closed Mouth, Dressed, 17 1/2 In.	365.00
Doll, Jumeau, Bisque Head, Composition Body, Marked 1907, 20 In.	275.00
Doll, Jumeau, Bisque Head, Open Mouth, Glass Eyes, Incised 1907, 20 1/2 In.	225.00
Doll, Jumeau, Bisque, Paperweight Eyes, Pierced Ears, Wig, 1907, 28 In.Tall	300.00
Doll, Jumeau, Blue Eyes, Applied Ears, 27 In.	850.00
Doll, Jumeau, Closed Mouth, Blue Eyes, Original Clothes, 18 In.Tall	500.00
Doll, Jumeau, Closed Mouth, Fully Signed, 27 In.Tall	585.00
Doll, Jumeau, Closed Mouth, Human Hair Wig, Dressed, 21 In.	425.00
Doll, Jumeau, Closed Mouth, Human Hair Wig, Dressed, 27 In.	595.00
Doll, Jumeau, Closed Mouth, Human Hair Wig, Pink Dress & Bonnet	425.00
Doll, Jumeau, Closed Mouth, Signed Head & Torso, 27 In.Tall	650.00
Doll, Jumeau, Fashion, Unmarked, 17 In.	375.00
Doll, Jumeau, French Fashion, Turned Neck	450.00
Doll, Jumeau, Gray Eyes, Clothed, 13 1/2 In.	375.00
Doll, Jumeau, Human Hair, Blue Paperweight Eyes, 1907, 33 In.Tall	395.00
Doll, Jumeau, Laughing, Stationary Eyes, Molded Teeth, Dressed, SFBJ 236	325.00
Doll, Jumeau, Open Mouth, Blue Eyes, Dressed, 19 In.	310.00
Doll, Jumeau, Open Mouth, Dressed In Peach Silk Coat, Marked 1907, 24 In.	260.00
Doll, Jumeau, Open Mouth, Dressed, 17 In.Tall	350.00
Doll, Jumeau, Open Mouth, Human Hair Wig, Signed, 22 In.	250.00
Doll, Jumeau, Original Clothes, 17 In.	375.00
Doll, Jumeau, Paperweight Eyes, Closed Mouth, Pierced Ears, Wig, 15 In.	550.00
Doll, Jumeau, Paperweight Eyes, Composition Body, Blonde Wig, Dressed, 28 In.	600.50
Doll, Jumeau, Pierced Ears, Open Mouth, Brown Eyes, Wig, Marked, 22 In.	265.00
Doll, Jumeau, Pierced Ears, Open Mouth, Teeth, Dressed	325.00
Doll, Jumeau, Sleep Eyes, Open Mouth, Teeth, Human Hair Wig, Dressed, 31 In.	350.00
Doll, Jumeau, Walker, Throws Kisses, Paperweight Eyes, Marked, 22 1/2 In.	326.00
Doll, Juno, Tin Head With Glass Eyes, 14 In.Tall	85.00
Doll, K & H Walkure, Sleep Eyes, Brown Wig, Green Satin Dress, 17 In.	90.00
Doll, K*r, Blue Sleep Eyes, Ball Jointed, Blonde Human Hair, 34 In.Tall	325.00
Doll, K*r, Boy, Bisque Head, Molded Hair, Glass Eyes, Teeth, Composition	125.00
Doll, K*r, Brown Eyes & Hair, 40 In.Tall	65.00
Doll, K*r, Brown Sleep Eyes, Kid Torso, Bisque Hands, 29 In.Tall	150.00
Doll, K*r, Celluloid Head, Flirty Eyes, Jointed, Undressed, 26 In.Tall	95.00
Doll, K*r, Girl, Ball Jointed, Closed Mouth, 28 In.Tall	500.00
Doll, K*r, Kaiser, Baby, Painted Eyes, Christening Dress, 14 In.Tall	295.00
Doll, K*r, Kaiser, Baby, Painted Eyes, White Christening Dress, 14 In.Tall	395.00
Doll, K*r, Kaiser, Baby, 14 In.Tall	210.00
Doll, K*r, No.100, Kaiser, Baby, Composition Body, Dressed, 14 In.Tall	195.00
Doll, K*r, No.128, Baby, Brown Sleep Eyes, 20 In.Tall	250.00
Doll, K*r, Pierced Ears, 33 1/2 In.Tall	230.00
Doll, K*r, Turns Head While Walking, 30 In.Tall	350.00
Doll, Kestner, Baby Girl, Two Teeth, Brown Eyes, 17 In.	100.00
Doll, Kestner, Baby, Stationary Blue Eyes, Marked H JDK, 15 In.	195.00
Doll, Kestner, Bisque Arms, Kid Body, Sleeping Brown Eyes, 30 In.Tall	125.00
Doll, Kestner, Bisque Head, Ball Jointed, Solid Plate Scalp Cover, Dressed	160.00
Doll, Kestner, Bisque Head, Stationary Eyes, Brown Wig, Ball Jointed, Dressed	125.00
Doll, Kestner, Blonde Curly Hair, Kid Body, Dressed, 27 In.	85.00
Doll, Kestner, Blue Stationary Eyes, Blonde Hair, Circa 1890, Germany, 23 In.	225.00
Doll, Kestner, Brown Sleep Eyes, Kid Body, 24 In.	95.00
Doll, Kestner, Character Baby Head, Incised 201	150.00
Doll, Kestner, Character Baby, Closed Mouth, Incised 211	250.00
Doll, Kestner, Character Baby, Incised 152	225.00
Doll, Kestner, Character Baby, Sleep Eyes, Composition Body, Gown & Hat	110.00
Doll, Kestner, Character Baby, Tongue, Teeth, Composition, Undressed	125.00

Doll, Kestner, Germany, Ball Point Body, 22 In.Tall	115.00
Doll, Kestner, Girl, Bisque Head, Sleep Eyes, Open Mouth, Lace Dress, 13 In.	68.00
Doll, Kestner, Girl, Kid Body, Brown Sleep Eyes, 24 In.	70.00
Doll, Kestner, Kid Body, Sleep Eyes, Blonde Wig, 24 In.	80.00
Doll, Kestner, Sleep Eyes, Human Hair Wig, Velvet Gown, 18 In.	105.00
Doll, Kestner, Toddler, Blue Open & Close Eyes	125.00
Doll, Kestner, Wax Over Composition, Open Mouth, Ball Jointed, Wig, 17 In.	240.00
Doll, Kestner, 152, Boy, Bisque, Kid Body, Painted Eyes, Closed Mouth, 12 In.	110.00
Doll, Kestner, 154, Bisque Head, Kid Body, Blue Eyes, Dressed, 18 In.Tall	85.00
Doll, King Henry VIII, Marked Madame Tussauds, London, Metal, 3 In.Tall	10.00
Doll, Kitten, Baby, 7 In.Tall	10.00
Doll, Knickerbocker, 2 Headed, 12 In.Tall	4.50
Doll, Lenci, Boy, Felt Clothes, Brown Wig, Brown Eyes, 11 In.Tall	75.00
Doll, Lenci, Girl, Felt Clothes, Yellow Braids, Blue Eyes, 9 In.Tall	60.00
Doll, Leuzzi, Sailor, Celluloid	12.00
Doll, Limoges, Bisque Head, Stationary Eyes, Composition Body, France	78.00
Doll, Limoges, 2 Rows Of Teeth, 18 In.Tall	275.00
Doll, Linda Williams, Marked, Original Dress, 15 In.Tall	12.50
Doll, Little Henry	12.00
Doll, Little Hugguns, Elastic Strung, 12 In.Tall	15.00
Doll, Little Lulu	12.00
Doll, Little Miss Revlon, 10 1/2 In.Tall	8.50 To 12.00
Doll, Madam Hendren, Whistling Sailor, Dressed	20.00
Doll, Man, Metal Head, Cloth Body, Bisque Hands, 11 In.	150.00
Doll, Man, Woman, Bisque Head, Kid Body, Molded Hair, Circa 1830, 10 In., Pair	500.00
Doll, Mannequin, Clothes, Patterns, Simplicity, 12 1/2 In.	25.00
Doll, Maybelle, 7 In.Tall	10.00
Doll, Mechanical, Girl On Music Box, Rolls Hoop, Head Turns, Legs Move, Paris	575.00
Doll, Mechanical, On Music Box, Head Turns, Legs Move, Pushes Hoop, France	575.00
Doll, Mickey & Minnie Mouse, Bisque, Marked Walt E.Disney, 4 1/2 In.Tall	48.00
Doll, Milliner's Model, Wax Face & Hands, Wire Torso, Beaded Gown, 15 In.	110.00
Doll, Milliner's Model, 8 1/2 In.Tall	45.00
Doll, Milliner's Model, 17 In.Tall	275.00
Doll, Minerva, Boy's Clothes, 11 In.	27.50
Doll, Minerva, Tin Head, Bisque Arms, Painted Features, Dressed, 12 In.Tall	28.00
Doll, Minnie Mouse, Rubber Face, Shoes, Hands, 13 In.	23.00
Doll, Minnie Mouse, Velvet, Straw And Cotton, 13 In.	50.00
Doll, Mon Tresor, Blue Paperweight Eyes, Blonde Human Hair Wig, 21 In.Tall	250.00
Doll, Morimura Bros., Bisque Head, Sleep Eyes, Bent Leg, C.1910	90.00
Doll, Morimura Bros., Bisque Shoulder Head, Cloth Body, 20 In.Tall	55.00
Doll, Mr.McGoo, Arms & Legs, Move, Original Dress, 12 In.Tall	35.00
Doll, Munster Girl	15.00
Doll, Nancy, Composition, 17 In.Tall	25.00
Doll, Negro, Celluloid, In Diaper, 4 In.High	1.00
Doll, Negro, Flirt Girl	40.00
Doll, Negro, Stuffed, 15 In.Tall	45.00
Doll, Nippon Bisque, Boy Toddler, Voice Box In Head, 16 In.	65.00
Doll, Nodder Of Colored Minstrel Man, Marked Germany, Bisque, 3 1/2 In.	25.00
Doll, Occupied Japan, 5 In.High	10.00
Doll, Oliver Hardy, Rubber Head, Stuffed Body, 11 In.Tall	5.00
Doll, Open Mouth, Teeth, Wig, Blue Eyes, Limoges, 24 In.	275.00
Doll, Paper, Betsy McCall, Goes Western, Uncut, 1955	3.00
Doll, Paper, Betty Bonnet, Patriotic Party, Seven Dolls & Costumes, 1917	10.00
Doll, Paper, Betty Bonnet's Big Brother, 1917, Uncut	8.00
Doll, Paper, Daisy & Her Baby Doll, May, 1930, Uncut	6.00
Doll, Paper, Dennison, Girl, One Coat, Six Dresses	7.00
Doll, Paper, Dolly Dingle Flies To Russia, March, 1928, Uncut	6.00
Doll, Paper, Dolly Dingle Visits Japan, February, 1928, Uncut	6.00
Doll, Paper, Dolly Dingle, Sept, 1926	5.00
Doll, Paper, Dolly Dingle's Trip To Persia, June, 1928	6.00
Doll, Paper, Hats, Signed Tuck, 4 3/4 In., Set Of 5	35.00
Doll, Paper, Sheila Young, Betty Bonnet's Big Brother, Uncut, May, 1917	6.00
Doll, Paper, Sheila Young, Betty Bonnet's Country Cousins, Uncut, March, 1917	6.00
Doll, Paper, Sheila Young, Lettie Lane, Minister, Best Man, January, 1910	3.50
Doll, Paper, Sunshine Biscuit, One Outfit, Dated April 26, 1916	5.00
Doll, Paper, Tuck, Advertising Leggings, Shoes, Boots, Set Of 5	38.00

Doll, Paper, Tuck, Four Costumes & Hats, 1894	35.00
Doll, Paper, Walking, Pat.1922, J.B.Caroll Co., 6 In.	9.75
Doll, Papier-Mache Head, Inset Glass Eyes, Closed Mouth, Cloth Body	275.00
Doll, Papier-Mache, Bulgy Eyes, Human Hair Wig, 31 In.Tall	120.00
Doll, Papier-Mache, Chinese With Speaker For Cryer, 8 In.Tall	17.50
Doll, Papier-Mache, Greiner Label, 1858, 25 1/2 In.Tall	115.00
Doll, Papier-Mache, 38 In.Tall	250.00
Doll, Parian, Cloth Body, Pierced Ears, Painted Eyes, Close Mouth, 16 1/2 In.	275.00
Doll, Parian, Girl, Taffeta Gown, Marked, 15 1/2 In.Tall	150.00
Doll, Patsy Ann, Bisque, German, 16 In.Tall	30.00
Doll, Patsy Ann, Molded Hair, Blue Sleeping Eyes, 14 In.	28.50
Doll, Penny, Blue Bonnet	5.00
Doll, Penny, Negro, Jointed Arms	10.00
Doll, Penny, Wooden, Dressed	2.50
Doll, Peter Pan	7.00
Doll, Piano Baby, see Bisque, Piano Baby	
Doll, Pincushion Head, Gold Band In Brown Hair, 4 In.Tall	10.00
Doll, Pincushion Head, Gray Molded Hair With Ribbon, 2 1/2 In.	3.00
Doll, Pincushion Head, Little Girl, Molded Clothing, 2 1/2 In.Tall	3.50
Doll, Pincushion, Arms Over Head, Pink Headband, Porcelain, Germany	8.00
Doll, Puncushion, Bisque, Movable Arms, 2 1/4 In.Tall	15.00
Doll, Puncushion, Bisque, Yellow Satin Cushion, Japan	8.00
Doll, Pincushion, Blonde Hair, Arms Folded On Chest, Porcelain, 4 In.	6.00
Doll, Pincushion, Blonde, Defined Bust, Porcelain, Germany	15.00
Doll, Pincushion, Blonde, Yellow Low Cut Gown, Hand On Hip, Porcelain	9.00
Doll, Pincushion, Brown China Molded Upsweep Hairdo, Pearls At Neck	10.00
Doll, Pincushion, Brown China Molded Upsweep Hairdo, Sequin Trim	10.00
Doll, Pincushion, Germany, Arms Extended, Blonde Molded Hairdo	30.00
Doll, Pincushion, Germany, 3 In.Tall	3.00
Doll, Pincushion, Loop For Skirt, Germany	8.00
Doll, Pincushion, Molded Blonde Hair, Porcelain, German, 5 In.Tall	10.00
Doll, Pincushion, Pink Hat With Red Roses, Yellow Hair, Holds Red Roses	9.50
Doll, Pinky Lee, Glass Eyes, 24 In.Tall	45.00
Doll, Pinocchio, Bisque, Japan, 4 1/2 In.Tall	12.00
Doll, Pinocchio, Composition, Walt Disney, 11 In.Tall	35.00
Doll, Pinocchio, Composition, 8 1/2 In.Tall	35.00
Doll, Pinocchio, Dressed, 9 In.	23.00
Doll, Pinocchio, Marked W.Disney Prod., U.S.A., 10 In.Tall	37.00
Doll, Pinocchio, Wood, 1935, Marked Ideal, 21 In.	150.00
Doll, Pinocchio, Wooden, Ideal, 10 In.Tall	55.00
Doll, Pinocchio, Wooden, Poland, 7 In.Tall	5.00
Doll, Pitiful Pearl, Glad, 1949, 19 In.	25.00
Doll, Plains Indian, Hide & Cloth, Multicolor Glass Beaded Dress, 15 In.	250.00
Doll, Pol Parrot Shoes, Bisque, 5 In.Tall	9.50
Doll, Popeye, Dressed, Gray, Blue, Cap, Moving Arms	25.00
Doll, Popeye, Wooden, Jointed, 5 In.Tall	25.00
Doll, Popeye, Wooden, Marked C, 1935, King Features, 12 In.Tall	55.00
Doll, Porcelain Head & Hands, Kid Body, 17 In.	60.00
Doll, Porcelain Head, Arms, Cloth Body, Red Dress, 18 In.	80.00
Doll, Porcelain Head, Recovered Cloth Body, Kid Arms & Hands, Curly Wig	250.00
Doll, Porcelain Head, Shoulders, Limbs, Molded Hair, Dressed, 7 In., Germany	50.00
Doll, Porcelain Shoulder Head & Limbs, Cloth Body, Red Eyelines, Dressed	225.00
Doll, Porcelain Shoulder Head, Closed Mouth, Painted Eyes, Cloth Body, 1850	275.00
Doll, Princess Elizabeth, Molded Felt Painted Face, Johnson Bros., Ltd.	75.00
Doll, Puppertrina	15.00
Doll, Puppet, Dream Baby, A & M, 8 1/2 In.Circumference	130.00
Doll, Puppet, Hand, Dopey, Disney	6.00
Doll, Puppet, Hand, Jiminy Cricket, Disney	6.00
Doll, Puppet, Hand, Minnie Mouse, Disney	6.00
Doll, Puppet, Hand, Pedro, Disney	6.00
Doll, Puppet, Man, Wooden, Russian, 7 3/4 In.Tall	15.00
Doll, Queen Louise, Bisque Head, Dressed, Germany, 24 In.	75.00
Doll, Queen Louise, Brown Wig, Brown Eyes, Dressed, 15 In.Tall	75.00
Doll, Queen Louise, Lashed Sleep Eyes, Ball Jointed, 24 In.	95.00
Doll, Queen Louise, Partially Dressed, 22 In.	135.00
Doll, Rabery & Delphien, Closed Mouth, Solid Wrists, Human Hair Wig, 18 In.	300.00

Doll, Rag, African Mother With Twin Babies Sucking, 22 In.Tall 12.00
Doll, Rag, Topsy, Knife Around Neck, Little Eva, Civil War Era 100.00
Doll, Raggedy Ann, Handmade, Washable, 20 In.Tall 11.00
Doll, Revalo, Germany, Dressed, 16 In.Tall 75.00
Doll, Rockabye Baby, Stationary Eyes, Composition Body, Christening Dress 80.00
Doll, Royal Canadian Mounted Police, Norah Wellings, Velvet Cloth 12.50
Doll, Ruth, China, Brunette, 20 In.Tall 125.00
Doll, S & C, Germany, Dressed, 9 1/2 In.Tall 45.00
Doll, S & H, Bisque Head, Composition Body, Paperweight Eyes, 7 In.Tall 75.00
Doll, S & H, Oriental Girl, Open Mouth, Kimono, 14 In. 355.00
Doll, S.F.B.J., Bisque Head, Composition Body, France, 25 In.Tall 275.00
Doll, S.F.B.J., Bisque Head, Composition Body, 16 1/2 In. 175.00
Doll, S.F.B.J., Bisque Head, Composition, 16 In.Tall 175.00
Doll, S.F.B.J., Bisque Head, Painted Eyes, Closed Mouth, Jointed 75.00
Doll, S.F.B.J., Bisque, Sleep Eyes, Human Hair Wig, 10 1/2 In.Tall 125.00
Doll, S.F.B.J., Bisque, Sleep Eyes, Wig, Undressed, 19 In.Tall 175.00
Doll, S.F.B.J., Composition Body, Bisque Head, Purple Velvet Clothes, 12 In. 87.50
Doll, S.F.B.J., Depose 7, Bisque Head, Lashed Eyes, Wig, Dressed, 18 In.Tall 250.00
Doll, S.F.B.J., France, Character, Toddler, Sleep Eyes, Human Hair Wig, 25 In. 425.00
Doll, S.F.B.J., Mechanical Head, Legs, Human Hair Wig, 20 In.Tal .... 200.00 To 225.00
Doll, S.F.B.J., No.60, Girl, Dressed, Blue Sleeping Eyes, Human Hair Wig 195.00
Doll, S.F.B.J., No.235, Jumeau, Boy, Laughing, Molded Hair, 21 In.Tall 400.00
Doll, S.F.B.J., Open Mouth, Human Hair Wig, Dressed, 20 In. 250.00
Doll, S.F.B.J., Open Mouth, Paperweight Purple Eyes, Human Hair Wig, 22 In. 195.00
Doll, S.F.B.J., Paperweight Eyes, Bisque Head, France, 60 Paris 3, 20 In. 195.00
Doll, S.F.B.J., Paperweight Sleep Eyes, Closed Pouty Mouth, 13 1/2 In. 1350.00
Doll, S.F.B.J., Paris, No.60, French Label On Torso, 20 In.Tall 125.00
Doll, S.F.B.J., Stationary Brown Eyes, Solid Wrists, 24 In. 175.00
Doll, S.F.B.J., 60 Paris 3, Bisque Head, Paperweight Eyes, Dressed 195.00
Doll, S.F.B.J., 236, Baby, Laughing, Hand-Knit Outfit, France 150.00
Doll, S.F.B.J., 301, Jumeau, Bisque, Sleep Eyes, Pierced Ears, Wig, 19 In.Tall 235.00
Doll, S.Schemarke, Turtle Mark, Germany, Celluloid, 16 1/2 In.Tall 18.00
Doll, Samurai Warrior, Suit Of Armor, Brocade, Stool, Wood, C.1800, 24 In.Tall ... 350.00
Doll, Santa Claus, Black Stocking Boots, C.1900, 26 In.Tall 17.00
Doll, Saroff, Character, Henry VIII, Composition Painted Head, Cloth Body 30.00
Doll, Saucy Walker, Circa 1945, 20 In. 20.00
Doll, Saucy Walker, Composition, Dark Wig, 16 In.Tall 15.00
Doll, Scarlet O'Hara, Composition, Pink Gown & Hat, 1937, 19 In. 30.00
Doll, Schlaggenwald, Boy, Bisque, Molded Hair, Socks, Shoes, 5 In. 40.00
Doll, Schoenhut, Boy 110.00
Doll, Schoenhut, Character, Girl, Intaglio Eyes, Closed Mouth, Mohair Wig 200.00
Doll, Schoenhut, Clown, 8 In.Tall 35.00
Doll, Schoenhut, Dressed, Wooden, 16 In. 175.00
Doll, Schoenhut, Girl, Dressed, 16 In.Tall 188.00
Doll, Schoenhut, Girl, Dressed, 17 In. 150.00
Doll, Schoenhut, Girl, Dressed, 20 In.Tall 80.00
Doll, Schoenhut, Girl, Intaglio Eyes, 22 In.Tall 175.00
Doll, Schoenhut, Girl, Pouty Closed Mouth, Brown Eyes, 19 1/2 In. 160.00
Doll, Schoenhut, Oriental Man, 8 In.Tall 50.00
Doll, Schoenhut, Painted Features, Molded Teeth, Mohair Wig, Dressed, 17 In. 135.00
Doll, Schoenhut, Sleep Eyes, Dressed, 15 In. 175.00
Doll, Schoenhut, Wooden, Dressed, 22 In. 140.00
Doll, Schutzmarke, Germany, Celluloid Head, 11 In.Tall 35.00
Doll, SH-PB In Star, Sleeping Eyes, Open Mouth, Four Teeth, Dressed 120.00
Doll, Shebee Hebee, Wood, Jointed, 13 In. 125.00
Doll, Shirley Temple, Flirty Eyes, Marked 115.00
Doll, Simon & Halbig, Ball Point Body, Pierced Ears, Dressed, 20 In.Tall 125.00
Doll, Simon & Halbig, Bisque Bald Head, 11 1/2 In.Tall 40.00
Doll, Simon & Halbig, Bisque Head, Composition Body, Wig, White Dress, 2 In. 150.00
Doll, Simon & Halbig, Bisque Head, Composition, Dressed, K Star R, 29 In. 205.00
Doll, Simon & Halbig, Brown Eyes, Composition Body, Human Hair Wig, 13 In. 95.00
Doll, Simon & Halbig, Character Baby, Blue Sleep Eyes, Closed Mouth, 20 In. 475.00
Doll, Simon & Halbig, Character Baby, Laughing Mouth, Flutter Tongue, 20 In. 175.00
Doll, Simon & Halbig, Colored, 11 In.Tall 120.00
Doll, Simon & Halbig, Dep, German Fashion, Bisque Body, Dressed, 15 1/2 In. 275.00
Doll, Simon & Halbig, Dressed, 32 In.Tall 225.00

Doll, Simon & Halbig, Gibson Girl, Sleep Eyes, Hourglass Figure, Dressed	295.00
Doll, Simon & Halbig, Girl, Marked, Sleep Eyes, Dressed, 31 In.Tall	175.00
Doll, Simon & Halbig, Handwerck, Pierced Ears, 25 In.Tall	135.00
Doll, Simon & Halbig, K*r, Baby, Weggle Tongue, Sleep Eyes, Gown, 19 In.Tall	175.00
Doll, Simon & Halbig, K*r, Walker, Bisque Head Moves, 15 In.Tall	225.00
Doll, Simon & Halbig, K*r, 703, Bisque, Turns Head, Walks, Sleep Eyes, 20 In.	235.00
Doll, Simon & Halbig, Shoulder Head, Pierced Ears, Dressed, 23 In.	225.00
Doll, Simon & Halbig, Sleep Eyes, Blonde Wig, Kid Body, Jointed, Dressed	145.00
Doll, Simon & Halbig, Sleep Eyes, Hair Eyelashes, Human Hair Wig, 11 In.	150.00
Doll, Simon & Halbig, Stationary Eyes, New Wig, Dressed, 28 In.Tall	110.00
Doll, Simon & Halbig, 949, Character, Closed Mouth, 16 In.Tall	325.00
Doll, Skippy, Bisque, Marked Percy L.Crosby, 5 In.Tall	24.00
Doll, Sleep Eyes, Human Hair Wig, Germany, 1912, 24 In.	150.00
Doll, Slumbermote	20.00
Doll, Snookums, Wood & Papier-Mache, Germany, 11 In.Tall	48.00
Doll, Snow White, Composition, 13 In.Tall	15.00
Doll, Soldier, World War I, Composition, Painted Features, Original Clothes	27.50
Doll, Sonja Henie, Fully Dressed, 18 In.	85.00
Doll, Sonja Henie, Madam Alexander, Suitcase, Tag .... 45.00 To 50.00	
Doll, Steiner, Closed, Unsigned, Dressed	350.00
Doll, Steiner, Cork Crown, Paperweight Eyes, Signed, Dressed, 11 In.	650.00
Doll, Steiner, Mechanical, Head & Arms Move, Cries, Key, Two Rows Of Teeth	595.00
Doll, Steiner, Paperweight Eyes, Solid Wrists, Closed Mouth, 22 In.	750.00
Doll, Steiner, Pierced Ears, Blue Eyes, Hat, Coat, Muff, 21 In.	550.00
Doll, Steiner, Unjointed Wrists, Wig, France, 9 In.	385.00
Doll, Storybook, Bisque, Dressed	5.00
Doll, Storybook, Nancy Ann, Bisque, Dressed, 5 In.Tall	5.00
Doll, Storybook, U.S.A., Bisque, 5 1/2 In.Tall	6.50
Doll, Sweet Pea, Plastic, 1 1/4 In.Tall	1.50
Doll, Sweet Sue, Silk Dress, 25 In.Tall	20.00
Doll, Sweet Tears	10.00
Doll, Tabatha	12.00
Doll, Terri Lee, Blue Gown, Box, 17 In.Tall .... 21.50 To 28.00	
Doll, Terri Lee, Brunette, Dressed	20.00
Doll, Terri Lee, Dark Hair, Dressed, 16 In.Tall	30.00
Doll, Terri Lee, Original Clothes, 10 In.Tall	16.50
Doll, Terri Lee, Original Clothes, 11 In.Tall	16.50
Doll, Thumbelina, Hand Knit Outfit	20.00
Doll, Tiny Tears, Rubber, Plastic Head, Lamb's Wool Wig	5.00
Doll, Toddler, SP Mark, Sleep Glass Eyes, 13 In.Tall	25.00
Doll, Toni	12.00
Doll, Unis, Bisque Head, Composition, Voice Box, New Wig, Marked, 32 In.	350.00
Doll, Unis, Bisque Head, Stationary Eyes, Wig, France, 18 In.	110.00
Doll, Unis, France, 251, Character Baby, Vaseline Bisque, Sleep Eyes, 17 In.	325.00
Doll, Unis, Girl, Open Mouth, Wig, Husky Body, France, 25 In.	210.00
Doll, Ventriloquist's, Red Hair, Dressed	25.00
Doll, Vogue, Ginny Type, Dressed	6.50
Doll, Voice Box, Ball Joint, Blue Eyes, Germany, 20 In.	65.00
Doll, Voice Box, Jointed Body, Brown Sleep Eyes, Germany, 20 In.	70.00
Doll, W.C.Fields, Bisque, German, 3 In.Tall	6.50
Doll, Walker, Sleep Eyes, Kid Body, Bisque Head, Ball Jointed, Pink Dress	85.00
Doll, Waltershousen, 10-1916, Bisque, Composition Body, 26 In.Tall	75.00
Doll, Wax, Blown Eyes, Pierced Ears, Molded Shoes, 26 1/2 In.Tall	80.00
Doll, Wax, Boy, Molded Hat, Blown Eyes, Wooden Hands & Feet, 11 In.Tall	50.00
Doll, Windy Ann	10.00
Doll, Wooden, Hinged, Painted Face, 6 1/2 In.Tall	45.00
Doll, Wooden, Miniature, Painted Face, 2 3/4 In.Tall	40.00
Doll, Wooden, Vermont, 21 1/2 In.Tall	60.00
Donald Duck, Camera, Black Plastic, Mini Photos, Original Box, C.1950	55.00
Donald Duck, Figurine, Bisque, 4 In.High .... 15.00 To 35.00	
Donald Duck, Holding Christmas Tree, 3 In.Tall	2.50
Donald Duck, Night-Light, Chalk, Sits On Base, Marked Wd Enterprises, 1938	9.00
Donald Duck, Tea Set, Pitcher, Sugar & Creamer, Cup, Early	15.00
Donald Duck, Toothbrush Holder, Siamese Model	40.00
Donald Duck, Watch, Rectangular, Ingersoll, 1946, Original Box .... 25.00 To 90.00	

Doorstop, see Iron, Doorstop

Doughty Birds were made by Dorothy Doughty for the Royal Worcester Porcelain Company of England from 1936 to 1962. They have become very collectible.

Doughty, Bird, Nightingale & Honeysuckle, Royal Worcester	2400.00
Doughty, Bird, Redstart & Beech	750.00
Doughty, Figurine, Apple Blossom Sprays	3500.00
Doughty, Figurine, Chiffchaff	1800.00

Doulton Pottery and Porcelain were made by Doulton and Co. of Burslem, England, after 1882. The name Royal Doulton appeared on their wares after 1902.

Doulton, see also Royal Doulton

Doulton, Lambeth, Vase, Hannah Barlow, Incised In Blue On Tan, 7 1/2 In.High	135.00
Doulton, Bottle, Whiskey, Yellow, Black, Animals, Cork Stopper, J.Dewar & Sons	85.00
Doulton, Cachepot, Ribbed, Blue, Raised White Garlands & Berries, 1884	45.00
Doulton, Candlestick, White, Blue, Brown Decoration, Lambeth, 6 In., Pair	34.00
Doulton, Coffeepot, Stoneware, Brown & Tan Figurals, Silver Rim & Spout	80.00
Doulton, Dish, Serving, Vegetable, Watteau, Flow Blue, 10 In.	16.00
Doulton, Humidor, Ships, Birds, Signed	23.00
Doulton, Jar, Cracker, Moose, Elk, Deer, Signed Hannah Barlow, 1879, Lambeth	150.00
Doulton, Jar, Tobacco, Blue & Copper Stylized Floral On Dark, Slater's	35.00
Doulton, Jar, Tobacco, Blue Floral On Tan, 5 In.High, Lambeth	35.00
Doulton, Jar, Tobacco, Brown, Tan, Applied Hunt Scene, Lambeth	40.00
Doulton, Jar, Tobacco, Tan, Blue, Cream, Marked, Lambeth, 5 1/2 In.	45.00
Doulton, Jug, Brown & Tan, Raised Figures, Lambeth, 7 In.	60.00
Doulton, Jug, Hunting Scenes In Relief, Tan & Reddish Brown, Lambeth, C.1895	28.00
Doulton, Jug, Milk, Brown, Tan, Raised Hunting Figures, Lambeth, 7 In.	40.00
Doulton, Jug, Tan, Brown, Scenes Of Monks Eating, Circa 1872, Lambeth	60.00
Doulton, Jug, Viking Ship Embossed On Side, Highland Whiskey, Circa 1883	45.00
Doulton, Mug, Brown, Black Design, By Florence Barlow, 1878, Lambeth	80.00
Doulton, Mug, Dogs Chasing Deer, Lambeth, Three Handles, Dated 1878	187.50
Doulton, Mug, Portrait, Queen Victoria, Dated 1837-1897, Blue, Signed, Lambeth	35.00
Doulton, Perfume, Green & White Mosaic, Inner Cover, Hinged Top, C.1877	70.00
Doulton, Pitcher, Brown Ground, Yellow Floral, Lambeth, Pair Tumblers	78.00
Doulton, Pitcher, Browns, Cameo Busts Of Victoria, Slipware, Lambeth	57.50
Doulton, Pitcher, Creamy Tan Tapestry, Green Leaves, Brown Handle & Rim	35.00
Doulton, Pitcher, Depicts Athenian Games, Green, Burslem, 7 In.High	45.00
Doulton, Pitcher, Drinking Scene, Hunter, Hound, Lambeth, 6 3/8 In.High	55.00
Doulton, Pitcher, Egyptian Figures, Head Of Sphinx Spout, Tans, Lambeth	40.00
Doulton, Pitcher, Green, Brown, & White On Buff In Relief, 5 1/2 In., Lambeth	25.00
Doulton, Pitcher, Lambeth, Decorator's Initials, Dated 1877	88.00
Doulton, Pitcher, Old Seadog, Noke, 6 1/2 In.Tall	33.00
Doulton, Pitcher, Sea Dog, They All Love Jack, 6 In.	35.00
Doulton, Pitcher, Silicon, 1884, Brown, Blue Rosettes, Lambeth	57.00
Doulton, Pitcher, Slater's Patent, Brown, Green Lining, Lambeth	45.00
Doulton, Pitcher, Tapestry Type, Green Handle, Circa 1890, 8 1/2 In.	29.00
Doulton, Pitcher, Water, Cream & Brown, Raised Flowers, Stoneware, Lambeth	35.00
Doulton, Pitcher, Water, Madras, Flow Blue, 2 1/2 Quart	65.00
Doulton, Pitcher, Water, Tan & Brown Glaze, Raised Floral, Lambeth	42.50
Doulton, Pitcher, Water, Watteau, Flow Blue, 2 1/2 Quart	65.00
Doulton, Pitcher, White, Green, Brown, 5 1/4 In.Tall	27.00
Doulton, Plaque, Flow Blue, Babes In The Woods, Gold Border	125.00
Doulton, Plate, Congressional Library, Dark Blue, 10 In.	14.00
Doulton, Plate, Dickensware, Signed Noke, 10 1/2 In.	30.00
Doulton, Plate, Flow Blue, Provincial Parliament Bldg., Victoria, B.C.	25.00
Doulton, Plate, Madras Pattern, Flow Blue	15.00
Doulton, Plate, Oxford, Brown & Ivory, Earthenware, Burslem, 8 In.	12.50
Doulton, Plate, Scenic, English Country Houses, 10 1/4 In.	15.00
Doulton, Plate, Turkey, Flow Blue, Watteau Doulton, Burslem, England, 1902	32.00
Doulton, Plate, Watteau, Blue & White, 10 1/4 In.	12.00
Doulton, Platter, Garden Scene, Flow Blue, Watteau, 17 1/4 X 14 In.	50.00
Doulton, Platter, Melrose Pattern, Flow Blue	58.00
Doulton, Platter, Oxford, Brown & Ivory, Earthenware, Burslem	35.00
Doulton, Platter, Watteau, Flow Blue, 13 1/4 In.	22.00
Doulton, Shaker, Cheese, Lambeth	18.00
Doulton, Tankard, Raised Blue Floral, White Dots, Tan, 1879, Lambeth	95.00

Doulton, Toby Mug, Sairey Gamp, 2 1/4 In. 8.00
Doulton, Toothpick, Brown & Beige Stoneware, Embossed Man & Dog, 2 Handles 27.00
Doulton, Tray, Butterfly, Artist Edith Barlow, 1891, Lambeth 45.00
Doulton, Tray, Dickensware, Mr.Squeers, Street Scene, Signed Noke 45.00
Doulton, Tureen, Madras, Flow Blue, Two Handles, Cover, Burslem, 12 In. 58.00
Doulton, Vase, Allover Floral, Lace Ground, Glazed Brown, Cobalt, Gold, Pair 195.00
Doulton, Vase, Beige Ground, Large Red Flowers, Burslem, 11 1/2 In. 88.00
Doulton, Vase, Beige Ground, Yellow Floral, Carrara, 12 1/2 In. 65.00
Doulton, Vase, Blue Incised Pattern On Tan Ground, Hannah Barlow, Lambeth 135.00
Doulton, Vase, Blue On Tan Pattern, Hannah Barlow, Lambeth, 7 1/2 In., Pair 250.00
Doulton, Vase, Blue Scrolls, Flowers, Dark Blue, Brown Trim, Lambeth 21.00
Doulton, Vase, Blue, Gilt, Daffodils, Burslem, England, 7 1/2 In. 45.00
Doulton, Vase, Blue, Tan, Signed, Lambeth, 7 1/2 In.Tall 135.00
Doulton, Vase, Brown, Applied Blue Decoration, Silicon, Lambeth, 4 In. 37.50
Doulton, Vase, Brown, Gilt, Slater Patent, 10 1/2 In. 38.00
Doulton, Vase, Brown, Yellow Floral, Faience, 16 1/2 In., Pair 228.00
Doulton, Vase, Bud, Blue Base, Morton Hall, Circa 1856, 5 1/4 In. 120.00
Doulton, Vase, Bud, Griccieth Castle, Wales, Circa 1855, 5 1/4 In. 120.00
Doulton, Vase, Burslem, Roman Garden Scene, Rose, Blue, Green, Yellow 185.00
Doulton, Vase, Cobalt, Green, Beige, Gold, White, Mark, 17 1/2 In. 165.00
Doulton, Vase, Cream, Sepia Scenic, Windsor Castle, Burslem, England 45.00
Doulton, Vase, Flower Design, Hand-Painted, 4 In.High 24.00
Doulton, Vase, Flying Geese, Signed Florence Barlow, 12 1/2 In., Pair 250.00
Doulton, Vase, Gold, White & Maroon Floral, Slender Neck, Lambeth, Pair 125.00
Doulton, Vase, Lace Flower Design, Blue, Gold, White, 16 In.High, Pair 395.00

Dresden China is any china made in the town of Dresden, Germany. The most famous factory in Dresden is the Meissen Factory.

Dresden, see also Meissen
Dresden, Bowl, Flowers, Marie Antoinette, Wreath Of Roses, 7 X 10 In. 48.50
Dresden, Bowl, Openwork, Scalloped Top, Allover Floral Inside & Outside 35.00
Dresden, Bowl, Pink & White Daisies, Handle 12.00
Dresden, Box, Powder, Rose Bud, Cherubs, Blue, White, Pink, 4 3/4 In.Diameter 125.00
Dresden, Butter Pat, Spring Flower Design, Gold Rim, Hand-Painted 5.00
Dresden, Candelabra, Fruit & Floral, Cherubs, 7 Branches, C.1850, Pair 450.00
Dresden, Candlestick, Applied Raised Flowers, Boy Figure, 3 Feather Mark 69.50
Dresden, Cane Handle, T Shape, Painted Town & River, Scrolls, Girl's Head 100.00
Dresden, Centerpiece, Reticulated Basket, Applied Garden Flowers, Marked 150.00
Dresden, Compote, Floral Motif, Pierced Border, 3 1/4 In.High 60.00
Dresden, Compote, Hand-Painted, Signed, 9 1/2 In.Diameter 32.50
Dresden, Creamer, Floral, Signed 35.00
Dresden, Creamer, Shell Shape, Floral, Stem Handle 15.00
Dresden, Creamer, Spring Flower Design, Gold Trim 20.00
Dresden, Cup & Saucer, Blue, Pink, Yellow Flowers, Gold Trim, Blue Mark 25.00
Dresden, Figurine, Bulldog, Lying Down, White, 5 In.Long 35.00
Dresden, Figurine, Calico Cat, 12 In.High 160.00
Dresden, Figurine, Cat Washing Paw, 5 1/2 X 3 1/2 In. 42.00
Dresden, Figurine, Cat, Sitting, 5 X 5 In. 42.00
Dresden, Figurine, Lady Seated On Chair, Strums Mandolin, Germany 32.50
Dresden, Figurine, Macaw, Green, On Stump With Mushrooms & Berries, 16 In. 160.00
Dresden, Figurine, Marshall Pully, On Horseback, Napoleonic 95.00
Dresden, Figurine, Monkey Sits On Stump, Holds Green Apple, Flowers, 16 In. 160.00
Dresden, Figurine, Monkey Smoking Pipe, 9 In.Tall 85.00
Dresden, Figurine, Prince Eugene, On White Stallion .... 90.00 To 95.00
Dresden, Figurine, Swan & Cherub 85.00
Dresden, Figurine, Swan, Birds Of Peace, Fernery, Male, Female, Pair 145.00
Dresden, Figurine, Swan, 11 X 9 In., Pair 150.00
Dresden, Garniture, Desk, 7 Piece 120.00
Dresden, Inkstand, Letter Box, Sand Pot, Candleholder, Cobalt, Scenics 250.00
Dresden, Inkwell On Tray, Floral Sprays, Romantic Scene, Gold Trim 100.00
Dresden, Lamp Base, Applied Cherub & Flowers 145.00
Dresden, Lamp Base, Cherubic Figure And Flowers, 14 In. 160.00
Dresden, Lamp Base, Cupid, Pastel Blue, Rose Color, Gold, Pink, 10 1/2 In. 87.50
Dresden, Lamp, Kerosene, Blue & White Applied Flowers & Cupid 225.00
Dresden, Mirror, Angels, Crossed Swords Mark, 6 1/2 In. .... *Illus* 175.00
Dresden, Name Plate, White & Gold, Flowers, Germany, Set Of 4 .... 8.00

Dresden, Mirror, Angels, Crossed Swords Mark, 6 1/2 In.
See Page 204

Dresden, Place Card, Hand-Painted Floral Border, Made In Saxony	6.00
Dresden, Plate, American Flag & Give Us This Day, 9 1/2 In.Diameter	6.00
Dresden, Plate, Cake, Pierced, Floral Center & Border, Gold Edge, Blue Mark	15.00
Dresden, Plate, Floral Center, Pierced Border Outlined In Gold, 8 In.	15.00
Dresden, Plate, Medallion, Marie Antoinette, Gold Floral, Artist A.Lamb	25.00
Dresden, Plate, Panels, Floral, Figures In Colonial Dress, 7 In.	12.50
Dresden, Plate, Signs Of Thaw, Pictorial, Prattsville, N.Y., 7 In.	18.00
Dresden, Sugar, Floral, Cover, Signed	37.50
Dresden, Tankard, Reverse Of Nude Lady, Green & White Glaze, 12 1/2 In.	195.00
Dresden, Tea Caddy, Floral, Gilt Trim, Marked	45.00
Dresden, Teapot, Spring Flower Design, Gold Trim	10.00
Dresden, Tray, Basket Weave, Applied Roses, Leaves, 7 In.	65.00
Dresden, Tray, Cake, Footed, Pierced, Colored Flowers & Leaves	45.00
Dresden, Tureen, Pair Mallard Ducks, 6 1/2 X 10 In.	165.00
Dresden, Urn, Double Scroll Handles, Spearhead & Leaves, Meissen Mark, Pair	375.00
Dummyboard, Dutch Boy & Girl, Painted, C.1650, Pair	500.00
Durand Type, Wine, Tapering, Pink & White Striated Feathers On Red & Clear	160.00

Durand Glass was made by Victor Durand from 1879 to 1935 at several factories. Most of the iridescent Durand Glass was made by Victor Durand, Jr., from 1912 to 1924 at the Durand Art Glass Works in Vineland, New Jersey.

Durand, Bowl, Centerpiece, Cobalt, Blue & White Feathers, Engraved Roses	285.00
Durand, Bowl, Cranberry On Clear, Ambergris Luster, Small	45.00
Durand, Bowl, Green, Orchid Iridescence, 4 In.Scalloped Top	100.00
Durand, Candleholder, Deep Blue To Light Blue To Yellow, Pair	275.00
Durand, Candlestick, Iridescent Rose Base, 5 3/8 In.	400.00
Durand, Cruet, Captain's, Gold, Signed	475.00
Durand, Jar, Amethyst, Signed, 10 In.	140.00
Durand, Jar, Covered, Pulled Feather Outlined In Gold, Threading, Signed	650.00
Durand, Lamp, Desk, Crackle Art Glass, 17 1/2 In.High	475.00
Durand, Lamp, Desk, Crackle Glass, Green, Gold, White To Orange, Gold, White	550.00
Durand, Lamp, Gold, Green Trailing Leaves & Vines	350.00
Durand, Plate, Cranberry, White & Pink Feather Decoration, 8 In.	125.00
Durand, Plate, Florentia Design, Cranberry Cut To Clear, Paperweight Floral	175.00
Durand, Rose Bowl, Purple, Threaded	250.00
Durand, Rose Bowl, Yellow Orange Ground, Green King Tut Motif, Yellow Lined	395.00
Durand, Vase, Blue Black Ground, Iridescent Blue Vines, 8 3/4 In.	825.00
Durand, Vase, Blue Iridescent, Nailsea Type Loopings, 5 1/2 In.	225.00
Durand, Vase, Blue Threads, Signed, 6 1/2 In.High	245.00
Durand, Vase, Blue, Double Handle, Unmarked, 9 1/2 In.High	130.00
Durand, Vase, Blue, Iridescent, Classic Shape, Signed, 6 3/4 In.	400.00
Durand, Vase, Blue, Iridescent, Gold Foot, Signed, 8 In.High	350.00
Durand, Vase, Butterscotch Color, Gold Threads, Ruffled Top, Signed, 7 In.	450.00
Durand, Vase, Car, Green & White, Ruffled Base	12.00
Durand, Vase, Gold Iridescent, Green Leaves & Tendrils, 8 In.High	250.00
Durand, Vase, Gold Iridescent, Signed, 5 In.High	275.00
Durand, Vase, Gold Iridescent, Signed, 8 In.High	239.00
Durand, Vase, Gold Iridescent, Threaded, Pedestal	325.00
Durand, Vase, Gold Iridescent, 6 1/2 In.	250.00

Durand, Vase, Gold Iridescent, 6 3/4 In. 275.00
Durand, Vase, Green, Gold, Rose Iridescent, Signed, 9 3/4 In.High 70.00
Durand, Vase, Green, Yellow Lining, Signed, 7 In.Tall 375.00
Durand, Vase, Pedestal, Threaded Gold 300.00
Durand, Vase, Pumpkin, King Tut Swirl Pattern, Signed 950.00
Durand, Vase, Ribbed, Green, Gold Aurene Inside, 7 1/4 In. 450.00
Durand, Vase, Silver Luster, Ambergris, Pulled Blue & Opal Design, Unsigned 195.00
Easter Egg, Bristol, Gold Cross Enamel 6.50
Easter Egg, Frosted Art Glass, Upright, Enameled, Opens, Four Brass Feet 85.00
Easter Egg, Hand-Painted Flowers, Milk Glass, 6 In.Long 25.00
Easter Egg, Opalescent, Hand Decorated, 7 In. 25.00
Easter Egg, Pink, Gold Edges, Roses, Basket Applied To Front, Base, Bisque 47.50
Easter Egg, Robin, Artist Orlik, Gold Trim, Porcelain 55.00
Easter Egg, Rose Decor, Porcelain, Beehive Mark, 5 1/2 In. 35.00
Enamel, Bowl, Blue, Pink Carnations, Leaves, Baby Breath, French, 8 In. 85.00
Enamel, Bowl, Underplate, Green, Blue & Pink Flowers, Set Of 12 .... 300.00
Enamel, Box, Portrait, Girl, Red Stones In Cap, France, 3 In.Diameter 125.00
Enamel, Dish, Blue, Applied Lotus Pods, Carved Jade Handle, China 85.00
Enamel, Plaque, French, Moses In Desert, Gray & Black Tones, 12 X 12 In. 475.00
Enamel, Tray, Viennese, Oval, Classical Sacrificial Scene, C.1850 .... 575.00
Enamel, Vase, French, Purple & Yellow Pansies, Clear To Amethyst, Pair 165.00
Enamel, Vase, Tree & Water Scene, French, 11 In. 85.00

End of Day Glass is now an out-of-fashion name for Spattered Glass.
The glass was made of many bits and pieces of colored glass. Traditionally,
the glass was made by workmen from the odds and ends left from the glass used
during the day. Actually it was a deliberately manufactured product popular
about 1880 to 1900, and some of it is still being made.
End-Of-Day, Basket, Red, Black, & Pink, Thorn Handle 97.00
End-Of-Day, Basket, White Cased, Thorn Handle, Fluted Top, 8 1/2 In. 69.00
End-Of-Day, Bottle, Barber's 98.50
End-Of-Day, Creamer, Tortoise Type Design 25.00
End-Of-Day, Cruet, Cobalt With Ocher, Round Bottom, 6 1/2 In.High 32.00
End-Of-Day, Figurine, Goldfish, Standing, 10 In.Tall 28.00
End-Of-Day, Figurine, Rooster 35.00
End-Of-Day, Marble, Pinks, Blues, Center Core Of Glass, 5 1/4 In. 30.00
End-Of-Day, Pitcher, Water, Cranberry & White In Clear Glass, Crimped Top 85.00
End-Of-Day, Rose Bowl, Flower Grill 125.00
End-Of-Day, Rose Bowl, White Ground, Pink & Green Spatter, Crimped Top 35.00
End-Of-Day, Tumbler, Pink, Red, White 22.50
End-Of-Day, Vase, Flower Top, Pink, Yellow, & White, 8 In.High 32.50
End-Of-Day, Vase, Inside Cased White, Flared Rim, 8 1/2 In.High 28.50
End-Of-Day, Vase, Jack-In-The-Pulpit, Blue, White, Pink, & Red, Ruffled Top 32.00
End-Of-Day, Vase, Multicolor Spatter, Clear Handles, White Lining, Pair 80.00
End-Of-Day, Vase, Multicolor, White Casing Inside, Flared, Three Lips 27.50
End-Of-Day, Vase, Orange Tones, Multicolor At Bottom, Fan Type Top 40.00
End-Of-Day, Vase, Orange Tones, Multicolor Bottom, Cased, 6 In.High 20.00
End-Of-Day, Vase, Red & White Marbling, White Lining, 5 3/4 In.High 65.00
End-Of-Day, Vase, Stick, Yellow & White, Gold Leaf Decoration On Front 35.00
End-Of-Day, Vase, Yellow, Multicolor Bottom, Cased, 6 In.High 20.00
Etruscan Majolica, see Majolica
Ezra Brooks, see Bottle, Ezra Brooks

Faberge, Carl Gustavovich, was a goldsmith and jeweler to the Russian
Imperial Court from about 1870 to 1914.
Faberge, Basket, Cake, Silver, Oval, Beaded, Anthemion, Channeling, C.1900 .... 575.00
Faberge, Bell Push, Gilded Silver & Nephrite, Karl Gustav Armfelt, C.1900 .... 1000.00
Faberge, Brooch Pendant, Diamond, Pearl, Garnet, C.1900 .... *Illus* 1700.00
Faberge, Cane Handle, Bowenite, Gold, & Translucent Enamel, Perchin, 1900 .... 1000.00
Faberge, Cane Handle, Rock Crystal, Enamel, Jeweled, 3 Color Gold, C.1900 .... 1500.00
Faberge, Canister, Sugar, Silver, Round, Monogram Cyrillic, Moscow, 1896 .... 450.00
Faberge, Case, Cigarette, Gold, Rectangular, Cushion Form, C.1900 .... 1500.00
Faberge, Charka, Gilded Silver & Horn, Catherine The Great Coin, C.1890 .... 725.00
Faberge, Charka, Silver, Repousse, Peacock's Head Handle, Moscow, C.1900 .... 700.00
Faberge, Figurine, Rhinoceros, Nephrite, Standing, St.Petersburg, C.1900 .... 4500.00
Faberge, Frame, Picture, Silver & Enamel, Hendrick Wigstrom, C.1900 .... 1900.00

Faberge, Frame, Picture, Silver, Translucent Enamel, Anders Nevalainen, 1900 .... 2300.00
Faberge, Knife, Paper, Jeweled, Gold Mounted Nephrite, Oblong, C.1900 .... 1100.00
Faberge, Kovsh, Silver, Enamel, Repousse, Flowers On Blue, Moscow, C.1900 .... 1500.00
Faberge, Pendant, Diamond, Sapphire, C.1900 .... *Illus* 1800.00
Faberge, Portes Menu, Silver, Karl Gustav Armfelt, Slit Arms, C.1900, Pair 575.00
Faberge, Rhinoceros, Carved Out Of Jade, Diamonds For Eyes, 8 In.Long 1500.00
Faberge, Seal, Jeweled, Gold, Enamel, & Lapis Lazuli, Initials EE, C.1900 .... 3700.00
Faberge, Tiger, Carved Out Of Cat's-Eye, Diamonds For Eyes, 8 In.Long 1500.00
Faience, Cachepot, French, Tulips, Puce & Green, Feather Rim, Pair 70.00
Faience, Figurine, Cockatoo, White Glaze, Pink Feet, Comb, Late 19th Century 95.00
Faience, Font, Wall, French, White, Black, Pink, & Green Transfer Scene 700.00
Faience, Hair Receiver, Brown Glaze Pottery, Designs 8.00
Faience, Mirror, Italian, Carved Rope Border, 23 X 46 In. 30.00
Faience, Pitcher, Glazed Redware, White Band, Blue & Gold Floral, Pewter Top 21.00
Faience, Plate, Nut, French, Filled With Walnuts, White, Floral, J.A.Lewis 700.00
Faience, Tureen, Covered, French, Boat Shape, Rococo Stand, Floral 100.00

*Fairings are small souvenir china boxes sold at country fairs during the
nineteenth century.*

Fairing, Boy On Dresser Looking In Mirror 35.00
Fairing, Boy, Dog, Cart 35.00
Fairing, Last One To Bed Turns Out The Light 40.00
Fan, Advertising, Glenwood Furniture, Taunton, Mass. 2.75
Fan, Advertising, Nature's Remedy, Cardboard 3.00
Fan, Bamboo, Silk Peacock Decoration 4.00
Fan, Birds, Trees, Red, Black, Gold, Artist B.llornes, Wooden 35.00
Fan, Black Silk, Painted Flower 5.00
Fan, Carved Black Wooden Spokes, Red Silk, Hand-Painted Bullfight Scene 15.50
Fan, Feather, Pink, Brass Frame 35.00
Fan, Ivory & Ostrich Feather, Large Size 15.00
Fan, Ivory, Carved Floral, Silk, Sequins, Beading, Portrait, Man, Woman, Signed 45.00
Fan, Ivory, Louis XV .... *Illus*   70.00

Faberge, Brooch Pendant, Diamond,
Pearl, Garnet, C.1900
See *Page 206*

Faberge, Pendant, Diamond, Sapphire, C.1900

Fan, Ivory, Louis XV

Fan, **Louis XV**, Ivory, Painted Classical Scene On Parchment, Carved	40.00
Fan, **Mother-Of-Pearl**, Ivory, Jeweled, Lot Of 5	150.00
Fan, **Mother-Of-Pearl**, Lace Inserts	35.00
Fan, **Mother-Of-Pearl**, Silver & Gold Sequins On Silk, Floral Design	42.00
Fan, **Parchment**, Hand-Painted Poppies, 14 Bamboo Stripes, Brass Ring	18.00
Fan, **Silk**, French, Hand-Painted, Ducks, Signed, Tassel	45.00
Fan, **Spanish Scene Of Conquistadore**, Peasants, Artist M.Esteve, Wooden	65.00
Fan, **Wedding**, White Lace, Pierced Ivory Sticks	18.00
Fan, **Wood & Paper**, Black Lacquer, Signed Painting	8.50
Fan, **Wooden Frame**, Scene, Two People In Boat	15.50
Fan, **36 Slats**, Two Paintings, Picking Grapes, Queen In Coach, France, 1894	36.00
Fenton, **Bottle**, Dresser, Melon Shape, Pink, Stopper	12.00
Fenton, **Bowl**, Scale Pattern, Flowers, Leaves, Cobalt Blue, 8 In.Diameter	27.50
Fenton, **Pitcher**, Cover, Vaseline, Cobalt Handle, 5 Mugs, Cobalt Handles	225.00
Fenton, **Pitcher**, Green Ground, Blue, White, Green Enamel, 1909, 5 Tumblers	78.00
Fenton, **Pitcher**, Vaseline, Amber Handle	67.50
Fenton, **Plate**, Chop, Grape Design, Purple, 11 In.Diameter	350.00
Fenton, **Salt & Pepper**, White, Grape, Circa 1900	20.00
Fenton, **Vase**, Satin Custard Glass, Peacock, 1972, 8 In.	7.00

Findlay, or Onyx, Glass was made using three layers of glass. It was
manufactured by the Dalzell Gilmore Leighton Company about 1889 in
Findlay, Ohio. The silver, ruby, or black pattern was molded into the glass.
The glass came in several colors, but was usually white or ruby.

Findlay Onyx, **Muffineer**, Silver Inlay	165.00 To 225.00
Findlay Onyx, **Muffineer**, White, Platinum Decoration	235.00
Findlay Onyx, **Spooner**, Floral, Pleated Top	225.00
Findlay Onyx, **Sugar**, Covered, Platinum On White, Platinum Finia	425.00 To 460.00
Findlay Onyx, **Toothpick**, Roughage	239.50
Findlay Onyx, **Tumbler**, White, Platinum	275.00
Fire, **Andiron**, Adam, Pair	150.00
Fire, **Andiron**, Bell Metal, Urn Top, Columnar, American, C.1790, Pair	1700.00
Fire, **Andiron**, Brass Ball, Double Branch, Ball Feet, 20 In.High, Pair	150.00
Fire, **Andiron**, Brass Ball, Slender Column, 28 In.High, Pair	125.00
Fire, **Andiron**, Brass Column & Ball, 29 In.High, Pair	100.00
Fire, **Andiron**, Brass, Acorn Top, Wittingham School, New York, C.1800, Pair	750.00
Fire, **Andiron**, Brass, Ball Feet, Arch Support, C.1810, 20 1/2 In.High, Pair	275.00
Fire, **Andiron**, Brass, Ball Top, Horizontal Reeding, American, C.1800, Pair	475.00
Fire, **Andiron**, Brass, Ball Top, Signed Hunneman, Boston, C.1810, Pair	550.00
Fire, **Andiron**, Brass, Urn Finial, Columnar Support, Bracket Feet, Pair	70.00
Fire, **Andiron**, Brass, Urn Top, Engraved, Pendant Swags, New York, C.1800, Pair	1100.00
Fire, **Andiron**, Brass, Urn Top, Signed Wittingham, New York, C.1790, Pair	2100.00
Fire, **Andiron**, Cast Iron, Ornate, 21 In.High, Pair	15.00
Fire, **Andiron**, Hammered Wrought Iron, Art Deco Style, Scrolls, C.1930, Pair	40.00
Fire, **Andiron**, Iron & Brass, Rosette Finial, French, C.1750, 24 In., Pair	30.00
Fire, **Andiron**, Key, Iron, 14 In.High, 15 In.Deep	35.00
Fire, **Andiron**, Owl, Bronze, Dated, Pair	85.00
Fire, **Andiron**, Wrought Iron, Goose Neck, 20 3/4 In.High, Pair	125.00
Fire, **Andirons**, Dutch Boy & Girl, Black, 14 In.High	25.00
Fire, **Andirons**, Fireplace Tools, Brass	45.00
Fire, **Bellows**, Hand-Painted Scenic, Brass Tip & Studs, C.1830, 15 In.	22.50
Fire, **Box**, Coal, Fireplace, Oak, Brass Trim, 13 X 20 In.	50.00
Fire, **Bucket**, Coal, Lion's Head Each Side, Copper, Blue & White Handle	45.00
Fire, **Bucket**, Coal, Tin, Victorian, Painted Flowers & Oak Leaves On Black	160.00
Fire, **Bucket**, Leather, American, 20 In.High *Illus*	350.00
Fire, **Bucket**, Leather, Dated 1817, Wm.Rotch, Jr., No.2 & 3, Pair	175.00
Fire, **Bucket**, Leather, Red With Gold, New England	100.00
Fire, **Bucket**, Red, Black, White, Leather, Bail, S.Tulinghuast, No.2, 1812	160.00
Fire, **Bugle**, Engraved Adams Fire Dept., Brass, 20 In.	140.00
Fire, **Certificate Of Membership**, Volunteer, N.Y., Dated 1855	14.50
Fire, **Coal Hod**, Copper Helmet, Painted Porcelain Handles, Lion Heads	185.00
Fire, **Coal Shuttle**, Liner, Shovel, Brass	100.00
Fire, **Crane**, Fireplace, Handwrought, 32 In.Arm	27.50
Fire, **Extinguisher**, Embossed Instructions, Wall Bracket, 1917, Brass, Pyrene	22.50
Fire, **Extinguisher**, Fireblown, Label, Yellow Amber, 6 In.High, 4 In.Wide	25.00
Fire, **Extinguisher**, Free-Blown Crackle Glass, Barrel, Amberina To Yellow	150.00

Fire, Extinguisher, Free-Blown Crackle Glass, Barrel, Chartreuse, 6 In.High	37.50
Fire, Extinguisher, Free-Blown Crackle Glass, Barrel, Crystal, 6 In.High	37.50
Fire, Extinguisher, Free-Blown Crackle Glass, Barrel, Emerald, 6 In.High	37.50
Fire, Extinguisher, Free-Blown Crackle Glass, Barrel, Turquoise, 6 In.High	37.50
Fire, Extinguisher, Free-Blown Crackle Glass, Barrel, Yellow Amber, 6 In.	37.50
Fire, Extinguisher, Harden's, Embossed, Molded Star In Circle, Blue, Grenade	26.00
Fire, Extinguisher, Harden's, No.2, Footed, Hand Grenade	45.00
Fire, Extinguisher, Impressed Hayward's Fire Grenade, 1871, Amber	16.00
Fire, Extinguisher, Phoenix, Red Metal Tube, Eagle, 21 In.Long	15.00
Fire, Firedog, French, Bronze Figure Of Egyptian Maiden, Iron, Pair	60.00
Fire, Fireplace & Garniture, Miniature, Brass, Pheasant Andirons, C.1850	225.00
Fire, Fireplace Cover, Victorian, Copper Plated, Cast Classical Figures	85.00
Fire, Fireplace Set, Andirons & Tools, Brass	150.00
Fire, Fireplace Set, Brass, Holder & 3 Tools	45.00
Fire, Fireplace Set, Brass, 3 Tools In Stand, Ball Andirons	200.00
Fire, Fireplace Set, Iron, Ball Finial, Andirons, Shovel, Tongs, & Poker	25.00
Fire, Fireplace Set, Iron, Fire Dogs, 2 Tools, Holder, & Coal Grate	170.00
Fire, Fireplace Set, Wrought Iron, Andirons, Shovel, & Tongs, Colonial	90.00
Fire, Fireplace Set, Wrought Iron, Andirons, Shovel, Tongs, & Screen	40.00
Fire, Fireplace, Cast Iron, American, C.1820 .... *Illus*	350.00

Fire, Bucket, Leather,
American, 20 In.High
See Page 208

Fire, Fireplace, Cast Iron, American, C.1820

Fire, Grate, George III, Brass, Iron, Pierced Front, June Portrait, C.1800	325.00
Fire, Grate, George III, Brass, Iron, Urn Center, Pierced Front, C.1800	250.00
Fire, Hat, Fireman's, Aluminum, Brass Eagle, Newburyport, Mass., Pat 1889	20.00
Fire, Hat, Fireman's, Black Leather, Shield, 'Lt.Engine 8 S.F.D., Salem'	20.00
Fire, Hat, Fireman's, Brass Eagle, Newburyport, Mass., Patent 1902	250.0
Fire, Hat, Fireman's, Pat.1889	40.00
Fire, Helmet, Fireman's, French, Brass, Sapeurs-Pompiers, Shield, Crown	19.50
Fire, Helmet, Fireman's, Leather, Shield, 'Engine 4 S.F.D.'	42.50
Fire, Hose Nozzle, Fireman's, Brass, 12 In.Long	15.00
Fire, Screen, Brass, Made In Europe, C.1890, Pair Lion Topped Fire Dogs	950.00
Fire, Screen, Brass, 15 1/2 X 25 In.	35.00
Fire, Screen, Federal, Mahogany & Cherry, Pole, Needlework, New England, 1780	700.00
Fire, Screen, Federal, Mahogany, Painted, Oval, Rhode Island, C.1790, Pair	3750.00
Fire, Screen, Federal, Mahogany, Pole, Shield Shape, Salem, C.1790	1500.00
Fire, Screen, Russian, Gros & Petit Point Of Nicholas I On Horse, C.1850	200.00
Fire, Stove, American, Gothic, Form Of Tower Building, C.1850	500.00
Fire, Stove, Franklin, Cast Iron & Brass, H.W.Cobert Co., N.Y., C.1830	375.00
Fire, Stove, Franklin, Ornate, Sliding Door Front, Dated 1856	115.00
Fire, Stove, Potbelly, Ornamental	300.00
Fire, Tongs, Circa 1860, Iron	11.00
Fire, Tongs, Ember, Fireplace, Iron	7.50
Fire, Tool Set, Brass, Urn Finials, Holder & Four Tools	80.00
Fire, Tool Set, Wrought Iron, Spool Handle, 4 Tools & Holder	17.50
Fire, Tools, Louis XVI, Husks & Strapwork, C.1850, 3 Piece	125.00
Fire, Warming Pan, Brass, Miniature, 9 In.	9.00

Fireglow Glass resembles English Bristol Glass. But a reddish-brown color can be seen when the piece is held to the light. It is a form of Art Glass made by the Boston and Sandwich Glass Co. of Massachusetts, and other companies.

Fireglow, Cruet, Opalescent, Bulbous, Flower Drape, Stopper	95.00
Fireglow, Jar, Biscuit, Satin Beige Ground, Enamel Floral	55.00
Fireglow, Vase, Bristol, Blue, 8 In.High	46.00
Fireglow, Vase, Bristol, Caramel, 9 In.High	9.00
Fireglow, Vase, Flowers, Robin, Bulbous, Satin Finish, 6 1/4 In.Tall	60.00
Fireglow, Vase, Gray Green, Blown, 6 1/2 In.High	29.00
Fireglow, Vase, Pink, Yellow, & Blue Floral On Beige, Signed P.K., 8 1/2 In.	65.00
-Fireplace Tools, See Fire, Tongs, Etc.	

Fischer porcelain was made in Herend, Hungary. The factory was founded in 1839, and has continued working into the twentieth century. The wares are sometimes referred to as Herend porcelain.

Fischer, Bowl, Blue, White, Openwork, Reticulated Knobs, Enamel Floral	65.00
Fischer, Teapot, Orange Floral On White, Gold, Rosebud Finial, Herend	52.50
Fischer, Vase, Art Nouveau Design, Encrusted Gold & Elongated Flowers	95.00
Fish Set, Bone Handle, Victorian, 12 Knives & Forks, Case	120.00
Fish Set, Pink & Rococo Shading, Gold Border, Platter, Sauceboat, 12 Plates	300.00

Flow Blue, or Flo Blue, was made in England about 1830 to 1900. The plates were printed with designs using a cobalt blue coloring. The color flowed from the design to the white plate so the finished plate had a smeared blue design. The plates were usually made of Ironstone China.

Flow Blue, see also Staffordshire	
Flow Blue, Bouillon, Saucer, Lyndhurst, Wm.Grindley	15.00
Flow Blue, Bowl, Albany, Johnson Bros., Central Medallion, Gold, 9 1/4 In.	20.00
Flow Blue, Bowl, Alton, Covered, Oval, Marked Grindley Co.	48.00
Flow Blue, Bowl, Berry, Russian Scene, 10 In.Diameter	15.00
Flow Blue, Bowl, Cereal, Albany, Johnson Bros., 6 3/4 In.Diameter	7.50
Flow Blue, Bowl, Cereal, Mongolia, Johnson Bros., 6 1/4 In.Diameter	7.50
Flow Blue, Bowl, Cereal, Normandy, Johnson Bros., 6 1/4 In.Diameter	8.00
Flow Blue, Bowl, Cereal, Wild Rose, Adams, Blue Gray, 6 3/4 In.Diameter	5.00
Flow Blue, Bowl, Coburg, Cover	165.00
Flow Blue, Bowl, Conway, New Wharf, Stylized Scrolls	20.00
Flow Blue, Bowl, Conway, New Wharf, 9 In.	18.00
Flow Blue, Bowl, Fairy Villas, W.Adams & Co., Stone China, England	25.00
Flow Blue, Bowl, Fairy Villas, 10 1/4 In.	30.00
Flow Blue, Bowl, Fairy Villas, 10 X 2 1/2 In.	30.00
Flow Blue, Bowl, Jenny Lind, Royal Staffordshire Pottery, 3 In.High	29.00
Flow Blue, Bowl, Knox, New Wharf, Central Medallion, Stylized Border	22.50
Flow Blue, Bowl, Kyber, W.Adams & Co., Deep, 9 In.Diameter	22.50
Flow Blue, Bowl, La Belle, 6 1/2 In.	8.00
Flow Blue, Bowl, Lorne, Cover, 8 In.	32.00
Flow Blue, Bowl, Mattean, 9 1/4 In.Diameter, 4 In.High	35.00
Flow Blue, Bowl, Melborne, 9 1/2 In.	18.00
Flow Blue, Bowl, Mikado, Wilkinson Co.	12.50
Flow Blue, Bowl, Mongolia, Johnson Bros., Peafowl Center, Cobalt, Floral	25.00
Flow Blue, Bowl, Oriental, Ridgway, 9 3/4 In.Diameter	30.00
Flow Blue, Bowl, Pekin, Wilkinson, Oriental Scene, Floral In Cobalt	35.00
Flow Blue, Bowl, Rebecca At The Well, Dark Blue, Clews, 5 3/4 In.	100.00
Flow Blue, Bowl, Salad, Base, Church, Gate, Wall, Abbey 1790 England	45.00
Flow Blue, Bowl, Serving, Avon, Floral & Gold, 3 Compartments, Handle, Mayer	50.00
Flow Blue, Bowl, Serving, Conway, New Wharf, 9 In.	25.00
Flow Blue, Bowl, Serving, Delph, Flower Basket Center, Burgess & Leigh	25.00
Flow Blue, Bowl, Serving, La Belle, Fluted Handle, Wheeling, 9 1/2 In.	35.00
Flow Blue, Bowl, Serving, La Belle, Fluted Shape, Floral & Gold, Wheeling	25.00
Flow Blue, Bowl, Serving, Nonpareil, Covered, Flower Finial, Burgess & Leigh	50.00
Flow Blue, Bowl, Serving, Normandy, Johnson Bros., 8 1/2 In.Diameter	17.50
Flow Blue, Bowl, Serving, Normandy, Johnson Bros., 9 1/4 In.Diameter	25.00
Flow Blue, Bowl, Serving, Pekin, By Wilkinson, 9 1/2 In.	16.00
Flow Blue, Bowl, Serving, Touraine, Stanley, 10 1/2 In.	30.00
Flow Blue, Bowl, Serving, Vegetable, Blenheim, Covered, Floral & Gold, Hancock	25.00
Flow Blue, Bowl, Serving, Vegetable, Cecil, Oval, Till & Son, 9 3/4 X 7 In.	22.50

Flow Blue, Bowl, Serving, Vegetable, Davenport, Cover, Floral, Gold, Wood & Son 30.00
Flow Blue, Bowl, Serving, Vegetable, Devon, Covered, Blue Floral, Ford & Sons 25.00
Flow Blue, Bowl, Serving, Vegetable, Haddon, Floral & Gold, Grindley 12.50
Flow Blue, Bowl, Serving, Vegetable, Leicester, Covered, Gray Blue Floral 25.00
Flow Blue, Bowl, Serving, Vegetable, Peach Royal, Johnson Bros. 12.50
Flow Blue, Bowl, Serving, Vegetable, Rose, Floral & Gold, Ridgway 17.50
Flow Blue, Bowl, Serving, Vegetable, Touraine, Covered, Oblong, Alcock 50.00
Flow Blue, Bowl, Serving, Victoria, Wood & Son, Cobalt Border, Floral 27.50
Flow Blue, Bowl, Soup, Bexley, Bisto, Holland, Floral & Gold, Flange Edge 15.00
Flow Blue, Bowl, Soup, Gironde, Grindley, Floral, 7 3/4 In. 12.00
Flow Blue, Bowl, Soup, Glenmore, Grindley, 7 3/4 In. 7.00
Flow Blue, Bowl, Soup, Holland, Meakin, Central Medallion, 7 1/2 In. 8.50
Flow Blue, Bowl, Soup, Hope Louise, Meakin, Floral & Gold, Flange Edge 12.00
Flow Blue, Bowl, Soup, Leicester, Burgess & Leigh, Central Medallion 15.00
Flow Blue, Bowl, Soup, Madras, Doulton, Blue Gray, 9 3/4 In. 12.00
Flow Blue, Bowl, Soup, Madras, Doulton, 10 1/4 In. 20.00
Flow Blue, Bowl, Soup, Madras, 10 In.Diameter 12.00
Flow Blue, Bowl, Soup, Manhattan, Alcock, Floral & Gold, 9 In. 12.00
Flow Blue, Bowl, Soup, Normandy, Johnson, 7 1/2 In. 10.00
Flow Blue, Bowl, Soup, Roseville, Thos.Hughes, Floral & Gold, 9 In. 12.00
Flow Blue, Bowl, Soup, Sefton, Ridgway, Stylized Cobalt Blue & Gold 11.00
Flow Blue, Bowl, Soup, Touraine, Alcock, Flange Edge, 9 In. 17.50
Flow Blue, Bowl, Tea, Scenes Of English Castles, Rington 18.00
Flow Blue, Bowl, Tonquin, 10 In. 20.00
Flow Blue, Bowl, Vegetable, Covered, Ironstone, Staffordshire, England 42.50
Flow Blue, Bowl, Vegetable, Crown & Shield Mark, Germany 17.50
Flow Blue, Bowl, Vegetable, Lois 10.00
Flow Blue, Bowl, Vegetable, Olympic, Oval, W.H.Grindley 9.00
Flow Blue, Bowl, Vegetable, Nonparell, Covered, 12 X 8 1/2 In. 75.00
Flow Blue, Bowl, Vegetable, Waldorf, 9 In.Diameter 18.50
Flow Blue, Bowl, Vegetable, Wentworth 18.00
Flow Blue, Bowl, Victoria, Wood & Son, England, 10 In. 18.00
Flow Blue, Bowl, Waste, Indian, 5 1/4 In.Diameter 35.00
Flow Blue, Bowl, Waste, Shanghai, Wm.Grindley, Oriental Scene, Floral Border 17.50
Flow Blue, Butter Pat, Blue Floral 7.50
Flow Blue, Butter Pat, Blue, Gold Tracery 3.50
Flow Blue, Butter Pat, Cambridge 7.50
Flow Blue, Butter Pat, Delph 7.50
Flow Blue, Butter Pat, Floral 5.50
Flow Blue, Butter Pat, Madras 8.00
Flow Blue, Butter Pat, Marechal Niel Pattern, Roses, Grindley, Set Of 6 .... 25.00
Flow Blue, Butter Pat, Marie Pattern, Grindley, Overall Floral, Scrolls, 5 .... 25.00
Flow Blue, Butter Pat, Ormonde Pattern 12.00
Flow Blue, Butter Pat, Paris Pattern 10.00
Flow Blue, Butter Pat, Pekin 8.00
Flow Blue, Butter Pat, Roseville 7.50
Flow Blue, Butter Pat, Stylized Floral 7.50
Flow Blue, Butter Pat, Touraine 9.00
Flow Blue, Butter, Albany 16.00
Flow Blue, Butter, Cover, Wentworth 35.00
Flow Blue, Butter, Lotus Pattern, Grindley 47.00
Flow Blue, Celery, Alaska, Grindley, 8 3/4 X 5 1/4 In. 12.50
Flow Blue, Celery, Lorne, Grindley, 9 1/4 X 5 1/4 In. 12.50
Flow Blue, Celery, Peach Royal, Johnson Bros., 8 1/2 X 4 3/4 In. 9.00
Flow Blue, Celery, Rustic, Grindley, Open Handled, 8 1/2 X 5 1/4 In. 8.00
Flow Blue, Chamber Pot, Covered, Geometric Floral, Embossed Scrolls, Gold 46.00
Flow Blue, Chamberstick, La Belle, Handled, Saucer Base, Signed 58.00
Flow Blue, Creamer, Indian, Jar 40.00
Flow Blue, Creamer, Mulberry, 6 In. 25.00
Flow Blue, Creamer, Normandy, Johnson Bros., Cobalt Leaf Border 40.00
Flow Blue, Creamer, Oregon, Johnson Bros., Floral With Gold 30.00
Flow Blue, Creamer, Oxford, Johnson Bros., Floral 30.00
Flow Blue, Creamer, Roseville, Thos.Hughes & Son, Floral Same As Maddocks 40.00
Flow Blue, Creamer, Touraine, Alcock 50.00
Flow Blue, Cup & Saucer, Amoy 22.00
Flow Blue, Cup & Saucer, Brooklyn 35.00

Flow Blue, Cup & Saucer, Demitasse, Idris 20.00
Flow Blue, Cup & Saucer, Duchess, Wm.Grindley 15.00
Flow Blue, Cup & Saucer, Celtic, Floral, Gold, Grindley 25.00
Flow Blue, Cup & Saucer, Haddon, Grindley 25.00
Flow Blue, Cup & Saucer, La Francis 15.00
Flow Blue, Cup & Saucer, Lois 24.00
Flow Blue, Cup & Saucer, Lorne, Grindley 25.00
Flow Blue, Cup & Saucer, Magnolia, Johnson Bros. 15.00
Flow Blue, Cup & Saucer, Manilla 23.00
Flow Blue, Cup & Saucer, Melbourne, Grindley 25.00
Flow Blue, Cup & Saucer, Navy, Floral, Gold, Till & Son 20.00
Flow Blue, Cup & Saucer, Normandy, Johnson Bros. 25.00
Flow Blue, Cup & Saucer, Oregon 23.00
Flow Blue, Cup & Saucer, Oriental, Alcock 35.00
Flow Blue, Cup & Saucer, Paris, Stanley 25.00
Flow Blue, Cup & Saucer, Rose, Floral, Gold, Grindley 25.00
Flow Blue, Cup & Saucer, Roseville, Floral, Thos.Hughes 25.00
Flow Blue, Cup & Saucer, Scinde 24.50
Flow Blue, Cup & Saucer, Shanghai, Grindley .... 18.50 To 25.00
Flow Blue, Cup & Saucer, Spinach, Libertas 20.00
Flow Blue, Cup & Saucer, Tonquin 23.00
Flow Blue, Cup & Saucer, Touraine, Alcock 30.00
Flow Blue, Cup & Saucer, Touraine, Stanley & Alcock 30.00
Flow Blue, Cup & Saucer, Troy 21.00
Flow Blue, Cup Plate, Amoy 22.50
Flow Blue, Cup Plate, Oriental In Boat, Circa 1850 .... 35.00
Flow Blue, Cup Plate, Oriental, Ridgway 15.00
Flow Blue, Cup Plate, Scinde 25.00
Flow Blue, Cup Plate, Simla, Elsmore & Forster, C.1860, 12 Sided, Oriental 15.00
Flow Blue, Cup, Demitasse, Manilla 20.00
Flow Blue, Cup, Manilla 18.50
Flow Blue, Cup, Watteau, Doulton 14.00
Flow Blue, Dinner Set, 52 Pieces 500.00
Flow Blue, Dish, Bone, Argyle, Johnson Bros., Set Of 5 .... 30.00
Flow Blue, Dish, Bone, Cambridge, Meakin, Floral & Gold 10.00
Flow Blue, Dish, Bone, Clarence, Set Of 6 .... 125.00
Flow Blue, Dish, Bone, Martha, Floral, Wilkinson 10.00
Flow Blue, Dish, Bone, Ophir, Floral, Burgess & Leigh 10.00
Flow Blue, Dish, Bone, Ormonde, Floral, Meakin 10.00
Flow Blue, Dish, Bone, Regal, Set Of 4 .... 72.00
Flow Blue, Dish, Bone, Regent, Floral & Gold, Meakin 10.00
Flow Blue, Dish, Bone, Versailles, Floral & Gold, Furnival 10.00
Flow Blue, Dish, Cheese, Dark Blue Handle 45.00
Flow Blue, Dish, Cheese, Lid, Roses, Marked Ironstone 32.00
Flow Blue, Dish, Honey, Touraine, Alcock 8.00
Flow Blue, Gravy Boat & Tray, Blenheim, Floral & Gold, Hancock 17.50
Flow Blue, Gravy Boat & Tray, Oxford 16.50
Flow Blue, Gravy Boat, Alaska, Floral & Gold, Grindley 20.00
Flow Blue, Gravy Boat, Argyle, F.& Sons 15.00
Flow Blue, Gravy Boat, Argyle, Floral & Gold, Grindley 20.00
Flow Blue, Gravy Boat, Brooklyn, Floral, Johnson Bros. 20.00
Flow Blue, Gravy Boat, Candia, Oriental Floral, Ridgway, C.1891 ..... 25.00
Flow Blue, Gravy Boat, Crescent, Grindley 17.50
Flow Blue, Gravy Boat, Devon, Alfred Meakin 17.50
Flow Blue, Gravy Boat, Osborne, W.H.Grindley & Co., England 22.50
Flow Blue, Gravy Boat, Princess, Floral & Gold, Grindley, 1800-1914 Mark 17.50
Flow Blue, Gravy Boat, Roseville, Thos.Hughes & Son 17.50
Flow Blue, Gravy Boat, Scenic, Grindley 15.00
Flow Blue, Gravy Boat, Touraine, Stanley 25.00
Flow Blue, Gravy Boat, Venus, Floral & Gold, Steel Blue, T.Till & Sons 15.00
Flow Blue, Holder, Toothbrush, Manhattan, Johnson Bros., Floral, Scalloped 25.00
Flow Blue, Jar, Biscuit, Roman Chariot Scene, Silver Handle & Top ... 60.00
Flow Blue, Mug, Scuttle, 5 In.High 35.00
Flow Blue, Pitcher, Arabesque, 40 Oz. 110.00
Flow Blue, Pitcher, Marked Lotus & Trademark, 5 In.High 30.00
Flow Blue, Pitcher, Milk, Clayton, Grindley, Floral, Embossing, 6 3/4 In.High 60.00

Flow Blue, Pitcher, Milk, Indian, Jar	55.00
Flow Blue, Pitcher, Milk, Touraine, Alcock, 6 1/4 In.High	50.00
Flow Blue, Pitcher, Water, Celtic	65.00
Flow Blue, Pitcher, Water, Geneva, Doulton, 2 1/2 Quart	50.00
Flow Blue, Pitcher, Water, Madras, 2 1/2 Quart	65.00
Flow Blue, Pitcher, Water, Nonpareil, Burgess & Leigh	60.00
Flow Blue, Pitcher, Water, Watteau, 2 1/2 Quart	65.00
Flow Blue, Plaque, Jenny Lind, Wilkinson, Picnic Scene, Lake, Castle	35.00
Flow Blue, Plate, Alaska, Grindley, 9 3/4 In.	20.00
Flow Blue, Plate, Alaska, 8 In.	10.00
Flow Blue, Plate, Albany, 9 1/2 In.	22.00
Flow Blue, Plate, Albion, 10 In.Diameter	10.00
Flow Blue, Plate, Alhambra, C.1860	9.00
Flow Blue, Plate, Amoy, 8 1/2 In.	23.00
Flow Blue, Plate, Amoy, 9 1/4 In.	20.00 To 26.00
Flow Blue, Plate, Argyle, Ford, 10 1/2 In.	18.00
Flow Blue, Plate, Argyle, Octagon	18.00
Flow Blue, Plate, Argyle, 9 In.	15.00
Flow Blue, Plate, Asborne, Ford & Son, 7 1/4 In.	6.00
Flow Blue, Plate, Ayr, W.& T.Corn, 9 In.Diameter	11.00
Flow Blue, Plate, Blenheim, Stylized Floral & Gold, Hood, 10 In.	12.00
Flow Blue, Plate, Blue Danube, Embossed, Stylized, Gold, Johnson, 8 In.	9.00
Flow Blue, Plate, Bread, Kyber, 7 1/2 X 10 In.	35.00
Flow Blue, Plate, California, Scenic, Pearl Stoneware, Wedgwood, Dated 1849	15.00
Flow Blue, Plate, Carlton, Oriental Stone, 12 Sided, Sam'L Alcock, C.1850	27.50
Flow Blue, Plate, Cattle, Herd In Center, 3 Scene Border, Wedgwood, 10 In.	20.00
Flow Blue, Plate, Cauldon, Gold Edge, 9 In.	9.00
Flow Blue, Plate, Chapoo, Ironstone, 7 1/2 In.	13.00 To 20.00
Flow Blue, Plate, Chop, La Belle, Wheeling, 11 1/4 In.	30.00
Flow Blue, Plate, Clover, Grindley, 9 In.	11.00
Flow Blue, Plate, Columbia, 9 1/2 In.	34.00
Flow Blue, Plate, Conway, 9 In.	22.00
Flow Blue, Plate, Conway, 10 In.	12.50
Flow Blue, Plate, Coral, 8 1/2 In.	5.00
Flow Blue, Plate, Crumlin, Floral & Gold, Myotts, 8 In.	10.00
Flow Blue, Plate, Cyprus, Davenport, Incised Anchor Mark & Date 1848	20.00
Flow Blue, Plate, Dahlia, E.Challinor, C.1845, 14 Sided, Oriental Stone	40.00
Flow Blue, Plate, Delamere, Alcock, Stylized Floral & Gold, 8 3/4 In.	10.00
Flow Blue, Plate, Duchess, 7 3/4 In.	8.00
Flow Blue, Plate, Duchess, 8 3/4 In.	9.00
Flow Blue, Plate, Duchess, 10 In.	
Flow Blue, Plate, Ebor	15.00
Flow Blue, Plate, Erie, Floral & Gold, Burgess & Leigh, 9 1/2 In.	11.00
Flow Blue, Plate, Eton, 9 In.	8.00
Flow Blue, Plate, Fairy Villas, Adams, 9 In.	15.00
Flow Blue, Plate, Fairy Villas, 7 3/4 In.	18.50
Flow Blue, Plate, Fish, Gold Swimming Fish, Stoke On Trent, 8 1/2 In.	18.00
Flow Blue, Plate, Floral Garlands	10.00
Flow Blue, Plate, Floral, Deep Cobalt, Copeland, Ironstone, C.1847, 10 1/2 In.	40.00
Flow Blue, Plate, Floral, Gold Edge, Fluted, Scalloped, 9 In.	15.00
Flow Blue, Plate, Game, Mountain Goats On Rocks, Scene, Uneven Edge, 9 In.	32.00
Flow Blue, Plate, Glenmore, Stylized Floral & Gold, Grindley, 10 In.	15.00
Flow Blue, Plate, Glenwood, Johnson, England, 9 In.	20.00
Flow Blue, Plate, Gothic, 12 Sided, Jacob Furnival & Co., C.1850	22.50
Flow Blue, Plate, Haddon, Stylized Floral, Grindley, 8 3/4 In.	11.00
Flow Blue, Plate, Hindustan, 7 1/2 In.	21.00
Flow Blue, Plate, Historical, Spanish Festivities, 1793, Half Moon Mark	30.00
Flow Blue, Plate, Hong Kong, 10 1/2 In.	20.00
Flow Blue, Plate, Indian Jar, 8 1/4 In.	22.50
Flow Blue, Plate, Indian Jar, 9 1/4 In.	32.00
Flow Blue, Plate, Iris, Blue & Gold, Wilkinson, Staffordshire, 10 In.	15.00
Flow Blue, Plate, Jeddo, Oriental Stone, 14 Sided, W.Adams & Sons, C.1845	25.00
Flow Blue, Plate, Kaolin, 9 1/2 In.	18.00
Flow Blue, Plate, Kelvin, Meakin, 9 In.	12.00
Flow Blue, Plate, Kinshan, E.C.& Co., 9 1/2 In.	20.00
Flow Blue, Plate, Kinshan, 10 1/2 In.	41.00

Flow Blue, Plate, Kyber, Adams, 10 1/4 In. 22.50
Flow Blue, Plate, Lahore, 10 In. 38.00
Flow Blue, Plate, Lancaster, New Wharf, 9 1/4 In. 12.00
Flow Blue, Plate, Landing Of Lafayette, Clews, 10 In. 185.00
Flow Blue, Plate, Leicester, Blue Gray With Gold, Burgess & Leigh, 9 In. 12.00
Flow Blue, Plate, Manhattan, Alcock, 9 In. 10.00
Flow Blue, Plate, Manila, 10 1/2 In. 35.00
Flow Blue, Plate, Manilla, Podmore Walker & Co. 25.00
Flow Blue, Plate, Marie, Grindley, 8 In. 9.00
Flow Blue, Plate, Marie, Grindley, 9 In. 15.00
Flow Blue, Plate, Ming, Davenport 16.00
Flow Blue, Plate, Mongolia, Peafowl Center, Floral, Johnson Bros., 7 1/4 In. 9.00
Flow Blue, Plate, Ning Po, 7 1/2 In. 18.00
Flow Blue, Plate, Nonpareil, Burgess & Leigh, 7 In. 10.00
Flow Blue, Plate, Nonpareil, Burgess & Leigh, 8 3/4 In. 15.00
Flow Blue, Plate, Nonpareil, Burgess & Leigh, 10 In. 20.00
Flow Blue, Plate, Nonpareil, 7 3/4 In. 16.00
Flow Blue, Plate, Normandy, Johnson Bros., 9 In. 12.00
Flow Blue, Plate, Olympia, Grindley, 9 In. 9.00
Flow Blue, Plate, Olympia, W.H.Grindley, 6 In. 3.50
Flow Blue, Plate, Olympia, W.H.Grindley, 10 In. 8.00
Flow Blue, Plate, Oregon, 9 In. 26.00
Flow Blue, Plate, Oriental, Ridgway, 8 In. 18.00
Flow Blue, Plate, Osborne, Ridgway, 8 In. 9.00
Flow Blue, Plate, Ovando, Alfred Meakin & Co., 10 In. .... 15.00 To 20.00
Flow Blue, Plate, Paisley, Mercer, 1890, 9 In. 12.00
Flow Blue, Plate, Paris, New Wharf, 9 In. 11.00
Flow Blue, Plate, Peking, C.1835-1859, 8 In. .... 13.00 To 18.50
Flow Blue, Plate, Peking, 10 1/2 In. 30.00
Flow Blue, Plate, Pelew, 10 In. 35.00
Flow Blue, Plate, Persian, Johnson Bros., 9 In. 12.00
Flow Blue, Plate, Pittsfield Elm, Clews, 8 In. 115.00
Flow Blue, Plate, Playing At Draughts, From Wilkie's Designs, Clews, 10 In. 130.00
Flow Blue, Plate, Princeton, Johnson Bros., 7 1/4 In. 7.00
Flow Blue, Plate, Regent, 9 In. 10.00
Flow Blue, Plate, Scenic, Castle, Trees, Clouds, Embroidered Blue Edge 23.50
Flow Blue, Plate, Scinde, 9 1/2 In. .... 23.00 To 26.50
Flow Blue, Plate, Scinde, 10 1/2 In. 32.00
Flow Blue, Plate, Shanghai, 9 3/4 In. .... 10.00 To 22.50
Flow Blue, Plate, Shell, 9 1/2 In. 24.00
Flow Blue, Plate, Spinach, Libertas, Ironstone 20.00
Flow Blue, Plate, Stanley, Johnson Bros., England, Patent Nov.1, '99 .... 8.50
Flow Blue, Plate, Summerset, Floral, Grindley, 8 In. 9.00
Flow Blue, Plate, Summertime, Floral, Malkin, Impressed, 1871-1903 .... 9.00
Flow Blue, Plate, Temple, Oriental Stone, Podmore Walker & Co., C.1850 .... 22.50
Flow Blue, Plate, Temple, The, P.W.& Co., 8 3/4 In. 25.00
Flow Blue, Plate, Tonquin, 9 1/2 In. 36.00
Flow Blue, Plate, Touraine, Alcock, 9 In. 15.00
Flow Blue, Plate, Touraine, Alcock, 10 In. .... 20.00 To 22.00
Flow Blue, Plate, Touraine, Gold, 9 7/8 In. 19.00
Flow Blue, Plate, Touraine, 8 1/2 In. 18.00
Flow Blue, Plate, Turkey, Scalloped Edge, Ridgway, 10 In. 30.00
Flow Blue, Plate, Valentine, Clews, 10 In. 95.00
Flow Blue, Plate, Views Of London, S.Hancock & Sons, C.1891 .... 21.50
Flow Blue, Plate, Waldorf, Floral, New Wharf, 8 In. 10.00
Flow Blue, Plate, Waldorf, New Wharf, 9 In. .... 12.50 To 18.00
Flow Blue, Plate, Waldorf, New Wharf, 10 In. 18.00
Flow Blue, Plate, Watteau, Doulton, 9 3/4 In. 20.00
Flow Blue, Plate, Watteau, Doulton, 10 1/2 In. 25.00
Flow Blue, Plate, Waverly, John Maddox & Sons, England, Crown 15.00
Flow Blue, Plate, Wild Turkey Center, Wedgwood 21.00
Flow Blue, Platter, Alaska, Floral & Gold, Grindley, 14 1/4 X 10 1/2 In. 20.00
Flow Blue, Platter, Alaska, Grindley, 16 X 11 3/4 In. 30.00
Flow Blue, Platter, Amoy, 10 X 14 In. 58.00
Flow Blue, Platter, Amoy, 14 X 17 3/4 In. 100.00
Flow Blue, Platter, Argyle, F & Sons, Burslem, 8 1/2 X 11 1/2 In. 20.00

Flow Blue, Platter, Argyle, Grindley, 17 1/4 X 12 In. 35.00
Flow Blue, Platter, Beaufort, 11 X 8 In. 26.00
Flow Blue, Platter, Blenheim, Stylized & Gold, Hancock, 16 1/4 X 13 1/4 In. 25.00
Flow Blue, Platter, Bouquet, Alcock & Co., 10 In.Square .... 20.00 To 25.00
Flow Blue, Platter, Cambridge, Central Medallion, Gold, Meakin 25.00
Flow Blue, Platter, Cambridge, 10 X 14 In. 21.00
Flow Blue, Platter, Canton, Octagon, 20 X 16 In. 75.00
Flow Blue, Platter, Cattle, Wedgwood, 13 1/2 X 16 3/4 In. 65.00
Flow Blue, Platter, Celtic, Central Medallion, Grindley 17.50
Flow Blue, Platter, Chinese Pagodas, Man, Eagle & Shield Mark 45.00
Flow Blue, Platter, Clayton, Johnson Bros., 16 1/4 X 12 1/4 In. 30.00
Flow Blue, Platter, Cleopatra, Ironstone, 17 X 13 1/2 In. 62.00
Flow Blue, Platter, Clover, Grindley, 12 X 9 In. 17.00
Flow Blue, Platter, Coburg, 12 X 16 In. 85.00
Flow Blue, Platter, Cyprus, Davenport, Incised Anchor Mark & Date 1848 .... 75.00
Flow Blue, Platter, Duchess, Floral, Grindley, 16 X 11 1/4 In. 27.50
Flow Blue, Platter, Duchess, W.H.Grindley & Co., England, 8 1/2 X 6 In. 12.50
Flow Blue, Platter, F.& Sons, Bute, Burslem, 15 1/2 X 11 In. 37.50
Flow Blue, Platter, Game, Turkey, Ducks, Partridge, Foliage, Cauldon, Ridgway 75.00
Flow Blue, Platter, Hong Kong, 14 X 18 In. 95.00
Flow Blue, Platter, Indian, 13 1/2 X 17 In. 88.00
Flow Blue, Platter, Indian, 15 1/4 In.Long 55.00
Flow Blue, Platter, Kelvin, Meakin, 14 In. 16.00
Flow Blue, Platter, Lonsdale, Grapevine, Ridgway, 12 1/2 X 9 1/4 In. 17.00
Flow Blue, Platter, Madras, Doulton, Burslem, 17 1/4 X 14 In. 55.00
Flow Blue, Platter, Madras, 13 1/4 X 10 3/4 In. 35.00
Flow Blue, Platter, Marechal Niel, Floral, Rose, Grindley 30.00
Flow Blue, Platter, Marguerite, Floral & Gold, Grindley, 16 X 11 1/4 In. 30.00
Flow Blue, Platter, Melbourne, Grindley 42.00
Flow Blue, Platter, Milton 10.00
Flow Blue, Platter, Nonpareil, Burgess & Leigh, 13 X 15 3/4 In. 40.00
Flow Blue, Platter, Nonpareil, 13 X 16 In. 65.00
Flow Blue, Platter, Nonpareil, 15 1/2 In.Long 45.00
Flow Blue, Platter, Normandy, Blue, Gold, 11 1/2 X 8 1/2 In. 30.00
Flow Blue, Platter, Normandy, 12 3/4 In.Long 32.00
Flow Blue, Platter, Olympia, W.H.Grindley 15.00
Flow Blue, Platter, Osborne, Cobalt Floral, Till & Sons 25.00
Flow Blue, Platter, Osborne, 12 1/4 In. 12.00
Flow Blue, Platter, Pekin, Royal Staffordshire, Burslem, England 25.00
Flow Blue, Platter, Rose, 11 3/8 In. 10.00
Flow Blue, Platter, Savoy, Oval, 12 In. 20.00
Flow Blue, Platter, Scinde, 10 1/2 X 16 1/2 In. 85.00
Flow Blue, Platter, Scinde, 12 1/2 X 16 In. 110.00
Flow Blue, Platter, Touraine, Alcock, 12 3/4 X 8 3/4 In. 27.50
Flow Blue, Platter, Touraine, Alcock, 15 X 10 1/2 In. 45.00
Flow Blue, Platter, Touraine, Alcock, 17 X 11 3/4 In. 60.00
Flow Blue, Platter, Touraine, Stanley, 12 3/4 X 8 3/4 In. 27.50
Flow Blue, Platter, Vincennes, Mulberry, 8 Sided, John Alcock, Cobridge 50.00
Flow Blue, Platter, Waldorf, 11 X 9 In. 18.00
Flow Blue, Platter, Waverly, Stylized Floral, Grindley, 12 X 8 1/2 In. 17.50
Flow Blue, Platter, White Granite, Spread Eagle With Shield Mark 55.00
Flow Blue, Relish, Pelew 35.00
Flow Blue, Sauce Set, Leicester, Floral & Gold, Burgess & Leigh, 4 Piece 40.00
Flow Blue, Sauce Set, Linnea, Gold, Grimwades, 1886-1900, 3 Piece 45.00
Flow Blue, Sauce, California, Blue Gray, Dated 1849 .... 8.00
Flow Blue, Sauce, Cecil, Till & Sons 7.50
Flow Blue, Sauce, Conway 7.50
Flow Blue, Sauce, Fairy Villas, Adams 7.50
Flow Blue, Sauce, Florida, Johnson Bros. 7.50
Flow Blue, Sauce, Iowa, Deep Cobalt, Wilkinson, 6 1/4 In. 8.50
Flow Blue, Sauce, Italia, Wood 7.50
Flow Blue, Sauce, K1, Grindley, 5 1/2 In. 6.00
Flow Blue, Sauce, K1, Grindley, 6 1/2 In. 7.50
Flow Blue, Sauce, Melrose, Doulton 7.50
Flow Blue, Sauce, Mongolia, Johnson Bros. 7.50
Flow Blue, Sauce, Peach Royal, Johnson Bros. 7.50

Flow Blue, Sauce, Racine, Johnson Bros.	6.00
Flow Blue, Sauce, Richmond, Johnson Bros.	7.50
Flow Blue, Sauce, Scinde	10.00
Flow Blue, Sauce, Shanghai, Grindley	7.50
Flow Blue, Sauce, Touraine	10.00
Flow Blue, Sauce, Waldorf, New Wharf	7.50
Flow Blue, Sauce, Wild Rose, G.Jones	6.00
Flow Blue, Saucer, Cambridge, Meakin	3.00
Flow Blue, Saucer, Clarence, Grindley	3.00
Flow Blue, Saucer, Devon, Coffee Cup Size, Meakin	5.00
Flow Blue, Saucer, Devon, Teacup Size, Meakin	4.00
Flow Blue, Saucer, Duchess	4.50
Flow Blue, Saucer, Marguerite, Grindley	3.00
Flow Blue, Saucer, Osborne, Ridgway	3.00
Flow Blue, Saucer, Tonquin, Deep, 6 In.	6.00
Flow Blue, Saucer, Touraine, Alcock	5.00
Flow Blue, Slipper, Scalloped, Leaves, Two Cherries In Upturned Toe, 5 In.	17.00
Flow Blue, Soup, Fairy Villas, 9 In.Diameter	12.50
Flow Blue, Soup, Hong Kong, 10 1/2 In.	20.00
Flow Blue, Soup, Kyber, Adams	14.00
Flow Blue, Soup, Mabelle, Burslem, 9 In.	10.00
Flow Blue, Soup, Sancho Panza At The Boar Hunt, Don Quixote Series, Clews	90.00
Flow Blue, Soup, Shanghai	13.00 To 18.00
Flow Blue, Sugar, Covered, Handled, Gold Star Garlands	10.95
Flow Blue, Sugar, Nonpareil, Burgess & Leigh	15.00
Flow Blue, Sugar, Normandy, Johnson Bros.	40.00
Flow Blue, Sugar, Shanghai, Grindley	35.00
Flow Blue, Sugar, Touraine, Alcock	50.00
Flow Blue, Sugar, Touraine, Stanley	50.00
Flow Blue, Tea Caddy, C.1840	38.00
Flow Blue, Teapot, Verona	85.00
Flow Blue, Tray, Watteau, Scrolls, Floral, Colonial Figures, Doulton, Burslem	30.00
Flow Blue, Tureen & Tray, Floral, Gilt, C.1890	24.00
Flow Blue, Tureen & Tray, Gravy, Covered, Japan	85.00
Flow Blue, Tureen & Tray, Landing Of Lafayette, Aug.1824, Clews	625.00
Flow Blue, Tureen, Covered, Floral Garlands	25.00
Flow Blue, Tureen, Covered, Nonpareil, Acorn Finial, Burgess & Leigh	75.00
Flow Blue, Tureen, Covered, Oblong	25.00
Flow Blue, Umbrella Stand, China	145.00
Flow Blue, Urn, Watteau, Losolle Ware, Pair	275.00
Flow Blue, Vase, Nankin, Gold Trim, England, 16 In., Pair	125.00
Flow Blue, Vase, Roses, Gold Trim & Handles, 8 1/2 In., Pair	60.00
Flow Blue, Vase, Willowware, Minton, 12 In.	65.00
Flow Blue, Vegetable, Cover, Wentworth	35.00
Flow Blue, Wash Basin, Flowers, Gilt, Scalloped, 19 X 15 In.	35.00
Flow Blue, Washstand Set, Atlas Pattern	175.00

Foo Dogs are mythical Chinese figures, part dog and part lion. They were made of pottery, porcelain, carved stone, and wood.

Foo Dog, Black Soapstone, Hand Carved, China, 2 3/4 In.High	22.00
Foo Dog, Gilt, 90 Set Turquoise Stones, Coral Stone Accent, 5 In.High	95.00
Foo Dog, Peacock Blue, Incised China Mark, 6 In., Pair	35.00
Foo Dog, Soapstone, Marblelike, Green Black Veins, Pedestal, 7 In., Pair	60.00
Foo Dog, Yellow, Green Mane, Holds Ball, Cub, Porcelain, China, 10 In., Pair	59.00

Fostoria Glass was made in Fostoria, Ohio, from 1887 to 1891. The factory was moved to Moundsville, West Virginia, and most of the glass seen in shops today is a twentieth century product.

Fostoria, Bowl, Baroque, Gold Tint, Handled, Three Sections, 10 In.	18.00
Fostoria, Bowl, Blue, Etched, Two Handles, 10 In.Diameter	22.00
Fostoria, Bowl, Versailles Etching, Azure, Handled, 10 In.	22.00
Fostoria, Bucket, Ice, Etched Grape Pattern, Green	22.00
Fostoria, Bucket, Ice, 8 In., Early American, Tongs	25.00
Fostoria, Candelabra, Three Holder, Deep Pink, Pair	60.00
Fostoria, Candelabra, 3-Light, Azure Blue, 3 In.High, Pair	25.00
Fostoria, Castor, Pickle, Victoria, Silver Plated Frame	48.00

Fostoria, Compote, Amber, 7 In. 6.00
Fostoria, Compote, Early American, 10 In. 25.00
Fostoria, Compote, Vesper, Amber, C.1926 .... 20.00
Fostoria, Dish, Lemon, Versailles, Azure Blue 4.50
Fostoria, Goblet, Art Nouveau, Curved Stem, Circa 1910, Signed, Set Of 6 .... 45.00
Fostoria, Pitcher, American, Clear, 7 In. 15.00
Fostoria, Pitcher, Clear, Applied Handle, 8 1/2 In.High 22.50
Fostoria, Plate, Cake, Honey Amber, Center Fleur-De-Lis Handle 12.50
Fostoria, Plate, Cake, Pioneer, Footed 9.00
Fostoria, Plate, Fairfax, Amber, 9 In. 3.00
Fostoria, Plate, Serving, Grape Pattern, Green & Frosted, Center Handle ,,,,,,,,,,,,,,,,, 8.50
Fostoria, Sauce & Plate, Holly 15.00
Fostoria, Shade, Iris, White With Green & Gold Leaf & Vine, Gold Interior 35.00
Fostoria, Sugar & Creamer, Baroque, Individual 10.00
Fostoria, Syrup, 'Virginia, 1923, ' Hinged Lid 10.00
Fostoria, Tumbler, Water, Swirl, Set Of 8 .... 15.00
Fostoria, Vase, Grape Brocade, Orchid Color, Circa 1927, 5 In. 20.00
    Foval, see also Fry
Foval, Vase, Gray Blue, Black Band, Footed 75.00
    Frame, see Furniture, Frame

     Francisware is an amber hobnail glassware.
    Francisware, see also Hobnail
Francisware, Bowl, Covered, Frosted, Yellow Band, Oval 25.00
Francisware, Bowl, Oval, Deep, Rich Gold Top 62.50
Francisware, Celery, Cupid And Venus 40.00
Francisware, Celery, Hobnail, Hobs Mint 80.00
Francisware, Dish, Nut, Amber Edge, 5 In.Square 27.00
Francisware, Relish, Swirl, Frosted, Amber Rim 39.00
Francisware, Sauce, Amber & Frosted 11.00
Francisware, Sauce, Frosted Hobnail, Amber Band 25.00
Francisware, Shaker, Salt, Swirls 19.00
Francisware, Toothpick, Frosted Hobnail, Amber Top 40.00
Francisware, Toothpick, Opalescent Swirl, Amber Ruffled Top 30.00
Francisware, Tray, Ice Cream, Leaf Shape, 12 In., Diameter 90.00
Francisware, Tumbler, Water, Hobnail 28.50

     Fry Glass was made by the famous H.C.Fry Glass Company of
     Rochester, Pennsylvania. It includes Cut Glass, but the famous Fry
     Glass today is the Foval, or Pearl, Art Glass. This is an opal ware
     decorated with colored trim. It was made from 1922 to 1933.
    Fry, see also Cut Glass
Fry Foval, Bowl, Covered, Opalescent, Signed, 4 1/2 In. 8.95
Fry Foval, Bowl, Fruit, Delft On Flared Rim & Stem, Footed 135.00
Fry Foval, Candlestick, Blue Spiral Threading & Connectors, Pair 165.00
Fry Foval, Candlestick, Fiery, No Decoration, 7 1/4 In.High, Pair 125.00
Fry Foval, Candlestick, Opalescent, Threading, Pair .... *Illus* 195.00

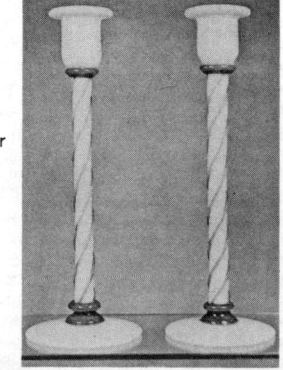

Fry Foval, Candlestick, Opalescent, Threading, Pair

Fry Foval, **Candlestick**, Spiral Pearl, Blue Trim, 12 1/2 In., Pair	310.00
Fry Foval, **Candlestick**, White, Blue Trim, Blue Coils, Pair	225.00
Fry Foval, **Casserole**, Covered, Dated, 9 In.	10.00
Fry Foval, **Cocktail Glass**, Smoke Black Bowl, Paperweight Base, Bubbles	35.00
Fry Foval, **Coffeepot**, Blue Handles, Finial On Cover	250.00
Fry Foval, **Coffeepot**, Silex, Removable Handle, 3 Piece	145.00
Fry Foval, **Coffeepot**, Underplate, Insert, Opalescent, Signed	185.00
Fry Foval, **Cruet**, Faceted, Applied Blue Handle, Blue Stopper, Pair	95.00
Fry Foval, **Cup & Saucer**, Green Handle	38.00
Fry Foval, **Cup & Saucer**, White Opalescent, Delft Blue Handle	40.00
Fry Foval, **Cup**, Custard, Opalescent, Dated 1936	3.50
Fry Foval, **Cup**, Custard, Set Of 4	20.00
Fry Foval, **Goblet**, Cone Top, Pink Base, Baluster Stem, Alabaster, Pearl Ware	37.00
Fry Foval, **Goblet**, Vaseline, Amber Foot	75.00
Fry Foval, **Iced Tea**, Green Handle & Base	48.00
Fry Foval, **Juicer**, Opalescent, Marked Ovenware	8.50 To 15.00
Fry Foval, **Lemonade Set**, Yellow, Blue Handled, Covered Pitcher, 11 Piece	245.00
Fry Foval, **Mug**, Blue Handle, Footed	75.00
Fry Foval, **Pan**, Bread, Opalescent, Dated, Patented	8.00
Fry Foval, **Perfume**, Petticoat Shape, Blue Capped Dauber	75.00
Fry Foval, **Pitcher**, Iced Tea, Covered, Green Handle & Finial	145.00
Fry Foval, **Pitcher**, Opal Stripes On Vaseline, Cobalt Handle, 9 In.	75.00
Fry Foval, **Pitcher**, White, Blue Handle, Blue Finial On Lid, 11 In.High	55.00
Fry Foval, **Plate**, Green Border, Signed, 8 1/2 In.	25.00
Fry Foval, **Plate**, Iridized, Milky, 8 1/2 In., Set Of 4	72.00
Fry Foval, **Plate**, Opalescent, Divided, Signed, 10 1/2 In.	10.00
Fry Foval, **Roaster**, Covered, Ovenware, Pearl, 14 In.	48.00
Fry Foval, **Rose Bowl**, Blue Opalescent Ribbon, Blown, Crimped Top	35.00
Fry Foval, **Sherbet**, Apple Green Base, Iridescent, Cone Shape	10.00
Fry Foval, **Sherbet**, Smoky Yellow Bowl, Blue Stem, Clear Base, Backward F	65.00
Fry Foval, **Trivet**, Footed, Signed	22.00
Fry Foval, **Vase**, Opal Stripes On Green, Crimped Top, Forms Six Point Star	65.00
Fry, **Mayonnaise Set**, Cut Glass, Signed, 2 Piece	110.00
Fry, **Pitcher**, Crackle, Transparent Lime Green Handle, Blown, 9 1/2 In.	65.00
Fry, **Tankard**, Cut Glass, Signed, 12 1/2 In.High	150.00
Fry, **Vase**, Crackle Glass, Applied Green Leaves, 10 In.High	75.00
Fry, **Vase**, Green, Opalescent Stripes, Top Crimped To Form Six Point Star	65.00
Fry, **Vase**, Jack-In-The-Pulpit, Lavender Border, 13 In.High	95.00 To 135.00
Fry, **Wine**, Smoky Crystal Bowl, Bubble Paperweight Ball Foot, Unsigned	35.00

*Fulper is the mark used by the American Pottery Company of
Flemington, New Jersey. The art pottery was made from 1910 to 1929.
The firm had been making bottles, jugs, and housewares from 1805. Doll heads
were made about 1928. The firm became Stangl Pottery in 1929.*

Fulper, **Bowl**, Frog, Turquoise & Black, 8 In.Bowl	28.00
Fulper, **Bowl**, Rose, Rose Color, Brown Inside	9.00
Fulper, **Box**, Powder, Figural, Lady In Puffed Skirt Forms Cover	48.00
Fulper, **Box**, Powder, Lady Top, Pink & Blue	48.00
Fulper, **Box**, Powder, Lady With Puffed Skirt Forms Cover, Artist Signed	48.00
Fulper, **Candlestick**, Pink, Gray, Handle, Mark	12.00
Fulper, **Jar**, Powder, Figural, Woman, Blue, Brown, Yellow, Floral On Base	18.00
Fulper, **Lamp**, Bisque Doll, Wired, Signed, 8 In.	45.00
Fulper, **Planter**, Green, Green & Brown Mottling, Bulbous, Short Neck, Handles	35.00
Fulper, **Rose Bowl**, Dark Green, Drips Down To Matte Blue, Paper Label	25.00
Fulper, **Urn**, Beige To Blue, Handles, High Glaze, Bar Mark, 9 1/2 In.High	25.00
Fulper, **Vase**, Blue & Green Mottling, Bulbous, Handle, 6 In.High	13.00
Fulper, **Vase**, Blue Gray, Deep Blue & Brown Mottling, Bulbous, 8 In.	45.00
Fulper, **Vase**, Blue Gray, Mottled, Three Handles, 5 1/4 In.High	35.00
Fulper, **Vase**, Blue Iridescent, 5 In.High	23.50
Fulper, **Vase**, Blue Shades, Drip Glaze Shades To Brown At Top, 5 In.	12.00
Fulper, **Vase**, Blue, Brown Gray Streaks	45.00
Fulper, **Vase**, Boat Shape, Rose & Green, 6 X 2 In.	12.00
Fulper, **Vase**, Brown Mottling, Blue Drip Finish Inside & Outside, 2 Handles	22.00
Fulper, **Vase**, Green, Brown Mottling, 8 Sided, Incised Signature	15.00
Fulper, **Vase**, Matte Glaze, Green Mark	35.00
Fulper, **Vase**, Tan Top, Brown Bottom, Glossy Drip Glaze, Two Handles, Squat	25.00

Fulper, Vase, Tan Top, Dark Brown Base, Two Handles, Glossy, 7 In.High 20.00
Furniture, Armchair, Austrian, Beechwood, Lyre Splat, Rush Seat, C.1890 .... 120.00
Furniture, Armchair, Beechwood, Carved Scallop Shells, C.1790, Pair 1000.00
Furniture, Armchair, Beechwood, Upholstered Back, Carved Acanthus, C.1790 .... 70.00
Furniture, Armchair, Biedermeier, Birch, Upholstered, Saber Legs, C.1850 .... 200.00
Furniture, Armchair, Brewster Style, C.1850 .... 200.00
Furniture, Armchair, Brewster, American, Rush Seat, 17th Century 550.00
Furniture, Armchair, Chinese, Huang-Huali, Horseshoe Back, Ch'len Lung 950.00
Furniture, Armchair, Chinese, Hung-Mu, Pair .... *Illus* 450.00
Furniture, Armchair, Chippendale, Mahogany, Open, High Back, Pair 800.00
Furniture, Armchair, Chippendale, Walnut, Cupid's Bow Crest Rail, Phila. 6500.00
Furniture, Armchair, Continental, Beechwood, Bowfront Seat, C.1850, Pair 125.00
Furniture, Armchair, Continental, Beechwood, Caned, Molded Back, C.1790 .... 90.00
Furniture, Armchair, Corner, Dutch, Walnut, Pierced Splats, C.1750 .... 300.00
Furniture, Armchair, Corner, George II, Elm, 2 Section Back, Pierced Splat 500.00

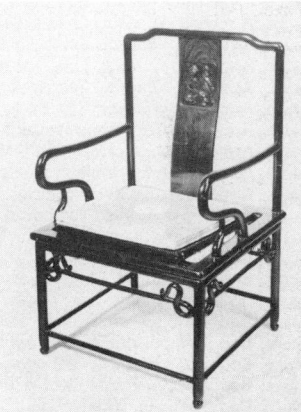

Furniture, Armchair, Chinese, Hung-Mu, Pair

Furniture, Armchair, Corner, George II, Walnut, Horseshoe Back, C.1780 .... 375.00
Furniture, Armchair, Doll's House, Wicker, 7 1/2 In.High 7.00
Furniture, Armchair, Federal, Inlaid Mahogany, Wing, Scrolled Arms, Penna. 400.00
Furniture, Armchair, Flemish Style, Walnut, Wine Damask, C.1650, Pair 225.00
Furniture, Armchair, Flemish, Arched Paneled Back, Box Base, C.1660 .... 85.00
Furniture, Armchair, French, Mahogany Frame, Open, Shield Back, Pair 250.00
Furniture, Armchair, George II, Elm & Beechwood, Gothic Back, C.1790 .... 310.00
Furniture, Armchair, George II, Walnut, Wing, Acanthus Carved Knees, C.1790 .... 1300.00
Furniture, Armchair, George II, Walnut, Wing, Carved Cartouches At Knees 1300.00
Furniture, Armchair, George III, Black Japanned, C.1790, Pair 375.00
Furniture, Armchair, George III, Gilt Wood, Black Leather Shield Back, 6 .... 3800.00
Furniture, Armchair, George III, Mahogany, Pierced Gothic Splat, C.1790 .... 225.00
Furniture, Armchair, George III, Mahogany, Pierced Vase Splat, C.1790 .... 90.00
Furniture, Armchair, George III, Mahogany, Shield Back, Carved, C.1750, Pair 1200.00
Furniture, Armchair, Iron, Shell & Seahorse Ornaments, Pair 350.00
Furniture, Armchair, Italian, Painted, Upholstered, Carved Acanthus, 1690 .... 60.00
Furniture, Armchair, Italian, Walnut, Corbel Finials, Ligurian, C.1650 .... 500.00
Furniture, Armchair, Italian, Walnut, Flemish Tapestry Upholstery, C.1650 .... 375.00
Furniture, Armchair, Italian, Walnut, Pierced Front Stretcher, C.1550 .... 300.00
Furniture, Armchair, Italian, Walnut, Red Velvet, Embroidery, Carved, C.1550 .... 225.00
Furniture, Armchair, Italian, Walnut, Tall Back, Carved Gilt Wood, C.1550 .... 150.00
Furniture, Armchair, Italian, Walnut, Upholstered, Carved, C.1760, Pair 800.00
Furniture, Armchair, James I, Oak, Paneled Back, Carved, C.1630 .... 600.00
Furniture, Armchair, Library, George II, Mahogany, Serpentine Top, C.1790 .... 1200.00
Furniture, Armchair, Library, George II, Mahogany, Upholstered Back, C.1750 .... 350.00
Furniture, Armchair, Library, George III, Mahogany, C.1750 .... 400.00
Furniture, Armchair, Library, Mahogany, Serpentine Top, C.1790 .... 450.00
Furniture, Armchair, Maple & Cherry, Slat Back, Turned, American, C.1720 .... 300.00
Furniture, Armchair, Maple, High Back, Upholstered 90.00
Furniture, Armchair, Maple, Ladder Back, Turned Stretcher At Front 275.00

Furniture, Armchair, Open Back, Pierced Splats, Carved, C.1790, Pair 650.00
Furniture, Armchair, Oval Wheel Back, Pierced, C.1790, Pair 1700.00
Furniture, Armchair, Painted, Open Backrest, Caned Seat, C.1750, 4 .... 950.00
Furniture, Armchair, Painted, Oval Back, Bowfront Seat, C.1790 .... 275.00
Furniture, Armchair, Regency, Beechwood, Pierced Splats, C.1820 .... 60.00
Furniture, Armchair, Shield Back, Victorian, Eastlake, Walnut 75.00
Furniture, Armchair, Spanish, Rectangular Tooled Leather Back, C.1650 .... 80.00
Furniture, Armchair, Spanish, Upholstered Back & Seat, C.1600 .... 225.00
Furniture, Armchair, Spanish, Walnut, Brass Finials, Upholstered, C.1650 .... 250.00
Furniture, Armchair, Venetian, Open, High Back, Cabriole Legs, C.1750, Pair 1300.00
Furniture, Armchair, Victorian, Black Japanned, Caned, C.1850, Pair 750.00
Furniture, Armchair, Wainscot, Open Back, Turned Legs, Molded Stretchers 125.00
Furniture, Armchair, William & Mary, Beechwood, Miniature, English, C.1700 .... 950.00
Furniture, Armchair, Windsor, Bow Back, Dark Finish 297.50
Furniture, Armchair, Windsor, Bow Back, Saddle Seat, H Stretcher, 7 Spindle 325.00
Furniture, Armchair, Windsor, Bow Back, 11 Turned Spindles, N.E., C.1790 .... 300.00
Furniture, Armchair, Windsor, Child's, Bow Back, Rhode Island, C.1790 .... 350.00
Furniture, Armchair, Windsor, Comb Back, Saddle Seat, 8 Spindles, H Stretcher 275.00
Furniture, Armchair, Windsor, Elm, Dished Seat, Stick Splats, C.1780, 3 .... 375.00
Furniture, Armchair, Windsor, Pennsylvania, C.1790 .... *Illus* 475.00
Furniture, Armchair, Windsor, Star Back, Bamboo Turned Legs, 7 Spindles 200.00
Furniture, Armchair, 18th Century, Center Base Stretcher, Coverlet Covered 575.00
Furniture, Armoire, Biedermeier, Birch, Molded Cornice, Doors, C.1820 .... 200.00
Furniture, Armoire, Dutch, Walnut, Molded Cornice, Veneered, C.1790 .... 675.00
Furniture, Armoire, Louis XVI Provincial, Fruitwood, Scroll Feet, C.1790 .... 575.00
Furniture, Bed, Brass, Curved Footboard, Twin 149.00
Furniture, Bed, Brass, Queen Size, Half Tester, 92 In.High 1050.00
Furniture, Bed, Brass, Springs 120.00
Furniture, Bed, Cannonball, Cherry, Eastern Kentucky, C.1810 .... 285.00
Furniture, Bed, Cannonball, Tiger Maple 300.00
Furniture, Bed, Child's, Flemish, Oak, Panel Decoration 30.00
Furniture, Bed, Companion Trundle, Applewood & Maple, Low Post, N.E., C.1750 .... 500.00
Furniture, Bed, Doll's, Federal, Mahogany, Tester, American, C.1800 .... 475.00
Furniture, Bed, Double, Painted Red & Brown, Gilded, Cartouche, C.1750 .... 375.00
Furniture, Bed, Eastlake, Ornate, Tall 850.00
Furniture, Bed, Federal, Cherry, Tester, Turned, Pennsylvania, C.1800 .... 550.00
Furniture, Bed, Federal, Curly Maple, Miniature, New England, C.1810 .... 350.00
Furniture, Bed, Florentine, Carved Wood, 3/4 Size, Painted White 100.00
Furniture, Bed, Four Poster, Single, Rope, Maple 95.00
Furniture, Bed, Maple & Pine, Restored, Twin, New Hampshire, C.1815, Pair 550.00
Furniture, Bed, Maple, High Post, Acanthus Carved Foot Posts, Turned Feet 350.00
Furniture, Bed, Oak, Carved Leaf & Flower Pediment, 17th Century 900.00
Furniture, Bed, Post & Tester, Dark Stained 695.00
Furniture, Bed, Post, Maple Finish, Acorn, C.1820 .... 185.00
Furniture, Bed, Provincial, Mahogany, Tester, C.1750 .... 70.00
Furniture, Bed, Shaker, Wood Rollers, Watervliet 475.00
Furniture, Bed, Spanish Nuptial, Embossed Nudes, Brass, Polished, Pair 750.00
Furniture, Bed, Venetian, Painted, Saint, Chains, Vases Of Flowers, C.1750 .... 1700.00
Furniture, Bench, Deacon's, Reversible Back, 7 Ft. 150.00
Furniture, Bench, Hall, Italian Renaissance Style, Walnut, Carved 400.00
Furniture, Bench, Hall, Italian, Walnut, Carved Apron, Upright Rail, C.1750 .... 160.00
Furniture, Bench, Huali, Chinese, Oblong, Caned Panel, C.1850, Pair 1600.00
Furniture, Bench, Louis XVI, Oak, Carved Apron, Floral, Material 125.00
Furniture, Bench, Mammy's, Handmade In Pennsylvania, 48 In.Wide 480.00
Furniture, Bench, Stone, 60 In.Long 100.00
Furniture, Bench, Table, Pine, Maple, C.1750 .... *Illus* 210.00
Furniture, Bench, Victorian Slipper, Walnut With Carved Ends 55.00
Furniture, Bench, Wainscot, Oak, Armed, 3 Panel Back, 17th Century 750.00
Furniture, Bench, Woodworking, Cabinetmaker's, Maple Top, 3 Drawer 55.00
Furniture, Bench, Work, Shaker, 5 Drawer, Turned Legs, 69 X 33 X 28 In. 800.00
Furniture, Bench, Wrought Iron, 23 X 18 X 20 In. 130.00
Furniture, Bergere De Bureau, Beechwood, Carved, Tub Form, C.1750 .... 1600.00
Furniture, Bergere De Bureau, Provincial, Caned, Tub Form, C.1790 .... 500.00
Furniture, Bergere, Louis XV, Beechwood, Carved, C.1750, Pair 2800.00
Furniture, Bergere, Louis XVI, Painted, Rectangular Back, Upholstered, 1750 .... 1600.00
Furniture, Book Table, Directoire, Mahogany, 1 Drawer, 3 Tiers, C.1850 .... 150.00

Furniture, Bench, Table, Pine, Maple, C.1750
See Page 220

Furniture, Armchair, Windsor, Pennsylvania, C.1790
See Page 220

Furniture, Bookcase Cabinet, George III, Mahogany, Breakfront, C.1790 .... 4100.00
Furniture, Bookcase Desk, Butler's, Federal, Mahogany, 2 Parts, American, 1810 .... 325.00
Furniture, Bookcase, Federal, Inlaid Mahogany, Miniature, American, C.1790 .... 4000.00
Furniture, Bookcase, Italian, Painted & Gilded, Open, C.1850 .... 225.00
Furniture, Bookcase, Mahogany, Breakfront, Carved Frieze, C.1790 .... 2000.00
Furniture, Bookcase, Mahogany, Red Lacquer, Breakfront, C.1820 .... 750.00
Furniture, Bookcase, Oak, 4 Shelves 40.00
Furniture, Bookcase, Shaker, 3 Tiered, Hancock, 18 1/2 X 19 X 10 In.Deep 87.50
Furniture, Bookshelf, George III, Mahogany, 4 Graduated Tiers, Footed 500.00
Furniture, Bookshelf, Mahogany, English, Cabinet Base 400.00
Furniture, Box On Stand, George III, Red Japanned, Rectangular, C.1790 .... 110.00
Furniture, Box, Candle, Dovetailed, Sliding Lid, Pine 32.50
Furniture, Box, Cutlery, Cutout Center Handle, Mahogany 55.00
Furniture, Box, For Wood, Lift Top, Turned Legs, Shaker 100.00
Furniture, Box, Knife, High Center Handle, Mortised Ends, Pine 14.50
Furniture, Box, Knife, Two Compartments, Carrying Handle, Pine 12.75
Furniture, Box, Spice, Victorian, Hanging, 8 Drawer 50.00
Furniture, Box, Writing, 3 Drawers, Mulberry, Handle, 8 In.Tall 22.50
Furniture, Buffet, Directoire, Mahogany, Rectangular, Breakfront, C.1750 .... 750.00
Furniture, Bureau Bookcase, Lacquered Chinese Landscapes, C.1790 .... 1500.00
Furniture, Bureau Cabinet, German, Fruitwood, Etched Coat Of Arms, C.1790 .... 1300.00
Furniture, Bureau Cabinet, Mahogany, Blind Fret Frieze, C.1790 .... 1700.00
Furniture, Bureau De Dame, Louis Philippe, Ebony Veneer, Ormolu, C.1850 .... 525.00
Furniture, Bureau Plat, Louis XVI, Tulipwood, Leather, Brass Rim, C.1790 .... 3500.00
Furniture, Bureau Plat, Satinwood, Rectangular, Brass, C.1750 .... 1600.00
Furniture, Bureau, George II, Mahogany, Slant Front, 5 Drawer, C.1750 .... 1100.00
Furniture, Bureau, Italian, Rectangular, Brass Gallery, White Marble, C.1780 .... 300.00
Furniture, Bureau, Mahogany, Fall Front, Green Leather Top, C.1790 .... 500.00
Furniture, Bureau, Queen Anne, Oak, Rectangular, Fall Front, C.1750 .... 400.00
Furniture, Bureau, White Paint, Bamboo Turned Rail, Paneled Sides, 3 Drawer 130.00
Furniture, Cabinet Chest, Biedermeier, Black Marble Top 275.00
Furniture, Cabinet-On-Chest, Display, Continental, Bowknot Crest 425.00
Furniture, Cabinet-On-Chest, Display, Dutch, Oak, Carved, Brass, C.1750 .... 500.00
Furniture, Cabinet On Stand, Chinese, Carved, Black, Red, Painted, C.1850 .... 450.00
Furniture, Cabinet Secretary, Venetian, Italian Landscape, C.1750 .... 3000.00
Furniture, Cabinet, Carved, Glass Door & Shelf, 1840, 24 X 24 In. 135.00
Furniture, Cabinet, Cheese, French, Oak, Center Door, 6 Turned Spindles 160.00
Furniture, Cabinet, Chippendale, Mahogany, English, Breakfront, C.1800 .... 2000.00
Furniture, Cabinet, Corner, George II, Mahogany, Arched Doors, C.1750 .... 350.00
Furniture, Cabinet, Corner, Louis XV Provincial, Walnut, Bowfront, C.1780 .... 170.00
Furniture, Cabinet, Corner, Mahogany, Inlaid Boxwood, C.1790 .... 575.00
Furniture, Cabinet, Doctor's, Oak, 4 Graduated Drawers Top, Paneled Door 350.00
Furniture, Cabinet, Ebon, Two Sevres Panels On Doors, Louis Philippe, 36 In. 1600.00
Furniture, Cabinet, English, Walnut Inlaid, 19th Century, Burl Sides 325.00

Furniture, Cabinet, Federal, French, Openwork, Yellow Marble Top, Pair 900.00
Furniture, Cabinet, Fruitwood, Open, Heart Cutouts On Each Side 90.00
Furniture, Cabinet, Miniature, Pine, 6 Drawer, 16 X 10 X 17 In. 110.00
Furniture, Cabinet, Napoleonic, Painted, Glass Doors, C.1815 .... 500.00
Furniture, Cabinet, Oak, Paneled Door, Dated 1726, 53 In.High 750.00
Furniture, Cabinet, Painted Red In Gesso, Rectangular, Raised Leaves 275.00
Furniture, Cabinet, Sevres Panels, Watteau Scenes On Doors, Black, 48 In. 1200.00
Furniture, Cabinet, Sheraton, Cherry, Glass, Two Doors, Four Shelves, C.1820 .... 295.00
Furniture, Cabinet, Side, Chinese, Inlaid Mother-Of-Pearl, Red Lacquer, Pair 1200.00
Furniture, Cabinet, Side, Flemish, Oak, Rectangular, Drawer In Frieze, C.1650 .... 650.00
Furniture, Cabinet, Side, George III, Satinwood, D Shape, C.1790 .... 650.00
Furniture, Cabinet, Side, Italian, Walnut, Rectangular, 5 Drawer, C.1650 .... 225.00
Furniture, Cabinet, Side, Italian, Walnut, 3 Drawer, Stepped, C.1550 .... 2800.00
Furniture, Cabinet, Side, Louis XVI Provincial, Beechwood, 2 Drawer, 1750 .... 230.00
Furniture, Cabinet, Side, Regency, Amboyna Wood, Rectangular, C.1820, Pair 550.00
Furniture, Cabinet, Side, Regency, Rosewood, Breakfront, 4 Grill Doors, 1890 .... 275.00
Furniture, Cabinet, Side, Spanish, Beechwood, Grotesque Masks, C.1550 .... 450.00
Furniture, Cabinet, Side, Victorian, Walnut & Fruitwood, Marquetry, C.1850 .... 300.00
Furniture, Cabinet, Smoker's, Glass Door, Inner Drawer, Pipe Rack, Golden Oak 48.00
Furniture, Cabinet, Smoker's, Pipe Racks, Shelf Inside, Lock, Ornate Hinges 35.00
Furniture, Cabinet, Smoker's, Rolltop, English, Edwardian Period, 1i In.Long 95.00
Furniture, Cabinet, Smoking, Glass Door, Inner Drawer, English Oak 59.00
Furniture, Cabinet, Spanish Renaissance Style, 2 Drawer, Carved 80.00
Furniture, Cabinet, Spice, Delft Knobs & Spice Plates, Seven Drawers, German 62.50
Furniture, Cabinet, Spice, Eight Drawers, White Knobs, Tin 45.00
Furniture, Cabinet, Spool, Liftup Top, Four Drawers, Oak 65.00
Furniture, Cabinet, Spool, Oak, 6 Drawer, Willimantic 120.00
Furniture, Cabinet, Spool, Star Thread 125.00
Furniture, Cabinet, Spool, Two Drawers, Oak 50.00
Furniture, Cabinet, Spool, Walnut, 3 Drawer 115.00
Furniture, Cabinet, Standing, Italian Renaissance Style, Metal Grill 250.00
Furniture, Cabinet, Standing, Italian, Walnut, Pair Of Doors, Masks, 1550 .... 780.00
Furniture, Cabinet, Two Sevres Panels, Ebonized, Inlayed, France, C.1850 .... 1600.00
Furniture, Cabinet, Vitrine, Victorian, Walnut, Stained, Pierced Crest, 1850 .... 275.00
Furniture, Cabinet, Writing, Tulipwood, I.F.Dubut, JME, C.1750 .... 1800.00
Furniture, Canape, Italian, Walnut, Double Arched Upholstered Back, C.1750 .... 350.00
Furniture, Candlestand, Birch, New England, Square, Spiral Carved Post 210.00
Furniture, Candlestand, Chippendale, Mahogany, Round Dished Top, C.1760 .... 750.00
Furniture, Candlestand, Chippendale, Mahogany, Round, Baluster Standard, 1760 .... 275.00
Furniture, Candlestand, Chippendale, Maple & Cherry, Tilt Top, Round, C.1760 .... 300.00
Furniture, Candlestand, Chippendale, San Domingo Mahogany, Phila., C.1760 .... 2600.00
Furniture, Candlestand, Federal, Cherry & Maple, Octagonal, New England, 1790 .... 110.00
Furniture, Candlestand, Federal, Cherry & Satin, Tilt Top, Octagonal, C.1790 .... 500.00
Furniture, Candlestand, Federal, Cherry, Oval, Tripod Support, Conn., C.1800 .... 475.00
Furniture, Candlestand, Federal, Inlaid Cherry, Tilt Top, Octagonal, American 425.00
Furniture, Candlestand, Federal, Inlaid Mahogany & Satin, Octagonal, C.1790 .... 1300.00
Furniture, Candlestand, Federal, Inlaid Mahogany, Tilt Top, Octagonal, Mass. 500.00
Furniture, Candlestand, Federal, Inlaid Maple & Birch, Serpentine Top 150.00
Furniture, Candlestand, Federal, Mahogany, Tilt Top, Octagonal, New England 500.00
Furniture, Candlestand, Federal, Mahogany, Tilt Top, Tripod, New York, C.1800 .... 225.00
Furniture, Candlestand, Federal, Maple & Cherry, C.1820 .... Illus 200.00
Furniture, Candlestand, Federal, Maple, Double Elliptic Top, C.1790 .... 850.00
Furniture, Candlestand, Federal, Pine & Maple, Square, New England, C.1800 .... 140.00
Furniture, Candlestand, French Walnut, Gray Marble Top, Brass, Pair 140.00
Furniture, Candlestand, Queen Anne, Mahogany, Arched Feet, C.1750 .... 400.00
Furniture, Canterbury, George III, Mahogany, 4 Divisions, Drawer, C.1790 .... 175.00
Furniture, Canterbury, Mahogany, Drawer In Frieze, 3 Slots, C.1750 .... 200.00
Furniture, Cellarette, Mahogany, New York, C.1820 .... Illus 750.00
Furniture, Cellarette, Mahogany, Rectangular, Lion Handles, C.1800 .... 125.00
Furniture, Chair Table, Oak, Cleated Top, Dentil Ornaments, 17th Century 2900.00
Furniture, Chair Table, Oak, Oval Top, Square Chamfered Legs, C.1750 .... 1000.00
Furniture, Chair Table, Oak, Round Top, Turned Legs, Stretcher Base, C.1750 .... 400.00
Furniture, Chair Table, Round Top, Lift Seat Contains Box 325.00
Furniture, Chair, Arrow Back, Plank Bottom, Maple, Signed B.Hagenbuch, Pair 85.00
Furniture, Chair, Austrian, Fruitwood, Arched Top Rail, Urn Splat, 1850, 10 .... 425.00
Furniture, Chair, Bergere En Cabriolet, 18th Century .... Illus 3400.00

Furniture, Chair, Biedermeier, Birch, Vase Splats, Dished Top Rail, C.1850, 6 .... 525.00
Furniture, Chair, Boudoir, French Provincial, Fruitwood, Rush Seat, C.1850, 3 .... 60.00
Furniture, Chair, Captain's, Oak, Bow Back, C.1900 .... 49.00
Furniture, Chair, Carved, Hip Rail, Walnut, Set Of 3 .... 95.00
Furniture, Chair, Child's, Edwardian, Rattan, Arched Back, Caned Seat, C.1890 .... 140.00
Furniture, Chair, Child's, Mahogany, Caned Back, Tub Form, C.1890 .... 80.00
Furniture, Chair, Child's, Wing, Scalloped Back, Brown Paint 155.00
Furniture, Chair, Chinese, Folding, Red Lacquer, Brass Mounted, Carved, C.1850 .... 250.00
Furniture, Chair, Chinese, Hung-Mu Back, Caned Seat, Chia-Ch'lng, 4 .... 1200.00
Furniture, Chair, Chippendale, Circa 1850, Set Of 6 .... 2000.00
Furniture, Chair, Commode, Pine, Child's, Blue Paint, 18th Century 54.00
Furniture, Chair, Corner, Chippendale, Red Paint 175.00
Furniture, Chair, Corner, Oak, 18th Century 150.00
Furniture, Chair, Corner, Queen Anne, Pegged, Maple, Hickory, C.1750 .... 385.00
Furniture, Chair, Corner, Queen Anne, Slanted Pierced Slats, Pine, Maple 395.00
Furniture, Chair, Curly Maple, Pennsylvania, C.1800, 4 .... *Illus* 350.00

Furniture, Candlestand,
Federal, Maple & Cherry,
C.1820
See Page 222

Furniture, Cellarette,
Mahogany, New York,
C.1820
See Page 222

Furniture, Chair,
Bergere En Cabriolet,
18th Century
See Page 222

Furniture, Chair,
Curly Maple,
Pennsylvania,
C.1800, 4

Furniture, Chair, Desk, Mahogany, Leather, Down Curved Supports 300.00
Furniture, Chair, Dining, Chippendale, Chinese, Mahogany, Upholstered, 12 .... 1080.00
Furniture, Chair, Dining, Empire, Mahogany, Demay, Rue De Clery, 1784, 8 .... 1500.00
Furniture, Chair, Dining, George III, Mahogany, Balloon Form, Upholstered, 6 .... 1700.00
Furniture, Chair, Dining, George III, Mahogany, Carved Acanthus, C.1790, 10 .... 2300.00
Furniture, Chair, Dining, George III, Mahogany, Carved Acanthus, Pierced, 6 .... 1400.00
Furniture, Chair, Dining, Italian, Painted, Grape Leaves & Fruit, C.1790, 11 .... 800.00
Furniture, Chair, Dining, Mahogany, Ladder Back, Pierced, C.1820, 4 .... 425.00
Furniture, Chair, Dining, Oak, High Back, Cushioned Seat & Back, Set Of 6 .... 400.00
Furniture, Chair, Dining, Regency, Mahogany, Pierced Leaf Carved Bracket, 6 .... 500.00
Furniture, Chair, Dining, William IV, Mahogany, Carved Shield, C.1890, 3 .... 200.00
Furniture, Chair, Fanback, Slant Arms, Cane Seat, 2 .... 70.00

Furniture, Chair, Federal Style, Carved, Mahogany, Set Of 8 .... 750.00
Furniture, Chair, Federal, Martha Washington, Lolling, Inlaid Mahogany, 1790 .... 1300.00
Furniture, Chair, Finger Carved, Hip Rail, Rose Back, Walnut, New Cane, 6 .... 280.00
Furniture, Chair, George III, Mahogany, Inlaid Cut Brass Stringing, Pair 200.00
Furniture, Chair, George III, Mahogany, Molded Rail, Stick Splat, C.1750, 4 .... 350.00
Furniture, Chair, Ice Cream Parlor, Loop Back 27.00
Furniture, Chair, Ice Cream, Doll's 25.00
Furniture, Chair, Italian, Oak, Carved Acanthus Finials, C.1580, 4 .... 625.00
Furniture, Chair, Italian, Oak, Upholstered Back & Seat, C.1650, Pair 175.00
Furniture, Chair, Italian, Walnut & Olivewood, Marquetry, C.1690, Pair 700.00
Furniture, Chair, Italian, Walnut, Hinged Seat, Carved, Low 160.00
Furniture, Chair, Italian, Walnut, Throne, Gray Linen Seat 150.00
Furniture, Chair, James I, Walnut, Gilt Carved Frame, Leather, C.1625, 14 .... 3600.00
Furniture, Chair, Ladder Back, Maple, American, C.1800, Set Of 5 .... 200.00
Furniture, Chair, Martha Washington, Lolling, Inlaid Mahogany, Salem School 700.00
Furniture, Chair, Martha Washington, Lolling, Inlaid Mahogany, Serpentine 110.00
Furniture, Chair, Oak, Cane Bottom, Set Of 6 .... 210.00
Furniture, Chair, Occasional, Louis XVI Style, Cane Back & Seat 200.00
Furniture, Chair, Office, Swivel, Mahogany 42.00
Furniture, Chair, Painted, Baltimore, C.1820, 6 .... *Illus* 700.00
Furniture, Chair, Potty, Child's Oak, Folding, Enamel Potty 6.00
Furniture, Chair, Queen Anne, Banister Back, Maple, Apple, Cherry, C.1710 .... 275.00
Furniture, Chair, Queen Anne, Cherry, C.1750 .... 150.00
Furniture, Chair, Queen Anne, Satinwood, Circa 1840, Set Of 6 .... 2000.00
Furniture, Chair, Reclining, Burled Walnut, C.1820 .... 175.00
Furniture, Chair, Regency Style, Mahogany, Curved Top Rail, X Splats, 4 .... 325.00
Furniture, Chair, Regency, Beechwood, Brass Mounted, Saber Legs, C.1820 .... 50.00
Furniture, Chair, Regency, Black Japanned, Caned Seat, Chinoiserie, 1850, Pair 100.00
Furniture, Chair, Rocking, Child's, Bent Wood, Oak 38.00
Furniture, Chair, Side, Banister Back, C.1710 .... *Illus* 800.00
Furniture, Chair, Side, Banister, Yoke Top, Maple, Apple, Chestnut, C.1720 .... 185.00
Furniture, Chair, Side, Biedermeier, Walnut, Pierced Fretwork Splat, C.1850, 4 .... 300.00
Furniture, Chair, Side, Black Paint, Curved Slats, Rush Seat, C.1850, 6 .... 110.00
Furniture, Chair, Side, Charles II, Maple, Painted, C Scroll Front, C.1660 .... 650.00
Furniture, Chair, Side, Chippendale, Birch, Crest, Conn., C.1770, Pair 325.00
Furniture, Chair, Side, Chippendale, Mahogany, C.1760 .... *Illus* 225.00
Furniture, Chair, Side, Chippendale, Mahogany, Carved Crest, Penn., C.1770 .... 250.00
Furniture, Chair, Side, Chippendale, Mahogany, Pierced Gothic Splat, Pair 600.00
Furniture, Chair, Side, Chippendale, N.Y., C.1790 .... *Illus* 550.00
Furniture, Chair, Side, Chippendale, Walnut, Carved, Serpentine Crest, C.1750 .... 1300.00
Furniture, Chair, Side, Dutch Colonial, Oak & Elm, Vase Splat, C.1750, Pair 325.00
Furniture, Chair, Side, English, Oak, Pierced Double Urn Slat, C.1780 .... 30.00
Furniture, Chair, Side, Federal Style, Carved, Mahogany, Set Of 4 .... 110.00
Furniture, Chair, Side, Federal, Inlaid Mahogany & Satin, Boston, C.1810 .... 1900.00
Furniture, Chair, Side, Federal, Inlaid Mahogany, Heart & Shield Back, Md. 1000.00
Furniture, Chair, Side, Federal, Inlaid Mahogany, McIntire, Mass., C.1800 .... 3000.00
Furniture, Chair, Side, Federal, Mahogany, Carved, Goddard, R.I., C.1780, Pair 7500.00
Furniture, Chair, Side, Federal, Mahogany, Carved, John Aitken, C.1790 .... 3500.00
Furniture, Chair, Side, Federal, Mahogany, Carved, Kneeland & Addams, Conn. 325.00
Furniture, Chair, Side, Federal, Mahogany, Carved, McIntire, C.1800, Pair 4250.00
Furniture, Chair, Side, Federal, Mahogany, Carved, New York, C.1800 .... 600.00
Furniture, Chair, Side, Federal, Mahogany, Carved, Salem, C.1790, Pair 3500.00
Furniture, Chair, Side, Federal, Mahogany, Carved, Shield Back, C.1780, Pair 6500.00
Furniture, Chair, Side, Federal, Mahogany, N.Y., C.1790 .... *Illus* 550.00
Furniture, Chair, Side, French Provincial, Carved Splats, Open Floral, C.1850 .... 40.00
Furniture, Chair, Side, French Provincial, Painted Rush Seat, C.1820, 3 .... 130.00
Furniture, Chair, Side, George III, Mahogany, Pierced Vase Splat, C.1790 .... 40.00
Furniture, Chair, Side, George III, Mahogany, Rectangular Top Rail, C.1780 .... 60.00
Furniture, Chair, Side, Hepplewhite, Hand Carved Rosettes, Mahogany 225.00
Furniture, Chair, Side, Italian, Gilt, Carved Acanthus Finials, C.1650, Pair 125.00
Furniture, Chair, Side, Italian, Oak, Cathedral Back, Upholstered 30.00
Furniture, Chair, Side, Italian, Painted, Parcel Gilt, Upholstered, 1850, 3 .... 100.00
Furniture, Chair, Side, Italian, Queen Anne Style, Walnut, C.1790, 3 .... 125.00
Furniture, Chair, Side, Italian, Rush Seat, 18th Century, Oval Back, Pair 175.00
Furniture, Chair, Side, Italian, Walnut, Shield Back, C.1760, Pair 90.00
Furniture, Chair, Side, John Belter 450.00

Furniture, Chair, Painted, Baltimore, C.1820, 6
See Page 224

Furniture, Chair, Side, Chippendale,
Mahogany, C.1760
See Page 224

Furniture, Chair, Side,
Banister Back, C.1710
See Page 224

Furniture, Chair, Side,
Chippendale, N.Y., C.1790
See Page 224

Furniture, Chair, Side,
Federal, Mahogany,
N.Y., C.1790 See Page 224

Furniture, Chair, Side, Ladder Back, Black Paint, Arched Splats, C.1800	90.00
Furniture, Chair, Side, Louis XV, Beechwood, Carved, Cartouche Back, C.1750	210.00
Furniture, Chair, Side, Maple & Birch, Banister Back, Turned, Rush Seat, 6	900.00
Furniture, Chair, Side, Queen Anne, English, C.1850, Carved, 4	1900.00
Furniture, Chair, Side, Queen Anne, Gumwood, Canted Back, Slip Seat, C.1750	475.00
Furniture, Chair, Side, Queen Anne, Walnut, Needlework, Philadelphia, C.1720	1900.00
Furniture, Chair, Side, Slat Back, Rush Seat, Painted, American, C.1850, 6	120.00
Furniture, Chair, Side, Spanish Style, Painted & Parcel Gilt, C.1650, Pair	110.00
Furniture, Chair, Side, Spool Turned, 17th Century	450.00
Furniture, Chair, Side, Venetian, Oval Open Back, Pair	700.00
Furniture, Chair, Side, Victorian, Finger Carving, New Fabric	165.00
Furniture, Chair, Side, Walnut, French, C.1820, Vase Splat	20.00
Furniture, Chair, Side, William & Mary, Banister Back, Conn., C.1720, Pair	250.00
Furniture, Chair, Side, Windsor, Bow Back, Curved Crest Rail, American, 1790	300.00
Furniture, Chair, Side, Windsor, Hoop Back, Conn., C.1800 .... *Illus*	250.00
Furniture, Chair, Slde, Windsor, Hoop Back, Saddle Seat, C.1800, Pair	300.00
Furniture, Chair, Side, Windsor, New England, C.1800, 4 .... *Illus*	475.00
Furniture, Chair, Side, Windsor, Star Back, 5 Bamboo Turned Spindles	70.00
Furniture, Chair, Slipper & Side, Chippendale, Mahogany, Salem, C.1760, Pair	5000.00

Furniture, Chair, Steer Horn, American, C.1890 .... *Illus* 900.00
Furniture, Chair, Victorian Style, Tapestry Seat 75.00
Furniture, Chair, Victorian, Mahogany, Serpentine Seat, C.1890, Pair 60.00
Furniture, Chair, Wainscot, Open Paneled Back, 17th Century .... 150.00 To 230.00
Furniture, Chair, Wainscot, Rawhide Seat & Back, 18th Century ....90.00 To 160.00

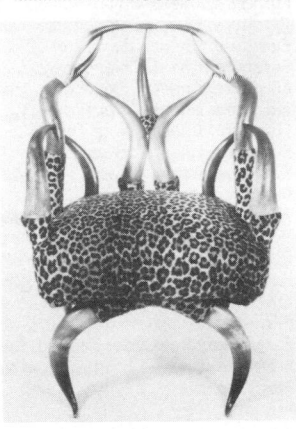

Furniture, Chair, Side, Windsor,   Furniture, Chair, Side,   Furniture, Chair, Steer Horn,
Hoop Back, Conn., C.1800   Windsor, New England,   American, C.1890
See Page 225   C.1800, 4 See Page 225

Furniture, Chair, Windsor, Bow Back, Saddle Seat, H Stretcher, 7 Spindle 250.00
Furniture, Chair, Windsor, Butterfly 85.00
Furniture, Chair, Windsor, Eight Spindle Back 250.00
Furniture, Chair, Windsor, Hitchcock, Pillow Back, Set Of 4 .... 169.00
Furniture, Chair, Windsor, Rabbit Ear, Raked, Set Of 4 .... 360.00
Furniture, Chair, Wing, Maple, Taper Leg, Stretcher Both Sides 550.00
Furniture, Chaise Longue, Stainless Steel & Fabric, Le Corbusier, C.1930 .... 550.00
Furniture, Chest On Frame, Queen Anne, Maple, Turned Legs, Button Feet 750.00
Furniture, Chest On Stand, Charles X, Lacquered, Cedar Lined, Hinged, C.1850 .... 675.00
Furniture, Chest On Stand, Chinese Painted Leather, Hinged Lid, C.1850 .... 450.00
Furniture, Chest-On-Chest, Chippendale, Carved, Mahogany, Maryland, C.1770 .... 3500.00
Furniture, Chest-On-Chest, Chippendale, Cherry, Delaware River Valley, 1760 .... 1000.00
Furniture, Chest-On-Chest, George I, Walnut, 9 Graduated Drawers, C.1720 .... 1700.00
Furniture, Chest-On-Chest, Mahogany, Bonnet Top, 7 Drawer, C.1850 .... 150.00
Furniture, Chest-On-Chest, North African, Inlaid Hardwood, 27 Drawer, 1850 .... 400.00
Furniture, Chest, Apothecary, Pine, 4 Drawers 85.00
Furniture, Chest, Austrian, Fruitwood, Rectangular Top, 8 Drawer, C.1790 .... 475.00
Furniture, Chest, Biedermeier, 2 Drawer, Rectangular Marble Top 375.00
Furniture, Chest, Blanket, Oak, Intaglio Carved, Candle Till, 17th Century 260.00
Furniture, Chest, Blanket, Penna.Dutch, Stippled, Dovetailed, Pine 100.00
Furniture, Chest, Blanket, Penna.Dutch, Turned Legs, Not Dovetailed, Pine 85.00
Furniture, Chest, Blanket, Pine & Oak, Paneled, Drawer In Base, C.1650 .... 175.00
Furniture, Chest, Blanket, Pine, Candle Box, 44 1/2 In. 210.00
Furniture, Chest, Blanket, Pine, Dovetailed, Bracket Feet, Strap Hinges 150.00
Furniture, Chest, Blanket, Pine, Molded Top, Deep Overhang, 54 In.Long 50.00
Furniture, Chest, Blanket, Pine, Molded Top, 18th Century 170.00
Furniture, Chest, Blanket, Pine, Oblong, Cleated Ends, American, C.1750 .... 130.00
Furniture, Chest, Blanket, Pine, Three Panel Front, Candle Box Inside 190.00
Furniture, Chest, Blanket, Pine, 1 Drawer, Arch Cut Ends, 18th Century 260.00
Furniture, Chest, Blanket, Pumpkin Pine, Handmade, Handmade Square Nails 75.00
Furniture, Chest, Blanket, Queen Anne, Pine, Oblong, Pennsylvania, C.1740 .... 250.00
Furniture, Chest, Blanket, Shaker, Bootjack End, Old Red, 42 X 23 X 17 In. 400.00
Furniture, Chest, Blanket, Shaker, Lift Lid, Red Paint, Leather Hinges 275.00
Furniture, Chest, Blanket, Shaker, Painted Brown, Three Drawer, Bracket Base 550.00
Furniture, Chest, Blanket, Two Drawers, Maple 55.00
Furniture, Chest, Bow Front, Mahogany, Brass Handles 750.00
Furniture, Chest, Carpenter's, Pine, 18th Century 140.00

Furniture, Chest, Carved Nut Pulls, Burl, Walnut, Mirror 240.00
Furniture, Chest, Charles II, Oak, Rectangular, 4 Drawer, C.1690 .... 400.00
Furniture, Chest, Charles II, Walnut, Rectangular, 4 Drawer, C.1690 .... 400.00
Furniture, Chest, Chippendale, Cherry & Birch, Serpentine Front, American 1100.00
Furniture, Chest, Chippendale, Cherry & Maple, Tall, Coved Cornice, 6 Drawer 1800.00
Furniture, Chest, Chippendale, Cherry, 7 Drawer, Scroll Feet, Penn., C.1760 .... 1000.00
Furniture, Chest, Chippendale, Maple & Cherry, High, 6 Graduated Drawers 800.00
Furniture, Chest, Chippendale, Maple, Reverse Serpentine Front, 4 Drawer 2300.00
Furniture, Chest, Chippendale, Pine & Maple, 6 Drawer, New England, C.1760 .... 750.00
Furniture, Chest, Chippendale, Walnut, High, 8 Drawer, Penna., C.1760 .... 2000.00
Furniture, Chest, Dome Top, Pine, 15 X 8 X 8 In. 14.00
Furniture, Chest, Dower, Austria, Pine, Hand-Painted Panels, 2 Drawer, C.1650 .... 1800.00
Furniture, Chest, Dower, Oak, Bootjack Ends, 17th Century, 37 1/2 In. Wide 225.00
Furniture, Chest, Dower, Oak, Carved Entwined Scrolls, Snipe Hinges, C.1650 .... 375.00
Furniture, Chest, Dower, Oak, Incised Carving, Bootjack Feet, 17th Century 160.00
Furniture, Chest, Dower, Oak, Intaglio Carving, Bootjack Ends, C.1650 .... 700.00
Furniture, Chest, Dower, Oak, Paneled, Carved Demilune Floral, C.1650 .... 425.00
Furniture, Chest, Dower, Oak, Paneled, Drawing Inside Of Cover, 17th Century 220.00
Furniture, Chest, Dower, Oak, Pine Cleated Lid, 17th Century 325.00
Furniture, Chest, Dower, Oak, 2 Carved Demilune Motifs On Front, C.1650 .... 500.00
Furniture, Chest, Dower, Oak, 2 Drawers In Base, 17th Century 375.00
Furniture, Chest, Dower, Pennsylvania Dutch Tulip 1500.00
Furniture, Chest, Dower, Pine, 2 Panel Front, Square Feet, 18th Century 210.00
Furniture, Chest, Dressing, George III, Mahogany, Hinged Top, 3 Drawer, 1750 .... 350.00
Furniture, Chest, Dutch, Marquetry, Rectangular, Brass Escutcheon, C.1750 .... 325.00
Furniture, Chest, Empire, Cherry, 4 Drawer 90.00
Furniture, Chest, Federal, Cherry, Bowfront, Molded Oblong Top, 4 Drawer, 1800 .... 2500.00
Furniture, Chest, Federal, Cherry, Bowfront, Oblong Top, American, C.1810 .... 800.00
Furniture, Chest, Federal, Cherry, Oblong, 4 Drawer, American, C.1820 .... 400.00
Furniture, Chest, Federal, Cherry, Oblong, 4 Drawer, Pennsylvania, C.1820 .... 375.00
Furniture, Chest, Federal, Curly Maple, Serpentine, 1800 .... *Illus* 1200.00

Furniture, Chest, Federal, Curly Maple,
Serpentine, 1800

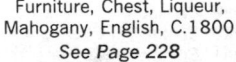

Furniture, Chest, Liqueur,
Mahogany, English, C.1800
See Page 228

Furniture, Chest, Federal, Inlaid Cherry, Bowfront, Inlaid, 4 Drawer, C.1780 .... 1300.00
Furniture, Chest, Federal, Inlaid Mahogany & Satin, Bowfront, N.H., C.1790 .... 3250.00
Furniture, Chest, Federal, Inlaid Mahogany, Bowfront, Oblong, 4 Drawers 1000.00
Furniture, Chest, Federal, Inlaid Mahogany, Serpentine Front, 4 Drawer, 1800 .... 1600.00
Furniture, Chest, Federal, Inlaid Maple & Birch, Elliptic Front, 4 Drawer 600.00
Furniture, Chest, Federal, Mahogany, Bowfront, Oblong, Pennsylvania, C.1810 .... 350.00
Furniture, Chest, Federal, Mahogany, Inlaid, Bowfront, C.1800 .... 800.00
Furniture, Chest, Five Drawers, Turned Legs, Sand Glass Knobs, Cherry 150.00
Furniture, Chest, Flemish, Oak, Hinged Top, Carved Panels, C.1550 .... 350.00
Furniture, Chest, George I, Walnut & Burr Walnut, Rectangular, 5 Drawer, 1750 .... 575.00
Furniture, Chest, George II, Burr Elm, Rectangular, 4 Drawer, C.1790 .... 575.00
Furniture, Chest, George II, Oak, Rectangular Top, 2 Drawer, C.1790 .... 100.00
Furniture, Chest, George III, Inlaid Mahogany, Miniature, Bowfront, C.1800 .... 300.00

Furniture, Chest, Hepplewhite, Inlaid Cherry, French Feet, C.1800 .... 775.00
Furniture, Chest, Hepplewhite, Inlaid Cherry, 4 Drawer 650.00
Furniture, Chest, Hepplewhite, Pine, Mahogany Veneered Drawer Fronts 595.00
Furniture, Chest, Italian, Lacquered, Rectangular, Gilt, 4 Drawer, C.1750 .... 775.00
Furniture, Chest, Liqueur, Mahogany, English, C.1800 .... *Illus* 200.00
Furniture, Chest, Louis XV Provincial, Oak, Rectangular Hinged Top, C.1780 .... 400.00
Furniture, Chest, Mahogany, Carved, Bowfront, Oblong, 4 Drawer, Mass., C.1810 .... 1000.00
Furniture, Chest, Miniature, Drawers, Doors, Dovetail, Teak, China, 9 1/4 In. 95.00
Furniture, Chest, Miniature, Victorian, Mahogany, Serpentine, 3 Drawer, 1890 .... 50.00
Furniture, Chest, Oak, Intaglio Carving, Strap Hinges, 17th Century 375.00
Furniture, Chest, Oak, Pierced Lid, Carved Corners, Bootjack Ends, C.1650 .... 160.00
Furniture, Chest, Painted, Decorated, Green, Red, Yellow, American, C.1800 .... 150.00
Furniture, Chest, Portuguese, Painted, Rectangular Marble Top, C.1750 .... 325.00
Furniture, Chest, Queen Anne, Cherry, L.Chapin, Conn. 1100.00
Furniture, Chest, Sea Captain's, Miniature, Pine, 15 In.Long 18.50
Furniture, Chest, Sea, Camphor Wood, Brass Strapping & Corners, 3 Piece Lid 32.50
Furniture, Chest, Sea, Pine, American, Hinged, Painted 44.50
Furniture, Chest, Sewing, Victorian, Slant Front, Spool Holders, Dated 1876 .... 40.00
Furniture, Chest, Shaker, Alfred Grain, Dovetailed Corners 425.00
Furniture, Chest, Shaker, Feather Graining, Watervliet, 3 Drawer 575.00
Furniture, Chest, Sheraton, Cherry, 4 Drawer, Penna., C.1810 .... 300.00
Furniture, Chest, Silver, Drop Lid Front, Mirror, Velvet Lined, 48 In.Long 285.00
Furniture, Chest, Silverware, Oak, Satin Lined, Velvet Holders 5.00
Furniture, Chest, Six Drawers, Chippendale, Dovetail, C.1770, Pine 875.00
Furniture, Chest, Spool, Two Drawers, Brass Drop Pulls, Oak 32.00
Furniture, Chest, Tea, Crotch Mahogany, Beveled, 19th Century 85.00
Furniture, Chest, Tea, Japanese, Iron Handles 80.00
Furniture, Chest, William & Mary Style, Pine & Maple, Oblong Top, 4 Drawer 150.00
Furniture, Chest, William & Mary, Walnut, Rectangular, 5 Drawer, C.1700 .... 650.00
Furniture, Coffer, Austrian, Pine, Hinged Top, Intarsia Decoration, 1599 .... 525.00
Furniture, Coffer, Oak, Strap Hinges & Lock, Carved Ornamentation, C.1650 .... 140.00
Furniture, Column, Green Marble, Ormolu Mounted, Red Base, 4 Ft.High, Pair 750.00
Furniture, Column, Italian, Painted & Parcel Gilt, Pierced, C.1750, Pair 225.00
Furniture, Commode, Black Lacquer, Marble Top, C.1790 .... 2500.00
Furniture, Commode, Bombe, Painted Blue, Floral Medallions, 2 Drawer, 1740 .... 300.00
Furniture, Commode, Charles X, Satinwood & Purpleheart, Rectangular, C.1850 .... 6200.00
Furniture, Commode, Corner, Ormolu Of Griffons, White Marble Top, Pair 450.00
Furniture, Commode, Empire, Mahogany, Rectangular Porphyry Top, C.1850 .... 400.00
Furniture, Commode, Fruitwood, Signed A.Gillabert, Black Marble Top 900.00
Furniture, Commode, George III, Olive & Rosewood, John Cobb Style, 1750 .... 4000.00
Furniture, Commode, Italian, Ebony, Inlaid Ivory Birds, Lombard, C.1690 .... 550.00
Furniture, Commode, Italian, Fruitwood, Rectangular Marble Top, C.1750 .... 400.00
Furniture, Commode, Italian, Walnut, Inlaid Ivory Birds, Lombard, C.1650 .... 650.00
Furniture, Commode, Italian, Walnut, 18th Century, 4 Drawer 450.00
Furniture, Commode, Kingwood, Marquetry, Serpentine, Bombe, C.1750 .... 3300.00
Furniture, Commode, Louis XVI Provincial, Fruitwood, Rectangular, C.1750 .... 200.00
Furniture, Commode, Mahogany, Tambour, D Shape Outline, C.1790 .... 800.00
Furniture, Commode, North Italian, Rosewood, Serpentine Front, C.1790 .... 425.00
Furniture, Commode, Oak, Padded Cover, 14 1/2 X 14 1/2 X 15 In. 60.00
Furniture, Commode, Petite, Italian, Walnut, Rectangular Top, 3 Drawer, C.1750 .... 500.00
Furniture, Commode, Petite, Louis XV, Marquetry, Serpentine Top, C.1790 .... 1300.00
Furniture, Commode, Petite, Rectangular, Brass Gallery, C.1750 .... 1600.00
Furniture, Commode, Petite, Tulipwood & Bois De Violette, C.1750 .... 1300.00
Furniture, Commode, Petite, Tulipwood, Rectangular, C.1750 .... 2100.00
Furniture, Commode, Pine, Refinished 85.00
Furniture, Commode, Provincial, Inlaid Burl, Rectangular, Pair 750.00
Furniture, Commode, Red Lacquer, Serpentine Front, 4 Drawer, C.1750 .... 4700.00
Furniture, Commode, Regence, Boulle, Berainesque Design, Ormolu, C.1750 .... 2900.00
Furniture, Commode, Regence, Walnut, Provincial, Rectangular, Carved, C.1730 .... 750.00
Furniture, Commode, Rosewood, Marquetry, J.Holthausen, JME, C.1750 .... 2000.00
Furniture, Commode, Sicilian, Painted, Serpentine, Concave Sides, C.1750 .... 3300.00
Furniture, Commode, Venetian, 2 Drawer, Painted Green, Floral Medallions 375.00
Furniture, Console, Charles X, Gilt Wood, Blackamoor, Carved, Serpentine, 1850 .... 1600.00
Furniture, Console, Continental, Gilt Wood, Carved, Rectangular, Marble, Pair 1000.00
Furniture, Console, German, Painted & Parcel Gilt, Carved, Pierced, C.1750 .... 400.00
Furniture, Console, Italian, Gilt Wood, Carved, Regence Style, C.1790 .... 1400.00

Furniture, Console, Italian, Paint & Gilt, Blue, White Marble, C.1650, Pair 250.00
Furniture, Console, Louis XV, Oak, Carved, Pierced Frieze, Marble, C.1750 .... 775.00
Furniture, Console, Louis XVI, Mahogany, 18th Century .... *Illus* 1900.00
Furniture, Cradle, Baby's, Wicker, Circa 1870 .... 48.00
Furniture, Cradle, Bentwood 125.00
Furniture, Cradle, Doll's, Oak, 4 Poster, 18 1/2 In.Long 34.00
Furniture, Cradle, Dovetailed Corners, Slat Bottom, Bow Shape Rockers, Pine 75.00
Furniture, Cradle, Elm, Seventeenth Century 250.00
Furniture, Cradle, English, Oak, 18th Century 250.00
Furniture, Cradle, Hooded, Red Paint 135.00
Furniture, Cradle, Oak, Hooded, Carved Pinwheels & Diamonds, 17th Century 350.00
Furniture, Cradle, Pine, Painted, Red Exterior, Blue Interior, C.1750 .... 300.00
Furniture, Credenza, Italian, Walnut, Armorial Cartouches, Cherubs, C.1690 .... 550.00
Furniture, Credenza, Spanish, Walnut, 2 Mask Front Drawers, C.1550 .... 375.00
Furniture, Cupboard, Corner, Architectural, Bowed Back, 18th Century 400.00
Furniture, Cupboard, Corner, Cherry, Glass Doors Above, Center Drawer, C.1840 .... 550.00
Furniture, Cupboard, Corner, Federal, Cherry, Pennsylvania, C.1790 .... 950.00
Furniture, Cupboard, Corner, Hanging, Pine, 35 In.High 150.00
Furniture, Cupboard, Corner, Oak Front, Shelves, Glass In Door 35.00
Furniture, Cupboard, Corner, Pegged, Pennsylvania, C.1820, Cherry 650.00
Furniture, Cupboard, Corner, Pine, Molded Cornice, 3 Shelves, 6 Ft.6 In.High 225.00
Furniture, Cupboard, Corner, Pine, 2 Piece, 18 Pane Doors, Painted 900.00
Furniture, Cupboard, Door, Shaker, 53 X 26 X 8 1/2 In.Sabbath Day Lake 275.00
Furniture, Cupboard, Flat, Softwood, Bracket Feet, 2 Top Drawers, C.1770 .... 425.00
Furniture, Cupboard, Flemish, Overhanging Cornice, Female Mask, C.1580 .... 800.00
Furniture, Cupboard, Food Storage, Oak, Ark Shape, Diamond Design, C.1650 .... 275.00
Furniture, Cupboard, French, Oak, 17th Century, Open Top, Birdcage Spindles 450.00
Furniture, Cupboard, Hanging, Pine, Linen Fold Molded Door, C.1750 .... 600.00
Furniture, Cupboard, Kitchen, Oak, 2 Piece 100.00
Furniture, Cupboard, Pewter, Pine, Slanting Open Upper Section, C.1750 .... 950.00
Furniture, Cupboard, Pewter, 18th Century 450.00
Furniture, Cupboard, Pine, Painted, Pennsylvania, C.1800 .... *Illus* 600.00
Furniture, Cupboard, Plate Rack, Painted, 18th Century, Pine 395.00
Furniture, Cupboard, Press, Shaker, C.1830, Restored Cornice, Cherry, 79 In. 625.00
Furniture, Cupboard, Shaker, Five Drawers, One Door 650.00
Furniture, Cupboard, Shaker, One Door, Double Raised Panels 450.00
Furniture, Cupboard, Shaker, Two Door, Clothespin Pulls 700.00
Furniture, Cupboard, Wall, Ash & Oak, One Piece 85.00
Furniture, Daybed, Regency, Painted, Pierced Horizontal Splats, C.1850 .... 75.00
Furniture, Desk On Stand, Federal, Camphorwood .... *Illus* 450.00

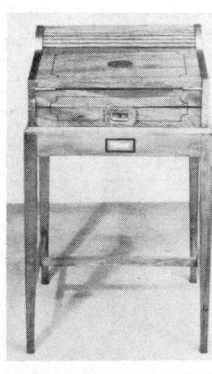

Furniture, Console,
Louis XVI, Mahogany,
18th Century

Furniture, Desk On Stand,
Federal, Camphorwood

Furniture, Cupboard, Pine, Painted
Pennsylvania, C.1800

Furniture, **Desk**, Biedermeier, Fruitwood, Rectangular, Marble Top 400.00
Furniture, **Desk**, Cherry, Slant Top, Secret Compartment, Brasses 1000.00
Furniture, **Desk**, Child's, Double Lift Top, Scissor Type Legs, Pine, 24 In.High 59.50
Furniture, **Desk**, Chippendale Federal, Mahogany, Slant Front, Penna., C.1790 .... 750.00
Furniture, **Desk**, Chippendale, Cherry & Mahogany, Serpentine Front, Slant Lid 1500.00
Furniture, **Desk**, Chippendale, Mahogany, Block Front, Carved, Mass., C.1760 .... 5750.00
Furniture, **Desk**, Chippendale, 2 Pedestal, Double Sides, Tooled Leather Top 1000.00
Furniture, **Desk**, Cylinder Top, Oak, Refinished, 44 In.High, 30 1/4 In.Wide 250.00
Furniture, **Desk**, Federal, Mahogany & Curly Maple, C.1810 .... *Illus* 550.00
Furniture, **Desk**, Federal, Mahogany, Mass. .... *Illus* 575.00
Furniture, **Desk**, French, Oak, Lift Lid, Raised Paneled Doors, 18th Century 150.00
Furniture, **Desk**, From Courthouse, Circa 1870, Slant Top, Walnut, 95 In. 600.00
Furniture, **Desk**, Italian Provincial, Fall Front, C.1750 .... 700.00
Furniture, **Desk**, Kneehole, C.1750 .... *Illus* 750.00
Furniture, **Desk**, Lady's, Federal, Inlaid Mahogany, Seymour School, C.1790 .... 2100.00
Furniture, **Desk**, Lawyer's, Victorian, Walnut 365.00
Furniture, **Desk**, Mahogany, Four Partners', Oval, 94 X 60 X 29 1/2 In. 1100.00
Furniture, **Desk**, Regency, Lady's, 4 Cabriole Legs 275.00
Furniture, **Desk**, Roll Top, Oak, Curve, 50 In.Wide 365.00
Furniture, **Desk**, Roll Top, 5 Ft. 300.00
Furniture, **Desk**, Schoolmaster's, Pennsylvania, C.1760 .... *Illus* 150.00
Furniture, **Desk**, Secret Drawers, Compartments, Irish, C.1850 .... 75.00
Furniture, **Desk**, Secretary, Green, Marble, 1920s 27.50
Furniture, **Desk**, Secretary, Oak, Smith Premier, 4 Drawer, 32 In.High 150.00
Furniture, **Desk**, Sewing, Shaker, Butternut And Maple, Elder Henry Green 3250.00
Furniture, **Desk**, Sewing, Shaker, 11 Drawer, Top Center Door, E.H.Green 3500.00
Furniture, **Desk**, Slant Front, Stepped Interior, Dovetail, Tiger Maple 1850.00
Furniture, **Desk**, Slant Top, Ball & Claw Feet, Brasses Replaced, Walnut 1250.00
Furniture, **Desk**, Slant Top, Bracket Base & Columns, L.Chapin, Conn., Cherry 1500.00
Furniture, **Desk**, Slant Top, Ogee Bracket Base, Cherry, Chippendale 1450.00
Furniture, **Desk**, Spinet, Mahogany, Lady's, Opens, 1 Drawer 175.00
Furniture, **Desk**, Table, Oak, Slant Lid, 2 Drawer, Foliate Carving, C.1650 .... 425.00
Furniture, **Desk**, Tambour, Federal, Mahogany, Inlaid, Massachusetts, C.1800 .... 1600.00
Furniture, **Desk**, Victorian, Traveling, Mahogany, Carved, Hinged, C.1850 .... 200.00
Furniture, **Desk**, Walnut, Boston, 2 Part, 7 Drawer, Black, 1870-1880 .... 750.00
Furniture, **Dhyana**, Buddha Of Kamurka Amida, Gilded Lacquer, Female, C.1650 .... 700.00
Furniture, **Doll's**, Wicker, Victorian, 4 Pieces 55.00
Furniture, **Door**, Swinging, Oak, Leaded Stained Glass, Brass, 65 In.High, Pair 350.00
Furniture, **Dresser**, Charles II, C.1675 .... *Illus* 1450.00
Furniture, **Dresser**, Derbyshire, Oak, C.1725 .... *Illus* 1000.00
Furniture, **Dresser**, George II, Oak, C.1750 .... *Illus* 2600.00
Furniture, **Dresser**, George II, Oak, Rectangular, 2 Drawer, 2 Doors, C.1790 .... 800.00
Furniture, **Dresser**, Pine, New England, C.1750 .... *Illus* 725.00
Furniture, **Dressing Glass**, Chippendale, Mahogany & Parcel Gilt, Brass Urns 250.00
Furniture, **Dressing Glass**, Federal, Mahogany, Oblong, New England, C.1810 .... 100.00
Furniture, **Dry Sink**, Deep Well, Pine, Refinished Lid, Circa 1880 .... 185.00
Furniture, **Dry Sink**, One Door, Pennsylvania, Small 170.00
Furniture, **Dry Sink**, Pennsylvania, Pine, Blue 295.00
Furniture, **Fauteuil**, Consulat, Painted White & Gold, Scrolled, C.1750 .... 300.00
Furniture, **Fauteuil**, Dieppe Carved Ivory, Cartouche Back, C.1750, Pair 7000.00
Furniture, **Fauteuil**, Directoire, Fruitwood, Gilt Wood Leaves, C.1750, Pair 200.00
Furniture, **Fauteuil**, Italian Provincial, Walnut, Carved Shell, C.1750 .... 350.00
Furniture, **Fauteuil**, Italian, Walnut, Carved Crest, Cartouche Back, C.1750 .... 225.00
Furniture, **Fauteuil**, Louis XV, Beechwood, Cartouche Back, Carved, C.1790 .... 325.00
Furniture, **Fauteuil**, Louis XV, Walnut, Carved, Cartouche Back, C.1750 .... 325.00
Furniture, **Fauteuil**, Louis XVI, Beechwood, Cartouche Back, C.1750, Pair 750.00
Furniture, **Fauteuil**, Louis XVI, Brown Paint, Tapestry, Carved, C.1750, Pair 750.00
Furniture, **Fauteuil**, Louis XVI, Painted Cream, Needlework, C.1750, Pair 900.00
Furniture, **Fauteuil**, Louis XVI, Painted, Oval Back, Upholstered, C.1780 .... 500.00
Furniture, **Fauteuil**, Louis XVI, Painted, Parcel Gilt, Red Damask, 1790, Pair 525.00
Furniture, **Fauteuil**, Painted & Parcel Gilt, C.1750, Pair 1600.00
Furniture, **Footstool**, Federal, Mahogany, Round Seat, Velvet, Salem, C.1800 .... *Illus* 325.00
Furniture, **Footstool**, Hand Carved Wood, Dark Finish, 12 1/2 X 7 1/2 In.High 22.50
Furniture, **Footstool**, Louis XV, Walnut, Serpentine Seat, Carved, C.1750 .... 250.00
Furniture, **Footstool**, Mahogany, Rectangular, Ogee Foot, Needlepoint Top 20.00
Furniture, **Footstool**, Needlepoint, Cabriole Feet, Metal Masks, Enamel, Brass 70.00

Furniture, Desk, Federal,
Mahogany & Curly
Maple, C.1810
See Page 230

Furniture, Desk,
Federal, Mahogany,
Mass.
See Page 230

Furniture, Desk, Kneehole, C.1750
See Page 230

Furniture, Desk, Schoolmaster's,
Pennsylvania, C.1760
See Page 230

Furniture, Dresser, Charles II, C.1675
See Page 230

Furniture, Footstool, Pennsylvania Dutch, Caned, 8 In.High	18.50
Furniture, Footstool, Pine, Bronze Fruit Stencil, Black Paint	22.00
Furniture, Footstool, Victorian, Beechwood, Serpentine, Needlework, C.1890	50.00
Furniture, Footstool, Victorian, Cast Iron, Tapestry Fabric	225.00
Furniture, Footstool, Victorian, Ornate Iron Feet, Gilt, Red Tapestry Top	30.00
Furniture, Footstool, Victorian, Round, Needlepoint Top, Scrolled Feet	30.00
Furniture, Frame, Brass, 12 1/2 In. *Illus*	25.00

Furniture, Dresser, Derbyshire, Oak, C.1725
See Page 230

Furniture, Dresser, George II, Oak, C.1750
See Page 230

Furniture, Dresser,
Pine, New England, C.1750
See Page 230

Furniture, Frame,
Brass, 12 1/2 In.
See Page 231

Furniture, Highboy, Queen Anne,
Maple & Walnut, C.1750
See Page 233

Furniture, Frame, Carved, Leaves Across Corners, Walnut, 8 1/2 X 10 In., Pair 19.00
Furniture, Frame, Cove Style, Carved, Gilt, C.1900, 11 1/4 X 13 1/4 In. 15.00
Furniture, Frame, Gold Leaf, Gesso Over Wood 99.00
Furniture, Frame, Gold Leaf, Ornate, 9 X 11 In. 4.50
Furniture, Frame, Gold Metal, Heavily Jeweled, 7 X 9 In. 26.50
Furniture, Frame, Heart & Flower Design, Victorian, 16 1/2 X 18 1/2 In.Pair 75.00
Furniture, Frame, Inlaid Wood Scrollwork Design, Art Nouveau, Wood, 11 In. 15.00
Furniture, Frame, Mahogany, Oval, Brass Liner, 11 X 13 In. 16.00
Furniture, Frame, Oval, Walnut, 10 X 8 In. 10.00
Furniture, Frame, Oval, Walnut, 1o X 11 1/4 In., Pair 65.00
Furniture, Frame, Picture, Victorian, Mahogany, Oval, Gold Liner 22.50
Furniture, Frame, Shadowbox, Flowers, Gold, 3 1/2 X 4 1/2 In. 30.00
Furniture, Frame, Stippled, Floral, Leaves, Carved, C.1870, 7 1/2 X 9 1/2 In. 25.00
Furniture, Frame, Votive, Italian, Gilt Wood, 2 Candle Branches, C.1750 .... 50.00
Furniture, Frame, Walnut, Crossed Corner, Porcelain Buttons, 12 X 8 In. 12.00
Furniture, Frame, Walnut, Embossed Fruit, Gold Liner, 14 X 11 1/2 In. 12.00
Furniture, Frame, Walnut, Gold Liner, 12 X 14 In. .... 10.00 To 21.00

Furniture, Frame, Walnut, Oval, Black, 8 X 10 In. 12.50
Furniture, Frame, Wooden, Carved, Large Balls & High Reliefs, 8 X 5 In. 15.00
Furniture, Frame, Wooden, Hand-Carved Walnut, 11 1/2 X 13 1/2 In. 5.00
Furniture, Globe, Terrestrial, Stand, Gilt Scrolls On Black 300.00
Furniture, Gueridon, Empire, Mahogany, Round, Octagonal Pedestal, 1850, Pair 180.00
Furniture, Hall Rack, Umbrella Holder, Marble Top Drawer, Mirror, Walnut 325.00
Furniture, Hassock, English, Leather, Elephant Form, 40 In.Long 160.00
Furniture, Hat Rack, Folding, 10 Hooks, White Porcelain Buttons, Walnut 15.00
Furniture, Hat Rack, Walnut, Folding, 6 Pegs, Porcelain Tips 7.50
Furniture, Highboy, Queen Anne Style, Maple, 19th Century 375.00
Furniture, Highboy, Queen Anne, Maple & Walnut, C.1750 .... *Illus* 3500.00
Furniture, Highboy, Queen Anne, Maple, Bonnet Top, 2 Parts, Carved, Conn., 1750 ...... 7750.00
Furniture, Highboy, Queen Anne, Tiger Maple, Flat Top, Allen Family, C.1750 .... 8000.00
Furniture, Highboy, Queen Anne, Walnut & Maple, Bonnet Top, 7 Drawer, 1750 .... 1500.00
Furniture, Highboy, William & Mary, Maple, 2 Part, 8 Drawer, C.1720 .... 675.00
Furniture, Highboy, William & Mary, Walnut, Crossbanded, Turned Legs 4200.00
Furniture, Highboy, William & Mary, Walnut, Flat Top, 2 Parts, American 1700 .... 9500.00
Furniture, Highchair, Horseshoe Back & Footrest, Flowers, Leaves 55.00
Furniture, Highchair, Maple, Open Paneled Back, 17th Century 550.00
Furniture, Highchair, Oak, Cane Seat, Lowers To Stroller, C.1895 .... 69.50
Furniture, Highchair, Various Woods, Splint Seat, 18th Century 50.00
Furniture, Highchair, Victorian, Walnut, Eastlake 125.00
Furniture, Highchair, Walnut, Lowers To Rocking Chair, Patent 1878 .... 150.00
Furniture, Holder, Roller Towel, Pine, 2 Sections Fit Into Frame 10.00
Furniture, Hunt Board, Federal, Inlaid Mahogany, Oblong, Square Legs, N.Y. 4750.00
Furniture, Hutch Table, Pine, C.1800 .... 165.00
Furniture, Hutch, Child's, 2 Door, Cream Paint, 14 In.High 12.00
Furniture, Hutch, Doll's, Pine, 3 Open Shelves, 2 Doors, 13 1/2 In.High 15.00
Furniture, Hutch, Open, 3 Shelves At Top, 2 Drawers, 6 Ft.Long 350.00
Furniture, Ice Cream Set, Child's, Handmade, Painted White, 5 Piece 39.50
Furniture, Ice Cream Set, Heart Back Chair, 2 Piece 50.00
Furniture, Ice Cream Set, Marble Top, 5 Piece 135.00
Furniture, Icebox, Pine 39.00
Furniture, Jardiniere, Regency, Mahogany, Slatted Body, Footed, C.1820 .... *Illus* 100.00
Furniture, Kas, Tulip, Poplar, & Maple, Penn., C.1760 .... *Illus* 1800.00
Furniture, Knickknack, Corner, Five Shelves, Hand Turned Spindles, Walnut 95.00
Furniture, Lit De Repos, Gilt Wood, Carved, Laurel, C.1750 .... 750.00
Furniture, Lit De Repos, Regence, Oak, Carved, Cartouche Shape, C.1720 .... 850.00
Furniture, Looking Glass, Mahogany, Convex, Handle, Ring Turnings, C.1800 .... 80.00
Furniture, Lowboy, Chippendale, Walnut, Carved, Oblong, Phila., C.1760 .... 8000.00
Furniture, Lowboy, Queen Anne, Cherry & Maple, Massachusetts, C.1750 .... 3350.00
Furniture, Lowboy, Queen Anne, Mahogany, Miniature, Delaware River, C.1750 .... 600.00

Furniture, Kas, Tulip, Poplar,
& Maple, Penn., C.1760

Furniture, Lowboy, Queen Anne, Walnut, Molded Oblong Top, Penna., C.1750 .... 7000.00
Furniture, Mirror With Candleholder, Carved, Rosette Plumes, C.1750, Pair 800.00
Furniture, Mirror, Acorn Inlay, Chippendale, American, Circa 1872 .... 135.00
Furniture, Mirror, American, Mahogany & Gilded Frame, C.1840, 18 X 29 In. 35.00
Furniture, Mirror, Art Deco, Silvered Bronze, Rectangular, French, C.1930 .... 1150.00
Furniture, Mirror, Bamboo, Folding, Japanese Print On Front, Patent 1879 .... 20.00
Furniture, Mirror, Bevel, Brass Open Edge Frame, Grapes, Bacchus, 8 X 5 In. 45.00
Furniture, Mirror, Chippendale Type, Finial, Mahogany, 35 1/2 X 17 3/4 In. 55.00
Furniture, Mirror, Chippendale, Chinese, Oval, Carved, Cartouche 900.00
Furniture, Mirror, Chippendale, Mahogany & Parcel Gilt, Carved, Phoenix, 1760 .... 2200.00
Furniture, Mirror, Chippendale, Parcel Gilt, C.1760 .... *Illus* 775.00
Furniture, Mirror, Chippendale, Walnut, Carved, Molded Slip, Crest, C.1760 .... 80.00
Furniture, Mirror, Courting, Eglomise Decoration, 19th Century 215.00
Furniture, Mirror, Dressing, Oak, 3 Mirror, Swivel, 7 1/2 Ft.Tall 325.00
Furniture, Mirror, Dressing, Swing, Acanthus Leaf & Shell Footing, Iron 35.00
Furniture, Mirror, Dressing, Walnut, Square Supports, Trestle Feet 120.00
Furniture, Mirror, Empire, Mahogany Frame, C.1800, 21 X 12 In. 60.00
Furniture, Mirror, Empire, Vanity, Sulfide, Swing, Gilt Metal Frame, Faceted 600.00
Furniture, Mirror, Federal, Gilt Wood & Gesso, C.1800 .... *Illus* 600.00
Furniture, Mirror, Federal, Gilt Wood, Overmantel .... *Illus* 250.00
Furniture, Mirror, Federal, New England, C.1790 .... *Illus* 1600.00

Furniture, Mirror,
Chippendale; Parcel Gilt,
C.1760

Furniture, Mirror, Federal,
Gilt Wood & Gesso, C.1800

Furniture, Mirror, Federal,
New England, C.1790

Furniture, Mirror, Federal, Gilt Wood, Overmantel

Furniture, Mirror, Footed Stand, Grape Pattern, Iron, 19th Century 15.00
Furniture, Mirror, Fretted Top, Mahogany Molded Frame, C.1760 .... 200.00
Furniture, Mirror, Full View, Low Stand, Walnut, 7 Ft. 200.00
Furniture, Mirror, George I, Walnut & Parcel Gilt, Rectangular, C.1720 .... 1300.00
Furniture, Mirror, George IV, Gilt & Ebonized Wood, Rectangular, 1850, Pair 550.00
Furniture, Mirror, Gilt Metal & Cut Glass, Classical Maiden, C.1820 .... 300.00
Furniture, Mirror, Gilt Wood, John Linnell Style, Oval, C.1790 .... 425.00
Furniture, Mirror, Gilt Wood, Oval, Acanthus, Lion's Mask, C.1790 .... 375.00
Furniture, Mirror, Gilt Wood, Rectangular, C-Scrolls, C.1750, Pair 1200.00
Furniture, Mirror, Hand Carved Angels, By Otto & Rosoni, 19th Cent.9 In. 35.00
Furniture, Mirror, Italian, Carved & Gilded, Star & Rosette Top, 1750 .... 225.00
Furniture, Mirror, Italian, Gilt Wood, Carved, Female Mask, C.1750 .... 1800.00
Furniture, Mirror, Italian, Gilt Wood, Carved, Rectangular, C.1750 .... 575.00
Furniture, Mirror, Italian, Gilt Wood, Rectangular, Pierced, Carved, C.1750 .... 750.00
Furniture, Mirror, Italian, Gold Leaf On Frame, Bowknot With Wheat Spray 500.00
Furniture, Mirror, Mantel, George II, Stripped Pine, Rectangular, Acanthus 700.00
Furniture, Mirror, Mantel, Neoclassic, Egyptian Motif 500.00
Furniture, Mirror, Mantel, Polished Gold Leaf, Carved, C.1850, 36 X 24 In. 175.00
Furniture, Mirror, Oriental, Gilt Wood, Rectangular, Pierced, Carved 85.00
Furniture, Mirror, Painted Green Border, Carved Wood Urn, Pair 250.00
Furniture, Mirror, Polished Gold Leaf, Carved, Victorian, 2 X 4 1/2 Ft. 175.00
Furniture, Mirror, Pot Metal Frame, Women's Arm Holding Mirror, 18 In. 20.00
Furniture, Mirror, Rectangular, Gold & Red Ground Frame, Birds & Animals 45.00
Furniture, Mirror, Repousse Brass Frame, Cabochons & Foliage, 54 In.High 90.00
Furniture, Mirror, Reverse Painting On Glass, Clipper Ship, American Flag 115.00
Furniture, Mirror, Rose Leaf Trim, Art Nouveau Handle, Pink, Green, 9 1/2 X 5 .... 17.50
Furniture, Mirror, Scrolled, Mahogany, Circa 1815, 18 X 11 1/2 In. 175.00
Furniture, Mirror, Shaving, Dovetail, Chippendale, Pink, 12 X 17 In. 95.00
Furniture, Mirror, Shaving, Drawer, Inlaid, 13 Stars, Moon, Tilts 35.00
Furniture, Mirror, Shaving, Metal American Eagle, Flags, Wooden Stand 35.00
Furniture, Mirror, Shaving, On Tin Tray, Wooden Ball Feet, Swivel, Bracket 22.00
Furniture, Mirror, Shaving, Wall Type, Beveled, Retractable, 8 In.Diameter 15.00
Furniture, Mirror, Spanish, Ebony & Leather, Ormolu Mounted, C.1690, Pair 650.00
Furniture, Mirror, Venetian Glass, Blue Applied Decorations, 19 In.High 155.00
Furniture, Mirror, Venetian, Italian, 19th Century, Green & Gold, Pair 275.00
Furniture, Mirror, Wall, Chippendale, Inlaid Mahogany, Carved & Gilded Slip 250.00
Furniture, Mirror, Wall, Chippendale, Inlaid Mahogany, Scroll Cut Crest, 1770 .... 500.00
Furniture, Mirror, Wall, Chippendale, Inlaid Mahogany, Scrolled Crest, 1750 .... 1200.00
Furniture, Mirror, Wall, Chippendale, Mahogany & Parcel Gilt, Carved, C.1770 .... 325.00
Furniture, Mirror, Wall, Chippendale, Mahogany, American, C.1770 .... 150.00
Furniture, Mirror, Wall, Empire, Brass & Mahogany, Rectangular, Crest, C.1820 .... 170.00
Furniture, Mirror, Wall, Empire, Fruitwood, Rectangular, Ebony, C.1850, Pair 450.00
Furniture, Mirror, Wall, Federal, Gilt Wood & Gesso, Eglomise Panel, C.1810 .... 1200.00
Furniture, Mirror, Wall, Federal, Gilt Wood & Gesso, Eglomise, N.Y., C.1800 .... 150.00
Furniture, Mirror, Wall, Federal, Gilt Wood & Marble, Bilboa, C.1790, Pair 2000.00
Furniture, Mirror, Wall, Federal, Mahogany, Broken Cornice, New York, C.1825 .... 100.00
Furniture, Mirror, Wall, Federal, Mahogany, Carved, Broken Cornice, N.Y., 1825 .... 200.00
Furniture, Mirror, Wall, George III, Gilt Wood & Eglomise, C.1790, Pair 300.00
Furniture, Mirror, Wall, Gilt Wood, Oval, Carved Laurel Leaves & Berries 200.00
Furniture, Mirror, Wall, Italian, Gilt Wood, Carved, Rococo, Pierced, Pair 925.00
Furniture, Mirror, Wall, Italian, Pine, Carved, Rectangular, C.1650, 4 Ft.High 725.00
Furniture, Mirror, Wall, Mahogany Frame, Rope Posts, Roof Top, Acorns, 17 In. 39.00
Furniture, Mirror, Wall, Venetian Style, Rectangular, Scrolling Crest 375.00
Furniture, Mirror, White Walnut Frame, New England, 34 X 21 In. 75.00
Furniture, Organ Stool, Upholstered Top, Fringe, Adjustable, Iron Legs, 1860 .... 22.00
Furniture, Panel, Oblong, Lacquer, Animals & Insects, J.M.Rothschild, C.1925 .... 200.00
Furniture, Pie Safe, Pine, Walnut Cathedral Doors, Drawers, 50 X 60 In. 215.00
Furniture, Pier Glass, George III, Gilt Wood, Rectangular Mirror, C.1890 .... 550.00
Furniture, Pier Glass, Queen Anne Style, Silvered Wood, Carved, Pair 1000.00
Furniture, Pier Glass, Victorian, Gilt Wood, Arched Plate, Vines, C.1850 .... 200.00
Furniture, Planter, Fruitwood, Three Tier Stand, Black Marble Top 275.00
Furniture, Planter, Fruitwood, Three Tier Stand, Wood Top 200.00
Furniture, Poudreuse, Directoire, Mahogany, Rectangular, Lift Lid, C.1780 .... 200.00
Furniture, Poudreuse, Italian, Tulipwood, Marquetry, Rectangular, C.1750 .... 200.00
Furniture, Press, Linen, Chippendale, Curly Maple, C.1760 .... *Illus* 3100.00
Furniture, Prie-Dieu, Italian, Painted, Serpentine, Faux Marbre, C.1750 .... 375.00

Furniture, Seat, Window, Regency, Mahogany, C.1825
See Page 237

Furniture, Press, Linen, Chippendale,
Curly Maple, C.1760
See Page 235

Furniture, Rack, Clothes, Wall, Oak, 4 Iron Hooks, 21 X 4 In.	7.50
Furniture, Rack, Coat & Umbrella, Revolving, Bronze Finish	70.00
Furniture, Rack, Hat, For Derbies & Bowlers	7.00
Furniture, Rocker, Boston, Painted Grain & Stencil	80.00
Furniture, Rocker, Camphored Runners, Queen Anne, Delaware	250.00
Furniture, Rocker, Cherry & Maple, Slat Back, Rush Seat, Penn., C.1720	250.00
Furniture, Rocker, Child's, Ladder Back, Cane Seat	38.00
Furniture, Rocker, Child's, Shaker, From Mt.Lebanon, N.Y., Colony	195.00
Furniture, Rocker, Corset Back, Tufted Red Velvet, Victorian	250.00
Furniture, Rocker, Empire, Mahogany, Fiddleback	90.00
Furniture, Rocker, Ladder Back, Five Slats, Bulbous Turning At Front	160.00
Furniture, Rocker, Ladder Back, Pennsylvania, Cheese Cutter Rockers	200.00
Furniture, Rocker, Ladder Back, Split Willow Seat	60.00
Furniture, Rocker, Lincoln, Upholstered	29.00
Furniture, Rocker, Queen Anne Style, Black Walnut, Needlepoint Seat	85.00
Furniture, Rocker, Windsor, Comb Back, Serpentine Crest Rail, C.1780	825.00
Furniture, Sconce, English, Mirrored Crystal, 2 Arms, C.1850, 4	800.00
Furniture, Sconce, Italian, Gilt Wood, Carved, Mirror Plate, C.1750, Pair	500.00
Furniture, Sconce, Wall, Italian, Acanthus Leaves Supporting 2 Candle Arms	70.00
Furniture, Screen, Black & Gold, 4 Fold, Pair Of Peacocks In Cage	125.00
Furniture, Screen, Chinese, Ivory, Mother-Of-Pearl, Wood, Lacquer, 2 Fold	375.00
Furniture, Screen, Chinese, Lacquer, Mother-Of-Pearl, Hardstone, 6 Fold, 1850	850.00
Furniture, Screen, Chinese, Painted Paper, Village Scenes, 6 Fold	1100.00
Furniture, Screen, Chinese, 3 Fold, Paper On Canvas, Family Scenes, C.1750	550.00
Furniture, Screen, Coromandel, Lacquer, Ch'len Lung Period, 8 Fold, Chinese	3200.00
Furniture, Screen, Coromandel, Lacquer, Landscape, Carved Wood, Chinese	185.00
Furniture, Screen, Coromandel, Lacquer, Tete De Negre Ground, 8 Fold, C.1820	550.00
Furniture, Screen, Coromandel, 4 Fold, Carved, Landscape, Figures, Black	1600.00
Furniture, Screen, Fire, Victorian, Satinwood, Yellow Damask, C.1850	110.00
Furniture, Screen, Florentine, 5 Fold, Painted Scenic Medallions	110.00
Furniture, Screen, French, 4 Fold, Canvas, Painting Couples In Garden, C.1850	70.00
Furniture, Screen, French, 6 Fold, Classical Medallions, C.1750	325.00
Furniture, Screen, Ivory Bird Scenes, Oriental, Panel 72 X 24 In., 4 Panel	800.00
Furniture, Screen, Japanese, Paper, 2 Fold, White Flowers, Marsh Reeds, Brown	350.00
Furniture, Screen, Japanese, 6 Fold, Gnarled Lotus Tree In Blossom	1500.00
Furniture, Screen, Japanese, 6 Fold, Gold Leaf Ground, Flowering Lotus Tree	1500.00
Furniture, Screen, Japanese, 6 Fold, Gold Leaf Ground, Marsh Scene	800.00
Furniture, Screen, Oriental, Black Lacquer, Silkwork Panel, 4 Fold, C.1850	300.00
Furniture, Screen, Painted Leather, Chinoiserie Pavilion, 3 Fold	150.00
Furniture, Screen, Painted Leather, Landscape, 4 Fold	450.00
Furniture, Screen, Painted Paper, French Cartoons, Black, 3 Fold	140.00

Furniture, Screen, 4 Fold, Painted Scenes Of Roman Buildings	60.00
Furniture, Seat, Buggy, Black Leather, Tufted	69.00
Furniture, Seat, Hall, Oak, Rack	59.00
Furniture, Seat, Marble, Carved Oak Leaf Supports, 71 X 18 In.	425.00
Furniture, Seat, Sleigh Back, Iron Frame, Brown Leather Like Material	100.00
Furniture, Seat; Vanity, Crushed Velvet Top, Victorian, Oak	18.50
Furniture, Seat, Window, Empire, Mahogany, Ormolu Mounted, C.1890	250.00
Furniture, Seat, Window, George II, Mahogany, Scroll Arms, Arched Back, 1790	550.00
Furniture, Seat, Window, Mahogany, Chair Back Ends, C.1790	225.00
Furniture, Seat, Window, Regency, Mahogany, C.1825 *Illus*	550.00
Furniture, Secretaire A Abattant, Biedermeier, Fruitwood, Marble, C.1850	200.00
Furniture, Secretaire A Abattant, Directoire, Mahogany, Marble Top, C.1750	700.00
Furniture, Secretaire A Abattant, Empire, Mahogany, Gilt Metal, Ormolu, 1850	250.00
Furniture, Secretaire A Abattant, Empire, Mahogany, Prophyry Top, C.1850	500.00
Furniture, Secretaire A Abattant, Louis XVI, King & Rosewood, Marquetry	3200.00
Furniture, Secretaire A Abattant, Tulipwood, Rectangular, C.1750	2750.00
Furniture, Secretaire Cabinet, George III, Mahogany, Marquetry, C.1820	1600.00
Furniture, Secretaire Cabinet, George III, Mahogany, Splay Feet, C.1790	1500.00
Furniture, Secretaire Cabinet, Mahogany, 13 Panel Doors, C.1790	950.00
Furniture, Secretaire Commode, Northern Italian, Walnut, Marble Top, C.1750	350.00
Furniture, Secretary Bookcase, Chippendale, Inlaid Mahogany, English, C.1775	950.00
Furniture, Secretary Bookcase, Chippendale, Mahogany, Coved Cornice, 2 Parts	3000.00
Furniture, Secretary Bookcase, Chippendale, Mahogany, 2 Parts, Conn., C.1760	4250.00
Furniture, Secretary Bookcase, Chippendale, Walnut, 1760 *Illus*	3000.00
Furniture, Secretary Bookcase, Oak	85.00
Furniture, Server, Table, Tapered Legs, Stenciled	59.00
Furniture, Settee, Biedermeier, Birch, Upholstered Back, Arms, & Seat, C.1850	325.00
Furniture, Settee, Ebene De Macassar, Silver Plate Ball Feet, Ruhlmann, 1925	850.00
Furniture, Settee, French Provincial, Fruitwood, Double Chair Back, C.1850	125.00
Furniture, Settee, French Provincial, Walnut, Rush Seat, Ladder Back, C.1750	350.00
Furniture, Settee, George I Style, Mahogany, Double Chair Back, Vase Splats	4000.00
Furniture, Settee, George III, Beechwood, Carved Guilloche Molding, C.1750	600.00
Furniture, Settee, George III, Beechwood, Carved, Red Velvet, C.1750	600.00
Furniture, Settee, Painted & Parcel Gilt, Carved Paterae, 1790	575.00
Furniture, Settee, Windsor, Duckbill Back, 20 Spindles, H Stretcher Base	750.00
Furniture, Settee, Windsor, New England, C.1790 *Illus*	675.00
Furniture, Shelf, Clock, Drawer, Honey Color Pine, Cut Corners, Refinished	38.00
Furniture, Shelf, Corner, Elk's Head, Carved, Walnut	12.50
Furniture, Shelf, Display, Pine, Yellow Paint	28.00
Furniture, Shelf, Folding, Lacquer, Fish, Flowers, Bug, Red, Gold	12.00
Furniture, Shelf, Folding, Lacquer, Mountain Scene, Mandarin, Red, Gold	12.00
Furniture, Shelf, Hanging, Victorian, Mahogany, Mirrored Back, 3 Tiers, C.1850	90.00
Furniture, Shelf, Wall, Folding, Wooden, Enamel, French, 13 In.Wide	37.50
Furniture, Shelf, Wall, Gilded Leaf, Pair	17.50
Furniture, Sideboard, Federal, Inlaid Mahogany, Bowfront, Oblong, Phila., 1810	375.00
Furniture, Sideboard, Federal, Inlaid Mahogany, Demilune, New York, C.1790	1200.00
Furniture, Sideboard, Federal, Inlaid Mahogany, Rectangular, New York, 1810	275.00
Furniture, Sideboard, Federal, Mahogany, C.1790 *Illus*	1200.00
Furniture, Sideboard, Federal, Mahogany, Phila., C.1835 *Illus*	475.00
Furniture, Sideboard, George III, Mahogany, D Shape Top, Frieze, C.1790	650.00
Furniture, Sideboard, George III, Mahogany, Rectangular, Frieze Drawer	275.00
Furniture, Sideboard, Mahogany, D Shape Outline, Drawer, C.1820	1500.00
Furniture, Sideboard, Mahogany, Oblong, Carved, Charles-Honore Lannuier, 1815	1400.00
Furniture, Sideboard, Sheraton, Mahogany	975.00
Furniture, Sofa Bed, Napoleonic Style, Sleigh Arms	250.00
Furniture, Sofa, Art Deco, High Back, Loose Cushions, William Lescaze, 1935	475.00
Furniture, Sofa, Chippendale, Mahogany, Miniature, Camel Back, Phila., C.1760	1300.00
Furniture, Sofa, Federal, Mahogany, Mass., C.1825 *Illus*	900.00
Furniture, Sofa, French Provincial, Fruitwood Frame, Upholstered	1000.00
Furniture, Sofa, George III, Mahogany, Arched Upholstered Back, Bowfront	850.00
Furniture, Sofa, Hepplewhite Transitional, Mahogany, Rhode Island	1850.00
Furniture, Sofa, Imperial, Walnut Frame, Rectangular Back & Side	400.00
Furniture, Sofa, Mahogany, Carved Ram's Head & Hoof Feet, 7 1/2 Ft.Long	450.00
Furniture, Sofa, Mahogany, Carved, Eagles, Serpentine Back, N.Y., C.1825	1000.00
Furniture, Sofa, Mahogany, New York, C.1820 *Illus*	900.00
Furniture, Sofa, Sheraton, Mahogany Frame, English, Serpentine, C.1850	850.00

Furniture, Secretary Bookcase,
Chippendale, Walnut, 1760
See Page 237

Furniture, Sideboard, Federal, Mahogany, Phila., C.1835
See Page 237

Furniture, Settee, Windsor, New England, C.1790
See Page 237

Furniture, Sideboard, Federal,
Mahogany, C.1790
See Page 237

Furniture, Stand, Art Deco, Marble, Square, Stepped Base, Reddish Brown, 1930 .... 200.00
Furniture, Stand, Boot, Hat, Umbrella, Walnut, Black Marble Top, Spiral Legs 350.00
Furniture, Stand, Candle, Sheraton, Scroll Base, Penna., Cherry, C.1810 .... 190.00
Furniture, Stand, Candle, Victorian Period, Tiger Maple 70.00
Furniture, Stand, Chinese, Hardwood, Pierced Frieze, C.1850, 5 .... 375.00
Furniture, Stand, Dumbwaiter, English, Mahogany, Dish Top, 2 Shelves, C.1850 .... 300.00

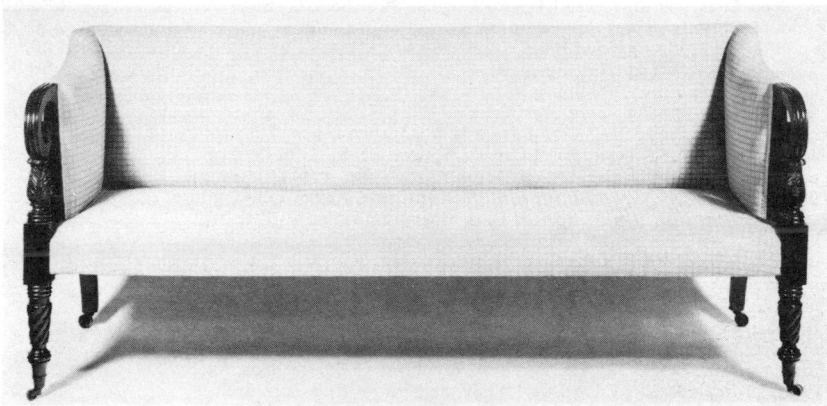

Furniture, Sofa, Federal, Mahogany, Mass., C.1825
See Page 237

Furniture, Sofa, Mahogany, New York, C.1820
See Page 237

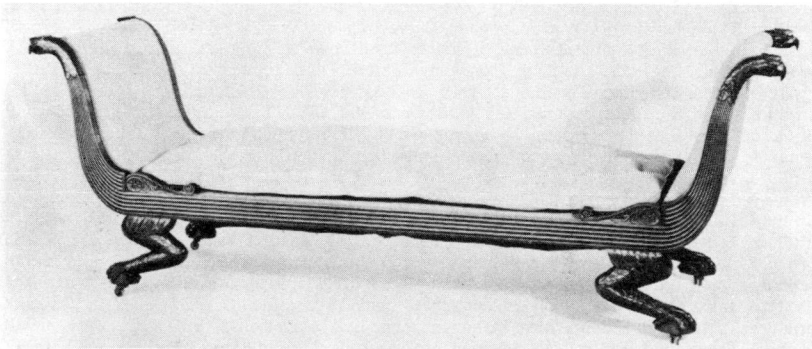

Furniture, Stand, French Provincial, 2 Tier, Painted & Gilded, Pair	350.00
Furniture, Stand, Italian, Walnut, Heart Corners, Cabriole Legs, C.1850	250.00
Furniture, Stand, Kettle, Mahogany, Oval, Candle Sill, C.1790	275.00
Furniture, Stand, Mahogany, English, Open, 5 Shelf, C.1850	450.00
Furniture, Stand, Metal, Glass Top, Bamboo Turned Frame, Square, Pair	160.00
Furniture, Stand, Music, Mahogany, Lyre Form, Ball Feet, C.1720	350.00
Furniture, Stand, One Drawer, Sheraton, Kentucky, C.1820, Cherry, 20 1/2 In.	65.00
Furniture, Stand, Reading, Continental, Fruitwood, Rectangular, Trestle	20.00
Furniture, Stand, Shaker, Turned Legs, 1 Drawer, 26 X 22 X 27 1/2 In.	325.00
Furniture, Stand, Teakwood, Marble Top, 37 In.High	165.00
Furniture, Stand, Victorian, Walnut, Scroll, Turned, 49 In.High, Pair	95.00
Furniture, Stand, Walnut, Splay Leg, Narrow Apron	160.00
Furniture, Stand, Wig, English, Mahogany, Circular Ring Top, Drawer	250.00
Furniture, Steps, Bed, Mahogany, 3 Red Leather Treads, C.1890	200.00
Furniture, Steps, Library, Regency, Mahogany, 3 Tiers, Gilt Leather, C.1750	200.00
Furniture, Stool, Chinese, Hung-Mu, Rectangular, Pierces Frieze, C.1850	250.00
Furniture, Stool, Claw Feet, Needlepoint Cover, 10 X 14 In.	25.00
Furniture, Stool, Continental, Beechwood, Carved Acanthus At Knees	50.00
Furniture, Stool, English, Walnut, Turned Hand Rails, Arched Stretcher	70.00
Furniture, Stool, Engraving On Seat, Brass, 13 X 11 In.	45.00
Furniture, Stool, Gout, V Shape, On Rockers, Green Velvet, 20 X 15 In.High	60.00
Furniture, Stool, Huali, Chinese, Square Top, Caned Panel, C.1850	250.00
Furniture, Stool, Italian, Painted & Parcel Gilt, Beige Velvet, C.1750, Pair	750.00

Furniture, **Stool**, Joined, Turned Legs, Rectangular Stretchers, C.1650	525.00
Furniture, **Stool**, Louis XVI, Square, Vase Legs, C.1750	750.00
Furniture, **Stool**, Milking, Hand-Hewn, Three Legged	20.00
Furniture, **Stool**, Milking, Pine, 3 Legged, 18th Century	50.00
Furniture, **Stool**, Milking, Three Legs Go Through To Top, Oak	10.00
Furniture, **Stool**, Milking, Three Legs, Gold Stencils On Legs, Signed	17.00
Furniture, **Stool**, Oak, Joined, Chip Carved Apron, Turned Legs, 17th Century	350.00
Furniture, **Stool**, Oak, Joined, Relief Carving, Shaped Apron, 17th Century	550.00
Furniture, **Stool**, Oak, Joined, Scrolled Apron, Molded Top, 17th Century	375.00
Furniture, **Stool**, Oak, Joined, Splay Legs, Molded Top & Apron, 17th Century	375.00
Furniture, **Stool**, Oak, Joined, Splayed Legs, Molded Stretcher	130.00
Furniture, **Stool**, Oak, Joined, 17th Century	300.00
Furniture, **Stool**, Saddle, Queen Anne Type Legs, Oak, 7 X 10 1/2 X 17 In.High	26.00
Furniture, **Stool**, Shaker, Painted Top, 24 X 12 X 19 In.	62.50
Furniture, **Stool**, Shaker, Turned Legs, Top, 18 X 10 X 15 In.Tall	85.00
Furniture, **Stool**, William & Mary Style, Oak, Rectangular, Needlework	100.00
Furniture, **Table Desk**, Oak, 3 Drawers, Slant Lid, Iron Escutcheon, C.1650	800.00
Furniture, **Table Screen**, Applied Carnelian, Amethystine Quartz, Jade, Agate	250.00
Furniture, **Table Screen**, Curved Crystal, Sterling Frame, Openwork Crowns	50.00
Furniture, **Table Screen**, Three Fold, Porcelain Inserts, Inlaid Wood Frame	110.00
Furniture, **Table**, Altar, Chinese, Hung-Mu, Oblong, Carved Frieze, Ch'len Lung	1000.00
Furniture, **Table**, Altar, Chinese, Red Lacquer, Rectangular, Scene, Floral, Bird	1900.00
Furniture, **Table**, Architect's, George III, Rectangular, Satinwood Urn, 1790	175.00
Furniture, **Table**, Baker's, Hickory	69.00
Furniture, **Table**, Banquet, Victorian, Black Walnut, Oval	185.00
Furniture, **Table**, Bedside, Cherry & Bird's-Eye Maple, Oblong, N.E., C.1800	130.00
Furniture, **Table**, Bedside, Federal, Mahogany, Carved, Oblong, N.Y., C.1810	375.00
Furniture, **Table**, Black Walnut, Gateleg, 1 Drawer, Oval Open	100.00
Furniture, **Table**, Bouillotte, Louis XVI, Mahogany, Marble, Pierced Brass	650.00
Furniture, **Table**, Breakfast, Biedermeier, Birch, Round, Hexagonal Column, 1820	250.00
Furniture, **Table**, Breakfast, Federal, Mahogany, Drop Leaf, C.1815	175.00
Furniture, **Table**, Breakfast, Federal, Mahogany, Oblong, 2 Serpentine Leaves	125.00
Furniture, **Table**, Breakfast, Rosewood, Oval Veneer Top, C.1790	525.00
Furniture, **Table**, Breakfast, Victorian, Mahogany, Round, Tilt Top, Carved, 1850	90.00
Furniture, **Table**, Card, Biedermeier, Birch, Rectangular, Square Legs, C.1820	180.00
Furniture, **Table**, Card, Boulle, Serpentine Baize Lined Top, Brass, C.1850	425.00
Furniture, **Table**, Card, Federal, Inlaid Cherry, Pelatiah Bliss, Mass., C.1790	2700.00
Furniture, **Table**, Card, Federal, Inlaid Mahogany & Satin, Boston, C.1790	1100.00
Furniture, **Table**, Card, Federal, Inlaid Mahogany & Satin, Serpentine, C.1790	2000.00
Furniture, **Table**, Card, Federal, Inlaid Mahogany & Satin, 5 Leg, Md., C.1790	2300.00
Furniture, **Table**, Card, Federal, Inlaid Mahogany, Demilune, Medallions, 1800	600.00
Furniture, **Table**, Card, Federal, Inlaid Mahogany, Demilune, Molded Edge, 1790	1300.00
Furniture, **Table**, Card, Federal, Inlaid Mahogany, Hinged Elliptic Top, 1810	375.00
Furniture, **Table**, Card, Federal, Inlaid Mahogany, Oblong, Frieze Drawer, 1800	1600.00
Furniture, **Table**, Card, Federal, Inlaid Mahogany, Serpentine Front, C.1800	300.00
Furniture, **Table**, Card, Federal, Inlaid Mahogany, Serpentine, S.C., C.1790	3500.00
Furniture, **Table**, Card, Federal, Mahogany & Satinwood, Serpentine, Mass., 1790	850.00
Furniture, **Table**, Card, Federal, Mahogany, Double Elliptic, Swivel Leg, 1810	1200.00
Furniture, **Table**, Card, George II, Burr Walnut, Veneered Top, Carved, C.1750	1250.00
Furniture, **Table**, Card, Hepplewhite, Mahogany & Bird's-Eye Maple	595.00
Furniture, **Table**, Card, Inlaid Mahogany & Parcel Gilt, Hinged, Pedestal, 1820	1000.00
Furniture, **Table**, Card, Inlaid Mahogany, Hinged, Lyre Support, Carved, C.1820	375.00
Furniture, **Table**, Card, Inlay, Hepplewhite, New England, Whitewood & Maple	475.00
Furniture, **Table**, Card, Mahogany, Semicircular, C.1790, Pair	800.00
Furniture, **Table**, Card, Mahogany, Thomas Astens, D Shape, Painted Decor, 1850	550.00
Furniture, **Table**, Card, Regency, Rosewood, D Shape, Satinwood Band, C.1850	200.00
Furniture, **Table**, Card, Regency, Rosewood, Rectangular, Maroon Leather, Pair	1000.00
Furniture, **Table**, Card, Serpentine, Mass., C.1815 *Illus*	600.00
Furniture, **Table**, Card, Turn Top, Virginia, C.1820, Walnut	225.00
Furniture, **Table**, Card, Victorian, Rosewood, Serpentine Top, Hinged, C.1850	250.00
Furniture, **Table**, Carved Legs, Mulberry, 13 1/2 X 9 1/2 In.Top	60.00
Furniture, **Table**, Center, Austrian, Oak, Rectangular Top, Drawer, C.1650	1200.00
Furniture, **Table**, Center, Charles I, Oak, Rectangular, Turned Legs, C.1650	800.00
Furniture, **Table**, Center, Charles II, Oak, Rectangular, Drawer In Frieze	400.00
Furniture, **Table**, Center, Chinese, Hardwood, Rectangular, Pierced, C.1850	400.00
Furniture, **Table**, Center, Continental, Beechwood, Rectangular, C.1780	380.00

Furniture, Table, Center, Directoire, Steel & Ormolu, Marble Top, C.1750 .... 3900.00
Furniture, Table, Center, Dutch, Mahogany, Round Brass Rimmed Top, C.1850 .... 225.00
Furniture, Table, Center, Elizabethan Style, Oak, Carved Frieze, C.1560 .... 1300.00
Furniture, Table, Center, Flemish, Oak & Elmwood, Rectangular, C.1630 .... 850.00
Furniture, Table, Center, Italian Renaissance Style, Round, 23 In.High 250.00
Furniture, Table, Center, Italian, Fruitwood, Marquetry, Oval, Scrolls, C.1750 .... 850.00
Furniture, Table, Center, Italian, Walnut, Hexagonal, Carved Frieze 225.00
Furniture, Table, Center, Italian, Walnut, Rectangular, Baluster Columns, 1600 .... 3750.00
Furniture, Table, Center, Regency, Inlaid Mahogany, Miniature, English, C.1820 .... 150.00
Furniture, Table, Charles II, Oak, Drop Leaf, Gateleg, Drawer, C.1790 .... 500.00
Furniture, Table, Chinese Lacquer Panel, Rectangular, Birds, Floral, Pair 500.00
Furniture, Table, Chinese, Inlaid Mother-Of-Pearl, Black Lacquer 500.00
Furniture, Table, Chinese, Lacquer, Mother-Of-Pearl, Hardstone, C.1850, Pair 325.00
Furniture, Table, Chinese, Lacquer, Oblong, Foliations On Brick Red 375.00
Furniture, Table, Chippendale Style, Cherry, Pembroke, Oblong, 1 Drawer 175.00
Furniture, Table, Chippendale, Mahogany, Carved, Tilt Top, Piecrust Edge 2000.00
Furniture, Table, Chippendale, Pembroke, Whitewood & Tiger Maple 495.00
Furniture, Table, Coffee, Six Carved Post Legs, Folds Flat, Brass Tray 58.00
Furniture, Table, Console, Dutch, Beech & Elm, Rectangular, Frieze, C.1750 .... 140.00
Furniture, Table, Console, French, Marble Top, C.1750 .... 600.00
Furniture, Table, Console, George III, Mahogany, D Outline, Carved, Pair 750.00
Furniture, Table, Console, Green D Shape Leather Top, Gilded, C.1790, Pair 525.00
Furniture, Table, Console, Portuguese, Rectangular, Red & Blue, C.1790, Pair 600.00
Furniture, Table, Coromandel Lacquer, Oriental Figures, Nest Of 4 .... 400.00
Furniture, Table, Couch, Chinese, Lacquer, Oblong, Scene On Black, Floral 125.00
Furniture, Table, Dining, Chippendale, Cherry, Ball & Claw Feet 1500.00
Furniture, Table, Dining, Federal, Cherry, Drop Leaf, Oblong, N.E., C.1820 .... 325.00
Furniture, Table, Dining, Federal, Inlaid Cherry .... *Illus* 1800.00
Furniture, Table, Dining, Federal, Mahogany, Pennsylvania, C.1800 .... 750.00

Furniture, Table, Card, Serpentine, Mass., C.1815   Furniture, Table, Drop Leaf, Curly Maple, Ohio, C.?
See Page 240   See Page 242

Furniture, Table, Dining
Federal, Inlaid Cherry

Furniture, Table, Dining, Federal, Tiger Maple, Drop Leaf, Oblong, American 300.00
Furniture, Table, Dining, George III, Mahogany, D Ends, Square Legs, C.1790 .... 650.00
Furniture, Table, Dining, George III, Mahogany, Rectangular, 3 Pedestal 3200.00
Furniture, Table, Dining, Pine, Crossbuck, 2 Board Cleated Top 950.00
Furniture, Table, Dining, Queen Anne, John Goddard, Rhode Island, Mahogany 1150.00
Furniture, Table, Dining, Queen Anne, Maple & Pine, Drop Leaf, Oval, N.H., 1740 .... 800.00
Furniture, Table, Dining, Regency, Rosewood, Rectangular, Brass, Carved, 1850 .... 2400.00
Furniture, Table, Directoire Style, Wrought Iron, Round Marble Top, Pair 180.00
Furniture, Table, Display, Chinese, Teakwood, Carved, Round, Brown Marble 220.00
Furniture, Table, Dressing, Double Pedestal, Kidney, 29 X 22 X 31 1/2 In. 60.00
Furniture, Table, Dressing, Federal, Inlaid Mahogany, Hinged Lid, Bowfront 750.00
Furniture, Table, Dressing, Federal, Mahogany, Inlaid, Serpentine Top, C.1790 .... 975.00
Furniture, Table, Dressing, Fruitwood, Mirror Glass, Stool, Paul T.Frankl, 1929 .... 700.00
Furniture, Table, Dressing, George II, Walnut, Kneehole, Rectangular, C.1750 .... 500.00
Furniture, Table, Dressing, Mirror, Art Deco, Lacquered Wood, Red Orange, Gilt 100.00
Furniture, Table, Dressing, Queen Anne, Oak, C.1725 .... *Illus* 800.00
Furniture, Table, Drop Leaf, C.1740, Cherry 500.00
Furniture, Table, Drop Leaf, Curly Maple, Ohio, c.1810 .... *Illus* 350.00
Furniture, Table, Drop Leaf, Cherry, American, Circa 1820, 44 X 66 1/2 In. 450.00
Furniture, Table, Drop Leaf, Queen Anne, Mahogany, C.1750 .... 850.00
Furniture, Table, Drop Leaf, Rope Legs, Butternut, Circa 1810, 42 X 43 In. 350.00
Furniture, Table, Drop Leaf, Tiger Maple & Cherry, 36 In. 180.00
Furniture, Table, Drop Leaf, Trestle, Gateleg, Square Drawer, C.1750 .... 950.00
Furniture, Table, Drum Top, Black Leather, Frieze Drawers, C.1790 .... 550.00
Furniture, Table, Drum, English, Inlaid Mahogany, C.1850 .... 700.00
Furniture, Table, Duncan Phyfe, Mahogany, Drop Leaf, 36 X 25 In.Closed 100.00
Furniture, Table, Empire, Burled Walnut Top, Pedestal 185.00
Furniture, Table, Federal, Cherry, Drop Leaf, Oblong, Conn., C.1800 .... 300.00
Furniture, Table, Federal, Mahogany, Inlaid .... *Illus* 225.00
Furniture, Table, Finger Carved, Walnut, White Marble Top, 20 X 16 In. 145.00
Furniture, Table, Flemish, Oak, Gateleg, Oval, Turned Supports, C.1690 .... 175.00
Furniture, Table, Galle, Thistles Of Scotland, Cross Of Lorrain .... 220.00 To 235.00
Furniture, Table, Gallery, English, Mahogany, Scalloped Edge, C.1850 .... 65.00
Furniture, Table, Gallery, Mahogany, Tilt Top, Spool Turned Legs 100.00
Furniture, Table, Game, Chippendale, Mahogany, 2 Tier, Lift Lid 300.00
Furniture, Table, Game, Directoire, Mahogany, Brass Rim, D Top, C.1750 .... 700.00
Furniture, Table, Game, George II, Mahogany, Rectangular, Acanthus Knees 625.00
Furniture, Table, Game, George III, Mahogany, Rectangular, C.1750 .... 125.00
Furniture, Table, Game, George III, Mahogany, Rectangular, Drawer, Pair 900.00
Furniture, Table, Game, Queen Anne Style, Walnut, 19th Century 500.00
Furniture, Table, Game, Victorian, Burr Walnut, D Shape, Drawer, C.1890 .... 120.00
Furniture, Table, George II, Mahogany, Piecrust, Tripod, Round, Birdcage 700.00
Furniture, Table, George II, Mahogany, Tripod, Rectangular Tray Top, Carved 275.00
Furniture, Table, George II, Mahogany, Tripod, Round Top On Birdcage, 1750 .... 250.00
Furniture, Table, George II, Mahogany, Tripod, Round, Piecrust Edge, Carved 525.00
Furniture, Table, George III, Elmwood, Tripod, Round, Vase Support, C.1750 .... 190.00
Furniture, Table, George III, Mahogany, Tripod, Rectangular, C.1790 .... 100.00
Furniture, Table, George III, Rosewood, Drum Top, Gilt Tooled Leather, 1750 .... 650.00
Furniture, Table, Harvest, Crossbuck, 1 Board Cleated Top, 26 X 84 In. 3200.00
Furniture, Table, Harvest, Pine Top, French, 19th Century 110.00
Furniture, Table, Harvest, Sheraton, Country, Curly Birch, New England, C.1810 .... 295.00
Furniture, Table, Harvest, Sheraton, Country, Maple, C.1820, 6 Ft.Long 895.00
Furniture, Table, Hutch, Pine, Long Leaf, Round Top, 38 In.Diameter 250.00
Furniture, Table, Hutch, Pine, Shoe Feet, 18th Century, 30 In.High 475.00
Furniture, Table, Inlaid, Pembroke, Cherry, Circa 1790 .... 385.00
Furniture, Table, Iron, Painted White, Figurehead Supports, 48 X 26 In. 200.00
Furniture, Table, Italian, Gray Paint, Rectangular, C.1850 .... 200.00
Furniture, Table, Italian, Gray Paint, 19th Century, 1 Drawer 175.00
Furniture, Table, Italian, Walnut, Lyre Legs, Rod Stretcher, 1 Drawer 200.00
Furniture, Table, Italian, Walnut, Oval, C.1750 .... 525.00
Furniture, Table, Italian, Walnut, Rectangular Top & Legs, C.1650 .... 450.00
Furniture, Table, Italian, Walnut, Round, Carved Floral Frieze 50.00
Furniture, Table, Kingwood, Marquetry, Floral Spray, C.1750 .... 4500.00
Furniture, Table, Lacquer, Chinese, C.1820 .... *Illus* 350.00
Furniture, Table, Lacquer, Chinese, C.1820, Nest Of 4 .... *Illus* 475.00
Furniture, Table, Lamp, Wicker 8.00

Furniture, Table, Library, George III, Mahogany, Drum Top, Round, Leather 850.00
Furniture, Table, Library, Mahogany, Drum Top, Green Leather, C.1750 .... 475.00
Furniture, Table, Library, Pennsylvania, Walnut 795.00
Furniture, Table, Magician's, Round Velvet Covered Top, Tripod, C.1925 .... 100.00
Furniture, Table, Mahogany, Cherry, C.1780 .... *Illus* 450.00

Furniture, Table, Dressing,
Queen Anne, Oak, C.1725
See Page 242

Furniture, Table,
Lacquer, Chinese, C.1820
See Page 242

Furniture, Table, Federal, Mahogany, Inlaid
See Page 242

Furniture, Table, Lacquer, Chinese,
C.1820, Nest Of 4
See Page 242

Furniture, Table,
Mahogany, Cherry,
C.1780

Furniture, Table,
Pier, Federal,
Mahogany,
Parcel Gilt
See Page 244

Furniture, Table, Mahogany, Dish Top, Tilt Top, Ball & Claw Feet, C.1900 .... 90.00
Furniture, Table, Mahogany, Rectangular, Shelf, Chamfered Legs, Pair 170.00
Furniture, Table, Mahogany, Tripod, Round, Carved, C.1890 .... 110.00
Furniture, Table, Maple & Pine, Turned, Drop Leaf, Oblong, New England, C.1820 .... 475.00
Furniture, Table, Monk's, Oak, 17th Century, 90 X 33 X 31 In. 700.00
Furniture, Table, Oak, Golden, Pedestal Base, C.1900 .... 145.00
Furniture, Table, Oak, Round Pedestal Base, Lion Claw Feet, 52 In.Diameter 285.00
Furniture, Table, Occasional, Austrian, Form Of 3 Leather Bound Tomes, 1750 .... 250.00
Furniture, Table, Occasional, Black Marble Top, Round, C.1820 .... 175.00
Furniture, Table, Occasional, Directoire, Mahogany, Drop Leaf, C.1750 .... 425.00
Furniture, Table, Occasional, Directoire, Mahogany, Rectangular, Drawer, 1850 .... 90.00
Furniture, Table, Occasional, Dutch, Marquetry, Drop Leaf, Rectangular 150.00
Furniture, Table, Occasional, Empire, Mahogany, Round, Glass Panel, C.1850 .... 500.00
Furniture, Table, Occasional, Empire, Oval, White Marble Top, C.1850 .... 120.00
Furniture, Table, Occasional, Flemish, Round Beechwood Top, C.1780 .... 60.00
Furniture, Table, Occasional, French, Walnut, 1 Drawer, Box Top, C.1850 .... 125.00
Furniture, Table, Occasional, George III, Black Japanned, Octagonal, 1750 .... 125.00
Furniture, Table, Occasional, Louis XV Provincial, Fruitwood, C.1750 .... 150.00
Furniture, Table, Occasional, Victorian, Green Lacquer, Mounted With Lamp 200.00
Furniture, Table, One Drawer, Hepplewhite Legs, C.1820, Cherry 85.00
Furniture, Table, One Drawer, Hepplewhite, Cherry, 20 1/2 X 24 In. 125.00
Furniture, Table, One Drawer, Sheraton, C.1815, 27 1/2 X 23 1/4 In. 125.00
Furniture, Table, Oriental Scenes, Round Top, Black, Japanned, Inlaid, C.1890 .... 220.00
Furniture, Table, Ormolu Plateau, Mirrored, Oval, C.1750 .... 1700.00
Furniture, Table, Papier-Mache, Mother-Of-Pearl Inlay, Tilt Top, 26 In.High 150.00
Furniture, Table, Pembroke, Drawer, Small Leg, Tiger Maple 245.00
Furniture, Table, Pembroke, Federal, Inlaid Mahogany, Oval, Drop Leaf, C.1790 .... 2300.00
Furniture, Table, Pembroke, George III, Mahogany, Rectangular, C.1750 .... 275.00
Furniture, Table, Pembroke, George III, Mahogany, Rectangular, C.1790 .... 200.00
Furniture, Table, Pembroke, George III, Satinwood, Elliptical, Medallion 775.00
Furniture, Table, Pembroke, Inlay, Chippendale, Cherry 495.00
Furniture, Table, Pembroke, Mahogany, D Shape Drop Leaves, C.1790 .... 500.00
Furniture, Table, Pembroke, Mahogany, Rectangular, Drawer, C.1790 .... 160.00
Furniture, Table, Pembroke, Queen Anne, C.1750, One Drawer, 45 In. 390.00
Furniture, Table, Pembroke, Mahogany, R%ctangular, Drawer, C.1790 .... 160.00
Furniture, Table, Piecrust, Chippendale, Mahogany, C.1760, Pair 1750.00
Furniture, Table, Pier, Federal, Mahogany, Parcel Gilt .... Illus 950.00
Furniture, Table, Pier, Queen Anne, Mahogany, Marble Top, Carved, American 2000.00
Furniture, Table, Pine & Chestnut, Penna., C.1775 .... Illus 4250.00
Furniture, Table, Pine, Double Gateleg, 46 In.Long, 17th Century 375.00
Furniture, Table, Provincial, Walnut, Rectangular, Carved, C.1790 .... 1100.00
Furniture, Table, Provincial, Walnut, Rectangular, Marble Top, C.1790 .... 1500.00
Furniture, Table, Queen Anne, Cherry, American, Drop Leaf, Round, Circa 1725 .... 1150.00
Furniture, Table, Queen Anne, Mahogany, Handkerchief, Triangular Top 275.00
Furniture, Table, Queen Anne, Maple & Cherry, Drop Leaf, New England, 1780 .... 700.00
Furniture, Table, Reading & Writing, Italian, Red Japanned, Drawer, C.1750 .... 225.00
Furniture, Table, Reading, Louis XVI, Mahogany, Lift Top Bookrest, C.1790 .... 750.00
Furniture, Table, Regency, Mahogany, Rectangular, C.1850, Nest Of 4 .... 150.00
Furniture, Table, Regency, Red Japanned, Tripod, Triangular, C.1850 .... 100.00
Furniture, Table, Rent, Mahogany, Round Red Leather Top, C.1790 .... 1400.00
Furniture, Table, Serving, English, Oak, Rectangular, 17th Century 575.00
Furniture, Table, Serving, Oak, Carved Front, 2 Drawers, 54 In.Long 150.00
Furniture, Table, Sewing, Drop Leaf, Rope Legs, Two Drawers, Maple 95.00
Furniture, Table, Sewing, Federal, Mass., C.1790 .... Illus 5500.00
Furniture, Table, Shaker, Enfield, Cabriole Legs, Two Drawers 700.00
Furniture, Table, Side, Charles II, Oak, Rectangular, 3 Frieze Drawers, 1650 .... 525.00
Furniture, Table, Side, Charles I, Oak, Rectangular, Frieze Of Floral, C.1650 .... 200.00
Furniture, Table, Side, Charles X Provincial, Fruitwood, Rectangular, C.1850 .... 110.00
Furniture, Table, Side, Chinese, Black, Pierced, Carved, Ch'len Lung 600.00
Furniture, Table, Side, Empire, Mahogany, Rectangular Marble Top, C.1820 .... 150.00
Furniture, Table, Side, George II, Mahogany, Rectangular, Frieze Drawer 650.00
Furniture, Table, Side, George III, Mahogany, Rectangular, Frieze Drawer 250.00
Furniture, Table, Side, Italian, Walnut, Rectangular Top, 2 Drawer, C.1600 .... 1000.00
Furniture, Table, Side, James I, Oak, Rectangular, Carved Frieze, C.1630 .... 1100.00
Furniture, Table, Side, Oak, 1 Drawer, Octagonal Chamfered Legs, C.1750 .... 500.00
Furniture, Table, Side, Regence Style, Gilt Wood, Rectangular Marble Top 325.00

Furniture, Table, Side, Spanish, Walnut, Rectangular, Frieze Drawer, C.1650 .... 550.00
Furniture, Table, Side, William & Mary, Walnut, Rectangular, 2 Drawers, C.1650 .... 1350.00
Furniture, Table, Sofa, George III, Mahogany, Rectangular, C.1750 .... 400.00
Furniture, Table, Sofa, George III, Mahogany, Rectangular, Pierced Fretwork 1600.00
Furniture, Table, Sofa, George III, Mahogany, 2 Drawers In Frieze, C.1750 .... 375.00
Furniture, Table, Sofa, Regency, Rosewood, Rectangular, Brass Handles, C.1820 .... 475.00
Furniture, Table, Square, Red Tooled Leather Top, Bamboo Legs, Shelves 125.00
Furniture, Table, Tavern, Hepplewhite 185.00
Furniture, Table, Tavern, Maple & Pine, New England, 1700 .... *Illus* 750.00

Furniture, Table, Pine & Chestnut, Penna., C.1775
See Page 244

Furniture, Table, Sewing,
Federal, Mass., C.1790
See Page 244

Furniture, Table, Tavern,
Maple & Pine, New England, 1700

Furniture, Table, Tavern, Maple, Turned, Oblong, 1 Drawer, New England, C.1720 .... 200.00
Furniture, Table, Tavern, Oak, 3 Legged Iron Base 60.00
Furniture, Table, Tavern, Pine & Maple, Oblong Breadboard Top, N.E., C.1710 .... 375.00
Furniture, Table, Tavern, Pine & Maple, Oblong, 1 Drawer, Penn., C.1720 .... 400.00
Furniture, Table, Tavern, Pine & Maple, Oval, New England, C.1700 .... 575.00
Furniture, Table, Tavern, Pine Top, Oak Base, Southern Origin 750.00
Furniture, Table, Tavern, Pine, Breadboard Top, Scalloped Corners, 1870 .... 475.00
Furniture, Table, Tavern, Queen Anne, Cherry, Pennsylvania 895.00
Furniture, Table, Tavern, Queen Anne, Duck Feet, Drawer, Pennsylvania 595.00
Furniture, Table, Tavern, Weathered Oak, Square Chamfered Legs, C.1750 .... 350.00
Furniture, Table, Tavern, Windsor, Turned Base, Ball Foot, Stretcher, Pine 395.00
Furniture, Table, Tea & Game, George II, Mahogany, Rectangular, Hinged, Pair 850.00
Furniture, Table, Tea, Chinese, Teakwood, Carved, Round, Scalloped, Marble 250.00
Furniture, Table, Tea, Chippendale, Walnut, Tilt Top, Carved, Piecrust, C.1760 .... 4250.00
Furniture, Table, Tea, George III Provincial, Mahogany, D Shape Top, C.1790 .... 925.00
Furniture, Table, Tea, George III, Mahogany, Rectangular, Hinged, 1790, Pair 750.00
Furniture, Table, Tea, Mahogany, Oval, Brass Band Tray Top, Bamboo Legs 170.00

Furniture, Table, Tea, Maple & Cherry, Turned, Oblong, New England, C.1750 .... 900.00
Furniture, Table, Tea, Maple & Curly Maple, Oval Top, C.1780 .... 550.00
Furniture, Table, Tea, Maple, Turned, Oblong, New England, C.1770 .... 325.00
Furniture, Table, Tea, Queen Anne, San Domingo Mahogany, Drop Leaf, C.1740 .... 5000.00
Furniture, Table, Tea, Queen Anne, Walnut, C.1800 .... 450.00
Furniture, Table, Tea, Tilt, Maple & Ash, American 300.00
Furniture, Table, Tilt Top, Dutch Foot, C.1740, Maple, 34 1/2 In.Square 375.00
Furniture, Table, Tilt Top, Three Footed Pedestal, C.1790, Pine 450.00
Furniture, Table, Toilet, Mahogany, Rectangular, Lift Top, C.1800 .... 375.00
Furniture, Table, Trestle Type, Oak, 6 Depressions With Drain Holes, C.1650 .... 425.00
Furniture, Table, Trestle, Shaker, Pine 2750.00
Furniture, Table, Tric-Trac, Directoire Style, Walnut, Rectangular, C.1850 .... 1500.00
Furniture, Table, Trivia, Beveled Glass, Key, Hepplewhite 265.00
Furniture, Table, Victorian, Satinwood, 61 X 42 In. .... *Illus* 2000.00
Furniture, Table, Victorian, Tilt Top, Round Iron Top, Checkerboard 120.00
Furniture, Table, Victorian, Walnut, Turtle Top, Castors 89.00
Furniture, Table, Walnut, Pennsylvania, Stretcher, Scallops Under 2 Drawers 7000.00
Furniture, Table, Walnut, Philadelphia, Tilt Top, Dish Top, Birdcage 170.00
Furniture, Table, Walnut, Tilt Top, Scalloped, Turned Pedestal, Shaped Feet 55.00
Furniture, Table, William & Mary, Maple, Butterfly, Oval, 2 Leaves, N.E., 1720 .... 550.00
Furniture, Table, Work, Federal, Inlaid Mahogany, Rectangular, American, 1800 .... 650.00
Furniture, Table, Work, Federal, Mahogany, Inlaid, C.1840 .... 170.00
Furniture, Table, Work, Federal, Mahogany, Jacob Forster, 1814, Carved, Oblong 2600.00
Furniture, Table, Work, Federal, Mahogany, Rectangular, 2 Drawers In Frieze 375.00
Furniture, Table, Work, Federal, Mahogany, Rectangular, 2 Drop Leaves, C.1800 .... 325.00
Furniture, Table, Work, Federal, Mahogany, Square, 2 D Shape Leaves, Boston 250.00
Furniture, Table, Work, Federal, Mass., C.1800 .... *Illus* 2500.00
Furniture, Table, Work, George III, Mahogany, Frieze With Drawer, C.1890 .... 400.00
Furniture, Table, Work, Hepplewhite, Leather Covered Top 1200.00
Furniture, Table, Work, Regency, Mahogany, Rectangular, 2 Drawer, C.1820 .... 100.00
Furniture, Table, Work, Shaker, Mt.Lebanon 495.00
Furniture, Table, Writing & Work, George III, Mahogany, Rectangular, C.1790 .... 475.00
Furniture, Table, Writing, Biedermeier, Birch, Rectangular, Leather, C.1850 .... 425.00
Furniture, Table, Writing, French Provincial, 1 Drawer, Fold Out Leaves 300.00
Furniture, Table, Writing, George II, Mahogany, Kneehole, Rectangular, 1790 .... 500.00
Furniture, Table, Writing, George III, Mahogany, Carlton House 275.00
Furniture, Table, Writing, George III, Mahogany, Gillows Of Lancaster Type 2500.00
Furniture, Table, Writing, George III, Mahogany, Oval, Green Leather, C.1790 .... 3600.00
Furniture, Table, Writing, George III, Mahogany, Tooled Green Leather Top 550.00
Furniture, Table, Writing, Lady's, George III, C.1775 .... *Illus* 1100.00
Furniture, Table, Writing, Mahogany, Pedestal, Rectangular, C.1820 .... 2200.00
Furniture, Table, Writing, Tulipwood, Galleried Top, C.1790 .... 2000.00
Furniture, Tea Caddy, Embossed Hearts, Copper 27.50
Furniture, Tea Caddy, Federal, Mahogany, Inlaid, C.1790 .... 100.00
Furniture, Tea Caddy, George II, Walnut, Brass Handle, 3 Compartments, 1750 .... 80.00
Furniture, Tea Caddy, George III, Pearwood, Carved To Resemble Pear, 1800 .... 250.00
Furniture, Tea Caddy, George III, Tortoiseshell, Bowfront, 2 Partitions 80.00
Furniture, Tea Caddy, Hardwood, Hexagonal, Tulip Inlay, C.1800 .... 70.00
Furniture, Tea Caddy, Lacquer On Wood, Pewter Liner 65.00
Furniture, Tea Caddy, Metal, Chinese, Hexagonal, Pictures Enclosed By Glass 22.00
Furniture, Tea Caddy, Regency, Inlaid Mahogany, Burl Walnut, Hinged, C.1820 .... 60.00
Furniture, Tea Caddy, Satinwood, Rectangular, Inlaid, C.1790 .... 60.00
Furniture, Throne, Italian, Walnut, Leather Upholstered, Coat Of Arms, 1650 .... 550.00
Furniture, Torchere, George III, Painted, Parcel Gilt, Carved, C.1750, Pair 400.00
Furniture, Torchere, Italian, Painted, Parcel Gilt, Round, Carved, Pair 425.00
Furniture, Torchere, Satinwood, Round, Carved, C.1890, Pair 1300.00
Furniture, Torchere, Walnut, Piecrust Border, Inlaid, C.1750, Pair 600.00
Furniture, Tray On Stand, Butler's, George III, Mahogany, Pierced, C.1850 .... 375.00
Furniture, Tray On Stand, George III, Mahogany & Satinwood Inlaid, Oval 850.00
Furniture, Tray On Stand, Victorian, Mahogany, Kidney Shape, Brass, C.1850 .... 225.00
Furniture, Tray On Stand, Victorian, Papier-Mache, Floral, Feathers, C.1850 .... 100.00
Furniture, Tray On Stand, Victorian, Papier-Mache, Lacquer, Oval, C.1850 .... 200.00
Furniture, Tray On Stand, Victorian, Papier-Mache, Rectangular, C.1850 .... 200.00
Furniture, Tray, Butlers, On Frame, English, Mahogany, Square Legs 400.00
Furniture, Tray, George III, Mahogany, Oval, Brass Gallery, Handles, C.1750 .... 170.00
Furniture, Trumeau, Federal, Canvas Panel Above 2 Part Mirror 175.00

Furniture, Trumeau, Italian, Gilded, Green, 2 Sections, Mirror, C.1820 .... 500.00
Furniture, Tub & Standard, Directoire, Painted Green, Floral, Pair 800.00
Furniture, Vitrine, Art Deco, French, Mahogany, Marble Insert, Carved, C.1930 .... 500.00
Furniture, Voyeuse, Painted, Padded Top Rail, U Back, C.1750, Pair 1650.00
Furniture, Washstand, Barber's 50.00
Furniture, Washstand, Corner, Federal, C.1790 .... *Illus* 700.00

Furniture, Table, Victorian, Satinwood, 61 X 42 In.
See Page 246

Furniture, Table, Work, Fede
Mass., C.1800
See Page 246

Furniture, Washstand,
Corner, Federal, C.1790

Furniture, Table, Writing
Lady's, George III, C.177
See Page 246

Furniture, Washstand, Federal, Inlaid Mahogany, Cupboard Section, N.Y., 1790 .... 1400.00
Furniture, Washstand, George III, Mahogany, Rectangular, Mirror, 2 Drawer 275.00
Furniture, Whatnot, Black Walnut, Scrollwork, 5 Graduated Shelves 100.00
Furniture, Whatnot, Corner, Five Shelves, Curly Maple 55.00
Furniture, Whatnot, Mahogany, Ball Finials, 4 Shelves, C.1800 .... 200.00
Furniture, Wine Cooler, Urn, Mahogany Frame, Metal Insert, Tapering Legs 400.00

> *Galle Glass was made by the Galle Factory founded by Emile Galle of
> France. The firm made Cameo Glass, furniture, and other art nouveau items
> from 1879 to 1905.*

Galle, see also Cameo, Furniture

Galle Pottery, Compote, Blue, White, Crest, Crown, Faience, Nancy St.Clement 125.00
Galle Pottery, Inkwell, French Mottos, Floral, Openings For Pens, Faience 125.00
Galle Pottery, Plate, Blue, White, Central Crest, Nancy St.Clement, Faience 45.00
Galle Pottery, Salt, Turtle Shape, Divided Center, Blue, White, Footed, Pair 75.00
Galle Pottery, Vase, Trees, Birds, & Fronds, White, Gold, & Blue, Signed, Pair 145.00
Galle, Bowl, Cut In Greens & Blues On Neutral, 8 X 5 In. 375.00
Galle, Bowl, Miniature, Green Spider Web On Frosted & Pink, 2 In.High 135.00
Galle, Bowl, Punch, Frosted, Green, Pink Trim, Berries, Pedestal, One Piece 995.00
Galle, Bowl, Stained Glass Window Technique, Signed E.Galle Nancy 200.00

Galle, Bowl, Three Colors, Lily Pads, Leaves, Blue, Purple, Camphor, Cameo 125.00
Galle, Box, Covered, Cut Brown Flowers On Honey Satin, Purple, Signed 195.00
Galle, Box, Powder, Covered, Lake Scene, Swans, Three Acid Cuttings, Cameo 375.00
Galle, Box, Powder, Signed, 2 1/4 X 5 In. 325.00
Galle, Candlestick, Sprigs Of Leaves, Yellow To Brown, Paper Sticker 235.00
Galle, Compote, Red Cherry Vines On Yellow, Signed, Cameo 375.00
Galle, Cup & Saucer, Amber, Enameled, Thistle & Leaf, Cup Signed In Gold 145.00
Galle, Cup & Saucer, Enameled Thistle Pattern, Signed 125.00
Galle, Decanter, Amber Swirl Ribbing, Enameled Butterflies, Applique, Signed 750.00
Galle, Decanter, Enameled Floral, Gold Trim, Blown, Cabochon Cover Stopper 185.00
Galle, Jar, Covered, Squat, Lavender Fuchsias On Mauve, Signed, 2 In.High 135.00
Galle, Lamp Base, Maroon Decoration On Lemon, Unwired, Signed, 11 In.High 185.00
Galle, Lamp, Flowers & Leaves, Red, Pink, & Maroon, Signed, Cameo, 12 1/2 In. 265.00
Galle, Lamp, Six Birds In Flight & Trees On Green, Cameo, 11 In.High 595.00
Galle, Liqueur Set, Vaseline Glass, Gold Enamel, Signed, 5 Piece 195.00
Galle, Liqueur, Square Body, Round Pedestal Base, Signed E.Galle Nancy 50.00
Galle, Perfume, Burnt Orange Nasturtiums On Frosted White, Cameo 178.00
Galle, Perfume, Camphor, Lavender & Purple Floral, Paper Label, Cameo 275.00
Galle, Perfume, Frosted Rose Ground, Brown Floral, 2 Acid Cuttings, Signed 165.00
Galle, Perfume, Mountain Scene, Blue, Amethyst, Orange, Signed, 6 3/8 In. 235.00
Galle, Perfume, Reds, Yellow, Signed 250.00
Galle, Perfume, Ribbed, Amber Glass, Allover Enamel, Signed Nancy, 4 In., Pair 250.00
Galle, Pitcher, Water, French Cameo, Signed Nancy 325.00
Galle, Plate, Frosted Green Ground, White Floral, Gold Stems & Leaves 250.00
Galle, Plate, Scroll Center, Blue, White, Basket Weave Border, 9 In. 49.00
Galle, Platter, Cake, Allover Enamel, Footed, Artist Brocard, Dated 1871 .... 595.00
Galle, Rose Bowl, Miniature, Pink, Frosted, & Chartreuse, Thistles, Signed 125.00
Galle, Rose Bowl, Mum Design, Green, Signed, 3 1/2 In.Tall 175.00
Galle, Rose Bowl, Pink, Frosted White, Chartreuse, Thistles 125.00
Galle, Shot Glass, Rose Colored Berries On Orange, Frosted White, Cameo 125.00
Galle, Toothpick, Camphor, Yellow & Brown, Floral, Cameo 95.00
Galle, Toothpick, Crystal, Swirled, Leaves, Gold Rim, Signed 90.00
Galle, Toothpick, Leaf & Berry, Purple To Lavender, Footed, Signed 135.00
Galle, Tumbler, Ovoid, Swan On Water On Burnt Orange, Cameo 175.00
Galle, Vase, Acid Cut Back, Enameled, 6 In.High .... *Illus* 375.00
Galle, Vase, Acid Cut Ground, Purple Leaves, Signed, 5 In.High 250.00
Galle, Vase, Amethyst & Green Wisteria On White & Peach, Cameo 225.00
Galle, Vase, Amethyst Floral On Lemon & Blue Mottled, Signed, 6 In.High 175.00
Galle, Vase, Amethyst Flowers On White & Yellow, Cameo, 7 In. High 170.00
Galle, Vase, Amethyst Leaf Design On Pale Orange, Signed, 5 In.High 175.00
Galle, Vase, Apricot & Clear Ground, Green Cactus Pattern, 4 In.High 145.00
Galle, Vase, Apricot Color, Nasturtiums On Frosted White, Signed, 14 In. 475.00
Galle, Vase, Baluster, Purple Clematis On Ocher, Acid Cut, Signed 190.00
Galle, Vase, Banjo Shape, Pink, White, & Lavender Ground, Flowers, Signed 195.00
Galle, Vase, Banjo, Green Acorn & Leaf Design On White & Rose, Cameo 170.00
Galle, Vase, Berries, Flowers, Leaves, Brown, Amber, Signed, 4 In.Tall 115.00
Galle, Vase, Berries, Leaves, & Stems, Cranberry & Camphor, Cameo, 12 1/2 In. 225.00
Galle, Vase, Berries, Leaves, Orange, Signed, 3 1/4 In.Tall 95.00
Galle, Vase, Blue, Cut Purple Flowers, Banjo, 7 In. 225.00
Galle, Vase, Boat Shape, Purple, Signed, 5 1/2 In.High 239.00
Galle, Vase, Brown Firs On Neutral, Cameo, 9 3/4 In.High 345.00
Galle, Vase, Brown Floral & Acorns On Frosted Blue, Pedestal Base, Cameo 300.00
Galle, Vase, Brown Floral & Leaves On Brown, Mottled, Amber, & Pink, Cameo 350.00
Galle, Vase, Brown Floral On Burnt Orange, Purple Base, Cameo, 3 3/4 In.High 135.00
Galle, Vase, Brown Narcissus & Grape Hyacinth On Citrine, Cameo, 6 In. 225.00
Galle, Vase, Brown To Golden, Three Layers Of Glass, Cameo, 4 In.High 175.00
Galle, Vase, Brown, Gray, & Yellow Flowers & Brown Leaves, Cameo, 10 1/2 In. 395.00
Galle, Vase, Bud, Cylindrical, Violets On Pink, Signed, 8 1/2 In.High 525.00
Galle, Vase, Bulbous, Hexagonal Rim, Ocher & Green Flora & Fauna On Frosted 175.00
Galle, Vase, Butterflies, Green, Blue, & Tan, Artist &.Nicholas, Cameo, 14 In 600.00
Galle, Vase, Cabinet, Beige To Chocolate, Inset, 4 1/2 In. 250.00
Galle, Vase, Cabinet, Orange, Cut, Signed, 4 1/2 In. 150.00
Galle, Vase, Cabinet, Purple To Yellow, Floral, 2 Cuttings & Casings, Signed 120.00
Galle, Vase, Cabinet, Red Frieze Of Cherries On White To Yellow, Signed 120.00
Galle, Vase, Cabinet, Three Layer Cutting, Elongated Neck 265.00
Galle, Vase, Cone, Three Colors, Cameo 250.00

Galle, Vase, Cut Amethyst Clematis & Leaf Design On White, Cameo, 2 1/2 In. 145.00
Galle, Vase, Deep Purple To Sky Blue, Lily Of The Valley, 7 In. 225.00
Galle, Vase, Dragonflies, Water Lilies, Pond, Burgundy On Yellow, Cameo 195.00
Galle, Vase, Drooping Vines In Full Leaf, Gold Tint, Champagne & Wine Color 250.00
Galle, Vase, Enameled Bleeding Hearts & Leaves, Cameo, 7 In.High 395.00
Galle, Vase, Enameled, Rose To Red On Clear, 12 1/2 In. .... *Illus* 300.00
Galle, Vase, Enameled, Signed, 4 1/2 In.High .... *Illus* 260.00
Galle, Vase, Fall Foliage, Fence, Fireglow & Green Haze 300.00
Galle, Vase, Fern Design, Yellow, Green, Signed, 3 3/4 In.High 125.00
Galle, Vase, Fernery, Acid Cut, Orange, White, 2 1/2 In.Tall 135.00
Galle, Vase, Flame Ground, Double Overlay Blue Floral, Green Leaves, 14 In. 395.00
Galle, Vase, Flaring, Acid Cut Lavender Berries On Frosted, Signed 200.00
Galle, Vase, Flat, Round, 2 Handles, 5 In.High 225.00
Galle, Vase, Floral Design, Blue, White, Amethyst, & Green, Signed 225.00

Galle, Vase, Acid Cut
Back, Enameled, 6 In.High
See Page 248

Galle, Vase, Enameled,
Signed, 4 1/2 In.High

Galle, Vase, Enameled,
Rose To Red On Clear,
12 1/2 In.

Galle, Vase, Floral Design, Light Blue, Clear, & Green, Signed, 4 1/4 In. 135.00
Galle, Vase, Floral Design, Pink, Blue, Green, Clear, Signed, 5 3/4 In. ;............................ 225.00
Galle, Vase, Floral In Blue, White, & Purple, Signed, 6 3/4 In.High 200.00
Galle, Vase, Floral In Orange, Yellow, & Brown, Signed, 3 1/2 In.High 240.00
Galle, Vase, Flower Design In Gold & Browns, Signed Body & Base, Cameo 895.00
Galle, Vase, Flower Sprays, Purple, White, Signed, Cameo, 4 1/2 In.High 160.00
Galle, Vase, Flowers & Confetti Design, Multicolor, Signed 250.00
Galle, Vase, Flowers, Brown & Tan, Bulbous, Signed, Cameo, 10 1/4 In.High 225.00
Galle, Vase, Flowers, Leaves, Orange, Camphor, Signed, 2 3/4 In.Tall 95.00
Galle, Vase, Four Layers, Acid Ground, Blue Floral, Green Leaves, Purple Base 475.00
Galle, Vase, Frost White Blue Ground, Purple & Lavender Cherries, Branches 325.00
Galle, Vase, Frosted Gold Ground, Coral Floral, 2 Acid Cuttings, Signed 115.00
Galle, Vase, Frosted Ground, Brown To Amber Cuttings, Floral, Signed, 5 In. 185.00
Galle, Vase, Frosted Ground, Mountains, Lake, Brown Foot, 6 1/4 In. 325.00
Galle, Vase, Frosted To Apricot Ground, Purple Violets, Squatty, 4 In. 265.00
Galle, Vase, Frosted To Yellow, Purple Fuchsia, Foliage, Bulbous, 6 In. 215.00
Galle, Vase, Frosted White To Pink Ground, Purple Violets, Bulbous, 4 In. 225.00
Galle, Vase, Frosty & Mauve Ground, Cut Brown Leaves, Foliage, Signed, 4 In. 175.00
Galle, Vase, Fuchsia Blossoms In Amethyst On Lemon, Bulbous, Signed 145.00
Galle, Vase, Gold Ground, Pink & Magenta Deep Cut Floral, 3 1/2 In. 125.00
Galle, Vase, Green Fernery On Clear Orange, Gloss Finish, Cameo, 3 In. 128.00
Galle, Vase, Green Fernery On Frosted Orange, Cameo, 17 In.High 325.00
Galle, Vase, Green Fernery On Frosted White & Orange, Cameo, 3 In.High 128.00
Galle, Vase, Green Fernery, White, Orange, 17 In.High 350.00
Galle, Vase, Heart Shape, 5 In.High 250.00
Galle, Vase, Honey Ground, Pink Red Flowers, Red Leaves, Glossy, 6 1/2 In. 250.00
Galle, Vase, Lake & Trees On Orange, Brown & Green, Signed, 6 1/2 In. 195.00
Galle, Vase, Landscape, Mountain Scene, Brown Trees, Blue Water, Cameo 290.00
Galle, Vase, Lavender Flowers & Leaves On Gold To Camphor, Cameo 335.00
Galle, Vase, Lavender Fuchsias, Leaves, & Birds On Frosted White, Signed 375.00

Galle, Vase, Leaf & Flower Design, White, Amethyst, Signed, 3 In.High 145.00
Galle, Vase, Leaf & Grape Design, White & Orange, Signed, 2 3/8 In.High 140.00
Galle, Vase, Leaf Design, Cranberry To Gold, Signed, 11 1/2 In.High 850.00
Galle, Vase, Lemon & Clear Ground, Fuchsia Floral In Amethyst, 3 1/2 In. 155.00
Galle, Vase, Lemon Ground, Brown Floral, Signed, 6 1/2 In.High 175.00
Galle, Vase, Light Blue Ground, Leaf & Flower Cluster, 2 1/2 In.High 145.00
Galle, Vase, Lime To Frosted Ground, Yellow, Amber & Brown Spider Flowers 185.00
Galle, Vase, Mahogany Lilies & Leaves On Yellow, Cameo, 4 In.High 220.00
Galle, Vase, Mauve Butterfly On Citrine, Cameo, 4 In. 210.00
Galle, Vase, Miniature, Signed, 4 In.High 95.00
Galle, Vase, Miniature, Trees, Foliage, Green To Purple, Signed, 5 3/8 In. 210.00
Galle, Vase, Orange Fernery On Frosted White, Signed, Cameo, 3 In.High 125.00
Galle, Vase, Orange Flowers On Frosted White, Cameo, 4 In.High 99.00
Galle, Vase, Orange Flowers On White Ground 135.00
Galle, Vase, Orange To Clear Ground, Brown & Green Ferns, Signed, 8 In. 285.00
Galle, Vase, Orange, Frosted Top & Bottom, Red Brown Leaves, Floral, Glossy 325.00
Galle, Vase, Orchid, Pyroform, 8 In.High 300.00
Galle, Vase, Ovoid Tumbler Shape, Pink To Green, Swans On Lake 225.00
Galle, Vase, Ovoid, Acid Cut, Purple & Blue Orchids On Milky, Signed 400.00
Galle, Vase, Ovoid, Red Frieze Of Nasturtiums On Ocher, Signed 190.00
Galle, Vase, Ovoid, Scenes On Water, Signed, Cameo 185.00
Galle, Vase, Pale Salmon To Orange Red, Carved Leaves & Berries, 3 1/2 In. 185.00
Galle, Vase, Pink & Purple Floral Sprays, Ribbed, 6 3/4 In. 300.00
Galle, Vase, Pink Ground, Green Floral, Bulbous, Signed, 9 In. 295.00
Galle, Vase, Pink To Burgundy Floral On Yellow, Cameo, 3 1/2 In. 185.00
Galle, Vase, Pink, White & Lavender Frosty Ground, Floral, Banjo Shape 195.00
Galle, Vase, Purple & White, Signed, Cameo 155.00
Galle, Vase, Purple Flowers On Vaseline Shaded, Cameo, 6 1/4 In. 155.00
Galle, Vase, Purple Flowers On Yellow, Two Casings, Two Cuttings, Cameo 120.00
Galle, Vase, Purple Shades, Green Decoration, 9 1/2 In. 245.00
Galle, Vase, Purple Trees & Blue Mountains On Pale Frosted Gold, Cameo 145.00
Galle, Vase, Pyroform, Blue Shades, Carved Iris 395.00
Galle, Vase, Red Berries & Leaves On Mottled Gray & Amber, Cameo, 5 In. 325.00
Galle, Vase, Red Currants & Leaves On Frosted To Peach, Cameo, 3 3/8 In. 125.00
Galle, Vase, Red Poppy, Signed, 9 In.High 265.00
Galle, Vase, Red, Yellow, Green, & Gold Enameled Floral On Translucent Amber 275.00
Galle, Vase, Rope Foliage, Leaf Design, Wine & Gold Tints 200.00
Galle, Vase, Rose & Green Ground, Green Acorns, Branches & Leaves, 5 In. 195.00
Galle, Vase, Scenic, Blue, Purple, & Green On Yellow, Acid Cut, Cameo 265.00
Galle, Vase, Scenic, Mountains & Lakes, Browns & Greens, Signed 325.00
Galle, Vase, Scenic, Signed, 5 1/4 In.High 250.00
Galle, Vase, Scenic, Three Colors 365.00
Galle, Vase, Scenic, Three Colors, Pink To Brown, Cameo, 6 1/2 In.High 285.00
Galle, Vase, Scenic, 5 3/4 In.High 220.00
Galle, Vase, Shaded Carnelians On Frosted Gray, Carved, Cameo, 4 1/2 In. 115.00
Galle, Vase, Stick Neck, Pinks, Greens, Lavenders, & Whites, Cameo, 17 1/2 In. 295.00
Galle, Vase, Stick, Beige, Green & Apricot, 12 In.High 350.00
Galle, Vase, Stick, Bleeding Hearts & Leaves In Violet Hues, Cameo, 13 In. 315.00
Galle, Vase, Stick, Rust, Gold, Pink, 13 In. 260.00
Galle, Vase, Stick, The Grasshopper 245.00
Galle, Vase, Swelling, Waisted Neck, Pendant Bluebells On Frosted Orange 600.00
Galle, Vase, Three Colors, Brown & Chartreuse Ferns, Signed, 8 In. 250.00
Galle, Vase, Three Colors, Cut, Cameo, 7 1/2 In.High 188.00
Galle, Vase, Violet Colored Flowers On Frosted White, Cameo, 4 In.High 99.00
Galle, Vase, Violet Leaves On Satin, Pinkish White Tinge, Cameo 85.00
Galle, Vase, Water Lilies & Lily Pads, Purple & Green, Allover Cut 250.00
Galle, Vase, Water Lily & Foliage On Lake Area, Salmon, Blue, Wine, Tapered 300.00
Galle, Vase, White Ground, Lavender Sweet Pea Vines, 13 1/2 In.High 275.00
Galle, Vase, White Ground, Purple Iris, 6 In.High 275.00
Galle, Vase, White, Amethyst, Floral Design, Signed, 3 1/2 In.High 145.00
Galle, Vase, Wine & Gold Tints, 10 In.High 175.00
Galle, Vase, Yellow Ground, Red Hawthornes, Acid Cut, 3 1/2 In. 160.00
Galle, Vase, Yellow, Red & Pink Floral, Signed, 3 In. 250.00
Galle, Wall Pocket, Basket Shape, White, Pink & Rose Floral, Galle Nancy 195.00
Galle, Wine, Allover Enamel, Thistles, Lorraine Cross 75.00
Galle, Wine, Clear, Two Cabochons, Amber Base, Signed .... 80.00 To 95.00

Game Plates are any type of plate decorated with pictures of birds, animals, or fish. The Game Plates usually came in sets consisting of twelve dishes and a serving platter. These Game Plates were most popular during the 1880s.

Game Plate, **Beehive**, 8 1/2 In. 65.00
Game Plate, **Buck & Doe By Stream**, Signed Megardee, 8 1/2 In.Diameter 9.00
Game Plate, **Dog & Rabbit In Wilds**, Hand-Painted, Uneven Edge, 9 In. 18.00
Game Plate, **Duck**, Flying, Coronet, Gold Border 85.00
Game Plate, **Grouse** 42.00
Game Plate, **Hunter Watches Ducks Flying**, Hand-Painted, Uneven Edge, 9 In. 18.00
Game Plate, **Mallard Ducks**, Lattice, Crown Bavaria 35.00
Game Plate, **Moose**, Deer, Scenes, Signed Edwin Megardee 10.00
Game Plate, **Moose**, Signed Edwin Megardee, 8 1/2 In. 10.00
Game Plate, **Mountain Goats On Rocky Ledges**, Flow Blue & Gold Edge, 9 In. 28.00
Game Plate, **Parrot**, Thomas 20.00
Game Plate, **Pheasant In Center**, Four Ducks On Rim, Blue Ground, Bavaria 47.50
Game Plate, **Quail**, Blue Wing, Duck & Quail Border, Turquoise Shading 35.00
Game Plate, **Sandpipers**, Coronet, Gold Border, Signed Max 95.00
Game Plate, **Snipe In Woods Scene**, Gold Lace Designs, Scalloped Edge 22.00
Game Plate, **Teal**, Blue Wings, Ducks & Grouse In Border, Turquoise Shading 37.50
Game Plate, **Wild Turkeys**, Gold Border, Signed, Heinz, Royal Austria 13.50
Game Set, **Birds**, Austrian, Platter & Seven Plates 65.00
Game, **A Trip Around The World**, Parker Bros., Lithograph Of Ship 10.00
Game, **Art Deco**, Mahogany, William Lescaze, C.1935, 5 Pieces 275.00
Game, **Capture The Cootie** 2.50
Game, **Card**, Fractions, Directions, Copyright 1902 .... 3.95
Game, **Card**, Howdy Doody, 1954, 32 Cards In A Box 1.00
Game, **Card**, Singer Domino, U.S.Playing Card Co., Maroon, Cardboard Box 3.00
Game, **Card**, Touring Auto 5.00
Game, **Card**, White Squadron, 52 U.S.Naval Vessels, Directions, Copyright 1896 .... 3.95
Game, **Checkerboard**, Hand-Painted On Glass, Framed To Hang 65.00
Game, **Chess Set**, Carved, English, 19th Century .... *Illus* 300.00
Game, **Chess Set**, Ivory, Oriental Motif, Every Pawn Different, 5 In.Tall 150.00
Game, **Chess Set**, Staunton, Jaques & Son, London 60.00
Game, **Country Auction**, Parker Bros., Scenic Lithograph 15.00
Game, **Croquet Set**, Wooden, Dovetailed Box, C.1860 .... 35.00
Game, **Cut-Up History**, Parker 10.50
Game, **Dissected Map Of U.S.**, Copyright 1887, Lithograph Of Indians, Box 20.00

Game, Chess Set, Carved, English, 19th Century

Game, Domino Set, Dated 1885, Boxed 5.00
Game, Domino Set, E.W.Willard & Co., N.H., Wooden Sliding Top Box 4.50
Game, Game Of Authors, H.H.Singer 4.50
Game, Game Of Authors, Parker Bros., Nickel Edition, Lithograph Of Man 4.50
Game, Indians, Germany, Tepee & Bonfire, 15 Pieces 125.00
Game, Intercollegiate Football, Tin, Frantz 35.00
Game, Jack Straws, M.Bradley 7.50
Game, Mah-Jongg Set, Brass On Box, Ivory On Bamboo Tiles 45.00
Game, Mah-Jongg Set, Tiles In Carved Square Teak Box, Chinese Figures 80.00
Game, Mrs.Casey Wants To Know, Parker Bros., Lithograph 3.00
Game, Parcheesi Set, Indian, Lapis Lazuli Men, Emerald, Ruby, & Quartz, C.1850 .... 1100.00
Game, Peter Coddles Trip, Milton Bradley, Lithograph Of Man & Trolley 9.00
Game, Pike's Peak Or Bust, Puzzle, Parker Bros., Lithograph 2.00
Game, Puzzle, Jigsaw, Chase & Sanborn, Men In General Store, 7 X 8 In. 45.00
Game, Snake Eyes, 1940s 15.00
Game, Tiddley Winks, Mcloughlin 5.00
Gardner, Bowl, Cranberry Red, Hand-Painted Floral, Russia, 1850 .... 62.50
Gardner, Bowl, Marigold Luster, Floral, Russia, 1860 .... 60.00
Gardner, Box, Light Blue, Cartouches, Floral, Russia 95.00
Gardner, Cup & Saucer, Green, Floral, Russia, 1850 .... 30.00
Gardner, Figurine, Dancing Coachman, C.1890 .... 225.00
Gardner, Tea Set, Floral On Green, Russia, 1850, 3 Piece 100.00
Gardner, Teapot, Cranberry Red, Hand-Painted Floral, Russia, 1850 .... 80.00
Gardner, Teapot, Floral On Green, Russia, 1850 .... 62.50

Gaudy Dutch Pottery was made in England for America from about 1810
to 1820. It is a white earthenware with Imari style decorations of red,
blue, green, yellow, and black.
Gaudy Dutch, Creamer, Butterfly, Pink Luster, Blue Designs 200.00
Gaudy Dutch, Cup & Saucer, Single Rose 195.00
Gaudy Dutch, Cup & Saucer, Urn 220.00
Gaudy Dutch, Cup Plate, Urn Pattern 230.00
Gaudy Dutch, Plate, Carnation, 8 1/4 In. 115.00
Gaudy Dutch, Plate, War Bonnet, 7 In. 110.00
Gaudy Dutch, Plate, War Bonnet, 7 1/4 In.Diameter 240.00
Gaudy Dutch, Plate, War Bonnet, 8 1/8 In.Diameter 180.00
Gaudy Dutch, Toddy Plate, Pierced For Hanging, 4 1/2 In. 275.00
Gaudy Ironstone, Coffeepot, Strawberry, Rose, 10 In. 130.00
Gaudy Ironstone, Dish, Leaf Shape, Mason, 11 X 7 1/4 In. 95.00
Gaudy Ironstone, Mug, Snake Handle, Octagon 45.00
Gaudy Ironstone, Pitcher, Milk, Tree Of Life, Blue, Gold, Allerton 68.00
Gaudy Ironstone, Pitcher, Orange & Blue, Serpent Handle, Mason's 65.00
Gaudy Ironstone, Pitcher, 5 In. 20.00
Gaudy Ironstone, Plate, Chinese Bird Pattern, 7 1/8 In. 25.00
Gaudy Ironstone, Plate, Flower Urn & Flower In Center, Mason, 9 3/8 In. 45.00
Gaudy Ironstone, Plate, Minton, Circa 1850, 8 1/2 In. 27.00
Gaudy Ironstone, Plate, Strawberries, Leaves, Copper Luster Trim, Octagonal 60.00
Gaudy Ironstone, Plate, Vase In Center, Cobalt, Rust Color, Mason 27.00
Gaudy Ironstone, Platter, Copper Luster Decoration, Colored Flower 100.00
Gaudy Ironstone, Platter, Copper Luster Decoration, Strawberry, 13 1/2 In. 75.00
Gaudy Ironstone, Platter, Octagon, Signed 45.00
Gaudy Ironstone, Soup, Urn & Flowers, Mason's Patent Ironstone China, 1825 .... 40.00

Gaudy Welsh is an Imari decorated earthenware with red, blue, green, and
gold decorations. It was made after 1820.
Gaudy Welsh, Bowl, Covered, Burnt Orange, Green, Copper & Pink Luster 95.00
Gaudy Welsh, Bowl, Tiger Paw Pattern, 7 In. 60.00
Gaudy Welsh, Bowl, Waste, Tulip Pattern 32.50
Gaudy Welsh, Creamer, Flower Basket Design 55.00
Gaudy Welsh, Creamer, Oyster Pattern, Circa 1850 .... 32.00
Gaudy Welsh, Creamer, Scalloped Rim & Base 43.00
Gaudy Welsh, Cup & Saucer 30.00
Gaudy Welsh, Cup & Saucer, Blue, Burnt Orange, Green, Copper & Pink Luster 17.50
Gaudy Welsh, Cup & Saucer, Demitasse 35.00
Gaudy Welsh, Cup & Saucer, Floral, Yellow, Cobalt, Green, Luster, Circa 1840 .... 28.00
Gaudy Welsh, Cup & Saucer, Handleless, Primrose 100.00

Gaudy Welsh, Cup & Saucer, Tulip .... 22.50 To 45.00
Gaudy Welsh, Cup & Saucer, Tulip Pattern, Luster 50.00
Gaudy Welsh, Cup & Saucer, Wagon Wheel 35.00
Gaudy Welsh, Cup, Demitasse 20.00
Gaudy Welsh, Dish, Cheese, Morning Glories 65.00
Gaudy Welsh, Jug, Snake Handle, 6 In. 88.00
Gaudy Welsh, Mustard, Lid, 2 X 3 In. 55.00
Gaudy Welsh, Pitcher, Serpent Handle, 4 1/2 In.High 42.00
Gaudy Welsh, Pitcher, Yellow Base, C.1820, 6 In. 100.00
Gaudy Welsh, Pitcher, 7 In.High 75.00
Gaudy Welsh, Plate, Dark Blue, Burnt Orange, Green, Copper & Pink Luster 25.00
Gaudy Welsh, Plate, Cake, Tulip Pattern, Closed Handles, 10 In. 35.00
Gaudy Welsh, Plate, Flower Basket Design 48.00
Gaudy Welsh, Plate, Oyster Pattern, Circa 1850, 5 1/2 In. 18.00
Gaudy Welsh, Plate, Oyster Pattern, Circa 1850, 6 In. 24.00
Gaudy Welsh, Plate, Tulip Pattern, Luster, 6 In. 20.00
Gaudy Welsh, Plate, Tulip Pattern, 5 7/8 In. 20.00
Gaudy Welsh, Plate, Wagon Wheel 38.00
Gaudy Welsh, Plate, Wagon Wheel, 7 In. 39.00
Gaudy Welsh, Platter, Strawberry Red Pattern, 12 X 15 In. 110.00
Gaudy Welsh, Teapot, Dark Blue, Burnt Orange, Green, Copper & Pink Luster 95.00
Gaudy Welsh, Teapot, Tulip Pattern 95.00

Gibson Girl Plates were made in the early 1900s by the Royal Doulton
Pottery at Lambeth, England. There are twenty-four different plates
featuring a picture of the Gibson Girl by the artist Charles Dana
Gibson.

Gibson Girl, Flask, Sterling, Gibson Girl On Front, Initials C.E.H. 50.00
Gibson Girl, Mirror, Hand, Triple, Hinged Together, Picture On Backs 90.00
Gibson Girl, Plate, A Quiet Dinner With Dr.Bottles .... 45.00 To 55.00
Gibson Girl, Plate, And Here Winning New Friends, Royal Doulton 45.00
Gibson Girl, Plate, Calendar, Portrait, Owatonna, Minn., 8 1/2 In. 20.00
Gibson Girl, Plate, Day After Journey's End, Royal Doulton 45.00
Gibson Girl, Plate, Message From Outside World, Blue & White, Royal Doulton 55.00
Gibson Girl, Plate, Miss Babbles Reads, Blue & White, Royal Doulton 55.00
Gibson Girl, Plate, Mr.Waddles Arrives Late, Blue & White, Royal Doulton 55.00
Gibson Girl, Plate, Mrs. Diggs Is Alarmed, Royal Doulton 47.50
Gibson Girl, Plate, Picture Center, Blue Border, 10 1/2 In. 47.00
Gibson Girl, Plate, She Becomes A Trained Nurse, Blue & White .... 45.00 To 55.00
Gibson Girl, Plate, She Contemplates The Cloister, Royal Doulton 45.00
Gibson Girl, Plate, She Decides To Die, Royal Doulton 45.00
Gibson Girl, Plate, She Finds Consolation, Blue & White, Royal Doulton 55.00
Gibson Girl, Plate, She Finds Exercise, Signed, Royal Doulton 45.00
Gibson Girl, Plate, She Goes Into Colors, Royal Doulton .... 45.00 To 55.00
Gibson Girl, Plate, She Goes To Dress Ball As Juliet .... 45.00 To 47.50
Gibson Girl, Plate, She Is Disturbed By A Vision, 1901, Royal Doulton 45.00
Gibson Girl, Plate, She Longs For Seclusion, Blue & White, Royal Doulton 55.00
Gibson Girl, Plate, She Looks For Relief, 10 1/4 In. 45.00
Gibson Girl, Plate, Some Think Retirement Is Too Long .... 35.00 To 47.50
Gibson Girl, Plate, They All Go Skating, Royal Doulton .... 45.00 To 55.00
Gibson Girl, Plate, They Go Fishing, Blue & White, Royal Doulto .... 35.00 To 55.00
Gibson Girl, Plate, Winning New Friends, Royal Doulton .... 45.00 To 55.00
Gibson Girl, Print, From 1902 Book 1.75
Gillinder, Buddha, Deep Ruby Red, 6 In.Tall 29.50
Gillinder, Muffineer, Melon Ribbed, Acid Finish, Blue To White 75.00
Gillinder, Muffineer, White Decorated 60.00
Gillinder, Slipper, Clear, Bows, Impressed Gillinder Centennial, Pair 55.00
Gillinder, Vase, Hand, Centennial 30.00
Ginori, Plate, Green Ground, Red Roses, Leaves, Artist P.Doncirbara 25.00
Ginori, Plate, Sweet Peas, Artist Signed, 7 1/2 In. 8.50
Girandole, Bronze Type Figure, Marble Base, Star Cut Prisms, 5 In., Pair 100.00
Girandole, Candlestick, Marble Base, Cherubs, Prisms, 14 In.High, Pair 85.00
Girandole, Federal, Gilt Wood & Gesso, New York, C.1800 .... 3750.00
Girandole, Federal, Gilt Wood & Gesso, Round, C.1800 .... 700.00
Girandole, Gilded Bronze, Philadelphia, Patent 1849, 3 .... *Illus* 250.00
Girandole, Italian, Gilt Wood, Cartouche Mirror, C.1790 .... 90.00

Girandole, Italian, Gilt Wood, Carved, Rococo, Shell Masks, Pair 175.00
Girandole, Venetian, Painted & Parcel Gilt, Rococo 140.00
Girandole, Venetian, Repousse Brass, 3 Arms, Tulip Nozzles, Pair 450.00
Girandole, 15 3/4 To 19 In.High, 3 .... *Illus* 225.00
Glasses, Pince-Nez, Gold, Gold Chain & Hairpin 9.50
Glasses, Pince-Nez, Metal Frame 2.00
Glasses, Pince-Nez, Thick Metal Frame 2.00
Glasses, Wire Frame 3.00

Girandole, Gilded Bronze, Philadelphia, Patent 1849, 3
See Page 253

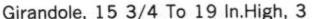

Girandole, 15 3/4 To 19 In.High, 3

Gold, Box, French, Empire, Round, Engine Turned, Arc Design, I.D.L., C.1815 .... 350.00
Gold, Box, Gold Dollar In Hinged Lid, 1 1/2 In.Diameter 65.00
Gold, Cane Handle, Knob Type 26.50
Gold, Case, Card, Lady's, Hand Chased, Chain On Wedding Band, Dated 1855, 18k 400.00
Gold, Case, Card, Presentation Maria Feodorovna, Jeweled, Enamel, Bolin, 1850 .... 3400.00
Gold, Case, Cigarette, Rectangular, Oval Rubies, Round Diamonds 250.00
Gold, Case, Cigarette, 15k, Russian Style, Ruby, Cartier, London 450.00
Gold, Cigar Cutter, 14k 15.00
Gold, Cuff Link, Double, Engraved Crests On All Sides, Oval, Pair 85.00
Gold, Etui, Louis XVI, 2 Color, Fluted, Chased, Leaves, Marked, Paris, C.1775 .... 250.00
Gold, Eyeglasses, Bifocals, In Papier-Mache Case, Black, Gold Decor 25.00

Gold, Lorgnette, Handle 85.00
Gold, Pencil, Automatic, 10k, 2 1/2 In. 15.00
Gold, Pencil, Retractable, Engraved 8.00
Gold, Snuffbox, French, Empire, Rectangular, Engine Turned, Chased, C.1815 .... 550.00
Gold, Snuffbox, Rectangular, Engine Turned, Lozenge Design, Marked 1798, 1809 ...... 325.00
Gold, Snuffbox, Ribbed Sides, Chased Shellwork, 2 Lovers Scene, C.1750 .... 1600.00
Gold, Snuffbox, Swiss, Rectangular, Champleve Blue Enamel, Musical, C.1810 .... 2100.00
Gold, Snuffbox, 15k, Round, Diamonds, Champleve Pink Enamel Floral, C.1900 .... 500.00
Goldscheider, Figurine, Seminude Female, Vienna, C.1930, 24 In.High 100.00
Goldscheider, Mask, Young Lady, Orange, Blue, C.1930 .... 100.00

*Goofus Glass was made from about 1900 to 1920 by many American factories.
It was originally painted gold, red, green, bronze, pink, purple, and other bright
colors.*
Goofus Glass, Banana Boat 18.00
Goofus Glass, Bowl, Flower & Leaf Design, Ruffled Edge, Red, Gold, 9 In. 45.00
Goofus Glass, Bowl, Green, Red Flower, Ruffled, Marked N 22.50
Goofus Glass, Bowl, Red Roses, Gold Ground, 9 1/2 In. 16.50
Goofus Glass, Bowl, Strawberries, Gold Leaves, Fluted, 10 In. 14.50
Goofus Glass, Compote, Green, Red Poppies 8.00
Goofus Glass, Jar, Powder, Lid, Embossed Rose Design, Overall Gold 15.00
Goofus Glass, Lamp, Kerosene 35.00
Goofus Glass, Pickle, Rose Embossed, Amethyst, Pint 8.50
Goofus Glass, Pickle, Rose Embossed, Amethyst, Quart 8.50
Goofus Glass, Pickle, Rose Embossed, Amethyst, 1/2 Pint 10.50
Goofus Glass, Plate, Apples, Gold, Red, 8 In. 12.50
Goofus Glass, Plate, Bread, The Last Supper 13.50
Goofus Glass, Plate, Egg, Red, Gold, 9 1/2 In.Diameter 18.00
Goofus Glass, Plate, Gay Nineties Type Girl 35.00
Goofus Glass, Plate, Little Bo Peep Embossed In Center 6.00
Goofus Glass, Rose Bowl, Paint 6.00

*Goss china has been made since 1858. English potter William Henry
Goss first made it at the Falcon Pottery in Stoke-on-Trent. In 1934
the factory name was changed to Goss China Company when it was taken over
by Cauldon Potteries. Goss China resembles Irish Belleek in both
body and glaze. The company also made popular souvenir china.*
Goss, Candle Snuffer, Form Of Dunce Cap, Signed, 2 1/2 In.High 12.00
Goss, Match Holder, Wall 6.50
Goss, Pitcher, Havant Crest, Falcon Mark, 3 3/4 In.High 10.00
Goss, Urn, Aladdin Lamp, 3 1/2 In.Long X 2 In.High 10.00
Goss, Washstand Set, King William IV, Coach, Riders, Horses, 2 1/4 In. 9.00
Gouda, Ashtray, Dark Blue, Gofdewaagen, 5 In.Diameter 16.00
Gouda, Bowl, Blue & Green Floral, Signed Damascus, Holland, 1885, 2 1/2 In. 42.50
Gouda, Bowl, Covered, Lid Shape Of Dog, Marked, Ivora, Gouda, Holland 42.00
Gouda, Candlestick, 12 In. .... *Illus* 65.00

Gouda, Candlestick, 12 In.

Gouda, Chamberstick, 4 1/4 In.High	35.00
Gouda, Compote, 1867, 8 In.Diameter	85.00
Gouda, Jar, Powder, Dark Blue, Seven Gold Florals	28.00
Gouda, Jug, 4 1/2 In.High	32.00
Gouda, Shoe, Blue Floral, Leaves, Swags, Marked Zenith, 7 In.Long	85.00
Gouda, Shoe, Dutch, Dark Blue, Gofdewaagen, 4 In.Long, Pair	18.50
Gouda, Tumbler, 3 3/4 In.High	28.00
Gouda, Vase, Cream & Green Ground, Yellow & Rust Floral, Artist Borodi	21.50
Gouda, Vase, Crocus, Signed, 11 In.High	25.00
Gouda, Vase, High Glaze, 6 1/2 In.High	55.00
Gouda, Vase, Miniature, Handles, 2 3/4 In.High	28.00
Gouda, Vase, Pastel Colors On Black, 5 1/2 In.High	50.00
Gouda, Vase, Red Flambe, Black Leaves & Designs, Pedestal, 7 In.High	49.00
Gouda, Vase, Stylized Croesus On Dark Green, Artist M.V.H., Signed	35.00
Gouda, Vase, Tan, Brown, Purple, Yellow Violets, 9 In.	18.00

Graniteware is an enameled tinware that has been used in the kitchen from the late nineteenth century to the present. Earlier Graniteware was green or turquoise blue, with white spatters. The later ware was gray with white spatters. Reproductions are being made in all colors.

Graniteware, Bowl, Ladle, White	6.00
Graniteware, Bucket, Blue	9.00
Graniteware, Coffeepot, Blue & White Speckles	12.00
Graniteware, Coffeepot, Brown, Hinged, Fluted Tin Lid, Pewter Finial	35.00
Graniteware, Coffeepot, Gray & White, 10 In.High	9.50
Graniteware, Coffeepot, Gray, Petger Top, Spout, & Handle, Copper Band Bottom	49.00
Graniteware, Coffeepot, Gray, 8 In.	3.00
Graniteware, Colander, 10 In.	5.00
Graniteware, Double Boiler, Gray, Tin Lid	6.50
Graniteware, Measure, Gray, One Quart	8.00
Graniteware, Measure, Liquid, Dark Blue, Tin Pouring Lip, Gallon	15.00
Graniteware, Mold, Cake, Tube, Fluted, Gray, 8 In.	6.00
Graniteware, Pail, Dinner, Gray	8.00
Graniteware, Pail, Lunch, Gray, Tin Bail, Cover, 5 In.High	6.00
Graniteware, Pan, Gray, Handle, 13 X 9 In.	4.00
Graniteware, Pot, Blue, White, Lid, Large	10.00
Graniteware, Pot, Wire Bail	2.00
Graniteware, Roaster, Gray, Marked Nesco On Lid, 13 X 20 In.	8.00
Graniteware, Teakettle, Blue, White, 9 In.Tall	3.00
Graniteware, Teakettle, White, Hand-Painted Fruit, Gold Leaf Trim	5.50
-Greentown, See Also Pressed Glass, Slag, Caramel	
Greentown, Bowl, Dewey, Canary, Footed, 8 In.	45.00
Greentown, Bowl, Ribbed Spiral, Clear, Fluted, 7 In.	18.00
Greentown, Bowl, Teardrop & Tassel, 9 In.	25.00
Greentown, Candlestick, Albany, Swirl, Miniature	10.00
Greentown, Cruet, Dewey, Amber	55.00
Greentown, Cup, Punch, Cord Drapery	8.00
Greentown, Dish, Candy, Wild Rose & Bowknot, Frosted	27.50
Greentown, Dish, Cat On Hamper, Covered, Chocolate, Square	200.00 To 225.00
Greentown, Jar, Cracker, Chocolate, Base, Cactus	25.00
Greentown, Mug, Blue Serenade, 5 In.	48.00
Greentown, Mug, Troubadour, Green, 5 In.	48.00
Greentown, Mug, Troubadours, Opaque White	15.00
Greentown, Pitcher, Water, Scalloped Flange, Clear	15.00
Greentown, Plate, Cake, Cord Drapery, Footed	22.50
Greentown, Plate, Serenade, Milk Glass, White, 6 1/2 In.Diameter	55.00
Greentown, Salt Shaker, Austrian	15.00
Greentown, Sauce, Cord Drapery	5.00
Greentown, Sugar & Creamer, Dewey, Canary, Covered, Large Size	85.00
Greentown, Toothpick, Paneled Holly, Clear	95.00
Greentown, Tumbler, Chocolate Uneeda Milk Biscuit	40.00
Greenwood Pottery, Chamber Pot & Lid, Blue & Gold Decor, 1861	25.00
Greenwood Pottery, Pitcher, Washstand, Blue & Gold Decor	25.00
Grindley, Platter, Spring, Blue Floral On White, No.5105b	4.50
Grueby, Vase, Dark Green Finish, Signed, 6 1/2 In.High	135.00
Grueby, Vase, Sculptured Rib, Artist S.L., Faience Mark, 7 7/8 In.High	150.00

Grueby, Vase, Speckled Green, Arches, W.Post 135.00
   Gun, see Weapon, Gun

Gunderson Glass was made at the Gunderson Pairpoint Works of New Bedford, Massachusetts, from 1952 to 1957. Gunderson Peachblow is especially famous.
   Gunderson, see also Peachblow
Gunderson, Basket, Pale Beige To Deep Rose, Scalloped Top & Base 225.00
Gunderson, Burmese, Creamer, Red To Yellow, Yellow Handle, Acid, Miniature 135.00
Gunderson, Goblet, Beige To Dark Rose 95.00
Gunderson, Peachblow, Creamer, Applied Handle 165.00
Gunderson, Peachblow, Creamer, Applied White Handle .... 120.00 To 135.00
Gunderson, Peachblow, Creamer, Deep Raspberry Color, Applied White Handle 110.00
Gunderson, Peachblow, Cruet, Reeded Handle, 5 In.High 110.00
Gunderson, Peachblow, Cup & Saucer, Deep Raspberry 200.00
Gunderson, Peachblow, Cup & Saucer, Raspberry To Blue Gray, White Handles 125.00
Gunderson, Peachblow, Decanter, 14 In. 160.00
Gunderson, Vase, Rose To White, Glossy, Ball Shape 125.00
-Gutta-Percha, See Album, Photo And Photography, Album ....

Philip Handel worked in Meriden, Connecticut, about 1885 and in New York City from about 1900 to the 1930s. His firm made Art Glass and other types of lamps.
Handel, Ceiling Fixture, Green Slag, Geometric, Ruby Border, 20 In.Diameter 450.00
Handel, Compote, Pansies, Signed, 8 1/2 In. 145.00
Handel, Humidor, Brown, Dog Scene, Hinged 75.00
Handel, Jar, Tobacco, Green, Two Deer, Silver Top, Pipe Match Holder 100.00
Handel, Lamp, Acid Cut Shade, Painted Scenic, 10 In.High 160.00
Handel, Lamp, Acorns & Oak Leaves On Yellow, Signed, 20 In.High 250.00
Handel, Lamp, Amber & Amethyst Mottle, Roses, Filigree Bronze, 21 In.High 395.00
Handel, Lamp, Blue Moon Shade, Moon, Ships, Palm Trees, Beaches, Bronze Base 635.00
Handel, Lamp, Boudoir, Flowers, Signed 150.00
Handel, Lamp, Boudoir, Gold Design, Signed 150.00
Handel, Lamp, Boudoir, Moon Scene, Signed, 15 1/2 In.High 175.00
Handel, Lamp, Boudoir, Neutral Ground, Overall Pink Flowers, Signed 175.00
Handel, Lamp, Boudoir, Reverse Painting, 13 In. 135.00
Handel, Lamp, Boudoir, The Setting Sun, Signed, 13 In.High 185.00
Handel, Lamp, Cameo Type, Ivrene, Green Coralene Type Glass, Scenic Base 875.00
Handel, Lamp, Chipped Ground Shade, Green Vines, Bronze Base, 23 In.High 350.00
Handel, Lamp, Crackle Acorn Shape Shade, Hand-Painted Flowers, Signed 75.00
Handel, Lamp, Desk, Art Deco, Yellow, Blue, Green, Red, Signed Base & Shade 185.00
Handel, Lamp, Desk, Bronze Overlay, Green Glass, Tulips, Cased Opalescent 145.00
Handel, Lamp, Desk, Milk Glass Elongated Shade, Green Exterior, Ivy Border 225.00
Handel, Lamp, Desk, Mottled Yellow To White Panels, Overlay Bronze Leaves 145.00
Handel, Lamp, Leaded Shade, Pink Flowers, Green Leaves 750.00
Handel, Lamp, Leaded Shade, Red, Orange, Yellow Floral, 16 In., Stick Base 550.00
Handel, Lamp, Leaded, Floral Border, 16 In.Diameter Shade 650.00
Handel, Lamp, Leaf Design, Cream To Yellow, Bronze Trim, 16 In.Diameter 250.00
Handel, Lamp, Mantel, Pine Trees & Mountains, Chipped Ice Ground, Signed 165.00
Handel, Lamp, Mushroom Type Shade, Brass Base, Signed 125.00
Handel, Lamp, Panels, Lake, Mountains, Sailboats, Palm Trees, 18 In.Shade 240.00
Handel, Lamp, Purple & Green, Lead Designs On 6 Sided Shade, Bronze Base 98.50
Handel, Lamp, Radio, Trees, Snow, Mountain, Cylindrical Shade, Signed 160.00
Handel, Lamp, Scenic Shade, Signed Base 125.00
Handel, Lamp, Scenic, Autumn Colors, Signed 425.00
Handel, Lamp, Scenic, Glowing Moon, Blue, Orange, Brown, Signed 165.00
Handel, Lamp, Scenic, Orange, Brown, & Red, Signed 425.00
Handel, Lamp, Stick, Blue Ground, Yellow Daisies, Shade, Rowena Cheney, 57 In. 250.00
Handel, Lamp, Table, Birds & Fronds, Base & Shade Signed 165.00
Handel, Lamp, Table, Blue, Birds, Signed, 7 1/2 In.Diameter Shade, 13 In.High 165.00
Handel, Lamp, Table, Forest Scene, Signed Base & Shade, 22 In.High 375.00
Handel, Lamp, Table, Green & White Cased Shade, Signed, 14 In.High 200.00
Handel, Lamp, White Ground, Trailing Leaves, Red Floral, Gold Leaf Base 110.00
Handel, Lamp, 288 Pieces Of Glass In Shade, Bronze Base, 28 In.High 650.00
Handel, Sugar, Prunus Blossom, Raised Design, Signed H.Bedigie, Handel 1909 .... 90.00
   Hatpin Holder, see also Porcelain

Hatpin Holder, Hand-Painted Floral	15.00
Hatpin Holder, White, Oak Leaves, Gold Trim, Hand-Painted	7.50
Hatpin, Amethyst, Faceted, Beaded Border, Basket Setting	7.50
Hatpin, Amethyst, Faceted, Filigree Oval Setting	15.00
Hatpin, Filigree Gold, Flattened Medallion, Stylized Openwork	15.00
Hatpin, Pink Cameo Set In Sterling Silver	10.00 To 15.00
Hatpin, Turquoise, Porcelain Beetle	15.00

18 C°
EPOSE
Haviland China has been made in Limoges, France, since 1846. The
factory was started by the Haviland Brothers of New York City.
Other factories worked in the town of Limoges making a similar chinaware. **Haviland & C° Limoges**

Haviland, see also Limoges	
Haviland, Basket, Beige, Purple Flowers, English Registry Mark, 1875	35.00
Haviland, Bowl & Pitcher, Miniature, Florals	17.00
Haviland, Bowl, Fluted Sides, 8 3/4 In.Diameter	8.00
Haviland, Bowl, Vegetable, Covered, C.1879	19.00
Haviland, Bowl, Vegetable, Covered, No.52b	22.50
Haviland, Bowl, Vegetable, Covered, No.78c	22.50
Haviland, Bowl, Vegetable, Covered, No.279	22.50
Haviland, Bowl, Vegetable, Covered, Pink Flowers	16.00
Haviland, Bowl, Vegetable, Covered, White	12.00
Haviland, Bowl, Vegetable, No.432, Round	12.00
Haviland, Bowl, White, Gold Trim, Fluted Border, 9 3/4 In.	15.00
Haviland, Bowl, Yellow, Pink & Red Roses, Two Gold Handles, 9 1/2 In.	18.50
Haviland, Butter Pat, No.19	4.50
Haviland, Butter Pat, No.251	3.50
Haviland, Butter Pat, Pastel Blue Firs, Scalloped Edge, Set Of 4	11.00
Haviland, Chocolate Set, Pink & Gold Trim, 11 Piece	85.00
Haviland, Cookie Jar, White, Small Floral, Maroon Borders Top & Bottom	35.00
Haviland, Creamer, Smooth Blank, White	7.50
Haviland, Cup & Saucer, Bouillon, Princess	12.50
Haviland, Cup & Saucer, Coffee, No.87c	14.50
Haviland, Cup & Saucer, Demitasse, Anniversary Pattern	10.00
Haviland, Cup & Saucer, Demitasse, Pink Roses On Yellow Band, Gold Handle, 8	95.00
Haviland, Cup & Saucer, Drop Rose, Pedestal	65.00
Haviland, Cup & Saucer, Five O'Clock Tea, No.621	12.00
Haviland, Cup & Saucer, Fuchsia, Green, Art Nouveau	20.00
Haviland, Cup & Saucer, No.57f	12.50 To 14.50
Haviland, Cup & Saucer, No.78c	15.00
Haviland, Cup & Saucer, No.103	14.00
Haviland, Cup & Saucer, No.279	14.00
Haviland, Cup & Saucer, No.432	12.50
Haviland, Cup & Saucer, No.15637, Gold Band, Haviland & Co., Factory	12.50
Haviland, Cup & Saucer, Roses In & Out, Gold Medallions, Limoges, France	8.50
Haviland, Cup & Saucer, Smooth Blank, White, Large Size	10.00
Haviland, Cup, Chocolate, No.261	8.00
Haviland, Dessert Set, No.114, Palette Shape Plates, 11 Piece	65.00
Haviland, Dish, Bone, Silver Pattern, Set Of 4	30.00
Haviland, Gravy Boat & Tray, Gold & White, Double Spout	15.00
Haviland, Gravy Boat On Tray, No.78c	20.00
Haviland, Gravy Boat On Tray, No.15637, Gold Band, Haviland & Co., Factory	10.00
Haviland, Ice Cream Set, R.B.Hayes, C.1880, 7 Piece	*Illus* 2800.00
Haviland, Jar, Biscuit, No.266b	32.00
Haviland, Pitcher & Six Glassed, Different Fruit On Each, Hand-Painted	150.00
Haviland, Pitcher, Gold Trim And Purple Pansies, 10 In.Tall	50.00
Haviland, Pitcher, Hand-Painted, Signed Haviland, 8 In.High	58.00
Haviland, Pitcher, Water, Mother-Of-Pearl Inside & Outside, Purple Peacocks	75.00
Haviland, Plate, Bird Group, Hand-Painted, Green, 8 1/2 In.Diameter	18.50
Haviland, Plate, Bread & Butter, No.103	6.50
Haviland, Plate, Bread & Butter, No.279	4.50
Haviland, Plate, Bread & Butter, Smooth Blank, White	3.50
Haviland, Plate, Cake, No.279, Handled	16.50
Haviland, Plate, Cake, Scalloped Border, Pink Garlands	10.50
Haviland, Plate, Dinner, No.19	9.00
Haviland, Plate, Dinner, No.103	7.50
Haviland, Plate, Dinner, Pattern No.432	8.00

Haviland, Ice Cream Set, R.B.Hayes, C.1880, 7 Piece
See Page 258

Haviland, Plate, Dinner, No.15637, Gold Band, Haviland & Co., Factory	7.00
Haviland, Plate, Game, Laurel Border	10.00
Haviland, Plate, Green Ground, Stylized Floral, Lavish Beading, 8 1/2 In.	9.00
Haviland, Plate, Hand-Painted Apples, Pears, Plums, & Violets, Gold, France	15.00
Haviland, Plate, Hand-Painted Flowers & Grapes, Artist-Signed, 9 In.	18.00
Haviland, Plate, Luncheon, No.19	8.50
Haviland, Plate, Luncheon, No.279	6.50
Haviland, Plate, No.279, Coupe	5.50
Haviland, Plate, Oyster, Color Shells, Seaweed, Fish, Sea Creatures	16.00
Haviland, Plate, Oyster, Gold Circles, Gold Border, C.1876, 8 1/2 In.	16.00
Haviland, Plate, Oyster, Green & Gray Floral, Gold Edges	25.00
Haviland, Plate, Oyster, Swirled, Scalloped, Pink Shaded Well	12.50
Haviland, Plate, Pheasant Center, Gold Floral Border	24.50
Haviland, Plate, Salad, No.103	6.50
Haviland, Plate, Stylized Floral, Lavish Beading, Green Ground	10.00
Haviland, Platter, Flowers, Gold, 16 X 11 In.	15.00
Haviland, Platter, No.78c, 13 1/2 X 9 1/4 In.	22.50
Haviland, Platter, No.103, Large Size	22.50
Haviland, Platter, No.103, Small Size	18.00
Haviland, Platter, No.15637, Gold Band, Haviland & Co., Factory, 12 In.	17.00
Haviland, Platter, Oval, Pointed End, Miniature Rose Garlands	14.00
Haviland, Platter, Wedding Band, 12 1/2 In.	12.00
Haviland, Ramekin, Clover Pattern, Set Of 6	40.00
Haviland, Relish, No.103	8.00
Haviland, Salt, Hand-Painted Florals, Three Ornate Feet	6.00
Haviland, Sauce, No.103	4.50
Haviland, Sauce, Smooth Blank, White	3.50
Haviland, Soup, No.103	6.50
Haviland, Soup, No.279	6.50
Haviland, Soup, Smooth Blank, White	4.00
Haviland, Sugar & Creamer, Hand-Painted Blue Posies, Twig Handles	14.00
Haviland, Sugar & Creamer, No.22, Gold, Covered Sugar	25.00
Haviland, Sugar & Creamer, No.66	27.00
Haviland, Sugar & Creamer, No.78c	27.00
Haviland, Sugar & Creamer, No.103	27.50
Haviland, Sugar & Creamer, No.15637, Gold Band, Haviland & Co., Factory	20.00
Haviland, Sugar & Creamer, Red & Blue Flowers, Gold Handles, Limoges	6.00
Haviland, Sugar, No.279	10.00
Haviland, Tea Set, White & Pink Flowers, Gold Lacework, Limoges, 3 Piece	85.00
Haviland, Teapot & Creamer, Gold Wedding Band, Basket Weave Pattern	18.50
Haviland, Tray, Dresser, Pink & Lavender Floral, Scroll Edge, Gold Stipple	9.00
Haviland, Tray, Tea, Blue Floral, Standing Scallop Edge, 9 1/2 In.Diameter	18.00
Haviland, Tureen, Pink Band, Flowers In Band, Gold Trim, July 22, 1871 Mark	35.00
Haviland, Tureen, Soup, Allover Floral, Leaves, Gold, Handles, Cover, C.1882	32.50
Haviland, Tureen, Soup, No.652, Baltimore Rose, Blank, Gold Trim	68.00
Haviland, Tureen, Soup, Pink Floral, Gold Decoration	20.00
Haviland, Vase, Abstract High Glaze, Floral, Pottery	28.00

The firm cut glass made at other firms until 1962. Many pieces are marked with the trademark, a trefoil ring enclosing a fleur-de-lis and two hawks.

Hawkes, see also Cut Glass

Hawkes, **Atomizer**, Blue Crystal, Gold Band, Bulb, Signed Block Letters, Label	30.00
Hawkes, **Bottle**, Dog & Hunting Scene, Signed	65.00
Hawkes, **Bottle**, Worcestershire, Venetian Pattern, Signed	150.00
Hawkes, **Bowl**, Buzz Star & Cane, Brilliant, Signed, 8 In.	70.00
Hawkes, **Bowl**, Covered, Engraved Flowers, Footed, Signed, 4 1/2 In.	38.00
Hawkes, **Bowl**, Crystal, Turned Down Rim Of Fine Cut Diamond Point, 9 1/2 In.	185.00
Hawkes, **Bowl**, Engraved Flowers & Vines, Applied Handles, 8 In.	85.00
Hawkes, **Bowl**, Hobstar & Fan, Signed, 8 In.	75.00
Hawkes, **Bowl**, Punch, Hobstar & Diamond, Brilliant, Signed	425.00
Hawkes, **Bowl**, Rock Crystal, Polished Floral Engraving, 10 In.	65.00
Hawkes, **Bowl**, Stars & Stripes, 9 In.Diameter	60.00
Hawkes, **Box**, Covered, Cut Leaf & Floral, Geometric Edge	60.00
Hawkes, **Box**, Covered, Hinged, Signed, 6 In.Diameter	165.00
Hawkes, **Candlestick**, Cut Scroll, Leaf, & Flower Bud, 9 In.High	65.00
Hawkes, **Candlestick**, Engraved Flower Baskets, Green, 4 3/4 In., Pair	35.00
Hawkes, **Candlestick**, Red Glass, Silver Cameo Cut Wide Borders, Cut Stem	65.00
Hawkes, **Cologne**, Copper Wheel Engraved, Stopper Full Length Of Bottle	95.00
Hawkes, **Cologne**, Cut, Sterling Stopper, Signed	60.00
Hawkes, **Compote**, Copper Wheel Engraved Hobstar & Floral	75.00
Hawkes, **Compote**, Copper Wheel Engraved Star & Floral, Signed	65.00
Hawkes, **Compote**, Engraved Floral, Fine Line Cutting, Etched Base	28.50
Hawkes, **Compote**, Etched Flowers, Fluted Top, Sterling Base	47.50
Hawkes, **Compote**, Yellow Engraved To Clear, Floral, Filigree Gold Band	35.00
Hawkes, **Cruet**, Oil & Vinegar, Clear, Double Lip, Signed Stopper & Base	45.00
Hawkes, **Dish**, Candy, Butterfly Shape, Hobstars, Two Cut Handles, Brilliant	45.00
Hawkes, **Goblet**, Gold Bands At Top & Base, Signed, Set Of 11	90.00
Hawkes, **Ice Bucket**, Row Of Cut Bar Ribs At Top, Silver Plate Lid & Handle	21.00
Hawkes, **Jar**, Dresser, Chrysanthemum Design, Sterling Top, 3 1/2 In.Tall	135.00
Hawkes, **Jar**, Jam, Etched, Two Handles, Lid, Signed, 4 In.High	43.00
Hawkes, **Perfume**, Bulbous, Allover Cut, Signed	32.00
Hawkes, **Perfume**, Engraved Floral Baskets, French Enamel Stopper	45.00
Hawkes, **Perfume**, Etched Floral & Leaves, Stopper, Signed, 8 In.High	110.00
Hawkes, **Perfume**, Etched, Cut Stopper	60.00
Hawkes, **Plate**, Gravic, Carnations, 7 In.	90.00
Hawkes, **Salt**, Individual, Etched, Stem, Signed	10.00
Hawkes, **Sugar**, Open, Trefoil, Signed, Brilliant Cut	36.00
Hawkes, **Tray**, Dresser, Anemone, Signed, Oval, 10 X 7 In.	95.00
Hawkes, **Tray**, Pen, Cut Crystal, Engraved, Signed	26.00
Hawkes, **Tumble-Up**, Intaglio, Signed, 7 In.High	100.00
Hawkes, **Vase**, Brunswick, 10 In.High	95.00
Hawkes, **Vase**, Dragon Design, Amethyst, Gold Rim, Signed, 12 In.High	150.00
Hawkes, **Vase**, Engraved Leaf & Berry, Pedestal Base, 11 In.High	135.00
Hawkes, **Vase**, Etched Checkerboard & Floral, 8 In.High	59.00
Hawkes, **Vase**, Etched Floral, Sterling Rim, Signed, 9 1/2 In.	55.00
Hawkes, **Vase**, Fan, Green, Frosted Band At Top, Gold Enameling, 7 1/2 In.	25.00
Hawkes, **Vase**, Flute, Signed, 13 In.High	50.00
Hawkes, **Vase**, Gravic, Intaglio Cosmos & Leaf, 9 In.High	85.00
Hawkes, **Vase**, Gravic, Intaglio Floral, Signed	185.00
Hawkes, **Vase**, Gravic, Rayed Bottom, Signed, 10 In.High	195.00
Hawkes, **Vase**, Rock Crystal, Polished Engraved Floral, Signed, 14 1/2 In.High	225.00
Hawkes, **Vase**, Trumpet, Allover Engraved Flowers, Amber	60.00
Hawkes, **Wine**, Carnation, Signed	49.50

Heisey Glass was made from 1895 to 1958 in Newark, Ohio, by A.H. Heisey and Co., Inc.

Heisey, **Ashtray**, Alexandrite, Diamond Shape, Marked	78.00
Heisey, **Ashtray**, Clear Diamond, Marked	40.00
Heisey, **Ashtray**, Flamingo 1389, Dog	12.50
Heisey, **Ashtray**, Ridgeleigh Pattern, Clear, Signed	5.00
Heisey, **Banana Boat**, Ribbed, Scalloped Rim, 13 X 7 1/2 In.	22.50
Heisey, **Basket**, Butterfly & Daisy Etching, Marked	32.50
Heisey, **Basket**, Double Rib, Panel, Marked, 6 In.High	35.00
Heisey, **Basket**, Recessed Panel, Etched Cut Flowers	32.50

Heisey, Basket, Round, Flamingo	30.00
Heisey, Basket, 9 In.Tall	37.50
Heisey, Bookend, Doe's Head ..... *Illus*	800.00
Heisey, Bookend, Figural, Scotty Dog, Pair	75.00
Heisey, Bookend, Fish, Pair ..... *Illus*	42.50
Heisey, Bookend, Horse's Head, Frosted, Clear Mane, Eyes, Nostrils, Pair	110.00
Heisey, Bottle, Bitters, Crystal, 1489, 4 Oz.	7.50
Heisey, Bottle, Water, Crystal, Grecian Border	50.00
Heisey, Bottle, Water, Crystal, 1205, Fancy Loop	25.00
Heisey, Bottle, Water, Fancy Loop	60.00
Heisey, Bottle, Water, Punty & Diamond Point	35.00
Heisey, Bowl & Base, Punch, Flamingo, Greek Key, Signed, 14 1/2 X 15 In.	375.00
Heisey, Bowl, Berry, Colonial Pattern, Scalloped, 9 In.Diameter	26.00
Heisey, Bowl, Berry, Prince Of Wales Plumes, Signed	45.00
Heisey, Bowl, Berry, 9 In.	20.00
Heisey, Bowl, Centerpiece, Clear, Blue, Gold Rim, Stand, 10 1/2 In.Diameter	20.00
Heisey, Bowl, Colonial, Cut & Etched	45.00
Heisey, Bowl, Colonial, Marked, 8 In.Diameter	12.50
Heisey, Bowl, Diamond Optic, Signed, 12 In.Diameter	45.00
Heisey, Bowl, Diamond Pattern, Scalloped Flange Rim, Marked, 12 3/4 In.	24.00
Heisey, Bowl, Diamond Thumbprint, Clear, Signed, 12 In.Diameter	25.00
Heisey, Bowl, Fandango, Star Shape, 2 1/2 In.Deep, 7 In.Diameter	20.00
Heisey, Bowl, Fish ..... *Illus*	350.00
Heisey, Bowl, Flared Side, Leaf Decor, Rayed, Marked, 7 1/2 In.Diameter	18.00
Heisey, Bowl, Floral, Sahara, Queen Anne, Dolphin Feet, 11 In.Diameter	25.00
Heisey, Bowl, Fruit, Clear Whirlpool, 12 In.	24.00
Heisey, Bowl, Fruit, Diamond Optic, Scalloped Edge, Signed, 12 In.	35.00
Heisey, Bowl, Ice Cream, Roman Key	35.00
Heisey, Bowl, Imprint Of Raised Petals, Scalloped Edge, Signed	22.50
Heisey, Bowl, Lariat, Paper Label, 7 In.Diameter	12.00
Heisey, Bowl, Narrow Ribbed, Signed, 9 In.Diameter	18.00
Heisey, Bowl, Oval, Rayed Bottom & Sides, Marked, 11 3/4 X 7 3/4 In.	12.00
Heisey, Bowl, Paneled Loops, Crown Shape, Rayed Base	20.00
Heisey, Bowl, Pink, Flare Shape, Star Base, Signed, 10 In.	24.00
Heisey, Bowl, Pink, Handle, Marked, 4 In.Diameter	8.00
Heisey, Bowl, Punch, Colonial	78.00
Heisey, Bowl, Punch, Scalloped, Paneled, Footed, Marked	47.50
Heisey, Bowl, Rolled Rim, Ribbed Panels, Rayed, Marked, 9 3/4 In.Diameter	20.00
Heisey, Bowl, Sahara, Queen Anne Flower	17.00
Heisey, Box, Cigarette, Rayed Design, Signed	20.00
Heisey, Box, Cigarette, Zircon, Crystolite	37.50
Heisey, Butter Tub, Cut Florals, Marked	10.00
Heisey, Butter Tub, Diamond Pattern, Marked	8.00
Heisey, Butter, Beaded Swag, Covered, Crystal	45.00
Heisey, Butter, Beaded Swag, Milk Glass, Cover	110.00
Heisey, Butter, Covered, Colonial	30.00
Heisey, Butter, Square, Floral Cutting, Signed	65.00
Heisey, Candelabra, Three Candle, Pineapple Base	18.00
Heisey, Candleholder, Triple, Waverly, Etched Rose, Pair	55.00
Heisey, Candlestick, Double, Orchid Pattern, 6 In., Pair	35.00
Heisey, Candlestick, Moongleam, Pair	10.00
Heisey, Candlestick, Notched, Petal Top, Purple Iridescence, Signed, Pair	55.00
Heisey, Candy, Pink Flamingo, Sticker, 3 Footed	7.00
Heisey, Canister Set, Green Glass, Signed, 7 Piece	22.50
Heisey, Celery, Block Pattern, Star Rayed Bottom	12.50
Heisey, Celery, Flamingo, Rayed Bottom, 12 In.	14.00
Heisey, Celery, Flamingo, Twisted Optic, 13 In.	16.00
Heisey, Celery, Greek Key	14.00
Heisey, Celery, Scallop, Panel, Signed	24.50
Heisey, Champagne, Sahara, Chintz Pattern	15.00
Heisey, Coaster, Lariat	8.00
Heisey, Cocktail, Rooster Head, Stemmed	12.50 To 22.50
Heisey, Compote, Candy, Pineapple Fan, Footed	18.50
Heisey, Compote, Clear, Double Mark, 4 1/4 In.High	18.00
Heisey, Compote, Covered, Green, 8 In.High	16.00
Heisey, Compote, Flowers, Engraved, Marked, Small	11.00

Heisey, Compote, Flowers, Hand-Painted, 10 In.	40.00
Heisey, Compote, Fluted Top, Marked	14.00
Heisey, Compote, Prince Of Wales, Plumes, Open	35.00
Heisey, Compote, Wagon Wheel, 8 In.Tall	14.00
Heisey, Console Set, Pink, Floral Decoration, Marked, 3 Piece	32.00
Heisey, Cornucopia, 7 1/2 In.High	28.00
Heisey, Creamer, Custard, Signed, Individual, Gold Scalloped	20.00
Heisey, Creamer, Fancy Loop, Miniature, 2 1/4 In.	16.00
Heisey, Creamer, Fandango, Miniature	18.50
Heisey, Creamer, Greek Key	14.00
Heisey, Creamer, Greek Key Oval, Marked	20.00
Heisey, Creamer, Rib, Blue Band, Gold Engraved Flowers, Pheasants	32.50
Heisey, Creamer, Tankard, Red Flashed Pineapple And Fan	35.00
Heisey, Cruet, Bell Shape, Paneled To Octagon Base, Signed	24.00
Heisey, Cruet, Clear, Slim, Paneled, Original Teardrop Stopper	28.50
Heisey, Cruet, Colonial Pattern, Stopper	12.00
Heisey, Cruet, Fancy Loop	22.00
Heisey, Cruet, Greek Key	15.00
Heisey, Cruet, Plain Band, Cut Stopper Etched Flowers On Band	20.00
Heisey, Cruet, Pleat & Panel, Flamingo	16.50
Heisey, Cruet, Stopper, 6 1/2 In.High	21.00
Heisey, Cup & Saucer, Crystolite, Signed	10.00
Heisey, Cup & Saucer, Empress, Queen Anne, Sahara	17.50
Heisey, Cup & Saucer, Flamingo, Pleat & Panel, Signed	8.50
Heisey, Cup, Nut, Colonial, Clear, Footed, Signed	3.50
Heisey, Cup, Nut, Sahara, Queen Anne	8.50
Heisey, Cup, Punch, Block Pattern, Set Of 6	22.00
Heisey, Cup, Punch, Colonial	4.50
Heisey, Cup, Punch, Signed	4.00
Heisey, Cup, Punch, Star Design, Clear, Signed	4.00
Heisey, Cup, Punch, Victorian Pattern, Signed, Set Of 8	30.00
Heisey, Dish, Candy, Floral Etching At Top, Pale Amber, Signed	18.75 To 20.00
Heisey, Dish, Cheese & Cracker, Etched, Silver Overlay, Cut Bottom, Signed	45.00
Heisey, Dish, Divided, Plantation Pattern, Sterling Base, Signed	35.00
Heisey, Dish, Lemon, Pleat & Panel, Flamingo, Signed	27.50
Heisey, Dish, Olive, Colonial, Signed	6.50
Heisey, Epergne, Pair Of One Light Candelabra With 12 Prisms, Crystal	425.00
Heisey, Figurine, Airedale	Illus 130.00
Heisey, Figurine, Donkey	Illus 85.00
Heisey, Figurine, Elephant, Amber, Small	Illus 550.00
Heisey, Figurine, Elephant, Large	Illus 95.00
Heisey, Figurine, Elephant, Small	Illus 55.00
Heisey, Figurine, Giraffe, Head Back	Illus 50.00
Heisey, Figurine, Horse, Clydesdale	Illus 110.00
Heisey, Figurine, Horse, Mare, Flying	Illus 700.00
Heisey, Figurine, Horse, Show	Illus 200.00
Heisey, Figurine, Mallard Duck, Wings Down	Illus 45.00
Heisey, Figurine, Mallard Duck, Wings Half Way Up	Illus 45.00
Heisey, Figurine, Mallard Duck, Wings Up	Illus 45.00
Heisey, Figurine, Pheasant, Asiatic	Illus 130.00
Heisey, Figurine, Pig	Illus 210.00
Heisey, Goblet, Cube Block, Dark Amber	22.50
Heisey, Goblet, Etched, Signed	3.00
Heisey, Goblet, Victoria, Clear	6.50
Heisey, Goblet, Water, Flamingo, Signed	9.00
Heisey, Hair Receiver, Clear, Signed	45.00
Heisey, Horse, Plug	40.00
Heisey, Humidor, Vertical Notched Ribs, Derby Silver Co.Lid, Signed	32.50
Heisey, Jar, Tobacco, Dated	70.00
Heisey, Jelly, Crystal, 433, Grecian Border, Handled, 5 In.Marked 'H'	15.00
Heisey, Jug, No.1509, Dolphin Footed, Queen Anne, Green, Signed	67.50
Heisey, Jug, Water, Crystal, Diana Etch	20.00
Heisey, Mayonnaise, Flamingo, Footed	4.00
Heisey, Mug, Pineapple & Fan	14.00
Heisey, Nappy, Fandango, Triangular, Handled	16.00
Heisey, Nappy, Fandango, 7 In.	20.00

168	169	170	171	172
Heisey, Figurine, Airedale	Heisey, Bookend, Doe's Head	Heisey, Figurine, Mallard Duck, Wings Halfway Up	Heisey, Figurine, Mallard Duck, Wings Up	Heisey, Figurine, Mallard Duck, Wings Down
See Page 262	See Page 261	See Page 262	See Page 262	See Page 262

173	174	175	176	177
Heisey, Paperweight, Rabbit	Heisey, Figurine, Pig	Heisey, Figurine, Elephant, Large	Heisey, Figurine, Elephant, Amber, Small	Heisey, Figurine, Elephant, Small
See Page 264	See Page 262	See Page 262	See Page 262	See Page 262

178	179	180
Heisey, Figurine, Horse, Clydesdale	Heisey, Figurine, Horse, Mare, Flying	Heisey, Figurine, Horse, Show
See Page 262	See Page 262	See Page 262

181	182	183	184	185
Heisey, Figurine, Giraffe, Head Back	Heisey, Figurine, Donkey	Heisey, Bowl, Fish	Heisey, Bookend, Fish, Pair	Heisey, Figurine, Pheasant, Asiatic
See Page 262	See Page 262	See Page 261	See Page 261	See Page 262

Heisey, **Nappy**, Gold, Winged Scroll 50.00
Heisey, **Nappy**, Greek Key, Handle, 5 In.Diameter 15.00
Heisey, **Paperweight**, Rabbit .... *Illus* 40.00
Heisey, **Paperweight**, Rabbit, Crystal 35.00
Heisey, **Perfume**, Pedestal, Ribbed Ball, Flamingo, Marked 22.50
Heisey, **Perfume**, Punty & Diamond Point, Sterling Top .... 18.00 To 22.00
Heisey, **Perfume**, Sterling Crest Stopper, Etched, 5 1/2 In.High, Signed 36.00
Heisey, **Pitcher**, Child's 5.00
Heisey, **Pitcher**, Clear, 10 Paneled, Rayed Base, Signed 28.00
Heisey, **Pitcher**, Colonial, Clear, Marked, 7 In.High 18.00
Heisey, **Pitcher**, Colonial, Quart .... 21.00 To 28.00
Heisey, **Pitcher**, Flute, Miniature, Child's, Marked 20.00
Heisey, **Pitcher**, Greek Key, 6 1/4 In.High 45.00
Heisey, **Pitcher**, Panels, Scalloped Top, Applied Handle, Star In Bottom. 19.00
Heisey, **Pitcher**, Water, Flamingo, Signed 60.00
Heisey, **Pitcher**, Water, Greek Key, Signed, 7 In.Tall, 6 In.Diameter 60.00
Heisey, **Pitcher**, Water, Greek Key, 6 3/4 In. 62.50
Heisey, **Pitcher**, 10 Paneled Rayed Base, Signed 38.50
Heisey, **Plate**, Beehive, Flamingo, 4 In.Diameter 9.50
Heisey, **Plate**, Cake, Octagonal Shaped, Pink, Signed 22.50
Heisey, **Plate**, Cheese, Hawthorne, Rib And Panel 15.00
Heisey, **Plate**, Comet, Marked, Set Of 12 .... 65.00
Heisey, **Plate**, Crystolite, Signed, 14 In.Diameter 15.00
Heisey, **Plate**, Deep, 8 In. 8.00
Heisey.**Plate, Flamingo**, Coarse Rib, Signed, 7 In. 5.00
Heisey, **Plate**, Lariat Pattern, Marked, 16 In.Diameter 15.00
Heisey, **Plate**, Maryland Pattern, 8 In.Diameter 8.00
Heisey, **Plate**, Pink Swirl, 7 In.Diameter 12.00
Heisey, **Plate**, Rib & Panel, Signed 5.00
Heisey, **Plate**, Square, Alexandrite, 8 In. 50.00
Heisey, **Punch Set**, Lariat, Signed, 15 Piece 52.00
Heisey, **Punch Set**, Queen Anne, Marked, 16 Pieces 240.00
Heisey, **Punch Set**, Ring Band Pattern, 8 Quart Size, Signed, 10 Piece 250.00
Heisey, **Punch Set**, Scalloped Rim, Signed, 8 Piece 125.00
Heisey, **Relish**, Cut Designs, 7 Compartments, Marked 16.00
Heisey, **Relish**, Divided, Round, Scalloped Top, Signed 10.00
Heisey, **Relish**, Etched Flowers & Fern, Green, 9 1/2 In.Long 22.50
Heisey, **Relish**, Sahara, Queen Anne, Triplex 22.50
Heisey, **Relish**, Spider Web Design On Sides, Marked, 12 1/4 In.Long 12.00
Heisey, **Relish**, 7 Compartments 25.00
Heisey, **Salt Dip & Underplate**, Diamond Point 8.00
Heisey, **Salt Dip**, Clear 5.00
Heisey, **Salt**, Fancy Loop 16.00
Heisey, **Salt**, Individual, Signed 5.00
Heisey, **Salt**, Open, Cobalt Blue 6.50
Heisey, **Sauce**, Flamingo, Pleat & Panel, Signed 4.00
Heisey, **Sauce**, Ridgeleigh, Signed 5.00
Heisey, **Sauceboat**, Footed, Marked, 6 In.Long 8.50
Heisey, **Scottie**, Crystal 27.50
Heisey, **Shaker**, Cocktail, Rooster Head, Strainer, 2 Quart 37.50
Heisey, **Sherbet**, Arcadia Pattern 8.00
Heisey, **Sherbet**, Colonial 3.00
Heisey, **Sherbet**, Colonial, Clear, Footed, Double, Signed 32.00
Heisey, **Sherbet**, Maryland Pattern 8.00
Heisey, **Sherbet**, Silver Overlay 6.00
Heisey, **Sherbet**, Victoria, Clear 5.00
Heisey, **Soda**, Kimberly Pattern, Footed 3.00
Heisey, **Spooner**, Beaded Swag, Sawtooth Scalloped Rim 18.50
Heisey, **Spooner**, Prince Of Wales Plumes, Signed 28.00
Heisey, **Sugar & Creamer**, Child's, Pink, Narrow Flute Pattern, Marked 13.50
Heisey, **Sugar & Creamer**, Colonial, Engraved 35.00
Heisey, **Sugar & Creamer**, Dawn, Lodestar 37.50
Heisey, **Sugar & Creamer**, Dolphin, Floral Cutting, Footed, Signed 47.50
Heisey, **Sugar & Creamer**, Etched Floral, Signed .... 15.00 To 55.00
Heisey, **Sugar & Creamer**, Etched, Marked .... 15.00 To 18.00
Heisey, **Sugar & Creamer**, Pink, Miniature 18.50

Heisey, **Sugar & Creamer**, Puritan, Marked	12.00
Heisey, **Sugar & Creamer**, Squatty, Stack Set	35.00
Heisey, **Sugar & Creamer**, Swirl, Green	15.00
Heisey, **Sugar**, Creamer, & Tray, Crystolite, Marked	16.00
Heisey, **Sugar**, Creamer, & Tray, Marked	15.00
Heisey, **Sugar**, Flute, Marigold, Miniature, 2 Handles, Signed	20.00
Heisey, **Sugar**, Greek Key, Marked	12.00
Heisey, **Sugar**, Roman Key, Two Open Handles	9.50
Heisey, **Syrup**, Colonial, Green, 8 Oz.	22.00
Heisey, **Syrup**, Covered, Green Paneled, 3 In., High, Metal Top, Signed	12.50
Heisey, **Syrup**, Etched, Signed	14.00
Heisey, **Syrup**, Flamingo 372, Sanitary	15.00
Heisey, **Syrup**, Metal Top, Patented 1909	15.00
Heisey, **Syrup**, Sahara, Paneled, Tin Lid, Signed	12.00
Heisey, **Table Set**, Beaded Swag, Clear, Gold, Clue, 4 Piece	195.00
Heisey, **Toothpick**, Button Arches, Marked, 2 In.Tall	15.00
Heisey, **Toothpick**, Pink, Diagonal Panels Of Raised Stars	22.50
Heisey, **Toothpick**, Ruby Punty Band	22.00
Heisey, **Toothpick**, Winged Scroll, Green	14.50
Heisey, **Tray**, Round, Rings Around Rim, Rayed Bottom, Marked, 12 7/8 In.	16.00
Heisey, **Tray**, Sugar Cube, Pattern No.394, Signed, 8 1/2 In.Long	14.00
Heisey, **Tumbler**, Flute, Gold Band, Marked	12.00
Heisey, **Tumbler**, Greek Key, 3 3/4 In. High	12.50
Heisey, **Tumbler**, Paneled Thumbprint, Marked	5.00
Heisey, **Tumbler**, Pineapple & Fan	10.00
Heisey, **Tumbler**, Sahara, Signed	15.00
Heisey, **Vase**, Colonial, No.353, 18 In.	50.00
Heisey, **Vase**, Fan, Applied Scrolls, Clear, 7 In.High	9.00
Heisey, **Vase**, Flamingo & Diamond Optic	19.50
Heisey, **Vase**, Fluted Top, Clear, Signed, 12 In.High	26.00
Heisey, **Wine**, Arcadia Pattern	8.00
Herend, see Fischer	
Heubach, **Butter Pat**, Hand-Painted Scenes, Ships, Castles, Set Of 12 In Box	170.00
Heubach, **Figurine**, Standing Baby In Walker, Pink Ribbons	40.00
Heubach, **Vase**, Red Roses, White Enamel Jewels, 5 In.High	38.00

Higbee Glass was made by the J.B.Higbee Company of Bridgeville, **H I G**
Pennsylvania, about 1900.

Higbee, **Bowl**, Cane Variant, Round, Footed, Marked W.Lee	35.00
Higbee, **Compote**, Hawaiian Lei, 7 3/4 In.Diameter	18.50
Higbee, **Compote**, Jelly, Hawaiian Lei, Bee Mark	15.00
Higbee, **Pitcher**, Milk, Hawaiian Lei, Bee Mark	22.50
Higbee, **Plate**, Hawaiian Lei, Bee Mark, 7 1/4 In.	14.00
Higbee, **Sugar & Creamer**, Hawaiian Lei, Miniature, Marked	45.00
Higbee, **Vase**, Signed, 7 In.High	12.00
Historic Blue, see Staffordshire	

*Hobnail Glass is a pattern of Pressed Glass with bumps in an allover
pattern. Dozens of hobnail patterns and variants have been made.
Reproductioins of many types of Hobnail Glass can be found.*
Hobnail, see also Francisware

Hobnail, **Bowl**, Berry, Ruffled Edge, Straw Markings In Glass, 8 1/2 In.	75.00
Hobnail, **Bowl**, Blue, 9 In.Square	75.00
Hobnail, **Candleholder**, Moonstone, Pair	5.00
Hobnail, **Creamer**, Opalescent, Child's, 3 In.High	17.00
Hobnail, **Cup**, Punch, Opalescent	25.00
Hobnail, **Eggcup**, Double, English	16.50
Hobnail, **Epergne**, Opalescent, Light Blue, Three Arms, Crisscross Design	28.50
Hobnail, **Ewer**, Blue, Pointed, Spatulated Handle, Ground Pontil, 7 1/2 In.	45.00
Hobnail, **Mug**, Blue	25.00
Hobnail, **Mug**, Child's, Blue	20.00
Hobnail, **Mug**, Child's, Blue, Pointed Hobs	18.00
Hobnail, **Perfume**, Opalescent, Cranberry	65.00
Hobnail, **Pitcher**, Water, Straw Markings In Glass, 2 Quart	30.00
Hobnail, **Plate**, Opalescent, White, Ruffled, 7 In.	7.50
Hobnail, **Sauce & Plate**, English, Westmoreland, Amber, 6 & 8 In.	18.00

Hobnail, Sauce, Opalescent, 5 In.	22.50
Hobnail, Shade, Gas Light, Opalescent, Blue, Scalloped Edge	30.00
Hobnail, Spooner, Opalescent	15.00 To 30.00
Hobnail, Spooner, Opalescent, Ruffled Edge	18.00
Hobnail, Spooner, Ruffled, Amber Rim	23.50
Hobnail, Sugar, Creamer, & Spooner, Opalescent, Clear, 3 In.High	27.50
Hobnail, Sugar & Creamer, Opalescent, Blue	18.00
Hobnail, Sugar & Creamer, Opalescent, Fiery	40.00
Hobnail, Syrup, Opalescent, Blue, Applied Handle, Silver Plate Top	45.00
Hobnail, Toothpick, Blue	4.50
Hobnail, Toothpick, Opalescent	15.00
Hobnail, Toothpick, Opalescent, Footed	14.00 To 18.00
Hobnail, Tray, Opalescent, 5 X 9 In., Oval	17.00
Hobnail, Tumbler, Opalescent	12.00
Hobnail, Tumbler, Opalescent, Seven Rows Of Hobs	24.00
Hobnail, Tumbler, Opalescent, Eight Rows Of Hobs	34.00
Hobnail, Vase, Opalescent, Green, Triangular Shape, 3 3/4 In.	5.00
Hobnail, Vase, Opalescent, Green, White Cased, Ruffled Top, 8 In.High	27.50

Hochst, or Hoechst, Porcelain was made in Germany from 1746 to 1796. It was marked with a six-spoke wheel.

Hochst, Cup & Saucer, Marked, Circa 1770	180.00
Hochst, Cup & Saucer, Miniature, C.1760	*Illus* 275.00

Holly Amber, or Golden Agate, Glass was made by the Indiana Tumbler and Goblet Company from January 1, 1903, to June 13, 1903. It is a pressed glass pattern featuring holly leaves in the amber shaded glass.

Holly Amber, Bowl, 8 1/2 X 4 In.Deep	450.00
Holly Amber, Butter, Covered	590.00
Holly Amber, Compote Covered, Large	1000.00
Holly Amber, Compote, Jelly	850.00
Holly Amber, Compote, Open On Standard, 8 In.Diameter, 6 1/2 In.High	325.00
Holly Amber, Compote, Open, 8 1/2 X 8 In., High	550.00
Holly Amber, Creamer	240.00
Holly Amber, Pickle, Handles	225.00 To 240.00
Holly Amber, Pitcher, 4 In.	*Illus* 490.00

Holly Amber, Pitcher, 4 In.

Hochst, Cup & Saucer, Miniature, C.1760

Holly Amber, Relish	110.00
Holly Amber, Sauce	150.00 To 175.00
Holly Amber, Spooner	395.00 To 600.00
Holly Amber, Spooner	600.00
Holly Amber, Sugar, Covered	275.00
Holly Amber, Syrup	795.00
Holly Amber, Syrup, 6 In.High	550.00
Holly Amber, Toothpick	155.00
Holly Amber, Tray	700.00
Hopalong Cassidy, Binoculars, Metal, Decals	5.00

Hopalong Cassidy, Clock, Alarm, U.S.Time Corporation	70.00
Hopalong Cassidy, Glass, White With Black Picture	5.00
Hopalong Cassidy, Mug, Milk Glass	2.50
Hopalong Cassidy, Wallet, Color Picture On Side	5.00
Hopalong Cassidy, Watch, Running	12.50
Hopalong Cassidy, Watch, U.S.Time, Band, Large Size	45.00
Hopalong Cassidy, Watch, U.S.Time, Band, Small Size	45.00

Hull Pottery is made in Crooksville, Ohio. The factory started in 1903 as the Acme Pottery Company.Art Pottery was first made in 1917.

Hull, Vase, Cream To Blue, Embossed Pink Flowers, Label	15.00
Hull, Vase, Embossed Flowers, Yellow Rose, Green, Two Handles	7.00
Hull, Vase, Pink To Blue, Embossed Yellow & Pink Floral, Handles, 9 In.	15.00
Hull, Vase, Pink To Blue, Matte, Floral, Artist-Signed, 8 In.	11.00
Hull, Vase, Pink To Cream To Blue, Raised Floral, 6 1/2 In.	10.00
Hull, Vase, Pink, White Spatter, Black Top & Handles, 11 In.High	12.00
Hull, Vase, Yellow To Pink, Handles, 6 1/2 In.High	5.00
Hummel, Figurine, Angel, Rust Robe, Blue Wings, Bee Mark	29.00
Hummel, Figurine, Goose Girl, Circa 1945, Mark, 5 3/4 In.High	35.00
Hummel, Figurine, Hear Ye, 5 1/4 In.High	22.50
Hummel, Figurine, Hear Ye, 6 In.High	31.00
Hummel, Figurine, Hear Ye, 7 In.High	53.00
Hummel, Figurine, Heavenly Angel, 4 1/4 In.High	15.00
Hummel, Figurine, Heavenly Angel, 6 In.High	20.00
Hummel, Figurine, Heavenly Angel, 6 3/4 In.High	25.00
Hummel, Figurine, Heavenly Angel, 8 3/4 In.High	48.00
Hummel, Figurine, Little Helper, 4 1/2 In.High	24.00
Hummel, Figurine, School Boy, 4 1/2 In.	21.00
Hummel, Figurine, Wayside Harmony, 4 1/2 In.	22.00
Hummel, Wine, Porcelain Figure Stem, Boy, Glass Bowl, Gold Overlay, Grapes	25.00
Hummel, Wine, Porcelain Figure Stem, Girl, Glass Bowl, Gold Overlay, Grapes	25.00
Hummel, Wine, Porcelain Figure Stem, Monk, Glass Bowl, Gold Overlay, Grapes	25.00
Icon, Russian, Archangel Michael, Repousse Gilt Metal, C.1850	160.00
Icon, Russian, Burning Bush, Repousse Gilt Metal, C.1850	150.00
Icon, Russian, Christ Pantocrator, C.1820, 12 1/8 X 10 1/2 In.	350.00
Icon, Russian, Christ Pantocrator, Repousse Gilded Silver, C.1850	425.00
Icon, Russian, Christ Pantocrator, Repousse Gilt Metal, C.1850	450.00 To 800.00
Icon, Russian, Christ Pantocrator, St.Joseph, St.Martyr Ulita, C.1820	650.00
Icon, Russian, Christ Pantocrator, St.Kozmas, Damian, & Anthony, C.1850	180.00
Icon, Russian, Complete Resurrection, Provincial School, C.1850	80.00
Icon, Russian, Crucifixion, Brass Crucifix, Wood, C.1850	300.00
Icon, Russian, Five Saints, Afanasi, Medost, Vlasi, Flor, Lavr, & Christ, 1850	170.00
Icon, Russian, Life Of St.Elijah, C.1850, 12 1/2 X 10 1/2 In.	140.00
Icon, Russian, Life Of St.John The Baptist, C.1850	125.00
Icon, Russian, Madonna & Child, Vladimir, Engraved Silver, Dated 1872	395.00
Icon, Russian, Our Lady Iverskaya, Repousse Gilt Metal, C.1850	400.00
Icon, Russian, Our Lady Kazanskaya, Chased Flowers, Enamel, C.1850	1300.00
Icon, Russian, Our Lady Kazanskaya, Parcel Gilt Silver Metal, C.1850	275.00
Icon, Russian, Our Lady Of Joy To Those Who Suffer, Repousse Metal, 1850	140.00
Icon, Russian, Our Lady Smolenskaya, Gilt Metal, C.1890	170.00
Icon, Russian, Our Lady Tichvinskaya, Gilded Silver, C.1900	950.00
Icon, Russian, Our Lady Tichvinskaya, Repousse Gilt Metal, C.1850	120.00
Icon, Russian, Our Lady Umilenie, Repousse Gilt Metal, C.1820	100.00
Icon, Russian, Our Lady Vladimirskaya, C.1820, 12 1/4 X 10 1/4 In.	600.00
Icon, Russian, Our Lady Vladimirskaya, Repousse Gilded Silver, C.1850	225.00
Icon, Russian, Our Lady With Three Hands, Troyaruchitsa, Infant, C.1890	160.00
Icon, Russian, Selected Saints, Bonifanti, Fomaida, Kornili, Moses, C.1850	70.00
Icon, Russian, Selected Saints, C.1820, 14 X 12 1/8 In.	250.00
Icon, Russian, Ss.Catherine, Yevdokia, Yephimi, Nadejda, & Barbara, C.1850	175.00
Icon, Russian, Ss.Foma & Simon, C.1850, 41 X 28 In.	325.00
Icon, Russian, St.Elijah, Biographical, C.1820, 12 3/8 X 10 1/4 In.	80.00
Icon, Russian, St.Elijah, Biographical, Repousse Parcel Gilt Metal, 1850	325.00
Icon, Russian, St.Gennady Of Kostroma Liubimograd, Repousse Silver, 1850	375.00
Icon, Russian, St.Loen, Bishop Of Catania, C.1850, 11 7/8 X 6 In.	130.00
Icon, Russian, St.Nicholas The Miracleworker, C.1820, 11 3/4 X 9 3/4 In.	90.00
Icon, Russian, St.Nicholas The Miracleworker, Christ & Virgin, C.1890	160.00

Icon, Russian, St.Nicholas The Miracleworker, Gilt Metal, C.182	110.00 To 200.00
Icon, Russian, St.Nicholas The Miracleworker, Repousse Gilt Metal, C.1850	125.00
Icon, Russian, St.Nicholas The Miracleworker, Repousse Metal, C.1820	200.00
Icon, Russian, St.Nicholas The Miracleworker, Repousse Silver Metal, 1850	225.00
Icon, Russian, St.Nicholas The Miracleworker, Silver Metal Rizza, C.1850	150.00
Icon, Russian, St.Panteleimon, Enamel Floral, C.1850	120.00
Icon, Russian, St.Panteleimon, Scalpel & Medical Casket, C.1890	100.00
Icon, Russian, Three Saints, Christ, C.1850, 13 1/2 X 11 1/2 In.	375.00
Icon, Russian, Traveling Iconostasis, 15 Arched Hinged Panels, C.1850	1700.00
Icon, Russian, Vernicle, Repousse Gilded Silver, Moscow, 1889	500.00
Icon, Russian, Virgin & Child, Silver, Enamel, G.P.Gratchev, C.1850	725.00

Imari Patterns are named for the Japanese Ware decorated with orange and blue stylized flowers. The design on the Japanese Ware became so characteristic that the name Imari has come to mean any pattern of this type. It was copied by the European factories of the eighteenth and early nineteenth centuries.

Imari, Berry Set, 5 Piece	65.00
Imari, Bottle, Snuff, Cylindrical, Enamel, Dragon, Peonies, Coral Stopper, 1850	80.00
Imari, Bowl, Bamboo Huts, Trees, Panels Inside, Scenes, Blue Printed Borders	110.00
Imari, Bowl, Blue & Red Floral, Turquoise & Blue Inside, 8 1/2 In.	32.50
Imari, Bowl, Blue & White, C.1850, 3 1/4 In.Diameter	15.00
Imari, Bowl, Blue & White, C.1850, 3 1/2 In.Diameter	15.00
Imari, Bowl, Blue & White, C.1850, 6 In.Diameter	15.00 To 20.00
Imari, Bowl, Blue Design, Nest Of 4, 5, 6, 7, & 9 In.	95.00
Imari, Bowl, Fan Shape, Blues & Oranges, 12 X 11 1/2 In.	75.00
Imari, Bowl, Hexagonal, Bombe Sides, 18th Century	225.00
Imari, Bowl, Imperial Grape, 10 1/2 In.	24.00
Imari, Bowl, Open Rose, Collar Base, 7 1/2 In.	16.00
Imari, Bowl, Orange & Blue, 6 In.	25.00
Imari, Bowl, Rectangular, Scenic, Cobalt Blue & White, C.1830	10.00
Imari, Bowl, Rice, Covered, Colored Panels, 6 In.	40.00
Imari, Bowl, White, Blue, Pagodas, Bridge, Fluted Edge, Circa 1850	6.50
Imari, Charger, Blue, White, White Peonies, Butterfly, Foliage, Circa 1820	72.50
Imari, Charger, Nine Immortals, 3 Ring, 16 In.	175.00
Imari, Charger, Panels, Cobalt, Red, Gold, Green, Scalloped Edge, 13 In.	90.00
Imari, Charger, Rust Orange & Blue, 15 In.Diameter	100.00
Imari, Charger, Six Medallions With Figures, 18 In.	225.00
Imari, Cricket Cage, Blue & White Clouds, Birds, Lion Head Handles, Dome Lid	45.00
Imari, Cup & Saucer, Panels, Medallions, Rusts, Blue, Gold, Green	22.00
Imari, Cup, Diaper Pattern, Blue, Handleless	18.00
Imari, Cup, Multicolor Panels, Gold, Blue & Gold Interior, Pedestal Base, 4	57.50
Imari, Cup, White Ground, Panels, Floral, Ring Base, Blue, White & Gold, 4	57.50
Imari, Plate, Basket Of Flowers Center	15.00
Imari, Plate, Blue & White	15.00
Imari, Plate, Blue & White, 9 1/2 In.	45.00
Imari, Plate, Deep Blue, Gold, Three Figures, 8 1/2 In.	45.00
Imari, Plate, Fishes, Blue, Tangerine, 8 1/4 In.	25.00
Imari, Plate, Pheasants, Butterflies, 14 1/2 In.	115.00
Imari, Plate, Scenic Medallions, 8 1/2 In.	22.50
Imari, Plate, Six Panels, Flower Urn Center, Blue Rings Underside	30.00
Imari, Plate, Terra-Cotta & Floral Medallions, Gold Trim	35.00
Imari, Platter, Crane Scene Center, Blue, Orange, Red, Gold, 14 1/2 In.Long	70.00
Imari, Platter, Scalloped Edge, Round	85.00
Imari, Platter, 11 X 9 In.	45.00
Imari, Seat, Garden, Octagonal, Blue & White, 19 1/2 In.High, Pair	450.00
Imari, Stand, Umbrella, Rust & Blue, People	185.00
Imari, Teabowl, Hexagonal	18.50
Imari, Tray, Flower & Leaf Design, Blue, Green, White, 5 X 7	12.00
Imari, Tray, Rectangular, Reds & Blues, Flared Sides, Bracket Edge, C.1880	65.00
Imari, Tureen, Covered, Iron Red Blossoms & Gold On White, 3 Handles	85.00
Imari, Urn, Blue, White, 8 In.High	285.00
Imari, Urn, Dark Blue, Orange, Gold, Lid, 18 In.High	280.00
Imari, Vase, Blue Figural Decoration, Red Petal Top, 16 1/2 In., Pair	375.00
Imari, Vase, Blue, Orange Red, Gold, Hexagon, 8 In.High, Pair	80.00
Imari, Vase, Medallions, Red, Cobalt, Gold, Circa 1800, Bottle Shape, 6 1/2 In.	95.00

Imari, Vase, White Ground, Orange & Blue Decoration, 5 In.High	17.00
Imperial Austria, Plate, Large Blossoms, Buds, Gold Leaves, Signed Renee	12.00
Imperial Austria, Plate, Portrait, Lady In Wreath Of White Blossoms, Marked	29.50
Imperial Austria, Plate, White, Blue, Magenta, & Gold Scrolls	7.50
Imperial Glass, Centerpiece, Floral & Leaf, Clear Crystal, Star Cut Base	60.00
Imperial Glass, Centerpiece, Purple Iridescent, Old Cross Signature	55.00
Imperial Glass, Bowl, Jewels, 10 In.Deep	200.00
Imperial Glass, Bowl, Opaque Iridescent Aqua, C.1920, 9 3/4 In.	60.00
Imperial Glass, Bowl, Stretch, Pink, Footed, 10 In.Diameter	15.00
Imperial Glass, Plate, Chop, Jewels, 12 1/4 In.	250.00
Imperial Glass, Salt, Individual, Candlewick	5.00
Imperial Glass, Vase, Art Glass, Bronze Gold Finish, Flared, Ruffled Top	90.00
Imperial Glass, Vase, Art Glass, Pulled Blue Green Loops On Opaque Orange	125.00
Imperial Glass, Vase, Art Glass, White Hearts, Blue Rim, Iridescent, 9 1/2 In	195.00
Imperial Glass, Vase, Iridescent Amethyst Base, Old Cross Mark	50.00
Imperial Glass, Vase, Jewels, Signed	10.00
Imperial Glass, Vase, White Hearts, Vines, Applied Rim, Cobalt Blue	110.00

Indian Tree is a china pattern that was popular during the last half of the nineteenth century. It was copied from earlier patterns of English China that were very similar. The pattern includes the crooked branch of a tree and a partial landscape with exotic flowers and leaves. It is colored green, blue, pink, and orange. King's Rose Pattern of soft paste Staffordshire was made in England from about 1820 to 1830. It was decorated in pink, red, yellow, and green. The pattern featured a large roselike flower.

Indian Tree; Cauldon, see also Coalport

Indian Tree, Platter, Meat	8.00

Indian Art from North America has attracted the collector for many years. Each tribe has its own distinctive designs and techniques. Baskets, jewelry, and leatherwork are of greatest collector interest.

Indian, Arrowhead, Birdstone	8.00
Indian, Arrowhead, Celt, Flint	.85
Indian, Arrowhead, Folsom	5.00
Indian, Arrowhead, Metates	.35
Indian, Arrowhead, Thunderbird	3.00
Indian, Ax, Fluted, Grooved	8.00
Indian, Bag, Bandolier, Cloth, Multicolor Glass Beads, Woodlands Region	325.00
Indian, Ball, Hide, Multicolor Glass Beads, Geometric Designs, Sioux	150.00
Indian, Banneystone	10.00
Indian, Basket, Alaska, Lid, 1946, 3 In.	30.00
Indian, Basket, Apache, Conical, Geometric Design, 14 1/2 In.Diameter	40.00
Indian, Basket, Apache, Shallow Round Body, Radiating Zig-Zag, 15 In.	325.00
Indian, Basket, Attu, 7 In.High *Illus*	100.00
Indian, Basket, Brown & Blue Thread, Cross & Rectangles, Tlingit	80.00
Indian, Basket, Coiled, Brown Thread, Geometric Motifs, Feathers, Tulare	110.00
Indian, Basket, Coiled, Brown Thread, Geometric, Floral, Southern California	170.00

Indian, Basket, Attu, 7 In.High

Indian, Basket, Lidded, Openwork, Multicolor Thread, Floral, Attu	375.00
Indian, Basket, Lidded, Openwork, Multicolor Thread, Geometric, Attu	340.00
Indian, Basket, North California, Coiled, Angular Geometric Design, 9 In.	160.00
Indian, Basket, Pima, Coiled, Circular Tondo, Rim Border, 11 1/2 In.Diameter	90.00
Indian, Basket, Pima, Flaring Cylindrical Body, Brown, Rim Border, 11 In.	170.00
Indian, Basket, Pima, Shallow, Brown, Stepped Design, 4 1/2 In.Diameter	40.00
Indian, Basket, Round, Multicolor Glass Bead Geometric Design, 4 1/2 In.	175.00
Indian, Basket, Southeastern, Footed, Geometric Design, 6 1/2 In.Diameter	100.00
Indian, Basket, Southwestern, Beaded, 5 In.Diameter _Illus_	325.00
Indian, Basket, Woven Designs, Lid, Nootka Tribe, 2 1/2 X 3 In.	30.00
Indian, Bead, Trade, Black Glass, 100	5.00
Indian, Bead, Trade, Chevron, Glass, Oval	.45
Indian, Bead, Trade, Coralene, D'Aleppo, Polychrome, 50	40.00
Indian, Bead, Trade, Hudson Bay, Red Glass, 20 In.String	2.50
Indian, Bead, Trade, Hudson Bay, 48 Polychromed Kitty Fisher Eyes	75.00
Indian, Bead, Trade, Mellon, Yellow, Glass	1.50
Indian, Bead, Trade, Millefiori, Grave Dug, 33 In.Long	35.00
Indian, Bead, Trade, Mosaic Type, Prismatic, Red, Glass, 20 In.String	7.00
Indian, Bead, Trade, Mosaics, Multicolored, Glass	.40
Indian, Bead, Trade, Nugget, Gold Red, Glass, 20 In.String	8.50
Indian, Bead, Trade, Overlay Barrel, Glass, 20 In.String	10.75
Indian, Bead, Trade, Venetian Glass, Millefiori, 26 In.Long	35.00
Indian, Bell, Ankle, Dance, River Crows, Montana	25.00
Indian, Bell, Dance, Ankle, On Leather, River Crows, Montana, Circa 1880	35.00
Indian, Belt, Butterfly Conchos, Pawn Silver, Buckle, Turquoise, Navajo	225.00
Indian, Belt, Conch, Navajo, Silver, Turquoise	125.00
Indian, Belt, Hide, Northern Ute, Fort Dueschene, Utah, Multicolor Beads	70.00
Indian, Belt, Hide, Rectangular, Multicolor Glass Beads, Metal Buckle, Sioux	120.00
Indian, Belt, Medicine Man's, Ceremonial, Beaded, Chippewa	95.00
Indian, Blanket, Navajo, Red, Cream, Brown	75.00
Indian, Blanket, Saddle, Hide, Tassel, Multicolor Glass Beads, Sioux	900.00
Indian, Boot, Hide, Yellow Stained, Multicolor Glass Beads, Sioux, Pair	375.00
Indian, Bracelet, Bangle, Navajo, Pair	10.00
Indian, Bracelet, Coral Stone, Sterling, Navajo	40.00
Indian, Bracelet, Navajo, Three Large Turquoises, Sterling Silver	50.00
Indian, Bracelet, Pawn, Butterfly, 5 Turquoise, Sterling Silver, Navajo	68.00
Indian, Bracelet, Seven Channel Turquoise Stones, Silver, Zuni, Pair	70.00
Indian, Bracelet, Turquoise Center, Two Corals, Navajo, Circa 1910, Silver	60.00
Indian, Breastplate, 67 Bones, 236 Peking Glass Trade Beads, Sioux	125.00
Indian, Button, Star Design, Silver, Navajo, 1 In.Diameter, Pair	10.00
Indian, Cap, Basketry, Brown Thread, Geometric Designs, Yurok-Karok	100.00
Indian, Doll, Ceremonial, Hopi Kachina, Wooden, C.1900, 9 1/2 In.Tall	18.00
Indian, Doll, Plains Region, 18 In.Tall _Illus_	525.00
Indian, Drum, Goatskin, Thunderbirds On Both Covers, Handmade, 10 In.	35.00
Indian, Earring, Hopi, Inlaid Turquoise, Sterling Silver, Pair	10.00
Indian, Earring, Santa Domingo, 92 Blue Turquoises, Pair	50.00
Indian, Fetish, Bear Skull, Hide, Bone, Carved, Northwest Coast Region	525.00
Indian, Fetish, Navajo, Snake Figure, 7 In.Long	15.00
Indian, Fish Hook, Flint	3.00
Indian, Holster, Sioux, Deerskin, Buckskin Fringe, Slotted For Belt, 1890	35.00
Indian, Knife, Horn Handle, Montana Crow	7.00
Indian, Ladle, Horn, Pierced Handle, Northwest Coast Region	60.00
Indian, Ladle, Mountain Sheep Horn, Abalone Shell Inlay, Carved, Haida	475.00
Indian, Mask, Dance, Corn, Pierced Eyes & Mouth, Fringed, Onondaga, N.Y.	100.00
Indian, Mask, Eskimo, Hide, Pierced Mouth & Eyes, Areas Of Fur	100.00
Indian, Moccasin, Child's, Beaded At Top & Front, Pair	25.00
Indian, Moccasin, Hide, Child's, Multicolor Glass Beads, Quills, Sioux, Pair	70.00
Indian, Moccasin, Hide, Ocher Stain, Multicolor Glass Beads, Plains, Pair	60.00
Indian, Moccasin, Sioux, Pair _Illus_	110.00
Indian, Moccasin, Squaw, Northwest Coast, Deerskin & Felt, C.1910, Pair	45.00
Indian, Moccasin, Tassels, Red, White, & Blue Glass Beads, Sioux, Pair	90.00
Indian, Moccasin, Yakima Tribe, Beaded, Pair	70.00
Indian, Moccasin, Yellow Stain, Multicolor Glass Beads, Sioux, Pair	70.00
Indian, Necklace, Honeycomb Coral, Navajo, 32 In.	55.00
Indian, Necklace, Hudson Bay Crows, Bear Claw, 28 In.Long	150.00
Indian, Necklace, Mother-Of-Pearl Bird Fetishes, Abalone Shell Beads	150.00

Indian, Basket, Southwestern, Beaded, 5 In.Diameter
See Page 270

Indian, Doll,
Plains Region,
18 In.Tall
See Page 270

Indian, Moccasin,
Sioux, Pair
See Page 270

Indian, Necklace, Navajo, Coral, Honeycomb, Three Strands, 11 1/2 In.Long 85.00
Indian, Necklace, Navajo, Squash Blossom, Silver Leaf, Turquoise, 1900s 475.00
Indian, Necklace, Navajo, Squash Blossoms, Blue Morenci .... 475.00 To 550.00
Indian, Necklace, Navajo, Squash Blossoms, Turquoise, Shadow Box Setting 500.00
Indian, Necklace, Navajo, Squash Blossoms, Sterling, 31 In., C.1930 .... 350.00
Indian, Necklace, Navajo, 18 Turquoises, 12 Silver Squash Blossoms 525.00
Indian, Necklace, Sioux, Bear Claw, Cobalt Beads, 32 In. 250.00
Indian, Necklace, Sleepy Eye, Turquoise, Sterling, Navajo 450.00
Indian, Necklace, Squash Blossom, Blue Diamond Turquoise, Sterling, Navajo 900.00
Indian, Necklace, Squash Blossom, Coral, Pawn, Sterling, Bracelet, Navajo 410.00
Indian, Necklace, Squash Blossoms, Pawn, Turquoise, Sterling, Navajo 595.00
Indian, Necklace, Sterling Silver, Squash Blossom, Turquoise, Fox Tail Chain 425.00
Indian, Needle, Bone 2.50
Indian, Painting, Sand, Navajo, Prehistoric Horses, 12 In.Square 22.50
Indian, Peace Pipe, Effigy 9.75
Indian, Pin, Silver, Crossed Arrows, Turquoise 12.00
Indian, Pipe Bowl, Black Steatite, Horse's Head Form, Arapaho 50.00
Indian, Pipe Tomahawk, Wooden Stem, Steel Head, Flaring Bowl, Plains Region 375.00
Indian, Pipe, Columbia River, Steatite Green, Carved, Cane Stem 125.00
Indian, Pipe, Effigy, Clay 5.00
Indian, Pipe, Effigy, Pottery 7.00
Indian, Pipe, Trade, Effigy Face 2.00
Indian, Pitcher, Sioux Pottery, White, Designs, Signed M.Black Tall Deer 50.00
Indian, Pottery, Vessel, Round, Angular Geometric Design, Pueblo, 6 5/8 In. 30.00
Indian, Pottery, Vessel, Round, Scrolling Geometric Design, Pueblo, 9 In. 90.00
Indian, Pouch, Basketry, Rectangular Corn Husk, Hide, Colored Wool, Nez Perce 100.00
Indian, Pouch, Cloth, Rectangular, Multicolor Glass Beads, Horse, Nez Perce 170.00
Indian, Pouch, Hide, Rectangular, Blue, Red, & Green Glass Beads, Sioux 50.00
Indian, Pouch, Hide, Rectangular, Glass Beads In Geometric, Plateau Region 325.00
Indian, Pouch, Hide, Rectangular, Multicolor Glass Beads, Shells, Plains 160.00
Indian, Quiver, Hide, Tassels, Multicolor Glass Beads, Painted, Sioux 1000.00
Indian, Ring, Lady's, Green Turquoise, Silver Rope Setting, Navajo 45.00

Indian, Ring, Lady's, Pawn, Green Turquoise Stone, Tan Matrix Stone, Navajo	65.00
Indian, Ring, Man's, Turquoise, Coral, Silver Leaf Design, Navajo	65.00
Indian, Ring, Navajo, Blue Gem Turquoise, Sterling Silver	45.00
Indian, Ring, Navajo, Blue Lone Mountain Turquoise, Sterling Silver	25.00
Indian, Ring, Navajo, Shadow Box Turquoise	25.00
Indian, Ring, Navajo, Sterling Silver, Coral Set Into Shadow Box	25.00
Indian, Ring, Turquoise, Coral, Sterling, Navajo, Circa 1900	29.00
Indian, Rug, see also Textile, Rug, Navajo	
Indian, Rug, Navajo, Beige, Brown, Red, 27 X 54 In.	85.00
Indian, Rug, Navajo, Geometric Design, Green, Brick, Black, 55 X 84 In.	300.00
Indian, Rug, Navajo, Gray, Black, Red, Tan, Double Tree Pattern, 43 X 60 In.	90.00
Indian, Rug, Navajo, Storm Pattern, Red, Gray, C.1900, 22 1/2 X 36 In.	200.00
Indian, Rug, Navajo, Woolen, Angular Motifs, Zigzag Border, 69 1/2 X 48 In.	225.00
Indian, Rug, Navajo, Woolen, Figures, C.1948, 43 X 56 In.	
Indian, Rug, Navajo, Woolen, Openwork Motif, 1895, 92 X 59 In.	190.00
Indian, Rug, Navajo, Woolen, Toothed Step Design, 122 X 51 In.	475.00
Indian, Rug, Navajo, Woolen, C.1925, 89 X 58 In. *Illus*	575.00
Indian, Rug, Navajo, Yei, Six Figures, Reversible, 1952, 2 1/2 X 4 1/2 In.	100.00
Indian, Rug, Navajo, Yei, Woolen, 34 1/2 X 68 In. *Illus*	275.00
Indian, Rug, Woolen, Toothed & Hooked Medallions, 64 X 33 In.	90.00
Indian, Scraper	.35 To .60
Indian, Spear, 15 In.	22.50
Indian, Spoon, Horn, Eskimo, Oval Engraved Bowl, Reindeer, Pierced Stem	100.00
Indian, Spoon, Horn, Haida, 6 3/4 In.Long *Illus*	250.00
Indian, Spoon, Mountain Goat Horn, Oval Bowl, Openwork, Carved, Haida	250.00
Indian, Teaspoon, Navajo, Coin Silver, Decorated	15.00
Indian, Throw, Woolen, Bands Of Varying Width, Navajo, 1900, 26 1/2 X 16 In.	45.00
Indian, Tom-Tom, Hollow Pine Log, Rawhide Heads	27.00
Indian, Tomahawk, Ceremonial, Multicolor Glass Beads, Steatite Head, Sioux	160.00
Indian, Tomahawk, Flint	3.75
Indian, Tomahawk, Pierced Wood, Steel Blade, Knopped Butt, Plains Region	250.00
Indian, Tomahawk, Stone	3.50
Indian, Totem Pole, Openwork, Raven, Bear, & Human, Haida	725.00
Indian, Trade Beads, Egg Shaped Peking Glass Beads, Cranberry, 66 Beads	25.00
Indian, Trade Beads, Yellow Onyx, Opaque, Hudson Bay, 24 In.	25.00
Indian, Vessel, Wooden, Seal Form, Inlaid Ivory, Shell, & Glass, Kwakiutl	400.00
Indian, Vest, Hide, Multicolor Glass Beads, Faceted Metal Beads, Sioux	280.00
Indian, Wand, Dance, Wooden, Notched, Figure Of Bird, Painted, Plains Region	500.00
Indian, Whip, Marine Ivory Handle, Plaited Hide Lash, Plains Region, 15 Ft.	80.00
Inkstand, Clear Glass, Twin Wells, Bakelite Covered, Marked Victor, 3 Pens	12.50
Inkstand, Continental, Steel & Brass, C.1790 *Illus*	450.00
Inkstand, Faience, Parrot On Stand, Two Wells, Shell Shape Base, Serpents	45.00
Inkstand, Figural, Opera Glasses On Fan, Blue Birds, Branch, France, 1890	55.00
Inkstand, Green Jade, Silver Mounted Carnelian Feet, Farmer, N.Y., C.1900	250.00
Inkstand, Six Holes On Flat Plate, Pewter, Pottery Insert, English, C.1840	55.00
Inkwell, see also Pewter, Inkwell	
Inkwell, Bakelite Top, Black, Marked Defiance Mfg.	4.75
Inkwell, Bear, Two Wells On Tray, Russian Porcelain, Kornilov, 1860	550.00
Inkwell, Black Marble, Marble Wells, Bronze Sphinx In Center, France	165.00
Inkwell, Blue, Cut Glass, Hexagon, Hinged Top, Ormolu Mounts	28.00
Inkwell, Brass Base, Lift Up Cover, Clear Glass Insert	8.75
Inkwell, Brass, Pierced, Leaf & Floral, Animal Like Faces, 6 In.High	110.00
Inkwell, Bronze, Double, Lid	6.50
Inkwell, Bronze, Negro On Lid With Hat, 6 In.Long	120.00
Inkwell, Cameo Cut Green Florals, Sterling Silver Hinged Cover, Signed	195.00
Inkwell, Car Shape, Glass Insert, Dated 1907, 5 In.Long, 3 In.High	49.50
Inkwell, Child's, Iron Rabbit By Head Of Lettuce, Painted	25.00
Inkwell, Clear Crystal, Octagon, Sets In Blue Triangle Holder, Pen Place	32.50
Inkwell, Clear Glass Horseshoe Base, Jockey Cap Lid, Hinged	26.50
Inkwell, Clear Glass, Pen Rack, Marked Paragon Stop Cover, Pat.1913	4.50
Inkwell, Crystal, Engraved Iris, Signed L.Parot, Art Nouveau	105.00
Inkwell, Crystal, Floral, Double, Sterling Hinged Tops	35.00
Inkwell, Crystal, Paperweight Type, Cover, Beaded Cut	19.50
Inkwell, Cut Stars, Thumbprint, Pewter Over Brass Collar, Chinese Crystal	55.00
Inkwell, Double Wells, Sphinx Covers, Ornate, Brass, 10 X 14 In.Long	125.00
Inkwell, Double, Hand-Wrought Iron, Hinged Covers, Relief Beetles, 7 X 5 In.	20.00

Inkwell, **Double**, Pen Rack Between, Bronze & Sterling, Pat.1912	9.75
Inkwell, **Figural**, Dog, Painted Features, Glass Eyes, Paperweight, 1900, 4 In.	18.00
Inkwell, **Figural**, German Helmet, Red Black Glass, Gold Spike Stopper	38.50
Inkwell, **Figural**, Monk, Hat Is Hinged Lid, Pewter	35.00
Inkwell, **Floral**, Gold, Attached To Plate, Two Liners, Porcelain, Germany	70.00
Inkwell, **German Commemorative**, Pewter, Bronze Finish, Kayserzinn, 1913	45.00
Inkwell, **Glass Slipper**, Circa 1850	25.00
Inkwell, **Glass**, Pen Rack In Front, Made By Defiance Mfg. Co., N.Y.	4.75
Inkwell, **Hinged Cover**, Letter & Pen Holder, Iron, Glass Well	24.00
Inkwell, **Hinged Lid**, Brass, Porcelain Liner, Attached To Brass Tray	16.50
Inkwell, **Horseshoe Base**, Hinged Jockey Cap Lid	25.00
Inkwell, **Houlin**, Double, Dated, 1864, Iron, Clear Glass Tip Up Wells	25.00
Inkwell, **House Scene**, Old Mission Church, Sepias, Hand-Painted, Porcelain	65.00
Inkwell, **Indian Warrior**, Glass Eyes, Enamel War Paint, Gilt Bronze	365.00
Inkwell, **Kaiser Wilhelm Helmet**, German Silver Over Pewter, Glass Well	45.00
Inkwell, **Lacy**, Cast Iron, Swirl Bottle	25.00
Inkwell, **Lion's Head**, Open Mouth, Red Tongue, Metal, Porcelain Insert	28.00
Inkwell, **Maiden Dressed In Blue Gown**, Shell Base, Majolica	30.00
Inkwell, **Marble**, Round Base, Brass Feet In Well With Lid, Peacock Finial	95.00
Inkwell, **Metal Pig**, Brass Well, C.1875	15.00

Indian, Spoon, Horn,
Haida, 6 3/4 In.Long
See Page 272

Inkstand, Continental,
Steel & Brass, C.1790

Indian, Rug, Navajo, Woolen,
C.1925, 89 X 58 In.
See Page 272

Indian, Rug, Navajo, Yei, Woolen, 34 1/2 X 68 In.
See Page 272

Inkwell, Metal, Glass, 5 In. .... *Illus*	80.00
Inkwell, Old Hindu Sitting On Rug, Playing Instrument, Signed	55.00
Inkwell, Ornate Design Of Scroll Masks, Brass, Glass Inset, 6 In.Square	50.00
Inkwell, Owl, Metal, Glass Eyes, Head Opens	32.00
Inkwell, Paperweight, Crystal, Tufted Design, Silver Hinged Top	75.00
Inkwell, Paperweight, Intaglio Roses, Lid, Signed Sinclaire	45.00
Inkwell, Pewter, Dead Bird, 6 In. .... *Illus*	60.00
Inkwell, Pink Opaque, Swirled, Gold Between Swirls, Hinged Lid	18.00
Inkwell, Pink To Rose, Roses, Scalloped Edge Underplate, Gold, Porcelain	28.00
Inkwell, Porcelain Stand, Enameled Floral, France	29.00
Inkwell, Porcelain, Dog Reclining At Back	40.00
Inkwell, Porcelain, Woman Reclining On Lounge, Book, Peacock At Her Side	225.00
Inkwell, Rainbow Iridescence, 4 In.Square, Brass Lid, Milk Glass Insert	35.00
Inkwell, Raised Lily Of The Valley, Morning Glory, Black Milk Glass, 1887	45.00
Inkwell, School Desk, Black Bakelite Top	2.50
Inkwell, School Desk, Southern Mexico, Hand Blown, Cobalt Blue	1.50
Inkwell, Seated Lady, Porcelain, 9 In. .... *Illus*	75.00

Inkwell, Metal, Glass, 5 In.   Inkwell, Pewter, Dead Bird, 6 In.

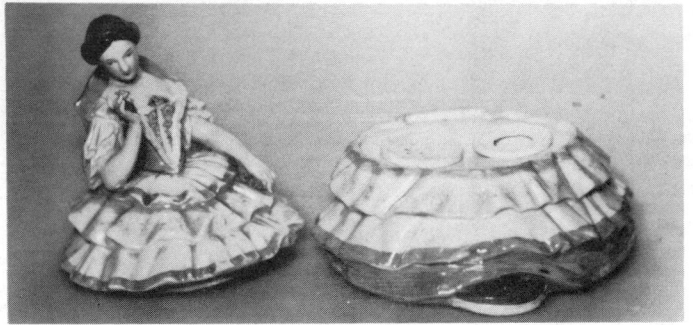

Inkwell, Seated Lady, Porcelain, 9 In.

Inkwell, Shape Of German Helmet, Metal, White Porcelain Insert, Hinged Lid	35.00
Inkwell, Ship's, Form Of Squat Teapot, Porcelain Liner	25.00
Inkwell, Silver Plate Stand, Crystal Inserts, Bud Vase Center, Art Nouveau	75.00
Inkwell, Single Well, Ornate, Brass, Griffin Cover & Insert, 8 X 11 In.Long	75.00
Inkwell, Swirl Design, Star In Base, Circa 1870, 2 1/8 In.Square	3.98
Inkwell, Swirl Design, Star In Base, Cover, Glass	5.98
Inkwell, Thick Glass, Stag's Head On Metal Base, Silver .... *Color*	25.00
Inkwell, Three Mold, Olive Green	125.00
Inkwell, Thumbprint, Cut Glass, Brass Hinged Top	20.00
Inkwell, Traveling, Leather Covered, Spring Latch	14.00
Inkwell, Traveling, Push Button Releases Spring Loaded Top, Glass Filler	19.00
Inkwell, Traveling, Rosewood Case	23.00

Inkwell, Traveling, Rosewood, Blown Glass Insert, 2 1/2 In.High	15.00
Inkwell, Traveling, Shape Of Satchel, Metal Top, Wooden Base, Miniature	20.00
Inkwell, Tree Trunk, Milk Glass Insert, Picture Of Monk On Cover	10.00
Inkwell, Violets, Cupid, Gold, Lavender, Two Wells, Covers, Place For Pen	30.00
Inkwell, White Friar, Paperweight, Candy Cane Bottom & Stopper, 6 In.High	185.00
Inkwell, White Lead, Milk Glass Insert, Oriental	6.50
Inkwell, White Porcelain Insert, Holder For Pens In Front, Iron, Pat.1873	11.75

Insulators of glass or pottery have been made for use on telegraph or telephone poles since 1844.

Insulator, A.T.& T.Co., CD 121	14.00
Insulator, A.T.& T.Co., Embossed On Crown, Aqua	6.50
Insulator, Agee, Tepee Shape, Purple	12.50
Insulator, American Insulator Co., Three Dates, Ice Blue	12.50
Insulator, Armstrong, CD 217, 51 C3, Dark Amber	7.00
Insulator, Armstrong, CD 511a	7.00
Insulator, Armstrong, CD 511a, Deep Amber	5.00 To 8.50
Insulator, Armstrong, No.51-C3, Amber	9.50
Insulator, Armstrong, No.51-C3, Root Beer Color	7.50
Insulator, B.T.C., Montreal, Pony, Ice Blue	5.00
Insulator, Beehive, Pleated	20.00
Insulator, Bell, Dark Purple	32.00
Insulator, Bennington Type	1.50
Insulator, Brookfield, Beehive	1.50
Insulator, Brookfield, CD 104, W.Brookfield, 55 Fulton St.	8.00
Insulator, Brookfield, CD 205	6.00 TO 10.00
Insulator, Brookfield, Hoopskirt, Deep Olive	7.50
Insulator, Brookfield, No.48, Blue	8.00
Insulator, Brookfield, No.48, Snowflake	8.00
Insulator, Brookfield, Railroad Signal Type, Embossed P.R.R., Green	6.00
Insulator, Brookfield, Spiral, 1907	2.50
Insulator, Brookfield, 45 Cliff St.	2.50
Insulator, Bullet, C.N.R., Canada, Emerald Green	11.00
Insulator, Bullet, Canada, Sun Colored Amethyst	100.00
Insulator, Bullet, Ice Blue, Canada	10.00
Insulator, C.D.& P.Tel.Co., Toll, Aqua	8.00
Insulator, C.P.R., Purple, Beehive	8.00
Insulator, C.P.R., White, Beehive	6.00
Insulator, Cable Top, CD 252, Embossed, H 62, Clear	50.00
Insulator, Cable, No.2, Pale Aqua	10.00
Insulator, Cable, No.3, Aqua	20.00 To 25.00
Insulator, Cable, No.3, Dark Green	35.00
Insulator, California, CD 145, V.N.M., Sun Colored Amethyst	20.00
Insulator, California, CD 152, Sun Colored Amethyst	5.00
Insulator, California, CD 166, Sage	6.00
Insulator, California, Signal, Burgundy	12.50
Insulator, California, Signal, Green	5.00
Insulator, California, Signal, Pink	7.50
Insulator, Canada, Bullet, Dwight Pattern, Green	8.00
Insulator, Canada, CD 190-191, Transposition, Embossed Diamond, Purple	75.00
Insulator, Canada, Ice Blue	12.00
Insulator, Canada, Lime Green	25.00
Insulator, Canada, N.M.	13.00 To 65.00
Insulator, Canada, Pony, Aqua	1.00
Insulator, Canada, Ridged, Vertical, Aqua	30.00
Insulator, Canadian Pacific Railroad, Baby Beehive, Purple	17.50
Insulator, Canadian Pacific, Beehive, Dark Amethyst	21.00
Insulator, Canadian, Ponies, Amethyst	5.00
Insulator, Canadian, Tolls, Amethyst	6.00
Insulator, Carnival Glass, Marigold, Giant, Pyrex, Usa	65.00
Insulator, Carnival Glass, 3 In.High	10.00
Insulator, Carnival, Pyrex, 3 1/2 In.	12.00
Insulator, CD 54ab, Transposition, Sun Colored Amethyst	35.00 To 37.50
Insulator, CD 120, Pleated Skirts, Aqua	8.00
Insulator, CD 145, B, Emerald & Olive Green	2.00
Insulator, CD 164, No.38, 20, Aqua	2.00

Insulator, CD 433	15.00
Insulator, CD 511a, Amber	7.00
Insulator, CD 512, Bug Eyes	5.00
Insulator, CD 512, Carnival Glass	20.00 To 25.00
Insulator, Chicago Electrical Supply, CD 133, Aqua	20.00
Insulator, City Fire Alarm Signal	50.00
Insulator, Columbia, Green	20.00
Insulator, Columbia, No.2, LSV, Threadless, Lime Green	20.00
Insulator, Corkscrew Salt Threads	125.00
Insulator, Corning, Large Size	50.00
Insulator, Diamond, Pony, Amber	5.00
Insulator, Diamond, Pony, Black Glass	6.00
Insulator, Diamond, Pony, Ice Blue	3.50
Insulator, Diamond, Transposition, Two Piece, Dark Amethyst	32.00
Insulator, Diamond, Transposition, Two Piece, Light Amethyst	35.00
Insulator, Dominion, No.42, Straw	8.00
Insulator, Dominion, No.614, Light Green	4.00
Insulator, Dominion, No.614, Straw	4.00
Insulator, Double Diamond, Pony, Ice Blue	3.50
Insulator, Double Star, CD 145, Aqua	6.00
Insulator, Duquesne Glass Co., Aqua	22.00
Insulator, Duquesne Keg	150.00
Insulator, Dwight, Beehive, Ice Blue	12.50
Insulator, Dwight, Bullet	12.50
Insulator, Dwight, CD 143, Aqua	4.00
Insulator, Edmonton, Dunvegan, & British Columbia Railway, CD 145, Blue	25.00
Insulator, English, Ceramic, White, 2 Piece	6.75
Insulator, Error, Lynchbor Made In No.44, U.S.A., Green, 44 Backwards	5.00
Insulator, Fireplug, No.1002	5.00
Insulator, Fireplug, No.10003, Large Style	15.00
Insulator, Fog Bowl, Gray, Porcelain	5.00
Insulator, G.E.Co., CD 134	10.00
Insulator, G.E.Co., Petticoat, Beehive, Ice Blue	1.00
Insulator, G.N.W.Tel.Co., Deep Purple	15.00
Insulator, Gaynor, CD 44	3.00
Insulator, Gaynor, CD 48-400, Aqua	8.00
Insulator, Gaynor, CD 530	25.00
Insulator, Gaynor, CD 530, Drip Points	15.00
Insulator, H.G.Co., Beehive, Jade Milk Glass	7.50 To 8.00
Insulator, H.G.Co., CD 151, Cornflower	30.00
Insulator, H.G.Co., Natco, Aqua	12.00
Insulator, H.K.Porter	3.50
Insulator, Hawley, Beehive	7.50
Insulator, Hawley, CD 102	10.00
Insulator, Helmet, Ceramic, Brown	10.00
Insulator, Hemingray, CD 128	1.50
Insulator, Hemingray, CD 168	4.00
Insulator, Hemingray, CD 238, Clear	4.50
Insulator, Hemingray, Mickey Mouse	6.00
Insulator, Hemingray, Muncie, Aqua, 7 In.	35.00
Insulator, Hemingray, No.D-510	5.00 To 35.00
Insulator, Hemingray, No.D-510, Aqua	3.00
Insulator, Hemingray, No.D-512	5.00
Insulator, Hemingray, No.D-512, Ice Blue	9.50
Insulator, Hemingray, No.D-514	4.50
Insulator, Hemingray, No.1	25.00
Insulator, Hemingray, No.1, CD 281, High Voltage	3.00
Insulator, Hemingray, No.8, Aqua	12.00
Insulator, Hemingray, No.9	1.00
Insulator, Hemingray, No.9, Clear	.50
Insulator, Hemingray, No.9, Green	6.00
Insulator, Hemingray, No.10	1.00
Insulator, Hemingray, No.12	1.00
Insulator, Hemingray, No.16	1.00
Insulator, Hemingray, No.16, Clear	.50
Insulator, Hemingray, No.17, Clear	.50

Insulator, **Hemingray**, No.19 .... 1.00
Insulator, **Hemingray**, No.19, Amber 9.50
Insulator, **Hemingray**, No.19, Green 10.00
Insulator, **Hemingray**, No.23, CD 241, Blue 15.00
Insulator, **Hemingray**, No.25 .... 17.50
Insulator, **Hemingray**, No.25, Aqua .... 9.00 To 35.00
Insulator, **Hemingray**, No.40 .... 1.00
Insulator, **Hemingray**, No.40, Aqua 5.00
Insulator, **Hemingray**, No.40, Emerald Green 4.00
Insulator, **Hemingray**, No.42 .... 1.00
Insulator, **Hemingray**, No.42, Aqua 8.00
Insulator, **Hemingray**, No.42, Blue 8.00
Insulator, **Hemingray**, No.42, Green 2.50
Insulator, **Hemingray**, No.42, Ice Blue 8.00
Insulator, **Hemingray**, No.42, White 2.50
Insulator, **Hemingray**, No.43, Blue 5.00
Insulator, **Hemingray**, No.43, Cable Top, Blue 5.00
Insulator, **Hemingray**, No.43, Emerald Green 7.50
Insulator, **Hemingray**, No.43, Grass Green 9.50
Insulator, **Hemingray**, No.45 .... 1.00
Insulator, **Hemingray**, No.55, Aqua .... 4.00 To 35.00
Insulator, **Hemingray**, No.55, Blue 9.50
Insulator, **Hemingray**, No.55, Triple Groove 9.50
Insulator, **Hemingray**, No.60 .... 15.00
Insulator, **Hemingray**, No.60, Clear 8.00
Insulator, **Hemingray**, No.60, Mickey Mouse 9.50
Insulator, **Hemingray**, No.60, Mickey Mouse, Aqua 12.50
Insulator, **Hemingray**, No.60, Mickey Mouse, Clear 11.00
Insulator, **Hemingray**, No.62, Aqua 35.00
Insulator, **Hemingray**, No.62, Cable Top .... 5.00 To 9.50
Insulator, **Hemingray**, No.76 .... 50.00
Insulator, **Hemingray**, No.94A, Purple 50.00
Insulator, **Hemingray**, No.94B, Purple 50.00
Insulator, **Hemingray**, No.109, Yellow Amber 20.00
Insulator, **Hemingray**, No.512, Bug Eyes, Amber 12.50
Insulator, **Hemingray**, No.512, Bug Eyes, Ice Blue 9.50
Insulator, **Hemingray**, No.820, Clear 15.00
Insulator, **Hemingray**, Patent Dec.19, 1871, Aqua 14.00
Insulator, **Hemingray**, Petticoat, Dated 1893, Amber 12.50
Insulator, **Hemingray**, TS, Double Groove 3.50
Insulator, **Isorex**, Aqua, Large Size 30.00
Insulator, **Isorex**, Aqua, Small Size 20.00
Insulator, **Isorex**, Purple 30.00
Insulator, **Jeffery Mine**, Aqua 65.00
Insulator, **Kimble**, CD 231, Clear 3.00
Insulator, **Kimble**, CD 531 .... 5.50
Insulator, **Kimble**, CD 820 .... 5.50
Insulator, **Kimble**, CD 820, Clear .... 3.00 To 10.00
Insulator, **Lowex**, CD 512, Amber 8.50
Insulator, **Lowex**, CD 512, Bug Eyes, Amber 12.50
Insulator, **Lynchburg**, Aqua 9.00
Insulator, **Lynchburg**, CD 53 .... 25.00
Insulator, **Lynchburg**, CD 530, Sun Deepened Purple 25.00
Insulator, **Lynchburg**, No.36 .... 5.00
Insulator, **Lynchburg**, No.38 .... 3.00
Insulator, **Lynchburg**, No.38, Emerald Green 5.00
Insulator, **Lynchburg**, No.38, Light Aqua 3.00
Insulator, **Lynchburg**, No.44 .... 3.00
Insulator, **M.L.O.D.**, CD 162, Deep Purple 40.00
Insulator, **Manhattan**, Blue, Dated 40.00
Insulator, **Manhattan**, CD 256 .... 55.00
Insulator, **Manhattan**, CD 256, Blue 50.00
Insulator, **Maydwell**, No.16, CD 122, Honey Color .... 4.00 To 5.00
Insulator, **Maydwell**, No.19, Light Amethyst 8.00
Insulator, **Maydwell**, No.20, Milk Glass .... 7.00 To 12.50
Insulator, **McLaughlin**, CD 115, Light Green 10.00

Insulator, **McLaughlin**, CD 160, Black Amber 15.00
Insulator, **McLaughlin**, No.16, Seven-Up Green 7.50
Insulator, **McLaughlin**, No.20, CD 164, Emerald Green 5.00
Insulator, **McLaughlin**, No.20, Ice Blue 5.00
Insulator, **McLaughlin**, No.42, Green 2.00
Insulator, **Mickey Mouse**, Bright Green, Dated 20.00
Insulator, **Mickey Mouse**, Clear 4.00
Insulator, **Mickey Mouse**, Electric Blue 10.00
Insulator, **Mickey Mouse**, Wide Groove, Aqua 15.00
Insulator, **N.D.P.**, 1673, Light Aqua 15.00
Insulator, **N.D.P.**, 1678, Light Aqua 12.00
Insulator, **N.M.**, CD 151, Cornflower Blue 20.00
Insulator, **Navy Submarine**, Chocolate Brown Glaze, 23 In.High 65.00
Insulator, **New England Telephone & Telegraph** 2.00
Insulator, **New England Telephone & Telegraph**, CD 104, Aqua 1.50
Insulator, **New England Telephone & Telegraph**, CD 162 .... 5.00
Insulator, **Oakman**, Embossed Rim, Helmet 20.00
Insulator, **P.L.W.**, CD 462 .... 55.00
Insulator, **Peak Top**, Ice Blue 34.00
Insulator, **Pennsylvania Railroad**, Embossed PRR On Top, Green 5.00
Insulator, **Pennsylvania Railroad**, Signal, Green 5.00
Insulator, **Pleated Beehives**, Aqua 22.00
Insulator, **Pony**, CD 102, Embossed Diamond 3.00
Insulator, **Pony**, Ceramic, Cobalt 5.00
Insulator, **Pony**, Purple 5.00
Insulator, **Pony**, Star, Double Groove, Aqua 3.50
Insulator, **Postal**, Emerald Green 5.00
Insulator, **Pyrex** 1.00
Insulator, **Pyrex**, Carnival Glass 16.00
Insulator, **Pyrex**, CD 63, Carnival Glass .... 8.00 To 10.00
Insulator, **Pyrex**, CD 662, Carnival Glass .... 8.00 To 12.50
Insulator, **Pyrex**, No.63, Clear 4.00
Insulator, **Pyrex**, Radio Broadcasting, Made In U.S.A., 1924, Patent No.1700 .... 12.50
Insulator, **Roman Helmet**, Porcelain, White .... 9.50 To 35.00
Insulator, **Signal**, Baby, Grayish Clear, Pair 15.00
Insulator, **Signal**, Baby, Light Purple 15.00
Insulator, **Signal**, California, Purple, Pair 12.00
Insulator, **So.Mass.Tel.Co.** 50.00
Insulator, **Sombrero**, Carnival Glass, Extra Dark, 10 In. 20.00
Insulator, **Sombrero**, Carnival Glass, Light, 10 In. .... 7.50 To 8.00
Insulator, **Sombrero**, Carnival Glass, Medium, 10 In. 10.00
Insulator, **Sombrero**, France, Translucent Green, 10 In. 65.00
Insulator, **Sombrero**, Metal On Glass, Green, 9 In. .... 4.00 To 5.00
Insulator, **Standard**, CD 143, Embossed, Ice Blue 6.00
Insulator, **Star**, Baby, Signal 10.00
Insulator, **Star**, CD 145, Dark Olive 10.00
Insulator, **Star**, CD 145, Pointed Top, Star Both Sides, Aqua 7.00
Insulator, **Star**, Signal, Green 7.00
Insulator, **Surge**, Chicago 5.00
Insulator, **T.H.E.Co.**, Beehive 200.00
Insulator, **Thomas**, Helmet, Porcelain, Brown 4.50
Insulator, **Thomas**, Helmet, Porcelain, White 6.00
Insulator, **Threadless Signals** 85.00
Insulator, **U.S.Tel.**, Chester, Threadless 225.00
Insulator, **U.S.Tel.Co.**, Toll, Aqua 18.00
Insulator, **Umr-Napoli**, Aqua 9.50
Insulator, **V.N.M.** .... 10.00 To 45.00
Insulator, **V.N.M.**, CD 190-191, Two Piece Transposition 12.00
Insulator, **W.F.G.Co.**, Denver, Colorado, Signal 4.50
Insulator, **W.F.G.Co.**, Denver, Ice Blue 9.50
Insulator, **W.G.M.Co.**, CD 106 .... 18.00
Insulator, **W.G.M.Co.**, CD 121 .... 12.00
Insulator, **W.G.M.Co.**, Toll, Royal Purple 12.50
Insulator, **W.U.T.Co.**, TS 2, Carnival Glass 9.00
Insulator, **Wade**, Threadless .... 110.00 To 225.00
Insulator, **Whitall Tatum & Armstrong**, CD 511a, Dark Amber 5.00

Insulator, Whitall Tatum, Amethyst, 3 1/2 In.	12.00
Insulator, Whitall Tatum, CD 165, Ice Blue	3.00
Insulator, Whitall Tatum, CD 511a, Deep Amber	8.50
Insulator, Whitall Tatum, Dark Amber	6.00
Insulator, Whitall Tatum, No.1, Amethyst	7.50
Insulator, Whitall Tatum, No.1, Green	1.00
Insulator, Whitall Tatum, No.1, Light Purple	7.50
Insulator, Whitall Tatum, No.1, Straw	8.00
Insulator, Whitall Tatum, No.2, Green	1.00
Insulator, Whitall Tatum, No.3, Green	1.00
Insulator, Whitall Tatum, No.9, Green	1.00
Insulator, Whitall Tatum, No.512-U, Amber	7.50
Insulator, Whitall Tatum, No.512-U, Root Beer Color	7.50
Iron, see also Kitchen, Tool, Store	
Iron, Ashtray, Girl With Hair & Outstretched Arm	9.00
Iron, Bed Warmer, Wrought, Pierced Brass Cover	35.00
Iron, Bill Clip, Marked Autofile Pat.1889-1894	5.95
Iron, Bill Spindle, Scrolls, Wall, 5 1/2 In.	6.50
Iron, Bill Spindle, Scrolls, Wall, 6 1/4 In.	7.50
Iron, Bookend, Abraham Lincoln, Pair	10.00
Iron, Bookend, Bust Of Lincoln, Painted Gold, Iron, Pair	4.95
Iron, Bookend, Copper Finish, 7 In., Pair	10.00
Iron, Bookend, Covered Wagon, Pair	8.50
Iron, Bookend, Elephant Shape, Trunk Up, Pair	4.95
Iron, Bookend, End Of Trail, Pair	12.00
Iron, Bookend, Girl Dancing, Bronze Plated, Pair	7.00
Iron, Bookend, Liberty Bell, Bronze Tone, Pair	12.00
Iron, Bookend, Owl, Pair	20.00
Iron, Bookend, Peacock, Cast	7.00
Iron, Bookend, Penguin, Painted, Pair	18.00
Iron, Bookend, Spirit Of St.Louis, Pair	12.00
Iron, Bookend, Three Puppies Singing, Paint, Pair	12.50
Iron, Boot, Hollow, 7 1/2 In.Long At Sole	11.75
Iron, Bootjack, Beetle	12.00
Iron, Bootjack, Fancy, 11 1/2 In.	16.00
Iron, Bootjack, Naughty Nellie	25.00 To 35.00
Iron, Bootjack, Rococo Scrolls	13.00
Iron, Bootjack, Shape Of Pistol, Folds	35.00
Iron, Bootjack, Two Prongs, Folds	25.00
Iron, Bracket, Plant, Hanging, Pair	10.00
Iron, Bracket, Shelf, Lacy, 8 X 6 In., Pair	4.50
Iron, Bracket, Shelf, Ornate, 9 X 7 In.	3.95 To 4.50
Iron, Bracket, Shelf, Scrollwork Back & Arms, Patent 1878	7.95
Iron, Branding Iron, Hand-Forged, Socket End Handle	4.50
Iron, Branding Iron, H.W.Miller-Bechtelsville, Circular Rod Handle, 21 In.	22.50
Iron, Candleholder & Rush Holder, Wrought, Floor	90.00
Iron, Candleholder, Jam Hook At Top	100.00
Iron, Candlesnuffer, Scissor Type	10.00
Iron, Candlesnuffer, Scissor Type, Peg Type Feet, 7 In.Long	12.50
Iron, Candlestick, Hogscraper, Hanging Hook, Dated 1853	20.00
Iron, Candlestick, Italian Renaissance Style, Columnar Stem, Pair	190.00
Iron, Candlestick, Spanish, Round Drip Pan, 16th Century, 5 Ft.7 In., Pair	425.00
Iron, Chair, Miniature, Red Plush Seat, Lattice Back, 3 In.High	9.00
Iron, Cherry Pitter, Enterprise	10.00
Iron, Coffee Grinder, see Coffee Grinder	
Iron, Cork Sizer, Four Slots, Handle, Design At Top	25.00
Iron, Corkscrew, Ornate	3.00
Iron, Cresset, Wrought	70.00
Iron, Cresset, 11 In.Long, 10 In.Diameter	195.00
Iron, Curling Iron, Handwrought	45.00
Iron, Cutter, Sugar, Engraved, Pair	27.50
Iron, Cutter, Tobacco, Spear Shape	25.00
Iron, Door Knocker, Basket	10.00

Iron Doorstops have been made in all types of designs. The vast majority of the doorstops sold today are cast iron and were made from about 1890 to

1930. Most of them are shaped like people, animals, flowers, or ships.

Iron, Doorstop, Airedale 25.00
Iron, Doorstop, Airedale, Full Figure, Standing, 11 In.Long, 10 In.High 16.75
Iron, Doorstop, Aunt Jemimah, 9 In.High 35.00
Iron, Doorstop, Basket Of Flowers .... 6.95 To 15.00
Iron, Doorstop, Basket Of Flowers With Ribbon At Top, 15 3/4 In.High 11.75
Iron, Doorstop, Basket Of Flowers, 6 In.High 6.00
Iron, Doorstop, Basket Of Flowers, 6 3/4 In.High 4.75
Iron, Doorstop, Basket Of Flowers, 8 3/4 In.High 7.75
Iron, Doorstop, Boston Terrier .... 18.00 To 24.00
Iron, Doorstop, Boston Terrier, Black & White 18.00
Iron, Doorstop, Boston Terrier, Full Figure, 13 In.Long, 10 In.High 14.75
Iron, Doorstop, Boston Terrier, Sitting, 7 3/4 In.High 14.75
Iron, Doorstop, Boston Terrier, Sitting, 8 1/4 In.Long 12.95
Iron, Doorstop, Boston Terrier, Standing .... 13.75 To 18.50
Iron, Doorstop, Bulldog .... 35.00 To 45.00
Iron, Doorstop, Bulldog, English, 4 In.Long, 2 1/2 In.High 8.00
Iron, Doorstop, Campbell Soup Kid, Teddy Bear, 10 In.High 20.00
Iron, Doorstop, Cat 6.00
Iron, Doorstop, Cornucopia With Fruit, 8 1/2 In. 12.00
Iron, Doorstop, Cottage 6.95
Iron, Doorstop, Cottage, Painted 10.50
Iron, Doorstop, Duck, 2 1/2 In.Tall 5.00
Iron, Doorstop, Elephant .... 18.00 To 27.50
Iron, Doorstop, Fish 12.50
Iron, Doorstop, Frog 8.50
Iron, Doorstop, German Shepherd, Flat Back, Wedge, 6 1/2 In.High 10.00
Iron, Doorstop, German Shepherd, Marked World Radio On Base, 12 1/4 In.High 8.95
Iron, Doorstop, Girl, Bonnet, Long Dress, Holds Basket Of Flowers, 9 In.High 12.75
Iron, Doorstop, Golfer .... *Illus* 12.00

Iron, Doorstop, Golfer

Iron, Doorstop, Golfer, Wears Cap, Holds Club, Bag Over Shoulder 14.75
Iron, Doorstop, House 15.00
Iron, Doorstop, Irish Terrier 19.00
Iron, Doorstop, Jenny Lind 14.50
Iron, Doorstop, Kitten, 7 1/4 In.High 20.00
Iron, Doorstop, Lady Sewing 13.50
Iron, Doorstop, Mammy 25.00
Iron, Doorstop, Mayflower Ship 6.00
Iron, Doorstop, Mayflower Ship, Green, Red, Gold, 12 In.High 15.00
Iron, Doorstop, Parrot, 6 1/2 In. 6.50
Iron, Doorstop, Peacock With Spread Tail, 6 1/4 In.High 12.50
Iron, Doorstop, Pot Of Tulips, 10 3/8 In.High 7.95
Iron, Doorstop, Ram, Black 25.00
Iron, Doorstop, Scottie Dog, Black 18.00
Iron, Doorstop, Scottie Dog, Painted 10.00
Iron, Doorstop, Scottie Dog, 5 In.High, 6 In.Long 12.00

Iron, **Doorstop**, Ship 15.00
Iron, **Doorstop**, Soldier 3.50
Iron, **Doorstop**, Stagecoach, Painted 12.25
Iron, **Doorstop**, Three Kittens In Basket 12.50
Iron, **Doorstop**, Windmill, 7 In.High 7.95
Iron, **Doorstop**, Wire Haired Fox Terrier 18.50
Iron, **Dressmaker's Form**, Ornate Iron Wheels, Victorian 25.00
Iron, **Duck**, 2 1/4 In.Tall 3.95
Iron, **Figurine**, Cat, Black, Yellow Eyes, 6 In.High 12.00
Iron, **Figurine**, Judith, Russian, Galbsheiber Factory, C.1850 .... 200.00
Iron, **Figurine**, Puppy With Bee, 1 5/8 In.High 5.75
Iron, **Flagstand**, G.A.R., Dated 1883 .... 8.00
Iron, **Flagstand**, 'stand By The Flag, ' Star Decoration 3.75
Iron, **Foot Scraper**, Scroll Ends 10.00
Iron, **Fork**, Inlaid With Brass, Engraved 140.00
Iron, **Frame**, Easel, Ornate Scroll Design, 9 In.High, 7 3/4 In.Wide 9.95
Iron, **Frypan**, Miniature, Don Rich Oil, Esso 3.00
Iron, **Grill**, Oval, Handled, Bussey & Mcleod, Troy, N.Y., Dated 1865 ...... 7.00
Iron, **Harpoon**, Hand-Forged, Single Barb, C.1850, 23 In. Long 34.50
Iron, **Harpoon**, Whaling, New Bedford, Hand-Forged, Rigged, 1840s, 56 In. 24.50
Iron, **Hitching Post**, Horse's Head, Two Rings 110.00
Iron, **Holder**, Iron, Troy Laundry Equipment Co. 12.00
Iron, **Holder**, Letter, Lacy, Boy With Letters, Painted Green, Removable 11.00
Iron, **Holder**, Light, Scissor Type, Knob Balance, Straight Stem, Saucer Base 85.00
Iron, **Holder**, Pot, Wall, Tile Inserts, Pair 35.00
Iron, **Holder**, Sadiron, Wall, Double 15.00
Iron, **Holder**, String, Beehive 12.50
Iron, **Holder**, Thread, Spool, 3 Tiers That Swivel, 4 Lion Feet Base 6.95
Iron, **Holder**, Twine, Standing, Lacy, 6 1/2 In.Tall 18.50
Iron, **Hook**, Ceiling, Ornate, Screw-In Type 2.75
Iron, **Hook**, Ceiling, Ornate, Screw-In Type, 10 In.Long 2.75
Iron, **Hook**, Ceiling, Victorian, Ornate, Screw-In Type, 11 In.Long 2.75
Iron, **Hook**, Wall Bracket, Birdcages, Planter's 2.75
Iron, **Hook**, Wall Bracket, Screw-In Type, Extends To 7 1/2 In.From Wall 2.75
Iron, **Horse**, Standing, 1820 .... 20.00
Iron, **Horse's Head**, Cast, Painted Black, Fits On 3 1/2 In.Post, 15 Lbs. 8.50
Iron, **Horse's Head**, For Hitching Post 32.00
Iron, **Horseshoe**, Eagle & Initials F.L.T.& L.O.O.F. 15.00
Iron, **Humidor**, Standing Figure Of A General, Signed Crowley, Round 30.00
Iron, **Key**, Eighteenth Century, 4 In. 1.00
Iron, **Key**, Eighteenth Century, 6 In. 2.00
Iron, **Key**, 7 In. 2.50
Iron, **Lance**, Whaling, Killing, Hand-Forged, Wood Shaft, 44 In. 24.50
Iron, **Lance**, Whaling, Killing, Hand-Forged, 44 In. 14.00
Iron, **Lifter**, Stove Lid, Spiral Handle 3.00
Iron, **Lock & Key**, Wood Encased, 6 X 10 In. 12.50
　　Iron, **Match Holder**, see also Match Holder
Iron, **Match Holder**, Advertising, R.Robbins & Co., Striker 22.00
Iron, **Match Holder**, Coal Bucket Shape, Iron Bail 6.00
Iron, **Match Holder**, Depicts Fireplace, Grate, Footed, Dated 1871 ...... 15.00
Iron, **Match Holder**, Hanging, Double, Openwork 9.00
Iron, **Match Holder**, Marked Pat.Dec.20, 1864, By D.M.& Co., New Haven, Conn. 30.00
Iron, **Match Holder**, Stove Shape, Embossed Economy Stove Co. 18.00
Iron, **Match Holder**, Table Type, Compartments, Handles, Striker 12.75
Iron, **Match Holder**, Wall, Double Pocket, Ornate Design 14.00
Iron, **Match Holder**, Wall, Double Pocket, Rabbit, Bird, & Bugle 25.00
Iron, **Match Holder**, Wall, Hanging, Pheasant & Rabbit 18.00
Iron, **Match Holder**, Wall, Hinged Lid, Marked Self Closing, For Matches, 1864 ...... 12.75
Iron, **Match Holder**, Wall, Lift Cover, Raised Hunting Dogs, Patent 1863 ...... 16.75
Iron, **Match Holder**, Wall, Lift Cover, Striker On Bottom 9.75
Iron, **Match Holder**, Wall, Lift Cover, Striker, Patent 1864, 5 1/2 In.Wide 16.75
Iron, **Match Holder**, Wall, Single Pocket, Openwork Back 9.95
Iron, **Match Holder**, Wall, Two Compartments, Marked Pat.Applied For, Striker 9.95
Iron, **Match Holder**, Wall, Two Compartments, Openwork Back 11.75
Iron, **Match Safe**, High Button Shoe, Crown Jewel Stoves, 6 X 6 In. 35.00
Iron, **Match Safe**, Wall, Holder Stands Out, Striker In Front, Embossed 9.00

Iron, **Mold**, Lamb .... 15.00 To 18.00
Iron, **Mold**, Muffin, Griswold 4.00
Iron, **Mortar & Pestle**, Clark, 6 In.High 25.00
Iron, **Mortar & Pestle**, Ring Turned Lip & Foot, C.1820 .... 70.00
Iron, **Mortar & Pestle**, 12 Lbs. 12.50
Iron, **Nutcracker**, Alligator, 1910, Bronzed, 15 1/2 In.Long 31.50
Iron, **Nutcracker**, Arcade 6.00
Iron, **Nutcracker**, Clamp On Table, Turn Screw To Crack Nut, Perfection 5.95
Iron, **Nutcracker**, Dog, Lift Tail & Jaws Open, 11 1/2 In.Long 13.75
Iron, **Nutcracker**, St.Bernard Dog 15.00
Iron, **Nutcracker**, Wooden Base, Marked Home, Patent 1915 .... 7.75
Iron, **Padlock**, Hand-Forged, Key, 16th Century, 4 Pounds 59.50
Iron, **Pan**, Cornstick, Griswold, 4 X 8 1/2 In. 8.50
Iron, **Parer**, Apple, Keen Cutter 10.00
Iron, **Parer**, Apple, Ornate, Pat.May 5, 1868 .... 14.50
Iron, **Planter**, Wrought, Painted Green, Openwork Basket Top, Pair 100.00
Iron, **Planter**, Wrought, 32 In.High 40.00
Iron, **Plaque**, Horseshoe Shape, 'Good Luck' 7.95
Iron, **Poker**, Stove, Spiral Handle 2.25
Iron, **Porringer**, Handle, 5 1/2 In.Diameter 65.00
Iron, **Porringer**, Signed Kendrick, Handle, 5 1/2 In. 70.00
Iron, **Pot**, Allaire, New Jersey, C.1850 .... *Illus* 45.00
Iron, **Press**, Fruit & Lard, 7 In.Diameter, 10 In.High 15.00
Iron, **Rushlight**, Wrought, Three Tripod Feet, 12 In.High 80.00
Iron, **Safe**, Embossed Fidelity Trust, By Henry Hart, Pat.1885, 8 1/2 In.High 125.00
Iron, **Salt & Pepper**, Old Lady In Rocker 6.00
Iron, **Sconce**, Wall, Italian, Acanthus, 3 Scrolling Arms, C.1660, Pair 250.00
Iron, **Skillet**, Miniature, 1 1/2 In.Diameter 4.00
Iron, **Skillet**, Three Legs, 10 In.Diameter 17.50
Iron, **Slicer**, Bean, Spongs 12.00
Iron, **Snowbird**, Eagle, Pair 25.00
Iron, **Spade**, Cutting, Whaling, Hand-Forged, 25 In. 14.00
Iron, **Spade**, Cutting, Whaling, To Cut Blubber, Hand-Forged, Wood Shaft 24.50
Iron, **Spike**, Bill, Wall, Openwork Back 2.75
Iron, **Spur**, European, Silver Floral Inlays, 5 Rowels, C.1660 .... 32.50
Iron, **Spur**, Spanish, Hand Engraved, Round Rowels, Pierced, Pair 22.50
Iron, **Spurs**, Spanish, 3 In.Rowels 2.25
Iron, **Stand**, Goffering, Miniature 20.00
Iron, **Stapler**, Dated Feb.10, '74 .... 5.00
Iron, **Teakettle**, Gooseneck Spout .... *Illus* 21.00
Iron, **Teakettle**, Hinged Cover 12.00
Iron, **Teakettle**, Sliding Cover, Dated 1861 .... 18.00
Iron, **Teakettle**, Swing Off Lid, Iron Handles 17.50
Iron, **Teakettle**, Swivel Lid, H.W.E.S., Bridgeport, Ohio, 1866 .... 39.00
Iron, **Torch**, Handle, Dated 1895, 10 In.High 20.00
Iron, **Torchere**, Spanish, Scrolled Strapwork, Tripod Legs, C.1650, Pair 160.00

Iron, Pot, Allaire, New Jersey, C.1850

Iron, Teakettle, Gooseneck Spout

Iron, Torchere, Wrought, Painted Yellow, Pair	125.00
Iron, Trammel, For Two Pots, Handwrought, Large Eye For Hanging	30.00
Iron, Trammel, Handwrought, 22 3/4 In.Long	55.00
Iron, Tsuba, Quatrefoil Design, Reticulation, 17th Century	85.00
Iron, Turtle, 3 1/4 In.Long	4.95
Iron, Wick Trimmer, Scissor Type, Chippendale Tin Tray, Black, Gold Stencil	38.00
Iron, Wig Hair Curler, Hand Forged, 17 1/2 In.Long	35.00

Ironstone China was first made in 1813. It gained its greatest popularity during the mid-nineteenth century. The heavy, durable, off-white pottery was made in white or was colored with any of hundreds of patterns. Much Flow Blue Pottery was made of Ironstone. Some of the pieces had raised decorations.

Ironstone, see also Chelsea Grape, Gaudy Ironstone

Ironstone, Bowl, Vegetable, Covered, Opaque, Anthony Shaw, England	15.00
Ironstone, Bowl, Vegetable, Panels, White, 7 In.	14.00
Ironstone, Bowl, Vegetable, White, Scalloped, Scrolls, Victorian	12.00
Ironstone, Box, Glove, Sepia Victorian Cattle Scene On Ivory, Mason's Pat.	15.00
Ironstone, Butter Chip, White, Square, J.& G.Meakin, England, Set Of 9	15.00
Ironstone, Butter, Round, Red Roses, 3 Pieces	6.50
Ironstone, Casserole, Lid, White, Wheat, Open End Handles, Elsmore & Forster	45.00
Ironstone, Coffeepot, White	32.00
Ironstone, Creamer, Fruit Basket, Animal Handle, Mason's	12.00
Ironstone, Creamer, Hamilton, Blue On White, John Maddock, C.1896	16.50
Ironstone, Cup & Saucer, Blue & Red Willow Pattern, Mason's, C.1862	25.00
Ironstone, Cup & Saucer, Peruvian Horse Hunt	27.50
Ironstone, Cup & Saucer, Plum, Excelsior	25.00
Ironstone, Cup Plate, White, Plain	6.00
Ironstone, Cup, 'Be Happy, ' Miniature	6.00
Ironstone, Dish, Pudding, 12 In.Diameter	8.00
Ironstone, Eggcup, Embossed Cable Trim, Pale Blue	8.00
Ironstone, Gravy Boat, J.W.Pankhurst & Co., Hanley, England	8.00
Ironstone, Gravy Boat, White, Wheat	14.00
Ironstone, Jug, Blue & Orange, Green Snake Handle, Mason's, C.1840, Pair	165.00
Ironstone, Jug, Mason's, 10 In., Pair	150.00
Ironstone, Mold, Sheaf Of Wheat	18.50
Ironstone, Pitcher, Canton Pattern, Mason's, 6 3/4 In.	75.00
Ironstone, Pitcher, Flower Design, Blue, White, Marked, 7 In.High	12.00
Ironstone, Pitcher, George Washington Transfer, Laurel Wreath, 10 In.Tall	75.00
Ironstone, Pitcher, Hydra Shape, Oriental Decoration, Green Handle, Mason's	35.00
Ironstone, Pitcher, Laurel Wreath In Relief, Elsmore & Forster, 1867	20.00
Ironstone, Pitcher, Meakin, 5 1/2 In.	18.00
Ironstone, Pitcher, Milk, Embossed Fuchsia, George Jones, Stoke-On-Trent	30.00
Ironstone, Pitcher, Milk, Lily Of The Valley	11.00
Ironstone, Pitcher, Milk, White, Blue Band, 8 1/4 In.Tall	20.00
Ironstone, Pitcher, Oriental Decoration, Snake Handles, Octagon, 5 1/2 In.	40.00
Ironstone, Pitcher, Oriental Decoration, Snake Handles, Octagon, 6 1/4 In.	45.00
Ironstone, Pitcher, Oriental Decoration, Snake Handles, Octagon, 7 In.	50.00
Ironstone, Pitcher, Purple, White, Carrara, Octagon Shape, 7 1/2 In.High	25.00
Ironstone, Pitcher, Red Willow Pattern, Lizard Handle, Mason's, 1862-1890	34.50
Ironstone, Pitcher, Sea Dragon Handle, Blue, Rust, & Gold, Mason's, 7 In.	135.00
Ironstone, Pitcher, Sheaf Of Wheat, Johnson	15.00
Ironstone, Pitcher, Water, Blue Decoration	19.00
Ironstone, Pitcher, Water, Farm Scene, Mason's	55.00
Ironstone, Pitcher, Water, White, Bulbous, James Edwards, 9 In.High	12.00
Ironstone, Plate, Blue, Lobella, Phillips Longport, 10 In.	28.00
Ironstone, Plate, Blue, Red, & White, Japan Pattern, Mason's, C.1830, 10 In.	30.00
Ironstone, Plate, Blue, White, Venus, By P.W.& Co.	15.00
Ironstone, Plate, Fig Pattern, Registry Nov.14, 1856, Davenport, Set Of 6	95.00
Ironstone, Plate, Floral, Blue, 'Bernard To Beckie '98, ' Johnson Bros.	8.00
Ironstone, Plate, Lavender Transfer, Italy Pattern, C.Meigh & Sons, C.1851	25.00
Ironstone, Plate, Oriental Motif, Floral Urns, Minton & Boyle, C.1836	17.50
Ironstone, Plate, Oriental Scenes, Enamel, C.1802, 7 In.	12.00
Ironstone, Plate, Pink Transfer, Canova Pattern, C.1826, T.Mayer	18.50
Ironstone, Plate, Red Orange Accents On Border, Mason's Patent	30.00
Ironstone, Plate, Soup, White, Plain	4.00

Ironstone, Plate, Wheat Pattern, Elsmore & Forster, Reg.1859	4.95
Ironstone, Plate, Wheat Pattern, 8 1/2 In., Pair	10.00
Ironstone, Plate, White, Raised Design, J.G.Meakin, 8 In.	3.00
Ironstone, Platter, Blue Pheasants, Mason's, 11 In.	25.00
Ironstone, Platter, Imari Type, A.J.Wilkinson, 9 In.	11.00
Ironstone, Platter, Meakin, 15 In.Long	20.00
Ironstone, Platter, White, Wheat Pattern, Elsmore & Forster, 15 3/4 In.	15.00
Ironstone, Pot & Attached Saucer, Mustard, Pear Finial	12.50
Ironstone, Pot, Bean, Trumpet Vine, Twig Handles, Acorn Finial, White	20.00
Ironstone, Potty, Covered	15.00
Ironstone, Relish, Blue & White	6.50
Ironstone, Sauce, Lavender, The Temple, By P.W.& Co.	6.00
Ironstone, Soup, Canova, T.Mayor, Stoke-On-Trent	15.00
Ironstone, Soup, Cyprus Pattern, Davenport	15.00
Ironstone, Stein, Hand-Painted French Porcelain Top, Pewter Edge & Grip	45.00
Ironstone, Sugar, Covered, J.W.Pankhurst & Co., Hanley, England	25.00
Ironstone, Syrup, Dark Green & White, Rope Handle, Sheffield Silver Top	28.00
Ironstone, Tea Leaf, Bowl, Square, Small	6.00
Ironstone, Tea Leaf, Bowl, Vegetable, Covered, Shaw	30.00
Ironstone, Tea Leaf, Butter Pat, Square, Meakin	4.00
Ironstone, Tea Leaf, Compote, Melon Rib, Scalloped Top, Meakin	35.00
Ironstone, Tea Leaf, Cup & Saucer, Handleless	15.00
Ironstone, Tea Leaf, Cup Plate, Luster	7.00
Ironstone, Tea Leaf, Dish, Bone	1.00
Ironstone, Tea Leaf, Gravy Boat, Meakin	24.00
Ironstone, Tea Leaf, Plate, Dinner, 8 3/4 In.	8.00
Ironstone, Tea Leaf, Plate, 8 In.	8.50
Ironstone, Tea Leaf, Plate, 8 1/4 In.	9.00
Ironstone, Tea Leaf, Platter, Burgess, 13 3/8 In.	12.00
Ironstone, Tea Leaf, Platter, Meakin	20.00
Ironstone, Tea Leaf, Platter, 12 In.Long	15.00
Ironstone, Tea Leaf, Platter, Meakin, 16 In.Long	22.50
Ironstone, Tea Leaf, Sauce, Square, Meakin	8.00
Ironstone, Tea Leaf, Shaving Mug, Alfred Meakin	65.00
Ironstone, Tea Leaf, Sugar, Bamboo Pattern, Meakin, C.1885	35.00
Ironstone, Tea Set, Child's, White, 16 Piece	55.00
Ironstone, Tea Set, Child's, 12 Piece	25.00
Ironstone, Teapot, Wheat Pattern, Ring Finial, Forster, Tunstall	35.00
Ironstone, Teapot, Wheat, Applied Handle, Tunstall, England	45.00
Ironstone, Tureen & Ladle	22.50
Ironstone, Tureen & Stand, Covered, Japan Pattern, Hicks & Meigh, 1815, Pair	700.00
Ironstone, Tureen & Tray, Soup, Covered, Miniature, White, Plain	25.00
Ironstone, Tureen, Covered, Mulberry, Scenery, Impressed Mark	17.50
Ironstone, Tureen, Gravy, White, Leaf Handles, Nut Finial, Pedestal	28.00
Ironstone, Tureen, Runic Pattern, Brown, 6 X 4 In.	15.00
Ironstone, Tureen, Underplate, & Ladle, Royal Pottery, Wilkinson, Ltd.	24.00
Ironstone, Tureen, Underplate, & Ladle, White	65.00
Ironstone, Vase, Black, Polychrome Enamel, Floral, Butterflies, Mason's, 9 In.	165.00
Ironstone, Vase, Blue & Gold, Birds, Fish, & Flowers, Gold Handles, C.1815	75.00
Ironstone, Vase, Oriental, Red & Green Birds, Blue Floral, Mason's	55.00
Ironstone, Washstand Set, Lily Of The Valley, 3 Piece	45.00
Ironstone, Washstand Set, Mason's Patent, 3 Piece	150.00
Ironstone, Washstand Set, White, From Athens, Texas Hotel, 2 Piece	25.00
Ironstone, Washstand Set, White, Signed J.& G.Meakin, 2 Piece	30.00
Ivory, see also Bottle, Snuff, Netsuke	
Ivory, Ball, Patience, Eight Movable Balls Within Outer Ball, Standard	120.00
Ivory, Ball, Patience, Seven Movable Balls Inside, On Carved Ivory Stem	115.00
Ivory, Birdcage, Oval, Repousse Silver Mounts, Engraved, Pierced	500.00
Ivory, Bottle, Snuff, Flattened, Carved Catlike Animal On Pine, Crane	60.00
Ivory, Bottle, Snuff, Flattened, Japanese, Carved Ladies, Tinted, Ch'len Lung	110.00
Ivory, Bottle, Snuff, Oval, Japanese, Carved Equestrian Figures, Ch'len Lung	120.00
Ivory, Bottle, Snuff, Tapering Cylindrical, Etched, Mountain Landscape	40.00
Ivory, Box, Carved, Hinged, Silver Bound, Tortoiseshell Lining, C.1840	74.00
Ivory, Box, Carved, Seated Figure On Lid Holds Fan, China, 12 In.Diameter	125.00
Ivory, Box, Embossed Monkey's Head, Monkey On Cover, 2 3/4 X 1 1/2 In.	45.00
Ivory, Bust, Buddha, Mounted On Silver Inlaid Teak, 11 1/2 In.	850.00

Ivory, Buttonhook, Glove	5.00
Ivory, Carving, Base Fiddle Player Standing On Barrel, 9 1/2 In.Tall	85.00
Ivory, Carving, Calla Lilies In Pot, 7 In.High	90.00
Ivory, Carving, Dog Sled, Eskimo, Openwork, Hide Thongs, Dog, 8 In.	325.00
Ivory, Carving, Kun Yin, 11 1/2 In.High	200.00
Ivory, Carving, Maggie & Jiggs, 5 1/4 & 5 1/2 In.Tall	225.00
Ivory, Carving, Nude Kneeling African Woman, 5 In.	24.00
Ivory, Carving, Nude Kneeling Pregnant Woman, 6 In.	29.50
Ivory, Carving, Trotty Veck, Dicken's Character, 5 1/2 In.High	55.00
Ivory, Carving, Trotty Veck, Dickens' Character, 5 1/2 In.High	55.00
Ivory, Carving, 20 Elephants On Bean	8.00
Ivory, Case, Card, Black, Green, & White Mosaic Design	25.00
Ivory, Case, Card, Ladies Calling, Oriental Scene, 2 1/4 X 3 3/4 In.	20.00
Ivory, Case, Cigarette, Hand Carved Native Dancing Girl In Native Costume	40.00
Ivory, Chess Set, Carved, 4 In.High	225.00
Ivory, Chess Set, Oriental Motif Pawns, Carved, 6 In.High, Case	225.00
Ivory, Chess Set, Velvet Lined Wooden Box, Hinged	59.00
Ivory, Comb, Carved, Hair	9.00
Ivory, Cribbage Board, Eskimo, Engraved & Painted, Nome, Alaska, 1904	550.00
Ivory, Cribbage Board, Eskimo, From Tusk, Engraved Figures, 5 1/8 In.	110.00
Ivory, Crochet Hook	2.00
Ivory, Doll, Doctor's, Lady, Amber Couch, Holds Amber Fan, Carved	225.00
Ivory, Doll, Doctor's, Lady, Carved, 3 In.Long, Wooden Stand	19.50
Ivory, Doll, Doctor's, Lady, Reclining, China, 5 1/2 In.Long	150.00
Ivory, Doll, Doctor's, Male, Lying On Stomach, Holds Flower, Carved	225.00
Ivory, Figurine, Bacchus & Diana, Hand-Carved, 9 In.High	250.00
Ivory, Figurine, Boy, Holding Books, Holding Fish & Pipe, 3 3/4 In., Pair	75.00
Ivory, Figurine, Chronos, South German, Kneeling On Lapis Lazuli Ball, 1760	650.00
Ivory, Figurine, Dog, Temple, Hand-Carved, Teak Stand, 9 In.High, Pair	500.00
Ivory, Figurine, Duck, Hand-Carved, 2 1/2 In.Long	25.00
Ivory, Figurine, Elephant, Curled Trunk, 6 In.Long, Wooden Stand	100.00
Ivory, Figurine, Emperor & Empress, Dragon Thrones, Teak Stands, 6 In., Pair	250.00
Ivory, Figurine, Farmer With Basket, Goose, Signed, 9 In.	117.00
Ivory, Figurine, Farmer, Artist Signed, 9 In.	115.00
Ivory, Figurine, Fisherman, Eskimo, Standing, Painted, 5 In.High	360.00
Ivory, Figurine, Fisherman, String Of Fish, Boy Helper, Basket, Ivory Base	95.00
Ivory, Figurine, Goddess Of Mercy, Yuki Shin, Meiji Period, 8 1/2 In.High	90.00
Ivory, Figurine, Kwan Yen, Carved, Rosewood Stand, 23 In.	800.00
Ivory, Figurine, Lady With Stringed Instrument, Carved, Signed, 5 In.	200.00
Ivory, Figurine, Man Holds Broom, Pipe & Pouch, Dog, Self Base, Carved, 7 In.	150.00
Ivory, Figurine, Mei Jen, Oriental Maid, 10 In.High, Wooden Stand	100.00
Ivory, Figurine, Monk, Carved Stand, 11 1/2 In.	140.00
Ivory, Figurine, Monk, Italian, Standing, Caritas On Chest, C.1750	750.00
Ivory, Figurine, Oriental Woman With Two Faces, One Face Revolves, 3 In.	45.00
Ivory, Figurine, Oriental Woman, Carved, Round Base, 15 In.High	125.00
Ivory, Figurine, Queen Elizabeth I, Triptych, Depicts Marriage Of Medici	350.00
Ivory, Figurine, The Persimmon Peddler, Tray, Umbrella, Artist Do Masa, 9 In.	100.00
Ivory, Figurine, Trumpet Player, Wears Derby & Waistcoat, Carved, 9 In.High	85.00
Ivory, Figurine, Woman Holding Lute, Carved, Tinted, Wooden Base, 12 In.	95.00
Ivory, Figurine, Young Girl, D.Chiparus, C.1925, Onyx Base	250.00
Ivory, Group, Elephant, Family Of Three, Carved	45.00
Ivory, Group, Reindeer Pulling Sled & Driver, Eskimo, Hide Thongs	325.00
Ivory, Head, Human, Eskimo, Sunken Mouth, Nostrils, & Eyes	200.00
Ivory, Holder, Cigarette, Carved	75.00
Ivory, Jar, Opium, Carved Birds, Floral, Dragon Handles, Finial, Teak Base	225.00
Ivory, Knife Rest, Carved, Silver Plate Knob Ends	7.00
Ivory, Napkin Ring, Carved	10.00
Ivory, Napkin Ring, Carved, 2 In.Diameter, Pair	30.00
Ivory, Night-Light, Carved Panels, Scenes, Footed, 12 1/2 In.High	185.00
Ivory, Pot, Mustard, Leaves, Vine, Silver Lid, Handle, Thomas Webb & Son	495.00
Ivory, Puzzle Ball, Ivory Base, Carved, 3 1/2 In.Diameter, 7 In.Tall	200.00
Ivory, Quill Sharpener	6.50
Ivory, Razor, Straight, Tortoise Ivory Case, Set Of 7	55.00
Ivory, Toothpick, 'Remember Me, ' 4 Toothpicks Unfold From Handle	8.00
Ivory, Vase, Ruffled Columns, Black Jade Foot, 9 In.High	165.00
Ivory, Vessel, Eskimo, Hinged Lid, Carved Figures, Four Footed	210.00

Jack-in-the-Pulpit Vases were named for their odd trumpetlike shape that resembles the wild plant called Jack-in-the-Pulpit. The design originated in the late Victorian years.

Jack-in-the-Pulpit, see also under specific Art Glass headings

Jack-In-The-Pulpit, Epergne, Vaseline To Opaque, Ruffled Bowl, Single Vase 37.50
Jack-In-The-Pulpit, Vase, Blue & Maroon, 6 In.High, Pair 65.00
Jack-In-The-Pulpit, Vase, Blue Encased With Green, Pair 60.00
Jack-In-The-Pulpit, Vase, Blue, Clear Decoration On Rim, Footed, Art Glass 30.00
Jack-In-The-Pulpit, Vase, Blue, Encased Maroon, 6 In., Pair 65.00
Jack-In-The-Pulpit, Vase, Clear Base To White Opalescent Top, Crimped 22.00
Jack-In-The-Pulpit, Vase, Cranberry, 9 1/2 In., Pair 95.00
Jack-In-The-Pulpit, Vase, End-Of-Day, Enamel Polka Dots, 7 In. 28.00
Jack-In-The-Pulpit, Vase, Flowers, Enamel, Amethyst To Clear, 16 1/2 In.High 120.00
Jack-In-The-Pulpit, Vase, Green To Mottled Ruby & White, Ruffled Top 33.00
Jack-In-The-Pulpit, Vase, Green, Lavender Trim 60.00
Jack-In-The-Pulpit, Vase, Opalescent, Blue, Twig Feet 32.00
Jack-In-The-Pulpit, Vase, Opalescent, Green, 6 1/2 In. 35.00
Jack-In-The-Pulpit, Vase, Prayer Rug, Custard, Pair 40.00
Jack-In-The-Pulpit, Vase, Ribbed, Swirled, Cranberry, Petal Feet, Blown 48.00
Jack-In-The-Pulpit, Vase, Rippled Edge, Cased Glass, White, Blue Inside 95.00
Jack-In-The-Pulpit, Vase, Rounded Ribs, Purple, 8 1/2 In.Tall 25.00
Jack-In-The-Pulpit, Vase, Swirls, Applied Pink Ribbons, Pink Lining, Bristol 45.00

Jackfield Ware was originally a black glazed pottery made in Jackfield, England, since 1630. A yellow glazed ware has also been called Jackfield Ware. Most of the pieces referred to as Jackfield are black pieces made during the Victorian era.

Jackfield, Creamer & Stand, Covered, Figural, Cow, Black, Gold Trim 30.00
Jackfield, Creamer, Figural, Cow, Black Glaze 48.00
Jackfield, Dish, Cheese, Black, Gold, Enamel Floral Sprigs, Butterflies 145.00
Jackfield, Hen On Nest, White Enamel Spots On Back, Gold Touchings 37.50
Jackfield, Inkwell & Attached Tray, Black, Gold Decoration, Brass Collar 29.50
Jackfield, Pitcher, Black, Glazed, Panels, Green Ivy, Gold, 7 1/2 In. 35.00
Jackfield, Pitcher, Hand-Painted Floral, Gold Trim, 8 In.High 27.50
Jackfield, Salt, Master, Hen Covered 19.50
Jackfield, Syrup, Pewter Cover, Thumbrest, & Bail 22.50
Jackfield, Tea Set, Cream & Gold Design, Gold Edges, 3 Piece 89.50
Jackfield, Teapot, Figural, Cat 45.00
Jackfield, Teapot, Hand-Painted Flowers, Leaves, Embossed Ribbed Border 38.00
Jackfield, Vase, Black Glaze, Gold & Green Trim, Handles, 10 1/2 In., Pair 85.00
Jackfield, Vase, Black, Multicolor Floral, Flask Shape, 9 In., Pair 62.50
Jade, Amulet, White & Green Nephrite, Lock Shape, Ming Dynasty, Stand, 2 In. 100.00
Jade, Box, Green, Cover, Frame, Bracket Feet, 3 1/2 In.Long 175.00
Jade, Box, Hinged Lid, Flowers, Leaves, Carved Hardstones, Ormolu, Footed 195.00
Jade, Buckle, White, Dragon, Chimera, Carved, 4 3/4 In.Long 175.00
Jade, Cup & Saucer, Demitasse, Marked China 100.00
Jade, Dish, Mutton Fat, Greenish Gray, C.1750 .... 650.00
Jade, Figurine, Child, Standing, Holds Flowers, Carved, 3 1/2 In.High 125.00
Jade, Figurine, Chinese Figure, Mutton Fat, 10 1/2 In., Pair 290.00
Jade, Figurine, Elephant, Yin Yang Symbolism, Ching Dynasty, 5 In.Long, Pair 450.00
Jade, Figurine, Fish, White, 2 In.Long 30.00
Jade, Figurine, Parrot, Green, Carved, C.1870, 5 In.High 225.00
Jade, Plant, Flower & Tree, White, Orange, Green, Cloisonne Pot, 27 In.High 1400.00
Jade, Plant, Six Flowers, White, Carnelian, Leaves, Cloisonne Pot, 27 In.High 1400.00
Jade, Plaque, Maiden, Flowers, Carved, White, Green Markings, China, 5 In.Oval 260.00
Jade, Plaque, White, Pierced Carving, Mythical Beasts, 2 1/2 X 2 In. 60.00
Jade, Prayer Wheel, Mutton Fat, Ching Dynasty, Stand 150.00
Jade, Sceptre, Ju-I, Spinach Green, Carved Polyporus Fungus, Chai Ch'Ing 1050.00
Jade, Sceptre, Ju-I, Spinach Green, Carved Shou, Medallions, Bats, C.1750 .... 1000.00
Jade, Tree With Buds & Flowers, In Jade Bowl, Marked, Chien Lung 425.00

Jasperware is a fine-grained pottery developed by Josiah Wedgwood in 1775. The jasper was made in many colors including the most famous, a light blue. It is still being made.

Jasperware, see also Wedgwood

Jasperware, Bowl, Green & White, Boar's Head 45.00

Jasperware, Box, Covered, Brown, White Glazed Insert, Lady & Cherub, Germany 15.00
Jasperware, Box, Green, John & Priscilla Embossed In White, 3 1/2 In.Square 14.00
Jasperware, Creamer, Light Green, White Cameo On Dark Green, Tankard Shape 22.50
Jasperware, Hair Receiver, Green & White, Germany 30.00
Jasperware, Hatpin Holder, Green, White Classical Ladies, Trees, Brass Rim 45.00
Jasperware, Jar, Cracker, Blue, Silver Rim, Lid, Bail 80.00
Jasperware, Pitcher, Gold Grecian Figures On Dark Blue, Coronet, England 50.00
Jasperware, Plaque, Blue, Girl Reclining With Flowers, 4 1/2 In. 25.00
Jasperware, Plaque, Green And White, Bust Of Emerson, 5 In.Diameter 17.50
Jasperware, Plaque, Green, Temple Block, Salt Lake City, 6 In. 26.00
Jasperware, Sugar, Covered, Dark Blue, Classical Figures, England 36.00
Jasperware, Teapot, Blue, Silver Plated Hinged Lid 65.00
Jasperware, Teapot, Light Green, White Figures, England 60.00
Jasperware, Toothpick, Three Cornered, Pink, Green, White 14.00
Jasperware, Vase, Light Blue, France, C.1850, 4 In. 42.50
Jewelry, Bar Pin, Arrow Through Circle Of Turquoise, Gold 75.00
Jewelry, Beads, African Amber 35.00
Jewelry, Beads, Amber, Honey Color, 15 In.Long 25.00
Jewelry, Beads, Baltic Amber, Knotted, 60 In. 150.00
Jewelry, Beads, Coral, 41 In. 60.00
Jewelry, Beads, Faceted Jet On Gold Chain, 62 In. 30.00
Jewelry, Beads, Green Jade, 24 In. 110.00
Jewelry, Beads, Sterling Silver Filigree With Alternating Opaque Blue 10.00
Jewelry, Beads, Tortoiseshell Separated By Gold Disks 35.00
Jewelry, Belt, Gold, Indian, Enameled Floral, Diamonds, Amethysts, Jaipur, 1850 .... 525.00
Jewelry, Bracelet, Bangle, Celluloid 4.00
Jewelry, Bracelet, Charm, 14K Gold 165.00
Jewelry, Bracelet, Coral, Carved Birds & Flowers All Around 250.00
Jewelry, Bracelet, Diamonds, Pearls, Turquoise, C.1880 .... Illus 950.00

Jewelry, Bracelet, Diamonds, Pearls, Turquoise, C.1880

Jewelry, Bracelet, Eight Amethysts, Faceted, Prong Set, Openwork, 14k Gold 175.00
Jewelry, Bracelet, Elephant Hair 5.00
Jewelry, Bracelet, Five Gold Graduated Enameled Panels, Jewels, C.1850 .... 1400.00
Jewelry, Bracelet, Five Paintings On Ivory, Butterfly, Floral, Silver Set 225.00
Jewelry, Bracelet, Garnet, 152 Faceted Stones In 3 Rows 200.00
Jewelry, Bracelet, Gold Filled Band, Engraved, C.1900 .... 35.00
Jewelry, Bracelet, Gold Filled, 1 In.Wide 25.00
Jewelry, Bracelet, Gold, Agate Cameo Spaniel's Head, Ruby, Pearls, C.1880 .... 1200.00
Jewelry, Bracelet, Gold, Oval Tubular, Gold Lion Mask, Diamond Eyes, C.1850 .... 200.00
Jewelry, Bracelet, Hair, Coiled Snake, Cabochon Garnet, C.1860 .... 225.00
Jewelry, Bracelet, Handmade, Gold, Lion's Head, Ruby Eyes, Diamonds 325.00
Jewelry, Bracelet, Indian, Gold, Tubular, Enameled Floral, Jaipur, C.1850, Pair 800.00
Jewelry, Bracelet, Indian, Navajo, Silver, Engraved, Triangular Brown Stone 60.00
Jewelry, Bracelet, Indian, Navajo, Silver, Oval Turquoise, Openwork, Engraved 70.00
Jewelry, Bracelet, Indian, Navajo, Silver, Rectangular Turquoise, Engraved 85.00
Jewelry, Bracelet, Interwoven Links, Garnet Charm, 14K Gold 100.00
Jewelry, Bracelet, Mesh, 12K Gold Filled, Wide 15.00
Jewelry, Bracelet, Mutton Fat Jade, Carved 70.00
Jewelry, Bracelet, Niello, Half Ball Shape Links, Russia, Circa 1900 .... 115.00
Jewelry, Bracelet, Openwork, Stiff, Five Diamonds, Platinum & Gold 350.00
Jewelry, Bracelet, Pinocchio, Gold & Enamel, 6 14K Gold Enameled Charms 65.00

Jewelry, Bracelet, Rectangular Crystal Center, Horses, Gold, English 225.00
Jewelry, Bracelet, Round Links Joined By Elongated Links, 14K Gold 50.00
Jewelry, Bracelet, Siberian Amethysts, Pair 185.00
Jewelry, Bracelet, Sterling Silver, Embossed, Narrow 6.00
Jewelry, Bracelet, Sterling Silver, Four Leaf Clover & Circles 10.00
Jewelry, Bracelet, Three Citrine Topaz Cameos, Women's Heads, Gold, Flexible 300.00
Jewelry, Bracelet, Victorian, Gold Bar Of 9 Graduated Diamonds, Enamel 700.00
Jewelry, Bracelet, Victorian, Gold Bar Of 11 Graduated Diamonds, Enamel 625.00
Jewelry, Bracelet, White Gold, Crystal & Diamond 150.00
Jewelry, Bracelet, 75 Garnets, Safety Chain 125.00
Jewelry, Brooch & Earrings, Gold & Chrysoprase, Egyptian Style, C.1870 .... 1000.00
Jewelry, Brooch & Earrings, Wedgwood, Blue & White, Marked, 1951 .... 55.00
Jewelry, Brooch, Amber, 14k Yellow Gold Roped Mounting 75.00
Jewelry, Brooch, 'Baby, 'sterling & Inlaid With Enamel 5.00
Jewelry, Brooch, Bird, Lily Pad, Plique A Jour Ground, Gold Encrusted, 1 In. 350.00
Jewelry, Brooch, Black Enamel Designs On Center Reliefs, Gold 45.00
Jewelry, Brooch, Cameo, Brown Ground, Bouquet Of Flowers, Gold Setting 30.00
Jewelry, Brooch, Cameo, Lady's Head, Lava, Open Loop Setting 125.00
Jewelry, Brooch, Cameo, Sardonyx, C.1870 .... *Illus* 450.00
Jewelry, Brooch, Cameo, Shell, Sea Goddess, Gold, 2 X 1 3/4 In. 88.00
Jewelry, Brooch, Cameo, Shell, Winged Woman, Full Figure, Brown, White, Gold 45.00
Jewelry, Brooch, Cameo, Triangular Pendants, C.1870 .... *Illus* 450.00
Jewelry, Brooch, Carved Cinnabar, Marked China, 2 X 1 In. 15.00
Jewelry, Brooch, Clover, Center Pearl, Chain & Pin Guard, Gold 22.50
Jewelry, Brooch, Cone Shape, 63 Faceted Garnets 76.00
Jewelry, Brooch, Florentine Mosaic, Gold Framed 95.00
Jewelry, Brooch, Four Cabochon Russian Lapis, Gold, 2 1/8 In.Long 75.00
Jewelry, Brooch, French, Miniature Signed Paillet, Diamonds, Gold 125.00
Jewelry, Brooch, Gold & Enamel, Baroque Pearls Form Buds, 1 1/4 In.Diameter 50.00
Jewelry, Brooch, Gold Sunburst, Openwork, Nine Diamonds, 1 1/8 In.Diameter 350.00
Jewelry, Brooch, Gold Top, 3 Blue Opals 65.00
Jewelry, Brooch, Hair, Engraving, Black Enamel, Gold 65.00
Jewelry, Brooch, Hair, Gold Border Frames Braided Hair, Black Enamel, Chain 45.00
Jewelry, Brooch, Hunting Scene On Mother-Of-Pearl, Austrian Silver, C.1870 .... 16.00
Jewelry, Brooch, Jet Tear Drops Encased In 14k Gold, Pearls 95.00
Jewelry, Brooch, Love Knot, Enameled Pansy, Pearls, 10k 125.00
Jewelry, Brooch, Lovers' Knots, England, Circa 1860, 15k Gold 43.00
Jewelry, Brooch, Lovers' Knot, Multicolor Enamel, Forget Me Nots, 1 In. 300.00
Jewelry, Brooch, Miniature Profile Of Woman On Ivory, C.1750 .... 425.00
Jewelry, Brooch, Mosaic, Parrot On Basket Of Fruit & Vegetables, Black Onyx 65.00
Jewelry, Brooch, Mosaic, Spaniel Dog On Green Cushion, Black Onyx, Gold 32.00
Jewelry, Brooch, Mourning, Chased Gold Plate, Hair In Center, Crest, C.1830 .... 75.00
Jewelry, Brooch, Mourning, Chased Rose Gold Snake Encircles Hair, 1830 .... 39.00
Jewelry, Brooch, Onyx Cameo, Relief Profile Bust Of Man, Diamonds, C.1880 .... 325.00
Jewelry, Brooch, Sardonyx Stone Cameo, Woman Wears Chain, Topaz Pendant 85.00
Jewelry, Brooch, Sardonyx Stone Cameo, 14k Yellow Gold Mounting 125.00
Jewelry, Brooch, Shell Cameo, Sea Goddess, Seaweeds, Anchor, 2 1/4 In. 85.00
Jewelry, Brooch, Small Ruby & Pearls Center, Etruscan Trim, 15k Gold 45.00
Jewelry, Brooch, Three Elephants, Sterling Silver, 1 1/2 In.Long 15.00
Jewelry, Brooch, Wedgwood, Light Blue & White, Chain, Pin, C.1860 .... 62.50
Jewelry, Brooch, Winged Dragon, Pearl In Mouth, Gold, Art Nouveau, 1 In. 75.00
Jewelry, Buckle, Shoe, Man's, Steel, C.1700, Pair 35.00
Jewelry, Chain & Fob, Watch, Man's, Double, Gold, 50 Point Diamond 350.00
Jewelry, Chain & Fob, Watch, Man's, Gold & Platinum, Diamond 160.00
Jewelry, Chain & Slide, Gold Filled, Jeweled 35.00
Jewelry, Chain & Slide, Watch, Gold, Red Stones & Seed Pearls 35.00
Jewelry, Chain & Slide, Watch, Lady's, Three Rubies, Six Pearls, 14K Gold 75.00
Jewelry, Chain & Slide, Watch, Raised Pattern, Two White Sapphires, 14K Gold 100.00
Jewelry, Chain & Slide, Watch, Vest Pocket, Gold, Double 25.00
Jewelry, Chain, Fob, & Watch Key, Gold, Lyre Shape Seals, Continental, C.1830 .... 220.00
Jewelry, Chain, Key, 18k Gold 140.00
Jewelry, Chain, Pendant, Roped, 14K Gold, 18 In. 95.00
Jewelry, Chain, Vest, Man's, Detailed Work, Victorian, 14k Gold 200.00
Jewelry, Chain, Watch, Braided Hair, Gold Fittings 22.50
Jewelry, Chain, Watch, Heavy, 14k Gold 50.00
Jewelry, Chain, Watch, Man's, Sterling, Engraved Medallion, 1907 .... 40.00

Jewelry, Chain, Watch, Marked Hamilton, Gold Filled, 13 In.Long	10.00
Jewelry, Chain, Watch, Three Ends, Bar, 14K Gold	58.00
Jewelry, Charm, Basket, Enameled Fruit, Inscribed Bon Voyage	15.00
Jewelry, Charm, Elk's Tooth, Silver Top	18.00
Jewelry, Charm, Sterling Silver, Heart, Scroll & Flowers, Amethyst In Center	12.95
Jewelry, Chatelaine, Silver, Brass, 6 Attachments	85.00
Jewelry, Choker, Carved Amethyst Quartz Beads, Carved Fruit Clasp	85.00
Jewelry, Clip, Dress, Turquoise & Lapis Lazuli, A.Marchak, C.1924	225.00
Jewelry, Comb, Spanish, Blue Stones	25.00
Jewelry, Cross, Azure, Blue Green, Circa 1910, Russia	150.00
Jewelry, Cross, Gold Filigree, Cabochon Garnets, Mediterranean, C.1850	80.00
Jewelry, Cross, Gold, Black Enamel, 11 Diamonds	750.00
Jewelry, Cuff Link, Fan Shape, Floral, Colored Gold, Pair	22.00
Jewelry, Earring, Amber, Pendant, Yellow Gold, Pair	48.00
Jewelry, Earring, Amethyst Clusters, France, 14K Gold, C.1870, Pair	74.00
Jewelry, Earring, Black, White Stone Cameo Center, Oval, Gold, Pair	95.00
Jewelry, Earring, Chinese Jade, Carved, 14 Carat Gold	175.00
Jewelry, Earring, Chinese Jade, Hoop, Carved, Gold Mountings, Handmade, Pair	365.00
Jewelry, Earring, Coral, Carved Grape Clusters, Pair	50.00
Jewelry, Earring, Coral, Dangle, High Cabochons, Ball Top, 14K Gold, Pair	125.00
Jewelry, Earring, Coral, Gold, Victorian, Dangling, Pair	40.00
Jewelry, Earring, Dangle, Angel Skin Corals, 14k Gold, Pair	68.00
Jewelry, Earring, Dangle, Black Opal Doublets Framed In 14k Gold, Pair	150.00
Jewelry, Earring, Drop, Silver, Enamel, Coral, Art Deco, Pair	60.00
Jewelry, Earring, Emerald & Diamond, Chased Foliate Pendants, C.1850, Pair	250.00
Jewelry, Earring, Four 4.10 Carat Andamooka Opals, Prong Set, 14K Gold, Pair	250.00
Jewelry, Earring, Jade, Green, Hoop, Carved, Pomegranates, Floral, China, Pair	375.00
Jewelry, Earring, Moss Jade, Hoop Pendant, 14k Gold, China, Screw On, Pair	85.00

Jewelry, Brooch, Cameo, Triangular Pendants, C.1870
See Page 288

Jewelry, Brooch,
Cameo, Sardonyx, C.1870
See Page 288

Jewelry, Pendant, Victorian,
Gold, Cameo, C.1870
See Page 291

Jewelry, **Earring**, Pendant, 4.10 Carat Opal, 14K Gold Mountings, Pair 250.00
Jewelry, **Earring**, Shell Cameo, 12k Gold Filled, Pair 18.50
Jewelry, **Hair Ornament**, Chinese, Jade, Rose Quartz, Fan Shaped Box 12.00
Jewelry, **Hatpin**, Bird Form, Gold, Cloisonne Enamel 100.00
Jewelry, **Lavaliere**, Black Cameo, White Head, Baroque Drop, 3 Pearls, 14K Gold 40.00
Jewelry, **Lavaliere**, Lapis Lazuli, Silver Loop, 1 X 2 In. 50.00
Jewelry, **Lavaliere**, Rose Gold, Birds, Diamond & Pearl 45.00
Jewelry, **Lavaliere**, Two Rubies, Pearl Drop 15.00
Jewelry, **Lavaliere**, Two Small Diamonds, Six Baroque Pearls, 14K Gold 1000.00
Jewelry, **Locket**, Gold, Oval, Engraved, Monogrammed 75.00
Jewelry, **Locket**, Pendant, Gold Mounted Bloodstone, Carved Roman Gods 325.00
Jewelry, **Locket**, Roman Mosaic, Floral, Etruscan Gold Border & Loop, 2 In. 175.00
Jewelry, **Locket**, Round, Diamond In Center, Turquoise Cluster, Gold 65.00
Jewelry, **Necklace & Earrings**, Gold & Topaz, Chased, Diamonds, C.1850 .... 600.00
Jewelry, **Necklace & Earrings**, Gold Mesh, Turquoise, Diamonds 625.00
Jewelry, **Necklace & Earrings**, Indian, Navajo, Silver, Turquoises 875.00
Jewelry, **Necklace**, Amber Beads, Gold Clasp, Double String, 26 In.Long 165.00
Jewelry, **Necklace**, Amber, Knot Strung, 84 Beads, Gold Clasp 95.00
Jewelry, **Necklace**, Bohemian Garnet, 239 Stones 175.00
Jewelry, **Necklace**, Cameo Carved On Sardonyx, Enamel Trim, Chain, 14k 175.00
Jewelry, **Necklace**, Carved Ivory Beads, Coral Beads, Graduated, 4i In. 80.00
Jewelry, **Necklace**, Carved Ivory Beads, Graduated, Ivory Clasp 35.00
Jewelry, **Necklace**, Carved Ivory Daisy Pendant On Ivory Beads 22.50
Jewelry, **Necklace**, Chinese Jade, 14 Carat Gold 175.00
Jewelry, **Necklace**, Chinese Jade, 39 Balls, 14k Gold Clasp 185.00
Jewelry, **Necklace**, Coral Beads, Matched, Carved, 20 In.Long 175.00
Jewelry, **Necklace**, Coral Beads, 49 In.Long 30.00
Jewelry, **Necklace**, Cut Glass, Dark Yellow, 32 Graduated Beads 20.00
Jewelry, **Necklace**, Facet Cut, Blue To Purple, Knots Between Beads, 64 In. 22.50
Jewelry, **Necklace**, Five Large Turquoise, Matrix, Seed Pearls, Gold Chain 150.00
Jewelry, **Necklace**, Gold, Etruscan Style, Quadruple Mesh, Scrollwork, C.1870 .... 325.00
Jewelry, **Necklace**, Green Jade Beads, Flat Crystal Rondels, 17 In.Long 150.00
Jewelry, **Necklace**, Hide Band, Tooth Pendants, Painted, Plains Indian 50.00
Jewelry, **Necklace**, Hide, Hoof & Blue Glass Beads, Plains Indian 70.00
Jewelry, **Necklace**, Honey Amber, Irregular Cut Pieces, Russia, 13 In.Strand 225.00
Jewelry, **Necklace**, Indian, Navajo, Silver, Turquoise, Openwork 300.00
Jewelry, **Necklace**, Indian, Navajo, Turquoise & Shell Beads, White Discs 130.00
Jewelry, **Necklace**, Indian, Navajo, Turquoise Beads, Shell & Silver Beads 210.00
Jewelry, **Necklace**, Ivory Beads, Carved, Ivory Clasp, 54 In. 30.00
Jewelry, **Necklace**, Jade, Double, Gold Clasp, 7 In. 75.00
Jewelry, **Necklace**, Jade, 41 Beads, Knot Strung, Gold Clasp, China, 28 In.Long 198.00
Jewelry, **Necklace**, Jade, 80 Beads, 25 In.Long 130.00
Jewelry, **Necklace**, Lapis Lazuli, 61 Balls, 14K Gold Clasp 195.00
Jewelry, **Necklace**, Lapis Lazuli, 63 Beads, Knot Strung, Gold Clasp 250.00
Jewelry, **Necklace**, Millefiori Oval Beads, Graduated, 18 In.Long 65.00
Jewelry, **Necklace**, Moonstone Beads, Graduated, 15 In.Long 20.00
Jewelry, **Necklace**, Peking Glass Beads, Blue, 26 In.Strand 25.00
Jewelry, **Necklace**, Plains Indian, Pendant Teeth & Tubular Glass Beads 80.00
Jewelry, **Necklace**, Rose Quartz Beads, Faceted, Graduate, 47 In.Long 125.00
Jewelry, **Necklace**, Sioux Indian, Amber, Blue, & Pink Glass Beads, Hide 60.00
Jewelry, **Necklace**, Sterling Silver Beads, 13 1/2 In. 15.00
Jewelry, **Necklace**, Tiger Eye Beads, Graduated, 31 In.Long 125.00
Jewelry, **Necklace**, Turquoise Nugget, Jokla, 220 Turquoise Disks 180.00
Jewelry, **Necklace**, Turquoise, Double, European, 14 3/4 In.Long 60.00
Jewelry, **Necklace**, Turquoise, Natural, Knotted, 14 3/4 In.Long 60.00
Jewelry, **Necklace**, 21 In.Long, Coral Beads, Each Bead About 1/4 In.Diameter 18.00
Jewelry, **Necklace**, 36 In.String Graduated Amber Glass 10.00
Jewelry, **Necklace**, 72 Garnets In Chain, 28 Garnets In Pendant, 18 In.Long 79.00
Jewelry, **Pendant & Brooch**, Silver Gilt, Enamel, St.George On Horseback, 1850 .... 225.00
Jewelry, **Pendant**, Amethysts & Pearls, 15k Gold 75.00
Jewelry, **Pendant**, Cameo, Lacy Gold Mount, Glass Back For Hair, 1890 .... 18.00
Jewelry, **Pendant**, Cameo, Pink & White, 10k Gold 25.00
Jewelry, **Pendant**, Cinnabar Ball, Slides On Cord, C.1920 .... 25.00
Jewelry, **Pendant**, Crystal, Oval, White Gold Border, Diamond Center 75.00
Jewelry, **Pendant**, Crystal, Rectangular, White Gold, Diamond .... 35.00 To 75.00
Jewelry, **Pendant**, Facet Amethyst, Baroque Pearls, Art Nouveau, Chain, Gold 75.00

Jewelry, Pendant, Filigree Gold, Seed Pearls, Turquoise, Baroque Pearl, Chain 30.00
Jewelry, Pendant, Gold Mounted Jade, Round, Turquoise, Mideastern, C.1750 .... 150.00
Jewelry, Pendant, Gold Washed Coin Silver, Heart Shape, Crest, Crown, England 85.00
Jewelry, Pendant, Horseshoe, Diamonds, Gold, Platinum, Chain 175.00
Jewelry, Pendant, Ivory, Carved Mother & Child, Wiener Werkstatte, C.1920 .... 100.00
Jewelry, Pendant, Jade Heart Framed In Gold 250.00
Jewelry, Pendant, Jade, White, Carved Flowers In Vase, 2 1/2 In. 35.00
Jewelry, Pendant, Pearl, Amethyst, Purple, Openwork Setting, 14k Gold 30.00
Jewelry, Pendant, Silver Gilt, Pelican Form, Garnets, Beryl, Openwork, C.1850 .... 225.00
Jewelry, Pendant, Topaz, Victorian Setting, Snake Chain, 17 In.Long 25.00
Jewelry, Pendant, Victorian, Gold, Cameo, C.1870 .... *Illus* 475.00
Jewelry, Pin & Earrings, Gold Enameled Plaques Of Venus & Cupid, C.1860 .... 225.00
Jewelry, Pin, Art Nouveau, Enameled Gold, Dancer Loie Fuller, Diamond, Ruby 250.00
Jewelry, Pin, Art Nouveau, Gilt Metal, Female Profile, Plique A Jour Enamel 425.00
Jewelry, Pin, Bar, Filigree, Diamond In Center, White Gold, 1 3/4 In.Long 200.00
Jewelry, Pin, Bar, Golf Club, Platinum & Gold, 2 In. 20.00
Jewelry, Pin, Bar, Lovers' Knot, Prong Mounted Diamond, Gold 125.00
Jewelry, Pin, Bar, White Filigree, Small Diamond 50.00
Jewelry, Pin, Betty Boop, Hand On Hip, 1 3/4 In. 7.50
Jewelry, Pin, Carved Coral 65.00
Jewelry, Pin, Etruscan Style Gold Work, Angel Skin Coral Disc Center, Gold 50.00
Jewelry, Pin, Garnet, Bowknot, 35 Flat Faceted Stones, 136 Pointed Stones 30.00
Jewelry, Pin, Garnet, 5 Heart Shaped Cabochon Stones, 1 Round Cabochon 175.00
Jewelry, Pin, Handy, Beaded Edge, 10k Gold 6.00
Jewelry, Pin, Horseshoe, Gold, Platinum Studs 25.00
Jewelry, Pin, Jockey Cap, Garnet Studded 125.00
Jewelry, Pin, Locket, Hair Under Glass, Pearl Border, Black Enamel, C.1850 .... 55.00
Jewelry, Pin, Moosehead, Garnet Eyes, Gold, 1 In.Long 35.00
Jewelry, Pin, Oval, Gold & Crystal, 2 Riders & 3 Hounds, English 175.00
Jewelry, Pin, Pedra Dura, Flowers, Place For Picture On Back 45.00
Jewelry, Pin, Portrait, Limoges, Signed, Garden Scene 35.00
Jewelry, Pin, Redheaded Duck, Flying, Perdew Of Henry, Illinois 125.00
Jewelry, Pin, Russian, C.1900 .... *Illus* 410.00

Jewelry, Pin, Russian, C.1900

Jewelry, Pin, Sword, Gold, Blue Enamel, Diamonds, Pearl, C.1850 .... 200.00
Jewelry, Pin, Watch, Lady's, Head In Relief, Marked 14k Yellow Gold 25.00
Jewelry, Pin, Watch, Reliefs & Cutouts, 14K Gold 25.00
Jewelry, Pin, Watch, Sterling, Fleur-De-Lis 6.50
Jewelry, Ring, Amethyst & Two Diamonds, 14k Gold 75.00
Jewelry, Ring, Art Nouveau, Head, Two Diamonds In Hair, 14K Gold 35.00
Jewelry, Ring, Band, Victorian, Small Diamond, 15K Gold 55.00
Jewelry, Ring, Cameo, Angel Skin Coral, Gold 45.00
Jewelry, Ring, Cameo, Standing Lady Playing Musical Instrument, 14k Gold 45.00
Jewelry, Ring, Carved Chinese Jade, Lady's, 14k Yellow Gold 150.00
Jewelry, Ring, Center Emerald, Diamond Studded, Platinum 300.00
Jewelry, Ring, Child's, Signet, Gold 17.00
Jewelry, Ring, Dinner, Opal, Black Tiffany Mounting, Yellow Gold 135.00

Jewelry, Ring, Dinner, Opal, White Gold Filigree Basket Mounting	195.00
Jewelry, Ring, Disc Top, Horse & Rider, Taking Hurdle, Gold, English	75.00
Jewelry, Ring, Domed Amber, Petals, Twigs, Insects, Wood Mold Inside, 14K Gold	135.00
Jewelry, Ring, Embossed, Engraved, 2 Pearls, 3 Rubies, Victorian, 14K Gold	25.00
Jewelry, Ring, Filigree, Diamond, Blue Sapphire, White Gold	180.00
Jewelry, Ring, Garnet Cluster	55.00
Jewelry, Ring, Garnet, Square Cut, Gold Mount	30.00
Jewelry, Ring, Garnet, 18k White Gold Filigree	32.00
Jewelry, Ring, Gold, Amethyst Flanked By 3 Diamonds	200.00
Jewelry, Ring, High Relief Sumac Leaves, Engraved Medallions, 1912, 10k Gold	48.00
Jewelry, Ring, Indian, Navajo, Silver, Triple Banded Hoop, Oval Turquoise	55.00
Jewelry, Ring, Indian, Zuni, Silver, Expanding Hoop, 16 Turquoises	55.00
Jewelry, Ring, Lady's, Andamooka Black Opal, 3 Carat, Seed Pearls	500.00
Jewelry, Ring, Lady's, Diamond, Tiffany, 14K Gold	95.00
Jewelry, Ring, Landy's, Jade, Carved Floral, Piercings, Engraved Gold Setting	150.00
Jewelry, Ring, Lady's, Opal Cluster, 14K Gold	65.00
Jewelry, Ring, Lady's, Opal, Two Diamonds, 14K Gold	175.00
Jewelry, Ring, Lady's, Pink Cameo, 10k Gold	20.00
Jewelry, Ring, Lady's, Signed Top, 15k Yellow Gold	95.00
Jewelry, Ring, Lady's, 3 Carat Peridot, 2 Small Diamonds, White Gold Setting	165.00
Jewelry, Ring, Lady's, 3 Cultured Pearls, 10k Yellow Gold, Size 6 1/2	15.00
Jewelry, Ring, Locket, Gold, Victorian, Paste Flowerhead, Pearls, C.1850	100.00
Jewelry, Ring, Man's, Dark Blue, White, Gold Setting, C.1850	95.00
Jewelry, Ring, Man's, Siberian Cabochon, Amethyst, 14K Gold	95.00
Jewelry, Ring, Marcasite, Carved Coral Flowers	35.00
Jewelry, Ring, Mizpah, English Hallmark, 14k Gold	35.00
Jewelry, Ring, Moss Agate, Gold	70.00
Jewelry, Ring, One Large Garnet, Ornate 14k Mounting	50.00
Jewelry, Ring, Opal, Heart Shape, Prong Mount, Gold	55.00
Jewelry, Ring, Opal, Lady's, 3.35 Carat, 27 Point Diamonds, 14K Gold	175.00
Jewelry, Ring, Opal, Oval Stone, 10K Gold	75.00
Jewelry, Ring, Opal, 18k White Gold Filigree	35.00
Jewelry, Ring, Persian Turquoise, Half Moon Set, Pearl, Dated 1889, 12K Gold	105.00
Jewelry, Ring, Railroad Conductor's, Enamel Inlay Design, 10K Gold	20.00
Jewelry, Ring, Sardonyx Stone Cameo, Carved Lady's Head, Openwork, 14K Gold	165.00
Jewelry, Ring, Scarab, Tiffany Type Glass, Blue, Art Nouveau Set ......70.00 To	130.00
Jewelry, Ring, Seven Opals In Cluster, 14K Gold Mounting	100.00
Jewelry, Ring, Signed, Gold, Engraved Arms Of Hermann Wilhelm Goering	650.00
Jewelry, Ring, Six Opals Clustered Around Rose Diamond, England, 15K Gold	30.00
Jewelry, Ring, Turquoise Surrounded By 12 Rose Cut Diamonds, 14K Gold	75.00
Jewelry, Ring, Victorian, Gold, Opals, Rubies & Pearls	125.00
Jewelry, Ring, White Opal, 14 Rose Cut Diamonds, 14K Gold	75.00
Jewelry, Set, Amethyst, Pearls, Silver Gilt .... *Illus*	400.00
Jewelry, Stickpin, Abalone Set In Silver	4.95
Jewelry, Stickpin, Amethyst Stone In Silver	4.50
Jewelry, Stickpin, Amethyst, Scarab, 14K Gold	75.00

Jewelry, Set, Amethyst, Pearls, Silver Gilt

Jewelry, Stickpin, Amethyst, Teardrop	7.00
Jewelry, Stickpin, Animal's Head Made From Gold Nugget, Diamond Eyes	37.50
Jewelry, Stickpin, Art Nouveau, Chip Diamond, 14K Gold	45.00
Jewelry, Stickpin, Art Nouveau, Girl With Flowing Hair, Gold Finish	3.95
Jewelry, Stickpin, Black Cameo, Gold Finish	3.50
Jewelry, Stickpin, Bust Of Woman, Cameo, White On Pink, Gold Setting	35.00
Jewelry, Stickpin, Cameo, White & Pink	6.00
Jewelry, Stickpin, Cameo, White Figure Of Classical Girl's Head	2.75
Jewelry, Stickpin, Carnelian Stone In 14k Gold	18.00
Jewelry, Stickpin, Cat Eye	10.00
Jewelry, Stickpin, Coral & Gold Snake	25.00
Jewelry, Stickpin, Coral Colored Cameo	15.00
Jewelry, Stickpin, Cut Design, Man On Winged Horse, Amber Stone	2.75
Jewelry, Stickpin, Diamond Shape Ruby, 10k Gold Setting	30.00
Jewelry, Stickpin, Diamond Shaped Amethyst In 10k Gold, 3 Pearls	14.50
Jewelry, Stickpin, Enameled Beetle, Two Tiny Blue Stones	2.95
Jewelry, Stickpin, Faceted Aquamarine, Engraved, Gold	48.00
Jewelry, Stickpin, Fleur-De-Lis Shape, Sterling Silver	2.95
Jewelry, Stickpin, Fleur-De-Lis, Twelve Pearls, 14k Gold	35.00
Jewelry, Stickpin, Four Baroque Pearls, One 5 Point Diamond, 15K Gold	60.00
Jewelry, Stickpin, Girl, Art Nouveau	12.00
Jewelry, Stickpin, Gold Finish, Brown Colored Stone	3.75
Jewelry, Stickpin, Gold Finish, Knot & Horseshoe	2.95
Jewelry, Stickpin, Gold Finish, Star & Crescent	2.95
Jewelry, Stickpin, Gold Nugget, Diamond, 14K Gold	30.00
Jewelry, Stickpin, Gold Nugget, Prong Set Diamond, 14K Gold	35.00
Jewelry, Stickpin, Gold, Art Nouveau Girl, Marked Garden City Tailoring Co.	5.95
Jewelry, Stickpin, Gold, Cameo	16.50
Jewelry, Stickpin, Gold, Circle Of 12 Seed Pearls, 4 Blue Sapphires	18.50
Jewelry, Stickpin, Gold, Crest	3.70
Jewelry, Stickpin, Green Zircon, Openwork, 14K Gold	15.00
Jewelry, Stickpin, Hand Shape, Gold	7.50
Jewelry, Stickpin, Head Of Moose, Glass Eyes, Gold Finish	3.75
Jewelry, Stickpin, Horseshoe, Seed Pearls, 14k Gold	12.50
Jewelry, Stickpin, Indian Moss Agate, Sterling Silver Mount	10.00
Jewelry, Stickpin, Initial, Gold Finish	3.75
Jewelry, Stickpin, Keystone Cop	10.00
Jewelry, Stickpin, Leaf Shape, Small Pearl, Gold	7.95
Jewelry, Stickpin, Lover's Knot, Gold Finish	3.75
Jewelry, Stickpin, Mosaic Flower	5.00
Jewelry, Stickpin, Mother-Of-Pearl, Oval	5.00
Jewelry, Stickpin, Mutt & Jeff	10.00
Jewelry, Stickpin, Opal	8.00
Jewelry, Stickpin, Oval, Blue Stone, Sterling Silver	2.95
Jewelry, Stickpin, Painting On Ivory, Nude, C.1800, 15K Gold	49.50
Jewelry, Stickpin, Pearl & Opal	15.00
Jewelry, Stickpin, Pearl, White Gold Setting	15.00
Jewelry, Stickpin, Pearls, Fleur De Lis, 14k Gold	22.00
Jewelry, Stickpin, Pink Cameo	4.50
Jewelry, Stickpin, Ruby Stone, Prong Setting	3.75
Jewelry, Stickpin, Silver Finish, Oval Mother-Of-Pearl Top	2.95 To 3.75
Jewelry, Stickpin, Small Opal, Gold	18.50
Jewelry, Stickpin, Sword, Garnet In Handle	7.50
Jewelry, Stickpin, Teardrop Citrine Stone Set In Wishbone, 14K Gold	14.50
Jewelry, Stickpin, Toad Shape, Carrying Cane & Hat, Silver Finish, 1894	3.95
Jewelry, Stickpin, Topaz, Sterling Silver	9.00
Jewelry, Stickpin, Turquoise Stone Circled By Eight Clear Stones	2.75
Jewelry, Stickpin, Woman's Head, Sterling Silver	2.95
Jewelry, Stickpin, Wreath Of Leaves & Berries Design	2.00
Jewelry, Tiepin, Sword Shape, Sterling	6.00
Jewelry, Watch, see Watch	

John Rogers Statues were made from 1859 to 1892. The originals were bronze. But the thousands of copies made by Rogers Factory were of painted plaster. Eighty different figures were made.

John Rogers, Group, A Matter Of Opinion	175.00

John Rogers, Group, Challenging The Union Vote	1000.00
John Rogers, Group, Henry Ward Beecher	2000.00
John Rogers, Group, Marguerite & Martha Trying On The Jewels	1500.00
John Rogers, Group, One More Shot	200.00
John Rogers, Group, The Bath	1250.00
John Rogers, Group, The Bushwhacker	2500.00
John Rogers, Group, The Mock Trial	500.00
John Rogers, Group, Uncle Ned's School	330.00
John Rogers, Group, Weighing The Baby	150.00
Johnson Brothers, Breakfast Set, Rosedawn, 10 Piece	15.00
Johnson Brothers, Butter, Wedding Band	9.25
Johnson Brothers, Platter, Cambridge Castle, Lavender On Cream, 1792	12.50
Judaica, Box, Spice, Brass, Silver, C.1720	50.00

Kate Greenaway, who was a famous illustrator of children's books, drew pictures of children in high-waisted empire dresses. She lived from 1846 to 1901. Her designs appear on china, glass, and other pieces.

Kate Greenaway, Book, Apple Pie	29.50
Kate Greenaway, Book, Little Ann, Color Illustrations	30.00
Kate Greenaway, Book, Marigold Garden	29.50
Kate Greenaway, Book, Pied Piper Of Hamelin, Color Illustrations	15.00
Kate Greenaway, Bookend, Figural, Girl, Red Clothes, Blue Hat, Muff, Pair	47.50
Kate Greenaway, Bowl, Little Boy Blue	50.00
Kate Greenaway, Butter Pat	15.00
Kate Greenaway, Cup & Saucer, Children & Flowers, Square	30.00
Kate Greenaway, Dish, Child's, Campbell Soup Kids, Buffalo Pottery	48.00
Kate Greenaway, Figurine, Boy & Girl, Carrying Posies In Basket, Bisque	58.00
Kate Greenaway, Figurine, Child, Sitting With Feet Crossed	25.00
Kate Greenaway, Figurine, Girl Sitting On Dog, Parian, 3 1n.High	14.00
Kate Greenaway, Match Safe, Pocket, Copper	35.00
Kate Greenaway, Muffineer, Boy On Long Coat & Stovepipe Hat	50.00
Kate Greenaway, Napkin Ring, Boy Against Ring, Silver Plate	65.00
Kate Greenaway, Napkin Ring, Dog, Boy, Signed Aurora, Replated	47.00
Kate Greenaway, Napkin Ring, Figural, Baby With Hat, Pairpoint	85.00
Kate Greenaway, Napkin Ring, Figural, Boy Wearing Hat, Pushes Ring	75.00
Kate Greenaway, Napkin Ring, Figural, Boy With Hat, Breeches, Pushes Ring	65.00
Kate Greenaway, Napkin Ring, Figural, Boy With Hat, Meriden	75.00
Kate Greenaway, Napkin Ring, Figural, Boy, Meriden 62.00 To	65.00
Kate Greenaway, Napkin Ring, Figural, Girl & Dog, Resilvered	65.00
Kate Greenaway, Napkin Ring, Figural, Girl Sitting By Ring	80.00
Kate Greenaway, Napkin Ring, Figural, Girl With Begging Dog, Meriden	80.00
Kate Greenaway, Napkin Ring, Girl Beating Drum	95.00
Kate Greenaway, Napkin Ring, Ring Sits On Column, Silver Plate, J.W.Tufts	95.00
Kate Greenaway, Picture, Watercolor	210.00
Kate Greenaway, Plate, Child's, Higgledy Piggledy, My Black Hen	40.00
Kate Greenaway, Plate, Three Maids Center, Gold Filigree, K.P.M.	25.00
Kate Greenaway, Print, Children In Meadow, Marcus Ward & Co., Ltd, Frame	41.00
Kate Greenaway, Salt & Pepper, Boy & Girl In Baskets 42.50 To	45.00
Kate Greenaway, Salt & Pepper, Boy & Girl In Period Clothes, Barrel Shape	40.00
Kate Greenaway, Salt Shaker, Figural, Girl	18.00
Kate Greenaway, Salt, Boy In Pink Coat	20.00
Kate Greenaway, Salt, Figural, Girl, Blue Coat, Fur Trim, Hat, Staffordshire	15.00
Kate Greenaway, Sauce, Colorfully Dressed Figure, 5 In.	6.00
Kate Greenaway, Toothpick, Girl With Bonnet, Gold Plated	59.00
Kate Greenaway, Tray, Pin, Seesaw	30.00
Kate Greenaway, Tray, Pin, Ten O'Clock Scholar	25.00
Kate Greenaway, Vase, Girl Skipping Rope, Majolica, 6 In.High	18.00

Kauffmann refers to the type of work done by Angelica Kauffmann, a painter and decorative artist, for Adam Brothers in England between 1766 and 1781. She designed small-scale pictorial subjects in the Neo-Classic manner. Most porcelains signed Kauffmann were made in the nineteenth century.

Kauffmann, Bowl, Royal Vienna, Beehive Mark, 4 1/2 In.	20.00
Kauffmann, Bowl, Scene, Classical Ladies, Infant, Marked Vienna, Beehive	35.00
Kauffmann, Bowl, Two Women, Child, Iridescent Inside, Pierced Edge, Mark	37.50
Kauffmann, Bowl, Women, Child, Green, Gold, Marked Victoria, Carlsbad, Austria	67.50

Kauffmann, Chocolate Pot, Mythical Scene, Signed & Numbered, 8 In.High	115.00
Kauffmann, Cup & Saucer, Demitasse, Man Holds Crown Over Two Ladies, 1750	65.00
Kauffmann, Cup & Saucer, Demitasse, Scene, Signed	45.00
Kauffmann, Cup & Saucer, Footed, Beehive, Gold Handle, Portrait On Front	48.00
Kauffmann, Dish, Candy, Gold, Burgundy, Cream, Scroll Handle, 2 Section, Signed	18.00
Kauffmann, Inkwell, Green, Gold, Center Medallion, Classical Figures	35.00
Kauffmann, Jar & Plate, Jam, Covered, Shaded Flow Blue, Scene Of Ladies, Gold	55.00
Kauffmann, Jar, Cracker, Scenic, Silver Plate Bail, Handle, & Cover, Signed	85.00
Kauffmann, Luncheon Set, Gold & Blue Borders, Classical Figures, 14 Piece	85.00
Kauffmann, Painting, On Porcelain, Cherub, Woman, Pot, Fire, Frame, 5 3/8 In.	185.00
Kauffmann, Plaque, Ladies Dancing, Signed, 3 3/4 In.	22.50
Kauffmann, Plate, Cake, Classical Center, Crown Mark, Gold, 9 1/2 In.Diameter	22.50
Kauffmann, Plate, Cake, Gold & Blue Borders, Classical Figures, Crown Mark	25.00
Kauffmann, Plate, Carlsbad, Austria, 14 In.	65.00
Kauffmann, Plate, Classic Scene, Deep Scallops, Ornate Border, Gold, 10 In.	33.00
Kauffmann, Plate, Classical Figures In Center, Gold Border, Raised Dots	47.50
Kauffmann, Plate, Classical Figures, Gold Shamrock Border, 7 1/2 In.	17.00
Kauffmann, Plate, Cupid & Nymphs Scene, Gold Border, Red Crown Mark	8.50
Kauffmann, Plate, Hanging, Classical Figures, Signed Victoria, Austria	32.00
Kauffmann, Plate, Ladies Dancing, Scroll Openwork In Corners, Cobalt Edge	23.00
Kauffmann, Plate, Lady, Cherub, Classic Figures, Green Border, Leaves, Pair	75.00
Kauffmann, Plate, Maroon On Gold Trim, Victoria Austria Mark, 8 1/4 In.	22.50
Kauffmann, Plate, Medallions, Four Women & Child, Gold Tracery Border	38.00
Kauffmann, Plate, Pierced, Cobalt To Pale Blue, Gold, Signed, Crown Mark	38.50
Kauffmann, Plate, Portrait, Classical Figures, Victoria, Austria, 10 In.	36.00
Kauffmann, Plate, Portrait, Figures Pull Chariot, Cupid Inside, Gold Scroll	35.00
Kauffmann, Plate, Sleeping Knight, Signed, 7 1/4 In.	18.00
Kauffmann, Plate, Woman, Child, Blue Green, Gold, E.P.Co., Stoke-On-Trent	65.00
Kauffmann, Plate, Yellow Border, Ladies & Cherub At Bath, Beehive, Austria	32.50
Kauffmann, Platter, Green & Gold Ground, Colorful Scene, Victoria, Austria	42.00
Kauffmann, Tea Set, Classical Center, Crown Marked, 3 Piece	95.00
Kauffmann, Teapot, Green, Gold, Woman & Child, Austria	49.00
Kauffmann, Teapot, Mythical Scene, Signed, Large Size	75.00
Kauffmann, Tray, Open Gold Handles, Cream, Classical Figures, Gold, Beehive	85.00
Kauffmann, Urn, Women Fix Hair, Cherub Watches, Maroon, Gold, Green, 11 In.	85.00
Kauffmann, Vase, Classic Greek Figures, Maroon, Signed, 5 3/4 In.High	15.00
Kauffmann, Vase, Classical Figures, Gold Handles, Beehive Mark, Pair	110.00
Kauffmann, Vase, Handles, Austria, Blue Beehive Mark, 6 1/2 In.	35.00
Kauffmann, Vase, Pink Luster, Gold Highlights, Seminude, Cherub, Carlsbad	75.00
Kauffmann, Vase, Portrait, Four Women, Grecian Gowns, Mountain Scene, Handles	60.00
Kauffmann, Vase, Portrait, Green Back, Blue & Rose Front, Gold Tracery	48.50
Kauffmann, Vase, Scene, Royal Blue, 18th Century Gold Designs, Signed	35.00

Kaziun Glass has been made by Charles Kaziun since 1942. His paperweights have been gaining fame steadily. Most of his glass and all of the paperweights are signed with A K designed cane worked into the design. He makes buttons, earrings, perfume bottles, and paperweights.

Kaziun, see also Paperweight

Kaziun, Earring, Paperweight, Sparkling Ground, Blue Floral, Signed, Pair	125.00
Kaziun, Paperweight, Snake	515.00

Kelva Glassware was made by the C.F. Monroe Company of Meriden, Connecticut, about 1904. It is a pale pastel painted glass decorated with flowers, designs, or scenes.

Kelva, Box, Blue, Red & Yellow Raised Leaf On Lid, Hinged, 4 In.Sq.	165.00
Kelva, Box, Cigar, Red, Signed	375.00
Kelva, Box, Jewel, Green With Coral Flowers, Silver Hinges, Signed	210.00
Kelva, Box, Jewel, Mottled Green, Large Orchids, Signed, 8 In.Diameter	385.00
Kelva, Box, Mottled Green Ground, Orange Blossoms, Signed	200.00
Kelva, Box, Mottled Sage Green, Orange Blossoms, Monroe, 4 1/2 In.Square	210.00
Kelva, Box, Signed, 3 1/2 In.High	225.00
Kelva, Box, Trinket, Hinged Cover, Embossed Pierced Brass Bottom, Floral	160.00
Kelva, Humidor, Covered, White, Abstract Mossy Green Pattern, White Floral	150.00
Kelva, Jar, Green, Cigar, Signed	300.00
Kelva, Planter, Enamel, Pink & White Floral, No Insert, 9 In.	175.00
Kelva, Vase, Apricot Color, Carnations, 8 In.High	68.00

Kelva, Vase, Salmon Pink, White Cosmos, Beaded Top, C.F.Monroe Wavecrest 165.00
Kelva, Vase, Sponged Green, Floral, 6 Panel, 4 Brass Ormolu Feet, Signed 225.00

*Kew Blas is the name used by the Union Glass Company of Somerville,
Massachusetts. The name refers to an iridescent golden glass made from the
1890s to 1924.*
Kew Blas, Creamer, Gold Iridescent, Mirror Finish, Snail Like Handle, Signed 225.00
Kew Blas, Plate, Gold, Signed, 6 In. 110.00
Kew Blas, Tumbler, Blue & Gold Iridescent, Pinched Sides, Signed 295.00
Kew Blas, Tumbler, Gold, Iridescent Blue & Rose, Pinched Body, Signed 150.00
Kew Blas, Tumbler, Signed 145.00
Kew Blas, Vase, Art Nouveau, Union Glass Co., Somerville, Mass. 750.00

*Kewpies were first pictured in the Ladies' Home Journal by Rose
O'Neill. The pixie-like figures became an immediate success, and Kewpie
dolls started appearing in 1911. Kewpie pictures and other items soon
followed.*
Kewpie, Bank, Advertising Calumet Baking Powder, Nods, Tin 47.50
Kewpie, Bank, Blue Wings, Chalk 8.00
Kewpie, Bell, Figural, Silver 28.00
Kewpie, Billiken, Celluloid, 2-Faced 15.00
Kewpie, Book, Christmas Party, Rose O'Neill, Ladies' Home Companion, 1911 .... 10.00
Kewpie, Box, Green Jasper, Signed Rose O'Neill, Cover 95.00
Kewpie, Box, Signed Rose O'Neill, 2 Kewpies Swinging, Tin, Black, Round 12.00
Kewpie, Box, Two Kewpies Swinging, Tin 13.50
Kewpie, Candy Container 28.00
Kewpie, Candy Container, Beside Barrel, Closure 32.00
Kewpie, Candy Container, Beside Barrel, Signed Borgfeldt 35.00
Kewpie, Candy Container, Doll Standing By Barrel, Painted 45.00
Kewpie, Candy Container, Signed Borgfeldt 35.00
Kewpie, Candy Container, Signed Rose O'Neill, Glass, 3 In.Tall 35.00
Kewpie, Card, Christmas, Hand-Drawn Kewpie, Verse 1.50
Kewpie, Card, Easter 5.00
Kewpie, Creamer, Signed O'Neill, 3 Kewpies, Trees, Rudolstadt 22.50
Kewpie, Creamer, Signed Rose O'Neill, Bavaria 45.00
Kewpie, Creamer, White Porcelain, 3 1/2 In. 39.50
Kewpie, Cup & Saucer, Signed Rose O'Neill, Royal Rudolstadt 65.00
Kewpie, Cup & Saucer, Signed Rose O'Neill, Wilson, Royal Rudolstadt 48.00
Kewpie, Cup, Saucer, & Cake Plate, Signed Rose O'Neill, Royal Rudolstadt 135.00
Kewpie, Cup, Saucer, & Plate, Carrying Flag, Signed Bavaria, Marked K 58.00
Kewpie, Dish & Cereal Bowl, Signed Rose O'Neill, Royal Rudolstadt 135.00
Kewpie, Dish, Feeding, Signed O'Neill 95.00
Kewpie, Dish, Feeding, Three Sections 25.00
Kewpie, Doll, Bisque, Droopy Drawers, Made In Japan, 4 1/2 In.Tall 10.00
Kewpie, Doll, Bisque, Katy O'Kewp, 4 1/2 In.Tall 62.50
Kewpie, Doll, Bisque, Label, Pat.1913, Made In Japan, 6 In. 30.00
Kewpie, Doll, Bisque, Molded Hair, Movable Arms, Marked Nippon, 5 3/4 In.Tall 19.00
Kewpie, Doll, Bisque, Nude, Made In Japan, 4 1/2 In.Tall 10.00
Kewpie, Doll, Bisque, Paper Label, 4 3/8 In.Tall 43.00
Kewpie, Doll, Bisque, Stands On Large Pearl Button, 4 5/8 In.Tall 51.00
Kewpie, Doll, Bisque, Thumb Sucker 12.50
Kewpie, Doll, Bisque, Traveler, 2 In.Tall 85.00
Kewpie, Doll, Bisque, Traveler, 2 1/2 In.Tall 60.00
Kewpie, Doll, Bisque, 4 In.Tall 65.00
Kewpie, Doll, Black, Japan, 3 In.Tall 15.00
Kewpie, Doll, Black, 7 In. .... *Illus* 125.00
Kewpie, Doll, Bride & Groom, Celluloid, Dressed, Crepe Paper, 6 In.Tall 20.00
Kewpie, Doll, Bride & Groom, Signed Rose O'Neill, Dressed, Germany, Pair 120.00
Kewpie, Doll, Cameo Squeeze, 11 In.Tall, Pair 17.50
Kewpie, Doll, Cameo, Ragsy, Red Vinyl, 11 In.Tall 9.50
Kewpie, Doll, Carnival, 13 In.Tall 15.00
Kewpie, Doll, Celluloid, Dressed, 2 In.Tall 5.00
Kewpie, Doll, Celluloid, Movable Arms, Blue Wings, Red Heart Label, Germany 18.50
Kewpie, Doll, Celluloid, 2 1/2 In.Tall 15.00
Kewpie, Doll, Chalkware, Elbows On Knees, Label, 1913 ...... 14.50
Kewpie, Doll, Composition, Dressed, 12 In.Tall 53.00

Kewpie, Doll, Composition, Jointed Arms & Legs, 13 In.Tall 296 .... 40.00
Kewpie, Doll, Composition, Movable Arms & Legs, 12 In.Tall .... 25.00 To 50.00
Kewpie, Doll, Composition, 11 In.Tall 45.00
Kewpie, Doll, Paper, Cutout, Little Assunta & Her Kewpie Doll, Rose O'Neill 18.00
Kewpie, Doll, Paper, Cutout, The Nurse & The Better Baby, Rose O'Neill, Uncut 18.00
Kewpie, Doll, Paper, The Flying Kewpies, May 1913, Rose O'Neill, Uncut 18.00
Kewpie, Doll, Ragsy 10.00
Kewpie, Doll, Rubber, Squeaks When Pressed, 9 In.Tall 4.00
Kewpie, Doll, Signed Rose O'Neill On Feet, Bisque, Red Heart Label, 5 1/4 In. 59.00
Kewpie, Doll, Signed Rose O'Neill, Action, 2 3/8 In.Tall 35.00
Kewpie, Doll, Signed Rose O'Neill, Bisque, Labels, 6 3/4 In.Tall 69.00
Kewpie, Doll, Signed Rose O'Neill, Bisque, Movable Arms, Sticker, 4 1/2 In. 55.00
Kewpie, Doll, Signed Rose O'Neill, Bisque, Seated, Holds Black Pencil 45.00
Kewpie, Doll, Signed Rose O'Neill, Bisque, Seated, 6 In.Tall 85.00
Kewpie, Doll, Signed Rose O'Neill, Bisque, 4 1/2 In.Tall 55.00
Kewpie, Doll, Signed Rose O'Neill, Bisque, 5 In.Tall 36.00
Kewpie, Doll, Signed Rose O'Neill, Bisque, 8 In.Tall 120.00

Kewpie, Doll, Black, 7 In.
See Page 296

Kewpie, Doll, Signed Rose O'Neill, Celluloid, Copyright Symbol, 9 In.Tall 50.00
Kewpie, Doll, Signed Rose O'Neill, Celluloid, 4 1/2 In.Tall 20.00
Kewpie, Doll, Signed Rose O'Neill, Composition, Heart Label, 11 1/2 In.Tall 35.00
Kewpie, Doll, Signed Rose O'Neill, Composition, Negro 100.00
Kewpie, Doll, Signed Rose O'Neill, Cuddle, Plush, 12 In.Tall 12.00
Kewpie, Doll, Signed Rose O'Neill, Glass Eyes 17.50
Kewpie, Doll, Signed Rose O'Neill, Impressed Mark, 5 In.Tall 40.00
Kewpie, Doll, Signed Rose O'Neill, Movable Arms, Paper Label, 4 1/2 In.Tall 59.00
Kewpie, Doll, Signed Rose O'Neill, Rubber, Jointed Arms, 10 In.Tall 30.00
Kewpie, Doll, Signed Rose O'Neill, Rubber, The Thinker, 3 1/2 In.Tall 15.00
Kewpie, Doll, Signed Rose O'Neill, Rubber, The Thinker, 5 In.Tall 25.00
Kewpie, Doll, Signed Rose O'Neill, Rubber, 11 In.Tall 38.00
Kewpie, Doll, Signed Rose O'Neill, Standing, 4 1/2 In.Tall 55.00
Kewpie, Doll, Signed Rose O'Neill, Standing, 8 In.Tall 110.00
Kewpie, Doll, Signed Rose O'Neill, The Traveler 85.00
Kewpie, Doll, Signed Rose O'Neill, 6 In.Tall 65.00
Kewpie, Doll, Signed Rose O'Neill, 8 1/2 In.Tall 87.50
Kewpie, Doll, Sitting, Red Plush, White Velvet Feet 15.00
Kewpie, Doll, Squeeze, Cameo Product, 10 In.Tall 30.00
Kewpie, Doll, Sticker, Small 50.00
Kewpie, Figurine, Kneeling, Sitting, Bisque, Marked Ider, 3 1/2 In., Pair 12.00
Kewpie, Figurine, Wings, 12 In.High 12.50
Kewpie, Flannel, Cutting Hair 13.00
Kewpie, Flannel, Kewpie With Berries In Hat 10.00
Kewpie, Flannel, Marching With American Flag, Marked Rose O'Neill, 1914 .... 10.00
Kewpie, Flannel, Scene 12.50
Kewpie, Flannel, Signed Rose O'Neill, 5 X 6 In. 8.00
Kewpie, Flannel, Target Practice, Marked Rose O'Neill, 1914, 5 X 6 In. 10.00
Kewpie, Flannel, The Ice Skaters, Signed Rose O'Neill .... 8.00 To 13.00
Kewpie, Hugger, Bisque, Rose O'Neill, Sticker On Back, 1913 .... 48.00
Kewpie, Hugger, Bisque, 3 1/2 In. 45.00
Kewpie, Hugger, Rose O'Neill, Sticker, 1913, 3 1/2 In. 75.00
Kewpie, Inkwell, Holds Pen Atop Well, Bisque, Signed O'Neill 200.00

Kewpie, Mirror	1.00
Kewpie, Mold, Chocolate, Tin, 1930s, 2 X 3 In.	4.00
Kewpie, Mold, Cookie, Tin, O'Neill	32.50
Kewpie, Mold, Ice Cream, Patent 3-4-13	43.00
Kewpie, Mold, Ice Cream, Pewter, Four Standing In A Row, 7 In.Tall	95.00
Kewpie, Muffineer, Two Kewpies, Pastel Blue, Gold, Porcelain, Germany	75.00
Kewpie, Mug, Six Actions, Rose O'Neill, Royal Rudolstadt, 2 In.High	75.00
Kewpie, Page, Rose O'Neill, Kewpieville	4.00
Kewpie, Perfume, Signed Germany	45.00
Kewpie, Picture, Signed Rose O'Neill, Wood Frame, 6 X 4 In.	8.00
Kewpie, Pillow Cover, Kewpie In The Moon, Painted, Embroidered, 1913	40.00
Kewpie, Pitcher, Kewpies Playing, Pastel Colors, Royal Rudolstadt, 4 In.	75.00
Kewpie, Pitcher, Signed Rose O'Neill	100.00
Kewpie, Planter, Pottery, Pink Glaze	55.00
Kewpie, Planter, Signed C In Circle, The Thinker, White	26.00
Kewpie, Planter, Signed Rose O'Neill, The Thinker, Pottery, Blue	31.00
Kewpie, Plaque, Signed Rose O'Neill, Heart Shape, White On Green Blue	110.00
Kewpie, Plate, Kewpie Carrying Flag Marked K, Bavaria, 5 1/4 In.	20.00
Kewpie, Plate, Signed Rose O'Neill, Green Trim, 5 7/8 In.	35.00
Kewpie, Plate, Signed Rose O'Neill, Pink Trim, 5 1/4 In.	35.00
Kewpie, Plate, Signed Rose O'Neill, Royal Rudolstadt, 7 5/8 In.	55.00
Kewpie, Plate, Signed Rose O'Neill, Wilson, Gold Edge, Royal Rudolstadt	58.00
Kewpie, Plate, Signed Rose O'Neill, Wilson, Kewpies Playing, Germany	65.00
Kewpie, Postcard	10.00
Kewpie, Postcard, Color, 12	10.00
Kewpie, Postcard, Mabel Bray	1.00
Kewpie, Postcard, Rose O'Neill At Bonnie Brook	1.50
Kewpie, Postcard, Signed Rose O'Neill, 'And I Cannot Swim A Stroke, ' Frame	14.00
Kewpie, Rattle & Teething Ring, English Silver, Dated 1925	75.00
Kewpie, Shaker, Talcum, Porcelain, Austria	34.00
Kewpie, Sheet, Signed Rose O'Neill, Kewpieville, 1926	4.25
Kewpie, Spoon, Baby's, Sterling Silver, Embossed Kewpie On Handle, Marked	32.50
Kewpie, Sugar & Creamer, Covered, Signed Rose O'Neill, Action Kewpies	110.00
Kewpie, Sugar & Creamer, Covered, Signed Rose O'Neill, Luster Ground	90.00
Kewpie, Sugar & Creamer, Signed Rose O'Neill, Seven Action Kewpies	135.00
Kewpie, Sugar & Creamer, Signed Rose O'Neill	125.00
Kewpie, Sugar, Covered, Signed Rose O'Neill, Luster Ground	45.00
Kewpie, Tea Set, Signed Rose O'Neill, Action Kewpies, Pink Luster, 13 Piece	350.00
Kewpie, Tea Set, Signed Rose O'Neill, 3 Piece	95.00
Kewpie, Teapot, Signed Rose O'Neill	60.00
Kewpie, Toothpick, Signed Rose O'Neill, Clear Glass	35.00
Kewpie, Toothpick, Thinker, 5 1/2 In.High	35.00
Kewpie, Tray, Signed Rose O'Neill, Action, Royal Rudolstadt, 10 In.	135.00
Kewpie, Tray, With Kewpish Love From Rose O'Neill	200.00
Kewpie, Truck, Yellow, 22 In.	150.00
Key, Dungeon, France, 6 In.Long	8.85
Key, Jail, 7 In.Long	1.75
Kimball, see Cluthra	
King's Rose, see Soft Paste	
Kitchen, see also Store, Tool, Wooden, Iron	
Kitchen, Basket, Splint, For Apples, 5 X 12 In.	12.00
Kitchen, Basket, Wire .... *Illus*	12.00
Kitchen, Board, Chopping, Heart Cutout, Pine	12.50
Kitchen, Board, Cookie, Clown, Wooden, 10 X 30 In.	40.00
Kitchen, Board, Cookie, Hand-Carved, Man, Ring For Hanging	27.50
Kitchen, Board, Cutting, Wooden, 1 In.Thick, Oval, 17 X 7 1/2 In.	4.00
Kitchen, Board, Pressing, Carved, Horse Handle, Flowers, Hex Signs	160.00
Kitchen, Board, Springerle, 2 Designs	15.00
Kitchen, Boiler, Potato, Wire, C.1830, 8 X 11 In.	58.00
Kitchen, Bottle Capper, Lever Action	4.50
Kitchen, Bowl & Ladle, Brass, Iron Handle On Ladle, Patent 1886	35.00
Kitchen, Bowl & Ladle, Maple, 11 In.Diameter	45.00
Kitchen, Bowl Set, Wooden, 13 To 15 In.Diameter, Set Of 4	10.00
Kitchen, Bowl, Burl, American Maple, 17 In.Wide, 9 In.Deep	250.00
Kitchen, Bowl, Chopping, Seasoned, Wooden, 10 1/2 In.Diameter, 3 In.High	10.00
Kitchen, Bowl, Chopping, Wooden, 17 In.Diameter	12.00

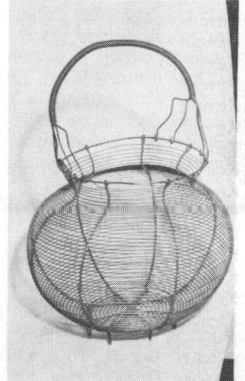

Kitchen, Basket, Wire
See Page 298

Kitchen, **Bowl**, Dough, Hand-Carved, Handles, 14 In.	37.50
Kitchen, **Bowl**, Wooden, Cone Shape, Deep, C.1750	29.00
Kitchen, **Bowl**, Wooden, 12 In.Diameter	9.00
Kitchen, **Bowl**, Wooden, 24 In.Diameter, 7 1/2 In.High	100.00
Kitchen, **Box**, Flour, Maple, Iron & Wood Handle, 11 In.Diameter	12.00
Kitchen, **Box**, Salt, Hanging, Green, Yellow, Pottery, 'salt, 'Wooden Lid	16.50
Kitchen, **Box**, Salt, Pine, Double, Handled, Figure Eight Shape	50.00
Kitchen, **Box**, Spice, Finger Lap, Rosehead Nails, 18th Century, 10 In.Diameter	45.00
Kitchen, **Box**, Spice, Tin, Round, 6 Stenciled Boxes & Nutmeg Grater Inside	18.00
Kitchen, **Bread Maker**, Universal, Metal, Pail Shape, Embossed, 15 In.High	40.00
Kitchen, **Butter Stamp**, Acorn, Plunger	22.00
Kitchen, **Butter Stamp**, Cow, Carved, Octagon, 3 In.	80.00
Kitchen, **Butter Stamp**, Pineapple & Leaf, Hand-Carved	27.50
Kitchen, **Butter Stamp**, Pineapple, Side Handle, Carved, 6 3/4 In.Long	165.00
Kitchen, **Butter Stamp**, Plunger Type, Nickel Plunger, Initial On Corners	25.00
Kitchen, **Butter Stamp**, Rooster, Carved, 3 In.Diameter	160.00
Kitchen, **Butter Stamp**, Wheat, Wooden	16.00
Kitchen, **Cake Turner**, Brass, Wrought Iron Handle, Pennsylvania	15.00
Kitchen, **Cherry Pitter**, Clamp Type, Iron	10.00
Kitchen, **Cherry Pitter**, Iron, Double Pronged, C.1867	10.00
Kitchen, **Cherry Pitter**, Iron, New Standard, Mt.Joy, Pennsylvania	6.00
Kitchen, **Cherry Pitter**, No.16	5.50
Kitchen, **Chopper**, Food, Iron, 6 Blades, UFFN, Pat.Appl'D 1894, Open Handle	10.00
Kitchen, **Chopper**, Food, Single Blade, Wooden Handle	2.75
Kitchen, **Chopper**, Food, 4 Sided	1.50
Kitchen, **Churn**, Butter, Double Dasher, Red Paint, Locked Laps, Wooden	85.00
Kitchen, **Churn**, Butter, Original Dasher	290.00
Kitchen, **Churn**, Butter, Wooden, Strapped, Floor Standing, Blue	62.50
Kitchen, **Churn**, Butter, Wooden, Strapped, Floor Standing, Red	62.50
Kitchen, **Churn**, Cylinder, Advertising, Wooden, 3 Gallon	27.50
Kitchen, **Churn**, Milk, Dazey Brand	19.00
Kitchen, **Churn**, Round Wooden Bucket, Patent Feb.27, 1872, 23 In.High	45.00
Kitchen, **Churn**, Staved Type, Green Wooden Dasher, Wooden, 19 In.High	55.00
Kitchen, **Cocktail Shaker**, Rooster Head, 2 Quart	65.00
Kitchen, **Coffee Grinder, see Coffee Grinder**	
Kitchen, **Colander**, Rolled Handle, Pedestal, Tin	10.00
Kitchen, **Cranberry Picker**, Child's, Wooden	18.00
Kitchen, **Cream Separator**	25.00
Kitchen, **Cream Whipper**, Tin, Marked Fries, 8 In.High	22.00
Kitchen, **Crock**, Butter, Gray, Blue Inside	10.00
Kitchen, **Cutter**, Biscuit, Tin, Embossed Jenny Wren	3.50
Kitchen, **Cutter**, Cabbage, Double, Walnut, Pennsylvania Dutch	32.50
Kitchen, **Cutter**, Cookie, Eagle Design, Tin, 5 X 6 In.	35.00
Kitchen, **Cutter**, Cookie, Miniature, Round, Tin, Box	15.00
Kitchen, **Cutter**, Kraut, Triple Blades, Tulip Wood	15.00
Kitchen, **Cutter**, Kraut, Wooden	3.00

Kitchen, **Dish Drainer**, Wooden, Bleached White With Lye Soap	35.00
Kitchen, **Eggbeater**, Dated Nov.24, 1908	7.00
Kitchen, **Eggbeater**, Dover, Pat.Nov.24, 1891	6.50
Kitchen, **Flatiron**, Advertising, Handle Is Tailor Holding Cloth	30.00
Kitchen, **Flatiron**, Brass, Wood Handle, Door At Back For Charcoal	60.00
Kitchen, **Flatiron**, Door In Back For Coal, Wooden Handle, Hand-Forged	29.50
Kitchen, **Flatiron**, Iron, Wooden Handle	3.00
Kitchen, **Flax Wheel**, American, Counting Hammer	190.00
Kitchen, **Flour Sifter**, Impressed Columbia, Tin, Turned Wooden Handle, Knob	5.00
Kitchen, **Fork**, Pie, Pennsylvania Dutch	5.00
Kitchen, **Funnel**, Sap, Turned Maple, 4 1/4 In.Diameter	25.00
Kitchen, **Grater**, Carrot, Punched, Tin, Wood Handled Back, 10 In.Long	22.00
Kitchen, **Grater**, Nutmeg, Pat.1891-1896	5.95
Kitchen, **Grater**, Nutmeg, Sliding Type, Two Parts, Wooden Knobs, Tin	12.00
Kitchen, **Grater**, Nutmeg, Tin, 5 In.	5.00
Kitchen, **Grater**, On Board, Punchwork, C.1830, 12 In.	25.00
Kitchen, **Grater**, Vegetable, Duplex, Iron & Tin	5.00
Kitchen, **Grinder**, Food, Child's, 3 In.Long	7.50
Kitchen, **Grinder**, Food, Universal, Iron, Wooden Handle, Patent 1899	7.00
Kitchen, **Grinder**, Meat, Wooden, Green Paint, 31 In.Long	30.00
Kitchen, **Ice Shaver**, Gem, North Bros.Mfg.Co.Of Philadelphia, C.1900	7.00
Kitchen, **Iron**, Charcoal, Brass & Copper, Engraved, Door At Rear	60.00
Kitchen, **Iron**, Charcoal, Brass, Wood Handle, Chinese	12.50
Kitchen, **Iron**, Fluting, Brass Rollers, Patent Nov.2, 1885	17.00
Kitchen, **Iron**, Fluting, Crank Type	20.00
Kitchen, **Iron**, Fluting, Two Parts	16.00
Kitchen, **Iron**, Ivory & Jade Insert In Handle, China	20.00
Kitchen, **Iron**, Marcel	5.00
Kitchen, **Iron**, Ruffling, Grand Union Tea Co., Removable Handle	9.50
Kitchen, **Iron**, Shape Of Duck, Iron, Miniature, 2 In.Long	12.00
Kitchen, **Iron**, Sleeve, Grand Union Tea Co., Pat.1897	4.75
Kitchen, **Iron**, Sleeve, Marked C8	4.75
Kitchen, **Jug**, Batter, Brown Pottery, Bail, 8 In.High	35.00
Kitchen, **Juicer**, Lemon, Hand Hewn Walnut	18.50
Kitchen, **Juicer**, Lemon, Iron	8.50
Kitchen, **Juicer**, Lemon, Superior	7.50
Kitchen, **Juicer**, Lemon, Two Handles, Wooden	17.50
Kitchen, **Juicer**, Lemon, Wooden	8.00 To 24.00
Kitchen, **Kettle Tilter**, Serpent Handle, Hand-Forged Iron	75.00
Kitchen, **Kettle**, Jelly, Copper, Burnished	68.00
Kitchen, **Kettle**, Side Handle, Three Legs, Iron, 7 In.Diameter, 6 In.High	18.00
Kitchen, **Ladle**, Wooden, Curved Handle, Pennsylvania	60.00
Kitchen, **Masher**, Maple	4.00
Kitchen, **Masher**, Potato, Cherry Wood	10.00
Kitchen, **Masher**, Potato, Long Handle, Wooden	8.00
Kitchen, **Masher**, Potato, Wire, Wooden Handle	1.50
Kitchen, **Masher**, Potato, Wooden	3.00
Kitchen, **Match Holder**, Iron, High Buttoned Shoe Shape	15.00
Kitchen, **Match Holder**, Iron, Hinged Cover, Marked	12.75
Kitchen, **Match Holder**, Two Sections, Blue, 3 X 3 1/2 In.	12.00
Kitchen, **Match Safe**, Built In Cigar Cutter, Woolworth Tower On Sides	10.00
Kitchen, **Mold**, Butter, Acorn & Leaves, Carved, Hand Mortised	14.50
Kitchen, **Mold**, Butter, Acorn Branch, Leaf Spray, Wood, 4 1/2 In.	40.00
Kitchen, **Mold**, Butter, Acorn Print, Wooden, 5 In.Square	24.00
Kitchen, **Mold**, Butter, Complex Swan, Wooden, 4 1/2 In.	58.00
Kitchen, **Mold**, Butter, Cow, Glass	35.00 To 65.00
Kitchen, **Mold**, Butter, Fern & Geometric, Round, Wooden, 1 Lb.	20.00
Kitchen, **Mold**, Butter, Fern Stamp	12.00
Kitchen, **Mold**, Butter, Flour Flower Prints, Dovetailed, Hook, Wooden, 1 Lb.	15.00
Kitchen, **Mold**, Butter, Four Flower Prints, Two Parts, Wooden, 1 Lb.	25.00
Kitchen, **Mold**, Butter, Fruit, Push-Up Type, Oblong	20.00
Kitchen, **Mold**, Butter, Grapes, Wheat, Fern, & Initials, Carved, Two Pounds	30.00
Kitchen, **Mold**, Butter, Pine Tree In Double Border, Wood	30.00
Kitchen, **Mold**, Butter, Pineapple & Leaves, Wooden, 4 1/2 In.	35.00
Kitchen, **Mold**, Butter, Pineapple, Deep Cut	22.00
Kitchen, **Mold**, Butter, Pineapple, Round, Wooden, 1 Lb.	25.00

Kitchen, Mold, Butter, Pineapple, Round, 1 Lb. 25.00
Kitchen, Mold, Butter, Pinecone, Ferns, Wooden, 4 1/4 In.Diameter 24.00
Kitchen, Mold, Butter, Plunger Type, Maple, 1/2 Lb. 6.50
Kitchen, Mold, Butter, Reindeer, Round, 1 Lb. 25.00
Kitchen, Mold, Butter, Rosebud & Leaves, Square, Push-Out, 1 1/2 Lbs. 35.00
Kitchen, Mold, Butter, Round, Wooden, 1 Lb. 25.00
Kitchen, Mold, Butter, Swan 35.00
Kitchen, Mold, Butter, Swan, Plunger Type, 1 Lb. 35.00
Kitchen, Mold, Butter, Tulip, Dovetailed, Two Piece, One Pound 14.50
Kitchen, Mold, Butter, Wooden, Plunger Type, Strawberry, 1/2 Pound 25.00
Kitchen, Mold, Butter, Wooden, 1 Lb. 8.00
Kitchen, Mold, Candle, see also Tin, Mold, Candle
Kitchen, Mold, Candle, 6 Tube 35.00
Kitchen, Mold, Candle, 8 Tube, Tin 9.00
Kitchen, Mold, Candle, 12 Tube, Tin 12.50
Kitchen, Mold, Candle, 24 Tube 85.00
Kitchen, Mold, Chocolate, Five Witches, Metal, Made In Germany 22.50
Kitchen, Mold, Corn Muffin, Glass, Wagner Ware 10.00
Kitchen, Mold, Corn Muffin, Iron 6.50
Kitchen, Mold, Food, Lamb, Iron 22.50
Kitchen, Mold, Jelly, White Porcelain, Oval 5.00
Kitchen, Mold, Melon, Covered, 2 Quarts 12.00
Kitchen, Mold, Plum Pudding, Covered, Tin 4.75
Kitchen, Mold, Pudding, Pottery, Handled, 9 In. 21.50
Kitchen, Mold, Pudding, Pottery, Handled, 10 In. 23.50
Kitchen, Mortar & Pestle, Bell Metal, Ring Turnings Above Molded Base, 1800 .... 160.00
Kitchen, Mortar & Pestle, Burl Footed Mortar, Maple Pestle 60.00
Kitchen, Mortar & Pestle, Burl Walnut 150.00
Kitchen, Mortar & Pestle, Lignum Vitae 28.00
Kitchen, Mortar & Pestle, Ring Turnings, Knop Finial, C.1850 .... 70.00
Kitchen, Mortar, Hand-Carved, Initials M.P. 25.00
Kitchen, Nutcracker, Lever Type 3.50
Kitchen, Nutcracker, Standing Dog, Tail Moves, English Registry Number 15.00
Kitchen, Paddle, Butter, Birch, Long Handle 12.00
Kitchen, Paddle, Butter, Wooden 7.50
Kitchen, Paddle, Butter, Wooden, Hand-Carved 6.50
Kitchen, Paddle, Butter, Wooden, 11 3/4 In.Long 2.75
Kitchen, Pan, Angel Cake, Fluted, Tin, 9 1/2 In.Diameter 4.75
Kitchen, Pan, Angel Food, Quilted, Tin 3.50
Kitchen, Pan, Cake, Fluted, Center Tube, Tin 5.00
Kitchen, Pan, Corn Stick, Iron 5.00
Kitchen, Pan, Muffin, Cutouts Between Cups, Diamond Shape, Iron 18.00
Kitchen, Pan, Muffin, For Six Seashell Shape Muffins, England, Tin 15.00
Kitchen, Pan, Muffin, 11 Deep Cups, Iron 6.95
Kitchen, Pan, Pie, Gray, Granite 2.00
Kitchen, Pan, Popover, Legs, Iron 3.75
Kitchen, Pancake Turner, Russell, Green River Works, Signed 8.50
Kitchen, Pastry Wheel, Brass 9.00
Kitchen, Peeler, Apple, Iron, Clamp Type, Dated 1872 .... 8.50
Kitchen, Peeler, Apple, Iron, Dated 1888 .... 15.00
Kitchen, Peeler, Apple, Leominster, Mass., 1904, Iron 10.00
Kitchen, Pie Crimper-Nipper, Brass, Revolving Wheel, 6 1/4 In. 12.50
Kitchen, Pie Lifter, Wooden Handle, 11 In.Long 20.00
Kitchen, Popcorn Popper, Lid, Turn Handle, Bottom Fits Into Cook Stove, Iron 32.50
Kitchen, Pot, Copper, Iron Handle, C.1790, 8 In.Diameter 65.00
Kitchen, Press, Cheese, Weathered Oak 12.00
Kitchen, Press, Fruit & Jelly, Brass, Dated 8/12/73, Quart 8.00
Kitchen, Pump, Gas Iron, Brass 3.00
Kitchen, Rack, Spoon, Hanging, Hand Dovetailed, Red Paint, Pennsylvania Dutch 45.00
Kitchen, Rack, Towel, Roller, Wooden 5.50
Kitchen, Rolling Pin, Aqua, Blown, Saratoga, 19 1/2 In.Long 40.00
Kitchen, Rolling Pin, Cherry, Wringer Type 42.50
Kitchen, Rolling Pin, Curly Maple, Nub Ends, 15 In.Long 35.00
Kitchen, Rolling Pin, Curly Maple, One Piece 12.00
Kitchen, Rolling Pin, Glass, Black, 8 In. 45.00
Kitchen, Rolling Pin, Glass, Imperial Mfg. Co., Cambridge, Ohio, Patent 1920 .... 35.00

Kitchen, Rolling Pin, Green, Glass, 15 In.Long	27.00
Kitchen, Rolling Pin, Impressed Stamps Of Birds, Floral, Fish, Wooden	14.00
Kitchen, Rolling Pin, Maple, Swivel Handle, 18 In.Long	6.00
Kitchen, Rolling Pin, Onion, Porcelain	35.00
Kitchen, Rolling Pin, Pine	6.00
Kitchen, Rolling Pin, Porcelain, Silver Trim, Floral Design One End	25.00
Kitchen, Rolling Pin, Tiger Maple	15.00
Kitchen, Sadiron, Child's	3.50
Kitchen, Sadiron, Enterprise, Philadelphia, Double Pointed, Removable Handle	6.00
Kitchen, Sadiron, Flat End, Embossed, Star, 5 3/4 In.	5.00
Kitchen, Sadiron, Handle	6.50
Kitchen, Sadiron, Hollow Handle, Molded, Embossed Lyno On A Shield	6.00
Kitchen, Sadiron, Hollow Handle, Oval Base, Embossed Silvester's Patent	6.00
Kitchen, Sadiron, Marked Carr & Haines, Philadelphia	4.50
Kitchen, Sadiron, Molded Handle, One Piece	6.00
Kitchen, Sadiron, Oval Base, Embossed T.Sheldon & Co., W.Hampton	5.00
Kitchen, Sausage Stuffer, Table Model, Two Eagles, Iron	45.00
Kitchen, Scoop, Butter, Hand Hewn, Wooden	12.50
Kitchen, Scoop, Hand Hewn, Wooden, 16 In.Long	15.00
Kitchen, Seeder, Raisin, Enterprise, Pat.1897	8.50
Kitchen, Seeder, Raisin, Marked	12.00
Kitchen, Sieve, 18th Century, 19 1/2 In.Diameter	35.00
Kitchen, Spatula, Hand Forged, Iron, 16 In.Long	15.00
Kitchen, Spatula, Rumford Baking Powder	2.00
Kitchen, Spice Chest, Six Drawer, Porcelain Knobs, Tin Labels, 7 In.High	32.00
Kitchen, Spinning Wheel, see Tool	
Kitchen, Spoon, Cream Separator, Milk Bottle	1.75
Kitchen, Strainer, Miniature, Drip Pan	7.50
Kitchen, Strainer, Tea, Ribbon Handle, Tin	9.50
Kitchen, Strawberry Huller, Cast Iron	4.00
Kitchen, Sweeper, Carpet, Walnut, Hatlinger, Mass., Hand Crank, 1890s	22.50
Kitchen, Teakettle, Ball Type, Iron	75.00
Kitchen, Teakettle, Brass & Copper Reliefs, Cutouts, Pennsylvania Dutch	135.00
Kitchen, Toaster, Circular Rotating, Three Feet, Iron, 18th Century	75.00
Kitchen, Tongs, Ice, Handwrought Iron	3.50
Kitchen, Tongs, Ice, Handwrought, 23 In.Long	7.50
Kitchen, Waffle Iron, Feb.22, 1910, Wooden Handles, 7 1/2 In.Diameter	4.50
Kitchen, Washboard, Pine, Zinc Rippled Liner, 12 X 24 In.	6.00
Kitchen, Washboard, Soap Saver	9.00
Kitchen, Wrench, Fruit Jar, Steel, Wizard	1.50
Kitchen, Wringer & Stand, Hand, Folding	40.00
Knowles, Taylor & Knowles, see Lotus Ware, KTK	
Koch, Bowl, Grapes, Purple & Green, Signed, 9 In.	25.00
Koch, Bowl, Grapes, 9 1/4 In.Diameter	27.50
Koch, Bowl, Peach, Signed, 8 1/2 In.	20.00
Koch, Cake Set, Grape Pattern, Open End, 5 Piece	75.00
Koch, Plate, Apple Decoration, Green, Cream, Beige, 6 1/4 In.	10.00
Koch, Plate, Apple Decoration, Scalloped Edge, 8 1/2 In.Diameter	28.00
Koch, Plate, Apples & Cherries, Signed, 8 1/2 In.	24.75
Koch, Plate, Apples & Cherries, 8 1/2 In.	22.00
Koch, Plate, Apples On Branch, Green Leaves, J & C Bavaria, 7 1/2 In.	14.00
Koch, Plate, Apples, 6 In.	15.00
Koch, Plate, Cake, Bunch Of Grapes, Green, Brown, Louise-Bavaria	45.00
Koch, Plate, Cake, Pierced Handles With Lush Grapes, Bavaria, Signed	42.50
Koch, Plate, Grape Design, Marked Louise, 12 1/2 In.Diameter	45.00
Koch, Plate, Grapes & Blackberries, Uneven Edge, Signed, 8 5/8 In.	39.50
Koch, Plate, Grapes, Fruit, Gold Uneven Edge, J.C.& Louise	35.00
Koch, Plate, Grapes, Hand-Painted, Green, Signed Louise, Bavaria	35.00
Koch, Plate, Grapes, Two Colors, Dark Ground, 8 3/4 In.	27.00
Koch, Plate, Grapes, 8 In.	22.00
Koch, Plate, Green & Purple Grapes, Signed, 9 In.	35.00
Koch, Plate, Peaches, 8 1/2 In.	33.00
Koch, Plate, Raspberries, 8 1/2 In.	27.75
Koch, Sauce, Grape Decoration, Green Ground	7.50

KPM is part of one of the marks used about 1723 by the Meissen Factory 𝒦. 𝒫𝑀

*Konigliche Porzellan Manufaktur. Other later firms using the letters
include the Royal Manufactory of Berlin, Germany, that worked from 1832
to 1847. A factory in Scheibe, Germany, used the mark in 1928. The mark
was also used in Waldenburg, Germany, and other German cities during the
twentieth century.*

KPM, Bowl, Child's, Children Sitting On Fence	14.50
KPM, Bowl, Fruit, Pastel, Roses, 10 In.	18.00
KPM, Bowl, Kauffmann Scene Of Cupids In Chariot, Green & Gold Interior	18.00
KPM, Painting On Porcelain, Boy, C.1840, Frame, 8 1/2 X 10 1/2 In.	600.00
KPM, Painting On Porcelain, Girl Watching Lions, Frame, Signed, 6 X 9 In.	595.00
KPM, Painting On Porcelain, Girl, Ornate Carved Frame, 8 X 10 In.	495.00
KPM, Painting On Porcelain, Girl, Ornate Gold Frame, 13 1/2 X 15 In.	500.00
KPM, Painting On Porcelain, Lovers In Boat, Hills, Church, Lithophane	185.00
KPM, Painting On Porcelain, Man, Woman, Signed Wirkner, Brass Frames, Pair	135.00
KPM, Painting On Porcelain, Woman, L.Sturn, 1871, 10 1/2 X 8 3/4 In.	350.00
KPM, Painting On Porcelain, Woman, Ornate Frame, 6 X 8 In.	450.00
KPM, Painting On Porcelain, 2 Children, Sitting, Book, C.1830	1150.00
KPM, Plaque, Bust Of Woman, Holds Roses, Signed Elm, Rococo Frame, 8 1/4 In.	275.00
KPM, Plaque, Man's Portrait, 9 X 6 1/2 In.	250.00
KPM, Plaque, Sistine Madonna, Frame, 15 X 17 In.	575.00
KPM, Plaque, Sistine Madonna, 10 X 12 In.	575.00
KPM, Plate, Cake, Forget-Me-Nots, Scrollwork, Gold Handles, Signed, 9 3/4 In.	12.00
KPM, Plate, Enameled Floral Bouquets In Center, Basket Weave Rim, C.1870	14.00
KPM, Urn, Cover, Blue Scepter Under Glaze, White Mark	40.00
KPM, Vase, Slate Blue, Floral, Butterfly, Gold, White, Green, Handles, Footed	250.00

K.T.&K. CHINA *KTK, initials of the Knowles, Taylor and Knowles Company of East
Liverpool, Ohio. was founded by Isaac W.Knowles in 1853. The company
is still working.*

KTK, Butter, Pink Flowers, Gold Trim, Round, 3 Pieces, Marked	15.00
KTK, Cup & Saucer, Child's, 2 Kittens In Stagecoach Pulled By 2 Kittens	12.00
KTK, Pitcher, Ironstone, 9 In.	15.00
KTK, Vase, Lotus, Jeweled & Reticulated, Floral, Signed	195.00
KTK, Washstand Set, White With Gold Trim, 6 Piece	85.00
Ku Klux Klan, Medal, German Silver, 'Without Fear & Without Reproach, '1866	34.50
Ku Klux Klan, Report, Conspiracy, Committee On Affairs, 1872, Official	50.00
Ku Klux Klan, Ring, Woman's	40.00
Ku Klux Klan, Sword, Hooded Man On Cross Guard	100.00

*Kutani Ware is a Japanese porcelain made after the mid-seventeenth
century. Most of the pieces found today are nineteenth century.*

Kutani, Bowl, Sparrow & Ducks In Flight, Rectangular, Signed	33.00
Kutani, Candlestick, Orange, Dragon, Birds, Floral, Footed, 9 In.High	45.00
Kutani, Incense Burner, Diamond Shape, Foo Dog Finial, Oriental Signature	20.00
Kutani, Plate, Hand-Painted Figures, Gold Trim, 7 3/8 In.	15.00
Kutani, Stringed Instrument, 21 In.Long, 4 In.Wide	210.00
Kutani, Sugar & Creamer, Ornate Design, Gold, C.1875	40.00
Kutani, Tea & Dessert Set, Scenes, 20 Piece	285.00
Kutani, Tea Set, Dragon Handles, Spouts, & Knobs, Lithophane, Hand-Painted	175.00
Kutani, Tray, Dresser, Oriental Scene, Hand-Painted, Mark	14.00
Kutani, Urn, Red Ground, Oriental Men, Gold Trim, Dome Cover, Foo Dog Finial	65.00
Kutani, Vase, Orange Gold Birds, Signed, 6 In.	56.00
Kutani, Vase, Stick, Cream Panels, Orange Floral, Gold Tracery, Pair	60.00

*Lalique Glass was made by Rene Lalique's Factory in Paris, France,
from 1860 to 1945. The glass was molded, pressed, and engraved. Many of the
most familiar designs were clear or with a bluish-tinged glass molded into
birds, animals, or foliage.*

Lalique, Ashtray, Four Nude Ladies At Edge, Blue, Signed R.Lalique	125.00
Lalique, Atomizer, Green, Round, Intaglio Cut Floral, Gold Cap, Marny, France	47.50
Lalique, Atomizer, Sea Foam Green, Nudes, Fully Signed	45.00
Lalique, Bookend, Bird, Signed, Pair	110.00
Lalique, Bookend, Kneeling Nude Female, Signed, C.1930, Pair	125.00
Lalique, Bottle, Cologne, Molded Poppy Shape, Enameled Black Stamens	75.00
Lalique, Bowl & Underplate, Clam Shell Design, Opalescent	55.00 To 85.00
Lalique, Bowl, Blue Opalescent, Beaded, Thumbprint, 8 In.	75.00

Lalique, Bowl, Blue Opalescent, 3 Robins In Flight, Flower, Signed	127.50
Lalique, Bowl, Centerpiece, Embossed Frosted Fruit, Pedestal Base, Signed	87.50
Lalique, Bowl, Fern & Leaf Design, Marked, 9 In.Across	120.00
Lalique, Bowl, Frosted Starfish, Yellow, Three Feet, 8 1/2 In.	75.00
Lalique, Bowl, Lily Design, Footed, Marked, 5 1/2 In.Tall	137.00
Lalique, Bowl, Milky Blue Opalescent, Swirling Fish In Relief, C.1925	140.00
Lalique, Bowl, Mistletoe Pattern, Berries Form Feet, Signed	65.00
Lalique, Bowl, Punch, Frosted & Molded Cherries, Leaves, Pedestal Foot	119.00
Lalique, Bowl, Round, Scalloped Rim, Cut Leafage, Footed, C.1935	90.00
Lalique, Bowl, Shallow, Sprays Of Opalescent Wisteria, 8 1/2 In.	37.50
Lalique, Bowl, Square, Panel Sides, Art Nouveau Frosted Medallions, Signed	55.00
Lalique, Bowl, Swan, Frosted & Molded Feathers, 9 In.Long	52.50
Lalique, Bowl, Water Lilies & Pads, Signed, 10 In.Diameter	75.00
Lalique, Bowl, Water Lilies In Relief On Satin, Signed R.Lalique	80.00
Lalique, Box, Cigarette, Rectangular, Clear, Leaf Motifs, Pair	225.00
Lalique, Box, Covered, Square, Cut Floral In Beige, Signed, C.1920, Pair	150.00
Lalique, Box, Divided, Satin Frosted, Embossed Bird Of Paradise, Signed	55.00
Lalique, Box, Powder, Angel Design, Signed, Block Letters, 2 1/2 In.Around	32.00
Lalique, Box, Powder, Covered, 3 Nudes	40.00
Lalique, Box, Powder, Five Cherubs On Lid, Signed R.Lalique	32.00
Lalique, Box, Powder, Three Dancing Women On Lid, Signed R.Lalique	23.00
Lalique, Bust, Madonna & Child, Satin Frosted, Carved, 5 In.High, Signed	68.00
Lalique, Butter Pat, Dragonflies	12.00
Lalique, Compote, Six Blue & Gold Opalescent Birds Around Nest, Brass	125.00
Lalique, Decanter, Allover Raised Scroll In Mauve, Signed In The Mold	95.00
Lalique, Decanter, Crystal, Octagon, Intaglio Cut Stopper, Nude & Cupid	110.00
Lalique, Decanter, Satin, Frosted, Raised Full Figure Nudes, Stopper, 11 In.	150.00
Lalique, Dish, Candy, Swan, Frosted & Molded Feathers	42.50
Lalique, Figurine, The Ice Maiden, C.1930, 30 1/2 In. *Illus*	1300.00

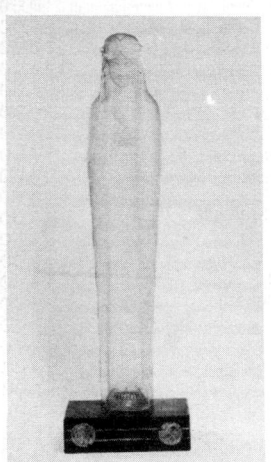

Lalique, Figurine, The Ice Maiden, C.1930, 30 1/2 In.

Lalique, Figurine, Two Men, Molded, Rust, Signed, Block Letters, 12 In.Tall	200.00
Lalique, Hood Ornament, Crouching Cock, Signed, 8 In.High	225.00
Lalique, Inkwell, Frosted, Signed, 3 In.Diameter	45.00
Lalique, Jar, Powder, Honeycomb, Applied Silver Flower, Emerald Jewel In Lid	42.50
Lalique, Lamp, Green, Allover Floral On Base, Signed	165.00
Lalique, Light, Wall, Art Deco, Frosted Panel, Fountain, C.1920, Pair	1300.00
Lalique, Paperweight, Eagle's Head, Signed	80.00
Lalique, Paperweight, Perch, Signed	35.00
Lalique, Paperweight, Plaque, Intaglio Cut Fish, Coral & Bubbles, Signed	59.50
Lalique, Paperweight, Pyramid, Frosted Flower In Base, Hexagon	38.00
Lalique, Paperweight, Rooster's Head, Signed	80.00
Lalique, Perfume Tester, Leaf & Vine Base, Five Flower Shaped Stoppers	125.00
Lalique, Perfume, Sculptured Stopper Of 2 Frosted Birds In Flight, Signed	55.00

Lalique, Perfume, Two Overlapping Blossoms, Hobnail Centers, Signed 32.00
Lalique, Pitcher, Water, Allover Pattern, Signed, 8 1/2 In.Tall 125.00
Lalique, Pitcher, Water, Crystal Ground, Leaves With Cut Edges, Signed 125.00
Lalique, Plate, Dragon, Fiery Opalescent, Footed, 14 In. 115.00
Lalique, Plate, Frosted Floral, Urns, Foliage, Signed, 10 3/4 In. 55.00
Lalique, Plate, White Opalescent, Olive Sprays, Clear Rim, 9 1/2 In. 51.50
Lalique, Tray, Molded Frosted Fish Figure, 5 In.Long 42.50
Lalique, Tray, Sculptured Leaves, Amber, Oval, Signed 110.00
Lalique, Tumbler, Artichoke Pattern, Camphor, Clear Bands, Signed 49.00
Lalique, Vase, Azure Opalescent, Embossed Cherries & Leaves, Signed 97.50
Lalique, Vase, Beaker Form, Relief Of Allover Leafage & Busts Of Pan 350.00
Lalique, Vase, Beaker Form, Relief Of Sparrows, Berries, & Leafage, Signed 100.00
Lalique, Vase, Beaker Form, 2 Semicircular Spiraling Tendril Handles 525.00
Lalique, Vase, Berries, Branches, Ball Shape, 7 In.High 95.00
Lalique, Vase, Berries, Leaves, Signed, 7 In.High, 4 In.Diameter 90.00
Lalique, Vase, Birds, Round Flattened Shape, 8 In. 50.00
Lalique, Vase, Blown Out Glass Roses, Signed R.Lalique 95.00
Lalique, Vase, Blue, Fish & Water Scene, Signed Joblings, 8 3/4 In. 59.50
Lalique, Vase, Blue, Gray, Band Of Frosted Birds In Cherry Tree, 7 1/4 In. 225.00
Lalique, Vase, Elongated Ovoid Shape, Vertical Ferns In Smoky, Signed 160.00
Lalique, Vase, Engraved Peacock Fantails, Clear & Satin Finish, 7 1/2 In. 65.00
Lalique, Vase, Fern Pattern, Bulbous, 19 1/2 X 7 1/4 In.High 68.00
Lalique, Vase, Frosted Allover Design Of Flowers, Leaves, 7 In. 65.00
Lalique, Vase, Frosted Crystal, Sunflowers, Signed, 4 1/2 In., Pair 150.00
Lalique, Vase, Frosted, Carved Flowering Trees, Crystal, 10 In. 110.00
Lalique, Vase, Frosted, Embossed Nude, Signed, 6 In., Pair 135.00
Lalique, Vase, Frosted, Ferns, Frosted Narrow Neck Opening, Bulbous, 9 In. 75.00
Lalique, Vase, Frosted, Opalescent Leaves, 5 1/4 In.High 95.00
Lalique, Vase, Intaglio Cut Leaves & Flowers, Ogilvies On Rim, 10 1/2 In. 200.00
Lalique, Vase, Inverted Pear Shape, Blossoms & Berries In Frosted, Signed 110.00
Lalique, Vase, Leaf Design, Charcoal, Molded, Bulbous, 7 In. 125.00
Lalique, Vase, Molded & Frosted Round Berries & Leaves, Script Signed 250.00
Lalique, Vase, Nude Children, Birds In Flight, Floral, Cut To Clear Foot 100.00
Lalique, Vase, Peacock With Feathers, Signed, 10 1/2 In.High 85.00
Lalique, Vase, Sloping Sides, Relief Of Thistles, Everted Rim, Signed 120.00
Lalique, Vase, Twelve Birds In Niches, Signed, 5 1/2 Pounds 110.00
Lalique, Vase, White Satin, Silver Enamel Violets, Leaves, Silver Bands 85.00
Lamp, Akro Agate, Made Of Seven Pieces Of White Glass, Signed 130.00
Lamp, Alabaster, Turtle, Lamp In Shell, Seminude Rider, Jockey Cap 250.00
Lamp, Alabaster, Urn Form, Carved Foliate Handles, 39 In.High, Pair 50.00
Lamp, Aladdin, Alacite, Electric 24.50
Lamp, Aladdin, Alacite, Urn, 2 Handles, Metal Base, 8 In.High 38.00
Lamp, Aladdin, Amber, 10 In., New Amber Shade 24.50
Lamp, Aladdin, Beehive, Amber 35.00
Lamp, Aladdin, Brass & Turquoise Porcelain, Dragon's Head, Gold Enamel 29.00
Lamp, Aladdin, Brass, Frosted Shade, Urns, New Mantle, Wick, Polished 65.00
Lamp, Aladdin, Brass, New Hand-Painted Champaign Dresden Satin Shade 55.00
Lamp, Aladdin, Brown Glaze, Pottery 15.00
Lamp, Aladdin, Glass Shade 45.00
Lamp, Aladdin, Green Milk Glass 35.00
Lamp, Aladdin, Lincoln Drape, Ivory 33.00
Lamp, Aladdin, Lincoln Drape, Off-White 22.50
Lamp, Aladdin, Lincoln Drape, Red 90.00
Lamp, Aladdin, Lincoln, Opaque Off-White 27.50
Lamp, Aladdin, Milk Glass 22.50
Lamp, Aladdin, Miniature, English Sterling, Signed Eaterling, Pair 50.00
Lamp, Aladdin, Nickel 12.50
Lamp, Aladdin, Nickel Plated Frame & Front, 12 In.Shade, 34 In.High 49.00
Lamp, Aladdin, 'Nu Tupe, 'Model B, Green Opaque Rib Font, Metal Base 17.50
Lamp, Aladdin, Oil, Flowers, Embossed, Bronze Finish, 6 In.Long, 4 1/2 In.High ... 25.00
Lamp, Aladdin, Opal Glass 35.00
Lamp, Aladdin, Opaque Glass, Ribbed 15.00
Lamp, Aladdin, Overlay Shade, Green, 22 In.High 45.00
Lamp, Aladdin, Quilted Shade, Green, 25 In.High 24.50
Lamp, Aladdin, Red 69.50
Lamp, Aladdin, Red, Ribbed Pattern, Pair 160.00

Lamp, Aladdin, Washington Drape, Amber	26.00
Lamp, Aladdin, White Quilted, Pair	40.00
Lamp, Alcohol, Brass	7.50
Lamp, Alcohol, Handle, Attached Snuffer, Sterling Silver	35.00
Lamp, Alcohol, Ornamented Handle & Rope Type Wick, Mfg.Miller Co., Brass	6.50
Lamp, Alcohol, Sterling Silver, Attached Snuffer, Miniature	28.00
Lamp, Amber Color Glass Shade, 13 Panels, Brass, Bradley Hubbard, 26 In.High	350.00
Lamp, Amber, Applied Clear Glass Decoration, Miniature	55.00
Lamp, Amberina Swirl, Applied Amber Leaves On Body & Base, Chimney	85.00
Lamp, Angle, Wall Mount, Single, Tin Font, Brass Burner, Frosted Shade	50.00
Lamp, Argand, Bronze, N.Y., C.1825, 20 3/4 In. High, Pair *Illus*	700.00
Lamp, Argand, Sheffield, C.1800, Pair *Illus*	1600.00
Lamp, Art Nouveau, Jeweled, Cobra Shape, 15 In.High	175.00
Lamp, Art Nouveau, Kneeling Female, Holds Lamp On Head, Green Opaque Globe	20.00
Lamp, Ball Base, Burner & Chimney	22.50
Lamp, Banquet, Aladdin, Opaque White Satin Glass, Baby Face Shade, 1896	325.00
Lamp, Banquet, B.& H., Brass Color Base, White Frosted Globe, Grapes	65.00
Lamp, Banquet, Christopher Columbus Figure, Milk Glass Ball Shade	85.00
Lamp, Banquet, Delft Blue Ball Shade, Dutch Windmill Scene, 29 In.	150.00
Lamp, Banquet, Embossed Brass, Milk Glass Ball Shade, Wired, 30 In.High	137.50
Lamp, Banquet, Juno, Brass Font, White Embossed Shade, 25 In.High	100.00
Lamp, Banquet, Kerosene, Five Yellow Shades & Fonts, Acid, Rib Swirl	1800.00
Lamp, Banquet, Mt.Washington Acid Etched Shade, Enamel Base, Signed Miller	295.00

Lamp, Argand, Bronze,
N.Y., C.1825, 20 3/4 In. High, Pair   Lamp, Argand, Sheffield, C.1800, Pair

Lamp, Banquet, Oil Font, Marble Base, Red Ball Shade, Prisms, Wired	95.00
Lamp, Banquet, Oil, Cranberry Thumbprint, 36 In.High	450.00
Lamp, Banquet, Pansy Design, Hand-Painted, Dated 1890	155.00
Lamp, Banquet, Ruby Font, Cut Shamrocks, Acorns, Lambert & Grafton, Dublin	165.00
Lamp, Banquet, Square Copper Base, Brass Standard, Amber Shade	175.00
Lamp, Banquet, Twisted Center Post, Ball Shade, Burner, Flowers, Acorns, Brass	75.00
Lamp, Banquet, Wavecrest & Satin, Victorian Cherubs, Floral, 24 In.High	250.00
Lamp, Banquet, 10 In.Ball Shade, 24K Gold Cherubs & Fleur-De-Lis, 23 In.	175.00
Lamp, Base, Aladdin, Oil, Amber	30.00
Lamp, Base, Camphor Glass, Nude Lady Reclining With Harp, 6 In.High	35.00
Lamp, Base, Floral China Base, Squatty, Brass Oil Font, 13 In.High	30.00
Lamp, Base, Gone With The Wind, Satin China, Brass Oil Font, Flowers, 14 In.	25.00
Lamp, Base, Oil, Emerald Green, Honeycomb, Bulbous	40.00
Lamp, Base, Pear Shape, Floral, Brass Oil Font, 17 In.High	30.00 To 35.00
Lamp, Betty, C.1750	39.00
Lamp, Betty, Double Crusie, Iron	25.00
Lamp, Betty, Double, Iron	48.50
Lamp, Betty, Double, Wall Spike	140.00 To 170.00
Lamp, Betty, Hook, Copper	65.00
Lamp, Betty, Iron, Engraved, Pierced, Toolwork, Hook	85.00
Lamp, Betty, Miner's, Iron	27.00

Lamp, **Betty**, Tin	39.00
Lamp, **Betty**, Tin, Hanging Hook	55.00
Lamp, **Betty**, Twisted Hook, Handwrought Iron, 6 In.High	28.00
Lamp, **Betty**, Wrought Iron	27.50
Lamp, **Betty**, Wrought Iron, Wood Trammel	105.00
Lamp, **Bible**, Candle Lantern, Cylindrical, Pierced, Sliding Shield, Tin, 1i In.	53.00
Lamp, **Bicycle**, The Dazzler, Coal Oil, Red & Green Reflectors	18.00
Lamp, **Bisque Pelican**, Shade, 16 1/2 In.High, Pair	175.00
Lamp, **Black**, Maiden, Upraised Arms, Arched Lights, Iron, Art Nouveau, 44 In.	425.00
Lamp, **Boudoir**, Puffy Satin	69.00
Lamp, **Bracket**, Brass Plated	20.00 To 25.00
Lamp, **Bradley & Hubbard**, Lake, Trees, Etched, 16 In.Shade, 22 In.High	425.00
Lamp, **Bradley & Hubbard**, Slant Shade, Blue Streaked Glass, Brass Base	300.00
Lamp, **Bradley & Hubbard**, Table, Amber Panels, Metal Leaves, Brown, Gold Base	175.00
Lamp, **Bradley & Hubbard**, Table, Embossed, Nickel, Brass, Signed, Dated 1896	59.00
Lamp, **Bradley & Hubbard**, Table, Metal Tiered Base, Pillar Stem, Cased Shade	70.00
Lamp, **Bradley & Hubbard**, Table, Panels, Flower Scenes, Filigree Base	175.00
Lamp, **Brass Cherub Holds Purple Glass Globe**, Enamel Font, Burnished, 30 In.	85.00
Lamp, **Brass**, Patent June, 1895, Painted Shade	85.00
Lamp, **Brass**, Saucer Bottom	7.50
Lamp, **Brass**, Saucer, Three Candlesticks, Red Tole Shade, 24 In.High	70.00
Lamp, **Bristol**, Overlay Enameled Birds & Butterflies, Pink, 24 In.High	35.00
Lamp, **Bronze Lady Holds Light**, Lavender Shade, Frosted Floral, Rene	235.00
Lamp, **Bronze Lobster**, Tail On Dore Base, Holds Dore Shade, Glass Jewels	525.00
Lamp, **Buggy**, Brass Bezel, Convex Lens, Smoke Bonnet, Pat.1906	15.00
Lamp, **Cameo**, Poppies, Mueller Freres, Luneville, France, 13 1/2 In.	350.00
Lamp, **Camphene**, Pewter, American	230.00
Lamp, **Candle Light**, French, Painted & Gilded, Pedestal, Brass, C.1830, Pair	650.00
Lamp, **Candle**, Brass Patina, Glass Flowers & Shades, France, Wired, Pair	68.00
Lamp, **Candle**, Hurricane, Brass, 13 In.	35.00
Lamp, **Candle**, Millefiori, Blues, Greens, Whites, 12 In.High	165.00
Lamp, **Candlestick**, Brass, Art Deco Pink Camphor Shade, 18 In.	37.50
Lamp, **Candlestick**, Metal, Knob Stem, Silk Shade, 28 In.High	50.00
Lamp, **Carbide**, Brass, Miner's	7.00
Lamp, **Carriage House**, Mercury Glass Reflector, Brass Kerosene Lamp, 19 In.	75.00
Lamp, **Carriage**, Beveled Glass, Brass Frames, Bottom Finial, Iron, Wired	40.00
Lamp, **Carriage**, Black Iron, Brass Trim, Silver Plate Inside, Convex, Pair	135.00
Lamp, **Carriage**, Brass, C.1820	200.00
Lamp, **Carriage**, Brass, Copper Trim, Bull's-Eye Lens, Beveled, Oil, Pair	295.00
Lamp, **Carriage**, Brass, Surmounted By Eagle, 21 In.High, Pair	300.00
Lamp, **Cased**, Pink, Swirl, Miniature	56.00
Lamp, **Cast White Metal**, Lion's & Lady's Heads Base	45.00
Lamp, **Ceiling Fixture Shade**, Crystal Beads, Fits 10 In.Fixture	35.00
Lamp, **Chandelier**, Brass Filigree, Four Shades, Gold, Blue, Loetz, Teplitz	165.00
Lamp, **Chandelier**, Cut Glass & Gilt Bronze, Teardrop Pendants, 2 Tiers	675.00
Lamp, **Chandelier**, Embossed, Kerosene, 33 In.Drop, 3 Branch	175.00
Lamp, **Chandelier**, Empire Style, Bronze & Ormolu, Anthemion Corona, 6-Light	375.00
Lamp, **Chandelier**, Empire, Ormolu & Cut Glass, Bronze Stem, Scrolled Arms	4500.00
Lamp, **Chandelier**, French Crystal, Metal Frame, Pear & Diamond Crystals	650.00
Lamp, **Chandelier**, Louis XV Style, Gilt Metal, Cut Glass, 15 Arms, Faceted	1500.00
Lamp, **Chandelier**, Louis XV Style, Gilt Metal, Rock Crystal, 8 Arms, Scrolls	1300.00
Lamp, **Chandelier**, Quezal Type, Hanging, Iridescent Glass, Teardrop Shape	200.00
Lamp, **Chandelier**, Venetian Glass, Spiral Column, 6 Arms, Urn Base, Flowers	5900.00
Lamp, **Chandelier**, Wall, Hanging, Crystal, 2 Arms, Diamond Cut Drops, Pair	250.00
Lamp, **Chandelier**, Waterford, Silver Plate Ring, Curved Arms, C.1820	750.00
Lamp, **Cherubs On Shade**, Hand-Painted, Scenes On Bottom, Brass Base, 18 In.	150.00
Lamp, **Chimney**, Oil, Cranberry Swirl, 10 1/2 In.High	25.00
Lamp, **Chimney**, Oil, Deep Cranberry, Diamond Pattern, Scalloped Top, 10 In.	25.00
Lamp, **Chimney**, Oil, Ruby Glass, Pair	45.00
Lamp, **Chinese Export Style Vase**, Iron, Green, Blue, & Gilt, Motto, Pair	375.00
Lamp, **Chinese Polychrome Decorated Vase**, Dragons, Gilt, 43 In.High	250.00
Lamp, **Clear Sandwich**, Free-Blown Font, Attached To Base	125.00
Lamp, **Cranberry Shade**, Fluted, Font, Hand-Painted Gold Floral, Brass Base	265.00
Lamp, **Cresolene**, Milk Glass Chimney	12.50
Lamp, **Cresolene Vapo**, Frame, Dated Aug.1888	21.00
Lamp, **Cresolene Vapo**, Miniature, White Chimney, Tin Holder Top	15.00 To 20.00

Lamp, Cresolene Vapo, Stand, Bottle With Labels, Boxed 17.50
Lamp, Cresset, Whaler's Torch, Iron, Long Armed 75.00
Lamp, Cruisie, Double, Iron, 8 In.High 32.00
Lamp, Cut Glass, Mushroom Shade, Intaglio Daisies On Leaves & Stems 375.00
Lamp, Delft Style Pottery Jar, Hexagonal, Blue, Floral, 21 In., Pair 90.00
Lamp, Depression Glass, English Hobnail, Clear, Adapter 60.00
Lamp, Depression Glass, English Hobnail, Pink, Electric Adapter 70.00
Lamp, Desk, Bronze, Leaded Floral Shade, 20 In.Base, 10 In.Diameter Shade ... 250.00
Lamp, Desk, Mottled Satin Shade, Black Iron Base, Art Nouveau 80.00
Lamp, Desk, Tiffany, Pinecone Pattern, Green Leaded Glass, Signed 225.00
Lamp, Desk, Two Kneeling Nudes, Bronzed, Ball Shade, Marble Base, Art Nouveau ... 45.00
Lamp, Doll's House, Hanging, Leaded 8.00
Lamp, Dome From 200 Year Old Hotel, Frosted Glass, Autumn Leaves, Wired 65.00
Lamp, Dresser, Carved Wood, 13 In.High, Pair 25.00
Lamp, End-Of-Day, Kerosene, Burner, Clear Chimney, 4 1/4 In.High 50.00
Lamp, Fairy, Amethyst With White Top, Blown Glass Wick Holder 60.00
Lamp, Fairy, Animal Head Of Wild Wolf, Brown Porcelain 85.00
Lamp, Fairy, Blue Diamond Point Top, Clear Base, Marked Clarke 27.50
Lamp, Fairy, Blue Satin, White Decor, Marked Fairy Pyramid, S.Clarke 75.00
Lamp, Fairy, Blue, Diamond Cut, Clarke Base, 5 In.High 50.00
Lamp, Fairy, Brass Base, Ornate Brass Filigree Shade 85.00
Lamp, Fairy, Burmese, Clear Clarke Base & Candleholder 120.00
Lamp, Fairy, Clambroth Ground, Cased, Spatter Glass Shade 85.00
Lamp, Fairy, Clear Base, Green Top, 'Clarke Fairy Pyramid' 22.50
Lamp, Fairy, Clear Diamond Point, Clarke 20.00
Lamp, Fairy, Clear Lacy Base, Diamond Point Beehive Shade, Clarke 22.50
Lamp, Fairy, Cobalt Blue, Applied Spiral Threads, Clarke Base 65.00
Lamp, Fairy, Cranberry, Diamond Puffed Shade 40.00
Lamp, Fairy, Diamond Pattern, Clarke 20.00
Lamp, Fairy, Eye Winker Pattern 9.95
Lamp, Fairy, Frosted Top, Pressed Bottom, Signed Clarke 55.00
Lamp, Fairy, Hanging, Jeweled Copper, Clarke Candleholder, 8 1/2 In.High ... 85.00
Lamp, Fairy, Hanging, Jeweled, Brass Frame & Chains 50.00
Lamp, Fairy, Hobnail, Amber, Clarke Base, 3 3/4 In.High 50.00
Lamp, Fairy, Jeweled, Set In Brass Plated Base With Handle 65.00
Lamp, Fairy, Multicolored, Jeweled, 4 In.High 135.00
Lamp, Fairy, Nailsea Shade, White Loopings, Ruffled Camphor Base 70.00
Lamp, Fairy, Nailsea, Pink & White Loopings, Marked Cricklite, Clarke's 185.00
Lamp, Fairy, Opaque Clambroth Ground, Cranberry Loops, Nailsea Shade 75.00
Lamp, Fairy, Owl, Open Head With Inner Candle, Porcelain 75.00
Lamp, Fairy, Peacock Blue, Hobnail, Clear Base, Cricklite, Clarke, 5 In.High ... 45.00
Lamp, Fairy, Pedestal, Base Signed, Registry Number, 12 In. 35.00
Lamp, Fairy, Pyramid, Blue Diamond Point, Clear Base, Signed Clarke 55.00
Lamp, Fairy, Pyramid, Food Warmer, Patent 1888, Clarke 68.00
Lamp, Fairy, Rainbow Satin, Camphor Glass Insert & Shade 450.00
Lamp, Fairy, Red, Diamond Cut, Clarke Base, 5 In.High 75.00
Lamp, Fairy, Red, Hobnail, Clear Base, Cricklite, Clarke, 5 In.High 45.00
Lamp, Fairy, Rose Nailsea, Three Parts, Signed Clarke, 6 In.Tall, 6 In.Wide ... 195.00
Lamp, Fairy, Shell Shape Overshot Glass Shade, Marked Clarke Base 45.00
Lamp, Fairy, Yellow, Mother-Of-Pearl, Clarke Base, 3 1/2 In.High 175.00
Lamp, Famille Rose Baluster Jar, Polychrome Prunus & Chrysanthemums 225.00
Lamp, Fat, Tin, Saucer Base, Handle 30.00
Lamp, Fat, Tin, 2 Round Burners 60.00
Lamp, Figurine, Bronze & White Metal, Signed, 36 In.High 350.00
Lamp, Figurine, Girl, Porcelain, Germany, White Shade 10.00
Lamp, Figurine, Lady Holds Swirled Opalescent Shade, French, Wired, 25 In. ... 65.00
Lamp, Finger, Amber Pattern, Pedestal, Chimney 58.00
Lamp, Finger, Brass Burner, Beaded Chimney Top, 4 1/2 In.High 11.00
Lamp, Finger, Chimney, Fluted Edge, Pedestal, Two Handles, Ripley Co., 1868 ... 22.00
Lamp, Finger, Frosted Yellow Font, Flower, Clear Base 19.50
Lamp, Finger, Kerosene, Footed, Embossed Patent Date 1876 .... 25.00
Lamp, Finger, Sperm Oil, Double Bull's-Eye, Brass Collar & Handle, C.1840 ... 50.00
Lamp, Finger, Whale Oil, Sandwich Loop, Pewter Collar, Drop Burner 60.00
Lamp, Floor, Art Deco, Bronze, Balls, Prisms & Cups, 3 Tiered Cone 3800.00
Lamp, Floor, Art Nouveau, Brass Lily Pond Base, Ten Lily Shades 350.00
Lamp, Floor, Bamboo Turned, Shade, Pair 90.00

Lamp, Floor, Brass, Marble Shelf, Blue Flowered Shade, 62 In.	69.50
Lamp, Floor, Iron Column, Tan Silk Shade	120.00
Lamp, Floor, Metal Stem, Brass Font, Etched Shade, 60 In.	49.50
Lamp, Flower Design, Enamel, Green Font, Brass Base, 12 In.High	20.00
Lamp, Fluid, Bronze & Glass, Animal Paw Feet, C.1830, 35 In.High	300.00
Lamp, Fluid, Pressed & Etched, Clear Font, Bronze, Marble, American, 1850	60.00
Lamp, French China Vase, Medallion Of Rural Scenery, Orange, Pair	140.00
Lamp, Gas, Figural, Viking, Metal, Bronze Patina, Wired, 19 In., Pair	150.00
Lamp, Gasoline, Ring Shade Holder, Brass, Polished, Lacquered, Wired, 10 In.	40.00
Lamp, Glass & Gilt Metal, Column On Square, Cast Leaf Tips, Pair	225.00
Lamp, Glass Shade, Hand-Painted Scene, Ivory Metal Stand, 12 1/2 In.High	34.00
Lamp, Glass, Bull's-Eye, Chimney, Square Base, 9 In.High	22.00
Lamp, Globe, Hanging, Frosted To Clear Designs, Brass Crown For Chains	12.00
Lamp, Gone With The Wind, Amethyst, Acanthus Leaf, Scroll, Miniature	85.00
Lamp, Gone With The Wind, Apple Green & White Ground, Pink Floral, 21 In.	145.00
Lamp, Gone With The Wind, Ball Chimney, Pink, White Roses, 19 In.High	95.00
Lamp, Gone With The Wind, Ball Shade, Lacy Iron Bottom, Brass Plated, Floral	185.00
Lamp, Gone With The Wind, Ball Shade, Shaded Blue, Pink Roses, Wired, 26 In.	175.00
Lamp, Gone With The Wind, Base, Miniature, Green Satin, Square Pattern	25.00
Lamp, Gone With The Wind, Base, Pink & White, Red Roses, Brass Fittings	45.00
Lamp, Gone With The Wind, Base, Pink To Aqua, Apple Blossoms, Brass Fittings	65.00
Lamp, Gone With The Wind, Beige, Green, Pink Chrysanthemums, 18 1/2 In.	75.00
Lamp, Gone With The Wind, Blue, White Sailboat Scene, Ornate Brass Base	225.00
Lamp, Gone With The Wind, Brown, Embossed Lion Heads, Scenes, Camels, Hunters	350.00
Lamp, Gone With The Wind, Camellias, Flared Base, White, Pink	225.00
Lamp, Gone With The Wind, Glass Font, Floral, Ornate Base, Brass Oil Tank	150.00
Lamp, Gone With The Wind, Green Ball Shade, Floral, Brass Font, Cast Base	140.00
Lamp, Gone With The Wind, Green, Medallions, Floral, Iron Base, Cupids, 1895	195.00
Lamp, Gone With The Wind, Kerosene, Green, Red Flowers	150.00
Lamp, Gone With The Wind, Light Pink & White Ground, Dark Pink Roses	165.00
Lamp, Gone With The Wind, Off White Ground, Roses, Not Wired	175.00
Lamp, Gone With The Wind, Oil, 24 In.High	250.00
Lamp, Gone With The Wind, Open Rose Design, Red Pink, Electric	125.00
Lamp, Gone With The Wind, Orange, Florals, Brass Mountings, 17 In.High	115.00
Lamp, Gone With The Wind, Pink To Pale Cream On Yellow, Pansies	285.00
Lamp, Gone With The Wind, Red Satin Glass, Large Size	50.00
Lamp, Gone With The Wind, Red Satin Glass, Miniature	35.00
Lamp, Gone With The Wind, Rust & Yellow Ground, Pink Floral Sprays, 21 In.	165.00
Lamp, Gone With The Wind, Satin Glass, Cranberry, 24 In.	400.00
Lamp, Gone With The Wind, Tan & Yellow, Red & Pink Roses, Brass Base	175.00
Lamp, Gone With The Wind, Vaseline, Hobnail, Brass Base, Raised Insects	950.00
Lamp, Gone With The Wind, White To Pink To Red, Camellias, Brass Fittings	250.00
Lamp, Grease, Stoneware, Saucer Base, Strap Handle	420.00
Lamp, Hall, Cranberry, Brass Rim & Bottom	125.00
Lamp, Hall, Cranberry, Panels, Ornate Brass Frame, Chain, Lift, Inner Lamp	95.00
Lamp, Hall, Hanging, Bell Shape, Cased, Font, Cranberry, 20 X 8 In.High	110.00
Lamp, Hall, Hanging, Cranberry Cut To Clear, Holds One Candle, Smoke Bell	175.00
Lamp, Hall, Hanging, Cranberry, Bell Shape Globe, Brass Frame, Canopy, Chain	65.00
Lamp, Hall, Hanging, Cranberry, Hobnail	89.50
Lamp, Hall, Hanging, Cranberry, Quilted, Chain	100.00
Lamp, Hall, Hanging, Cranberry, Swirls, Brass & Iron Frame, No Burner	115.00
Lamp, Hall, Hanging, Pink Candy Swirl Stripe Ball, Brass Fixtures, Chains	150.00
Lamp, Hall, Hanging, Red Paneled Glass Shade, Brass Canopy, Base, Chains	175.00
Lamp, Hall, Hanging, Satin Glass, Pink Shading, Raised Pattern, Chains	135.00
Lamp, Hall, Metal Frame, Stripes, White, Clear, 24 In.High	79.00
Lamp, Hall, Satin Glass, Pear Shape, Pink, 13 In.High	140.00
Lamp, Hall, Tree, House, Blue, Pink, Hand-Painted, 12 In.Around	100.00
Lamp, Hand, Blown, Clear Glass, Applied Handle & Thumb Rest	75.00
Lamp, Hand, Blue, Melon Ribbed, Ring Handle	21.50
Lamp, Hand, Clear, Cabbage Rose Pattern Fonts, Bell Shape Base, Pair	35.00
Lamp, Hand, Cone Shape, Brass, Tin Base, Attached Snuffer, 'Made In U.S.A.'	8.00
Lamp, Hand, Fishscale & Beads, Clear, 11 In.	22.50
Lamp, Hand, Glass, Conical Shape Brass Burner, Applied Handle, Pat.1860	25.00
Lamp, Hand, Glass, Embossed Heart Design, Burner, Chimney, Applied Handle	17.50
Lamp, Hand, Opal Spot Resist, Burner, Chimney, Footed	28.00
Lamp, Hand, Pressed Leaf Pattern	18.00

Lamp, Hand, Raised Design, Green	35.00
Lamp, Handel Type, Table, Brass Base, Chipped Effect Shade, Scenic, 19 In.	95.00
Lamp, Handel, see also Handel, Lamp	
Lamp, Handel, Clear Glass, Chimney, Dated 1870, 13 1/2 In.High	
Lamp, Handel, Clear Glass, Little Buttercup, 8 In.High	24.00
Lamp, Hanging Shade, Caramel Slag Panels, Crown, Windmills, Lily Pads, Leaded	450.00
Lamp, Hanging Shade, Caramel, Fruit, Leaded, 20 In.	450.00
Lamp, Hanging Shade, Green, Yellow Flowers, Leaded, 24 In.	500.00
Lamp, Hanging, Brass Frame, Pink, 14 In.Shade, 27 In.High	89.00
Lamp, Hanging, Brass, Six Sided, Red, Green, & Blue Glass, 13 In.High	95.00
Lamp, Hanging, Cast Iron, White Opaque Font & Shade	65.00
Lamp, Hanging, Cranberry Swirl Shade, Brass Frame, Cut Prisms, Chain	325.00
Lamp, Hanging, Cranberry, Hobnail, Brass Frame, Double Row Of Prisms	345.00
Lamp, Hanging, Cranberry, Inverted Thumbprint, Brass Holder, Prisms	175.00
Lamp, Hanging, Frosted Inside Globe, Iris Outlined In Gold, Brass Fittings	42.00
Lamp, Hanging, Glass Prisms, Hobnail Cranberry Shade	395.00
Lamp, Hanging, Hall, Cranberry Swirl Shade, Large	48.00
Lamp, Hanging, Hall, 4 Panels Of Daisy & Button, Brass Frame & Prisms	160.00
Lamp, Hanging, Hand-Painted Shade, Brass Frame, Spring Reel Canopy	85.00
Lamp, Hanging, Hobnail, Cranberry, Brass, Victorian	800.00
Lamp, Hanging, Kitchen, Cast Iron Frame, Pattern Glass Font, Bristol Shade	79.50
Lamp, Hanging, Leaded Dome, White Slag Glass, Leaded	275.00
Lamp, Hanging, Leaded Shade, Grapes On Bottom & Trailing Down From Top	125.00
Lamp, Hanging, Leaded, Ribbon Intertwining Flowers Design	525.00
Lamp, Hanging, Leaded, Small Pieces Form Roses & Buds, Twelve 3 In.Roses	850.00
Lamp, Hanging, Pierced, Embossed Burner, Handmade Chains, Oriental	62.00
Lamp, Hanging, Vaseline Glass, Hobnail, Vaseline Drop, Faceted, Brass Frame	245.00
Lamp, Hanging, White Ground, Pastel Floral, Brass Frame, Prisms, Canopy	345.00
Lamp, Hanging, White Shade, Pink & Red Flowers, Prisms, Brass Rim, Font, Frame	275.00
Lamp, Hanging, White Slant Glass Shade, Ornate Iron Frame, Chains	85.00
Lamp, Heater, Brass, Cranberry Overshot Shade, 18 1/2 In.High	185.00
Lamp, Heater, Brass, 19 In., Cranberry Overshot Shade, 21 In.Circumference	135.00
Lamp, Heater, Central Oil-Gas Stove Co., 1900, 43 In.High	750.00
Lamp, Hobnail, Amber, Electrified, 19 In.High, Pair	175.00
Lamp, Hobnail, Globe Shape Chimney, 7 In.High	15.00
Lamp, Icicle Pattern Glass	22.00
Lamp, Jade, Green, Figural, Brass Base, Tan Silk Shade, Jade Finial	200.00
Lamp, Kerosene, Brass Base & Burner, Amber, 1, 000 Eye, 19 In.High	55.00
Lamp, Kerosene, Brass, Quart Font, Incised Grapes, Chimney	28.00
Lamp, Kerosene, Bull's-Eye	27.50
Lamp, Kerosene, Clear, Ribbon Pattern	23.50
Lamp, Kerosene, Dietz & Smith, Patent 1864, Globe Dated 1868	40.00
Lamp, Kerosene, Figurine, Boy With Lamb Stem, Metal, Glass Font	45.00
Lamp, Kerosene, Footed, Dated 1876	28.00
Lamp, Kerosene, Hand, Brass, Ring Handle	9.95
Lamp, Kerosene, Intaglio Grapes, Leaves, Marked Schneider Co., Leipzig, Brass	32.00
Lamp, Kerosene, Iron Font, Wall Bracket, Round	15.00
Lamp, Kerosene, Milk White Base, Clear Font, Brass Connection, 9 1/2 In.	35.00
Lamp, Kerosene, Miniature, Illinois, Globe, Signed, Left & Right Rib Swirls	22.50
Lamp, Kerosene, Opalescent Coin Spot, Amber Stem & Foot, Herringbone	45.00
Lamp, Kerosene, Ribbed Blue Opalescent Stripe Font, Patterned Base, 9 In.	45.00
Lamp, Kerosene, Ribbed Cranberry Opalescent Stripes, Brass Collar, C.1876	55.00
Lamp, Kerosene, Upright, Green	45.00
Lamp, Kerosene, Vaseline & Clear Shade, Floral, Brass, 19 In.High	165.00
Lamp, Kitchen, Hanging, Brass Frame, Clear Diamond Font, White Shade	85.00
Lamp, Lace Maker's, Blown, Clear, 5 In.High	20.00
Lamp, Lard Oil, Kinnear, American Patent	95.00
Lamp, Leaded Glass Shade, Tulips, Signed Royal Art Glass Co., 23 In.High	900.00
Lamp, Leaded Shade, Blue & Yellow Ground, Purple Floral, 9 X 15 In.High	450.00
Lamp, Leaded, Bronze Base, Shade, Caramel, Pink, Green, 16 In.Diameter	325.00
Lamp, Light, Whale Oil, Two Tubes, Round, Tin	75.00
Lamp, Lincoln Drape, Shade, 6 1/2 In.High	38.00
Lamp, Loom Light, Rush Type Holder & Candle Socle	170.00
Lamp, Marriage, Clambroth & Opaque Blue, Lyre Center, Brass Connector	400.00
Lamp, Metal Sculpture, Fry Custard Glass Shade, Rosewood Standard, Pair	195.00
Lamp, Mica Shading, Amber Finial, Gold Fringe, Gilt Wooden Base, 29 In.High	175.00

Lamp, **Milk Glass**, Apple Blossom, Blue, 7 In.High 63.00
Lamp, **Miner's Light**, Hook, Marked Dunlap, Pitts., Tin 26.00
Lamp, **Miner's**, Carbide, Brass 10.50
Lamp, **Miniature**, Acorn, Wick Turner Says, The P & A Mfg.Company 47.50
Lamp, **Miniature**, Blue Satin Glass, Daisy & Button Paneled Base 11.50
Lamp, **Miniature**, Clear Glass, Raised Flowers & Leaves, 7 1/2 In.High 55.00
Lamp, **Miniature**, Clear, Brass Burner, 3 3/4 In.High 22.00
Lamp, **Miniature**, Cresolene 12.00
Lamp, **Miniature**, Cresolene, Cast Iron Frame, Clear Chimney, Tin Tray 12.00
Lamp, **Miniature**, Handy, Cobalt Blue 22.50
Lamp, **Miniature**, Hobnail Globe, Painted Floral On Base, 7 In.High 14.00
Lamp, **Miniature**, Hobnail, 7 1/2 In.High, Pair 8.00
Lamp, **Miniature**, Kerosene, Clear Swirled Pattern, 8 In.High 8.50
Lamp, **Miniature**, Kerosene, Green Milk Glass, Marked Night Queen 35.00
Lamp, **Miniature**, Lincoln Drape 20.00
Lamp, **Miniature**, Little Buttercup, Amethyst 58.00
Lamp, **Miniature**, Little Buttercup, Blue Base 17.50
Lamp, **Miniature**, Little Duchess, Milk Glass 18.50
Lamp, **Miniature**, Marked Little Buttercup, Cobalt Blue 48.00
Lamp, **Miniature**, Nutmeg, Cobalt Blue 22.50
Lamp, **Miniature**, Nutmeg, Opaline, Brass Fittings, Clear Chimney 28.00
Lamp, **Miniature**, Swirl Pattern, Clear Glass, Parchment Shade 10.00
Lamp, **Miniature**, Wall, Brass Font, White Globe, Horizontal Ribs 27.50
Lamp, **Miniature**, Whale Oil, Blown Font, Pressed Ribbed Base, 5 3/4 In.High 60.00
Lamp, **Mottled Orange & Lemon Shade**, Medallion In Base, Girl, Flowing Hair 125.00
Lamp, **Mt.Washington**, Winter Scene On Shade & Column, Electric, 14 In.High 105.00
Lamp, **Murano Glass**, Baluster Stem, Flowering Branches, 32 In., Pair 40.00
Lamp, **Niagara Falls**, Scene, Action, 1920s 45.00
Lamp, **Night-Light**, Cameo Shell 60.00
Lamp, **Night-Light**, Carved Cameo Shell, Aurora In Her Chariot 75.00
Lamp, **Night-Light**, Carved Jade, Mahogany Base 22.00
Lamp, **Night-Light**, Clear Glass Base, Embossed Nutmeg, Ribbed Chimney 16.00
Lamp, **Night-Light**, G.E., No.U90896, Brass, Screws Into Socket, Patent 1904 .... 4.75
Lamp, **Night-Light**, Ivory, Carved Scenes Of Ladies, Footed, 10 In.High 285.00
Lamp, **Nude Women**, Chinese Scenes, 2 Candlestick Lamps .... *Illus* 150.00
Lamp, **Nun's**, Oil, Pewter, Handle, Saucer Base, 1855, 10 3/4 In.High 150.00
Lamp, **Nutmeg**, Green 20.00
Lamp, **Oil**, Amber, Clear Crystal Overlay, Miniature 52.00
Lamp, **Oil**, Ball Shape Font, Ribbed Pedestal Base, Chimney, 18 In.High 25.00

Lamp, Nude Women, Chinese Scenes, 2 Candlestick Lamps

Lamp, **Oil**, Banquet, Fleur-De-Lis Design, Yellow, Gold, 28 In.High 185.00
Lamp, **Oil**, Bronze & Cast Iron, 28 In.High 375.00
Lamp, **Oil**, Burner, Pink Porcelain, Hand-Painted Floral, Brass Pedestal Base 35.00
Lamp, **Oil**, Cherub, Squat, White Metal 85.00
Lamp, **Oil**, Clear Glass Bulbous Bowl, Brass Connection, Marble Base, 8 In. 23.50
Lamp, **Oil**, Cranberry, Opalescent Swirl, Beaded Chimney 65.00
Lamp, **Oil**, Crystal, Hand-Painted Floral, Ruffled Shade, St.Louis, 11 1/2 In. .. 85.00
Lamp, **Oil**, Frosted Font, Etched Floral, Brass Plate Top, Porcelain Pedestal 27.50

Lamp, Oil, Grecian, Burner Swings In Holder, Saucer Base, Handle, Hinged Top 45.00
Lamp, Oil, Heart & Thumbprint, Flint 85.00
Lamp, Oil, Milk Glass, Christmas Flower, Double Wick, Metal Base 34.00
Lamp, Oil, Miniature, Europe, Porcelain Elephant Base, Cased Shade, C.1888 .... 225.00
Lamp, Oil, Mold Blown, Blue Slag, Embossed Greek Key, Russia, 10 1/2 In.High 75.00
Lamp, Oil, Palmette, Pressed Glass, Iron Base, Clear, C.1870 .... 38.50
Lamp, Oil, Panels, Plain Bow, Chimney, Pedestal Base, 19 In. 15.00
Lamp, Oil, Peg, Sandwich Chain Pattern Font, Brass Connector, Dated 1868 .... 48.00
Lamp, Oil, Pink Glass, 12 In. 16.50
Lamp, Oil, Princess Feather, Pressed Glass 49.50
Lamp, Oil, Sandwich Glass, Ribbed Bellflower, Single Vine, Applied Base 75.00
Lamp, Oil, Saucer Type, Center Post, Oval Font On Top, Tole 65.00
Lamp, Opium, Jade Base, Silver Holder, Glass Chimney 125.00
Lamp, Pairpoint, Blown-Out, Flowers & Butterflies, Signed 395.00
Lamp, Pairpoint, Cut Glass, Butterfly & Tulip Intaglio, Prisms, 19 In.High 575.00
Lamp, Pan On Trammel, Hand-Forged, Four Wicks, American, 20 In.High 175.00
Lamp, Parlor, Caramel Glass 75.00
Lamp, Peg, Clear Glass Candlestick Insert, 4 In.High, Pair 40.00
Lamp, Peg, Cranberry, Gold Floral, Applied Crystal Leaves, Brass Base 185.00
Lamp, Peg, Flint Shade, Swirls, Brass Egyptian Base, Cut Glass Font, Pair 225.00
Lamp, Peg, Green Opaque, Brass Candlestick 65.00
Lamp, Peg, Tin 35.00
Lamp, Peg, White Satin Glass, Gold Ribbon Decoration, Pair 235.00
Lamp, Petticoat, Tin, Camphene Burner 27.00
Lamp, Pewter, American, Saucer Base, Ring Handle, 2 Burners, Gimbal 125.00
Lamp, Pewter, Blue Swirl Shade, Engraved Cherubs & Fish, 20 In.High 250.00
Lamp, Phoebe, Hammered Design, Brass 50.00
Lamp, Phoebe, Iron 25.00
Lamp, Phoenix, Custard, Grapes & Leaves In Turquoise & Tangerine 35.00
Lamp, Pink & White Swirl Rib, Embossed Yellow Floral, Milk Glass, 3 1/2 In. 30.00
Lamp, Pink Depression Glass, Hexagonal Base 12.50
Lamp, Pole, Whale Oil, Reflector, Tin, 8 X 8 In. 95.00
Lamp, Pressed Glass, Heart Pattern, Handled 15.00
Lamp, Queen Anne Burner, Wick, Chimney, Pressed, Princess Feather, Pair 55.00
Lamp, Rabbi's, Whale Oil, Saucer Base, Wick, Pick, & Chain, Hinged Lid 135.00
Lamp, Railroad, Caboose, Wick, Chimney, Wall Holder For Chimney, Adlake 10.00
Lamp, Railroad, Union Carbide, Oxeld 23.00
Lamp, Raised Flowers On Ball Base & Shade, White Milk Glass, 7 1/2 In.High 65.00
Lamp, Rayo, Brass, Embossed, Paneled Red Glass Shade, White Lining, 17 In. 41.50
Lamp, Rayo, Brass, Green Shade, White Lined, Wired 35.00
Lamp, Rayo, Brass, Hand-Painted Shade, Electrified 55.00
Lamp, Rayo, Nickel Plated, Burner 18.50
Lamp, Red Satin Glass, Puffy, Beaded Panels, Burner, Chimney, 4 1/2 In.High 49.50
Lamp, Reflector, Kerosene, Cylindrical Font, Tin 26.75
Lamp, Ribbed Font & Shade, Metal Stem, Electric, 21 In.High 32.50
Lamp, Ripley, Twin Clambroth Fonts, Bridal, Pressed White Base, Match Cup 550.0
Lamp, Ruby, Cut, C.1930 .... 18.50
Lamp, Rushlight, Scrolled Wooden Base, Wrought Iron Top 95.00
    Lamp, Sandwich Glass, see also Sandwich Glass, Lamp
Lamp, Sandwich Glass, Dated 45.00
Lamp, Satin Glass, Pink, Raised Avocado Pattern, Square Base, 8 In.High 150.00
Lamp, Satin Glass, Red, Puffy Panels, Beading, Burner, Chimney, 8 1/2 In. 59.00
Lamp, Saucer, Miniature, Brass 14.00
Lamp, Sconce, Art Nouveau, Bronze, Three Purple Tulip Shades, French 175.00
Lamp, Shade, Pink Apple Blossoms, White To Blue At Top, Satin Finish, 10 In. 25.00
Lamp, Ship's, Chimney, Brass, 17 In.High, Pair 165.00
Lamp, Ship's, Copper, Clear White Ribbed Lens, Dated 1894, 25 Pounds 54.50
Lamp, Signed Delatte Nancy, Cameo, Red On Frosted .... *Illus* 700.00
Lamp, Signed Shade & Base, Woodbine, 14 In. 2400.00
Lamp, Silver, Crystal, Children At Seashore, Art Nouveau, 18 In., Pair 150.00
Lamp, Sinumbra, Bronze, Cut Glass, J.& I.Cox, N.Y., C.1840 .... *Illus* 450.00
Lamp, Six Panels In Shade, 16 In.Diameter, Tiffany Type, 22 In.High 135.00
Lamp, Skater's, Brass, Bail Handle 24.00
Lamp, Skater's, Tin, Bail Handle 18.00
Lamp, Skaters, Miniature, Brass 24.00
Lamp, Slag, Green & Ruby Panels, Heavy Filigree, 17 1/2 X 24 In. 160.00

Lamp, Spout, Sheet Iron, American, C.1850, 15 In.High .... *Illus* 100.00
Lamp, Staffordshire, Owl, Milk Glass Shade 410.00
Lamp, Store, Brass Font, Old White Shade 75.00
Lamp, Store, Hanging, Brass, Iron Frame, White Shade, 36 In.High 400.00
Lamp, Store, Hanging, Brass, Tin Shade 60.00
Lamp, Store, Hanging, Milk Glass Font, Shade, Smoke Bell, Brass Frame, 1890 .... 185.00
' amp, Store, Hanging, Tin Shade, Iron Bracket, Nickel 75.00

Lamp, Signed Delatte Nancy,
Cameo, Red On Frosted

See Page 312

Lamp, Sinumbra, Bronze, Cut Glass,
J.& I.Cox, N.Y., C.1840
See Page 312

Lamp, Spout, Sheet Iron, American, C.1850, 15 In.High

Lamp, Street Post, Deitz & Ham 95.00
Lamp, Student, Double, Burnished Brass, Dimmer Switch, New Shades 150.00
Lamp, Student, Double, White Shades, Not Polished Or Electrified 245.00
Lamp, Student, Green Shade, White Cased, One Arm, Pewter Plate Over Metal 135.00
Lamp, Student, Pewter Over Metal, Green Shade Cased In White 135.00
Lamp, Student, Pewter Over Metal, One Arm With Green Shade, White Cased 135.00
Lamp, Student, Single Light, Green, White Lined Shade, Brass, Wired 187.50
Lamp, Student, Single, Chimney, White Shade, Brass 85.00
Lamp, Student, Single, Nickel, Electrified 150.00
Lamp, Student, White Shade, Brass, Not Electrified, 7 In.Shade 125.00
Lamp, Student, White, Slant Sides, Ringed Neck, Flared 16.00
Lamp, Student's, Brass, American, 2 Light Branches, Yellow Glass, C.1850 .... 160.00
Lamp, Student's, Brass, Single, White Bristol Shade 110.00
Lamp, Table, Caramel Slag, Red Glass On Shade 125.00
Lamp, Table, Conical Shade, Bulbous, Orange, Red, & Black, Zigzags, Arrowheads 425.00
Lamp, Table, Filigree Bronze Shade, Panels, Holly Amber Colors, Blue, Pink 145.00
Lamp, Table, Glass & Gilt Bronze, Waterfall Shade, Geometrics, French, C.1930 .... 175.00
Lamp, Table, Green & Pink Shade, 380 Pieces, Leaded, Bronze Base, Relief Work 1050.00
Lamp, Table, Green Slag Shade, Bronzed Metal Base, Art Nouveau, 21 In.High 75.00
Lamp, Table, Matching Shade & Base, Slag Panels 225.00
Lamp, Table, Oil Guard, Patent Sept.20, 1870, 8 In. 18.00
Lamp, Table, Oil, Lacy Iron Base, Filigree Panels, Hand-Painted Ball Shade 150.00
Lamp, Table, Oil, Umbrella Shape Shade, Water Scene, Etched Chimney, 16 In. 95.00
Lamp, Table, Paneled Clambroth Umbrella Shade, Brass & Bronze Base, 2-Light 100.00
Lamp, Table, Panels, Mother-Of-Pearl Inlaid Base, Flowers, Brass Leaves 375.00
Lamp, Table, Princess Feather, 7 3/4 In.High 16.00
Lamp, Table, Reverse Painting On Glass Dome, Brown Shades 275.00
Lamp, Table, Signed B & H, Brass Base, Dated Feb.1888, White Shade, 20 In. 125.00
Lamp, Table, Slag Panels, Matching Shade & Base 225.00
Lamp, Teardrop With Eyewinkers, Clear 20.00
Lamp, Tiffany Type Domical Shade, Green Tiles, Square Bronze Base, 24 In. 225.00
Lamp, Tiffany Type, Palm Leaves In Green On Beige Shade, Bronze Base 750.00

Lamp, Tiffany Type, Table, 20 In.High	125.00
Lamp, Tiffany, see Tiffany	
Lamp, Tin, Brass Oil Font	60.00
Lamp, Tin, Queen Anne Burner, Ring Handle, 5 1/2 In.High	9.00
Lamp, Tole, Can, Black Paint, Chinoiserie Figures In Gold, Pair	350.00
Lamp, Tole, Empire, Red, Columnar Standard, Pedestal, Gold Decor, C.1850	140.00
Lamp, Tole, Small Font, 4 In.High	12.00
Lamp, Torpedo, Pygmy, 7 In.High	23.50
Lamp, Trammel Rush Light Holder With Candle Socle	250.00
Lamp, Vanity, Cranberry, Prism, Electric	18.00
Lamp, Vanity, Paperweight Ball On Standard, Electrified, 10 1/2 In.High	27.50
Lamp, Wall, Double, Embossed Brass, Fonts, Ribbed Chimneys, 10 In.High	95.00
Lamp, Waterford Crystal, 13 In.High	125.00
Lamp, Whale Oil, American Pewter, C.1825	125.00
Lamp, Whale Oil, Blown, Clear	30.00
Lamp, Whale Oil, Blown, Sandwich Glass	75.00
Lamp, Whale Oil, Blue Purple, Ellipse, Flint	225.00
Lamp, Whale Oil, Brass, 10 1/2 In.High	45.00
Lamp, Whale Oil, Bull's-Eye, Flint, Marble Base, Brass Column & Collar	60.00
Lamp, Whale Oil, Clear Font, Octagon Base, Flint	55.00
Lamp, Whale Oil, Clear Sandwich, Heart & Thumbprint, Wired	125.00
Lamp, Whale Oil, Diamond Point, Sandwich Glass	65.00
Lamp, Whale Oil, Dolphin, Sandwich Glass	75.00
Lamp, Whale Oil, Excelsior Pattern, Maltese Cross, Two Prong Burner, Flint	195.00
Lamp, Whale Oil, Factory, Copper	23.00
Lamp, Whale Oil, Giant Prism And Thumbprint, Flint, C.1840	95.00
Lamp, Whale Oil, Gothic Arch, Sandwich Glass	95.00
Lamp, Whale Oil, Hanging, Small Dove Perches On Cross, Two Chains	22.50
Lamp, Whale Oil, Hearts With Alternating Thumbprint & Diamond Point, Flint	70.00
Lamp, Whale Oil, Horn Of Plenty, Flint, 10 In.	90.00
Lamp, Whale Oil, Horn Of Plenty, No Burner, 9 1/4 In.	105.00
Lamp, Whale Oil, Light Green, Handle, Bell Shape, 5 In.High	45.00
Lamp, Whale Oil, Loop & Punt, Sandwich Glass	26.00
Lamp, Whale Oil, Miner, Brass, Mark Star, M.Hardsogg	20.00
Lamp, Whale Oil, Petticoat, Handle, Black, Tin	55.00
Lamp, Whale Oil, Petticoat, Tin, Japan, 4 1/2 In., Pair	125.00
Lamp, Whale Oil, Pewter, American, 10 In.	165.00
Lamp, Whale Oil, Pewter, S.Rusts Patent, New York	200.00
Lamp, Whale Oil, Pewter, Urn Form, Round Base, Ring Handle, C.1850	60.00
Lamp, Whale Oil, Pewter, Urn Shape, Short Pedestal	65.00
Lamp, Whale Oil, Pressed Base, Rayed, Clear Font, 6 1/4 In.	31.00
Lamp, Whale Oil, Round Single Burner, Chimney, Flint	60.00
Lamp, Whale Oil, Sandwich Glass, Clear, McKearin 194, No.2, 12 In., Pair	250.00
Lamp, Whale Oil, Sandwich Glass, Heart, Flint, 2 Prong Burner, 11 1/2 In.High	185.00
Lamp, Whale Oil, Sandwich Glass, Pewter Rim, 9 In.High	62.50
Lamp, Whale Oil, Sandwich Glass, Tulip Pattern, Flint, 10 1/2 In.High	95.00
Lamp, Whale Oil, Sandwich, Blown Engraved Font, Pressed Base, Blown Center	80.00
Lamp, Whale Oil, Sandwich, Clear, Elongated Bull's-Eye, Burner, 9 3/4 In.	45.00
Lamp, Whale Oil, Sandwich, Inverted Sawtooth & Bull's-Eye, Pair	155.00
Lamp, Whale Oil, Sandwich, Vaseline, Elongated Font, Oval & Circle Design	85.00
Lamp, Whale Oil, Sawtooth Concave Hexagonal Base, Flint, 10 1/2 In.High	85.00
Lamp, Whale Oil, Tole, Flowers, Scrollwork, Initials N.A.	49.50
Lamp, Whale Oil, Two Prong Burner, Heart Pattern, Flint, Clear, Collar, Pair	185.00
Lamp, Whale Oil, Waffle	60.00
Lamp, Whale Oil, 4 Wick, Tin	39.00
Lamp, White Shade, Clear Drape, Nickel Plate On Brass, Rochester	75.00
Lantern Globe, For Post, Dietz, 11 In.High, 5 3/4 In.Diameter	15.00
Lantern, Battle, Nazi Wehrmacht, Iron, Square Battery Box, Gray	14.50
Lantern, Beveled Glass, Cross On Top, Iron, Ornate Bracket, Roses	75.00
Lantern, Boat's, Bull's-Eye Lens, Sliding Signaling Shutter	70.00
Lantern, Boy Scout, Dated 1914	11.50
Lantern, Brass, Clear Globe, Brass Bail, Whale Oil, 3 Round Burners	125.00
Lantern, Brass, Etched Clear Glove, Jas.Stevenson & Masonic Emblem	75.00
Lantern, Brass, Patent Date 1885, 19 In.High	49.00
Lantern, Brass, Ruby Chimney, 'Deitz Jr.Cold Blast, 'Brass Bail	38.00
Lantern, Candle, Brass, Globe, Ring On Top	45.00

Lantern, Candle, Folding, Mica Windows, Stonebridge 35.00
Lantern, Candle, Four Glass Sides In Wooden Frame, Metal Handle 45.00
Lantern, Candle, Horn Panes, Marked Lanthorne, 17 In.High 150.00
Lantern, Candle, Paul Revere Type, Pierced, Iron 80.00
Lantern, Candle, Pierced, Paul Revere Type, Tin 75.00
Lantern, Candle, Quadrangular, One Clear & Three Red, Tin 45.00
Lantern, Candle, Tin & Glass, 10 In.High 10.00
Lantern, Candle, Wooden, Square, Tin Holder, 9 In.Tall, 4 1/2 In.Square 95.00
Lantern, Civil War, Wire Bail Handle, Clear Globe, Woodward's Patent, 1864 .... 27.00
Lantern, Clear Globe, Dietz Fire Dept., No Inside Oil Font, Brass 50.00
Lantern, Conductor's, Three Colored Lenses, Handle, Brass 60.00
Lantern, Fire Department, Copper Bottom, Brass Handle, Dietz 27.50
Lantern, Folding, Isinglass Panel, Paul Revere, Square, 10 1/2 In.High 18.00
Lantern, Frame, Barn, Tin, Fold Out Mirrored Sides 85.00
Lantern, Hanging, Caramel Art Glass, Decorative Bracket, Iron, 11 In.High 95.00
Lantern, Hanging, Signed C.T.Ham Mfg.Co., Dated 1886, Green Paint 90.00
Lantern, Horn Panes 60.00
Lantern, Keystone & P.R.R., Etched Globe 29.00
Lantern, Miner's Patent 1865, Candle, Folding, Japanned 60.00
Lantern, Miner's, Whale Oil, Tin, Leather Strap 55.00
Lantern, Paul Revere, Quadrangular, Hoops Cover Glass, Pointed Roof, C.1870 .... 69.50
Lantern, Police, Whale Oil, Dietz, Tin 32.00
Lantern, Queen Anne, Brass & Horn, Hanging, Embossed, Double Doors, C.1700 .... 227.50
     Lantern, Railroad, see also Railroad, Lantern
Lantern, Railroad, Box Shape, Tin Kerosene Font, Red Lens, England 22.50
Lantern, Railroad, Brass, Clear Globe, Whale Oil Burners 125.00
Lantern, Railroad, Caboose, Amber, Green, Cm & St.P., Pair 125.00
Lantern, Railroad, Clear Globe, Adams & W, Staten Island Rapid Transit 52.00
Lantern, Railroad, Clear Globe, NYO & W 30.00
Lantern, Railroad, Dietz Vesta, Clear Chimney 15.00
Lantern, Railroad, Dietz 39 Vulcan N.Y.N.H.&h.On Globe & Frame 25.00
Lantern, Railroad, Dietz, Blue Globe 16.50
Lantern, Railroad, Glass Font, B&A RR, Patent 1864, Tin 35.00
Lantern, Railroad, Marked N.Y.C.S. 9.95
Lantern, Railroad, Oil Font, Clear Globe, Boston Elevated No.210 Supreme 25.00
Lantern, Railroad, Red & Blue, Adlake 55.00
Lantern, Railroad, Red Globe, Bell Bottom, Dietz 39 .... 15.00
Lantern, Railroad, S.T.L.S.W., Clear Globe 16.50
Lantern, Railroad, Short Clear Globe, M.K.T. 18.00
Lantern, Railroad, Switch, Bull's-Eye Lens, Adlake Railway 45.00
Lantern, Railroad, Tall Clear Globe, Snap On Bottom, St.L & S.W. 19.00
Lantern, Railroad, Two Red, Two White Fresnel Lenses, Marked Dressell 25.00
Lantern, Railroad, Wabash 17.50
Lantern, Revere Type, Tin, Swirl Design 65.00
Lantern, Scott, 6 In.High 15.00
Lantern, Scout, Miniature, Kerosene 22.50
Lantern, Ship, Brass, Electrified, Perkins Marine Lamp Corp. 80.00
Lantern, Ship's, Brass, Corner Type, Handle, Blue Lens, 10 Pounds 34.50
Lantern, Ship's, Copper, Clear Ribbed Glass, 14 Pounds 39.50
Lantern, Ship's, Copper, Clear White Glass, Kerosene, Brass, 9 Pounds 34.50
Lantern, Ship's, Copper, Clear White Lens, Top Removes, 14 Pounds 39.50
Lantern, Ship's, Copper, Clear White Lens, 15 Pounds 42.50
Lantern, Ship's, Copper, Corner Type, Ribbed Clear White Lens, Port Hole Top 34.50
Lantern, Skater's, Brass, 11 1/2 In.High 25.00
Lantern, Skater's, Red Glass Globe, Pewter Base & Bail, Place For Battery 13.00
Lantern, Skater's, Tin .... 7.00 To 15.00
Lantern, Skating, Ring, Chain, Brass, Tapered Glass Chimney, Dated 1864 .... 65.00
Lantern, Tin, Horn Panels, 18th Century .... 170.00 To 210.00
Lantern, Vessel, Kerosene, Font, Burner, Blue Ribbed Glass, Iron, Brass Crown 47.50
Lantern, Wall, Barn Type, Tin, Cone Shape Reflector 27.50
Lantern, Whale Oil, Patent 1869 .... 100.00
Lantern, Whaler's, Metal, Brass Top & Lock, 9 In.Tall 35.00
Lantern, Wooden, Glass Sides, Candleholder Inside, Door, 7 In.High 85.00
Lapis Lazuli, Bottle, Snuff, Flattened Ovate, Green Corundum Stopper 110.00
Lapis Lazuli, Bottle, Snuff, Flattened Ovate, Stopper 80.00
Lapis Lazuli, Bottle, Snuff, Flattened Shield Shape, Aventurine Stopper 40.00

Lapis Lazuli, Candlestick, German Rock Crystal, Silver, C.1850, Pair 675.00
Lapis Lazuli, Vase, Beaker Shape, Flair Top, Carved Stand, 3 1/4 In.High 135.00

Le Gras glass was made by August J.F. Le Gras in Saint-Denis,
France. Between 1864 and 1914. Cameo, acid cut and enameled glass was made.
Le Gras, Bowl, Winter Scene, Pinched Four Places At Top, Signed, 4 1/2 In. 60.00
Le Gras, Box, Covered, Winter Scene, Orange, Signed, 3 In.High 55.00
Le Gras, Jar, Cracker, Scenic, Allover Enamel, Silver Plated Cover, Unsigned 125.00
Le Gras, Rose Bowl, Cut Purple Floral On Frosted Lavender, Signed 145.00
Le Gras, Rose Bowl, Enameled Winter Scene On Orange, Signed 95.00
Le Gras, Rose Bowl, Winter Forest Scene, Yellow, Red Orange, Brown, & White 110.00
Le Gras, Rose Bowl, Winter Scene, Crimped Top, Signed, 4 1/2 In.High 55.00
Le Gras, Vase, Art Deco, Raised, Blue, Frosted, Signed 85.00
Le Gras, Vase, Bulbous, Blue & Purple On Chartreuse Acid Etched, Signed 160.00
Le Gras, Vase, Cameo, Cup Purple Flowers, Signed, 8 In. 175.00
Le Gras, Vase, Cameo, Dogs, Weeping Willow Tree, Frosted Green Ground 245.00
Le Gras, Vase, Cameo, Hunting Dogs, Weeping Willow, Frosted Green Ground 225.00
Le Gras, Vase, Cameo, Lake, Trees, Green, Brown, Black, Gray, Enamel 145.00
Le Gras, Vase, Cameo, Red Floral, 8 1/4 In.High, 22 In.Circumference 139.00
Le Gras, Vase, Cameo, Scenic, Forest, Mountains, Lake, 7 1/2 In. 155.00
Le Gras, Vase, Cameo, Seaweed Pattern, 13 In.High, Signed 175.00
Le Gras, Vase, Cameo, Seaweed, Signed, 10 In.High 195.00
Le Gras, Vase, Cameo, Venice Scene, Gondola, Man, Homes, Trees, Garden, Urn 195.00
Le Gras, Vase, Clear Frost, Satin, Bird & Grape Pattern, Orange, Cobalt, Green 100.00
Le Gras, Vase, Cylindrical, Brown Landscape Frieze On Pink To Cream, Signed 90.00
Le Gras, Vase, Enamel, Scenic, Signed, 11 In. 95.00
Le Gras, Vase, Enameled Forest Scene, White, Yellow, Orange, Blue, & Brown 90.00
Le Gras, Vase, Floral On Pale Blue, Green, & Yellow, Signed, 14 1/4 In.High 450.00
Le Gras, Vase, Floral, Pink, Clear, & Maroon, Signed, 8 1/2 In.High 225.00
Le Gras, Vase, Frosted Ground, Raised Blue Art Decor Design, 5 1/2 In. 45.00
Le Gras, Vase, Green To Yellow To Green, Brown Sailboats, Shoreline, 5 In. 220.00
Le Gras, Vase, Mottled, Yellow, Orange, Blue, Enamel Peacock, 6 In.High 95.00
Le Gras, Vase, Mulberry Color Flowers On Rough Acid Cut, Signed, Pair 350.00
Le Gras, Vase, Pale Orchid Ground, Purple Flowers, 8 1/2 In.High 195.00
Le Gras, Vase, Scenic, Bridge, Trees, Water, Lilac To Green, 4 In.High 165.00
Le Gras, Vase, Scenic, Cameo, 8 1/2 In.High 165.00
Le Gras, Vase, Scenic, Dark Green, Foliage, 7 In. 250.00
Le Gras, Vase, Spatter, Red Poppies, Green Leaves, Art Glass, France, 9 In. 98.00
Le Gras, Vase, Speckled Red, Orange, Green Leaves, Brown Trees, House, 5 In. 180.00
Le Gras, Vase, Swelling, Cased, Brown Near Eastern Motifs On Yellow Green 90.00
Le Gras, Vase, Tapering, Cased, Blue Green Fruit & Leafage On Blue, Signed 200.00
Le Gras, Vase, Tortoiseshell Glass, Enamel Floral, 11 In. 65.00
Le Gras, Vase, Trees & Water Scene, Green, Brown, Signed, 14 In.High 145.00
Le Gras, Vase, Violet Design, Crimped Top, Frosted, 6 In.Tall 95.00

Le Verre Francais cameo glass was made in Paris during the late 19th
and early 20th centuries. The glass is mottled and usually decorated with
floral designs.
Le Verre Francais, Bowl, Blue, Lemon, & Orange, Cut Abstract Design, 9 In. 250.00
Le Verre Francais, Bowl, Cameo, Art Deco, Orange & White 135.00
Le Verre Francais, Bowl, Tortoiseshell, Geometric Pattern, Cameo, Charder 150.00
Le Verre Francais, Lamp, Mushroom, Cobalt, Green, Scene, One Piece, 10 1/2 In. 650.00
Le Verre Francais, Night-Light, Acid Cut Orange & Tortoiseshell On Green 152.00
Le Verre Francais, Pitcher, Art Deco, Red Geometrics On Blue Green, Signed 165.00
Le Verre Francais, Pitcher, Cameo, 13 In. 275.00
Le Verre Francais, Rose Bowl, Blue Frosted, Signed Charder 95.00
Le Verre Francais, Vase, Animal Cameo, Candy Cane, Green, Orange, Signed 235.00
Le Verre Francais, Vase, Beige, Dark Brown, Deep Cut, 11 In.High 210.00
Le Verre Francais, Vase, Brown Beetles On Orange, Cameo, Signed 215.00
Le Verre Francais, Vase, Cameo, Dark Blue To Orange Shades, 11 1/2 In. 125.00
Le Verre Francais, Vase, Cameo, Floral, Blue, Yellow, Orange 145.00
Le Verre Francais, Vase, Cameo, Frosted Pink Shading To Frost, Birds, 9 In. 175.00
Le Verre Francais, Vase, Cameo, Geometric, Yellow, Orange, Tortoise, Handles 133.00
Le Verre Francais, Vase, Cameo, Hand Cut, Footed, 7 In. 350.00
Le Verre Francais, Vase, Cameo, Yellow, Turquoise, White, Allover Mushrooms 225.00
Le Verre Francais, Vase, Carved, Orange, Green Spots, Frosted White Ground 125.00

Le Verre Francais, Vase, Cobalt, Orange, & Yellow, France, Cameo 175.00
Le Verre Francais, Vase, Fuchsia Cameo, Hanging Cherries, Art Glass, 15 In. 225.00
Le Verre Francais, Vase, Handled, Orange Yellow, Pomegranates, 2 Casings 175.00
Le Verre Francais, Vase, Orange To Brown Design On White, 3 In.High 98.00
Le Verre Francais, Vase, Ovoid, Cranberry Bluebells On Yellow To Red, Pair 200.00
Le Verre Francais, Vase, Trumpet, Flowers, Purple To Amethyst, 19 In.High 225.00
Le Verre Francais, Vase, Trumpet, Mottled Pink, Chrysanthemums 300.00
Le Verre Francais, Wine, Cameo, Flowers, Frosted Ground, Yellow, Brown, Pink 95.00
Leather, Boots, Western, Brown, Padded, Lined, C.1870, Pair 59.50
Leather, Chest, Money, Red, Gilt, Tooled, 2 Tiers Of Drawers 250.00
Leather, Sabretache, British Officer's, Queen Victoria Embroidered, C.1850 .... 57.50
Leather, Shoe, Woman's, Civil War Era, High Laces, Brown, Square Toe, Pair 17.50
Leather, Sporran, Scottish, Child's, Silver Edge, Crest, Horsehair, Tassels 9.50

> Leeds Pottery was made at Leeds, Yorkshire, England, from 1774 to 1878.
> Most Leeds Ware was not marked. Early Leeds pieces had distinctive
> twisted handles with a greenish glaze on part of the creamy ware. Later ware
> often had blue borders on the creamy pottery.

Leeds, Bowl, Oval, Reticulated, Footed 50.00
Leeds, Figurine, Courtier, Pink Tunic, Holds Scroll, 11 1/4 In. 75.00
Leeds, Mug, Pink Luster, House Pattern, 2 1/2 In.High 35.00
Leeds, Plate, Green Border, 7 1/2 In. 15.00
Leeds, Plate, Orange Flower Decoration, Green Edge, 7 1/2 In.Diameter 35.00
Leeds, Plate, Peafowl Center, 8 3/4 In.Diameter 200.00
Leeds, Plate, Soft Paste, Blue Decoration, 7 3/4 In.Diameter 40.00
Leeds, Platter, Blue Feather Border 60.00
Leeds, Platter, Oval, Color Decoration At Center, 15 1/2 In. 270.00
Leeds, Pot, Punch, Mottled Green & Brown On Yellow, 1765 .... Illus 475.00

Leeds, Pot, Punch, Mottled Green & Brown On Yellow, 1765

Leeds, Potty, Child's, Handle, Blue Decoration Of Flowers & Leaves 60.00
Leeds, Sugar, Covered, Leaf & Flower 20.00
Leeds, Teapot, Creamware, Globular, Green Monochrome Leaves & Laurel, C.1770 ...... 120.00
Lehnware, Bucket, Covered, 19 In.High 550.00
Lehnware, Sugar, Covered, Decorated 180.00

> Lenox China was made in Trenton, New Jersey, after 1906. The firm
> also makes a porcelain similar to Belleek.

Lenox, see also Belleek

Lenox, Bonbon, Leaf Shape, Pink 6.00
Lenox, Chamberstick, Gold Border, Green Wreath Mark 17.00
Lenox, Cream Soup, Sterling Silver Holder, Set Of 6 .... 90.00
Lenox, Creamer, Painted May Flowers, Gold Handle, Signed Hackett, 1914 .... 18.00
Lenox, Cup & Saucer, Demitasse, Sterling Frames, Cream, Gold Rims, Set Of 6 .... 180.00
Lenox, Cup & Saucer, Demitasse, White, Art Nouveau, Stubby Handle 17.50
Lenox, Cup, Chocolate, Sterling Silver Holder, Alvin Silver Co., Set Of 10 .... 98.00
Lenox, Figurine, Girl's Head In Profile, White, Green Rectangular Base 27.50
Lenox, Figurine, Swan, White, Green Mark, 4 3/8 In. 10.00

Lenox, Holder, Flower, Sterling Center Handle, Sterling Overlay 35.00
Lenox, Mug, Brown, Corn Decoration, Palette Mark 40.00
Lenox, Mug, Football Player In Old Time Uniform, Marked C.A.C. 47.50
Lenox, Mug, Painted Portrait Of Cavalier, Artist Signed, 5 1/2 In. 38.00
Lenox, Mug, William Penn Treaty, Green Wreath, 6 1/2 In.High 50.00
Lenox, Mustard, Gold Border, Silver Frame, Green Mark 24.00
Lenox, Pitcher, Shell Spout, Beading At Shoulder, White, 5 1/4 In.High 14.00
Lenox, Pitcher, White, Gold Trim, Applied Handle, Swirled Ribs, Wreath & L 22.00
Lenox, Plate, Dinner, Cattails, Set Of 8 .... 45.00
Lenox, Plate, Luncheon, White, Washington Wakefield Pattern, Set Of 12 .... 78.00
Lenox, Salt & Pepper, Cobalt, Sterling Overlay, Six Panels, Initial 25.00
Lenox, Salt, Floral, Gold Rim, Round, Artist-Signed, Belleek 6.00
Lenox, Sauceboat, Enameled Florals, Gold Trim, Handles 18.00
Lenox, Sugar & Creamer, Sterling Overlay, Blue Wreath Mark 27.50
Lenox, Swan, Creamy White, Green Mark, 4 3/8 In.Long 8.00
Lenox, Swan, Pink, Green Wreath Mark, 4 1/2 In. 8.00
Lenox, Tazza, Ming Pattern, Raised Foot 24.00
Lenox, Teapot, Sugar, Creamer, Cobalt, Silver Overlay 95.00
Lenox, Urn, Cream, Gold, Rust, Gold Handled, Square Base, 10 In., Pair 90.00
Lenox, Urn, Swan Handles, 10 1/2 In., Pair 75.00
Lenox, Vase, Bud, Pedestal, Flowers & Leaves Embossed, Cream White 18.50
Lenox, Vase, Cornucopia, Bouquets, Gold Trim, C.1930, Pair 30.00
Lenox, Vase, Cream Top, Green Base, Blue Mark 35.00
Lenox, Vase, Cream, Pink Base, Flowers, Green Wreath Mark, 10 In. 17.50
Light Bulb, Hand Blown 5.00
    Lighting Devices, See Candleholder, Candlestick, Lamp, etc.

    Lightning Rod Balls are collected for their variety of shape and color.
    These glass balls were at the center of the rod that was attached to the
    roof of a house or barn to avoid lightning damage.
Lightning Rod, Ball, Barnett, Emerald Green, 4 1/2 In. .... *Illus* 25.00
Lightning Rod, Ball, D & S, Amber 25.00
Lightning Rod, Ball, D & S, Milk Glass, Blue 15.00
Lightning Rod, Ball, D & S, Sun Colored Amethyst 20.00
Lightning Rod, Ball, Electra, 5 In. .... *Illus* 45.00
Lightning Rod, Ball, Embossed, D & S, Milk Glass 12.00
Lightning Rod, Ball, Grape Pattern, Milk Glass 10.00
Lightning Rod, Ball, Hawkeye, Red, 5 1/2 In. .... *Illus* 50.00
Lightning Rod, Ball, Large Mouth, 1 5/16 In., Milk Glass, Purple 12.00
Lightning Rod, Ball, Large Mouth, 1 5/16 In., Sun Colored Amethyst 10.00
Lightning Rod, Ball, Moon & Stars, Sun Colored Amethyst 25.00
Lightning Rod, Ball, Pottery, Blue & White 10.00
Lightning Rod, Ball, Ribbed, Cobalt 40.00
Lightning Rod, Ball, Ribbed, Shinn, Milk Glass, Blue 22.00
Lightning Rod, Ball, Ribbed, Shinn, Sun Colored Amethyst .... 27.00 To 32.00
Lightning Rod, Ball, Ribbed, W.C.Shinn Lincoln, Nebraska, Milk Glass 18.00
Lightning Rod, Ball, Round, Milk Glass .... 3.00 To 4.00
Lightning Rod, Ball, Round, Milk Glass, Blue .... 6.00 To 7.00
Lightning Rod, Ball, Round, Sun Colored Amethyst 8.00
Lightning Rod, Ball, Ruby 8.00
Lightning Rod, Ornament, Acorn, Cobalt, 5 1/2 In. .... *Illus* 80.00

    Limoges Porcelain has been made in Limoges, France, since the
    mid-nineteenth century. Fine porcelains were made by many factories,
    including Haviland, Ahrenfeldt, Guerin, Pouyat, Elite, and others.
    Limoges, see also Haviland
Limoges, Ashtray, Pink, White, Shell Shape, Footed, 3 3/4 In.Diameter 3.50
Limoges, Basket, Waste Paper, Floral, Brown, Gold, Green, Four Gold Feet 85.00
Limoges, Basket, White, 8 Gold Stars, Rim, P Handle, 8 Sided, Signed 25.00
Limoges, Berry Set, Rose Design, Artist Signed, 7 Piece 125.00
Limoges, Bonbon, Roses, Gold, Signed Florence, Dated 1800, Handles, Finial 48.00
Limoges, Bottle, Dresser, Ball Shape, Painted Flowers, 6 In.High, Pair 20.00
Limoges, Bowl, Blue Delft Scene, Scalloped Blue & Gold Rim, 10 In. 25.00
Limoges, Bowl, Centerpiece, Cherry Pattern, Scalloped, Gold Encrusted, Footed 115.00
Limoges, Bowl, Forget-Me-Nots, Scalloped, Gold Handle, Flower Finial 22.50
Limoges, Bowl, Poppies, Slotted Gold Handles, Guerin, 9 1/4 In. 39.00

Lightning Rod,
Ball, Barnett, Emerald
Green, 4 1/2 In.
See Page 318

Lightning Rod,
Ball, Electra, 5 In.
See Page 318

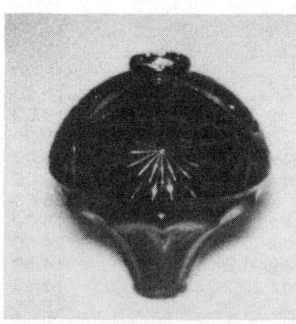

Lightning Rod,
Ball, Hawkeye,
Red, 5 1/2 In.
See Page 318

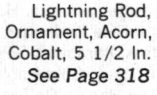

Lightning Rod,
Ornament, Acorn,
Cobalt, 5 1/2 In.
See Page 318

Limoges, Bowl, Punch, Base, Grapes & Foliage, Signed, 16 In.	225.00
Limoges, Bowl, Vegetable, Covered, Gold & Green Design	25.00
Limoges, Bowl, Vegetable, Covered, Gold, White, Raised Design	10.00
Limoges, Bowl, Vegetable, Gold Band, 8 In.Diameter	5.00
Limoges, Bowl, Vegetable, Hand-Painted Roses, Gold, 7 1/2 In.	6.00
Limoges, Box, Covered, Flower & Gold Design, White, Yellow, Marked, 3 In.High	27.50
Limoges, Box, Floral, Orange, Gold, 3 In.Long	50.00
Limoges, Box, Peach, Flower Top, Gold Swags, Sides Flair In, 6 In.Square	45.00
Limoges, Box, Pin, Covered, Gold Roses, Hexagonal	4.50
Limoges, Box, Powder, Covered, Man, Lady, Allover Gold Trim	27.50
Limoges, Box, Powder, Portrait, Enameled, T&V	75.00
Limoges, Box, Powder, Vines, Flower, Bird Center, Footed, Signed	24.50
Limoges, Box, Queen Louise, Covered, Green Outside, Signed Limoges, France	30.00
Limoges, Butter Pat, Allover Gold Floral, Gold Border, Set Of 6	28.00
Limoges, Butter, Covered, Pansy Decoration	30.00
Limoges, Cake Set, Ruffled Rim, White, Pink Roses, Blue Ribbons, 13 Piece	45.00
Limoges, Chocolate Pot, Cream To Pink, Leaf Overlay In Gold	38.00
Limoges, Chocolate Pot, Silver Overlay, 9 1/2 In.High	55.00
Limoges, Chocolate Pot, Two Rows Of Life Like Peaches, Gold Bands	25.00
Limoges, Chocolate Pot, White, Cream, Gold, Forget-Me-Nots	38.00
Limoges, Chocolate Pot, White, Pink & Orchid Floral Sprays, Gold, Haviland	45.00
Limoges, Chocolate Set, Carnations, Gold Handles, C.1890, 13 Piece	195.00
Limoges, Chocolate Set, Flower Design, Pot, 4 Cup & Saucer	65.00
Limoges, Chocolate Set, White To Pink Roses, Prunts, 9 Piece	295.00
Limoges, Cup & Saucer, Beige, Pink Floral Spray, Fluted, Marked	12.00
Limoges, Cup & Saucer, Demitasse, Floral Decor, Luster Finish Inside & Out	12.95

Limoges, **Cup & Saucer**, Demitasse, Floral Trimmed In Gold	4.00
Limoges, **Cup & Saucer**, Demitasse, Gold Border, Raised Design	9.00
Limoges, **Cup & Saucer**, Demitasse, Gold Encrusted Roses	18.00
Limoges, **Cup & Saucer**, Demitasse, Holly Berry Border, Gold Handle, Set Of 12	48.00
Limoges, **Cup & Saucer**, Demitasse, Pink Rose & Gold Border	4.50
Limoges, **Cup & Saucer**, Demitasse, White, Gold Border, Set Of 8	75.00
Limoges, **Cup & Saucer**, Flowers, Blue, Gold Trim, Demitasse	5.50
Limoges, **Cup & Saucer**, Miniature, Hand-Painted Floral, Gold	13.00
Limoges, **Cup & Saucer**, Peach Ground, Birds, Hand-Painted	9.50
Limoges, **Cup & Saucer**, White, Etched Gold Border, Set Of 12	120.00
Limoges, **Cup**, Saucer, Plate, Pink & White Roses, Set Of 4	45.00
Limoges, **Dish**, Bone, Roses, Gold, Haviland	12.50
Limoges, **Dish**, Candy, Gold Wishbone Handle, Flower Thumb Rest, White Floral	16.00
Limoges, **Dish**, Candy, Hand-Painted Forget-Me-Nots, Gold, Artist-Signed	18.00
Limoges, **Dresser Set**, Pinecone Decoration, 5 Piece	110.00
Limoges, **Dresser Set**, 10 Piece	150.00
Limoges, **Fernery**, Tiny Roses On Sides, Gold Rim, 8 In.Diameter, 3 In.High	28.00
Limoges, **Fish Set**, Artist-Signed, 23 In.Platter, 7 Piece	95.00
Limoges, **Game Plate**, Coronet, Signed Duval, 13 In.	35.00
Limoges, **Game Set**, Pheasant Design, 7 Piece	265.00
Limoges, **Game Set**, Quails, Cornfield, Marked, 5 Piece	28.50
Limoges, **Gravy Boat & Attached Underplate**, Blue Border, Floral, T & V	12.00
Limoges, **Gravy Boat & Underplate**, Flower Design, Pink	14.00
Limoges, **Hair Receiver & Powder Jar**, Flower Border, Gold Trim	26.50
Limoges, **Hair Receiver**, Pastel Shadings, Apple Blossoms	8.75
Limoges, **Hair Receiver**, Rose Design, Hand-Painted, Signed	14.50
Limoges, **Hair Receiver**, Roses, Blue, Yellow, Artists Initials	24.50
Limoges, **Hatpin Holder**, Pink Wild Roses, Gold Top, Artist Miller	18.00
Limoges, **Hatpin Holder**, White Ground, Apricot Color Base, Pink Roses, Gold	15.00
Limoges, **Hatpin Holder**, Yellow Roses, Hand-Painted	18.00
Limoges, **Holder**, Letter, Green, Flowers, Sailboat	35.00
Limoges, **Holder**, Matchbox, White, Gold Trim, Attached Saucer Base	14.00
Limoges, **Humidor**, Bat, Moon, Blue Ground, Pipe On Cover, Dated 1916	35.00
Limoges, **Jar**, Cracker, Flowers, Dimpled, Blue, Gold	35.00
Limoges, **Jar**, Dresser, Covered, Green Ground, Hand-Painted Pink Roses, Marked	15.00
Limoges, **Jar**, Milk, Flower Design, Blue, Lavender, Gold, Log Handle	24.50
Limoges, **Jar**, Mustard, Pink Asters, Baroqued Gold Decoration, Nugget Finial	14.50
Limoges, **Jar**, Powder, Wild Pink Roses, Gold Knob & Trim, Signed	11.50
Limoges, **Jar**, Tobacco, Floral, Pipe Handle On Lid, 6 In.High	45.00
Limoges, **Jardiniere**, Roses, Pink, White, 8 In.Tall, 11 In.Diameter	105.00
Limoges, **Lavabo**, White, C.1870	295.00
Limoges, **Painting On Porcelain**, Two Cupids, Artist Ester Kline, Frame	450.00
Limoges, **Perfume**, Atomizer, Pearlized Blue Glass, Gold Leaf Trim	9.00
Limoges, **Pitcher**, Flowers & Doves, Hexagon Shape, Signed, 8 In.Tall	95.00
Limoges, **Pitcher**, Lemonade, Grape Pattern, Hand-Painted, 14 1/2 In.High	175.00
Limoges, **Pitcher**, Milk, Black, Green & Yellow Luster Parrots, Gold Band, 1907	20.00
Limoges, **Plaque**, Birds, Signed James B.Graff, 1907, Gold Border	125.00
Limoges, **Plaque**, Female Nude, Filmy Draperies, Taupe Ground	65.00
Limoges, **Plaque**, Game, Moose Looking At Wounded Chicken, Rococo Edge	95.00
Limoges, **Plaque**, Portrait, Girl, Flowers In Hair, Shawl, Artist J.Soustre	375.00
Limoges, **Plaque**, Wall, Pink, White Chariot & Rider, Ornate Brass Holder	225.00
Limoges, **Plaque**, Wall, Three Large Roses, Red, Pink, Yellow, Gold Trim	85.00
Limoges, **Plate**, Berry Clusters, Artist Signed, 7 1/2 In.	7.00
Limoges, **Plate**, Bird, Artist Signed, Gold Art Nouveau Border	30.00
Limoges, **Plate**, Bird, Blue Jar On Yellow Ground, Signed Bay, Mark, Limoges	35.00
Limoges, **Plate**, Bird, Signed A.Broussillon, Coronet	65.00
Limoges, **Plate**, Bird, Signed Lavoy, Coin Gold Border, Pair	42.00
Limoges, **Plate**, Bust Of Indian Holding Headdress, Artist Luc, Coronet	65.00
Limoges, **Plate**, Cake, Flowers, Pink, Blue, Yellow, 6 In.Diameter, Set Of 6	24.00
Limoges, **Plate**, China Bird With Pheasant Flying, 12 In.	65.00
Limoges, **Plate**, Chop, Bowl, Orchid, T & V	87.50
Limoges, **Plate**, Chop, Hand-Painted, Yachting Souvenir, Motto, Crossed Flags	12.00
Limoges, **Plate**, Chop, Yachting Souvenir, Motto, Crossed Flags, C.1900	10.00
Limoges, **Plate**, Chop, Yachting Souvenir, Motto, Crossed Flags, T & V	12.00
Limoges, **Plate**, Coronet, Hand-Painted Purple Poppies, Gold	45.00
Limoges, **Plate**, Coronet, Hand-Painted Roses In Water Scene, Gold, Duval	20.00

Limoges, Plate, Cream, Oak Leaves, Floral, Gold Outline, Gold Embossed Rim 14.00
Limoges, Plate, Cupid Center, Lacy Gold Edge, 8 1/2 In. 25.00
Limoges, Plate, Daisy Design, Raised, Marked, 9 3/4 In.Diameter 16.00
Limoges, Plate, Duck, Signed Max, 10 In. 42.50
Limoges, Plate, European Peasant Girl In Wedding Dress, Signed Lanoy 145.00
Limoges, Plate, Fish Swimming From Dark Into Sunlight, Signed Lanoy 22.00
Limoges, Plate, Fish, Hand-Painted Scene, Pastel Border, Set Of 6 .... 90.00
Limoges, Plate, Fish, Hand-Painted, Coronet, 8 1/2 In., Pair 29.50
Limoges, Plate, Fish, Hand-Painted, Gold Edge, Signed, 9 In., Set Of 4 .... 125.00
Limoges, Plate, Fish, Signed Max, Hand-Painted 16.00
Limoges, Plate, Flower Center, Green Border, 10 1/2 In.Diameter 4.50
Limoges, Plate, Flowers, Gold Handle, Scalloped, Artist-Signed, 8 1/2 In. 23.00
Limoges, Plate, Game Bird, Gold Border, Hand-Painted, 11 In.Diameter 91.00
Limoges, Plate, Game Bird, Gold Scalloped Border, Signed Lobc Flambeau 63.00
Limoges, Plate, Game, Bird, 8 In. 15.00
Limoges, Plate, Game, Duck, Signed Max, Coronet, Gold Border, 10 In. 30.00
Limoges, Plate, Game, Ducks, Walking, Flying, Signed A.Broussellon, Pair 85.00
Limoges, Plate, Game, Gold Border, Signed 45.00
Limoges, Plate, Game, Golden Pheasant, Signed Max, Coronet, 10 In. 30.00
Limoges, Plate, Game, Mallard Duck, Pink Ground, Signed Max 45.00
Limoges, Plate, Game, Pheasant By Leon, Ducks By Rene, Pierced To Hang, Pair 55.00
Limoges, Plate, Game, Pheasant, Rococo Gold, Scalloped, Embossed Border 145.00
Limoges, Plate, Game, Signed Ludov, Cobalt Border, Gold Trim, Marked 36.00
Limoges, Plate, Game, Two Snipes, Water, Gold Scrolled Edge, Artist Felix 115.00
Limoges, Plate, Gold Oak Leaves & Floral, Gold Rim Band, 8 1/4 In. 15.00
Limoges, Plate, Green Ground, Rose Sprays, Gold Ferns, Mark 52.00
Limoges, Plate, Hand-Painted Blackberries, Flowers, Signed, 9 1/2 In. 15.00
Limoges, Plate, Hand-Painted Pink Wild Roses, Artist-Signed, J.P.Limoges 10.00
Limoges, Plate, Hand-Painted Purple Violets, Artist-Signed, T.& V. 10.00
Limoges, Plate, Hand-Painted Purple Violets, J.P.Limoges 10.00
Limoges, Plate, Hand-Painted Red Roses, Gold Scrolls, J.P.Limoges 12.00
Limoges, Plate, Hand-Painted Stylized Florals, Gold Band 9.00
Limoges, Plate, Irregular Fluted Edge, Purple Pansies, 12 1/2 In. 18.00
Limoges, Plate, Lavender Floral, Gold Border 9.00
Limoges, Plate, Lily Of The Valley, Scalloped Gold Edge, 8 1/2 In. 1.80
Limoges, Plate, Oyster, Azure Blue, Gold Border Shape Inserts 20.00
Limoges, Plate, Oyster, Pairpoint, White, Brown, Sailboats, 8 In. 35.00
Limoges, Plate, Oyster, Pink Rose In Each Insert, Floral Border, Gold Rim 17.50
Limoges, Plate, Peonies, Haviland, 8 1/2 In. 12.00
Limoges, Plate, Pink Poppies, Ornate Gold Border, Coronet, 10 1/2 In. 37.50
Limoges, Plate, Pink Poppy, 10 In.Diameter 4.25
Limoges, Plate, Poppies & Wheat, Gold Edge, Signed Pouyat Limoges, 10 In. 10.00
Limoges, Plate, Poppies, Signed Baralhe, Coronet, 6 1/2 In. 15.00
Limoges, Plate, Poppy Design, Red, Gold, Signed, 8 1/2 In.Diameter 25.00
Limoges, Plate, Portrait, Hand-Painted Grecian Maiden At Bath, L.S.& S. 35.00
Limoges, Plate, Portrait, Woman, Jeweled, Green Rim, 8 3/4 In. 24.00
Limoges, Plate, Quail, Leaves, Bright Hues, Hand-Painted, Signed, 10 5/8 In. 65.00
Limoges, Plate, Quail, Signed Max, Coronet Mark, Pierced For Hanging 35.00
Limoges, Plate, Red Foxes, Signed Pradst, Coronet, 10 In. 67.50
Limoges, Plate, Rose & Leaf Design, Gold Rim, 8 1/2 In.Diameter 4.50
Limoges, Plate, Roses, Green Rim, Hand-Painted, 8 1/2 In. 5.50
Limoges, Plate, Scene Of Fish, Embossed Florals, 9 In.Diameter 18.00
Limoges, Plate, Ships On Rocky Shore, Artist-Signed 15.00
Limoges, Plate, Strawberries, Artist-Signed, 7 1/2 In. 7.00
Limoges, Plate, Stylized Floral, Gold Rim Band, Decorated Border Design 9.00
Limoges, Plate, Stylized Floral, Wide Gold Band Rim, Inner Decorated Rim 9.00
Limoges, Plate, Thistle Design, Green, Gold, Scroll Edge, 8 1/2 In. 18.50
Limoges, Plate, Tiny Rose Swags Around Border, Gold Scallop Rim, Haviland 7.50
Limoges, Plate, Two Large Blue Flowers, Gold Band, Artist-Signed 18.00
Limoges, Plate, Venice Canal Scene, Gold Trim, Artist-Signed 20.00
Limoges, Plate, Violets, Cherubs, Vine, Signed, Dated 1896, Set Of 12 .... 59.00
Limoges, Plate, Wall, Hand-Painted, Gloucester Fisherman, 8 1/4 In. 15.00
Limoges, Plate, White Daisies, Pink Roses, Gold, Marked France, 10 1/2 In. 45.00
Limoges, Plate, White Ground, Painted Ram's Head, Green Border 14.00
Limoges, Plate, White To Blue, Floral, Gold, Irregular Gold Border 30.00
Limoges, Plate, Wine, Yellow, Apricot Floral Decoration, Crown Pairpoint 35.00

Limoges, Plate, Wreath & Rosebud Design, 9 In.Diameter 3.75
Limoges, Plates, Hand-Painted, April 9, 1902, 7.1/4 In., Set of 6 .... 45.00
Limoges, Platter, Bleeding Heart Spray, 11 X 15 1/2 In. 9.00
Limoges, Platter, Butterflies, White, Deep, 20 X 14 In. 20.00
Limoges, Platter, Game, Pheasant, Ransom Pattern, Gold, Signed Artist Felix 69.00
Limoges, Platter, Game, Rococo Border, Elk, Bird, 12 1/2 In.Diameter 125.00
Limoges, Platter, Garlands, Gold Handles, Gold Border, Haviland, Oval 28.00
Limoges, Platter, Pheasants, White Medallions, Gold Rococo, 19 In.Long 195.00
Limoges, Platter, Pink Roses On Border, 22 In. 22.00
Limoges, Platter, Rosebuds, 16 In., 8 Plates 65.00
Limoges, Platter, Tiny Roses, Leaves, Gold Trim Border, Maker J.P.L. 55.00
Limoges, Platter, Yellow Bleeding Heart, Floral 8.00
Limoges, Portrait, Gold Ground, Woman, Rose Diamonds In Hair, 1 In.Diameter 400.00
Limoges, Punch Bowl, Grapes Inside & Outside, Pink Scalloped Border 225.00
Limoges, Ramekin, Saucer, Roses On Border, Signed Elite, Set Of 6 .... 70.00
Limoges, Ramekin, White & Gold 4.50
Limoges, Relish, White, Enameled Berries, Gold Leaves, Haviland 27.50
Limoges, Ring Tree, Green, Gold Border 22.50
Limoges, Shaving Mug, Red, White, Blue, U.S.Shield, 42 Stars, Name 14.75
Limoges, Stein, Hand-Painted Butterflies, Heavy Gold 12.50
Limoges, Sugar & Creamer, Roses, Gold Trim, Signed C.A.D.N.1906 .... 35.00
Limoges, Sugar & Creamer, Small Flowers, Red & Gold 26.00
Limoges, Sugar & Creamer, Violets, Hand-Painted 28.00
Limoges, Sugar & Creamer, Violets, Leaves, Gold, Artist R.H., 1898 .... 74.00
Limoges, Sugar & Creamer, Violets, Leaves, Gold, 1898, Pickard 45.00
Limoges, Sugar, Covered, Yellow Roses, Dated Dec.25, 1916 .... 30.00
Limoges, Tankard, Autumn Colors, Hand-Painted 45.00
Limoges, Tankard, Grape Design, Dragon Handle, 14 In.High 200.00
Limoges, Tea Set, Banding Of Green Fern Between 2 Rows Of Gold, 21 Piece 75.00
Limoges, Tea Set, Floral Design, Silver Overlay, 3 Piece 69.50
Limoges, Tea Set, Portrait Scene, Tray, Miniature, 10 Piece 16.50
Limoges, Teapot, Pale Blue, Pink Florals, Wide Gold Handle 10.00
Limoges, Teapot, Poppy Decoration On Cream, Satin Finish, Signed JPL 50.00
Limoges, Teapot, 11 1/4 In. .... *Illus* 35.00
Limoges, Tile, Stylized Nature Forms, Art Deco, 14 X 10 In. 14.00
Limoges, Toothpick, Pink, Gold Trim, Ship Scenes 15.00
Limoges, Tray, Dresser, Four Rose Bouquets, Foliage, Vines, Shaded Ground 14.00
Limoges, Tray, Dresser, Hand-Painted Florals 20.00
Limoges, Tray, Dresser, Hand-Painted Rose Bouquets, Foliage, Vines 14.00
Limoges, Tray, Dresser, Kidney Shape, Gold & Bronze Chrysanthemums, Handles 35.00

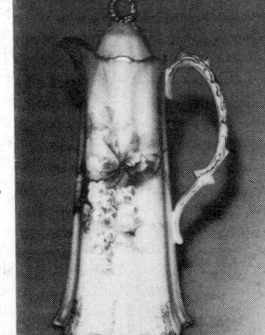

Limoges, Teapot, 11 1/4 In.

Limoges, Tray, Dresser, Painting Of 17th Century Man Courting Woman 27.00
Limoges, Tray, Dresser, Rose Bouquets, Vines, Hand-Painted 14.00
Limoges, Tray, Dresser, Roses, Green, White, Pine, Kidney Shape, 12 1/2 X 9 In. 26.00
Limoges, Tray, Kidney Shape, Gold Bronze Chrysanthemums, Handles 35.00
Limoges, Tray, Peach Blossom Springs, Ornate Gold Border, 1895 .... 26.00
Limoges, Tray, Perfume, Rosebuds, 5 1/2 X 8 In. 12.50
Limoges, Tray, Pin, Green Sailboat On Green 28.00
Limoges, Tray, Pin, Hand-Painted Baby, Initials F.L.L., 1911, Oval 25.00

Limoges, Tray, Pink Dish, Talcum Bottle, Rose Sprays, Gold	45.00
Limoges, Tureen, Old Abbey, 14 In.Long	28.00
Limoges, Tureen, Soup, Flowers, Gold	19.00
Limoges, Tureen, Soup, Hand-Painted, Brown, Green Floral, C.1885	30.00
Limoges, Urn, Sarah Bernhardt In Art Nouveau Attire, Pair	875.00 To 1200.00
Limoges, Vase, Gourd Shape, Fluted, Pink Asters, Gold, Artist-Signed	35.00
Limoges, Vase, Obverse Design, Enamel, Deer, Forest, Gothic Castle, 7 1/2 In.	495.00
Limoges, Vase, Overall Iris Decoration, Hand-Painted, Artist-Signed, 11 In.	37.50
Limoges, Vase, Pink Enamel Ground, Frosted Leaves, Floral, Signed Faure	500.00
Limoges, Vase, Portrait, Girl With Flowing Hair, Enamel, 3 1/2 In.	245.00
Limoges, Vase, Stag, Doe, Mountain, Trees, Signed J.P.L., France, 13 In.High	75.00
Lindbergh, Airplane, Iron, Blue Paint, Steel Wheels, 3 1/2 In.Wingspan	32.50
Lindbergh, Bank, White Metal	30.00
Lindbergh, Bookend, Spirit Of St.Louis, Iron, Pair	12.00
Lindbergh, Bookend, With Plane, Marked The Aviator, Iron, Pair	10.00
Lindbergh, Kit, Spirit Of St.Louis, By Metalcraft, C.1930, Never Assembled	125.00
Lindbergh, Pinback, Photo, Plane On Ribbon	4.50
Lindbergh, Plate, N.Y.To Paris, May 20, 1927, Photo, Marked Sarreguimines	15.00
Lindbergh, Tapestry, Statue Of Liberty, Spirit Of St.Louis, Skylines, Frame	25.00

Lithophanes are porcelain pictures made by casting clay in layers of various thicknesses. When a piece is held to the light, a picture of light and shadow is seen through it. Most lithophanes date from the 1825 to 1875 period. A few are still being made.

Lithophane, American Scenes, 5 Panel Shade	125.00
Lithophane, Cup & Saucer, Dragon, White Ground, Oriental Girl In Cup, Japan	15.00
Lithophane, French, Scenic Panels Of People & Forest, Brass Hanger	25.00
Lithophane, French, White, Lady With Birdcage, Cupid, Brass, Impressed 1856	30.00
Lithophane, Grandmother, Child, Dog, Marked Paris, 1804, Brass Hook Hanger	30.00
Lithophane, Hudson River Valley Scene, Scrollwork At Top & Bottom	35.00
Lithophane, K, P.M., Man Leaning Against Keg, Lead Frame	55.00
Lithophane, Lady, 4 X 5 In.	25.00
Lithophane, Panel, Pierced For Hanging, 4 X 4 1/2 In.	35.00
Lithophane, Picture, Niagara Falls, Lacy Nickel Frame, Chain, 8 X 10 In.	8.50
Lithophane, Picture, Pastoral Scene, Maid On Bridge, Hunter With Gun	45.00
Lithophane, Plaque, Colored Leaded Glass Frame, Triangular Shape	65.00
Lithophane, Plaque, People Scene, Brass Chain, 6 X 7 In.	55.00
Lithophane, Plaque, Scenic, People, Leaded Glass Frame, Brass Chain	45.00
Lithophane, Scenic, 2 X 3 1/2 In., Set Of 5	75.00
Lithophane, Stein, Character, Monk, Brown Robe, Porcelain	155.00
Lithophane, Stein, Character, Munich Maid, Black Robe, Porcelain	155.00
Lithophane, Stein, Duck Hunt	135.00
Lithophane, Stein, Floral, Bum Andenhen In Gold, Ornate Pewter Top & Rest	65.00
Lithophane, Tea Warmer, Four Round Scenics, Brass Holder, Bail, Burner	65.00
Lithophane, Tea Warmer, Four Scenic Panels, Nickel Plated Stand	85.00

Liverpool, England, has been the site of several pottery and porcelain factories from 1716 to 1785. Some Earthenware was made with transfer decorations. Sadler and Green made print-decorated wares from 1756. Many of the pieces were made for the American market and featured patriotic emblems such as eagles, flags, and other special-interest motifs.

Liverpool, Jug, Transfer Printed, Inn Yard, Skating Scene, C.1800	120.00
Liverpool, Mug, Handled, Scene Of Ships, Inscription, Frog Inside Base, 1795	175.00
Liverpool, Pitcher, Black Transfer Washington & Lafayette, Eagle	200.00
Liverpool, Pitcher, Washington Memorial, 19th Century *Illus*	450.00
Loetz Type, Compote, Crimped Edge, Hobs In & Out, Metal Female Frame	145.00
Loetz Type, Vase, Green & Amber Iridescence On Red, Triangular, 5 1/2 In.	180.00
Loetz Type, Vase, Green, Bulbous Top, 5 In.	50.00
Loetz Type, Vase, Purple, Threaded Outside, 5 In.	55.00

Loetz Glass was made in Austria in the late nineteenth century. Many pieces are signed Loetz, Loetz-Austria, or Austria, and a pair of crossed arrows in a circle. Some unsigned pieces are confused with Tiffany Glass.

Loetz, Bowl & Underplate, Finger, Green Gold	70.00
Loetz, Bowl, Blue Purple, Iridescent, Ruffled, 6 1/4 In.	90.00
Loetz, Bowl, Green Iridescence, Threading, Oval, Sterling Rim	375.00

Loetz, **Bowl**, Green, Fluted Top, Unsigned, 8 In.Diameter	65.00
Loetz, **Candlestick**, Iridescent Gold, Green, & Red Leaf Decoration On Base	60.00
Loetz, **Centerpiece**, Cabochon Jewels, Gold Flecks, Gold Band, Footed, 12 In.	575.00
Loetz, **Inkwell**, Green, Ribbed, Iridescent Brass Lid, Unmarked	75.00
Loetz, **Jar**, Sweetmeat, Green, Pulled Glass, Silver Lid	65.00
Loetz, **Rose Bowl**, Confetti Design, Brass Rim, Purple Iridescent	85.00
Loetz, **Rose Bowl**, Green Iridescent, Plain & Honeycomb Panels, Gold Feet	95.00
Loetz, **Rose Bowl**, Melon Rib, White Iridescent Cased Glass, Green Feet	145.00
Loetz, **Vase**, Amber, Silver, Red Iridescence, 9 1/2 In. .... *Illus*	850.00
Loetz, **Vase**, Blue, Green, Purple, Silver Iridescent, 8 In.	100.00
Loetz, **Vase**, Bronze Flowers, Bronze Holder	195.00
Loetz, **Vase**, Clear To Cranberry, Swirls, Scalloped, Unsigned, 9 1/4 In.High	70.00
Loetz, **Vase**, Cobalt Blue Teardrop, 7 In.High	85.00
Loetz, **Vase**, Crackle Glass, Favrile Coloring, Snail Shells, Bulbous, 3 In.	50.00
Loetz, **Vase**, Experimental, Fuchsia To Gold, Teardrop, Applied Serpent	175.00
Loetz, **Vase**, Gold Decorated, Bronze Leaf Stand, 4 1/4 In.	125.00
Loetz, **Vase**, Gold Iridescent Base Applied To Emerald Green Top	195.00
Loetz, **Vase**, Gold Teardrop, 9 In.High	75.00
Loetz, **Vase**, Gold, Green, Blue Iridescent, Silver Overlay, 11 In.	95.00
Loetz, **Vase**, Green Blue, Purple Iridescent, 9 1/2 In.	135.00
Loetz, **Vase**, Green Iridescent, Banana Bowl Style Top, 12 In.High	145.00
Loetz, **Vase**, Green Iridescent, Blue Mottle, Bronze Iris, Floral, Unsigned	135.00
Loetz, **Vase**, Green Iridescent, Signed, Austria, 7 1/2 In.High	135.00
Loetz, **Vase**, Green Teardrop, 5 1/2 In.High	55.00
Loetz, **Vase**, Iridescent Green To Magenta, Pedestal Base, Flared Top	65.00
Loetz, **Vase**, Iridescent, Onion Form, Turquoise Loopings On Bronze, Signed	375.00
Loetz, **Vase**, Jack In Pulpit Shaped Top, Metal Holder	195.00
Loetz, **Vase**, Jack-In-The-Pulpit, Gold Iridescent, Zipper Pattern, Holder	175.00
Loetz, **Vase**, Jack-In-The-Pulpit, Ornate Bronze Stand	175.00
Loetz, **Vase**, Light Blue Iridescent, Loopings, Dimpled In Center, 7 1/4 In.	250.00
Loetz, **Vase**, Metal Trim, 8 1/2 In. .... *Illus*	72.00
Loetz, **Vase**, Pinch Bottle Type, Tulip Top, Iridescent, 7 In.	200.00
Loetz, **Vase**, Pink, Cased In Pink, 10 In.High	95.00
Loetz, **Vase**, Purple, Gold & Green Iridescent, Fluted, Unsigned, 10 1/4 In.	90.00
Loetz, **Vase**, Rainbow, Signed, 8 In.	100.00
Loetz, **Vase**, Red, Ruffled Top, Signed, 7 In.	95.00
Loetz, **Vase**, Red, 4 In.	40.00
Loetz, **Vase**, Ruffle Top, Swirl, Blue Iridescent, 5 In.High	45.00
Loetz, **Vase**, Ruffled Top, 9 1/2 In.	75.00
Loetz, **Vase**, Signed, 4 1/2 X 2 1/2 In.High	100.00
Loetz, **Vase**, Silver & Blue Iridescent, Ruby Interior, Polished Pontil, 8 In.	385.00
Loetz, **Vase**, Silver Loops, Red Mottled Glass, 8 In.Diameter	75.00
Loetz, **Vase**, Silvery Blue Iridescence, Green Base Glass	200.00
Loetz, **Vase**, Swirled Design In Blue, Silver, & Fuchsia, Polished Pontil	125.00
Lone Ranger, Book, Dead Men's Mine, 1939	7.00
Lone Ranger, Radio, Light Up, Figural Front In Color	145.00
Lone Ranger, Statue, Pressed Wood, 1938	32.00

Lotus Ware was made by the Knowles, Taylor & Knowles Company of East Liverpool, Ohio, from 1890 to 1900.

Lotus Ware, Creamer, White, Molded Fishnet Decoration, Bamboo Handle	50.00
Lotus Ware, Cup & Saucer .... *Illus*	165.00
Lotus Ware, Pitcher, Pink Roses, Green & Gold Scrolls, Signed K.T.K.	275.00
Lotus Ware, Pitcher, Signed, 7 1/2 X 5 In.	125.00
Lotus Ware, Vase, Hobs, Gold Trim, Hand-Painted Violets, Covered, Signed	300.00
Lotus Ware, Vase, Pitcher Type, Hobs, Gold Trim, Hand-Painted Violets, Signed	300.00
Lowestoft, see Chinese Export	

Luneville, a French faience factory, was established in 1731 by Jacques Chambrette. It is best known for its fine biscuit figures and groups and for large faience dogs and lions. The early pieces were unmarked. The Terre de Lorraine or T.D.L.impression was used after 1766.

Luneville, Figurine, Lion, Recumbent, Green Base, Open Mouth, Pair	750.00
Luneville, Plate, Fruit, Apples, Cherries, Pierced, Obert, K.& G.	20.00
Luneville, Plate, Grape Design, Signed Obert, 8 3/4 In.Diameter	17.00
Luneville, Plate, Grape On Pink Ground, Signed Obert, 8 3/4 In.Diameter	22.00

Liverpool, Pitcher,
Washington Memorial,
19th Century
See Page 323

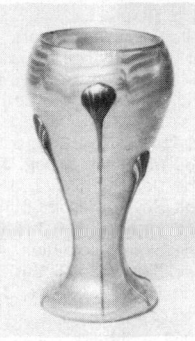

Loetz, Vase, Amber,
Silver, Red Iridescence,
9 1/2 In.
See Page 324

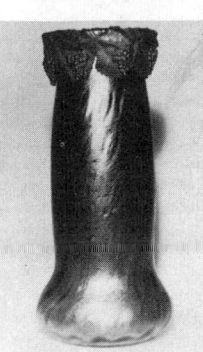

Loetz, Vase,
Metal Trim, 8 1/2 In.
See Page 324

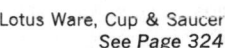

Lotus Ware, Cup & Saucer
See Page 324

Luneville, Plate, Pears On Bronze Ground, Signed Obert, 8 3/4 In.Diameter	24.00
Luneville, Platter, Pink Roses, Pink Edge	30.00

Lusterware was meant to resemble copper, silver, or gold. It has been used since the sixteenth century. Most of the Luster found today was made during the nineteenth century.

Luster, Blue & Silver, Cup & Saucer, Gold	14.00
Luster, Blue, Bowl, Sailing Ship, Gulls, Gold, Devon Lustrine Fieldings	95.00
Luster, Canary, Creamer, Birthplace Of Abraham Lincoln, 3 1/2 In.High	15.00
Luster, Canary, Pitcher, American Independence Emblems, 19th Century	600.00
Luster, Canary, Pitcher, 4 In.	95.00
Luster, Copper, Beading Around Top & Bottom, Raised Figures Each Side	45.00
Luster, Copper, Bowl, Footed, 4 3/4 In.	17.50
Luster, Copper, Chalice, Lavender Band, White Vine Design, Copper Lining	55.00
Luster, Copper, Creamer, Blue Band	35.00
Luster, Copper, Creamer, Blue Flowers, Brown & Gold Leaves	40.00
Luster, Copper, Creamer, Footed, 4 1/2 In.High	27.50
Luster, Copper, Creamer, House Pattern, 4 In.	42.50
Luster, Copper, Cup & Saucer, E.Wood, 1790	35.00
Luster, Copper, Figurine, Spaniel, 9 In.High, Pair	75.00
Luster, Copper, Goblet, Flower Design, Hand-Painted, 4 3/4 In.High	75.00
Luster, Copper, Goblet, Pink Luster Leaves & Flowers On Band	60.00
Luster, Copper, Mug, Band, Beads, White Lining, C.1845, 2 3/4 In.High	32.00
Luster, Copper, Mug, Child's, Blue & Yellow Band Around Middle	25.00
Luster, Copper, Mug, Child's, C.1860	27.00
Luster, Copper, Mug, Child's, 2 3/4 In.	15.00

Luster, Copper, Mug, Orange Band, Floral 47.00
Luster, Copper, Mug, Pink & White Enameled Flowers, 2 1/3 In.High 35.00
Luster, Copper, Mug, Pink Luster Band, House Decoration, 3 In. 35.00
Luster, Copper, Mug, Pink Luster Decoration 32.50
Luster, Copper, Mug, Russet Band, Raised Flowers Both Sides & Front 45.00
Luster, Copper, Pitcher, Allerton's 35.00
Luster, Copper, Pitcher, Beading, Tan, Blue, & Copper Bands, 3 1/2 In.High 30.00
Luster, Copper, Pitcher, Blue Band With Lady & Dog, 3 3/4 In. 58.75
Luster, Copper, Pitcher, Blue Band, Beading, 3 1/2 In. 35.00
Luster, Copper, Pitcher, Blue Band, Boy With Dog Sitting On Bench, 3 3/4 In. 29.00
Luster, Copper, Pitcher, Blue Band, Embossed, 5 1/4 In. 40.00
Luster, Copper, Pitcher, Blue Band, Floral Decoration, 4 1/2 In.High 32.00
Luster, Copper, Pitcher, Blue Band, Raised Girl & Cat Decoration, 3 1/2 In. 44.00
Luster, Copper, Pitcher, Blue Band, Roses & Grapes, 3 1/2 In.High 45.00
Luster, Copper, Pitcher, Blue Band, 3 1/2 In. 22.00
Luster, Copper, Pitcher, Blue Bands, 5 In.High 35.00
Luster, Copper, Pitcher, Blue Border In Center, Relief Girl, C.1845, English 32.50
Luster, Copper, Pitcher, Blue Panel, Embossed Rose, 4 In.High 10.00
Luster, Copper, Pitcher, Caramel Band 23.00
Luster, Copper, Pitcher, Cherubs & Flowers, Raised, Handle 65.00
Luster, Copper, Pitcher, Dark Blue Band, Raised Painted Figure & Dog 37.50
Luster, Copper, Pitcher, Dolphin Handle, Tan Band With Floral, 8 In. 85.00
Luster, Copper, Pitcher, Double Blue Band, 5 1/2 In.High 25.00
Luster, Copper, Pitcher, Eight Raised Deer, Hound, Blue Drape At Top, 8 In. 85.00
Luster, Copper, Pitcher, Flower Design, Raised, Beading, 3 1/2 In.High 50.00
Luster, Copper, Pitcher, Gold Color, Bulbous, 5 In.High 50.00
Luster, Copper, Pitcher, Greek Key, 4 Sided 32.00
Luster, Copper, Pitcher, Green & Yellow Bands, White Lined 36.00
Luster, Copper, Pitcher, Green Band, 4 In.High 37.50
Luster, Copper, Pitcher, Honeycomb Around Base, Enamel Around Top & Sides 57.50
Luster, Copper, Pitcher, Inverted Pear Shape, Orange Frieze, 19th Century 110.00
Luster, Copper, Pitcher, Off-White Sanded Band, England, 1820, 2 1/2 In. 22.50
Luster, Copper, Pitcher, Pink Band, Schoolhouse & Trees, Beading, 4 1/2 In. 100.00
Luster, Copper, Pitcher, Pink Florals, English, 3 In.High 10.00
Luster, Copper, Pitcher, Pink Luster Schoolhouse & Scrolls, 6 1/2 In.High 55.00
Luster, Copper, Pitcher, Pink, White Bands, Lavender, Orange, Green Decoration 50.00
Luster, Copper, Pitcher, Schoolhouse Clock Front, Religious Scene Back 90.00
Luster, Copper, Pitcher, Tan & Blue Bands, 3 1/4 In. 35.00
Luster, Copper, Pitcher, Tan Band, Basket Of Flowers, Dolphin Handle 85.00
Luster, Copper, Pitcher, Two Decorated Tan Bands, 4 1/2 In.High 22.50
Luster, Copper, Pitcher, White Band, Blue & Yellow Flowers, Pink Luster 45.00
Luster, Copper, Pitcher, White Band, Red Roses, Leaves, Wade, England, 4 In. 11.00
Luster, Copper, Pitcher, Yellow Band, 4 1/2 In.High 32.00
Luster, Copper, Pitcher, Yellow Bands, 5 In.High 40.00
Luster, Copper, Pot, Pepper, Apricot Band 43.00
Luster, Copper, Salt, Blue Band, White Lining, Footed 36.00
Luster, Copper, Salt, Master, Blue Band, Footed, 3 In. 15.00
Luster, Copper, Salt, Master, Blue Decoration 22.50
Luster, Copper, Salt, Master, Cream Band, Footed, 3 In. 17.50
Luster, Copper, Salt, Pink & Cream Motif Band, Copper Lining, Footed, Open 35.00
Luster, Copper, Salt, Yellow Band Around Center, Open 32.50
Luster, Copper, Shaving Mug 48.75
 Luster, Copper, Tea Leaf, see Ironstone, Tea Leaf
Luster, Copper, Teapot, Deep Green Band, Lion Finial, Eagle Band 55.00
Luster, Copper, Teapot, Lid, Blue Band 50.00
Luster, Copper, Toby Mug, Allerton, Cobalt, Snufftaker, C.1912 ....65.00 To 145.00
Luster, Copper, Toby Mug, Man, Seated, Allerton, C.1915, 5 1/2 In. 60.00
Luster, Copper, Tumbler, Blue Band, 3 In.High 26.50
Luster, Copper, Urn Vase, Flowers Front & Back 17.50
Luster, Copper, Vase, Square, Stippled, 8 In.High 40.00
 Luster, Fairyland, see also Wedgwood
Luster, Fairyland, Bowl, Mottled Gray Blue, Wedgwood, England, No.Z 4828 .... 105.00
Luster, Fairyland, Bowl, Mottled Lavender, Gold Butterflies, Portland Mark 110.00
Luster, Gold, Cup & Saucer, Demitasse ....12.00 To 15.00
Luster, Gold, Pitcher, Gold Flower Design, Beading, 4 In.High 45.00
Luster, Pink, Boot, Flower Design, Raised, Gold, Cobalt Blue Trim 20.00

Luster, Pink, Bowl, Church Scene, Pedestal, 6 1/2 In.	25.00
Luster, Pink, Bowl, Pig Listens To Phonograph Horn, Germany, 5 1/2 In.	35.00
Luster, Pink, Bowl, Scenic Design, Deep, Davenport	15.00
Luster, Pink, Box, Figural, Colonial Lady, Tiered Skirt, Impressed Germany	12.00
Luster, Pink, Creamer, Red, Yellow, Pink, & Green Floral Band, 5 1/2 In.	45.00
Luster, Pink, Cup & Saucer, C.1820, Set Of 4	80.00
Luster, Pink, Cup & Saucer, Child's	19.00
Luster, Pink, Cup & Saucer, Child's, Lions	12.50
Luster, Pink, Cup & Saucer, Demitasse, Child's, Cow In Color	12.00
Luster, Pink, Cup & Saucer, Demitasse, Church Scene	17.50
Luster, Pink, Cup & Saucer, Demitasse, 'Remember Me, 'Made In Germany	8.50
Luster, Pink, Cup & Saucer, England	12.00
Luster, Pink, Cup & Saucer, Floral, C.1835	20.00 To 25.00
Luster, Pink, Cup & Saucer, Floral, Wishbone Handle	16.00
Luster, Pink, Cup & Saucer, Handleless	15.00 To 50.00
Luster, Pink, Cup & Saucer, Handleless, House Scene	20.00
Luster, Pink, Cup & Saucer, Leaf & Flower	10.00
Luster, Pink, Cup & Saucer, Leaf Pattern, Handleless	15.00
Luster, Pink, Cup & Saucer, 'Present'	12.50
Luster, Pink, Cup & Saucer, Primrose, Rust, Yellow, Blue, Green, C.1835	25.00
Luster, Pink, Cup & Saucer, Strawberries & Leaves, 19th Century, Set Of 12	350.00
Luster, Pink, Cup & Saucer, Tulip Pattern	15.00
Luster, Pink, Invalid Feeder, Porcelain	12.50
Luster, Pink, Jug, Transfer, 'The Mariner's Compass, 'sunderland, C.1805	90.00
Luster, Pink, Mug, Child's, Goldfinch Bird Scene	25.00
Luster, Pink, Mug, Child's, White Ground, Floral, 'For A Good Child'	8.50
Luster, Pink, Pitcher, House Pattern, 3 1/4 In.High	32.00
Luster, Pink, Pitcher, Hunting Scene With Horses & Dogs, 5 In.High	55.00
Luster, Pink, Pitcher, The Tythe Pig, C.1850 *Illus*	80.00
Luster, Pink, Pitcher, Transfer Print, Bulbous, 9 In.High, 19th Century	150.00
Luster, Pink, Pitcher, Verses, C.1850, 7 1/2 In. *Illus*	70.00
Luster, Pink, Plate, Lily Of The Valley, 8 1/4 In.	18.00
Luster, Pink, Plate, Pink Flower, 7 In.	40.00
Luster, Pink, Plate, Raised Flower Border, Colored Flower Center	20.00
Luster, Pink, Plate, Schoolhouse, 8 In.Diameter	22.50
Luster, Pink, Plate, 6 Swags, Green Leaves, 8 In.	14.00
Luster, Pink, Saucer, Carnation	10.00
Luster, Pink, Saucer, Red, Yellow, Pink, & Green Floral	20.00
Luster, Pink, Soup, Fence Pattern	22.00
Luster, Pink, Sugar & Creamer, Staffordshire, C.1800 *Illus*	140.00
Luster, Pink, Tea Set, Child's, White Medallion Of Apple Blossoms, 8 Piece	37.50
Luster, Pink, Tea Set, Strawberry Vines, 1920, 21 Piece	135.00
Luster, Pink, Vase, Altar, Luster Heart, Hand-Painted Floral	16.00
Luster, Pink, Waste Bowl, Faith, 6 In.Diameter	15.00
Luster, Purple, Cup & Saucer, Grapevine & Leaf, Gray's Pottery	25.00
Luster, Purple, Vase, Ormulu Base, Male In 17th Century Court Costume	125.00
Luster, Silver, Chalice, 4 1/2 In.High	27.50
Luster, Silver, Coffeepot, Footed	75.00
Luster, Silver, Creamer, 3 1/2 In.	70.00
Luster, Silver, Pitcher, Ribbed Base, Black Handle, Porcelain Lined, Hanover	80.00
Luster, Silver, Salt, Footed, Pair	20.00
Luster, Silver, Sugar, Open, Pedestal, 5 In.High	22.50
Luster, Silver, Tea Set, Oval Shape, 13 Piece	9.00
Luster, Silver, Tea Set, Porcelain Lined, 4 Piece	130.00
Luster, Silver, Teapot, Brown, White Relief Figures	38.00

*Lustre Art Glass Company was founded in Long Island, New York
in 1920 by Conrad Vahlsing and Paul Frank. The company made lamp
shades and globes that are almost indistinguishable from those made by Quezal*

Lustre Art, Shade, White, Gold Pulled Feather, Gold Interior, Set Of 4	190.00
Lustre Art, Vase, Carriage, Threaded, Bronze Holder With Birds, Signed	225.00

*Lustres are mantel decorations, or pedestal vases, with many hanging glass
prisms. The name really refers to the prisms, and it is proper to refer to a
single glass prism as a lustre. Either spelling, luster or lustre, is correct.*

Luster, Pink, Pitcher,
The Tythe Pig, C.1850
See Page 327

Luster, Pink, Pitcher,
Verses, C.1850, 7 1/2 In.
See Page 327

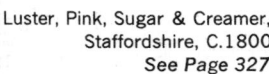

Luster, Pink, Sugar & Creamer,
Staffordshire, C.1800
See Page 327

Lustres, Bohemian, Gothic Lobed Border, White & Gold On Blue, C.1850, Pair	350.00
Lustres, Flowers, Birds, Cranberry Glass, Bohemian, Pair	400.00
Lustres, Forest Green, Two Rows Of Drops, Large Balls On Drop Ends, Pair	275.00
Lustres, Green, Gold & White Enamel Trim, Double Row Spear Prisms, Pair	350.00
Lustres, Green, Gold, Hand-Painted Decoration, Scalloped, Prisms, 11 In., Pair	155.00
Lustres, Ruby Glass, Enamel Decorations, Prisms, Pair	350.00
Lustres, Ruby Glass, England, Pair	125.00
Lustres, Ruby Glass, White Floral, Gold Leaves, Spear Prisms, Pair	250.00
Lustres, Ruby, Gold & White Enameling, Cut Glass Prisms, 13 1/2 In., Pair	265.00
Lutz Type, Plate, Whirling Stripes, Gold Mica, Ruffled, 7 In.	11.00
Lutz Type, Tumbler, Pink, White, Clear	12.00

*Lutz Glass was made in the 1870s by Nicholas Lutz at the Boston and
Sandwich Company. He made a delicate and intricate threaded glass of
several colors. Other similar wares are referred to as Lutz.*

Lutz, Bottle, Cologne, Stopper, Blue Stripes With White Latticinio	30.00
Lutz, Bowl & Plate, Cranberry, Amber Threading, Ruffled	35.00
Lutz, Bowl & Underplate, Finger, Bluish Opalescent, Vaseline Trim	95.00
Lutz, Bowl, Finger, Cherub Face Handle, Purple & White, 4 1/2 In.Diameter	65.00
Lutz, Bowl, Finger, Gold, Cherub Handles	60.00
Lutz, Cruet, Striped, Pair	305.00
Lutz, Plate, Gold Swirls, Gold Threading, White Threading Panels, 7 In.	55.00
Maastricht, Plate, Apples, Embossed Scalloped Rim, Pierced For Hanging	10.00
Maastricht, Plate, Canton, 8 3/4 In.	15.00
Maastricht, Plate, International Eucharistisch Congress, 1924	22.00 To 45.00
Maastricht, Plate, Peaches, Embossed Scalloped Rim, Pierced For Hanging	10.00
Maastricht, Plate, Pompeia, 8 1/2 In.Diameter	17.50
Maastricht, Plate, Toko, P.Regout & Co., 8 1/2 In.	12.50
Maastricht, Plate, White Ground, Blue Flowers, 9 In.	30.00
Maastricht, Plate, Winter Scene Of Church, Houses, & Children, Embossed Rim	12.00

Maastricht, Saucer 4.00

Maize glass, sold by the W.L.Libbey & Son Company of Toledo,
Ohio, was made by Joseph Locke in 1889. It is pressed glass formed like
an ear of corn. Most pieces were made for household use.
Maize, Toothpick, Barrel Shape, Joseph Locke For Libbey & Son 295.00
Maize, Vase, Locke, 6 1/2 In. .... *Illus* 95.00

Majolica is any pottery glazed with a tin enamel. Most of the Majolica
found today is decorated with leaves, shells, branches, and other natural
shapes and in natural colors. It was a popular nineteenth century product.
Majolica, Ashtray, Match Holder, Frog Beside Playing Uke 25.00
Majolica, Basket Bowl, Basket Weave With Berry Cluster, Branch Handle 22.50
Majolica, Bowl, Centerpiece, Pink, 3 Green Snail Feet, 12 In. 40.00
Majolica, Bowl, Fan, Flowers, Blue 16.50
Majolica, Bowl, Fruit, Basket Weave, Impressed Monogram, 9 In.Diameter 36.50
Majolica, Bowl, Green Basket Weave, Fruit & Flowers In Relief, Marked 25.00
Majolica, Bowl, Green, Yellow, & Red Flowers 28.00
Majolica, Bowl, Leaf Design, Pink, Green, Brown 20.00
Majolica, Bowl, Leaf Shape, Cauliflower, Etruscan, 9 1/2 In.Diameter 32.00
Majolica, Bowl, Leaf Shape, Green & Brown 14.00
Majolica, Bowl, Leaf Shape, Green, Apricots In Center, Gold Handle 9.50
Majolica, Bowl, Leaf Shape, Yellow Top, Brown, Green, & Yellow, Etruscan, GSH 21.00
Majolica, Bowl, Maple Leaf Shape & Pattern, 10 1/4 In.Diameter 15.00
Majolica, Bowl, Maple Leaf Shape, Pink, Green, & Yellow, 5 1/2 In.High 20.00
Majolica, Bowl, Maple Leaf Shape, Pink, Green, & Yellow, 8 In.Wide 12.00
Majolica, Bowl, Pink, Lavender Chrysanthemums, George Jones Mark, English 32.50
Majolica, Bowl, Raised Maple Leaf In Center, Leaf Shape, 10 In. 16.00
Majolica, Bowl, Serving, Leaf Shape, Green Leaf Center, Signed, Etruscan 20.00
Majolica, Bowl, Shell Shape, Pink & Blue, Shell Feet 60.00
Majolica, Bowl, Shell Shape, Shell & Coral On Base, Brown & Turquoise Lined 35.00
Majolica, Bowl, Yellow And White, Gold Trim, Handle Across Top 37.50
Majolica, Box, Tobacco, Arab's Head 50.00
Majolica, Butter Pat, Flower 4.00
Majolica, Butter Pat, Leaf Shape 7.00
Majolica, Butter Pat, Marked Etruscan 9.25
Majolica, Compote, Green, Brown, Leaf Center, Scalloped Border, On Stand 35.00
Majolica, Compote, Multicolor, Gold, Foliate Handles, Pedestal Base 35.00
Majolica, Cup & Saucer, Demitasse, Brown, Green, Flower & Leaf Decoration 9.00
Majolica, Cup & Saucer, Shell & Seaweed, Pink Lined, Etruscan .... 58.00 To 75.00
Majolica, Cup, Pineapple Pattern 16.75
Majolica, Cuspidor, Stippled White, Pink Lining, Embossed Birds On Trees 19.50
Majolica, Figurine, Parrot, Bright Blue & Greens On Green Gray Base, 13 In. 90.00
Majolica, Figurine, Young Girl Holding Flowers, 7 1/2 In.High 24.00
Majolica, Ginger Jar, Cream Color, Brown Bird 18.00
Majolica, Humidor, Arab's Head Shape, Beard, Turban, 5 1/2 In. .... 20.00 To 40.00
Majolica, Humidor, Covered, Bowl Shape, Flower Design, Green & Tan, 5 1/2 In. 12.50
Majolica, Humidor, Covered, Girl's Head Shape, Embossed, Flowers 35.00
Majolica, Humidor, Fagin Shape, Dickens' Character, 5 In.High 37.50
Majolica, Humidor, Indian's Head Shape, Feather Headdress 48.50
Majolica, Incense Burner, Elf With Pipe 25.00
Majolica, Jar, Ginger, Tan & Brown, Raised Bird Each Side, Footed, Knobbed 18.00
Majolica, Jardiniere, Cabbage Leaf, Raised, Green, Brown, 9 1/2 In.Diameter 27.50
Majolica, Jardiniere, Grape & Leaf Decoration, Green & Brown 55.00
Majolica, Jardiniere, Green Flowered Base, Embossed Flower Top, 10 In. 19.00
Majolica, Jug, Ear Corn, Yellow & Green, Metal Lid & Rim, 6 1/2 In. 50.00
Majolica, Juice, Red Basket Weave, 3 Colored Birds Sitting Among Flowers 5.00
Majolica, Match Holder, Monkey & Organ Grinder 29.50
Majolica, Pitcher, Bird, 8 1/2 In. .... *Illus* 40.00
Majolica, Pitcher, Blue, Yellow & Green Sheaf Of Wheat, 7 In.High 25.00
Majolica, Pitcher, Brown, Green Fence Trim, White Flowers, Pink Lining 16.00
Majolica, Pitcher, Ear Of Corn, Brown Husks, Pink Lined, Brown Handle 41.00
Majolica, Pitcher, Ear Of Corn, Lavender Lining .... 18.50 To 25.00
Majolica, Pitcher, Ear Of Corn, Yellow, Brown, 8 1/4 In.Tall 49.00
Majolica, Pitcher, Fan & Owl Design, Tricornered, 8 In.High 35.00
Majolica, Pitcher, Flowers, Basket Weave, Brown, White, Yellow, & Red, 6 In. 30.00

Maize, Vase,
Locke, 6 1/2 In.
See Page 329

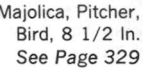

Majolica, Pitcher,
Bird, 8 1/2 In.
See Page 329

Majolica, **Pitcher**, Mustard To Green, 5 1/2 In.	12.00
Majolica, **Pitcher**, Owl, 10 1/2 In.High	75.00
Majolica, **Pitcher**, Rooster, Green, Yellow, White, 10 In.High	95.00
Majolica, **Pitcher**, Signed Italy 7412, Japanese Mark	28.50
Majolica, **Pitcher**, Sunflower, Butterfly Spout, Basket Weave Bottom, 8 In.	55.00
Majolica, **Pitcher**, Water, Etruscan, Shell & Seaweed	85.00
Majolica, **Pitcher**, Water, Fan Design, Hummingbird, Blossoms, Lavender Lined	65.00
Majolica, **Pitcher**, Water, Rose Design, Yellow, Flow Blue Top, Mark England	20.00
Majolica, **Pitcher**, Water, Stork, Cattail, Flowers, White, Green, Yellow, 12 In.	79.50
Majolica, **Plate**, Cobalt Blue Center, Flowers, Aqua Border, 8 In.	7.00
Majolica, **Plate**, Doghouse, 10 1/2 In.	28.50
Majolica, **Plate**, Green, Tan, Brown, Etruscan, 7 In.	15.00
Majolica, **Plate**, Grey Ground, Raspberries, Floral Border, French	7.50
Majolica, **Plate**, Leaf	15.00
Majolica, **Plate**, Red Apple, Green Leaves, Cream Ground, France, 8 1/2 In.	12.50
Majolica, **Plate**, Sheep Dog & Dog House	25.00
Majolica, **Plate**, Shell & Seaweed, Etruscan, 8 1/2 In.	25.00
Majolica, **Plate**, Shell Pattern	12.00
Majolica, **Plate**, Star Pattern	12.00
Majolica, **Plate**, Starfish Pattern, Etruscan, 9 In.	25.00
Majolica, **Plate**, Tan Basket Weave Ground, Green Leaf, Incised Monogram	14.50
Majolica, **Plate**, Three Large Pansies, France	6.50
Majolica, **Plate**, Two Love Birds, Marked Salins, 8 In.	12.50
Majolica, **Platter**, Blackberry, Cliftonware, Marked	35.00
Majolica, **Platter**, Green Ribs, Raised Lily Of The Valley, Pink Floral	17.50
Majolica, **Platter**, Leaf Pattern, Green, Brown, Beige, 9 In.Long	12.50
Majolica, **Platter**, Pink Floral, Green Ferns, English Registry Mark	23.75
Majolica, **Relish**, Dewdrop Pattern, Signed Etruscan	6.50
Majolica, **Sauce & Plate**, Blue, Entwining Sprigs, Floral, Marked 1873	40.00
Majolica, **Seashell**, Blue, Pink Interior, Floral Applique, Coral Base	120.00
Majolica, **Shoe**, 8 1/2 In.Long, 3 3/4 In.High	17.50
Majolica, **Spittoon**, Lady's, Green & Brown	20.00
Majolica, **Stein**, Pewter Lid	45.00
Majolica, **Syrup**, Cornflowers, Etruscan	50.00
Majolica, **Teapot**, Bamboo, Raised Green Bowknot, Leaves, Blue Spatter On Top	23.00
Majolica, **Teapot**, Shell & Seaweed, Etruscan, Pink Lining, 7 In.	98.00
Majolica, **Tray Set**, Green With 2 Ears Of Yellow Corn, 7 Piece	25.00
Majolica, **Tray**, Leaf Shape, Bright Colors, 12 In.	12.00
Majolica, **Tray**, Leaf Shape, Etruscan	40.00
Majolica, **Trivet**, White, Turquoise Border, Blue & Yellow Spray, Frame, Feet	10.00
Majolica, **Vase**, Figural, Troubadour Holds Mandolin, Stands Beside Trumpet	70.00
Majolica, **Vase**, Green Ground, Raised White Lilies, Art Nouveau	65.00
Majolica, **Vase**, Italian, Animals & Classical Figures In White On Blue	100.00
Majolica, **Vase**, Old Man Of The Sea Design, Hand-Painted, Purple, Blue, 14 In.	75.00
Majolica, **Vase**, Raised Rose, 5 1/4 In.	18.00
Majolica, **Vase**, Red, Sanded	25.00
Majolica, **Vase**, Sanded, Oval, Applied China Floral, 2 Handles, 6 In.High	10.00
Majolica, **Vase**, Seashell, Pedestal, Gray, White, Yellow Seaweed, Pair	35.00

Majolica, Vase, Shell & Seaweed, 14 In.High, Pair	65.00
Majolica, Vase, Sunflowers, Scalloped, Lavender Lining, Etruscan, Marked	25.00
Majolica, Vase, Water Scene, Lilies, Lavender Interior, 7 1/2 In.High	22.50
Malachite, Egg, Banded, 2 1/2 In.	85.00
Malachite, Figurine, Sailor, Silver, Russian, C.1870, 4 In.High	95.00

Marbles of glass were made during the nineteenth century. Venetian swirl, clear glass, sulfides, and marbles with frosted white animal figures embedded in the glass were popular. Handmade clay marbles were made in many places, but most of them came from the pottery factories of Ohio and Pennsylvania.

Occasionally, real stone marbles of onyx, carnelian, or jasper can be found.

Marble, Agate, C.1915, 1/2 In.Diameter, Lot Of 38	5.00
Marble, Bennington Type, Blue	5.00
Marble, Bennington Type, 1 1/2 In.	8.00
Marble, Bennington, Blue, Large, 2	14.00
Marble, Bust, Emperor, Italian, Pale Yellow, Inscribed Tito, C.1790	170.00
Marble, Candy Stripe, Paperweight, Extra Large	22.00
Marble, Candy Stripe, Paperweight, Large	18.00
Marble, Candy Stripe, Paperweight, Medium	12.00
Marble, Candy Stripe, Paperweight, Small	8.50
Marble, Clay, Glass, Bag Of 60	5.00
Marble, Clay, 1 In., Pair	3.00
Marble, Cocker Spaniel Begging, Sulfide, 1 In.Diameter	48.00
Marble, Dog, Sulfide, 1 1/4 In.	18.00
Marble, Dog, Sulfide, 2 1/2 In.	32.00
Marble, End-Of-Day, Red, Blue, Yellow, White, & Black, Some Swirl, 2 In.	35.00
Marble, Figurine, Hercules, White, Leaning On Tree Trunk, 19 In.High	100.00
Marble, Green Glass, Circa 1915, 3/4 In.Diameter, Lot Of 11	3.00
Marble, Stripe, 1 1/8 In.Diameter	2.00
Marble, Sulfide, Ape Man, Upright, 1 13/16 In.	27.50
Marble, Sulfide, Bear, Clear Glass, 2 In.Diameter	28.00
Marble, Sulfide, Bear, Standing, 4 3/4 In.Circumference	40.00
Marble, Sulfide, Bear, Walking	35.00
Marble, Sulfide, Bear, 1 1/2 In.	35.00
Marble, Sulfide, Bird, 1 1/4 In.	25.00
Marble, Sulfide, Bird, 6 In.Circumference	45.00
Marble, Sulfide, Cow, Reclining, 2 In.Diameter	28.50
Marble, Sulfide, Cow, 5 In.Circumference	35.00
Marble, Sulfide, Cow, 5 1/4 In.Circumference	40.00
Marble, Sulfide, Dog, Sitting, 1 3/4 In.	22.00
Marble, Sulfide, Dog, 6 1/2 In.Circumference	45.00
Marble, Sulfide, Eagle, 4 1/2 In.Circumference	45.00
Marble, Sulfide, Elephant, 6 3/4 In.Circumference	50.00
Marble, Sulfide, Fish, 2 In.	35.00
Marble, Sulfide, Horse	18.50
Marble, Sulfide, Horse, Rearing, 2 In.	35.00
Marble, Sulfide, Horse, 1 In.Diameter	20.00
Marble, Sulfide, Lamb, Large	18.00
Marble, Sulfide, Lamb, 5 1/2 In.	32.00
Marble, Sulfide, Lion, Large	22.00
Marble, Sulfide, Lion, 6 3/4 In.Circumference	45.00
Marble, Sulfide, Porcupine, Small	15.00
Marble, Sulfide, Rabbit, 1 3/4 In.	22.00
Marble, Sulfide, Rabbit, 5 In.Circumference	35.00
Marble, Sulfide, Rooster, Very Large	38.00
Marble, Swirl, Cane Center, 2 In.Diameter	18.00
Marble, Swirl, End-Of-Day, Rose, Blue, & White, 1 3/4 In.	16.50
Marble, Swirl, Webbing, Purity, Lot Of 5	28.00
Marble, Swirl, Yellow Stripes, Mica Specks, Red, Blue, Green Core, 5 1/4 In.	30.00
Marble, Swirl, 1 In.	12.00
Marble, Swirl, 1 9/16 In.	10.00
Marble, Swirl, 1 3/4 In.	21.00

Marblehead Potteries were started in 1904 by Dr.Herbert J.Hall in Marblehead, Massachusetts. Many of the pieces were decorated with marine motifs. The pottery closed in 1936.

Marblehead, Pitcher, Lapis Blue, Slightly Ribbed, Signed, 3 1/2 In.High 28.00

Martinware is a salt-glazed stoneware made by the Martin Brothers of Middlesex, England, between 1873 and 1915. Many figural jugs and vases were made.

Martinware, Jug, Dragon Fighting, Brown, Beige, Signed, Dated 1897 .... 350.00
Martinware, Vase, Cucumber Form, Blue & Green, Signed, 5 In.High 95.00

Mary Gregory Glass is identified by a characteristic white figure painted on dark glass. It was made from 1870 to 1910. The name refers to any glass decorated with a white silhouette figure and not just the sandwich glass originally painted by Miss Mary Gregory.

Mary Gregory, Atomizer, Blue 95.00
Mary Gregory, Atomizer, Blue, White Figure 95.00
Mary Gregory, Bell, Cranberry 8.45
Mary Gregory, Bottle, Barber, Amethyst, Little Girl 68.00
Mary Gregory, Bottle, Barber, Blue & Cranberry, Boy In Woods, Tinted Face 60.00
Mary Gregory, Bottle, Barber, Girl Playing Tennis, Cobalt Blue, 9 1/2 In. 75.00
Mary Gregory, Bottle, Wine, Crystal, White Boy, Teardrop Stopper 45.00
Mary Gregory, Bottle, Wine, Crystal, White Girl, Teardrop Stopper 45.00
Mary Gregory, Bowl, Apple Green, Faint Panels, White Boy & Girl With Ball 150.00
Mary Gregory, Bowl, Rose Design, 7 X 3 1/2 In. 32.00
Mary Gregory, Box, Amber, Foliage, Boy, Butterfly Net, White Enamel 85.00
Mary Gregory, Box, Black Amethyst, Girl With Umbrella, Ormolu Stand 250.00
Mary Gregory, Box, Camphor Satin, White Garland On Base & Cover 65.00
Mary Gregory, Box, Covered, Girl, Enamel On Glass, Cobalt, 2 1/2 In.Diameter 57.50
Mary Gregory, Box, Cranberry, Head & Shoulders White Enamel Girl On Lid 75.00
Mary Gregory, Box, Jewel, Amber, White Enamel Girl, Foliage, Brass Base, Feet 95.00
Mary Gregory, Box, Patch, Girl Holding Flower, Amber, 1 3/4 In.Diameter 50.00
Mary Gregory, Box, White Enameled Boy, Flowers, Hat In Hand, Foliage 42.00
Mary Gregory, Cologne, Clear, White Enamel, Stopper 25.00
Mary Gregory, Compote, Amber, White Lady On Tree Branch, Dots On Pedestal 165.00
Mary Gregory, Cordial, Tinted Child, Blown Stem & Foot 25.00
Mary Gregory, Creamer, Green, White Enamel Boy, Applied Handle 50.00
Mary Gregory, Creamer, Green, White Enamel Girl Reaching For Butterfly 48.00
Mary Gregory, Cruet, Clear Glass, Girl In White, Tinted Face, 8 In.High 35.00
Mary Gregory, Cruet, Cranberry Glass 140.00
Mary Gregory, Cruet, Green Panel Glass, White Enamel Girl, Foliage, Blown 65.00
Mary Gregory, Decanter, Green, Boy, Tinted Face & Hands, Lilies, Gold Leaves 75.00
Mary Gregory, Decanter, Green, White Boy & Flowers, Crystal Stopper, Handle 65.00
Mary Gregory, Ewer, Green, Rigaree Handles, 11 In., Pair 160.00
Mary Gregory, Goblet, Blue, Blue Pedestal Foot, White Enamel Girl, Foliage 38.00
Mary Gregory, Goblet, Green, Enameled Children, Foliage, Birds, Pair 50.00
Mary Gregory, Jar, Biscuit, Green, White Girl, Pink Dress, Barrel Shape 95.00
Mary Gregory, Jar, Candy, Cranberry 85.00
Mary Gregory, Juice, Blue, Boy 42.75
Mary Gregory, Juice, Blue, Girl 42.75
Mary Gregory, Lamp, Custard Glass, Girl Catching Butterflies 225.00
Mary Gregory, Lamp, Kerosene, Black, White Girl, Open Pontil 165.00
Mary Gregory, Lamp, Kerosene, Tan Bristol, White Figure In Garden 150.00
Mary Gregory, Muffineer, Red 62.00
Mary Gregory, Muffineer, Ruby, Girl 18.00
Mary Gregory, Mug, Boy, Girl, Flower Borders, Blown, Pair 45.00
Mary Gregory, Mug, Green, Boy With Flowers In Hand, Inverted Thumbprint 75.00
Mary Gregory, Mug, Lime Green, White Enamel Boy & Girl, Clear Handle, Pair 50.00
Mary Gregory, Perfume, Atomizer, Blue Glass, White Figure Of Boy, Pedestal 85.00
Mary Gregory, Perfume, Blue, White Enameled Girl, Brass Chain, Ring, & Cap 45.00
Mary Gregory, Perfume, Clear, Pharmacist's Label, Plush Case 65.00
Mary Gregory, Perfume, Cranberry, Girl, Foliage, Brass Top, Chain, Ring 75.00
Mary Gregory, Perfume, White Enameled Girl, Tinted Face, Floral, Cut Stopper 50.00
Mary Gregory, Pitcher, Amber, Girl Jumping Rope, Pewter Cover 125.00
Mary Gregory, Pitcher, Amber, Thumbprint, White Enamel, Amber Handle 125.00
Mary Gregory, Pitcher, Bell, Toothpick, Cranberry, White Child & Foliage 55.00
Mary Gregory, Pitcher, Blue, Coin Spots, White Enamel Girl, White Floral 85.00
Mary Gregory, Pitcher, Boy, Flowers, Pewter Cover, White, 12 1/2 In.Tall 135.00
Mary Gregory, Pitcher, Clear To Amethyst, White Decoration, 10 In.High 155.00

Mary Gregory, **Pitcher**, Clear, Girl Picking Wheat, 5 In. 85.00
Mary Gregory, **Pitcher**, Cobalt, Boy, Foliage, Miniature, 1 3/4 In.High 68.00
Mary Gregory, **Pitcher**, Cranberry Bulbous, Clear Handle 95.00
Mary Gregory, **Pitcher**, Girl, Flora & Fauna In White, Applied Ribbed Handle 75.00
Mary Gregory, **Pitcher**, Green, Applied Handle, White Cherub, Floral, Blown 85.00
Mary Gregory, **Pitcher**, Green, White Cherub & Floral, Blown, 6 1/4 In.High 88.50
Mary Gregory, **Pitcher**, Olive Amber, Inverted Thumbprint, Boy, 12 In. 135.00
Mary Gregory, **Pitcher**, Ruby Glass, 6 1/2 In.High 125.00
Mary Gregory, **Rose Bowl**, Cranberry, 5 In.High 85.00
Mary Gregory, **Shot Glass**, Cranberry, Boy 39.00
Mary Gregory, **Stein**, Amber, Tinted Face 85.00
Mary Gregory, **Stein**, Blue, Thumbprint, 6 1/2 In.High 55.00
Mary Gregory, **Sugar & Creamer**, Green Panel Glass, Open Sugar 65.00
Mary Gregory, **Syrup & Sugar Shaker**, Boy, Girl, Tinted Features, Cranberry 29.00
Mary Gregory, **Syrup**, Red 62.00
Mary Gregory, **Tankard**, Blue, Clear Handle, Girl In Garden 90.00
Mary Gregory, **Tankard**, Cobalt, Boy With Rake In Garden, 9 1/2 In. 125.00
Mary Gregory, **Tankard**, Covered, Cobalt, Inverted Thumbprint, Boy Holds Stick 95.00
Mary Gregory, **Tankard**, Green, Pewter Lid, Insert, White Enamel Girl 75.00
Mary Gregory, **Toothpick**, Blue 10.00
Mary Gregory, **Tray**, Cranberry Overlay, 2 Figures Skating Scene 250.00
Mary Gregory, **Tumbler**, Amber Ground, White Figure Of Girl, 4 1/2 In. 35.00
Mary Gregory, **Tumbler**, Baby Thumbprint, Cranberry Center, White Child, Dots 35.00
Mary Gregory, **Tumbler**, Blue, Boy, Girl, Tinted Features, Pair 110.00
Mary Gregory, **Tumbler**, Blue, White Figure, World's Fair, 1893 .... 55.00
Mary Gregory, **Tumbler**, Boy Walking, Corset Shape, Olive Green, Ribbed 35.00
Mary Gregory, **Tumbler**, Clear, Enamel Boy, World's Fair, 1893 .... 50.00
Mary Gregory, **Tumbler**, Cranberry, Girl Figure With Flower In Hand 42.00
Mary Gregory, **Tumbler**, Cranberry, White Enamel Boy, Foliage 35.00
Mary Gregory, **Tumbler**, Girl Amid Foliage, Frosted Cranberry, 4 In. 45.00
Mary Gregory, **Tumbler**, Girl Sitting, Sapphire Blue, 2 1/4 In.High 30.00
Mary Gregory, **Tumbler**, Green, One Boy, One Girl, Pair 50.00
Mary Gregory, **Tumbler**, Shot Glass Size, Cranberry, White Figure 65.00
Mary Gregory, **Tumbler**, Topaz, Boy 44.00
Mary Gregory, **Tumbler**, Topaz, Girl 44.00
Mary Gregory, **Tumbler**, Water, Cranberry, Girl Holding Flower 40.00
Mary Gregory, **Vase**, Amber, All White Figure, Ruffled Top, 6 In. 65.00
Mary Gregory, **Vase**, Amberina, Inverted Thumbprint, White Figure, Pedestal 75.00
Mary Gregory, **Vase**, Amberina, Thumbprint, White Girl, Ruffled, 10 1/2 In. 125.00
Mary Gregory, **Vase**, Black Amber, With Boy & Flower, Enameled 10 In. 75.00
Mary Gregory, **Vase**, Black Amethyst, Baby Angels Drop Flowers, 9 In., Pair 200.00
Mary Gregory, **Vase**, Black Amethyst, White Enamel Girl, Foliage, 10 1/4 In. 75.00
Mary Gregory, **Vase**, Blue Green, White Figure Of Boy, Coralene Suit 75.00
Mary Gregory, **Vase**, Blue, 14 In.High 125.00
Mary Gregory, **Vase**, Boy Angel, Foliage, Blue, 7 In.High 35.00
Mary Gregory, **Vase**, Boy Fishing From A Tree Stump, Ruffled Top, 9 In.High 75.00
Mary Gregory, **Vase**, Boy, Butterfly Net, Bulbous, Cranberry, 9 1/2 In.High 69.00
Mary Gregory, **Vase**, Champagne Color, Boy With Flower Pot, Pedestal, 10 In. 75.00
Mary Gregory, **Vase**, Cranberry, Amber, Flange Top, Girl, 6 7/8 In.High 55.00
Mary Gregory, **Vase**, Cranberry, Panels, White Boy & Foliage, 6 3/8 In. 60.00
Mary Gregory, **Vase**, Cranberry, White Girl, Pedestal, 6 In.High 79.00
Mary Gregory, **Vase**, Figure Detail, Cranberry, 9 In.High 95.00
Mary Gregory, **Vase**, Flowers, Vines, Girl, Cobalt Blue, 6 1/2 In.High 78.00
Mary Gregory, **Vase**, Golden Amber, White Enamel Boy & Girl, Ruffled, Pair 78.00
Mary Gregory, **Vase**, Green, Girl Picking Flowers, Coralene Dress 85.00
Mary Gregory, **Vase**, Green, Girl With Tinted Face, Ruffled Top 95.00
Mary Gregory, **Vase**, Green, Rippled Top, Girl, 8 1/2 In.High 55.00
Mary Gregory, **Vase**, Honey Amber Satin Ground, White Enameled Girl At Play 38.00
Mary Gregory, **Vase**, Olive Green, Girl Skips Rope, Tinted Skin & Hair, 9 In. 75.00
Mary Gregory, **Vase**, Pale Blue, Girl, Boy, 5 1/2 In., Pair 115.00
Mary Gregory, **Vase**, Rubena, Pixie Climbing Flower Stalk 125.00
Mary Gregory, **Vase**, White Figures Of Two Girls, Cranberry Glass, Pair 450.00
Mary Gregory, **Vase**, Young Girl, Cobalt Blue, Bronze Foot 78.00
Mary Gregory, **Water Set**, Green, Lady On Pitcher, Girls, Boys On 6 Tumblers 475.00
Mary Gregory, **Water Set**, Thumbprint, Clear, 3 Piece 100.00
Mary Gregory, **Wine**, Clear, White, Gold, Blue Boy Fishing, Foliage, Stem 30.00

Masonic Shrine Glassware was made from 1893 to 1917. It is occasionally called Syrian Temple Shrine Glassware. Most pieces are dated.

Masonic, Ashtray & Match Holder, Medinah Athletic Club, Bavarian	9.00
Masonic, Belt, Indian Beadwork, Symbols, Circa 1910	37.50
Masonic, Brooch, Shrine, High Priestess, Can Be Worn On Chain, 14k Gold	50.00
Masonic, Chain, Double, Gold, Hinged 32nd Degree Fob	250.00
Masonic, Champagne, 1900, Washington, D.C., Syria	70.00
Masonic, Champagne, 1902, San Francisco, Syria Shrine	70.00
Masonic, Champagne, 1908, New Orleans, Shriner, Alligator Handles	48.00
Masonic, Champagne, 1909, Kentucky, Shriner, Tobacco Leaf Base	40.00 To 55.00
Masonic, Champagne, 1910, New Orleans, Syria, Alligator, Man	52.50 To 75.00
Masonic, Champagne, 1911, Rochester, N.Y., Shriner, Mounted On Pewter Base	65.00
Masonic, Cup & Saucer, 1906, Los Angeles, Syria, Orange	39.00 To 60.00
Masonic, Cup, Loving, 1899, Commemorative	68.00
Masonic, Cup, Loving, 1905, Niagara Falls, Syria	55.00 To 59.00
Masonic, Goblet, 1899, Pittsburgh, Pa., Syria, June, Gilt	41.00
Masonic, Goblet, 1900, Pittsburgh, Pa., Syria, May 22, 3 Swords	29.50
Masonic, Goblet, 1902, San Francisco, Syria, Solomon's Temple, Bear	58.00
Masonic, Goblet, 1907, Los Angeles, Syria	55.00 To 62.00
Masonic, Goblet, 1908, St.Paul, Syria	32.00 To 55.00
Masonic, Goblet, 1909, Louisville, Syria	48.00
Masonic, Match Safe, Pocket, Nickel Plate, 1904	10.50
Masonic, Mug, E.Pluribus Unum	38.00
Masonic, Mug, 1867-1907, Philadelphia Lodge, Anniversary, Gold Trim	22.50
Masonic, Mug, 1903, Pittsburgh, Saratoga, Scimitar Handle	55.00 To 65.00
Masonic, Mug, 1903, Saratoga, Syria, Indian	50.00
Masonic, Mug, 1904, Atlantic City, Syria, Fish Handle	48.00 To 55.00
Masonic, Mug, 1905, Pittsburgh, Pa., Shriner, Three Handles	55.00
Masonic, Mug, 1907, Shriner Emblem, Arabic Scene, P.F.& Co.	28.00
Masonic, Mug, Shriner, Syria, Niagara Falls View, Three Handles	38.00
Masonic, Paperweight, Etched Insignias, Resembles Goblet, Open Top	75.00
Masonic, Paperweight, Shrine Emblem On Bubbly Red Ground, 3 In	19.00 To 25.00
Masonic, Paperweight, Temple, Chicago, Glass	3.95
Masonic, Pin, Ohio Valley Association, Vevay, Ind.June 24, 1898, Gold	1.75
Masonic, Pipe Rack, Holds Six Pipes, Bronze	23.00
Masonic, Pitcher, Commemoration, Grant Lodge Of Penna., 1911, 11 In.	50.00
Masonic, Plate, Camel, Rider, Insignia Border, Tin, 10 In.	18.00
Masonic, Plate, Hand-Painted Star Emblem, Gold Trim, Poppies, 7 5/8 In.	10.00
Masonic, Plate, Hand-Painted Star Emblem, Gold Trim, 7 5/8 In.	8.00
Masonic, Plate, Hand-Painted Star Emblem, Gold Trim, 8 3/8 In.	10.00
Masonic, Plate, I.O.O.F., Star Emblem, 6 3/8 In.	8.00
Masonic, Plate, Star Emblem, Fluted Edge, Gold Trim, 10 In.	10.00
Masonic, Plate, 1781-1956, Utica Chapel, 175th Anniversary, Officers On Back	9.00
Masonic, Plate, 1906, Los Angeles, Shriner, Gold & Silver Saber, Flowers	29.00
Masonic, Plate, 1910, Acacia Fraternity, Franklin Chapter, Symbols, Porcelain	6.75
Masonic, Shaving Mug, Emblems, Name, Flowers, Green Ground, Porcelain	45.00
Masonic, Shaving Mug, Gold Compass On Blue Circle	25.00
Masonic, Shaving Mug, Name, Porcelain	28.50
Masonic, Sword, American Eagle On Roman Helmet Pommel, White Metal, 1850	19.00
Masonic, Sword, American Fraternal Order, Lodge, Brass Hilt, Engraved	19.50
Masonic, Sword, American Fraternal Order, Lodge, Roman Helmet Pommel	18.50
Masonic, Sword, Dress, Knights Templar	50.00
Masonic, Sword, Templar, Rural Amity Lodge, Athens, Pa., Chartered 1796	35.00
Masonic, Toasting Glass, 1908, St.Paul, Syria, Cranberry Glass, Gold	47.50
Masonic, Toothpick, Chas.A.Titus Lodge, Handles, Silver Plate, Reed & Barton	4.95
Masonic, Tumbler, 1916, Pittsburgh, Syria, Milk Glass, White	35.00
Masonic, Uniform, Chaplain, Feathered Hat, Chest Band, Medals, Circa 1865	75.00
Masonic, Watch Fob, Emblem, Silver, Brown Strap	3.50
Masonic, Watch Fob, Hinged, 32nd Degree On One Side, Shrine On Other, Ruby	58.00
Masonic, Watch Fob, 19th Century Lady, Reverse Sailboat Scene, Gold	15.00
Masonic, Watch Fob, 32nd Degree, Hinged, White Gold	48.00

Massier pottery is iridescent French art pottery made by Clement Massier in Golfe-Juane, France in the late nineteenth and early twentieth centuries. It is characterized by a metallic lustered glaze.

Massier, Plate, Reddish Blue Swirls, Like Weller's Sicardo, Signed	100.00

Massier, Vase, Blue Green Iridescent Swirls, Signed, 4 In.High 40.00
Massier, Vase, Two Iridescent Sea Serpents Around Vase, Signed 225.00
Massier, Vase, Volcano Rock Design, Blue, Signed, 18 1/2 In.Tall 175.00
Massier, Vase, Volcano Rocks, Blue Iridescent, Signed, 15 1/2 In.High 175.00
Match Holder, Black Boot, White & Tan Puppy On Foot, Porcelain 12.50
Match Holder, Button, Hole For Hanging, Place For Used Matches, Honey Amber 16.95
Match Holder, Ceramic, Modeled Old Police Figure, 8 1/2 In.High, C.1895 .... 100.00
Match Holder, Figural, Shoe, Amber, On Stand 35.00
Match Holder, Hand, Blue Glass, 3 1/2 In. .... *Illus* 24.00
Match Holder, Hanging, Half Coal Hod, Scratchers, Iron, J.Robbins & Co. 20.00
Match Holder, Head, Tibetan, 5 1/2 In. .... *Illus* 25.00
Match Holder, Negro, Porcelain, 6 1/2 In.High 18.00
Match Holder, Silver, Frogs On It, 'I'M No Match For You' 19.50
Match Holder, Standing, Boy, Holds Racket, Bisque 18.00
Match Holder, Swimming Scene, Standing Nude Female, Art Nouveau, Sterling 45.00
Match Holder, Table Type, Metal, Tree Trunk & Flowers, Cherub, Birds 9.95
Match Holder, Wall, Raised Hunting Dog On Lift Up Cover, 1862, Iron 16.75
Match Holder, Wall, Single Pocket, Openwork Back, Iron 12.75
Match Safe, Advertising, Val Blatz Brewing Co. 18.50
Match Safe, Basket, Pewter, World's Exposition, Chicago, 1893 .... 4.50
Match Safe, Blue, Asphaltum Scratch Surface, Japanned, 4 In.High 35.00
Match Safe, Brown Palace Cigar, Denver, Colo., Stag On Front 16.00

Match Holder, Head, Tibetan, 5 1/2 In.

Match Holder, Hand, Blue Glass, 3 1/2 In.

Match Safe, Celluloid, Book Shape, Black 8.50
Match Safe, Cupids, Roses, Heart, Dart, Ring, Sterling Silver 15.00
Match Safe, Fleur-De-Lis, Relief, Sterling Silver 15.00
Match Safe, Ostrich Farms, Book Match Type 4.00
Match Safe, Plumes & Roses, Sterling Silver 18.50
Match Safe, Pocket, Allover Chased Design, Sterling, Loop For Hanging 16.50
Match Safe, Pocket, Bryant & May, England, Tin 2.50
Match Safe, Pocket, Donkey Drawn Team, Brass 15.00
Match Safe, Pocket, Tin, 'Diamond' 2.50
Match Safe, Potter's Shoes, Celluloid 14.00
Match Safe, Rainier Beer 8.50
Match Safe, Scrolls, Laurel Wreath, Sterling Silver 18.50
Match Safe, Sterling Silver, Embossed Maple Leaves & Berries 22.00
Match Safe, Sterling Silver, Figure Of Nude Woman Embossed On Front 35.00
Match Safe, Three Flying Swallows, Relief, Sterling Silver 15.00
Match Safe, Tin, Red Celluloid Insert Photo Of Marguerite, Havana Cigars 15.00
Match Safe, Wall, 'Watchman' In High Relief, Iron 17.50
Match Striker, Metal, Black Leather Covering, Lettering 2.00

McCoy pottery is made in Roseville, Ohio. The J.W.McCoy
pottery was founded in 1899. It became the Brush McCoy Pottery
Company in 1911. The name changed to the Brush Pottery in 1925. The
Nelson McCoy Sanitary and Stoneware Company was founded in
Roseville, Ohio in 1910. This firm made art pottery after 1926. In 1933
it became the Nelson McCoy Pottery. Pieces marked McCoy were made
by the Nelson McCoy company.

McCoy, Jar, Cookie, Chef's Head	12.50
McCoy, Jar, Cookie, Covered, Wagon	29.95
McCoy, Kettle, Cookie, Black, Metal Handle	8.00
McCoy, Lamp, Cowboy Boots, Electric	15.00
McCoy, Planter, Sculptured Bird Of Paradise, White & Tan, 7 In. High	8.00
McCoy, Planter, Wishing Well	6.00
McCoy, Tea Set, Pinecone, Green	10.00
McCoy, Vase, Double Tulip	7.50

Mechanical Bank, see Bank, Mechanical

Meerschaum Pipes and other carved pieces of Meerschaum date from the nineteenth century to the present time.

Meerschaum, Cigar Holder, Amber Stem, Full Figure Of Horse & Dog	85.00
Meerschaum, Cigar Holder, Amber Stem, Stag Stands On Top, Velvet Lined	27.50
Meerschaum, Cigar Holder, Carved Dog, Case	25.00
Meerschaum, Cigar Holder, Carved Stag, Case	25.00
Meerschaum, Cigarette Holder, Three Dogs Carved On Top, Case	35.00
Meerschaum, Pipe, Amber Stem, Carved Figure Of Dog, 4 1/2 In., Case	55.00
Meerschaum, Pipe, Carved Bearded Man's Head, New Stem, 5 1/2 In.	50.00
Meerschaum, Pipe, Carved Figure Of Girl, 7 In.	58.00
Meerschaum, Pipe, Carved Sailor Head, Glass Eyes, 5 1/2 In. Long	45.00
Meerschaum, Pipe, Carved Turk's Head Bowl	18.00
Meerschaum, Pipe, Horse At Top, 4 In. Long, Case	37.50
Meerschaum, Pipe, In Holder, Nude Girl Reclining	225.00
Meerschaum, Pipe, Nude Lady On Tulip Shape Ground, Rose Garlands, Case	225.00
Meerschaum, Pipe, Two Pug Dogs On Small Block Pipe	30.00
Meerschaum, Pipe, Wooden Stem, Unscrews In Center, Leather Case	16.00

Meissen is a town in Germany where porcelain has been made since 1710. Any china made in that town can be called Meissen, although the famous Meissen Factory made the finest porcelains of the area.

Meissen, see also Dresden, Onion

Meissen, Ashtray, Oval, White, Rose Design, Crossed Swords Mark, Pair	12.50
Meissen, Basket, Open Lattice, Allover Blue & Pink Applied Floral, 1860	160.00
Meissen, Bonbonniere, C.1860, Pair	300.00
Meissen, Bowl, Black & White, Floral, Crossed Sword Mark	90.00
Meissen, Bowl, Cobalt, Hand-Painted Floral, Crossed Swords Mark, C.1810	220.00
Meissen, Bowl, Cobalt, White, Gold, Pierced, Crossed Sword Mark	125.00
Meissen, Bowl, Diamond Shape, Allover Pink Roses, Green Leaves, Marked	65.00
Meissen, Bowl, Lacy Cutout Sides, Handles	85.00
Meissen, Bowl, Leaf Shape, Twig Handle, Floral On Yellow, Impressed Mark	18.50
Meissen, Bowl, Leaf Shape, Watteau Type Center, Purple Rim, Handle, A.R.	65.00
Meissen, Bowl, Leaves In White & Gold, C.1863, 11 1/2 In. Across	137.50
Meissen, Bowl, Red, White, & Gold, Two Handles, Crossed Swords Mark	162.00
Meissen, Box, Blue, Floral, Gold, Cliff & Water Scene, Sailing Ships, Cover	125.00
Meissen, Candelabrum, Lady Figure, Holds Hurdy-Gurdy, French Ormolu, C.1790	1300.00
Meissen, Candelabrum, Three Branches, Pair	1000.00
Meissen, Candlestick, Burgundy Luster, Gold Dots, Floral Medallion, Pair	40.00
Meissen, Centerpiece, Pair Shepherd 3 Branch Candelabra, 1845, 22 In. High	1400.00
Meissen, Chamberstick, Cobalt, White, Gold Trim, Circa 1750-1818, Mark	45.00
Meissen, Chamberstick, Small Floral Pattern	55.00
Meissen, Chamberstick, White, Floral, Yellow Border, Bird Tail Thumbrest	60.00
Meissen, Cheese Server, Multicolor Floral, Finger Hole, C.1890	90.00
Meissen, Clock, Mantel, Dragon Head Base, Brass Holder, Ornate Feet	175.00
Meissen, Coffeepot, Colorful Costumes, Gold, C.1818	425.00
Meissen, Coffeepot, Rose Finial, Crossed Sword Mark	55.00
Meissen, Compote, Children & Lady	425.00
Meissen, Compote, Two Tiers, Flower Holder At Top, Onion Base, Mark	135.00
Meissen, Compote, Woman & Child, Lattice Rim, Applied Roses, 1760-1774 Mark	900.00
Meissen, Compote, Woman, Child, Roses, Lattice Rim, Crossed Sword Mark, C.1760	750.00
Meissen, Cup & Saucer, Demitasse, C.1890	30.00
Meissen, Cup & Saucer, Demitasse, Red, Gold, Yellow, Signed, Cross Sword	75.00
Meissen, Cup & Saucer, Fable Of Loewenfinch	75.00
Meissen, Cup & Saucer, Posset, Castle Scenes, Floral Scenes, Rose Finial	75.00
Meissen, Cup, Saucer, Plate, White, Tiny Orange Floral, Crossed Sword Mark	25.00
Meissen, Dish, Candy, Open Lace Pattern, C.1890	23.00

Meissen, **Ewer**, Rococo, White Ground, Scrollwork, Gilding, Bearded Mask 160.00
Meissen, **Figurine**, Apollo & Cupid, Chariot, Horses, 16 In.Long, 12 In.High 950.00
Meissen, **Figurine**, Bird In The Gilt Cage, Blue Crossed Swords, 6 1/2 In. 285.00
Meissen, **Figurine**, Child Harlequin, C.1765, 4 3/4 In. .... *Illus* 500.00
Meissen, **Figurine**, Collie, Standing, 4 1/2 X 5 In. 135.00
Meissen, **Figurine**, Cow, Horns, Lying Down, 3 In. 135.00
Meissen, **Figurine**, Duck, White, Brown Feather Tips, Orange Feet & Bill 125.00
Meissen, **Figurine**, Dutch Boy, Shoes Under Arm, Rococo Base, 9 1/4 In.High 110.00
Meissen, **Figurine**, Goat Stands On Overturned Onion Saucer Of Milk 95.00
Meissen, **Figurine**, Mallard Ducks Sit On Haunches 135.00
Meissen, **Figurine**, Mallard, Sitting Among Fernery, 4 In., Pair 125.00
Meissen, **Figurine**, Man, Red Coat, Tricorner Hat, Reads Pocket Watch, Cane 190.00
Meissen, **Figurine**, Pair Of Swimming Mallard Ducks, Base, 4 X 4 3/4 In. 135.00
Meissen, **Figurine**, Pug Dog, Miniature, Blue Collar, Six Gold Bells 60.00
Meissen, **Figurine**, Woman Holds Basket Of Flowers, Man Holds Bouquet, Pair 165.00
Meissen, **Group**, Huntress, Hound, Ormolu, C.1750 .... 2300.00

Meissen, Figurine, Child Harlequin, C.1765, 4 3/4 In.

Meissen, **Jar**, Jam, Rose Finial, Crossed Sword Mark 17.00
Meissen, **Knife Rest**, Blue & White Floral, Gold Trim, Turned Up Ends 12.00
Meissen, **Knife Rest**, Green Leaves 16.50
Meissen, **Mush & Milk Set**, Crossed Sword Mark 30.00
Meissen, **Napkin Ring**, Floral 18.00
Meissen, **Pitcher**, Ivy Pattern, 3 1/2 In.High 28.00
Meissen, **Plate**, Cameo Scrollwork, Baroque Medallions, Crossed Sword Mark 22.50
Meissen, **Plate**, Cobalt, Gold Floral, Pierced Rim, Crossed Sword Mark, Pair 48.00
Meissen, **Plate**, Molded Border, Gold Vines, Leaves, Grapes, X Swords Mark 55.00
Meissen, **Plate**, Pastoral Scene Of Lovers, Reticulated Rim, Deep Blue, 10 In. 85.00
Meissen, **Plate**, Porcelain Cameo Scrollwork, Baroque Medallions, Gold Trim 20.00
Meissen, **Plate**, White, Cobalt Floral, Gold Tracery, Pierced Edge, 8 In. 22.50
Meissen, **Relish**, Ivy Pattern 42.00
Meissen, **Rolling Pin**, Wooden Handles, 16 In.Long 40.00
Meissen, **Salt**, Double Scalloped 45.00
Meissen, **Sugar & Creamer**, Colorful Costumes, Gold, C.1818 .... 375.00
Meissen, **Sweetmeat**, Leaf Shape, Handle, Blue, White, Crossed Sword Mark 17.50
Meissen, **Tea & Coffee Set**, Colorful Figures, Gold, C.1818, 4 Piece 1100.00
Meissen, **Teapot**, Colorful Costumes, Gold, C.1818 .... 425.00
Meissen, **Tureen**, Covered, Stand, Oval, Scroll Feet, Figural Handles, C.1745 .... 2000.00
Meissen, **Tureen**, White, Oval, Branch Handles, Lemon Slice Finial, C.1750 .... 1000.00
Meissen, **Vase**, White, Gold, Roses, Forget-Me-Nots, Butterflies, Mark, 17 In. 285.00

Mercury, or Silvered, Glass was first made in the 1850s. It lost favor for a while but became popular again about 1910. It looks like a piece of silver.

Mercury Glass, **Ball**, Darning, Handle 4.75
Mercury Glass, **Ball**, On Pedestal, 6 In.Round, 11 In.High, Pair 100.00
Mercury Glass, **Candlestick**, Gold, Flower Decoration, 7 1/2 In.High, ... 12.50

Mercury Glass, **Candlestick**, Point For Candle, 1o In.High, Pair 110.00
Mercury Glass, **Candlestick**, 4 1/2 In.High 5.00
Mercury Glass, **Candlestick**, 12 In.High 3.00
Mercury Glass, **Compote**, Decoration Pair 105.00
Mercury Glass, **Compote**, Etched Band, Gold Effect Inside 32.00
Mercury Glass, **Compote**, Pink Design, Hand-Painted, 7 In.Diameter & Tall 35.00
Mercury Glass, **Compote**, White Decoration Outside, Gold Inside, Open 27.50
Mercury Glass, **Cup**, Wine, Geometric Design, Gold Lining, Footed 30.00
Mercury Glass, **Ornament**, Christmas Tree, Green, Acorn Shape, 6 1/2 In.Long 35.00
Mercury Glass, **Reflector**, 6 In. 12.00
Mercury Glass, **Salt**, Open, Pedestal 10.50
Mercury Glass, **Tieback**, Floral, Pewter Mount, Pair 37.50
Mercury Glass, **Tieback**, 3 1/2 In. 12.50
Mercury Glass, **Urn**, Pedestal, White Enamel Decoration, Gold Line 35.00
Mercury Glass, **Vase**, Bud, Ribbed, Bulbous, 4 1/4 In.Tall 8.50
Mercury Glass, **Vase**, Frosted, Wreath Of Flowers, Gold Butterfly, Pair 25.50
Mercury Glass, **Vase**, 6 3/4 In. 5.00
Mercury Glass, **Wig Stand**, 10 In.High 55.00

Mettlach, Germany, is a city where the Villeroy and Boch Factories
worked. Steins from the firm are known as Mettlach Steins. They date
from about 1842.
Mettlach, **Beaker**, Gray, Applied Cherubs & Panels, Silver Luster Ivy 85.00
Mettlach, **Beaker**, No.2327, Kansas City Coat Of Arms .... 26.00 To 30.00
Mettlach, **Beaker**, No.2775 .... 55.00
Mettlach, **Bowl & Underplate**, Punch, No.2339 & 1028 .... 290.00
Mettlach, **Bowl & Underplate**, Punch, No.3379, Covered, Fruit Handles 300.00
Mettlach, **Bowl**, Fruit, No.2415, Etched, Gray Blue, Stylized Decoration 250.00
Mettlach, **Bowl**, No.1325, Blue, Beige, Rose, Brass Cover & Handle, Castle Mark 35.00
Mettlach, **Bowl**, Old Strasbourg, Tulips, Green Banded Top, Villeroy & Boch 80.00
Mettlach, **Bowl**, Punch, No.2339, Dwarfs At Work, 4 Quart .... 215.00 To 260.00
Mettlach, **Bowl**, Punch, No.2602, Cameo & Relief, Underplate, 4 Quart 550.00
Mettlach, **Bowl**, Punch, No.3037, Castle On The Rhine, Tray & Top, Set 285.00
Mettlach, **Bowl**, Salad, No.1339, Silver Plate Rim, Silver & Porcelain Servers 175.00
Mettlach, **Candlestick**, No.3339, Geometric Pattern, White, Brown, Rust, Pair 125.00
Mettlach, **Compote**, Incised Floral Geometric, Signed, 6 1/2 In.High 125.00
Mettlach, **Jardiniere**, No.418, 2 Gallon, Mercury Mark 310.00
Mettlach, **Mug**, Barthololmay's Rochester Beer, Red Wings On Wheel, 1 1/2 In. 45.00
Mettlach, **Mug**, No.95, 1/4 Liter, 'Imported Humbser Beer, Fred K.Hollender' 45.00
Mettlach, **Mug**, No.1526, 'Adolph Hinderson, 'J.D.S.In Blue 45.00
Mettlach, **Mug**, No.1526, Princeton University Reunion, 1900, Crest, Colors, Pug 30.00
Mettlach, **Mug**, No.1526, 3/10 Liter, 'It's Hell To Be Poor' 45.00
Mettlach, **Mug**, No.1526, 3/10 Liter, 'May Dame Fortune Ever Smile On You' 45.00
Mettlach, **Mug**, No.1526, 4/10 Liter, 'staten Island Quartet Club, 1861-1911' 45.00
Mettlach, **Mug**, No.1526, 4/10 Liter, '1898 Harvard 1913, 'Red 45.00
Mettlach, **Mug**, No.1526, 1/2 Liter, F.H.& Co.Imported, V.& B. 45.00
Mettlach, **Mug**, No.1526, 1/2 Liter, '88 Decennial, 'Harvard, Red 45.00
Mettlach, **Mug**, No.2027, Hire's Root Beer, Boy Holds Mug, Villeroy & Boch 55.00
Mettlach, **Mug**, No.2189, 1/4 Liter, Plain 18.00
Mettlach, **Mug**, No.2327, Hamburg 29.00
Mettlach, **Pitcher**, Copyrighted 1910, Signed, 7 1/2 In. 48.00
Mettlach, **Pitcher**, No.1492, Castle Mark, Floral Pattern, 15 In.High 200.00
Mettlach, **Pitcher**, No.2076, 3 Liter, Cream Ground Panels, Red Body, Eagle 325.00
Mettlach, **Pitcher**, No.2210, 2 1/2 Liter 275.00
Mettlach, **Pitcher**, No.2332/1031, 2 Liter, Dwarfs, Pug 135.00
Mettlach, **Pitcher**, No.2418, Pewter Top, White & Crafts Malsters, N.Y. 395.00
Mettlach, **Plaque**, No.167a, Fairyland Castle, Pug, Villeroy & Boch, 10 1/2 In. 125.00
Mettlach, **Plaque**, No.167a, 15 In. 225.00
Mettlach, **Plaque**, No.167b, Fairyland Castle, Pug, Villeroy & Boch, 18 In. 250.00
Mettlach, **Plaque**, No.1044-1143, Drinking Scene, Pug, 17 In.Diameter 225.00
Mettlach, **Plaque**, No.1044, Castle Scene, Knight & Maiden .... 85.00 To 250.00
Mettlach, **Plaque**, No.1044, Church, Mercury, Pug, 13 1/2 In. 100.00
Mettlach, **Plaque**, No.1044, Dutch Girl With Cat, Mercury, Pug, 17 In. 200.00
Mettlach, **Plaque**, No.1044, Dutch Girl With Chickens, Mercury, Pug, 17 In. 200.00
Mettlach, **Plaque**, No.1044, Lichtenstein & Neuschwanstein, Pug, Pair 295.00
Mettlach, **Plaque**, No.1044, Pug, Castle, 11 In.Diameter 85.00

Mettlach, Plaque, No.1260, Etched, 11 In. 125.00
Mettlach, Plaque, No.1365 .... 550.00
Mettlach, Plaque, No.1384, Etched 400.00
Mettlach, Plaque, No.1570, Birds, Villeroy & Boch 25.00
Mettlach, Plaque, No.2070, Etched, Signed, 15 In. 475.00
Mettlach, Plaque, No.2101 & 2102, Deer Scene, Blue On White, 18 In.High 500.00
Mettlach, Plaque, No.2142 .... 400.00
Mettlach, Plaque, No.2143 .... 400.00
Mettlach, Plaque, No.2195 & 2196, Pair 895.00
Mettlach, Plaque, No.2195, Etched, Castle 600.00
Mettlach, Plaque, No.2196, Etched, Castle 600.00
Mettlach, Plaque, No.2199, Etched, Signed, 15 In. 500.00
Mettlach, Plaque, No.2199, 15 1/4 In. 395.00
Mettlach, Plaque, No.2200, Etched, Signed, 15 In. 500.00
Mettlach, Plaque, No.2316, P.U.G.12 In. 75.00
Mettlach, Plaque, No.2351, Multicolor Nasturtiums, Etched 400.00
Mettlach, Plaque, No.2445, Cameo, Oval, 10 1/2 In. 245.00
Mettlach, Plaque, No.2445, Children With Musical Instruments, 10 1/2 In. 550.00
Mettlach, Plaque, No.2517, Etched 525.00
Mettlach, Plaque, No.2534, Etched, 17 In.Diameter 495.00
Mettlach, Plaque, No.2534, 17 1/2 In.Diameter 525.00
Mettlach, Plaque, No.2541, Engraved, Signed R.Thevenin, 16 In. 395.00
Mettlach, Plaque, No.2541, Etched, Signed, 15 In. 475.00
Mettlach, Plaque, No.2542, Etched, Signed, 15 In. 475.00
Mettlach, Plaque, No.2558, Etched, 15 1/2 In.Diameter 250.00
Mettlach, Plaque, No.2596 .... 400.00
Mettlach, Plaque, No.2874, Green, White Cameo, Figures Showing Skills 475.00
Mettlach, Plaque, No.3165 .... 450.00
Mettlach, Plaque, No.7013, Blue, Cameo, Signed, 18 In. 750.00
Mettlach, Plaque, No.7014, Blue, Cameo, Signed, 18 In. 750.00
Mettlach, Plaque, No.7043, Cameo, Man & Maidens Play With Dolphin 1000.00
Mettlach, Plaque, No.7066, Cameo, Frame, 5 1/2 In.Sq. 225.00
Mettlach, Plaque, No.7069, Cameo, Brass Frame, 3 X 4 In. 175.00
Mettlach, Plaque, No.7069, Cameo, 3 X 4 In. 110.00
Mettlach, Plaque, No.7070, Cameo, Oval, Woman, 3 X 4 In. 110.00
Mettlach, Plaque, No.8033, Pheasant In Flight 95.00
Mettlach, Plaque, Nuremberg, Castle Scene, Villeroy & Boch, 13 1/2 In. 45.00
Mettlach, Plaque, Ruins Of Castle, Scalloped Edge, Mercury Mark, 10 1/2 In. 70.00
Mettlach, Plate, Christmas, Nazi Emblem, 1940 .... 100.00
Mettlach, Plate, Spoke Wheel Design, Mulberry Colored Edge Decoration 35.00
Mettlach, Platter, Blue, White, Villeroy & Boch, Signed 35.00
Mettlach, Sachet, No.3147, Rose Petal, Castle Mark 80.00
Mettlach, Smoking Set, No.465, Bird, Lizard, Leaves, 7 In.Tall 155.00
Mettlach, Stein, Lithophane, Porcelain, Coaching Scene, Pewter Lid, Germany 125.00
Mettlach, Stein, No.6, 3 Liter, Inlaid Top 335.00
Mettlach, Stein, No.24, 1/2 Liter, Brown Tankard, V.& B. .... 137.00 To 175.00
Mettlach, Stein, No.62, 1/2 Liter, Silver Lid, Villeroy & Boch .... 135.00 To 145.00
Mettlach, Stein, No.171, 1/4 Liter, Blue Ground, White Figures, Pewter Lid 175.00
Mettlach, Stein, No.171, 1/2 Liter 90.00
Mettlach, Stein, No.202, 1 Liter, Relief, Pewter Lid 165.00
Mettlach, Stein, No.209, 1/4 Liter, Adelweiss Flowers, Etched 250.00
Mettlach, Stein, No.279, 3 Liter, Signed V.& B. 300.00
Mettlach, Stein, No.279, 5 Liter, Fired On Hand-Painted Scene 400.00
Mettlach, Stein, No.280, 1/2 Liter, Pug .... 100.00 To 135.00
Mettlach, Stein, No.675, 1/4 Liter, Barrel, Acorn At Top 59.50
Mettlach, Stein, No.675, 1/2 Liter, Barrel, Acorn On Lid .... 85.00 To 105.00
Mettlach, Stein, No.783, 1/2 Liter 110.00
Mettlach, Stein, No.817, 1/2 Liter 135.00
Mettlach, Stein, No.1004, Humpen, Lid With Cherub, 21 In.High 325.00
Mettlach, Stein, No.1028, 1/2 Liter, Cameo, Boy & Girl In Browns .... 85.00 To 155.00
Mettlach, Stein, No.1028, 1/2 Liter, Tree Bark Lid 145.00
Mettlach, Stein, No.1132, 1/2 Liter, Inlaid Lid 240.00
Mettlach, Stein, No.1133, 1/2 Liter, Pewter Lid 145.00
Mettlach, Stein, No.1144, 1/2 Liter, Inlaid Lid 125.00
Mettlach, Stein, No.1146, 1/2 Liter, Etched .... 225.00 To 275.00
Mettlach, Stein, No.1164, 1/2 Liter, Etched 245.00

Mettlach, Stein, No.1171, 1/2 Liter 200.00
Mettlach, Stein, No.1180, 1/2 Liter ....95.00 To 125.00
Mettlach, Stein, No.1261, 1/2 Liter, Stylized Mosaic Flowers, Scallops 275.00
Mettlach, Stein, No.1266, 1/4 Liter ....95.00 To 130.00
Mettlach, Stein, No.1266, 1/2 Liter, Coral 135.00
Mettlach, Stein, No.1370 .... 180.00
Mettlach, Stein, No.1394, 1/2 Liter, Tarot Card Symbols, Wheat, Barley 295.00
Mettlach, Stein, No.1395, 1/2 Liter 265.00
Mettlach, Stein, No.1395, 1/2 Liter, Etched 195.00
Mettlach, Stein, No.1403, 1/2 Liter, Bowlers, Etched .... 265.00 To 290.00
Mettlach, Stein, No.1453, 1/2 Liter, Etched Hunter, Dogs, Chasing Boars 250.00
Mettlach, Stein, No.1467, 1/2 Liter, Panels, Oak Sprays, Acorns, Figures 175.00
Mettlach, Stein, No.1479, 1/2 Liter, Etched 275.00
Mettlach, Stein, No.1480, 1/2 Liter 275.00
Mettlach, Stein, No.1492, Floral, Glazed Colors, Castle Mark, No Lid, 15 In. 250.00
Mettlach, Stein, No.1494, 5 Liter, Etched 850.00
Mettlach, Stein, No.1508, 1/2 Liter, Etched, Inlaid Top 285.00
Mettlach, Stein, No.1512, 1/2 Liter, Etched, Pewter Lid 235.00
Mettlach, Stein, No.1519, 1/2 Liter 250.00
Mettlach, Stein, No.1526-1076, 1/2 Liter, Pug, Spread Eagle Thumb Lift 125.00
Mettlach, Stein, No.1526, Here's To Good Old Yale, U.S.Seal, Eagle, Pug 165.00
Mettlach, Stein, No.1526, 1/4 Liter 95.00
Mettlach, Stein, No.1526, 1/2 Liter ....65.00 To 135.00
Mettlach, Stein, No.1526, 1/2 Liter, Pug, Hansel & Gretel 70.00
Mettlach, Stein, No.1526, 1/2 Liter, 'Wir Sind Die Levte 20th Reunion, 1913' 45.00
Mettlach, Stein, No.1526, 1 Liter 150.00
Mettlach, Stein, No.1527, 1/2 Liter, Etched, Pewter Lid .... 185.00 To 290.00
Mettlach, Stein, No.1527, 1/2 Liter, Etched, With Music Box 325.00
Mettlach, Stein, No.1527, 1/2 Liter, Knights In Drinking Scene, Dark Blue 260.00
Mettlach, Stein, No.1527, 1/2 Liter, Knights In Drinking Scene, Light Blue 260.00
Mettlach, Stein, No.1566, 1/2 Liter 275.00
Mettlach, Stein, No.1570, 1/2 Liter 195.00
Mettlach, Stein, No.1625, 1/2 Liter 125.00
Mettlach, Stein, No.1632, 5 Liter 750.00
Mettlach, Stein, No.1644, 1/2 Liter .... 175.00 To 190.00
Mettlach, Stein, No.1645, 1/2 Liter 175.00
Mettlach, Stein, No.1652, 5 Liter 1100.00
Mettlach, Stein, No.1675, 1/2 Liter, Inlaid Lid 275.00
Mettlach, Stein, No.1725, 1/2 Liter, Silver Lid 210.00
Mettlach, Stein, No.1732, 1/2 Liter, Inlaid Lid 245.00
Mettlach, Stein, No.1734, 3 Liter, Etched 550.00
Mettlach, Stein, No.1740, 1/4 Liter 130.00
Mettlach, Stein, No.1740, 3/10 Liter, Relief, Pewter Lid 110.00
Mettlach, Stein, No.1742, 1/2 Liter, Inlaid Lid 255.00
Mettlach, Stein, No.1745, 1/4 Liter, Brown Ground, Cameo, Scrolls, Leaves 125.00
Mettlach, Stein, No.1786, 1 Liter, Etched, Pagoda Lid, St.Florian & Dragon 495.00
Mettlach, Stein, No.1799, 1/2 Liter, Etched 250.00
Mettlach, Stein, No.1861, 1/2 Liter, Gambrinus Front Circle 235.00
Mettlach, Stein, No.1885, Blue Etched, White & Gold Trim, Castle Mark 195.00
Mettlach, Stein, No.1909-11, 1/2 Liter, Pug, Man Smoking Cigar, Mercury Mark 70.00
Mettlach, Stein, No.1909-942, 1/2 Liter, Pug 140.00
Mettlach, Stein, No.1909, 1/2 Liter 125.00
Mettlach, Stein, No.1914, 1/2 Liter, Etched 325.00
Mettlach, Stein, No.1915, 1/2 Liter, Inlaid Lid 275.00
Mettlach, Stein, No.1923, 3/10 Liter 122.00
Mettlach, Stein, No.1927, 2 Liter 175.00
Mettlach, Stein, No.1932, 1/2 Liter, Pewter Lid, Castle Mark, Signed, E.Warth 275.00
Mettlach, Stein, No.1932, 1/2 Liter, Two Cavaliers 315.00
Mettlach, Stein, No.1932, 1 Liter, Etched, Inlaid Top .... 315.00 To 425.00
Mettlach, Stein, No.1938, 1/4 Liter, Mosaic 165.00
Mettlach, Stein, No.1947, 1/4 Liter, Etched .... 195.00 To 290.00
Mettlach, Stein, No.1947, 1/2 Liter, Etched Jesters 270.00
Mettlach, Stein, No.1968, 1/4 Liter, Stork, Couple, Bower Of Flowers, Etched 250.00
Mettlach, Stein, No.1972, 1/4 Liter 175.00
Mettlach, Stein, No.1972, 1/2 Liter, Etched, Pewter Lid 250.00
Mettlach, Stein, No.1997, 1/2 Liter, Etched .... 175.00 To 225.00

Mettlach, Stein, No.1998, 1/2 Liter, Etched, Inlaid Lid .... 175.00 To 250.00
Mettlach, Stein, No.2001, 1/2 Liter, A Book Lawyer, Inlaid Lid 350.00
Mettlach, Stein, No.2001, 1/2 Liter, German Saying, Time Is Money 350.00
Mettlach, Stein, No.2001a, 1/2 Liter, Book, Lawyer, Inlaid Lid 300.00
Mettlach, Stein, No.2001b, 1/2 Liter, Book, Doctor, Inlaid Lid .... 280.00 To 325.00
Mettlach, Stein, No.2001d, 1/2 Liter, Etched 275.00
Mettlach, Stein, No.2001f, 1/2 Liter, Architect, Inlaid Lid 325.00
Mettlach, Stein, No.2001g, 1/2 Liter, Electrical Engineer, Inlaid Lid 300.00
Mettlach, Stein, No.2002, 1/2 Liter, Munich Maid, Inlaid Lid .... 255.00 To 280.00
Mettlach, Stein, No.2002, 1 Liter, Munich, Etched 300.00
Mettlach, Stein, No.2005, Castle, 1/2 Liter 225.00
Mettlach, Stein, No.2007, 1/2 Liter, Etched Black Cat, Inlaid Li .... 335.00 To 350.00
Mettlach, Stein, No.2007, 1/2 Liter, Signed F.Stuck 195.00
Mettlach, Stein, No.2008, 1/2 Liter 300.00
Mettlach, Stein, No.2024, 1/2 Liter 295.00
Mettlach, Stein, No.2025, 3/10 Liter, Cupids, Blue Ground .... 145.00 To 235.00
Mettlach, Stein, No.2027, 1/2 Liter 265.00
Mettlach, Stein, No.2028, 1/2 Liter, Etched, Inlaid Lid .... 265.00 To 335.00
Mettlach, Stein, No.2035, 1/2 Liter, Inlaid Lid .... 245.00 To 265.00
Mettlach, Stein, No.2035, 1 Liter, Etched, Pewter Lid 275.00
Mettlach, Stein, No.2042, 1/2 Liter 125.00
Mettlach, Stein, No.2052, 1/4 Liter, Man Holds Two Steins, Cherub On Lid 195.00
Mettlach, Stein, No.2054, 1/2 Liter, Man Drinking, Against Keg .... 225.00 To 295.00
Mettlach, Stein, No.2057, 1/2 Liter, Etched, Inlaid Top 315.00
Mettlach, Stein, No.2057, 1/2 Liter, People Dancing, Inlaid Top .... 250.00 To 265.00
Mettlach, Stein, No.2076, 3 Liter .... 275.00 To 300.00
Mettlach, Stein, No.2082, 1/2 Liter, William Tell 425.00
Mettlach, Stein, No.2085, 4 Liter, Dancing Figures, Relief 300.00
Mettlach, Stein, No.2088, 5 Liter 1400.00
Mettlach, Stein, No.2090, 3/10 Liter 175.00
Mettlach, Stein, No.2090, 1 Liter, Etched 295.00
Mettlach, Stein, No.2092, 1/2 Liter, Dwarf Winding Clock, Schlit .... 235.00 To 300.00
Mettlach, Stein, No.2093, 1/2 Liter, Etched Jacks & Kings Of Cards 350.00
Mettlach, Stein, No.2097, 1/2 Liter, Music, Inlaid Lid .... 250.00 To 275.00
Mettlach, Stein, No.2099, 3/10 Liter 125.00
Mettlach, Stein, No.2100, 1/2 Liter, Etched Prosit Stein, Pewter Lid 240.00
Mettlach, Stein, No.2102, 23 In.High 1500.00
Mettlach, Stein, No.2105, 2 Liter 500.00
Mettlach, Stein, No.2123, 3/10 Liter, Knight Drinking 275.00
Mettlach, Stein, No.2131, 1/2 Liter, Relief, Inlaid Top .... 200.00 To 275.00
Mettlach, Stein.No.2131, 1 Liter, Relief, Inlaid Top .... 250.00 To 325.00
Mettlach, Stein, No.2140, Regimental, Ornate Pewter Lid, Eagle Thumb Lift 200.00
Mettlach, Stein, No.2140, 1/2 Liter, P.U.G.Chicago Brewery 130.00
Mettlach, Stein, No.2140, 1/2 Liter, P.U.G.Dance Scene 115.00
Mettlach, Stein, No.2141, 1/2 Liter 150.00
Mettlach, Stein, No.2152, 1/2 Liter 95.00
Mettlach, Stein, No.2179, 1/4 Liter 145.00
Mettlach, Stein, No.2181, 1/4 Liter, Pug, Castle Mark 120.00
Mettlach, Stein, No.2182, 1/2 Liter, Bowling Scene, Presentation, Dated 1897 .... 195.00
Mettlach, Stein, No.2182, 1/2 Liter, Man Bowling, Innkeeper, Relief 350.00
Mettlach, Stein, No.2182, 1/2 Liter, Terra-Cotta, Beige, Inlay Lid 180.00
Mettlach, Stein, No.2184, 1/2 Liter, Dwarfs, Mandolin, Rats 245.00
Mettlach, Stein, No.2194, 5 Liter 650.00
Mettlach, Stein, No.2217, 1/2 Liter 115.00
Mettlach, Stein, No.2217-960, 1/4 Liter, Pug 125.00
Mettlach, Stein, No.2230, 1/2 Liter, Etched .... 275.00 To 290.00
Mettlach, Stein, No.2231, 1/2 Liter .... 275.00 To 285.00
Mettlach, Stein, No.2235, 1/2 Liter, Etched Girl With Flowing Steins, Target 375.00
Mettlach, Stein, No.2246, 3/10 Liter 135.00
Mettlach, Stein, No.2247, 3/10 Liter 145.00
Mettlach, Stein, No.2248, 3/10 Liter 145.00
Mettlach, Stein, No.2271, 1/2 Liter 150.00
Mettlach, Stein, No.2277, Nuremberg 245.00
Mettlach, Stein, No.2277, 3/10 Liter 175.00
Mettlach, Stein, No.2278, 1/2 Liter 265.00
Mettlach, Stein, No.2280, 1/2 Liter, Pewter Lid .... 250.00 To 285.00

Mettlach, Stein, No.2285, 1 Liter, Lovers 360.00
Mettlach, Stein, No.2286, 3 Liter 600.00
Mettlach, Stein, No.2302, 1/2 Liter 200.00
Mettlach, Stein, No.2333-1033, 3/10 Liter, Dwarfs, Pewter Lid 70.00
Mettlach, Stein, No.2349, 3/10 Liter, Pug 70.00
Mettlach, Stein, No.2349, 3 Liter, Pug, Dance Scene 225.00
Mettlach, Stein, No.2358, 1/2 Liter, Fiddler, Girl, Tavern Scene, Relief 300.00
Mettlach, Stein, No.2373, 1/2 Liter, Allgator Head & Handle 385.00
Mettlach, Stein, No.2373, 1/2 Liter, Etched 375.00
Mettlach, Stein, No.2382, 1/2 Liter, Etched Tower Lid, Signed H.Schlitt 395.00
Mettlach, Stein, No.2382, 1/2 Liter, Thirsty Rider 310.00
Mettlach, Stein, No.2382, 1 Liter, Thirsty Knight, Tower Lid, H.Schlitt 495.00
Mettlach, Stein, No.2408, 1/2 Liter, Etched 275.00
Mettlach, Stein, No.2430, 3 Liter, Etched 475.00
Mettlach, Stein, No.2442, 18 In., Plaque Cameo 615.00
Mettlach, Stein, No.2488, 3 Liter 500.00
Mettlach, Stein, No.2532, 1/2 Liter 310.00
Mettlach, Stein, No.2547, 1/2 Liter 165.00
Mettlach, Stein, No.2556, 1/2 Liter, Blue Ground Panels On Tan Body 230.00
Mettlach, Stein, No.2557, 1/2 Liter 187.75
Mettlach, Stein, No.2580, 1/2 Liter 385.00
Mettlach, Stein, No.2582, 1/2 Liter, Jester, Audience, Etched .... 245.00 To 300.00
Mettlach, Stein, No.2639, 1/2 Liter 290.00
Mettlach, Stein, No.2716, 1/2 Liter, Tavern Scene, Inlaid Lid, Signed F.Q. 295.00
Mettlach, Stein, No.2719, 1/2 Liter, Pewter Lid 250.00
Mettlach, Stein, No.2755, 1/2 Liter, Cameo Panels, Tavern Scenes, Castle Mark 315.00
Mettlach, Stein, No.2776, 1/2 Liter, Keeper Of Wine Cellar, Inlaid Lid 295.00
Mettlach, Stein, No.2780, 1/2 Liter, Inlaid Lid 270.00
Mettlach, Stein, No.2790, 1/2 Liter, Dark Brown Shades, Cavalier, Pug 160.00
Mettlach, Stein, No.2802, 1/4 Liter, Etched 200.00
Mettlach, Stein, No.2829, 1/2 Liter 495.00
Mettlach, Stein, No.2833, 3/10 Liter 195.00
Mettlach, Stein, No.2833, 1/2 Liter, Soldiers Advancing Through Woods 240.00
Mettlach, Stein, No.2833b, 1/2 Liter .... 245.00 To 275.00
Mettlach, Stein, No.2833d, 1/2 Liter, Brick Series, Etched .... 225.00 To 285.00
Mettlach, Stein, No.2833e, 1/2 Liter, Soldiers In Forest, Inlaid Lid 240.00
Mettlach, Stein, No.2836, 1/2 Liter, Cameo .... 225.00 To 350.00
Mettlach, Stein, No.2844, 1/2 Liter, Farmer, Fisherman, Hunter, Etched 325.00
Mettlach, Stein, No.2845, 1/2 Liter, Hunter And Mountains, Etched 300.00
Mettlach, Stein, No.2871, 1 Liter, Etched, Inlaid Lid, Cornell Stein 565.00
Mettlach, Stein, No.2880, 1/2 Liter, Bartender Pouring Ale On Customer 285.00
Mettlach, Stein, No.2892, 1/2 Liter 265.00
Mettlach, Stein, No.2893, 3 Liter, Rampant Lions Hold Shield, Pug 250.00
Mettlach, Stein, No.2900, 1/2 Liter, Argentina, White Quilmas .... 325.00 To 350.00
Mettlach, Stein, No.2900, 1/2 Liter, Train, Buildings 310.00
Mettlach, Stein, No.2922, 1/4 Liter, Etched, Castle Mark 200.00
Mettlach, Stein, No.2936, 1/2 Liter 315.00
Mettlach, Stein, No.2943, 1/2 Liter 150.00
Mettlach, Stein, No.2953, Cup, Four Suits Of Cards 90.00
Mettlach, Stein, No.2957, 1/2 Liter, Etched Bowlers 290.00
Mettlach, Stein, No.3085, 1 Liter, Pewter Lid 250.00
Mettlach, Stein, No.3172, 1/2 Liter, Etched 235.00
Mettlach, Stein, No.3221, 1/2 Liter, Etched, Inlaid Top 300.00
Mettlach, Stein, No.3251, 1/2 Liter 265.00
Mettlach, Tazza, Famille Rose Decoration, Villeroy & Boch, 9 1/2 In. 39.00
Mettlach, Tile, Blue & White, Barnyard Scene, Signed, 5 3/4 In.Square 20.00
Mettlach, Tile, Hand-Painted Bumblebees, Water Lily Scene, Laura N.O'Neill 150.00
Mettlach, Tumbler, Ale, Scenic, 1/4 Liter 29.50
Mettlach, Tumbler, No.2327, Munchen 29.00
Mettlach, Urn, No.1537, Four Seasons, Pedestal Base, Pair 375.00
Mettlach, Urn, No.2172, Browns & Blacks, Small Handles, Castle Mark 115.00
Mettlach, Vase, Blues & Browns, Castle Mark, 6 In.High ....95.00 To 100.00
Mettlach, Vase, No.1336, Glazed Jewel Colors, Castle Mark, 11 1/2 In.Tall 150.00
Mettlach, Vase, No.1596, Red Ground, Bulbous Body, Castle Mark, 7 1/2 In.Tall 150.00
Mettlach, Vase, No.1728, 7 3/4 In.High, Pair 185.00
Mettlach, Vase, No.1829, 9 1/4 In.High, Pair 325.00

Mettlach, Vase, No.1899, 7 3/4 In.High 87.00
Mettlach, Vase, No.2252, Two Girls, One With Star, One With Flask 195.00
Mettlach, Vase, No.2505, 13 1/4 In.High, Pair 295.00
Mettlach, Vase, No.2907, Blue, Tan, & White, Castle Mark, 4 1/2 X 2 1/2 In. ... 45.00
Mettlach, Vase, No.2907, Cream, Tan, Blue Ground, Castle Mark, 2 1/2 In.High 45.00
Mettlach, Vase, No.2913, Floral, Art Nouveau Panels, Castle Mark 70.00
Mettlach, Vase, Portrait 285.00
Mettlach, Vase, Tan Tree Trunk Body, Blue Berries, Vine Handles, 10 In. 150.00
Mettlach, Vase, Tree Bark Surface, Brown Vines, Blue Berries, White Lining 150.00
Mettlach, Wine Dispenser, Relief, 18 In.Tall 135.00
Mexican War, Writing Kit, Sheldon's Patent Escritoir, Metal Box, 1045 .... 110.00
Mickey Mouse And Pluto, Holder, Toothbrush, Mickey Washing Pluto's Face 30.00
Mickey Mouse, Airplane, Mail, Rubber 25.00
Mickey Mouse, Album, Picture Card, 11 Gum Cards, Drawings By Walt Disney 27.50
Mickey Mouse, Ashtray, Minnie Mouse, Pie Shape, Six Sections For Cigarettes 60.00
Mickey Mouse, Bank, Dime Register, Walt Disney Prod., 1939 .... 50.00
Mickey Mouse, Bank, Tin, Post Office, 1940s, 5 In. 15.00
Mickey Mouse, Bank, Treasure Chest Form, Mickey With Minnie, C.1935 .... 40.00
Mickey Mouse, Bicycle Belt 3.00
Mickey Mouse, Book, In Giantland, 1934, Mckay Co., 44 Pages, Hardbound 30.00
Mickey Mouse, Book, Mother Goose, 1937, Whitman, 140 Pages, Hardbound 40.00
Mickey Mouse, Button, Pinback, 3 1/2 In.Diameter, C.1935 .... 40.00
Mickey Mouse, Button, 'sincerely Yours, ' C.1935, 3 1/2 In.Diameter 70.00
Mickey Mouse, Button, White Circular Face, Inscribed, 'Mickey Mouse Club' 10.00
Mickey Mouse, Camera 12.50
Mickey Mouse, Christmas Lights, Electrical, Bell Shaped, 1935 .... 55.00
Mickey Mouse, Clock, Alarm, Circular Dial, Original Box, Ingersoll, 1946 .... 100.00
Mickey Mouse, Clock, Alarm, Electric, Movable Figure, Ingersoll, 1933 .... 300.00
Mickey Mouse, Clock, Alarm, Ingersoll, C.1935 .... 150.00
Mickey Mouse, Clock, Alarm, Minnie, Designed By Alberto Horen, Ingersoll 200.00
Mickey Mouse, Clock, Alarm, Original Box, Ingersoll, 1946 .... 100.00
Mickey Mouse, Cloth, Pie-Eyed, 12 1/2 In.Tall 45.00
Mickey Mouse, Crayons, Giant Size 1.00
Mickey Mouse, Cup, Mickey, Minnie, Pluto, Orange & Blue Ground, Tin, 1 1/2 In. 12.00
Mickey Mouse, Cup, Orange, Blue, Mickey, Minnie, Pluto, Tin 12.00
Mickey Mouse, Dish, Soap, Rubber, Donald Duck 8.00
Mickey Mouse, Doll, Cloth, Mickey & Minnie, Pair 38.00
Mickey Mouse, Doll, Holding Flowers, Rubber, Dell, 7 In. 13.00
Mickey Mouse, Doll, Knickerbocker, Mickey & Minnie, 1930s 80.00
Mickey Mouse, Doll, Seiberling, Rubber, Pie Wedge Eyes 16.50
Mickey Mouse, Doll, Small, Wooden, Flexible Arms And Legs, 1933 .... 40.00
Mickey Mouse, Doll, Stuffed Cloth, 12 In.Tall, 1935 .... 50.00
Mickey Mouse, Doll, Sun Rubber Company, 8 In. 15.00
Mickey Mouse, Figure, Bisque, Dressed As Santa, 3 In.Tall 2.50
Mickey Mouse, Figure, Bisque, Mickey & Minnie, 4 In.Tall, Pair 46.50
Mickey Mouse, Figure, Bisque, Minnie, Playing Accordion 40.00
Mickey Mouse, Figure, Bisque, One Movable Arm, Japan, 5 In.Tall 6.25
Mickey Mouse, Figure, Bisque, Playing Saxophone 48.00
Mickey Mouse, Figure, Bisque, 1 1/2 In.Tall 15.00
Mickey Mouse, Figure, Holding Catcher's Mitt, Standing On Rock 20.00
Mickey Mouse, Figure, Soap, Carved, C.1936, 4 1/2 In.Tall 35.00
Mickey Mouse, Fire Truck, Rubber 5.00
Mickey Mouse, Game, Bagatelle, Mickey Among Numerals, C.1935 .... 100.00
Mickey Mouse, Holder, Toothbrush, Bisque, Japan 17.50
Mickey Mouse, Holder, Toothbrush, Mickey & Minnie, Signed Walt Disney 25.00
Mickey Mouse, Lamp Base, Decal Figures Of Mickey Mouse, 1935 .... 15.00
Mickey Mouse, Lamp Base, Tin 12.50
Mickey Mouse, Magazine, Summer Quarterly, 1935 .... 90.00
Mickey Mouse, Mug, Ceramic, Mickey & Pluto, 'Pluto-The Pup, ' 1935 .... 15.00
Mickey Mouse, Mug, Mickey In Fireman's Attire Holding Ax, C.1935 .... 35.00
Mickey Mouse, Pail, Minnie & Mickey, Walt Disney Enterprises 17.50
Mickey Mouse, Pen & Pencil, Inkograph, 1934 .... 75.00
Mickey Mouse, Plate, Mickey Playing Horn, 1930s .... 6.00 To 9.00
Mickey Mouse, Projector, Marked C.W.D., Eight Rolls Of Colored Film 65.00
Mickey Mouse, Puppet, Hand, Disney .... 3.00 To 6.00
Mickey Mouse, Puppet, Wooden, 1930s 8.00

Mickey Mouse, **Ruler**, By Disney 5.00
Mickey Mouse, **Snow Shovel**, Mickey & Pluto, 1935, 26 In.Long 125.00
Mickey Mouse, **Spoon**, Soup, Silver Plate, William Rogers .... 5.00 To 9.00
Mickey Mouse, **Stand Up Set**, Cardboard, Post's Radio Theatre, 1934 .... 100.00
Mickey Mouse, **Sugar**, Japanese 6.50
Mickey Mouse, **Tea Set**, Signed Disney, Box, 20 Piece 65.00
Mickey Mouse, **Toy**, Airplane, Rubber, Sun, Air Mail 25.00
Mickey Mouse, **Toy**, Donald Duck's Duet, Spring, Key, Dated 1946 .... 40.00
Mickey Mouse, **Toy**, Grand Piano, Decal, Mickey With Minnie, 1935 .... 45.00
Mickey Mouse, **Toy**, Musical Group, Drummer, Pianist, Leader, Dancer, Marx, Tin 150.00
Mickey Mouse, **Toy**, Musician, Windup, Marx, Tin 75.00
Mickey Mouse, **Toy**, Puddle Jumper, Pull, Wooden 10.00
Mickey Mouse, **Toy**, Telephone Bank, Painted Cardboard Figure, C.1935 .... 50.00
Mickey Mouse, **Toy**, Telephone, Metal & Wood, Upright, Bell, Signed Walt Disney 37.50
Mickey Mouse, **Toy**, The Magician, Windup, Tin, Marx .... 35.00 To 65.00
Mickey Mouse, **Toy**, Three Small Mickeys Crossing Plastic Bridge, 1933 .... 30.00
Mickey Mouse, **Toy**, Truck, Hook & Ladder, Donald Duck On Back, Rubber 11.00
Mickey Mouse, **Tractor**, Rubber, Sun 12.00
Mickey Mouse, **Tray**, 1935 .... 6.00
Mickey Mouse, **Washing Machine**, 7 In.High 25.00
Mickey Mouse, **Watch**, Chrome Strap, Ingersoll, C.1938 .... 120.00 To 200.00
Mickey Mouse, **Watch**, Circular Dial, Ingersoll, 1935 .... 45.00
Mickey Mouse, **Watch**, Disneyland, First Series, C.1968 .... 40.00
Mickey Mouse, **Watch**, Ingersoll, C.1933, Round 80.00
Mickey Mouse, **Watch**, Ingersoll, C.1948 .... 50.00
Mickey Mouse, **Watch**, Ingersoll, 1936 .... 95.00
Mickey Mouse, **Watch**, Pocket, Mickey Tells Time, Ingersoll, 1935 .... 125.00 To 165.00
Mickey Mouse, **Watch**, Rectangular Dial, Ingersoll, 1946 .... 75.00 To 95.00
Mickey Mouse, **Watch**, Rectangular Shape, C.1948 .... 40.00
Mickey Mouse, **Watch**, Seconds Dial With Mickeys, Mickey Band, Ingersoll, 1933 .... 260.00
Mickey Mouse, **Watch**, Wrist, Ingersoll, By U.S.Times, C.1939 .... 100.00
Mickey Mouse, **Watch**, Wrist, Ingersoll, Red Band 20.00
Mickey Mouse, **Watch**, Wrist, Metal Figures On Leather Band, Ingersoll 195.00
Mickey Mouse, **Watch**, Wrist, Red Band, U.S.Time, Walt Disney 65.00
Mickey Mouse, **Watering Can**, Mickey Watering His Garden, 1935 .... 70.00
Mickey Mouse, **World Globe**, Donald Duck 15.00

Milk Glass was named for its milky white color. It was first made in
England during the 1700s. The height of its popularity in the United
States was from 1870 to 1880. It is now correct to refer to some colored
glass as Blue Milk Glass, Black Milk Glass, etc. The numbers b-xx
refer to the book Milk Glass by E.Belknap.

Milk Glass, see also Cosmos
Milk Glass, **Banana Boat**, Blue, Open Lattice Edge, Pedestal 21.00
Milk Glass, **Basket**, Blue 14.00
Milk Glass, **Bathtub**, Ornate, Footed, 6 1/2 In.Long 10.00
Milk Glass, **Bobeche**, Alternate Rib, Chartreuse, Pair 30.00
Milk Glass, **Bottle**, Barber, Metropolitan Art Co., 9 1/2 In.High 12.00
Milk Glass, **Bottle**, Black, Sitting Bear, Green Base 40.00
Milk Glass, **Bottle**, Blue, Oval, Atterbury 25.00
Milk Glass, **Bottle**, Camphor, Stopper, Scrolls, Eged In Gilt, 11 1/2 In.High 20.00
Milk Glass, **Bottle**, Cologne, Bulbous, Hollow Stopper, Hand-Painted, Gold 50.00
Milk Glass, **Bottle**, Dresser, Gargoyle Head Pattern, Matched Stopper, Pair 45.00
Milk Glass, **Bottle**, Gemel, Free-Blown, Applied Stem & Foot, McKearin 229 ..... 65.00
Milk Glass, **Bottle**, Toilet Water, Blue, Enameled Floral 30.00
Milk Glass, **Bottle**, Toilet, Bulbous, Stopper, 10 In.High 30.00
Milk Glass, **Bottle**, World's Fair, 1939 .... 9.00
Milk Glass, **Bowl**, Apple Blossom Design, 9 In.Diameter 60.00
Milk Glass, **Bowl**, Basket Weave Design, Dated Patented June 30, 1874 .... 20.00
Milk Glass, **Bowl**, Black, 12 In. 25.00
Milk Glass, **Bowl**, Covered, Blackberry 45.00
Milk Glass, **Bowl**, Daisies, Pink & Blue Floral, Green Leaves 77.50
Milk Glass, **Bowl**, Double Open Lace Edge 30.00
Milk Glass, **Bowl**, Eye & Scroll, Oyster Center, Blue, 7 In. 28.00
Milk Glass, **Bowl**, Floral, Panels, Tree Of Life & Daisy Pattern 85.00
Milk Glass, **Bowl**, Flower, Opalescent, Threaded, Lamb's Leg Pattern, 4 In. 30.00

Milk Glass, Bowl, Fruit, Pink, Pedestal 12.75
Milk Glass, Bowl, Grape Pattern, 8 X 4 In. 15.00
Milk Glass, Bowl, Lattice Edge, Apple Blossom Decoration, 9 In.Diameter 60.00
Milk Glass, Bowl, Lattice Work, 12 In.Diameter 38.00
Milk Glass, Bowl, Ruffled, Relief, 10 1/2 In.Diameter 22.00
Milk Glass, Bowl, Victorian Hands, Satin Finish, Red & Gold Trim, English 49.50
Milk Glass, Bowl, White, Daisy & Tree-Of-Life, Hexagonal, 4 In.Deep 75.00
Milk Glass, Bowl, White, Ruffled Lacy Edge 20.00
Mikl Glass, Box, Covered, Heart Shape, 3 1/2 In.Diameter 15.00
Milk Glass, Box, Covered, Rectangular, 3 X 4 In. 15.00
Milk Glass, Box, Handkerchief, Rectangular, 5 X 5 1/2 In, ,,,,,, ,,,,,,,,,,,,,,,,,,,,,,,,,,,,,,,,, 30.00
Milk Glass, Box, Pin, Covered, Raised Scrollwork 10.00
Milk Glass, Box, Powder, Covered, Round, 3 1/2 In.High 27.50
Milk Glass, Box, Shell Design, 4 In.Diameter 18.00
Milk Glass, Box, Square, 2 In.High 15.00
Milk Glass, Box, Trinket, Covered, Raised Florals, 3 1/2 X 4 1/2 In. 10.00
Milk Glass, Box, Trinket, Flowers, Enamel, Gold, 4 X 3 1/2 In. 12.00
Milk Glass, Butter, Child's, Wild Rose 55.00
Milk Glass, Butter, Covered, Child's, White, Sawtooth Edge, Pressed Pattern 22.50
Milk Glass, Butter, Covered, Panels, Herringbone, Opalescent 15.00
Milk Glass, Cake Stand, Decorated, Flint 35.00
Milk Glass, Cake Stand, Fluted Pattern, Chartreuse, Atterbury & Co. 95.00
Milk Glass, Camphor, Stopper, Scrolls, Edged In Gilt, 11 1/2 In.High 20.00
Milk Glass, Candlestick, Climbing Rose 5.00
Milk Glass, Candlestick, Crucifix, Pair 50.00
Milk Glass, Candlestick, Loop Handle, 4 1/2 In.High 15.00
Milk Glass, Candlestick, Mermaid Supports Holder, Signed Portieux, Pair 85.00
Milk Glass, Candlestick, Scroll Pattern, Squared Base, 6 1/2 In.High 15.00
Milk Glass, Candlestick, Swirled Design, Opalescent, France, 3 1/2 In., Pair 12.00
Milk Glass, Candlestick, Twist, Black 17.50
Milk Glass, Cat On Drum, Blue, Marked Portieux 25.00
Milk Glass, Christmas Light, Humpty Dumpty 4.00
Milk Glass, Compote, Blue, Basket Weave Center, 10 In.Diameter 50.00
Milk Glass, Compote, Blue, C-Scroll With Eye, Octagon, 12 In.High 122.50
Milk Glass, Compote, Diamond Pattern, Scalloped Edge, 6 In. 6.00
Milk Glass, Compote, Flowers, Tall 55.00
Milk Glass, Compote, Jenny Lind, Flint 75.00
Milk Glass, Compote, Lacy Edge, Blue 50.00
Milk Glass, Compote, Lattice Border, Floral Inside, High Standard 70.00
Milk Glass, Compote, Open Lattice Edge, Diamond Pattern Pedestal Base 65.00
Milk Glass, Creamer, Blue, Horn Of Plenty, Gold 12.00
Milk Glass, Creamer, Blue, Swan & Cattails, Gold 25.00
Milk Glass, Creamer, Diamonds In Ovals 22.00
Milk Glass, Creamer, Grapes Overlapping Leaves 22.00
Milk Glass, Creamer, Royal Oak, Green Top 37.50
Milk Glass, Creamer, Scroll Pattern, Raised, White, Green, Gold 16.00
Milk Glass, Creamer, Sunflower 18.00
Milk Glass, Cruet 11.00
Milk Glass, Dish, Candy, Blue, Cabbage Rose 23.00
Milk Glass, Dish, Battleship Cover, Marked Dewey, B-161b 27.50
Milk Glass, Dish, Battleship Cover, Marked Maine, B-162 .... 35.00
Milk Glass, Dish, Battleship Cover, Marked Olympia 40.00
Milk Glass, Dish, Battleship Cover, Marked Oregon, B-184b .... 20.00 To 40.00
Milk Glass, Dish, Battleship Cover, Marked Wheeling 32.00
Milk Glass, Dish, Cat Cover, Reclining 22.00
Milk Glass, Dish, Cat Cover, Ribbed Base 48.50
Milk Glass, Dish, Chick & Eggs Cover, Dated 1889, Atterbury 145.00
Milk Glass, Dish, Chick In Egg Cover, Sleigh Base 45.00
Milk Glass, Dish, Chicken Cover, Blue 30.00
Milk Glass, Dish, Dewey & Gunboat Cover, Greentown 45.00
Milk Glass, Dish, Dog Cover 28.50
Milk Glass, Dish, Dove Cover, Basket-Weaved Base, Fiery Opalescent, White 275.00
Milk Glass, Dish, Duck Cover, Wavy Base 60.00
Milk Glass, Dish, Duck Cover, White, Wavy Base 67.50
Milk Glass, Dish, Fish Cover 20.00
Milk Glass, Dish, Fish Cover, White, Entwined, Atterbury 145.00

Milk Glass, Dish, Fish On Skiff Cover 39.50
Milk Glass, Dish, Fox Cover, Dated 1889 .... 98.00
Milk Glass, Dish, Hand & Dove Cover, Eye, Atterbury, Dated 1889 .... 72.50 To 95.00
Milk Glass, Dish, Hand & Dove Cover, Lacy Edge 115.00
Milk Glass, Dish, Hen Cover, Basket-Weaved Base 68.00
Milk Glass, Dish, Hen Cover, Basket-Weaved Base, 5 1/2 In. 12.00
Milk Glass, Dish, Hen Cover, Blue, Basket-Weaved Base, 5 1/2 In.Long 35.00
Milk Glass, Dish, Hen Cover, Blue, Nest Base, 9 In.Diameter 37.50
Milk Glass, Dish, Hen Cover, Blue, White Head 45.00
Milk Glass, Dish, Hen Cover, Blue, 6 In. 24.50
Milk Glass, Dish, Hen Cover, Lacy Edge 60.00
Milk Glass, Dish, Hen Cover, Old Vallerystahl Type 19.50
Milk Glass, Dish, Hen Cover, Red Comb 8.00
Milk Glass, Dish, Hen Cover, The American Hen, B-162a 59.00
Milk Glass, Dish, Hen Cover, White, Blue Marbled, Lacy Base, Atterbury 135.00
Milk Glass, Dish, Hen Cover, White, Vallerystahl Type 26.50
Milk Glass, Dish, Hen Cover, 8 3/4 In.Long 85.00
Milk Glass, Dish, Lamb Cover, Blue, 5 In. 28.50
Milk Glass, Dish, Lamb Cover, White, Bopeep Base 215.00
Milk Glass, Dish, Lion Cover 55.00
Milk Glass, Dish, Lion Cover, Reclining 75.00
Milk Glass, Dish, Lion Cover, White, Lacy Base, Atterbury 75.00
Milk Glass, Dish, Pintailed Duck Cover 45.00
Milk Glass, Dish, Pope Leo XIII Cover 55.00
Milk Glass, Dish, Quail Cover, White 45.00
Milk Glass, Dish, Rabbit Cover, Blue, Patent March 9, 1886, 10 In .... 130.00 To 350.00
Milk Glass, Dish, Rooster Cover, Blue, 5 In. 36.00
Milk Glass, Dish, Snail On Strawberry Cover, Painted 35.00
Milk Glass, Dish, Swan Cover, Lacy Base, Raised Wings 95.00
Milk Glass, Dish, Turkey Cover, Imperial Glass 30.00
Milk Glass, Egg, Easter .... 9.00 To 10.00
Milk Glass, Egg, Hand Blown, Painted Easter Greeting 12.00
Milk Glass, Eggcup, Blue, Chicks, Signed Portieux 8.50
Milk Glass, Eyecup 5.00
Milk Glass, Eyecup, Panels 15.00
Milk Glass, Fernery, Footed, Raised Scrolls, Scalloped Top, 7 1/2 In. 15.00
Milk Glass, Figurine, Hen, Red Comb, 2 1/2 In. 7.50
Milk Glass, Figurine, Owl, Blue 4.22
Milk Glass, Figurine, Swan, Blue 4.22
Milk Glass, Flask, Klondyke 35.00
Milk Glass, Hat, Dogwood, Flared, Blue 30.00
Milk Glass, Hatchet, Cherries 7.00
Milk Glass, Holder, Playing Card, Spades, Hearts, Diamonds, Clubs, Beading 20.00
Milk Glass, Jar, Covered, Ivy 11.00
Milk Glass, Jar, Covered, Victoria 45.00
Milk Glass, Jar, Cracker, Apple Blossom Pattern, Pink Flowers, Green Band 65.00
Milk Glass, Jar, Cuff, Cylinder Shape, Lid, 5 In.High 35.00
Milk Glass, Jar, Ginger, Covered, Blue, Plume 35.00
Milk Glass, Jar, Honey, Form Of Woven Hive 20.00
Milk Glass, Jar, Mustard, Blue, Swirl 29.00
Milk Glass, Jar, Mustard, Owl 50.00
Milk Glass, Jar, Tobacco, Brass Lid, Brown, Pipe, Matches, Birds 37.50
Milk Glass, Juicer, Sunkist 10.00
Milk Glass, Knob, Dresser Drawer, Blue, Self-Thread Base 3.00
Milk Glass, Lamp Base, Spider Web 40.00
Milk Glass, Lamp, Hexagonal Shade, 6 In.High 35.00
Milk Glass, Lamp, Night, Wick & Chimney 27.50
Milk Glass, Lamp, Pink, Brass Column, Font, White To Pink Shade, 20 In. 55.00
Milk Glass, Lamp, Raised Swirls, Blue, 4 1/4 In.High 35.00
Milk Glass, Match Holder, Figural, Hand, Floral Decoration 17.00
Milk Glass, Match Holder, Horse's Head Each Side, Herringbone 10.00
Milk Glass, Match Holder, Uncle Sam's Hat, Star Band 12.00
Milk Glass, Muffineer, Carnations 17.50
Milk Glass, Muffineer, White, Blue Flowers 23.00
Milk Glass, Muffineer, White, Mauve Flowers 20.00
Milk Glass, Mug, Child's, Stork & Peacock 18.00

Milk Glass, Mug, Child's, Washington & Lafayette 18.00
Milk Glass, Mug, Davy Crockett 2.50
Milk Glass, Mug, Ivy In Snow 7.00
Milk Glass, Mug, Pink White, Greentown 15.00
Milk Glass, Mug, Roses In Gothic Arches 22.00
Milk Glass, Mug, Shaving, Rose Design, Signed Hazel Atlas 5.00
Milk Glass, Mustard, Swirl Pattern, Cover 27.50
Milk Glass, Ornament, Lilies Mounted On Brass Stem, Round Base, Pair 125.00
Milk Glass, Pickle, Blackberry, Flint 18.00
Milk Glass, Pitcher, Apple Blossoms, Green Band, Six Tumblers 100.00
Milk Glass, Pitcher, Blown, 8 1/2 In. 45.00
Milk Glass, Pitcher, Owl, White, 3 1/2 In.High 32.50
Milk Glass, Plate, Apple Blossom, Latticework 28.00
Milk Glass, Plate, Black, Gothic, 9 In. 15.00
Milk Glass, Plate, Black, Keyhole Border, 7 1/2 In. 9.00
Milk Glass, Plate, Black, Scalloped, Two Handles, 9 In. 9.00
Milk Glass, Plate, Block Border, 8 1/2 In. 9.50
Milk Glass, Plate, Blue, Peg Border, Round, 7 1/4 In. 28.00
Milk Glass, Plate, Blue, Scroll & Eye, 8 In. 27.50
Milk Glass, Plate, Bread, Actress 50.00
Milk Glass, Plate, Bread, Basket Weave 37.50
Milk Glass, Plate, Bread, Basket Weave, June 30, 1874 On Reverse 60.00
Milk Glass, Plate, Bread, Diamond Grill, Give Us This Day Borde .... 32.50 To 49.00
Milk Glass, Plate, Cake, Open Handles, Ornate Edge, Black 8.00
Milk Glass, Plate, Center Scene 16.00
Milk Glass, Plate, Club & Shell, Waffle Center, 9 1/2 In.Diameter 9.00
Milk Glass, Plate, Columbus, 1492-1892, 9 1/4 In. .... 17.50 To 35.00
Milk Glass, Plate, Contrary Mule, 7 In. 24.00
Milk Glass, Plate, Cupid & Venus 22.50
Milk Glass, Plate, Eagle, Arrow, & Fleur-De-Lis 16.00
Milk Glass, Plate, Eagle, Flag & Star Border, 7 In. 25.00
Milk Glass, Plate, Eagle, Fleur-De-Lis, Flag, Dated 1903 .... 15.00
Milk Glass, Plate, Easter Design, Chick & Egg 25.00
Milk Glass, Plate, Flower Center, Open Lattice Edge, 10 In.Diameter 30.00
Milk Glass, Plate, Forget-Me-Nots, Lacy Border, Opalescent 8.00
Milk Glass, Plate, Give Us This Day, Patent Date 40.00
Milk Glass, Plate, Iris, Hand-Painted, 10 In. 18.00
Milk Glass, Plate, Mother Goose, 6 1/4 In.Diameter 27.50
Milk Glass, Plate, Ribbon 8.75
Milk Glass, Plate, Scroll & Eye, 8 In.Diameter 11.00
Milk Glass, Plate, Star Shape, 5 1/2 In. 9.50
Milk Glass, Plate, Star, 5 In. 9.75
Milk Glass, Plate, Three Bears 22.00
Milk Glass, Plate, Three Kittens .... 16.00 To 22.00
Milk Glass, Plate, Three Kittens, Painted 15.00
Milk Glass, Plate, Three Owls .... 18.00 To 22.00
Milk Glass, Plate, U.S.Battleship Maine, Club & Heart Border 22.00
Milk Glass, Plate, U.S.Battleship Maine, Transfer 29.50
Milk Glass, Plate, View Of Lachine Rapids, Reticulated Edge, Gold Rim 10.50
Milk Glass, Plate, White, Lacy Edge, 8 In.Square 12.00
Milk Glass, Plate, White, Serenade, Greentown, 6 1/2 In. 55.00
Milk Glass, Plate, White, Spring Meets Winter, Round, 7 1/4 In. 31.00
Milk Glass, Plate, Wicket, 7 3/4 In. 14.00
Milk Glass, Plate, Wicket, 8 3/4 In. 15.00
Milk Glass, Plate, Wicket, 9 In. 7.00
Milk Glass, Plate, Woof Woof 40.00
Milk Glass, Plate, 101, 5 1/2 In.Diameter 4.00
Milk Glass, Platter, Dog Swimming To Retrieve A Bird .... 62.50 To 95.00
Milk Glass, Platter, White, John Hancock 165.00
Milk Glass, Pot, Preserve, Shape Of Strawberry, Portieux-Marked 35.00
Milk Glass, Rolling Pin, Signed Imperial Glass, Cambridge, Ohio 24.00
Milk Glass, Rolling Pin, White, Wooden Handled, C.1885, 17 In.Long 10.00
Milk Glass, Rolling Pin, Wooden Handles 15.00
Milk Glass, Salt & Pepper, Blue, Original Lids, 3 1/4 In.High 30.00
Milk Glass, Salt & Pepper, Blue, Tassel 25.00
Milk Glass, Salt & Pepper, Blue, 6 In. 5.00

Milk Glass, Salt & Pepper, Bulbous, Raised Scrolls & Beading, Paint	15.00
Milk Glass, Salt & Pepper, Embossed Floral, Pewter Tops	27.50
Milk Glass, Salt & Pepper, Enamel Design, Ribbed, Squatty	20.00
Milk Glass, Salt & Pepper, G.E.Monitor Refrigerators, Pink Tri	12.00 To 16.50
Milk Glass, Salt & Pepper, Grape & Leaf, Gold Paint, Footed	15.00
Milk Glass, Salt & Pepper, Green, Ribbon Band	24.00
Milk Glass, Salt & Pepper, Hand-Painted Farm Scenes, Silver Holder, Handle	16.50
Milk Glass, Salt & Pepper, Hand-Painted Pink Floral	10.00
Milk Glass, Salt & Pepper, Light Blue, Swirl Princess	25.00
Milk Glass, Salt & Pepper, Light Blue, 6 In.High	15.00
Milk Glass, Salt & Pepper, Owl Shape, Round Base, 6 In.High	175.00
Milk Glass, Salt & Pepper, Pink, Artichoke	35.00
Milk Glass, Saltshaker, Blue, Paneled Scroll	14.00
Milk Glass, Saltshaker, Blue, Paneled Shell	15.00
Milk Glass, Saltshaker, Egg Shape, Rabbit, Squatty	9.00
Milk Glass, Saltshaker, Four Raised Palmer Cox Brownies	18.00
Milk Glass, Saltshaker, Leaf Panel, Footed	25.00
Milk Glass, Saltshaker, Pink, Cone	15.00
Milk Glass, Saltshaker, White, Cactus	9.00
Milk Glass, Saltshaker, White, Creased Bail	16.00
Milk Glass, Saltshaker, White, Pee Wee Forget-Me-Not	5.00
Milk Glass, Salt, Blue, Palm Leaf	15.00
Milk Glass, Salt, Charioteer, Rectangular, Footed, Sandwich	95.00
Milk Glass, Salt, Master, Pedestal	15.00
Milk Glass, Salt, Pale Green, Tulip, Footed	12.00
Milk Glass, Salt, Pink, Twisted Leaf	15.00
Milk Glass, Salt, Rectangular, Footed, Sandwich, N.E.Glass Co., Boston	85.00
Milk Glass, Salt, Triple Bud, Raspberry	17.00
Milk Glass, Saucer, Blue, Cherry Blossom	5.00
Milk Glass, Shoe, Painted Black, Painted Dog's Head	20.00
Milk Glass, Slipper, Daisy & Button, Cat's Head	16.00
Milk Glass, Slipper, Daisy & Button, Kitten's Head, 6 In.	15.00
Milk Glass, Slipper, Opalescent, Two Parts, 8 1/2 In.Long	110.00
Milk Glass, Spooner, Apple Blossoms, Yellow Band At Top, C.1860	27.50
Milk Glass, Spooner, Blackberry	15.00 To 20.00
Milk Glass, Spooner, Double Loop	13.00
Milk Glass, Spooner, Horses' Heads Medallions	35.00
Milk Glass, Spooner, Oval Medallion, Painted Pansy	12.50
Milk Glass, Spooner, Roses & Ribbons	16.00
Milk Glass, Spooner, Scenic & Wild Rose Design, Ruffled Rim	29.00
Milk Glass, Spooner, Sunflower	18.00
Milk Glass, Spooner, Wild Rose Design, Ruffled Rim	29.00
Milk Glass, Stein, Juliette	15.00
Milk Glass, Sugar & Creamer, Child's, Blue, Hobnail	7.50
Milk Glass, Sugar & Creamer, Covered, Crown	15.00
Milk Glass, Sugar & Creamer, Orange, Green Handle, 3 1/2 In.High	22.00
Milk Glass, Sugar & Creamer, Swan, Swan Finial	27.50
Milk Glass, Sugar, Covered, Embossed Grape, Scalloped Top, Vine Finial, Oval	18.00
Milk Glass, Sugar, Covered, Forget-Me-Not	15.00
Milk Glass, Sugar, Covered, White, Beaded Swirl, Oval	15.00
Milk Glass, Sugar, Covered, White, Double Loop	77.50
Milk Glass, Sugar, White, Sawtooth, Footed	30.00
Milk Glass, Syrup, Blue, Tree Of Life	65.00
Milk Glass, Syrup, Dahlia	18.00
Milk Glass, Syrup, Grape & Leaves, Blue, Applied Handle	75.00
Milk Glass, Syrup, Spider Web	22.50
Milk Glass, Syrup, White, Embossed Morning Glories, Tin Top	45.00
Milk Glass, Table Set, Miniature, Covered, C.1930, 3 Piece	16.00
Milk Glass, Toothpick, Barrel Shape, Snake Coiled Around Bottom Half	15.00
Milk Glass, Toothpick, Beaded Swag, Rose Decoration, 'Mom, State Fair'	30.00
Milk Glass, Toothpick, Boy Kneeling Playing Marbles, French	12.50
Milk Glass, Toothpick, Daisy & Button, Blue, Hat Shape	9.50
Milk Glass, Toothpick, Elephant's Head	22.50
Milk Glass, Toothpick, Green, Hand Holds Container	18.00
Milk Glass, Toothpick, Hand-Painted Underglaze, 3 Handles, Kemple Mark	8.00
Milk Glass, Toothpick, Swan Handles	12.00

Milk Glass, Toothpick, Tramp's Shoe, Orange Paint 12.50
Milk Glass, Toothpick, Tramp's Shoe, Paint 23.50
Milk Glass, Toothpick, Uncle Sam's Hat, Red, White And Blue 25.00
Milk Glass, Toothpick, White, Cat-O'-Nine Tails, Swan Handles 9.75
Milk Glass, Tray, Cameo Bust Of Woman, Oval, 7 1/2 X 11 1/2 In. 45.00
Milk Glass, Tray, Double Hand 35.00
Milk Glass, Tray, Dresser, Actress .... 35.00 To 50.00
Milk Glass, Tray, Dresser, Chrysanthemum, Gilt 25.00
Milk Glass, Tray, Dresser, Gray Cast, Scroll-Type Flowers In Center 35.00
Milk Glass, Tray, Dresser, Scalloped Border 10.50
Milk Glass, Tray, Embossed Scrolls, Beading, Lions' Heads, Oval 7.50
Milk Glass, Tray, Heart Shape, 5 X 4 1/2 In. 15.00
Milk Glass, Tray, Pin, Blue, Flower Design, Diamond Shape, Hand-Painted 7.50
Milk Glass, Tray, Pin, Delaware, Cranberry Flowers 15.00
Milk Glass, Tray, Pin, Heart Shape, Scrollwork 7.50
Milk Glass, Tray, Pin, Shell Border 8.50
Milk Glass, Tray, Pink, 16 In.Long 8.00
Milk Glass, Tumbler, Blossom 20.00
Milk Glass, Tumbler, Louisiana Purchase 8.00
Milk Glass, Tumbler, Paneled Daisy & Tree Of Life, Barrel Shape 20.00
Milk Glass, Tumbler, St.Louis Exposition 12.50
Milk Glass, Tumbler, Waffle, Leaf Rosette On Bottom 22.50
Milk Glass, Tumbler, Water Lily 20.00
Milk Glass, Tumbler, White, Scroll 20.00
Milk Glass, Tumbler, White, Scroll, 4 In.High 22.50
Milk Glass, Tureen, Blue, Hen On Nest, 9 In. 37.50
Milk Glass, Vase, Black, Flared, Pedestal, 8 In.High 15.00
Milk Glass, Vase, Blue, Hand With Ring Holding Vase, 8 In. 25.00
Milk Glass, Vase, Blue, Raised Flowers, Fluted Neck, 8 In. 20.00
Milk Glass, Vase, Hand & Torch, 6 In. 40.00
Milk Glass, Vase, Lamb's Leg Pattern, 4 1/2 In. 30.00
Milk Glass, Vase, Pink & Red Roses, Artist Signed, 9 7/8 In. 12.00
Milk Glass, Vase, Pink, Horn Of Plenty, 4 In. 8.75
Milk Glass, Vase, Pink, 7 In.High 5.00
Milk Glass, Vase, White, Pink Casing, Amber Overlay In Flower Design, Footed 85.00
Milk Glass, Vase, White, Tree Of Life .... 20.00 To 25.00

Millefiori means many flowers. It is a type of glasswork popular in paperweights. Many small flower-like pieces of glass are grouped together to form a design.

Millefiori, see also Paperweight
Millefiori, Cruet, Squatty Shape 26.00
Millefiori, Epergne, Four Lilies, Ruffled Dish Base 175.00
Millefiori, Jar, Pomade, Covered, Blue 20.00
Millefiori, Slipper, High Heel, 5 1/2 In.Long 175.00
Millefiori, Toothpick, Colored Canes 20.00
Millefiori, Toothpick, Flared 15.00
Millefiori, Toothpick, Two Horns 15.00
Millefiori, Vase, Amethyst Ground, Green, Red Floral, Handles, 4 1/4 In. 67.50
Millefiori, Vase, Bud, Slender Neck, Flared Top 38.00
Millefiori, Vase, Green, Brown, & White, Gold Mica Flecks, Two Handles 85.00
Millefiori, Vase, Green, Brown, Purple, Yellow, 7 In. 75.00
Millefiori, Vase, Handles, Blue & Green 65.00
Millefiori, Vase, Inlay Of Cane Flowers Among Seaweed Leaves 75.00
Millefiori, Vase, Muted Green, Red, Yellow 137.00
Miniature, Andirons, Brass, 1 3/4 In. 8.00
Miniature, Anvil, Brass, 3 1/2 In.Long 8.00
Miniature, Bed Warmer, Brass Pan, Turned Mahogany Handle, 9 3/4 In.Long 36.50
Miniature, Bed, Armoire, Night Table, Ivory, Circa 1814, Scale 1/2 In.To Foot 150.00
Miniature, Boiler, Oval, Copper, 2 1/2 In. 6.50
Miniature, Book, Fairy Tales From Grimm, Christmas Stocking Series, 3 In. 8.50
Miniature, Bowl, Blue Swirl, Folded Rim, 3 3/4 In.Diameter 55.00
Miniature, Bowl, Clear, Welded Rim, 3 1/2 In.Diameter 17.50
Miniature, Cake Stand, Cobalt Blue, Swirled, Fluted, 5 In.Tall, 7 In.Diameter 35.00
Miniature, Candlestick, Glass, 3 3/4 In.High, Pair 15.00
Miniature, Candlestick, Pressed Glass, 2 In.High, Pair 75.00

Miniature, Chair, Mahogany, Velvet Seat, Lifts, Compartment, 7 In.High	35.00
Miniature, Chair, Wing, Upholstered, Petit Point, Ball & Claw Feet	650.00
Miniature, Chest, Dovetailed Drawers, Mahogany, 4 Drawer, 5 1/2 In.High	75.00
Miniature, Churn, Butter, Stoneware, Blue Bands, Pine Plunger & Cover, 6 In.	18.00
Miniature, Coffee Grinder, Brass, 1 1/2 In.	5.00
Miniature, Couch & Two Chairs, Ivory, Carved, C.1814	150.00
Miniature, Creamer, Pittsburgh, Applied Handle, Extended Base, 2 1/4 In.	70.00
Miniature, Crock, Signed John Bell	160.00
Miniature, Cruet, Hobnail, Clear, Applied Handle, Stopper, 1 3/4 In.	30.00
Miniature, Desk, Black, Lacquered, Drop Front, Drawers, Japanese, 7 In.	27.00
Miniature, Figurine, Duck, Green, Marked China, 1 1/2 In.	2.00
Miniature, Jug, Applied Handle, Embossed Our Little Pet Jug, Milk Glass	45.00
Miniature, Jug, Signed John Bell, Splotching	210.00
Miniature, Kettle, Wire Bail, Supermaid Cookware, Salesman Sample, 4 1/2 In.	5.00
Miniature, Knife Sharpener, Silver & Ivory, 1 3/4 In.Long	7.50
Miniature, Lamp, Fire-Fly, Complete, 4 1/2 In.High	17.50
Miniature, Lamp, Flowers, Raised, Pink, Clear, Tin Base, 7 1/2 In.High	60.00
Miniature, Mortar & Pestle, Brass, 1 1/4 In.	12.00
Miniature, Mug, Clear, Opalescent, Pressed Glass, 1 2/3 In.	15.00
Miniature, Mug, Raised Figures, Men Drinking, 1 In.High	9.00
Miniature, Pitcher, Marked India, Brass, 2 1/2 In.	3.00
Miniature, Plaque, Ten Commandments, Copper, 1 3/4 In.	2.00
Miniature, Purse, Silver Mesh, France	12.50
Miniature, Rooster, Pottery, Incised Feathers In Tail	95.00
Miniature, Spittoon, Brass, 2 3/4 X 2 In.	20.00
Miniature, Staffordshire, Hen On Nest	32.00
Miniature, Table Set, Clear Glass, Swirl, 2 In.High, 4 Piece	25.00
Miniature, Table, Birds, Floral, Cabriole Legs, French Silver, 1 1/2 In.High	56.00
Miniature, Teakettle, Brass Swing Handle, Riveted, Copper, 1 3/8 In.	7.50
Miniature, Tumbler, Panel Sides, Plain Rim, Clear, Sandwich Glass, 1 3/4 In.	14.00
Miniature, Wash Set, Flower Band, White, Bowl, 6 In.Diameter, Pitcher, 5 In.	37.50

Minton China has been made in England from 1793 to the present time.

Minton, Box, Patch, Round, Forget-Me-Nots, Roses, Pansies, Gilt	19.75
Minton, Can, Coffee, Blue & White Willow Pattern, C.1830	15.00
Minton, Compote, Blue Border, Enameled Roses In Panels, R.D.57705	32.50
Minton, Compote, Indian Tree, Two Handles, C.1874	20.00
Minton, Compote, Wild Flowers, Gold Band	12.00
Minton, Cup & Saucer, Burgundy And Gold, Made For Tiffany & Co.	20.00
Minton, Cup & Saucer, Floral, Pale Blue Reserved Trim, C.1830	20.00
Minton, Cup & Saucer, Pink, Girl, Green Sprigs, C.1820	30.00
Minton, Figurine, Europa & The Bull, Dated 1881, Parian	185.00
Minton, Figurine, Majolica Child Riding Sea Horse	420.00
Minton, Inkstand, Green, Pink Roses & Floral, 3 Pots, Taperstick, C.1830	160.00
Minton, Inkstand, Rectangular, Flower Encrusted, 2 Pots, Scrolls, C.1835	100.00
Minton, Pitcher & Toothbrush Holder, White, Blue, 4 Sided	25.00
Minton, Pitcher, Genevese, Bulbous, 6 In.High	30.00
Minton, Pitcher, Gray, Raised Leaf Design, Blue Floral, Circa 1851, 5 In.	42.50
Minton, Pitcher, Royal Blue, Raised White Cherubs & Floral, No.229, Parian	75.00
Minton, Plate, Botanical, Center Lathyrus Retifolius, Gray & White Border	12.50
Minton, Plate, Buffalo Scene, 9 In.	14.00
Minton, Plate, Cake, Hand-Painted Red Roses, Signed	46.00
Minton, Plate, Delft Pattern, Blue, White, Circa 1879, 10 1/2 In.	17.50
Minton, Plate, Dinner, Gold With Dark Blue, Gold Spray Edge, 10 In.Diameter	10.00
Minton, Plate, Fish, 8 In.Diameter	3.60
Minton, Plate, Fish, 9 In.Diameter	3.60
Minton, Plate, Florentine, Red & White, Marked, 9 In.	6.50
Minton, Plate, Gold Decoration, Gold Rim, Burgundy Border, 9 In.	10.50
Minton, Plate, Green & Pink Diamond Border, Roses, Enameled, R.D.542509	6.00
Minton, Platter, Copper Luster, 12 1/2 In.	20.00
Minton, Platter, Queen Anne, Pink & Blue Floral	12.00
Minton, Relish, Gold & Blue Trim, Strawberry Top, 11 In.Diameter	30.00
Minton, Soap Dish, White, Blue Leaves, Ridged Inside	30.00
Minton, Sugar, Covered, Fleur-De-Lis	6.00
Minton, Teapot, Blue, Acanthus Leaf, Gold Decoration, England, 1810	37.50
Minton, Tile, Blue, White, Farmland Scenes, People, Children, Imperial Mark	18.00

Minton, Tile, Pastoral Scene With Donkey, 6 In.Square 18.00
Minton, Umbrella Stand, White Ground, Blue Decoration, Footed, 21 1/2 In. 155.00
Minton, Vase, Hand-Painted Birds, Kensington Gore, 8 1/2 In. 58.00
Minton, Vase, Red, Green & Ivory Leaves, 6 1/2 In.High 20.00
    Mirror, see Furniture, Mirror

*Mocha Ware is an English-made product that was sold in America during
the early 1800s. It is a heavy pottery with pale coffee and cream coloring.
Designs of blue, brown, green, orange, or black or white were added to the
pottery.*

Mocha, Bowl, Blue & Brown, Footed, 6 1/4 In.Diameter 40.00
Mocha, Bowl, Blue, White, Black, Green, Feathers, Pleated Ribbon, 7 In. 85.00
Mocha, Bowl, Earthworm Pattern, 6 1/4 In.Diameter 85.00
Mocha, Bowl, Seaweed Band, 11 In. .... 30.00 To 46.00
Mocha, Chamber Pot 70.00
Mocha, Jug, Seaweed, 6 In. 128.00
Mocha, Mug, Worm Pattern, Blue, Gray, & Black, 6 In.High 210.00
Mocha, Mustard Pot, Lid 60.00
Mocha, Pitcher, Blue & Brown Bands 60.00
Mocha, Tankard, Seaweed Pattern, Blue Band, Pint Mark, 5 In. 85.00
    Mold, Candle, see Tin, Mold, Candle
    Mold, Ice Cream, see Pewter, Mold
    Mold, see Kitchen, Weapon, Pewter, Tin, etc.
Monmouth Pottery, Vase, Melon Rib, Fluted Top, Green, 6 3/4 In.Tall, Pair 12.00
    Mont Joye, see Mt.Joye
Montieres, Vase, Purple Blue Iridescence, Applique Decoration, 2 Handles 60.00

*Moorcroft Pottery was founded in Burslem, England, in 1914 by William
Moorcroft. The earlier wares are similar to those made today, but color and
marking will help indicate the age.*

Moorcroft, Ashtray, Floral Decorated 12.00
Moorcroft, Ashtray, Fruit Decoration, Flip Top & Rim, Silver Plate 30.00
Moorcroft, Ashtray, Round, Floral, Script W.Moorcroft Impressed 30.00
Moorcroft, Bowl, Blue, Green, Fall Leaves, Grapes, 10 In. 55.00
Moorcroft, Bowl, Cobalt To Light Blue, Raised Green Trees 65.00
Moorcroft, Bowl, Cobalt, Fruit Decoration, W.M.In Green Script 27.00
Moorcroft, Bowl, Covered, Green, Amaryllis Design, Signed, 6 In. 35.00
Moorcroft, Bowl, Covered, Red & Green, Signed, 6 In. 40.00
Moorcroft, Bowl, Dark Blue, Floral Center, 5 3/4 In. 20.00
Moorcroft, Bowl, Footed, Fruit Decoration, Signed WM In Green Script 30.00
Moorcroft, Bowl, Fruit Design, Cobalt Blue, 5 In.Diameter 27.50
Moorcroft, Bowl, Pomegranate Decoration, Footed, Signed WM, 4 In. 30.00
Moorcroft, Bowl, Pomegranates, Footed, 4 In. 25.00
Moorcroft, Box, Blue, Large Flowers, Paper Label, 4 1/2 X 3 1/2 In. 15.00
Moorcroft, Box, Covered, Floral, Signed W.Moorcroft In Blue Script 40.00
Moorcroft, Box, Floral Decoration, Signed, 4 X 5 In. 22.00
Moorcroft, Candlestick, Floral Decoration, Cobalt, 6 In. 30.00
Moorcroft, Candlestick, Olive Green, Orange Flower, Low, Pair 25.00
Moorcroft, Compote, Multicolored, Burslem, 8 In.Wide, 5 3/4 In.High 78.00
Moorcroft, Compote, Pomegranates & Leaves On Dark Blue, Script-Signed 75.00
Moorcroft, Compote, Pomegranates, Grapes, Leaves On Blue Interior & Foot 75.00
Moorcroft, Cup & Saucer, Demitasse, Red Floral On Green Yellow, Marked 10.50
Moorcroft, Cup & Saucer, Green Ground, Floral 20.00
Moorcroft, Dish, Candy, Blue Green Base, Floral Top 42.00
Moorcroft, Dish, Candy, Flower Design, Green, Cover 35.00
Moorcroft, Dish, Candy, Rust Glaze, Floral, Cover 35.00
Moorcroft, Inkwell, Blue Ground, Red Flower, Signed 35.00
Moorcroft, Jar, Covered, Floral, Signed, 3 1/2 In. 30.00
Moorcroft, Jar, Covered, Yellow & Purple Blossoms On Green, Bulbous 35.00
Moorcroft, Jar, Covered, Yellow, Pink, & Green Leaf With Berries On Blue 28.00
Moorcroft, Jar, Ginger, Dark Blue, Red & Blue Flowers, Impressed Mark 25.00
Moorcroft, Lamp Base, Maroon, Allover Floral, Brass & Iron Base, Label 195.00
Moorcroft, Lamp Base, Raised Flowers, Green To Blue Ground, 10 In.High 94.00
Moorcroft, Lamp Base, Raised Flowers, Signed, 10 In.High 94.00
Moorcroft, Lamp, Green Ground, Large Blossoms, Polished Wooden Base 250.00
Moorcroft, Match Holder, Floral Decoration, Round, Pair 6.00

Moorcroft, Pitcher, Blue Script Mark, 8 1/2 In.High	87.50
Moorcroft, Pitcher, Leaf & Grape Decoration, WM In Blue Script, 8 1/2 In.	85.00
Moorcroft, Planter, Green, Blue Decoration At Four Corners, Liberty & Co.	52.00
Moorcroft, Plate, Green Ground, Red & Purple Flowers, 8 3/4 In.	45.00
Moorcroft, Teakettle, Cobalt, Floral, Signed Burslem & WM In Green	85.00
Moorcroft, Vase, Ball, Green Ground, Orchids, Script Signature	50.00
Moorcroft, Vase, Blue Ground, Red Fruit, Script Signature, 6 3/8 In.High	47.50
Moorcroft, Vase, Blue Ground, Red, Blue, Tan Decoration, 6 1/2 In.	40.00
Moorcroft, Vase, Blue Ground, Red, Yellow, Blue Fruit, Signed, 7 In.	77.00
Moorcroft, Vase, Blue, Plum Color Fruit, 3 1/2 In.	18.50
Moorcroft, Vase, Blue, Red, High Glaze, 4 1/2 In.High	25.00
Moorcroft, Vase, Bud, Florian Ware, Signed MacIntyre, 6 In.High	50.00
Moorcroft, Vase, Cobalt Ground, Yellow & Purple Pansies	28.50
Moorcroft, Vase, Cobalt Pomegranates, 4 1/2 In.	15.00
Moorcroft, Vase, Cobalt With Pink, Yellow, & Green Raised Flowers, Signed	45.00
Moorcroft, Vase, Cobalt, Floral, Signed WM, Label, 7 In.	40.00
Moorcroft, Vase, Cobalt, Rose Pink Orchids, 4 In.	25.00
Moorcroft, Vase, Cobalt, Rose, Blue, Yellow Floral, Green Foliage, 7 In.	60.00
Moorcroft, Vase, Cream, Red & Yellow Blossoms, 4 1/4 In.	22.00
Moorcroft, Vase, Creamy Ground, Pink & Yellow Blossoms, 4 1/2 In.	20.00
Moorcroft, Vase, Dark Blue, Fruits, Leaves, 'Potter To H.M.The Queen'	25.00
Moorcroft, Vase, Dark Green Ground, Purple, Red & Blue Floral, Bulbous, 4 In.	12.00
Moorcroft, Vase, Foliage On Green, Signed Made For H.M.The Queen In Blue	25.00
Moorcroft, Vase, Fruit & Grapes, 15 In.High	125.00
Moorcroft, Vase, Fruit, Cobalt, Signed WM, Silver Rim, 7 In.	30.00
Moorcroft, Vase, Grape & Leaf Decoration, Signed, 6 In.High	42.00
Moorcroft, Vase, Green Ground, Floral, 6 1/2 In.	38.00
Moorcroft, Vase, Green, Red, Yellow, Purple Floral, 'Potter To H.M.The Queen'	34.00
Moorcroft, Vase, Multicolored, Script Signature, Burslem, England, 11 1/2 In.	88.00
Moorcroft, Vase, Ovoid, Fruits, Cobalt, Yellow, Green, England, 7 1/2 In.	45.00
Moorcroft, Vase, Pansy Design, Cobalt Blue To Blue Green, Signed, 4 In.High	15.00
Moorcroft, Vase, Pomegranates, Grapes, Leaves, Dark Blue Ground, 8 In.High	40.00
Moorcroft, Vase, Red & Blue, Red Iris, Pink Camellia, 2 3/4 In.	45.00
Moorcroft, Vase, Red & Yellow Flowers, Bulbous, Label, 3 3/4 In.	10.00
Moorcroft, Vase, Red Roses On White, Blue Touches, J.MacIntyre, 8 In.	65.00
Moorcroft, Vase, Silver Luster Ground, Enameled Floral, Vines, Signed	105.00
Moorcroft, Vase, Tree Design, Signed, 8 In.High, 3 1/2 In.Diameter	45.00
Moorcroft, Vase, Yellow, 1913 Burslem Mark, 9 In.	35.00
Moser Type, Wine, Jeweled, Hollow Stem, Green, Gold Enamel, 7 1/2 In.High	60.00

Moser Glass was made by Kolomon Moser in the early 1900s. The Art Nouveau type glassware had detailed exotic enamel designs.

Moser, Bottle, Cordial, Applied Lizard & Turtle, Enamel, Crystal Stopper	65.00
Moser, Bottle, Etched, Stopper, Karlsbad, Signed	85.00
Moser, Bottle, Scent, Blue, Flutes, Expanded, Matching Stopper	95.00
Moser, Bowl, Bell Shape, Paneled Border Inside, Blue, Unsigned	35.00
Moser, Bowl, Crystal, Gold Band At Top, Oval, Signed, 6 3/4 In.Long	55.00
Moser, Bowl, Custard, Blue Lining, Hand-Painted Ferns, Fluted Rim	120.00
Moser, Bowl, Green Chintz, Footed, Signed & Numbered	80.00
Moser, Bowl, Leaf Shape, Enameled Leaf Decoration On Amber, Shallow	50.00
Moser, Bowl, Squat, Domed Foot, Green, Frieze Of Gilt Elephants, Signed	60.00
Moser, Box, Amethyst, Gold Bands, Cameo Cut Amazons, Four Curled Feet, Lid	110.00
Moser, Box, Covered, Amazon Pattern, Footed, 5 In.	90.00
Moser, Cocktail Glass, Emerald Green, Pyramidal Base, Blown Bowl, Set Of 9	195.00
Moser, Compote, Amethyst, Cameo Cut Figures On Horseback, Signed	200.00
Moser, Compote, Amethyst, Pedestal, Gold Cameo Cut Figures, Signed	225.00
Moser, Creamer, Amberina, Enameled Oak Leaves, Applied Acorns, Gold Foliage	950.00
Moser, Cup & Saucer, Amethyst To Crystal With Gold Enameling, Signed	110.00
Moser, Decanter, Enameled Acorns, Leaves, & Branches On Blue, Brass Acorns	135.00
Moser, Decanter, Yellow, Bees, Signed, 9 1/2 In.	90.00
Moser, Ewer, Enamel, Applied Fish, Unsigned	200.00
Moser, Ewer, Smoky Topaz Color, Enamel Floral & Berries, Blue Handle	95.00
Moser, Finger Bowl, Plate, Intaglio Cut, Signed	80.00
Moser, Goblet, Blue Ground, Enameled Acorn, Leaves, Branches, Brass Acorns	75.00
Moser, Goblet, Intaglio Cut Flowers, Leaves Trail Down Stem, Signed	125.00
Moser, Goblet, Intaglio Cut, Flowers To Stem, Signed, Amethyst	75.00

Moser, Goblet, Lavender, Intaglio, Cut Flowers In Bowl Extend To Foot 85.00
Moser, Goblet, Water, Intaglio, Lavender, Floral Cutting Down Stem, Signed 125.00
Moser, Juice, Enameled Birds On Cranberry, Diamond Shape Panels 155.00
Moser, Juice, Gold Overlay On Cranberry, Signed 58.50
Moser, Liqueur Set, Blue, Enameled Acorn Leaves, Applied Acorns, 5 Piece 435.00
Moser, Perfume, Enameled Gold Filigree, Jeweled Flowers On Stopper, Signed 80.00
Moser, Perfume, Jeweled Flowers, Enamel, Gold Filigree, Stopper, Signed 80.00
Moser, Pitcher, Cranberry, Gold & White Enamel, Applied Bees, Shell Feet 295.00
Moser, Plaque, Opalescent Glass, Tangerine, Enamel, Applied Acorns 395.00
Moser, Rose Bowl, Cranberry, Signed 175.00
Moser, Rose Bowl, Enameled Fish Among Coral & Sea Flowers, Crystal Ground 55.00
Moser, Sherbet, Green, Porcelain Portrait 75.00
Moser, Tumbler, Pale Amber, Enameled Grapes, Leaves, & Insects, 3 1/2 In.High 75.00
Moser, Tumbler, Plum Color, Gold Flowers & Foliage, Signed 110.00
Moser, Vase-Bowl, Acid Cut Ground, Cameo Cut Birds, Elephants, Trees 375.00
Moser, Vase, Amethyst To Clear, Enameling & Gold, 11 In.High 55.00
Moser, Vase, Amethyst To Clear, Ovoid, Panels, Gold Decoration Upper Half 40.00
Moser, Vase, Amethyst, Gold Decoration, Acid Mark, 9 In. 60.00
Moser, Vase, Amethyst, Swirl Cut Pattern, Signed Royalit Moser, 7 1/2 In. 127.00
Moser, Vase, Blue To Amethyst, Enameled Floral In Panels, Applied Gold Bees 300.00
Moser, Vase, Blue, Enameling, Applied Hanging Grapes, Bee, Gold Feet, 4 In. 295.00
Moser, Vase, Bud, Amber Ground, Enameling, Signed, 6 In. 70.00
Moser, Vase, Bud, Carved Glass, Clear Flowers & Leaves, Unsigned 10.00
Moser, Vase, Bud, Cranberry, Applied Acorns & Oak Leaves, Butterfly, Pair 290.00
Moser, Vase, Clear To Amethyst Top, Gold Leaves, Acorns, Butterfly, 1885 .... 60.00
Moser, Vase, Clear To Amethyst, Carved Flowers & Leaves, Quadrangular 75.00
Moser, Vase, Crackle Glass, Blue, Pink, & White, Bulbous, 4 Handles, 6 In.High 125.00
Moser, Vase, Cranberry Glass, Enameled Floral, Applied Glass Ruffling 75.00
Moser, Vase, Cut & Enameled, Figure Of Pied Piper On Front, Signed 150.00
Moser, Vase, Enamel Flowers, Triangular, Metal Holder, Embossed Acorns, 6 In. 125.00
Moser, Vase, Flower Form, Gold Hearts, Enameled Floral, 10 In. 127.50
Moser, Vase, Flowers & Leaves On Green, Beading, Scrolls, 8 In.High 175.00
Moser, Vase, Frosty Satin Ground, Floral, Silver & Gold Overlay, 10 In. 135.00
Moser, Vase, Gold & Black Hunt Scene, Gold Decorated Panels, 5 1/2 In. 50.00
Moser, Vase, Green Inner Layer, Red Particles, Carved Peasant Boy & Girl 395.00
Moser, Vase, Paperweight, Intaglio Cut, Signed, 11 In. 150.00
Moser, Vase, Purple Panels, Band Of Figures, Signed, 6 In.High 65.00
Moser, Vase, Smoky, Wide Gold Warrior Band, Gold Scroll, 14 In. 125.00
Moser, Vase, Teal, Enamel, Bees, Signed, 11 1/2 In. 95.00
Moser, Wine Set, Cobalt, Blue, Panels, Scrolls, Stemmed Glasses, 7 Piece 350.00
Moser, Wine Set, Engraved Grapes, Gold Band, Ruby Color, Signed, 7 Piece 350.00
Moser, Wine, Applied Grapes, Tall Stem 95.00
Moser, Wine, Cranberry, Signed, Set Of 6 .... 210.00
Moser, Wine, Cut Birds & Foliage, Signed, Clear Stem 79.00
Moser, Wine, Green To Clear, Gold Borders, Cut Iris On Bowl 39.50

*Moss Rose China was made by many firms from 1808 to 1900. It refers to
any china decorated with the Moss Rose flower.*

Moss Rose, Biscuit Barrel, Pairpoint 125.00
Moss Rose, Creamer, Pink Edge 18.00
Moss Rose, Cup & Saucer, Demitasse, Stem & Thorn Handle, Relief Pattern 14.00
Moss Rose, Cup, Mustache, Limoges 12.50
Moss Rose, Dresser Set, Porcelain, 3 Piece 15.00
Moss Rose, Eggcup, Set Of 6 .... 12.50
Moss Rose, Plate, Cake, Cutout Handles 15.00
Moss Rose, Plate, Ironstone, 8 In. 8.50
Moss Rose, Platter, Ironstone, W.H.Grindley & Co., 12 In.Long 15.00
Moss Rose, Sauce 3.00
Moss Rose, Sugar, Covered, Finial, Haviland 35.00
Moss Rose, Sugar, Covered, Pink Edge 22.00
Moss Rose, Teapot, Ground Spout, Porcelain 12.50
Moss Rose, Teapot, Haviland 60.00
Moss Rose, Teapot, Pink Edge 28.00
Moss Rose, Tray, Oval, Irregular Shape, Impressed Mark 45.00

Mother-of-pearl, or Pearl Satin, Glass was first made in the 1850s in

England and in Massachusetts. It was a special type of mold-blown satin glass with air bubbles in the glass, giving it a pearlized color.

Mother-of-Pearl, see also Pearl

Mother-Of-Pearl, **Bowl**, Amberina, Herringbone Pattern, Satin Glass	300.00
Mother-Of-Pearl, **Bowl**, Blue, Diamond Quilted, Ruffled Top, 4 1/2 In.	60.00
Mother-Of-Pearl, **Bride's Bowl**, Blue Satin, Ribbed Herringbone	325.00
Mother Of Pearl, **Bride's Bowl**, Pink Satin, Ribbed Herringbone	375.00
Mother-Of-Pearl, **Cup & Saucer**, Demitasse, Red Millefluri	75.00
Mother-Of-Pearl, **Pitcher**, Pink To Plum, Diamond-Quilted, 5 1/2 In.High	135.00
Mother-Of-Pearl, **Pitcher**, Satin Glass, Pink, Diamond Quilted	275.00
Mother-Of-Pearl, **Pitcher**, Satin Glass, Raindrops Pattern	325.00
Mother-Of-Pearl, **Salt**, Rainbow	195.00

Mother-Of-Pearl, Satin Glass, see Satin Glass, Tiffany, etc.

Mother-Of-Pearl, **Shoe**, Lady's, Luster, Applied Gold Flowers, 3 1/2 In.	6.00
Mother-Of-Pearl, **Vase**, Aqua & Gold Coralene	395.00
Mother-Of-Pearl, **Vase**, Blue, Diamond-Quilted, 8 In.High	175.00
Mother-Of-Pearl, **Vase**, Blue, Diamond-Quilted, 12 In.	100.00
Mother-Of-Pearl, **Vase**, Diamond-Quilted, Pink, 6 1/4 In.High	115.00
Mother-Of-Pearl, **Vase**, Federzeichnung, 7 In. .... *Illus*	1200.00
Mother-Of-Pearl, **Vase**, Pink, 14 In.High	400.00
Mother-Of-Pearl, **Vase**, Rose Color, Coralene Beads, Camphor Handles	350.00
Mother-Of-Pearl, **Vase**, Satin Glass, Raindrop Pattern, 6 In.	35.00

Mother-Of-Pearl, Vase, Federzeichnung, 7 In.

Mother-Of-Pearl, **Vase**, Yellow, White Casing, Ruffled Top	100.00

Moustache Cup, see Mustache Cup

Mont Joye is an enameled cameo glass made in the late nineteenth and twentieth centuries by Saint-Hilaire Touvior de Varraux and Co.of Pantin, France. This same company produced De Vez glass.

Mt.Joye, Rose Bowl, Frosted, Violets, Gold Wash Rim, Unsigned, 2 1/2 In., Pair	65.00
Mt.Joye, Vase, Bulbous, Flared Top, Gold Edge, Purple Violets	140.00
Mt.Joye, Vase, Cameo, Red Flowers, 10 In.	65.00
Mt.Joye, Vase, Flask Shape, Floral Design, Signed	95.00
Mt.Joye, Vase, Frosted, Enamel Pansies, Gold Wash Rim, Ruffled, Signed	95.00
Mt.Joye, Vase, Green & White Floral, Pair	145.00
Mt.Joye, Vase, Iris, Yellow & White Flowers, 14 In.High	110.00
Mt.Joye, Vase, Leaves, Ferns, Frosted, Green, Gold, 7 1/2 In.High	105.00
Mt.Joye, Vase, Oak Leaf & Acorn Design, Green, Gold, Silver, Signed, 12 In.	155.00
Mt.Joye, Vase, Red Flowers, 10 In.	69.00
Mt.Joye, Vase, Stippled, Beige, Green, Carnations, Gold Trim, 11 1/2 In.High	185.00
Mt.Joye, Vase, Wine Color, Twisted, Gold & Enamel, 4 In.	145.00

Mt.Washington Glass was made at the Mt.Washington Glass Co. located in New Bedford, Massachusetts. Many types of Art Glass were made there from 1850 to the 1890s.

Mt.Washington Glass, see also Burmese

Mt.Washington, Bowl, Finger, Inverted Thumbprint, Cranberry, Square Top	45.00
Mt.Washington, Bride's Basket, Acid Etched Woman's Head In Medallions	400.00
Mt.Washington, Bride's Basket, Cameo, Pink	410.00
Mt.Washington, Cologne, White, Lusterless, Floral, Stopper	19.00

Mt.Washington, **Compote**, Red Rim, Frosted 40.00
Mt.Washington, **Egg**, Lay Down, Columbian Exposition, 1893, Acid Finish 45.00
Mt.Washington, **Flower Frog**, Mushroom Shape, Shasta Daisies 145.00
Mt.Washington, **Hair Receiver**, White Satin Decoration 12.50
Mt.Washington, **Holder**, Toothbrush, White, Floral 35.00
Mt.Washington, **Holder**, Toothbrush, White, Tiny Flowers 40.00
Mt.Washington, **Jar**, Biscuit, Brown, Yellow, Gold Scroll, Blue Cornflowers 180.00
Mt.Washington, **Jar**, Biscuit, Pairpoint, Hexagon, Pink Morning Glories, White 250.00
Mt.Washington, **Jar**, Biscuit, Pink To Ivory, Enamel Cosmos, Silver Lid, Bail 265.00
Mt.Washington, **Jar**, Biscuit, Rose Ground, White Poppies, Egg Shape, Pairpoint 185.00
Mt.Washington, **Jar**, Cookie, Apple Blossoms, Mt.Washington Lid 195.00
Mt.Washington, **Jar**, Cookie, Gold Scrolls, Multicolor Pansies, Signed 250.00
Mt.Washington, **Jar**, Cracker, Tomato Shape, Peach Ground, Enamel Floral 325.00
Mt.Washington, **Jar**, Pin, Covered, Tomato, Burmese Coloring, Enameled Floral 150.00
Mt.Washington, **Jar**, Powder, Painted Flowers, Hinged, 5 In. 79.00
Mt.Washington, **Jardiniere**, Floral, Beaded Top, 7 3/4 In.High 420.00
Mt.Washington, **Muffineer**, Egg Shape, Burmese Coloring, Enameled Daffodils 165.00
Mt.Washington, **Muffineer**, Egg Shape, Lemon To Peach, Pink & Green Leaves 135.00
Mt.Washington, **Muffineer**, Figure Shape, Blue, Flower Design 210.00
Mt.Washington, **Muffineer**, Flower Design, Melon Rib, Unsigned, 4 1/2 In. 95.00
Mt.Washington, **Muffineer**, Green To White, Pink & White Floral 119.00
Mt.Washington, **Muffineer**, Melon Ribbed Satin, White To Blue Top, Floral 195.00
Mt.Washington, **Muffineer**, Peach To White, Blue Floral & Butterfly 140.00
Mt.Washington, **Muffineer**, Satin Glass, Leaves, Blackberries, Tin Top 125.00
Mt.Washington, **Muffineer**, Squatty, Melon Ribbed, Enameled, Silver Plated Top 155.00
Mt.Washington, **Muffineer**, Squatty, Melon Ribbed, Metal Top 65.00
Mt.Washington, **Muffineer**, Tomato Shape, White Daisies, Silver Plated Top 165.00
Mt.Washington, **Muffineer**, Tomato Shape, Melon Ribbed 125.00
Mt.Washington, **Muffineer**, Violets 85.00
Mt.Washington, **Muffineer**, White, Pink & Blue Enameled Ferns, Lusterless 85.00
Mt.Washington, **Plate**, Lusterless Satin, Pink Blossoms, Foliage, 10 1/2 In. 25.00
Mt.Washington, **Plate**, River & Bridge Scene, 9 In. 28.00
Mt.Washington, **Plate**, Roses, Leaves, 11 In. 25.00
Mt.Washington, **Plate**, Satin Glass, Blue Bachelor Buttons, 10 In. 20.00
Mt.Washington, **Pot**, Mustard, Blue To White, Pink & Wine Floral, Pleated Ribs 65.00
Mt.Washington, **Pot**, Mustard, Reverse Shading, Yellow To Pink, Floral, Leaves 50.00
Mt.Washington, **Rose Bowl**, Clear Ground, Pulled Up Opalescent White Loops 60.00
Mt.Washington, **Salt & Pepper**, Apple Shape 45.00
Mt.Washington, **Salt & Pepper**, Egg Shape, Pewter Tops 60.00
Mt.Washington, **Salt & Pepper**, Enameled Flowers, Satin Glass 35.00
Mt.Washington, **Salt & Pepper**, Fig Shape, Cranberry .... 125.00 To 150.00
Mt.Washington, **Salt & Pepper**, Fig Shape, Enameling 145.00
Mt.Washington, **Salt & Pepper**, Floral, Pewter Tops 38.00
Mt.Washington, **Salt & Pepper**, Melon Ribbed, Red Florals 48.00
Mt.Washington, **Salt & Pepper**, Standing Egg Shape, Satin Finish, Enameling 60.00
Mt.Washington, **Salt & Pepper**, White, Pansies 55.00
Mt.Washington, **Salt Dip**, Melon Rib, Floral 32.00
Mt.Washington, **Salt**, Acorns, Pine Needles, Pewter Top, 3 In.High 65.00
Mt.Washington, **Salt**, Egg Shape, Satin, Blue To White, Enameled Strawberries 35.00
Mt.Washington, **Salt**, Ribbed, Burmese 55.00
Mt.Washington, **Salt**, Textured Clear Glass, Enameled Floral 85.00
Mt.Washington, **Saltshaker**, Burmese, Ribbed 68.00
Mt.Washington, **Saltshaker**, Egg Shape, Blue, Pewter Top 35.00
Mt.Washington, **Saltshaker**, Egg Shape, Violets, 'A Bright Easter' In Yellow 28.00
Mt.Washington, **Saltshaker**, Melon Ribbed, White To Blue, Pink Flowers 30.00
Mt.Washington, **Saltshaker**, Pink, Tied In Middle Effect With Knotted Rope 25.00
Mt.Washington, **Saltshaker**, Ribbed, Dusty Rose To Lemon 65.00
Mt.Washington, **Sugar & Creamer**, White Satin Glass 150.00
Mt.Washington, **Sugar & Creamer**, White To Pale Yellow, Pink Flowers 125.00
Mt.Washington, **Sweetmeat**, Holly Decoration On Green, Silver Plated Cover 325.00
Mt.Washington, **Toothpick**, Acid Finish, Flower Enameling 55.00
Mt.Washington, **Toothpick**, Dusty Rose 245.00
Mt.Washington, **Toothpick**, Flower Clusters, Pink, White, Enamel 165.00
Mt.Washington, **Toothpick**, Ribbed, Decorated, Albertine Coloring, Square 150.00
Mt.Washington, **Toothpick**, Ribbed, Satin 110.00
Mt.Washington, **Toothpick**, Venetian, Folded In Tricorn Rim, 2 In. 325.00

Mt.Washington, Toothpick, White Ground, Blue Shading, Raised Floral	150.00
Mt.Washington, Toothpick, White Satin, Relief Lion Heads In Corners	12.50
Mt.Washington, Tumbler, Milan Stripe	45.00
Mt.Washington, Vase, Burmese, Encrusted Enamel Decoration	950.00
Mt.Washington, Vase, Cameo, Pink, Brass Rim At Top, 7 In.Diameter	850.00
Mt.Washington, Vase, Decorated Clear Glass, 9 1/2 In.High	125.00
Mt.Washington, Vase, Embossed Ribbing, Ruffled Top	45.00
Mt.Washington, Vase, Purple & Wine Violets, Gold Outline, Verona	75.00
Mt.Washington, Vase, Satin Glass, Coral To White, Fluted Top, Pontil	108.00
Mt.Washington, Vase, Swirl Rib, Ruffled, Flared, Lusterless, White	30.00
Mt.Washington, Vase, Verona, Mums Outlined In Coin Gold, Panel Ribbed	125.00
Mt.Washington, Vase, Verona, Panel Ribs, White & Wine Mums, Gold Outline	95.00
Mt.Washington, Vase, Verona, Paneled Crystal, Enamel Iris & Foliage	95.00
Mt.Washington, Vase, Verona, Rose & White Mums, Outlined In Coin Gold, Clear	120.00
Mt.Washington, Vase, Verona, Violets, Coin Gold Outline, Flared, Ruffled	55.00
Mt.Washington, Vase, White, Satin Glass, Lusterless, Hourglass Shape, 11 In.	60.00
Muffineer, Floral, Clear Color, Six Panels, Silver Plated Top	18.00
Muffineer, Night Desert Scene, Silver Plated Top	18.00
Muffineer, Panel Cut, E.P.N.S.Top	25.00
Muffineer, Paneled, Cut Sides, Silver Plated Top	12.00
Muffineer, Pierced Sterling Silver Top, Engraved Around Holes	42.00
Muffineer, Puffed Pineapple Pattern, Pink Cased	55.00
Muffineer, Raised Cobalt Blue Panels	28.00
Muffineer, Sheraton Ivory, W.H.Grindley & Co., Lid., Ornate Gold & Floral	6.00
Muffineer, Sterling Silver, Acron Pattern, 6 In.	40.00
Muffineer, Vase Shape, Embossed Rose Garland, Silver On Brass, Crown Mark	25.00

Muller Freres, French for Muller Brothers, made cameo and other art glass from the early 1900s to the late 1930s. Their factory was first located in Luneville and later moved to Croismaire, France.

Muller Freres, Bowl, Cameo, Purple, Gold, Tangerine, Turquoise Moths, Signed	850.00
Muller Freres, Chandelier, Chains Down To Bunches Of Iron Fruit, Luneville	375.00
Muller Freres, Chandelier, Red & Gold Fruit, Chains, Fittings, Luneville	275.00
Muller Freres, Chandelier, Royal Blue & Orange Mottlings, Signed	125.00
Muller Freres, Chandelier, Rust, Orange, & White Mottlings, Signed	125.00
Muller Freres, Rose Bowl, Orange & Purple, Signed	145.00
Muller Freres, Vase, Art Glass, Luneville, Signed, 4 1/2 In.High	125.00
Muller, Freres, Vase, Cameo, Peonies, Leaves, Luneville	525.00
Muller Freres, Vase, Frosted Ground, 5 Colors, 2 Layers, Cut Poppies	295.00
Muller Freres, Vase, Magenta & Pink Peonies On Lemon, Luneville	425.00
Muller Freres, Vase, Multicolor, 8 In.High	250.00
Muller Freres, Vase, Tree Landscape & Scenic On Coral, Luneville, Signed	168.00
Music, Accordion Roll, Tanzabar Player, 5	125.00
Music, Banjo, Schoenhut, 21 In.Long	15.00
Music, Box, Barrel Organ, 4 Tune, 13 3/4 X 8 3/4 X 10 3/4 In.	300.00
Music, Box, Brass, Crank, Porcelain Knob, Picture Of Children, 2 Tune	22.00
Music, Box, Cylinder, Four Tunes	195.00
Music, Box, Cylinder, Tune Sheet, Swiss, 8 Tune, Refinished	325.00
Music, Box, Keywind, B.B.& Cie, 17 1/2 X 6 1/4 X 5 In.	425.00
Music, Box, Mahogany, Mira, Twenty Four 12 In.Discs	425.00
Music, Box, Nicole Freres, Key Wind, 4 Tune, 15 X 6 X 5 In.	600.00
Music, Box, Nicole Freres, No.43673, Inlaid Case, 128 Tooth Comb	1700.00
Music, Box, Nicole Freres, Pianoforte, Brass Bedplate, Inlaid Lid	1495.00
Music, Box, Organ, Gately Mfg.Co.Of 72 Pearl St., Boston, Civil War Era	450.00
Music, Box, Paillard, Six Brass Bells, 13 In.Cylinder	650.00
Music, Box, Piano Form, Silver Gilt, Blue Enamel, Garnets, Pearls	800.00
Music, Box, Piano, Painting Of Chopin On Lid, Lid Opens	90.00
Music, Box, Regina, Mahogany Case, 13 1/4 X 12 1/4 X 7 3/8 In.	425.00
Music, Box, Regina, Oak Case, 23 X 20 X 12 In.	950.00
Music, Box, Regina, Serpentine Mahogany Case, 12 Discs	1500.00
Music, Box, Regina, Table Model, Mahogany, Inlays, 15 1/2 In., 4 Discs	725.00
Music, Box, Regina, 8 Discs	350.00 To 375.00
Music, Box, Silver, Gold Wash, Jewels, Enamel, Open Lid, Bird's Wings Flutter	600.00
Music, Box, Swiss, 8 In.Cylinder	425.00
Music, Box, Symphonion, Double Comb, 10 In.Disc, 12 Discs	375.00

Music, Box, Symphonion, Floor Model, Double Comb, Coin, 20 In.Disc, 18 Discs 1000.00
Music, Box, Symphonion, 11 7/8 In.Discs 500.00
Music, Box, Thorens, Swiss, Lorely, Blue Danube, & Lohengrin Betrothal March 100.00
Music, Box, 12 Tune Cylinder 425.00
Music, Bugle, Boy Scout, Brass, Rexcrott 27.50
Music, Bugle, Brass, Spanish Cavalry, Cord Wraps & Tassel 19.50
Music, Bugle, U.S.Army Regulation, Brass 17.50
Music, Calliope, Tangley, Automatic & Manual, Gasoline Motor, 43 Note 5800.00
Music, Calliope, Tangley, Automatic, Gasoline Motor .... 5200.00 To 5800.00
Music, Calliope, Tangley, Manual, Electric & Gasoline Motor, 43 Note, Rebuilt 4000.00
Music, Calliope, Tangley, Manual, Gasoline Motor, 43 Note 4000.00
Music, Celestina, 3 Rolls 375.00
Music, Clariona, Reed Pipe, Unrestored 165.00
Music, Coinola, Orchestrion, Plays Superior O Rolls, Restored 4000.00
Music, Cremona, Art Glass, Coin Slot, Seeburg, Rebuilt 2450.00
Music, Disc, Regina Music Box, Metal, 27 1/2 In., 4 .... 100.00
Music, Disc, Symphonion, 12 In., 30 .... 250.00
Music, Disc, Symphonion, 25 1/2 In., 7 .... 50.00
Music, Drum, American, Maple Center, 14 In.Diameter, C.1850 .... 32.50
Music, Drum, British Regimental, Hand-Painted Polychrome, 8th Hussars, 1870 .... 69.50
Music, Drum, Indian, Hide, Dance, Round, Wooden, Blue & Brown Paint, Plains 125.00
Music, Drum, Jungle, Handmade From Hollow Tree, Hand-Painted Scenes 15.00
Music, Drum, Leather Covered, Dragon's Head & Peacock's Head, Signed 15.00
Music, Flute, Civil War Period, Rosewood, German Silver Keys, 3 Piece 29.50
Music, Gramophone, Brass Horn, Decals, G. & T.Ltd.Berliner 395.00
Music, Graphophone, Key Wind, Two Minute, Model B, Carrying Case .... 175.00 To 225.00
Music, Harmonica, Hohner, With Horn 12.50
Music, Harp, Zither, Lap, 43 Strings, 19 In.Long, 14 In.Wide 18.00
Music, Hexaphone, Regina, Refinished Case, Rebuilt 1275.00
Music, Horn, Cylinder Phonograph, Concert, Brass, 45 In.Long 80.00
Music, Horn, Quimby, Boston, Civil War Military Type, Brass, Rotary Valve 79.50
Music, Horn, Victrola, Green, Red Roses, Scalloped, 22 X 30 1/2 In.Tall 35.00
Music, Jew's Harp 3.50
Music, Juke Box, Rock-Ola, Wood Paneled, Light Front, C.1940, 78 Rpm 300.00
Music, Lute, Miniature, Inlaid Wood, Mother-Of-Pearl 24.00
Music, Mandolin, Gennaro Arienzo, Mother-Of-Pearl Inlay, 1893, Case 200.00
Music, Melodeon, Bishop, 1860 .... 1150.00
Music, Metalophone, Schoenhut, Marked, 12 Key 15.00
Music, Mutoscope, Table Model, Coin Slot, C.1920 .... 300.00
Music, Needles, Gramaphone, 'songster, ' In Tin 5.50
Music, Needles, Gramaphone, Victor Dog, 'His Master's Voice, ' In Tin 7.50
Music, Nickelodeon, Mills, Double Violin Violano Virtuoso, 8 Rolls 3750.00
Music, Nickelodeon, Seeburg, Art Glass In Cabinet, Restored 1990.00
Music, Nickelodeon, Seeburg, Plays G Rolls, Rebuilt 3200.00
Music, Nickelodeon, Seeburg L, Plays G Roll, Rebuilt 3200.00
Music, Nickelodeon, Seeburg L, With Instruments, Plays G Roll, Rebuilt 3200.00
Music, Orchestrion, Baldwin, Player, O Roll 3000.00
Music, Orchestrion, Decap, 88 Note, 101 In.High, Restored 5000.00
Music, Orchestrophone, Limonaire Frere, Drums, Cymbal, Triangle, 60 Note 4000.00
Music, Organ, Band, Artison 105 .... 2800.00
Music, Organ, Band, Wurlitzer, Double Track, Drums, Cymbal, Restored 6850.00
Music, Organ, Band, Wurlitzer, No.125, 13 Brass Pipes 3000.00
Music, Organ, Celestina, Paper Roll, 6 Rolls 245.00
Music, Organ, Concert, Roller, 6 Cobs 150.00
Music, Organ, Gem Roll, 5 Rolls 200.00
Music, Organ, Mouth, Jazz King, Germany 4.50
Music, Organ, Pipe, 8 Rank, Chimes, 2 Manual 1000.00
Music, Organ, Pump, Lehr, Piano Cased, Beveled Glass Mirrors, 85 Key, Stool 300.00
Music, Organ, Pump, Mahogany, Refinished, Weak Bellows, C.1875, 82 In.High 875.00
Music, Organ, Pump, Shoninger, Full Range Of Bells 350.00
Music, Organ, Pump, Walnut, Stool 500.00
Music, Organ, Roller, Gem, Four Cobs 225.00
Music, Organ, Street, Player, Luis Casali, Barcelona, Spain 800.00
Music, Organ, Wurlitzer, Folding 500.00
Music, Organette, Mechanical, Several Rolls 150.00

The Phonograph, invented by Thomas Edison in the 1880s, has been made by many firms.

Music, Phonograph, Amets, Chicago Talking Machine, 1893, Crank 495.00
Music, Phonograph, Austrian Concert, 'Veritas Grammophonograph,' Horn 495.00
Music, Phonograph, Berliner Trademark 495.00
Music, Phonograph, Busy Bee, Disc, 1 Disc 250.00
Music, Phonograph, Busy Bee, Key Wind, Horn, 2 Cylinder Records 300.00
Music, Phonograph, Chicago Talking Machine Co., Chicago 395.00
Music, Phonograph, Columbia Home Grand Graphophone, Six Spring Motor 575.00
Music, Phonograph, Columbia, Key Wind, Horn, 2 Cylinder Records, Case 150.00
Music, Phonograph, Columbia, Nickel Works, 4 Spring Motor, Mahogany Case 215.00
Music, Phonograph, Columbia, Ornate Case, Decals, Wooden Tone Arm 245.00
Music, Phonograph, Double Spring, Underslung Reproducer Carriage, Horn 245.00
Music, Phonograph, 'Edison Suitcase Home,' Date 1893, Crank, Brass Mandrel 335.00
Music, Phonograph, Edison, Amberola, Built In Horn, Pat.1903, 40 Cylinders 195.00
Music, Phonograph, Edison, Amberola B80, Mahogany, Belt Driven Diamond Disc 200.00
Music, Phonograph, Edison, Amberola 30, Table Model, Inside Horn .... 165.00 To 175.00
Music, Phonograph, Edison, Amberola 50, Mahogany Cabinet, Inside Horn 200.00
Music, Phonograph, Edison, Cylinder, No Horn, 8 Records 125.00
Music, Phonograph, Edison, Diamond Disc, Console, Mahogany Cabinet 140.00
Music, Phonograph, Edison, Diamond Needle, Four Minute, Blue Flower Horn 225.00
Music, Phonograph, Edison, Fireside, Cygnet Horn, Horn Crane 250.00
Music, Phonograph, Edison, Gem, C Reproducer, 10 In.Horn 230.00
Music, Phonograph, Edison, Model E, Cygnet Morning Glory Horn, 120 Records 450.00
Music, Phonograph, Edison, Oak Case, Black Horn, Copper Trim, 10 Cylinders 135.00
Music, Phonograph, Edison, Oak Cygnet Horn, Model C ....;............... 235.00
Music, Phonograph, Edison, Standard Model C, Reproducer, Brass Bell Horn 175.00
Music, Phonograph, Edison, Standard Model E, Morning Glory Horn, 12 Rolls 350.00
Music, Phonograph, Edison, Suitcase Model 175.00
Music, Phonograph, Edison, Triumph, Model C, Reproducer, 14 In.Brass Horn 325.00
Music, Phonograph, Excelsior, Cylinder, Red Striping On Mechanical Parts 195.00
Music, Phonograph, Nickel Works, Spun Aluminum Horn, Brass Rooster Inlay 325.00
Music, Phonograph, Pathe Triplex, Rooster Trademark, Horn, C.1903 .... 675.00
Music, Phonograph, Phoenix, Nickel Works, Spun Aluminum Horn, 2 In.Mandrel 350.00
Music, Phonograph, Queen Bee, Table Model, Cylinder, Enclosed Lower Works 275.00
Music, Phonograph, Regina, Cylinder, Hexaphone 1250.00
Music, Phonograph, Standard, Keyshift Replay, 15 In.Horn .... 135.00 To 145.00
Music, Phonograph, Standard, 32 In.Horn 185.00
Music, Phonograph, Thornward, Cylinder, Gutta-Percha Reproducer, Dated 1894 .... 275.00
Music, Phonograph, Twenty Century Grand, Cylinder, 5 In.Reproducer 825.00
Music, Phonograph, Victor, Model D, Black, Brass Cygnet Horn 135.00
Music, Phonograph, Victor, Spring Driven, Oak Case, 15 In.High 75.00
Music, Phonograph, Zon-O-Phone, Concert, Ornate Case, Decal, Brass Horn 295.00
Music, Phonograph, Zon-O-Phone, Front Mount, Horn, Decal On Case 290.00
Music, Phonograph, Zon-O-Phone, Grand Opera, Pillars, Glass Windows, Horn 415.00
Music, Phonograph, Zon-O-Phone, Iron, Brass Horn, Oak Base 150.00
Music, Piano Roll, Artempo, Lot Of 90 .... 22.50
Music, Piano, Baby Grand, Steinway & Sons, N.Y., Ebonized Wood, 7 Ft. 2600.00
Music, Piano, Burled Walnut, Carved, Brass Candelabra Attached, 54 In.High 795.00
Music, Piano, Dulcimer, C.1700 .... 550.00
Music, Piano, Grand, Chickering, Square, Rosewood, 125 Years Old 3400.00
Music, Piano, Grand, Knabe Gaehle Concert, Dated 1839-1854 .... 3500.00
Music, Piano, Grand, Steinway Concert, Autographed Joseph Lhevinne, 1907 .... 4000.00
Music, Pinao, Grand, Weber, Carved Legs, Pedal Support, Music Rack, 1881 .... 550.00
Music, Piano, Grand, Weber, Rose Mahogany 1500.00
Music, Piano, Guilbaud Freres Of Paris, Barrel, Coin Operated, 36 Note 500.00
Music, Piano, Henry Miller, Upright, Pedal Clavier 1000.00
Music, Piano, Morgan Davis, N.Y., Stenciled, Painted, 1825 .... *Illus* 2000.00
Music, Piano, Player, A.B.Chase, Grand, Black Lacquer, Oriental Motif 6000.00
Music, Piano, Player, Coin Operated, Coin Slot, Art Glass 2100.00
Music, Piano, Player, Coinola, Coin Slot, Art Glass, Rebuilt 2450.00
Music, Piano, Player, Cremona, Art Glass, Coin Slot, Rebuilt, Refinished 2450.00
Music, Pinao, Player, Deagn Una-Fon, Keyboard, 33 Note 2000.00
Music, Piano, Player, Dreiter, Coin Operated, A Roll, French Repeating Action 2150.00
Music, Piano, Player, Seeburg, Art Glass, Coin Slot, Rebuilt 2300.00
Music, Piano, Player, Seeburg, Coin Operated, Mandolin Bar 2100.00

Music, **Piano**, Player, Seeburg, Coin Slot, Art Glass, Rebuilt 2450.00
Music, **Piano**, Player, Seeburg, Kt With Eagle Art Glass, Coin Slot 3500.00
Music, **Piano**, Player, Seeburg, 25 Cents Coin Slot, Eagle Glass 3500.00
Music, **Piano**, Schoenhut, Grand, Matching Bench 35.00
Music, **Piano**, Steinway, Baby Grand, Ebony Case, No.5289035, 60 In.Long 1500.00
Music, **Piano**, Steinway, Upright, Ebony Case, Seat 1200.00
Music, **Piano**, Waters, Grand, Green Painted Case, Floral Vases, Gold, Red 750.00
Music, **Piano**, Welte Mignon, Grand, Black Painted Case, Floral 1600.00
Music, **Polyphone**, Shield Design On Lid, 12 X 11 X 7 In.12 Discs 375.00
Music, **Record**, Cylinder, Edison, Blue Amberole 1.00
Music, **Record**, Cylinder, Edison, Blue Amberole, 43 .... 25.00
Music, **Record**, Cylinder, 2 Minute 2.50
Music, **Record**, Cylinder, 4 Minute 2.00
Music, **Record**, Disc, Edison 2.00
Music, **Record**, Disc, Edison, Diamond Disc, C.1920
Music, **Rolls**, Piano, Box, 5 .... 8.00
Music, **Sheet**, Battle Call Of Freedom, Chicago, Dated 1862 .... 5.00
Music, **Sheet**, Charcoal, A Study In Black, Gibson Cooke, Coon Songs 5.00
Music, **Sheet**, Colonel Baker's Funeral March, Philadelphia, Dated 1861 .... 5.00
Music, **Sheet**, Columbia The Gem Of The Ocean, Philadelphia, Dated 1861 .... 7.50
Music, **Sheet**, Ho For The Kansas Plains, Boston, 1856 .... 22.50
Music, **Sheet**, Ku Klux Klan, 1913 .... 10.00
Music, **Sheet**, Major General Hallock's Grand March, Philadelphia, 1862 .... 7.50
Music, **Sheet**, Marches & Quick Steps, Hempstead, Dated 1864 .... 6.00
Music, **Sheet**, Marching Through Georgia, Civil War, 1865 .... 7.50
Music, **Sheet**, Mollie's Dream Waltz, Duncan Of Columbia 7.50
Music, **Sheet**, Negro, De Bullys Wedding Night, 1896 .... 6.00
Music, **Sheet**, Nora O'Neal, 1866 .... 5.00
Music, **Sheet**, Old Black Joe, 1892 .... 4.00
Music, **Sheet**, Ole Black Joe, Picture, 1905 .... 5.00
Music, **Sheet**, Pennies From Heaven, Bing Crosby On Cover, 1936 .... 18.00
Music, **Sheet**, Pickaninnies Pastime Schottische, Jean Howard, 1903 .... 3.00
Music, **Sheet**, The Knot Of Blue & Grey, Civil War 4.00
Music, **Sheet**, The Maiden's Prayer, Shirner, Macon & Savannah 7.50

Music, Piano, Morgan Davis, N.Y., Stenciled, Painted, 1825
See Page 358

Music, **Sheet**, The Parting Song, Soldier's Farewell, Brooklyn, 1865 .... 5.00
Music, **Sheet**, The Plantation, 3 Dancing Negroes On Cover 6.00
Music, **Sheet**, The Scarecrow From The Wizard Of Oz, 1903 .... 5.00
Music, **Sheet**, The Song Of Blanche Alpen, Confederate, Steven Glover 7.50
Music, **Sheet**, Yellow Rose Of Texas, Confederate, John Shriner Of Macon 7.50
Music, **Sheet**, You'Re A Dangerous Girl, Al Jolson, 1916 .... 15.00

Music, Symphonion, Imperial, Cherry Case, 9 Discs, 24 X 20 3/4 X 11 In. 1000.00
Music, Ukelin, Lap, 32 Strings, Mahogany Frame, 28 X 8 In., Bow, Sheet Music 21.00
Music, Viola, Heinrich Roth, Bow, Velvet Lined Case 125.00

*Mustache Cups were popular from 1850 to 1900. A ledge of china or silver
held the hair out of the liquid in the cup.*
Mustache Cup & Saucer, **Embossed**, Gold Flowers, Curlicues 27.00
Mustache Cup & Saucer, **Floral** 25.00
Mustache Cup & Saucer, **Floral**, H & Co. 32.00
Mustache Cup & Saucer, **Floral**, Pink Roses, Green, Gold 22.00
Mustache Cup & Saucer, **Flow Blue** 30.00
Mustache Cup & Saucer, **Flow Blue**, Marked Victoria Ironstone, Staffordshire 55.00
Mustache Cup & Saucer, **Fox Hunt Scene**, 1939 Mark 16.50
Mustache Cup & Saucer, **German Verse**, Ornate 37.50
Mustache Cup & Saucer, **Germany**, C.T.With Eagle, Pink Roses, Violets, Gold 35.00
Mustache Cup & Saucer, **Hand-Painted Pink Wild Roses On Cream**, Gold, Bodley 28.00
Mustache Cup & Saucer, **Ivory**, Pink Floral, Marked Weimer-Germany 24.00
Mustache Cup & Saucer, **Lavender & Gold**, Floral Panels, Think Of Me 30.00
Mustache Cup & Saucer, **Luster**, Lavish Gold 32.00
Mustache Cup & Saucer, **Norway Plains Mill** 18.50
Mustache Cup & Saucer, **Pale Green Luster**, Gold, Raised Florals, Germany 20.00
Mustache Cup & Saucer, **Pink Luster**, Floral, Blue, Pink, Green, German Script 35.00
Mustache Cup & Saucer, **Pink Luster**, Footed 22.50
Mustache Cup & Saucer, **Pink Luster**, Gold Decor, Painted Leaves, Beaded Rims 50.00
Mustache Cup & Saucer, **Pink**, Blue Forget-Me-Nots, Gold, Limoges 55.00
Mustache Cup & Saucer, **Pink**, Painted Flower, Pair 35.00
Mustache Cup & Saucer, **Portrait**, Young Couple, Bench, German, Pink Luster 27.50
Mustache Cup & Saucer, **Rose Trim**, Three Crown China 22.50
Mustache Cup & Saucer, **Rust & Green Shades**, Brandenburg 24.50
Mustache Cup & Saucer, **Scene Of Soldier's Home**, Tilton, N.H. 27.00
Mustache Cup & Saucer, **Silver Plate** 25.00
Mustache Cup & Saucer, **Sunderland Luster**, Compass & Verse, Pink 32.50
Mustache Cup & Saucer, **Sunderland Luster**, Pink, Compass On One Side, Navy 32.00
Mustache Cup & Saucer, **Think Of Me**, Spray Of Flowers, Porcelain 25.00
Mustache Cup & Saucer, **White With Gold Beading In High Relief**, Pink Trim 25.00
Mustache Cup & Saucer, **White**, Gold, Floral Decoration On Front 32.50
Mustache Cup, **Cabbage Rose Shape**, Heavy Gold On White, Scalloped Base 25.00
Mustache Cup, **Flanged Base**, Etched Floral, Pairpoint, Silver Plate 22.50
Mustache Cup, **Floral Swags**, Deep Red & Gold Border, Porcelain, Hand-Painted 17.50
Mustache Cup, **Flowers**, A Present, Germany 15.00
Mustache Cup, **Left Handed** 15.00
Mustache Cup, **Silver Plate**, Engraved Designs On Swirl 48.50
Mustache Cup, **Think Of Me**, Square Handle 18.00
Mustache Cup, **Transfer Picture**, The Race Of The Century, Gold Edge 12.00
Mustache Cup, **White**, Gold Trim 10.50
Mustache Cup, **White**, Raised Gold Berries & Leaves, Footed 24.00

*Nailsea Glass was made in the Bristol District in England from 1788
to 1873. Many pieces were made with loopings of colored glass as decorations.*
Nailsea, **Basket**, Pink, Blue & White Loops, White Cased, Cameo Heads On Ends 185.00
Nailsea, **Basket**, Pink, Overlay, Footed, Rosette Prunts, Loopings, Braid Handle 110.00
Nailsea, **Bell**, Crystal Ground & Clapper, White Loops, Spear Handle, 10 In. 75.00
Nailsea, **Bell**, Green, Clear Handle, 9 3/4 In. 55.00
Nailsea, **Cruet**, Blue Shades 17.50
Nailsea, **Flask**, Reclining, Opaque, Red & Blue Specks On Yellow White 65.00
Nailsea, **Jar**, Cranberry, White Loopings, Silver Mount, Bail 120.00
Nailsea, **Lamp**, Fairy, Red & White 400.00
Nailsea, **Lamp**, Fairy, Satin Glass, Cranberry & White, Clear Base, 6 In.High 150.00
Nailsea, **Lamp**, Pink & White Globe & Chimney, 25 In.High 1150.00
Nailsea, **Muffineer**, Looping, White, Clear, Stopper 68.00
Nailsea, **Pitcher**, 6 Tumblers, 13 In. .... *Illus* 400.00
Nailsea, **Rolling Pin**, Green Glass, Red & Blue Speckles, 14 In.Long 45.00
Nailsea, **Shade**, Cranberry & White, 3 1/2 In.High 75.00
Nailsea, **Shade**, Gas, Vaseline Glass .... 65.00 To 75.00
Nailsea, **Tumbler**, Ruby, White Loops, White Cased 18.00
Nailsea, **Vase**, White Swirls, Enamel Floral, Pontil, Urn Shape, 6 In. 30.00

Nakara is a trade name for a white glassware made around 1900 that was decorated in pastel colors. It was made by the C.F.Monroe Company of Meriden, Connecticut.

Nakara, Box, Blue, Ornate Ormulu, Attached Swivel Mirror, Signed 295.00
Nakara, Box, Brown With Pink Trim, 4 In. 195.00
Nakara, Box, Dusty Pink, Blue Daisies, White Beading, Hinged Lid, Hexagon 125.00
Nakara, Box, Hinged, Blue, Signed, Small 115.00
Nakara, Box, Jewel, Cherubs & Floral, Hinged, Brass Collar & Clasp, Marked 200.00

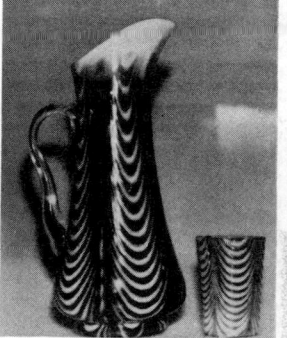

Nailsea, Pitcher, 6 Tumblers, 13 In.
See Page 360

Nakara, Box, Jewel, Floral Cover, Pink, Signed 95.00
Nakara, Box, Jewelery, Octagonal, Open, Olive Green, Hand-Painted Orchids 158.00
Nakara, Box, Open, Brass Rim, Pink Ground, White Enameled Flowers, C.F.Monroe 45.00
Nakara, Box, Orange Floral On Green To Mauve, Scrolled Gold .... 155.00 To 185.00
Nakara, Box, Powder, Hinged, Celery Green Lid 150.00
Nakara, Box, Round, Green Iridescent Beaded Scroll 180.00
Nakara, Box, Round, Hinged Cover, Floral On Beige 160.00
Nakara, Box, Vanity, Swivel Mirror, 4 In.Diameter, Signed 350.00
Nakara, Dish, Candy, Green, Allover Floral, Brass Collar & Bail, Signed 125.00
Nakara, Fernery, Olive Green, Hand-Painted Orchids, Brass Collar, Signed 195.00
Nakara, Fernery, Yellow To Red To Green, Enamel Floral, Brass Rim 125.00
Nakara, Hair Receiver, Flowers, Beaded, Scrolls, Pink, Blue, White, Signed 160.00
Nakara, Hair Receiver, Peachblow, Pink & White Ground, Beaded Scrolls 165.00
Nakara, Hair Receiver, Pink To White, Enamel Floral, Beads, Lid 25.00
Nakara, Humidor, Old Sport & English Bulldog On Front, Brass Lid 150.00
Nakara, Planter, Dark Rose To Pale Pink, Shasta Daisies, Plated Rim 115.00
Nakara, Vase, Pink, Green, White, Signed 250.00

Nanking China is a blue-and-white procelain made in China for export during the eighteenth century.

Nanking, Bowl, Basket Border, Florettes, Blue, White, 1780, 9 In. 150.00
Nanking, Bowl, Blue, White, Lattice Border, 1780, 9 1/2 In.Diameter 125.00
Nanking, Cup & Saucer, Blue, Gilt Edges 22.00
Nanking, Plate, Blue & White, Oriental Willow Pattern, C.1800 .... 50.00
Nanking, Plate, Blue, Hand-Painted Scene, Men, Boats, Temples 28.00
Nanking, Plate, Blue, White, Landscape, 8 1/2 In. 45.00
Nanking, Teapot, Gold Decoration 385.00

Napkin Rings were popular from 1869 to about 1900.

Napkin Ring & Toothpick, Silver Plate, U.S.S.Battleship Maine, 1898 .... 8.00
Napkin Ring, Beaded Edge, Two Branches 45.00
Napkin Ring, Brass, Allover Enamel Fruit & Flowers, Place For Initial 12.75
Napkin Ring, Carved Ivory 15.00
Napkin Ring, Carved Shell, Leaves, Scrolls 8.00
Napkin Ring, Cloisonne 16.00
Napkin Ring, Cut Glass, Crosshatching & Diamond Puff, 6 Sided, Pair 25.00
Napkin Ring, Cut Glass, Diamond Puff Pattern, Oval, 3 X 1 1/4 In. 12.50
Napkin Ring, Engraved Children Praying, 'Good Child Says Prayers, 'silver 12.50
Napkin Ring, Engraved Name, Signed Heimendinger 6.00
Napkin Ring, Figural, Antelope Holds Ring, Meriden 75.00

Napkin Ring, Figural, Antlered Deer, Meriden	75.00
Napkin Ring, Figural, Barrel On Twig Legs, Simpson, Hall Miller & Co.	36.00
Napkin Ring, Figural, Barrel With Leaves, Silver Plate	18.50
Napkin Ring, Figural, Barrel, Stemmed Maple Leaf, Silver Plate, Meriden	28.50
Napkin Ring, Figural, Bird & Fan, Base With Ring, Silver Plate, Derby	55.00
Napkin Ring, Figural, Bird & Fan, Silver Plate, Footed	85.00
Napkin Ring, Figural, Bird Guarding Nest With 3 Eggs	75.00
Napkin Ring, Figural, Bird Guards Nest With Three Eggs, Webster	60.00
Napkin Ring, Figural, Bird On Leaf, Silver Plate, Meriden, Encrusted Base	80.00
Napkin Ring, Figural, Bird On Nest On Oval Ring	38.00
Napkin Ring, Figural, Bird On Openwork Ring, William Rogers	48.00
Napkin Ring, Figural, Bird Perched On Stem, Leaf, Silver	42.50
Napkin Ring, Figural, Bird With Leaf Stem In Mouth, Ring On Top	75.00
Napkin Ring, Figural, Bird, Long Tail, Footed, Derby Co., Silver	85.00
Napkin Ring, Figural, Bird, Spread Wing, Fretwork Ring, Signed Wm.Rogers	45.00
Napkin Ring, Figural, Boy Kneeling Holding Grapes, Ornate Base	75.00
Napkin Ring, Figural, Bud Vase, Kate Greenaway Child At Base	155.00
Napkin Ring, Figural, Butterflies & Fans, Silver Plate	85.00
Napkin Ring, Figural, Butterfly & Fan, Engraved Name, Meriden Silver Co.	50.00
Napkin Ring, Figural, Butterfly & Fan, Silver Plate, Rogers Silver Co.	50.00
Napkin Ring, Figural, Chair, High Back	42.00 To 45.00
Napkin Ring, Figural, Cherub On Scroll, Lacy Openwork, M.B.& Co., Silver	65.00
Napkin Ring, Figural, Cherubs Sitting On Base, Barrel Ring, Silver	49.50
Napkin Ring, Figural, Chicken Looks At Rake, Ornate Base, Webster Mfg.	65.00
Napkin Ring, Figural, Chicken On Wishbone, Broken Egg Shape, Silver	45.00
Napkin Ring, Figural, Cupid On Ends, Scalloped Base, Silver Plate, Wilcox	50.00
Napkin Ring, Figural, Cupids Holding Easel, Footed Base	85.00
Napkin Ring, Figural, Dog On Sides Looking Out Doghouse, Engraved, Silver	39.50
Napkin Ring, Figural, Dog Stands On Ring, Cat On Top, Meriden Silver Co.	85.00
Napkin Ring, Figural, Dog Trying To Get To Cat On Top Of Ring, Ornate Base	75.00
Napkin Ring, Figural, Dog With Ring On His Back, Silver Plate	75.00
Napkin Ring, Figural, Dog, Doghouse, Meriden	75.00
Napkin Ring, Figural, Driftwood, Seashell Base, Wide Ring, Meriden	65.00
Napkin Ring, Figural, Dripping Pear With Entwined Leaves, Leaf Base	50.00
Napkin Ring, Figural, Eagles, Wings Open, On Each Side, Marked Meriden	55.00
Napkin Ring, Figural, Elk On Stand, Holds Ring	70.00
Napkin Ring, Figural, Flower & Swirl On Pellet Type Ring, Rogers	20.00
Napkin Ring, Figural, Flower On Leaf Base, Meriden	24.00
Napkin Ring, Figural, Fox, Flower Sprays, Silver	40.00
Napkin Ring, Figural, Fretwork Arch, Birds, Leaves, Scroll Feet, Meriden	85.00
Napkin Ring, Figural, Giraffe, Standing, Silver Plate	85.00 To 95.00
Napkin Ring, Figural, Girl Holding Flowers	95.00
Napkin Ring, Figural, Girl In Grecian Attire, Holds Ring, Meriden	95.00
Napkin Ring, Figural, Girl With Dog, Silver Plate, Meriden Silver Co.	95.00
Napkin Ring, Figural, Girl, Dated 1880	110.00
Napkin Ring, Figural, Girl, Dog	95.00
Napkin Ring, Figural, Girl, Ponytail, Basket, Footed, 4 In.High	110.00
Napkin Ring, Figural, Goat At Side Of Ring, Meriden	55.00
Napkin Ring, Figural, Griffon Each Side, Oval, Silver Plate, 3 In.Long	34.00
Napkin Ring, Figural, Halfmoon, Royal Austria	9.00
Napkin Ring, Figural, Hen Attached To Ring, Rogers	65.00
Napkin Ring, Figural, Jester Sitting On Ring Holding Torchere, Meriden	110.00
Napkin Ring, Figural, Kangaroo On Leaf, Australian Silver	42.50
Napkin Ring, Figural, Kangaroo, Ostrich, Boomerang, Bird, Australian Silver	47.50
Napkin Ring, Figural, Koala Bear On Tree Stump Beside Ring, Leaf Base	48.00
Napkin Ring, Figural, Lily Pad With Ring, Flower Cluster On Side, Silver	65.00
Napkin Ring, Figural, Lion Standing On Hind Feet, Ring On Paws, Silver	49.50
Napkin Ring, Figural, Naked Child Holding Cup Of Wine Over Head, Rockford	110.00
Napkin Ring, Figural, Nude Child, One Foot Up Touches Ornate Ring, Base	55.00
Napkin Ring, Figural, Owl Mother & 2 Owl Babies On Branch, Simpson	75.00
Napkin Ring, Figural, Parrot One Side, Bud Vase Other, Webster Silver Co.	65.00
Napkin Ring, Figural, Peacock On Ring, Meriden	60.00
Napkin Ring, Figural, Pear On Sides, Leaf & Stem Attached To Ring, Silver	32.50
Napkin Ring, Figural, Prehistoric Bird, Holding Ring, 4 Ball Feet	70.00
Napkin Ring, Figural, Rabbit Crouching Against Leaves & Berries Bower	75.00

Napkin Ring, Figural, Rooster Beside Ring, Pairpoint Silver 69.00
Napkin Ring, Figural, Rooster, Sterling Silver 35.00
Napkin Ring, Figural, Roses, Leaves, Silver Plate, Rogers Silver Co. 60.00
Napkin Ring, Figural, Scotty Dog, Sterling Silver, Marked J.B. 47.00
Napkin Ring, Figural, Scotty With Ring On Back 65.00
Napkin Ring, Figural, Squirrel Eating Nut, Silver Plate, Rogers Silver Co. 75.00
Napkin Ring, Figural, Swan Beside Ring, Silver Plate, Rogers & Bros., Footed 49.00
Napkin Ring, Figural, Tulip With Petal Shape Base, Meriden Co. 38.00
Napkin Ring, Figural, Two Birds Hold Ring, Engraved Monogram, Meriden 65.00
Napkin Ring, Figural, Two Butterflies Hold Ring, Ornate Fan Base 45.00
Napkin Ring, Figural, Two Cherubs Hold Barrel, Seated, Meriden 65.00
Napkin Ring, Figural, Two Cherubs With Rings On Backs 47.50
Napkin Ring, Figural, Two Children With Barrel Resting On Shoulders 85.00
Napkin Ring, Figural, Two Draped Women, Ring Aloft Between Their Backs 95.00
Napkin Ring, Figural, Two Fans Hold Ring, Bat Under Ring, Ornate Base 45.00
Napkin Ring, Figural, Two Horseshoes, Jockey Cap, Silver Plate, Derby Silver 35.00
Napkin Ring, Figural, Water Lily On Leaf Base, Silver Plate, Meriden 22.50
Napkin Ring, Figural, Winged Doves On Footed Base, Silver Plate 70.00
Napkin Ring, Figural, Wishbone Between Ring & Base, Silver Plate, Wilcox 22.50
Napkin Ring, Figural, Wishbone With Folded Napkin, Best Wishes, Cox Silver 30.00
Napkin Ring, Figural, Wishbone, Silver Plate, 'Best Wishes, ' Footed 28.00
Napkin Ring, Glass, Green, Triangle, Square Cut Design 20.00
Napkin Ring, Gold Plate, Design, Pair 19.00
Napkin Ring, Gold Plate, Design, Silver, Pair 19.00
Napkin Ring, Ivory, Carved 15.00
Napkin Ring, Ivory, Hand Carved 11.50
Napkin Ring, Ivory, Handmade, 3/4 In.Wide 8.50
Napkin Ring, Porcelain, Bracelet Shape, Blue & Gold Scrolls 30.00
Napkin Ring, Porcelain, Cherubs 20.00
Napkin Ring, Porcelain, Flowers, Coalport 4.50
Napkin Ring, Porcelain, Girl, Sitting, Bonnet, Yellow, 4 In.High 12.50
Napkin Ring, Rococo Oval Medallion, Footed, Standard Silver Co., Toronto 45.00
Napkin Ring, Russian Enamel, Troika Design 52.50
Napkin Ring, Russian Silver, Multicolor Enamel 225.00
Napkin Ring, Seashell, Los Angeles Painted On Front, Pair 10.50
Napkin Ring, Shell, Carved Leaves & Scrolls 8.00
Napkin Ring, Silesia, Hand-Painted Flowers, Signed 10.00
Napkin Ring, Silver Plate, Floral, Engraved 4.50
Napkin Ring, Silver Plate, Mother Goose Figures 20.00
Napkin Ring, Silver Plate, Nautical, Engraved Captain, U.S.S.B., Oval 8.00
Napkin Ring, Silver Plate, Pair Of Eagles, Meriden 22.50
Napkin Ring, Silver Plate, Pair Of Wishbones Over Triangular Shaped Ring 22.50
Napkin Ring, Silver Plate, Two Little Girls, Meriden 50.00
Napkin Ring, Silver, Sterling, Black Enamel Russian Landscape 15.50
Napkin Ring, Sterling Silver, Art Nouveau Type, Cat & Dog, Pair 30.00
Napkin Ring, Sterling Silver, Engraved, Hallmarked, Birmingham, 1891, Case 22.50
Napkin Ring, Sterling Silver, Engraved, 'Mother' 12.50
Napkin Ring, Sterling Silver, Four Cherubs' Heads 20.00
Napkin Ring, Sterling Silver, Lacy Openings Between Etched Flowers 6.00
Napkin Ring, Sterling Silver, Name Betty 6.00
Napkin Ring, Tortoiseshell, Florals & Birds 3.50
Napkin Ring, Trumpet Shape Bud Vase Atop Ring, Tiered Base, Floral 85.00
Napkin Ring, Two Children On Side, Pink, Blue, Butterfly 25.00
Napkin Ring, Wooden, Souvenir, Whirlpool, Niagara Falls 2.75

Nash Glass was made in Corona, New York, by Arthur Nash and his sons after 1919. He had worked at the Webb Factory in England and for the Tiffany Glassworks in the United States.

Nash Type, Vase, Chintz, Baluster, Blue Vertical Bandings On Clear 80.00
Nash, Plate, Gold, Blue & Red Highlights, Signed, 5 In. 155.00
Nash, Shade, Lamp, Pleated Beige Body, Paperweight Color Flower .... 68.00 To 88.00
Nash, Shade, Lamp, Signed 95.00
Nash, Vase, Chintz, Cobalt, Blown, Unsigned, 4 In.High 50.00
Nash, Vase, Chintz, Red Ground, Blue Gray Stripes, Signed, 6 In.Diameter 675.00
Nash, Vase, Chintz, Transparent Green, Orange & Yellow Decoration, 8 In. 165.00

Needlework, see Textile, Picture

Netsuke are small ivory, wood, metal, or porcelain pieces used as the button on the end of a cord holding a japanese money pouch. The earliest date from the sixteenth century.

Netsuke, Ascetic, Seated On Rocky Base, Ivory, C.1750	90.00
Netsuke, Ascetic, Fasting, Seated, Ivory, C.1750	200.00
Netsuke, Bamboo Shoot, Ivory, Tomotada School ...... *Illus*	375.00
Netsuke, Charging Boar, Ivory ...... *Illus*	1400.00
Netsuke, Chrysanthemums, Leaves, Gold, 18th Century, Signed, Case, Lid	165.00
Netsuke, Cooper, Ivory ...... *Illus*	525.00
Netsuke, Dog & Pup, Ivory, Playing, Tametaka Of Nagoya	600.00
Netsuke, Dutchman, Ivory, C.1850 ...... *Illus*	1350.00
Netsuke, Elephant, Ivory, Signed, 1 1/2 In.	32.00
Netsuke, Farmer, Wood, Lacquer, Standing On Barrel, C.1850	325.00
Netsuke, Fat Man, Ivory	20.00
Netsuke, Futen, Ivory, Standing On One Foot, C.1750	70.00
Netsuke, Group Of Carved Birds On Stand Catching Fish	75.00
Netsuke, Horse, Running, Carved Ivory, Signed, On Top Of Bean Bag	22.00
Netsuke, Horse, Shibayama, Ivory, Inlaid Mother-Of-Pearl, Lacquer, C.1850	650.00
Netsuke, Ho-Ti Treasure Box In Boat, Signed	25.00
Netsuke, Itinerant, Ivory, Standing, Samurai Armor, Hogyoku, C.1850	400.00
Netsuke, Kabuki Theater Figure, Tragedy & Triumph, Carved Ivory, Signed	125.00
Netsuke, Kagamibuta, Ivory, Kneeling Before Teakettle, Ryuei	110.00
Netsuke, Kirin, Mythical Beast, Ivory, C.1750 ...... *Illus*	2000.00
Netsuke, Kite Boy, Fan, Lobster, Feather, Ivory Inlaid Wood, Signed, Case, Lid	195.00
Netsuke, Kneeling Man, Holding Full Sack, Signed	25.00
Netsuke, Maiden, Horned God Of Thunder, Seated, Ivory, C.1750	225.00
Netsuke, Man Lying On Lotus Leaf, Wooden, Signed	135.00
Netsuke, Man Seated On Head Of Wise Man, Polychrome, Ivory, Signed	145.00
Netsuke, Man With A Bag, Ivory	20.00
Netsuke, Man With Long Arms, Wooden, 3 In.	47.50
Netsuke, Man's Face	10.00
Netsuke, Manju, Ivory, Signed Hakusai ...... *Illus*	400.00
Netsuke, Mouse, Ivory, Gnawing On Fan Handle, C.1750	150.00
Netsuke, Noh Mask Carved, Wood, Seated, Gyokkei	375.00
Netsuke, Okame, Ivory, Standing, Engraved Maple Leaves, Hidekaku	200.00
Netsuke, Peasant Tradesman, Ivory	18.00
Netsuke, Peddler, Ivory, Profile, Carrying Wicker Basket, C.1750	90.00
Netsuke, Purse, Carved Wooden Bear, Bead Eyes, Ivory Fittings, 4 1/2 In.High	45.00
Netsuke, Revolving Face, Happy Face, Sad Face, Ivory, 2 In.	28.00
Netsuke, Rolling Face, Ivory	29.00
Netsuke, Sage, Ivory, C.1750	75.00
Netsuke, Sennin, Ivory, Holding Gourd & Branch, C.1750	225.00
Netsuke, Sennin, Stagshorn, Standing, Peony On Shoulder, C.1750	200.00
Netsuke, Shishi, Ivory, Muscular Animal, Bushy Tail, On Haunches, C.1850	75.00
Netsuke, Shishimai Dancer, Ivory, Seated, Engraved, Inlaid Horn, C.1850	300.00
Netsuke, Shoki, Stagshorn, Standing, C.1750	150.00
Netsuke, Sleeping Teamaster Resting On Hibachi, Wooden	95.00
Netsuke, Snail, Wooden, 1 1/2 In.	37.50
Netsuke, Tiger, Ivory, C.1750 ...... *Illus*	425.00
Netsuke, Two Men Holding Fish, Ivory	60.00
Netsuke, Woman, Shugetsu School, Wood, Ivory, Kawamoto Shuraku	675.00
Netsuke, Wrestlers, Ivory, On Lotus Leaf, Seimin	625.00

New Geneva stoneware was made in New Geneva, Pennsylvania, between 1854 and 1900.

New Geneva, Crock, Blue Decoration Of American Eagle, Williams, 2 Handles	140.00
New Geneva, Jug, Water, Tan With Brown Flowers & Leaves, Handle, 2 Spouts	475.00
New Geneva, Pitcher, Dark Brown Decorated, Initials 'H.V.', '1888, 9 1/2 In.	240.00
New Geneva, Pitcher, Decorated, 6 1/2 In.High	80.00
New Geneva, Pitcher, Milk, Light Brown With Dark Brown Decoration	40.00

Newcomb Pottery was founded by Ellsworth and William Woodward at Sophie Newcomb College, New Orleans, Louisiana, in 1896. The work

continued through the 1940s. Pieces of this art pottery are marked with the letter N inside the letter C.

Newcomb, Lamp, Tiffany Type Shade, 20 In.High 475.00
Newcomb, Plaque, Cyprus, Hanging Moss, N In C Signature, 5 1/2 In. 225.00
Newcomb, Vase, Blue Loopings On Green, Artist-Signed, 3 1/2 In.High 75.00
Newcomb, Vase, Blue, Daffodils In Relief At Top, Green Band Rim, Signed S 135.00
Newcomb, Vase, Blue, Narcissus, Artist AM 90.00
Newcomb, Vase, Cyprus Tree, Moss, Signed, Artist's Initials 225.00
Newcomb, Vase, Oak Trees, Mountains, Artist J.M., Paper Label 125.00
Newcomb, Vase, Ovoid, Bluish Ground, Green & White Floral, Henrietta Bailey 120.00
Newcomb, Vase, Pink To Blue Geometrics, Sadie Irvine 95.00

Newhall Porcelain Manufactory was started at Newhall, Shelton, Staffordshire, England in 1782. Simple decorated wares were made. Between 1810 and 1825, the factory made a glassy bone porcelain marked with the factory name.

Newhall, Bowl, Floral Inside & Outside, Cobalt Rim Band, Pink Floral 50.00
Newhall, Cup & Saucer, Transfer Print, C.1810 .... *Illus* 225.00
Newhall, Platter, Oval, Blue & Gold Border, Scenic Center, 15 X 17 1/2 In. 425.00

Niloak Pottery (Kaolin spelled backwards) was made at the Hyten Brothers Pottery in Bremen, Arkansas, between 1909 and 1946. Although the factory did make cast and molded wares, collectors are most interested in the marbleized art pottery line.

Niloak, Pitcher, Milk, Marbleized Blue, Rust, Beige, & Cream, 8 In.High 25.00

Netsuke, Bamboo Shoot,
Ivory, Tomotada School
See Page 364

Netsuke, Tiger, Ivory, C.1750
See Page 364

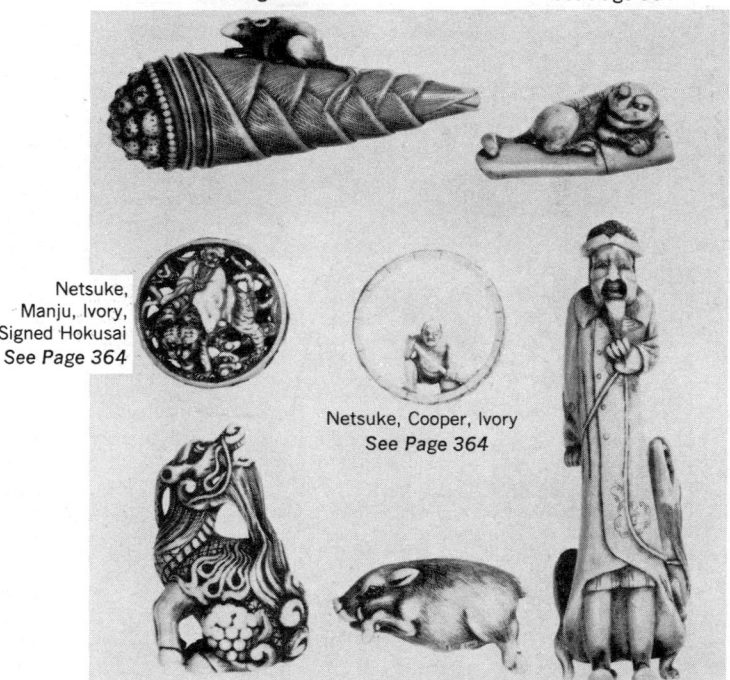

Netsuke,
Manju, Ivory,
Signed Hokusai
See Page 364

Netsuke, Cooper, Ivory
See Page 364

Netsuke, Kirin,
Mythical Beast,
Ivory, C.1750
See Page 364

Netsuke,
Charging Boar, Ivory
See Page 364

Netsuke, Dutchman,
Ivory, C.1850
See Page 364

Newhall, Cup & Saucer, Transfer Print, C.1810
See Page 365

Niloak, Pitcher, Water, Maroon	12.00
Niloak, Pitcher, White, Square, 9 In.	15.00
Niloak, Planter, Deer, Green Matte Glaze, Marked, 5 In.High	8.00
Niloak, Planter, Elephant, Green	12.00
Niloak, Planter, Frog, Tan Matte Finish, Dot & Bar, Signed	15.00
Niloak, Planter, Mother & Baby Rabbit	18.00
Niloak, Rose Bowl, Ovoid, Blue, Beige, Wine & Brown Swirls	32.50
Niloak, Tile, Marbleized Blue, Rust, Beige, & Cream, 4 In, Square	8.00
Niloak, Vase, Corset Shape, Swirls, 4 5/8 In.High	8.00
Niloak, Vase, Marbleized Blue, Rust, Beige, & Cream, 3 1/2 In.High	15.00
Niloak, Vase, Marbleized, Marked, 3 3/4 In.High	15.00
Niloak, Vase, Marbleized, Pair	22.00
Niloak, Vase, Marbleized, 6 1/2 In.	35.00
Niloak, Vase, Paper Label, 6 1/2 In.High	17.50
Niloak, Vase, Swirled Cream, Brown, & Blue, Soft Matte Finish, Signed	10.00

Nippon-marked porcelain was made in Japan after 1891.

Nippon, Basket, Bluebirds, Pink Flowers, Gold Handle, 7 1/2 In.	28.00 To 30.00
Nippon, Basket, Hand-Painted Black Silhouettes Lace Scene, Gold	13.00
Nippon, Basket, Handled, Blue Flower Decoration, Signed	25.00
Nippon, Berry Set, Orange, Brown Flowers, Gold Trim, 7 Piece	32.00
Nippon, Berry Set, White, Geisha Motif, Scalloped, 5 Piece	35.00
Nippon, Bottle, Perfume, Floral Decoration Outlined In Gold Beading	29.00
Nippon, Bowl, Acorn & Walnuts	10.00
Nippon, Bowl, Allover Lake Scene, Three Lobes & Handles, 7 In.	22.00
Nippon, Bowl, Apple Blossoms, Foliage, Rising Sun, Pierced Handles	12.00
Nippon, Bowl, Berry, Medallions Inside, Roses Outside, Gold-Beaded, 9 In.	18.00
Nippon, Bowl, Blossoms, Beaded Band, 3 Lobed Shape, Magenta Wreath	10.00
Nippon, Bowl, Bulbous Areas Form Scallops, Oriental Scenes Inside	12.00
Nippon, Bowl, Cobalt & Gold Trim, Roses, 5 In.	9.50
Nippon, Bowl, Cover, Green, Gold, 6 In.	26.00
Nippon, Bowl, Cream Border, Blue, Yellow, & Pink Pansies, Gold Flower Center	13.50
Nippon, Bowl, Cucumber, Flowers, Pink, Enamel, Pierced, 7 1/2 In.Diameter	12.00
Nippon, Bowl, Cucumber, Footed, Gold, Pagoda Mark	20.00
Nippon, Bowl, Cucumber, Magenta, Pink And White Flowers, Marked	24.00
Nippon, Bowl, Floral Border, 5 In.	5.00
Nippon, Bowl, Floral, Gold Outline, Beaded Gold Bands, 5 1/2 In.	15.00
Nippon, Bowl, Flower Design, Pink, Black, Purple, Orange, Handle, Green Wreath	10.00
Nippon, Bowl, Flowers Inside, Panels Of Gold Scrolls Outside, Gold Handles	15.00
Nippon, Bowl, Flowers, Leaves, Open Handle, Green Mark, M Wreath, 7 In.	15.00
Nippon, Bowl, Flowers, Orange, Yellow, Black Beaded Trim, Hand-Painted	15.00
Nippon, Bowl, Footed, Blue, Gold Trim	5.00
Nippon, Bowl, Footed, Gold Ground, Pink Roses, Marked	35.00
Nippon, Bowl, Four Large Bluebirds, Rural Allover Scene, Pierced Handles	20.00
Nippon, Bowl, Green, Gold Bands, Green Wreath Mark	32.50
Nippon, Bowl, Handles, Oval, Flowers, 7 1/2 In.	9.50
Nippon, Bowl, Hand-Painted Pinecones On Tree Branches, Gold, Handled	28.00
Nippon, Bowl, Hand-Painted, Flowers, Blue Butterflies	18.00

Nippon, Bowl, Jeweled, Hand-Painted Scene, Mark 4 .... 17.00
Nippon, Bowl, Lake, Swans, Water Lilies In Lavender, Yellow, & Green, Signed 22.00
Nippon, Bowl, Mayonnaise, Azalea, Ladle, Hand-Painted 7.00
Nippon, Bowl, Melon Ribbed, Lacy Design, Gold, Pink, Wreath & M Mark 14.00
Nippon, Bowl, Noritake, Double Pierced Handles, Rising Sun Mark 12.50
Nippon, Bowl, Nut, Acorns, Oak Leaves, Beaded Drape Rim, Mark M In Wreath 24.00
Nippon, Bowl, Nut, Cobalt Medallions, Gold Swags, Ribbons, Green Wreath Mark 12.00
Nippon, Bowl, Nut, Nuts, Leaves, Scallop, Marked 22.50
Nippon, Bowl, Nut, Satsuma Type, Blue, Gold Decoration, Scene, 3 Feet 7.00
Nippon, Bowl, Oblong, Open Handles, Bird & Flowers 5.00
Nippon, Bowl, Octagon Shape, Enamel Florals & Beading, Green M Mark 20.00
Nippon, Bowl, Pastoral Scene, Gold Encrusted Band, Enamel, 10 In. 45.00
Nippon, Bowl, Pierced Gold Handles, Hand-Painted Blossoms, Rising Sun Mark 8.00
Nippon, Bowl, Pink Roses, Gold, Footed, Underplate 8.50
Nippon, Bowl, Punch, Hand-Painted Grapes & Leaves, Gold Legs & Band 65.00
Nippon, Bowl, Raised Gold Roses, Leaves In Beaded Band, Beaded Rim, Footed 18.00
Nippon, Bowl, Roses, Gold Marked 27.50
Nippon, Bowl, Round, Pale Blue & Pink, Sailboat Center, Windmills 10.00
Nippon, Bowl, Rural Home Scene, Lake, Beaded Trim, Jeweling, Strap Handles 22.00
Nippon, Bowl, Sailing Ship Scene, Signed, Footed, 6 X 8 In. 20.00
Nippon, Bowl, Scene, Trees, Lake, Boats, 6 3/8 In. 10.00
Nippon, Bowl, Scenic, Island, Boats, Trees, Gold, 7 1/2 In. 26.00
Nippon, Bowl, Scenic, Windmill, House, Trees, Raised Border, Two Handles 22.50
Nippon, Bowl, Scroll Design, Raised, Beading, Gold, Green, Hand-Painted, 7 In. 22.50
Nippon, Bowl, Serving, Pierced Handles, Hand-Painted Violets On Tinted Gold 8.00
Nippon, Bowl, Serving, Scenic 10.00
Nippon, Bowl, Square, Pink, Gold Embossed Roses, Marked 16.00
Nippon, Bowl, Square, White With Gold Enameling, Green Mark 15.00
Nippon, Bowl, Wine & Rose Color Blossoms, Gold Bands, Scalloped, Maple Leaf 30.00
Nippon, Box, Band, Covered, Flowers Outlined In Raised Gold, Pinched Sides 12.00
Nippon, Box, Covered, Stylized Design On Top, Gold Trim, Rising Sun Mark 8.50
Nippon, Box, Lilacs, Raised Beaded Pompoms, Blue Leaf, Marked 16.50
Nippon, Box, Pin, White, Gold Pink, Six Tiny Feet, Hexagon 19.00
Nippon, Box, Powder, Covered, Lake Scene, Gold Beads Around Cover 22.50
Nippon, Box, Powder, Pink & Yellow Floral, Gold Beading, Wreath Mark 37.50
Nippon, Box, Trinket, Colorful Geometric And Gold, Rising Sun Mark 10.00
Nippon, Box, Trinket, Violet Design, Blue, Gold Trim, Hand-Painted 9.00
Nippon, Breakfast Set, Blue, White Birds, Marked, Hand-Painted, 22 Piece 150.00
Nippon, Butter Tub, Three Large Bluebirds, Rising Sun, Insert, Two Handles 14.00
Nippon, Butter, Covered, Hand-Painted Violets On Tinted Gold 18.00
Nippon, Cake Set, Blue Lake Scenes, White Swans, 7 Piece 37.50
Nippon, Cake Set, Open Handles, Lake Scene, 6 Piece 29.00
Nippon, Cake Set, Pierced Handles, Pink & White Roses, Green Wreath, 7 Piece 35.00
Nippon, Cake Set, Pink Roses, 7 Piece 20.00
Nippon, Cake Set, Scenic Design, Raised Border, Yellow, Green, 7 Piece 30.00
Nippon, Celery Set, Daffodils, Gold, Green Wreath Mark, 7 Piece 25.00
Nippon, Celery Set, Floral & Gold, 6 Piece 12.50
Nippon, Celery, Gold Beading, Scrolls, Florals, Pierced Handles, Spoke Mark 15.00
Nippon, Celery, Lake Hills, Farm, Trees, Autumn Colors, Matte Finish 18.00
Nippon, Celery, Pierced Handles, Hand-Painted Blossoms, Gold Beading, Wreath 15.00
Nippon, Celery, Pink Roses And Gold, Royal Crown Mark, 8 In. 20.00
Nippon, Chamberstick, Orchid, Raised Beading, Green, Gray, White, M In Wreath 25.00
Nippon, Charger, Green & Yellow Grasses, Distant Field, Pond, Lilies, House 38.00
Nippon, Chocolate Pot, Blue & White, Hand-Painted Violets, Green Wreath 22.00
Nippon, Chocolate Pot, Blue Forget-Me-Nots, Rising Sun Mark 16.00
Nippon, Chocolate Pot, Flower Design, Handle, Gold Beaded Trim, Hand-Painted 33.00
Nippon, Chocolate Pot, Flowers, Garland, Purple 18.00
Nippon, Chocolate Pot, Gold Beaded, Ornate Handle And Finial 29.00
Nippon, Chocolate Pot, Green, Gold, Pink Enamel, Hand-Painted 28.00
Nippon, Chocolate Pot, Pierced Handle, Yellow, Red, & Pink Roses, Gold, Marked 67.50
Nippon, Chocolate Pot, Pink Flowers, Cobalt Trim 25.00
Nippon, Chocolate Pot, Raised Gold Floral, Beaded Bands, Green Wreath 18.00
Nippon, Chocolate Pot, Scenic, Gold Decoration, Leaf Mark 45.00
Nippon, Chocolate Set, Flower Design, Blue, Gold Trim, 9 Piece 49.00
Nippon, Chocolate Set, Footed, Enameled, Gold, 12 Piece 250.00
Nippon, Chocolate Set, Raised Gold & Wine Enamel, Footed, 12 Piece 250.00

Nippon, Chocolate Set, Rose Decoration, 7 Piece	35.00
Nippon, Chocolate Set, Rose Medallion Border, Beading, 13 Piece	70.00
Nippon, Chocolate Set, Roses, Pink Bands, Gold, Rising Sun Mark, 9 Piece	42.00
Nippon, Chocolate Set, Roses, Signed, 13 Piece	110.00
Nippon, Chocolate Set, Sailboats, 9 Piece	55.00
Nippon, Chocolate Set, Scenic, 11 Piece	35.00
Nippon, Chocolate Set, Scenic, Rising Sun Mark, 9 Piece	60.00
Nippon, Chocolate Set, White Ground, Pink Floral, Gold, 13 Piece	95.00
Nippon, Chocolate Set, White, Gold & Green Cast, Hand-Painted, 13 Piece	50.00
Nippon, Chocolate Set, White, Gold, Floral, Green Mark, 11 Piece	55.00
Nippon, Coaster, Floral Band, Sun Mark, Set Of 4	8.00
Nippon, Coffeepot, Gilt, Pink Flowers, Green Leaves, Blue Bows, Signed	15.00
Nippon, Compote, Chinese Rose Design In Relief, 7 X 2 1/2 In.	5.00
Nippon, Compote, Flower Design, Gold Beaded Trim, Handles	13.00
Nippon, Compote, Gold Handles, Beaded Trim	11.00
Nippon, Compote, Pink Apple Blossoms, Foliage, Rising Sun Mark	12.00
Nippon, Compote, Pink Jewel Inserts, Beading, Gold, Signed	30.00
Nippon, Compote, Rose Design, Beaded, Gold, Yellow, Pink, 4 In.High	14.00
Nippon, Condiment Set, Floral Grouping On Tan & Blue, Marked 31, 6 Piece	15.00
Nippon, Creamer & Sugar, Orange Ground, Scenic, Mark	18.50
Nippon, Creamer, Blue & White Floral, Green Foliage, Bulbous	8.50
Nippon, Creamer, Covered, Underplate, Scenic, Beaded, Yellow, Brown, & Green	22.00
Nippon, Creamer, Figural, Child's Face, Signed	25.00
Nippon, Creamer, Flowers, Pink, Blue, Gold, Marked	13.50
Nippon, Cup & Bowl, Child's Face, Marked	24.50
Nippon, Cup & Saucer, Blue & White	15.50
Nippon, Cup & Saucer, Bouillon, Pink Azaleas, Blue Leaves & Border	4.25
Nippon, Cup & Saucer, Demitasse, Hand-Painted Pink Rose, Gold	5.00
Nippon, Cup & Saucer, Octagonal, Gold & Green Scrollwork, Iris	18.00
Nippon, Cup & Saucer, Panama Calif.Expo., San Diego, 1915, Machinery Bldg.	20.00
Nippon, Dish & Tray, Sardine, Art Nouveau Ocean Scene, Sardine Handle	50.00
Nippon, Dish, Candy, Fluted, Scalloped, Hand-Painted Flower, Marked 46	7.00
Nippon, Dish, Candy, Inside Lake Scene, Footed	15.00
Nippon, Dish, Candy, Pedestal, Boats, Sunset Interior, Green Wreath Mark	12.00
Nippon, Dish, Candy, Shamrocks, Gold Tracery, Footed	10.00
Nippon, Dish, Canoe Shape, Interior Palm Tree, Sailboat Scene Outside	12.00
Nippon, Dish, Cheese & Cracker, Hand-Painted Florals, Gold Vines, Wreath	20.00
Nippon, Dish, Cheese & Cracker, Tiered, Leaves, Gold Flowers, Beading, Marked	22.00
Nippon, Dish, Cheese, Covered, Hand-Painted	20.00
Nippon, Dish, Cheese, Covered, Hand-Painted Roses, Red, Blue, & Yellow	29.00
Nippon, Dish, Cheese, Rectangular, Hand-Painted Flowers, Green Wreath Mark	37.00
Nippon, Dish, Cheese, Slant Top, Cobalt, Yellow And Green, Marked	28.00
Nippon, Dish, Nut, Hand-Painted Clover Leaves, Gold Tracery, Footed, Square	8.00
Nippon, Dish, Nut, Nuts & Leaves Inside, Jeweled Border & Three Handles	27.50
Nippon, Dish, Nut, Raised Nuts, Handles, Round	65.00
Nippon, Dish, Pancake, Covered, Dome, Pink, White Flowers, Rising Sun Mark	25.00
Nippon, Dish, Sweetmeat, Shaded Green Ground, Gold, Apple Blossoms, Matte	12.50
Nippon, Dish, Tidbit, 3 Compartment, Blue Rim, Florals, Handles	10.00
Nippon, Dresser Set, Flower Design, Raised, Hand-Painted, 4 Piece	36.00
Nippon, Eggcup, Rose Design, Aqua, M In Wreath, Set Of 4	15.00
Nippon, Ewer, Gold Jeweling & Roses, Handles, Pedestal, 12 1/2 In.High	58.00
Nippon, Ewer, Pastel Blue & Green Scenic, Beaded Handle, 11 In.High	60.00
Nippon, Ewer, Rose Panels, Gold, 6 In.	25.00
Nippon, Gravy Boat & Underplate, Magenta, Pink Flowers, Gold Trim, Marked	28.50
Nippon, Hair Receiver & Powder Jar, Violets, Gold, Hand-Painted	28.00
Nippon, Hair Receiver, Azalea Decoration, Gold Beading & Trim	15.00
Nippon, Hair Receiver, Flower Border, 3 Gold Feet	11.50
Nippon, Hair Receiver, Pink Poppies, 2 In., Legs	18.00
Nippon, Hair Receiver, Turquoise & Coral Enamel Jeweling, Gold Beads, Legs	25.00
Nippon, Hair Receiver, White & Turquoise Ground	22.50
Nippon, Hair Receiver, White, Rising Sun, Floral, Footed	8.00
Nippon, Hatpin Holder, Apple Blossom, Pink, Green, Marked, Hand-Painted	5.95
Nippon, Hatpin Holder, Butterflies, Gold Outline	15.00
Nippon, Hatpin Holder, Dragon Design, Raised, Beaded Eyes, Gray, Blue	18.00
Nippon, Hatpin Holder, Gold Beading	15.00
Nippon, Hatpin Holder, Gold Ground, Pink Roses, Marked	18.00

Nippon, Humidor, Brown & Yellow Marbleizing, Bulldog Holds Pipe, Marked 68.00
Nippon, Humidor, Heavy Jeweling, Gold 75.00
Nippon, Humidor, Large Dog Decoration, Shades Of Brown, Green Wreath Mark 22.00
Nippon, Jar & Underplate, Condensed Milk, Hand-Painted Flowers, Gold 27.00
Nippon, Jar & Underplate, Jam, Garlands Of Multicolor Floral, Gold Handles 32.00
Nippon, Jar, Biscuit, Flowers, Brown, Green, Lavender 26.00
Nippon, Jar, Cookie, Rose Design, Pink, Gold Trim 18.00
Nippon, Jar, Covered, Roses, Leaves, Gold 28.00
Nippon, Jar, Cracker, Blue Gilt Scrolled Borders, Floral, Latticework 32.75
Nippon, Jar, Cracker, Double Handle, White, Flower Border 16.00
Nippon, Jar, Cracker, Gold Decoration, Gold Beading, Finial On Lid 25.00
Nippon, Jar, Cracker, Hexagonal, Gold Floral, Beaded 35.00
Nippon, Jar, Cracker, Old Scrolls, Florals And Beading, 6 Footed, Marked 40.00
Nippon, Jar, Cracker, Pink & Lavender Roses 17.50
Nippon, Jar, Cracker, Red, Yellow Flowers, Gold Scroll 35.00
Nippon, Jar, Cracker, Scenic Ovals, Rose Medallions, Gold, Beading 70.00
Nippon, Jar, Cracker, Tannish Brown, Yellow Roses, Gold Handles, Blue Mark 30.00
Nippon, Jar, Cracker, Yellow Rose, Marked 37.50
Nippon, Jar, Ginger, Covered, Birds, Red Berries, Gold Edged Trees, Marked 20.00
Nippon, Jar, Rose, Covered, Hexagonal, Floral, Gold 23.00
Nippon, Ladle, Mayonnaise, Pink Roses 5.00
Nippon, Lazy Susan, Seven Compartments, Signed 50.00
Nippon, Lemonade Set, Yellow, Violets, Gold Trim, Handles On Glasses, 6 Piece 55.00
Nippon, Match Holder, Scenic, Satin Finish, Pierced For Hanging 28.00
Nippon, Mayonnaise Set, Azalea Pattern, Rising Sun Mark, 3 Piece 18.00
Nippon, Mayonnaise Set, Pink Roses, Rising Sun Mark, 3 Piece 14.00
Nippon, Mayonnaise Set, Roses, Hand-Painted, 3 Piece 14.00
Nippon, Mayonnaise Set, Scenic, Crown Mark 10.00
Nippon, Mayonnaise Set, Violets, Signed, 3 Piece 26.00
Nippon, Muffineer, Flower Design, Pink, Gold Scroll, 6 Sided, Pair 30.00
Nippon, Muffineer, Roses, Gold, Hexagon, Handle, Signed 38.00
Nippon, Mug, Lemonade, Violet Decoration, E-OH Mark, Set Of 6 .... 20.00
Nippon, Mug, Scenic, Blowout Reindeer, Rustic Handle, M In Wreath Mark 75.00
Nippon, Mug, Shaving, Windmill Scene, Hand-Painted 18.00
Nippon, Mustard Pot & Attached Underplate, Covered, Pastel Florals, Green M 12.00
Nippon, Mustard Pot & Attached Underplate, Hand-Painted 10.00
Nippon, Mustard Pot, Pink Roses, Gold Banding & Beading, Blue Leaf Mark 17.00
Nippon, Mustard Pot, Poppies, Cobalt, Gold Trim 15.50
Nippon, Mustard Pot, White With Blue Hand-Painted Butterflies 7.00
Nippon, Mustard Set, Attached Underplate, Flower & Scroll Design, 2 Piece 18.00
Nippon, Mustard Set, Attached Underplate, Multicolor Floral, Marked, 2 Piece 27.50
Nippon, Mustard Set, Cobalt, Yellow And Green Flowers, Marked, 2 Piece 12.50
Nippon, Mustard Set, Green Wreath Mark, 4 Piece 37.50
Nippon, Mustard Set, Hand-Painted Pink Flowers, Green & Gold, 3 Piece 10.00
Nippon, Mustard Set, Violets, Orange & Brown Ground, 2 Handles, Gold, 2 Piece 15.00
Nippon, Napkin Ring, Flowers, Marked 27.50
Nippon, Napkin Ring, Geisha Girls, Gold, Pink, Red 15.00
Nippon, Napkin Ring, Hand-Painted Scene, Green M Mark 17.50
Nippon, Nappy, Ring Handle, Scalloped Edge, Raised Gold On White 12.50
Nippon, Nappy, Scenic Center, White Blossoms, Green Border, Footed 37.00
Nippon, Nut Set, Flower Design, Beading, Purple Wreath Mark, 6 Piece 18.50
Nippon, Nut Set, Fluted, Orange & Yellow Florals, Rising Sun Mark, 5 Piece 12.00
Nippon, Nut Set, Hand-Painted, 7 Piece 15.00
Nippon, Nut Set, Oval, Florals, Gold, Marked 17, 7 Piece 32.00
Nippon, Nut Set, Pierced Handles, Footed, Nuts, Currants, Berries, 5 Piece 55.00
Nippon, Perfume, Flower Design, Gold Beaded Trim, Hand-Painted 33.00
Nippon, Pitcher, Lemonade, Bisque Finish, E-OH Mark 36.00
Nippon, Pitcher, Lemonade, Ice Lip, Scene 35.00
Nippon, Pitcher, Shaded Gray, Raised Enamel Dragon 5.00
Nippon, Planter, Bowl Hanging On Three Chains, 5 In.Diameter 25.00
Nippon, Plaque, Blown Out Bison, Signed, 10 1/2 In.Diameter 175.00
Nippon, Plaque, Pink Roses, Leaves And Buds, Green Leaf, Marked 26.00
Nippon, Plaque, Scene, Ships, Black Border, Flowers & Leaves, Beading, Gold 18.00
Nippon, Plate, Applied Raised Dragon, 7 1/2 In.Diameter 9.00
Nippon, Plate, Bird On Branch, Blue, Black, Yellow, Maple Leaf, Hand-Painted 24.00
Nippon, Plate, Blossoms, Leaves, & Boughs, Gold Tracery, Spoke Mark 8.00

Nippon, Plate, Cake, Applied Raised Dragon, 10 In.Diameter 18.00
Nippon, Plate, Cake, Bluebirds, Florals, Gold, Green M Mark 15.00
Nippon, Plate, Cake, Colorful Blossoms, Gold Trim, Pierced Handles 18.00
Nippon, Plate, Cake, Daisy Sprays, Gold Outline, Two Incised Handles 14.00
Nippon, Plate, Cake, Handles, Gold Floral Border, Green & Gold Band 10.00
Nippon, Plate, Cake, Lakeside Scene, Jeweled Border, Cutout Handle 22.50
Nippon, Plate, Cake, Pierced Gold Handles, Blossoming Tree, Swans On Yellow 14.00
Nippon, Plate, Cake, Pink & Blue Flowers, Encrusted Gold, Green Mark 7.50
Nippon, Plate, Cake, Rose Design, Gold, Hand-Painted 10.00
Nippon, Plate, Child's, Girl Opening Mail, Dog 20.00
Nippon, Plate, Fish, Three Fish, Black, Blue And Orange, 8 3/8 In., Marked 13.50
Nippon, Plate, Floral Border, 10 In. 4.50
Nippon, Plate, Flower Design, Purple, Blue, Maple Leaf Mark 14.00
Nippon, Plate, Hand-Painted Autumn Lake Scene, Beaded, Pierced, Green Wreath 15.00
Nippon, Plate, Hand-Painted Blossoms With Vines, Raised Gold Beading 8.00
Nippon, Plate, Hand-Painted Currants, Foliage, Shaded Ground, Crown Mark 8.00
Nippon, Plate, Hand-Painted Dutch Girl, Signed Jack McConnel 8.00
Nippon, Plate, Hand-Painted Pink Flowers, Gold, Handled, Marked Rising Sun 8.00
Nippon, Plate, Hand-Painted Stylized Floral, Dragon Mark 8.00
Nippon, Plate, Hanging, Floral On Pink Border, Parrots On Black Center 30.00
Nippon, Plate, Japanese Women, Cobalt, Gold, Red Seal Mark, 9 In. 18.00
Nippon, Plate, Man On Skiff Scene, Gray Edge, Signed 7.50
Nippon, Plate, Pair Heavily Raised Peacocks, 8 In. 25.00
Nippon, Plate, Portrait, Heavily Jeweled Gold, 10 In. 57.50
Nippon, Plate, Portrait, Two Girls In Garden, Blue, Hand-Painted, 10 1/2 In. 45.00
Nippon, Plate, Purple Violets, Hand-Painted, 8 1/4 In. 8.00
Nippon, Plate, Raised Gold Decoration, Pink & Red Roses, 12 In. 45.00
Nippon, Plate, Raised Tapestry Rooster, 8 In. 25.00
Nippon, Plate, Roses, Hand-Painted, 7 1/4 In. 7.00
Nippon, Plate, Roses, Tinted, Hand-Painted, 5 In. 2.50
Nippon, Plate, Scene, Ducks, Brown Border, Bead Trim, Green Wreath Mark 12.00
Nippon, Plate, Scene, Scallops Accented With Gold, Cobalt, 8 1/2 In. 8.00
Nippon, Plate, Scenic Center, Raised Floral, Beading, Turquoise, Green, Purple 55.00
Nippon, Plate, Serving, Center Handle, Landscape Scene, Embossed Edge 10.00
Nippon, Pot De Creme, Tea Roses, Gold Bands & Beads, Green Wreath Mark 12.50
Nippon, Relish, Hand-Painted Lake Scene 13.00
Nippon, Relish, Pink & Yellow Roses, Scalloped, Scroll Handles, Rising Sun 14.00
Nippon, Ring Tree, Figural, Hand, Beading, Cobalt Border On Base 21.50
Nippon, Ring Tree, Gold Hand On Square Base 20.00
Nippon, Ring Tree, Gold Luster Hand Forms Tree, Flowers, Hearts, Mark 16.50
Nippon, Ring Tree, Red Roses, Gold Beaded 27.00
Nippon, Ring Tree, Saucer Type, Outstretched Hand, Gold Beading, Pink Floral 22.50
Nippon, Ring Tree, Shape Of Woman's Hand, Marked 12.00
Nippon, Salad Set, Flower Design, Gold Trim, Hand-Painted, 6 Piece 19.00
Nippon, Salt & Pepper, Grapes, Enameled Jewels, Gold Vines, RC Mark 10.00
Nippon, Salt & Pepper, Hand-Painted Violets On Tinted, Gold 7.00
Nippon, Salt & Pepper, Pink Florals, Enamel Beading 10.00
Nippon, Salt & Pepper, Pink Roses, Gold, 3 Little Feet, Signed 20.00
Nippon, Salt & Pepper, Scenic, Raised Design On Tops 27.50
Nippon, Salt & Pepper, Tree In The Meadow, Signed 18.00
Nippon, Salt & Pepper, Violets, Orange & Brown Ground, Gold, Scalloped 7.00
Nippon, Salt & Pepper, Windmill Design 12.00
Nippon, Salt Shaker, Side Handle 5.00
Nippon, Salt, Flowers, 3 Feet 4.00
Nippon, Salt, Individual, Gold Beading, Scrolls, Florals, Spoke Mark 4.00
Nippon, Salt, Rose Design, Pedestal, Hand-Painted, Marked 2.25
Nippon, Sauce, Hand-Painted Pink Flowers 2.00
Nippon, Sauce, Windmill 5.00
Nippon, Strainer & Bowl, Tea, Cobalt, Gold, Colorful Floral, White Ground 14.00
Nippon, Strainer & Bowl, Tea, Purple & Pink Roses, Gold 16.50
Nippon, Strainer, Tea, Floral 18.00
Nippon, Strainer, Tea, Floral Top, Gold Trim, Signed 30.00
Nippon, Strainer, Tea, Gold Decoration, 2 Piece 14.00
Nippon, Strainer, Tea, Hand-Painted Blue & Pink Decoration, Gold Beading 14.50
Nippon, Strainer, Tea, Rose & Gold Enamel Decoration, Hand-Painted 18.00
Nippon, Sugar & Creamer, Beige, Violets, Covered 30.00

Nippon, Sugar & Creamer, Floral Band At Top 7.00
Nippon, Sugar & Creamer, Flower Design, Hand-Painted 12.50
Nippon, Sugar & Creamer, Flower Design, White, Gold, Purple M, Wreath Mark 15.50
Nippon, Sugar & Creamer, Flowers, Leaves, Gold, Rim Design 14.00
Nippon, Sugar & Creamer, Flowers, Orange, Blue, Green, Hand-Painted, Marked 14.00
Nippon, Sugar & Creamer, Footed, Oriental Ladies, Lake Scene, E-Oh Mark 14.00
Nippon, Sugar & Creamer, Hand-Painted Florals, Gold, Marked 25.00
Nippon, Sugar & Creamer, Hand-Painted Pink Roses, Gold Trim 12.00
Nippon, Sugar & Creamer, Hand-Painted Sailboats On South Seas Setting 18.00
Nippon, Sugar & Creamer, Hand-Painted Scene, Gold Beaded, Sugar Cover 45.00
Nippon, Sugar & Creamer, Hand-Painted Violets On Tinted, Gold Handles 12.00
Nippon, Sugar & Creamer, Hand-Painted, Gold 11.00
Nippon, Sugar & Creamer, Melon Rib, Jeweled, Pink Floral, Gold Mark 50.00
Nippon, Sugar & Creamer, Moriyoga Ware .... *Illus* 55.00
Nippon, Sugar & Creamer, Orange Poppies, Green, Gold, Beading, RC Mark 16.00
Nippon, Sugar & Creamer, Ornate, Jeweled, Heavy Gold, Footed 59.00
Nippon, Sugar & Creamer, South Sea Isle Scene 18.00
Nippon, Sugar & Creamer, White Ground, Pink Roses, Gold Encrusted 20.00
Nippon, Sugar & Creamer, White, Pink, & Green, Gold Beaded Trim 36.00
Nippon, Sugar & Creamer, Yellow & Lavender Cosmos, Gold 20.00

Nippon, Sugar & Creamer, Moriyoga Ware

Nippon, Sugar, Covered, Azalea 12.00
Nippon, Sugar, Covered, Miniature 5.00
Nippon, Sugar, Covered, White, Pink, Blue, White Floral, Green Band, Gold 7.00
Nippon, Sugar, Gold Banding, Beading, Florals, RC Mark 10.00
Nippon, Sugar, Roses 6.50
Nippon, Syrup & Underplate, Covered, Medallion, Gold, Marked 13.00
Nippon, Syrup & Underplate, Covered, Scenic, Rising Sun Mark 17.00
Nippon, Syrup & Underplate, Oval, Raised Gold & Pink Flowers 18.50
Nippon, Syrup, Covered, Pink & Blue Florals, Rising Sun Mark 9.00
Nippon, Syrup, White, Gold Flowers, Beading, Black & Gold Border, Green Mark 10.00
Nippon, Tea Set, Blue & Pink Flowers, Gold Trim, 3 Piece 47.00
Nippon, Tea Set, Blue Floral, Enamel Tracery, Gold, Cobalt Blue, 4 Piece 35.00
Nippon, Tea Set, Demitasse, Roses & Tulips, Red Wreath Mark, 15 Piece 38.00
Nippon, Tea Set, Hand-Painted Pink Roses, Forget-Me-Nots, Gold, 3 Piece 35.00
Nippon, Tea Set, Hand-Painted Roses, Gold Trim, 16 Piece 65.00
Nippon, Tea Set, Octagon, Floral & Butterflies, Gold, Green Mark, 11 Piece 75.00
Nippon, Tea Set, Pink Roses, Gold Beading, 11 Piece 52.00
Nippon, Tea Set, Pink Roses, White Enamel Beading, TT Mark, 15 Piece 40.00
Nippon, Tea Set, Roses, Leaves, Pink, Green, Gold, Blue Border, Mark, 3 Piece 28.00
Nippon, Tea Set, Violets, Gold, All Pieces With 4 Feet, 3 Piece 45.00
Nippon, Teapot, Floral Design 8.00
Nippon, Teapot, Rose & Gold Design, Pink, Footed 14.00
Nippon, Teapot, Rose Design, Pink, Gold, Melon Shape, Footed 15.00
Nippon, Teapot, Scenic, Beaded Flowers, Signed 18.00
Nippon, Teapot, Scroll & Medallion, Lacy, Gold, Mark 15.00
Nippon, Toothpick, Beaded, Gold, Handle, Mark 6.00
Nippon, Toothpick, Hand-Painted Flowers, Gold Trim, Handles, Rising Sun Mark 5.00
Nippon, Toothpick, Pedestal Type, Marked 12.50
Nippon, Toothpick, Sailing Ships, Beaded Edge, Matte Finish, Three Handles 14.00

Nippon, Toothpick, Scene, Three Handles	65.00
Nippon, Tray & Cup, Pink Flowers, Gold	16.50
Nippon, Tray, Basket Shape, Scenic Center, Gold Handle & Border	22.50
Nippon, Tray, Blue Border, Pink Florals, Gold, 8 1/4 X 6 In.	7.50
Nippon, Tray, Forget-Me-Nots, Pink, Blue, Gold, Hand-Painted, 10 X 7 In.	14.00
Nippon, Tray, Multicolored Geometric Design, Rising Sun Mark, 8 1/2 In.Long	6.50
Nippon, Tray, Oriental Garden Scene, Water, Geisha Girls, Two Handles	20.00
Nippon, Tray, Oval, Cream Border, Pink & Yellow Floral Wreath, Gold	5.00
Nippon, Tray, Pin, Blue & Brown Border Decoration, Round	9.50
Nippon, Tray, Pin, Gold, Hand-Painted, Washington D.C., Capitol In Center	12.00
Nippon, Tray, Pin, Royal Koya	12.00
Nippon, Tray, Relish, Scene, House, Trees, Lake, Brown Colors, Open Handle	19.00
Nippon, Vase, Allover Yellow Rose, Gold Beaded Neck & Apron, 11 1/4 In.	60.00
Nippon, Vase, Beaded Top, Poppies, 2 Handles, Yellow, Brown, & Green	35.00
Nippon, Vase, Bulbous, Gold Handles And Feet	39.00
Nippon, Vase, Bulbous, Hand-Painted Horses In Pasture Scene, Pair	45.00
Nippon, Vase, Cabinet, Footed, Arab Desert Scene, 5 3/4 In.High	15.00
Nippon, Vase, Calla Lily, Art Nouveau, Pair	60.00
Nippon, Vase, Dutch Windmill Scene, Pastel, Gold Trim, Handles, Pedestal Base	22.50
Nippon, Vase, Fall Country Scene, Blue & Gold Stripes, Beading, 2 Handles	16.00
Nippon, Vase, Floral, Leaves, Gold Beaded Outline, 10 In.	37.00
Nippon, Vase, Flowers & Birds, 13 In.	35.00
Nippon, Vase, Gold, Pink, White Flowers, Marked, 7 In.	15.00
Nippon, Vase, Gold, Red & Pink Roses, Enamel Dots, Maple Leaf Signature	75.00
Nippon, Vase, Green & Beige Ground, Red Roses, Gold Overlay, 7 In.	20.00
Nippon, Vase, Green Iridescent Ground, Pastel Flowers, Beading, Handles	45.00
Nippon, Vase, Green, Gold Raised Enamel Decoration, Marked, 10 In.	40.00
Nippon, Vase, Green, Scenes Front & Back, Gold Beading, 6 1/2 In.	27.50
Nippon, Vase, Hand-Painted Landscape Scenes, Jeweled Border, Handles, Pair	50.00
Nippon, Vase, Heavy Brocade, Gold, Roses, Signed Blue Leaf	32.00
Nippon, Vase, Heavy Jeweling, Flowers, Two Handles, Footed, 7 1/2 In.	45.00
Nippon, Vase, House, Trees, Lake, Handles, Mark M In Wreath, 5 3/4 In.High	35.00
Nippon, Vase, Houses, Windmill, River, Sunset Colors, 7 In.	18.00
Nippon, Vase, Lake Scene, Roses, Gold Trim, 10 In.High	28.00
Nippon, Vase, Lake Scene, 9 1/2 In.High, 6 1/2 In.Wide, Green Mark	29.00
Nippon, Vase, Mountains, Lake, Trees, Satin Finish, Handle, Gold, 12 In.High	53.00
Nippon, Vase, Painted Lilies & Panel Ground, Gold Handles, Green Wreath	12.00
Nippon, Vase, Pink & Green Floral, Allover Gold Beading, Handles	40.00
Nippon, Vase, Pink Morning Glories, Handles, Cherry Blossom Mark	12.00
Nippon, Vase, Raised Allover Decoration, Green & Cranberry Floral, Marked	95.00
Nippon, Vase, Red Roses, Gold Handles, 10 In.High	35.00
Nippon, Vase, Rose Medallions, Turquoise Beading, Footed, 7 1/2 In.High	42.00
Nippon, Vase, Roses, Leaves, Gold Footed, Gold Handles, Bisque Finish, 10 In.	65.00
Nippon, Vase, Ruffle Top, Pastels, Gold, Open Handle, 6 In.High	20.00
Nippon, Vase, Sailboats, Brown Enameled Handles, 7 In.	25.00
Nippon, Vase, Sailboats, Handle, Pink, Brown, Hand-Painted, 3 X 3 1/2 In.	26.00
Nippon, Vase, Scene, Jeweled, Two Handles, 8 In.	55.00
Nippon, Vase, Scenery, Jeweled, Double Handles	65.00
Nippon, Vase, Scenic And Floral, Gold Ram's Heads For Handles	45.00
Nippon, Vase, Scenic, Floral, Three Gold Looped Handles, 14 In.	150.00
Nippon, Vase, Scenic, Gold Beading, Gold Handles, 9 In.	42.00
Nippon, Vase, Scenic, Sailboats, Gold, Beading, Two Handles, Mark, 11 In.	40.00
Nippon, Vase, Scenic, Swan, Lake, Cottage, Blue Border, Basket Of Flowers	45.00
Nippon, Vase, Scenic, Two Handles, 8 In.	25.00
Nippon, Vase, Sunset, Blossoming Branch, 2 Handles, 12 In.High	18.00
Nippon, Vase, Swan On A Lake, Gold Beaded, 10 In.High	45.00
Nippon, Vase, Swans, Pond, Gold, Three Handles, Footed, 12 In., Pair	75.00
Nippon, Vase, Three Pink Orchids, Yellow Ground	42.50
Nippon, Vase, Urn Shape, Purple Iris, Gold, Handles, 2 Piece, Marked	55.00
Nippon, Vase, Water Scene, Jeweled Top, Two Handles, 5 1/2 In.	11.50
Nippon, Vase, Winter Scene, Gold Trim & Handles, 3 Footed	30.00
Nippon, Vase, Wisteria, Gold Overlay, Two Handles, 7 In.	16.00

*Nodders or Nodding Figures, or Pagods, are porcelain figures with heads
and hands that are attached to wires. Any slight movement causes the parts to*

move up and down. They were made in many countries during the eighteenth and nineteenth centuries.

Nodder, Andy Gump, Bisque	40.00
Nodder, Boy, White Suit & Hat, Bisque, Germany, 3 In.	19.00
Nodder, Mandarin & His Lady, Porcelain, 2 1/4 In., Pair	45.00
Nodder, Sailor Boy Sits In Chair	63.50
Nodder, Wooden, Figures, Carved	75.00

Noritake-marked porcelain was made in Japan after 1904 by Nippon Toki Kaisha.

Noritake, Bowl, Black & Gold Leaves, Yellow Bird, Blue Floral, Handles	35.00
Noritake, Bowl, Gray Panels, Apple Blossoms, Gold Festoons, 11 1/2 In.	55.00
Noritake, Bowl, Hand-Painted Orchid Colored Roses Inside, Scalloped	25.00
Noritake, Bowl, Lake Scene, Swan, Trees, Gold Band, Handles, 7 1/2 In.	8.00
Noritake, Bowl, Lake, Trees, Mountains, Pastel Colors, Open Handle, Gold Rim	10.00
Noritake, Bowl, Nut, Brown To Amber To White, Blossoms, Leaves, Two Handles	12.00
Noritake, Bowl, Nut, Tan To Brown Roses & Buds, 6 In.Square	15.00
Noritake, Bowl, Roses, Fluted	15.00
Noritake, Bowl, Scene, Trees, Lake, Sunset, Handles, 6 In.Square	7.00
Noritake, Bowl, Shell Shape, Floral, Red Mark	12.00
Noritake, Butter, Cream, Black Fleur-De-Lis, Dome Lid, M In Wreath Mark	10.00
Noritake, Cake Plate, Brown, Tan, Large Yellow Flowers, Open Handles	7.50
Noritake, Cake Plate, Violets, 7 1/2 In.	5.50
Noritake, Cake Set, Pink & White Carnations, Gold, M In Wreath, 7 Piece	28.00
Noritake, Candleholder, Handle	7.50
Noritake, Candlestick, Blue & Orange Decoration, Open Handle, 2 In., Pair	12.00
Noritake, Chocolate Set, Medallion Design, Maroon, 11 Piece	65.00
Noritake, Compote, Raised Gold Rose Bouquets, Ribbons, Scrolls, 2 Handles	18.00
Noritake, Condiment Set, Sahara, 4 Piece	10.00
Noritake, Cruet, Syrup & Sugar Shaker, Azalea	97.50
Noritake, Cup & Saucer, The Rheims	3.75
Noritake, Cup & Saucer, White, Gold Band, Green Mark	2.50
Noritake, Demitasse Set, White Dogwood On Black, Gold, 13 Piece	45.00
Noritake, Dish, Cheese & Cracker, Purple & Pastel Colors, Gold	16.00
Noritake, Dish, Child's, Animals, Three Sections	7.50
Noritake, Egg, Easter, 1971, 1st Edition	45.00
Noritak, Gravy Boat & Attached Tray, Pink Roses, Gold, Marked 515 & Merida	8.00
Noritake, Jam Set, Gold Swags, Flowers, 3 Piece	12.00
Noritake, Jar, Tobacco, Black Desert Scene, Arab, Camel, Orange Ground, Lid	35.00
Noritake, Jar, Tobacco, Scenic, Embossed Pipe On Lid, Miniature	18.00
Noritake, Muffineer & Creamer, Flowers, Bluebirds, Orange, Yellow, Blue	16.50
Noritake, Muffineer & Creamer, Lake, House, Trees, Blue, Brown, Yellow	25.00
Noritake, Mustard Set, Gold Flowers On Blue Band, E.P.N.S.Cover, 2 Piece	12.00
Noritake, Nut Set, Brown Bisque Finish, 3-Petaled Acorn Shape, 5 Piece	38.50
Noritake, Plate, Cake, Yellow, Open Yellow Roses, Dark Green Foliage, Handle	10.00
Noritake, Plate, Dogwood, Artist Signed, 8 In.	9.00
Noritake, Plate, Dresden Decoration, 6 1/4 In.	2.25
Noritake, Plate, Fruit, Scene, Lake, Trees, Swan, Gold Decoration, Green Mark	10.00
Noritake, Plate, Lavender & Yellow Ground, Roses, Violet Leaves, 8 5/8 In.	12.00
Noritake, Plate, Open Handles, Yellow Flowers On Shaded, 9 1/2 In.	6.00
Noritake, Plate, Swirls, Leaves, Beading, Raised, Gold, White, 8 3/4 In.	18.50
Noritake, Plate, Yellow Ground, Salmon & Yellow Roses, Violets, 8 5/8 In.	10.00
Noritake, Relish, Azalea	12.00
Noritake, Relish, Raised Gold, Florals, Jewels, Maroon Accent Panels, Marked	16.00
Noritake, Salt & Pepper, Covered Mustard, Tray, Azalea	18.00
Noritake, Server, Sandwich, Floral, Green Border, Center Handle, M In Wreath	9.00
Noritake, Soup, Cream, Underplate, Shasta	6.00
Noritake, Spooner, Pink Roses, Signed F.Horda, Gold Trim & Handles	15.00
Noritake, Sugar & Creamer, Azalea Pattern	16.00
Noritake, Sugar & Creamer, Gold Birds & Water Lilies, Orange Border	20.00
Noritake, Sugar & Creamer, Tree In The Meadow	10.00
Noritake, Sugar, Nirvana Pattern, C.1920	7.00
Noritake, Syrup & Underplate, Petal Form Plate, Bud Finial	6.00
Noritake, Tea Set, Floral, Signed F.Honda, 11 Piece	65.00
Noritake, Tea Set, Yellow Flowers, 3 Piece	16.50

Noritake, Teapot, Individual, Multicolor Florals, Gold 12.50
Noritake, Tile, Tea, White & Gold 6.00
Noritake, Toast Rack, Yellow Rings, Relief Bluebird On Top, Wreath Mark 18.00
Noritake, Tray, Dresser, White, Butterflies, Cream & Gold Border, Handles 18.00
Noritake, Urn, Scene, Swans, Pond, Water Lilies, Cover, Pair 57.50
Noritake, Vase, Apricot Color, Roses, Gold Tracery, Gold Ears, 6 1/2 In. 25.00
Noritake, Vase, Flowers, Pink, Applied Handles, Mark Red M, 7 1/2 In.High 12.00
Noritake, Vase, Gray Matte, Brown Rim & Handles, Raised White Enamel Dragon 22.50
Noritake, Vase, Hand-Painted Azaleas, 7 In. 10.00
Noritake, Vase, Purple, Floral, Gold Handles & Edge, Nippon, Pickard, 6 In. 48.00
Noritake, Vase, Scenic, 12 In. 25.00
Noritake, Vase, White, Roses, Artist-Signed, 8 1/2 In.High 32.00

Northwood Glass Company worked in Martins Ferry, Ohio, from 1888.
They marked some pieces with the letter N in a circle. Many pieces of
Carnival Glass were made by this company.

Northwood, see also Carnival Glass
Northwood, Berry Set, Fan, Gold, 5 Piece 235.00
Northwood, Bowl, Berry, Clear Blue, Gold Band, Enamel Trim, Rayed Star 35.00
Northwood, Bowl, Berry, Clear, Cherry Thumbprint 25.00
Northwood, Bowl, Fluted Scrolls, Blue, Opalescent, Footed 17.50
Northwood, Bowl, Grape & Cable, Clear 30.00
Northwood, Bowl, Grape, Red, 6 1/2 In.Diameter 250.00
Northwood, Bowl, Green Fiery Opalescent, Ruffles & Rings, Footed 20.00
Northwood, Bowl, Green, Hand Fluted Edge, Netted Roses, 8 1/2 In.Diameter 22.50
Northwood, Bowl, Green, Opal Ribbed Top, Beaded Circle Design, Footed, Signed 30.00
Northwood, Bowl, Ice Cream, Grape & Basket Weave, Green, Signed, 10 In. 93.00
Northwood, Bowl, Intaglio Gold Leaves, Red Cherries, Unmarked, 9 3/4 In. 12.00
Northwood, Bowl, Key & Fishscale, Green, Mark N In Circle 28.75
Northwood, Bowl, Meander, Green Opalescent, Spatula Footed, 6 1/2 In. 18.00
Northwood, Bowl, Opalescent Block, Fluted, Blue, 8 In. 22.00
Northwood, Bowl, Opalescent, Ruffles & Rings, Footed, 9 In. 20.00
Northwood, Bowl, Star Of David, Amethyst 65.00
Northwood, Butter, Covered, Everglades, White Opalescent, Gold Trim 55.00
Northwood, Butter, Maple Leaf, Green, Dome Cover 43.00
Northwood, Celery, Block, Blue Opalescent 26.00
Northwood, Celery, Clear, Marked 7.50
Northwood, Compote, Chalice, 6 1/2 In. 36.00
Northwood, Compote, Jelly, Emerald Green, Gold, Intaglio 27.00
Northwood, Compote, Jelly, Intaglio, Blue Opalescent 37.50
Northwood, Creamer, Blue, Opalescent, Alaska 35.00
Northwood, Creamer, Everglades, White Opalescent, Gold Trim 32.00
Northwood, Creamer, Sapphire Blue, Opalescent, Drapery Pattern, N Mark 37.50
Northwood, Cruet, Blue Opalescent, Intaglio, Clear Facet Stopper 65.00
Northwood, Cruet, Opalescent Intaglio, Bulbous, Stopper 68.00
Northwood, Dish, Card, Argonaut Shell, White, Opalescent, Footed 28.50
Northwood, Goblet, Singing Bird, Clear 50.00
Northwood, Mug, Embossed Dads, Stippled, Barrel Shape, Signed N 5.00
Northwood, Mug, Singing Bird, Blue, Signed 28.00
Northwood, Pitcher, Water Lily & Cattails, Blue, Opalescent 17.50
Northwood, Pitcher, Water, Atlas, Flashed Gold Edge, Six Tumblers 85.00
Northwood, Pitcher, Water, Singing Bird, Clear 125.00
Northwood, Plate, Custard, Three Fruits, Nutmeg Trim, Marked N, 7 1/2 In. 28.00
Northwood, Plate, Rose & White, Pleated Edge, Satin Glass, Threads, C.1885 ...... 225.00
Northwood, Rose Bowl, Fluted, Scrolls, Footed, Blue Opalescent 30.00
Northwood, Rose Bowl, Lions Leg, Opal White To Clear, Ruffled, Pedestal Base 25.00
Northwood, Sauce, Cherry, Marked N 8.50
Northwood, Shade, Drapery, White, Mark Block Letters 40.00
Northwood, Spooner, Everglades, White Opalescent, Gold Trim 20.00
Northwood, Spooner, Paneled Holly, Gold On Leaves & Berries, Green, Handles 38.00
Northwood, Spooner, Wild Bouquet, White Opalescent 22.50
Northwood, Sugar & Creamer, Grape & Gothic Arches, Green Crystal 43.00
Northwood, Sugar, Cherries, Crystal, Red Flashed, Gold Leaves, Cable, Signed 21.00
Northwood, Sugar, Covered, Drapery, Blue, Opalescent, Gold 45.00
Northwood, Sugar, Covered, Everglades, White Opalescent, Gold Trim 45.00
Northwood, Sugar, Covered, Fan, Gold 80.00

Northwood, Sugar, Covered, Inverted Feather & Fan, Green 55.00
Northwood, Sugar, Paneled Sides, Beveled Scalloped Top, Handles, Green, 1910 .... 35.00
Northwood, Sweetmeat, Strawberry & Cable, Clear, Signed 30.00
Northwood, Table Set, Atlas, Clear, Gold, 6 Piece 125.00
Northwood, Table Set, Cherry & Plum, 4 Piece 250.00
Northwood, Tray, Clear, Holiday Pattern, Signed, 11 In. 25.00
Northwood, Tumbler, Gold Rose Pattern, Pink, Gold Trim 22.00
Northwood, Tumbler, Green Frosted, Enameled Flowers, N Mark 18.50
Northwood, Tumbler, Peach, Green, Mark N 18.75
Northwood, Vase, Blue, Iridescent, Signed, 10 In.High 35.00
Northwood, Vase, Corn, Blue, Wavy Stalks As Lower Handles 49.00
Northwood, Vase, Fluted Top, Signed, 8 1/4 In. 28.50
Northwood, Vase, Leaf Column, Green, 12 In. 23.00
Northwood, Water Set, Atlas, Gold, Signed N, 7 Piece 110.00
Northwood, Water Set, Green, Enameled Flowers & Leaves, Gold, 7 Piece 145.00
Northwood, Water Set, Maple Leaf, Custard Glass, 6 Piece 350.00

Nymphenburg, a German porcelain factory, was established at
Neudeck-ob-der-Au in 1753 and moved to Nymphenburg in 1761. The company
is still in existence. Modern marks include a shield superseded by a star or
crown, and a crowned CT with a checkered shield.
Nymphenburg, Figurine, Group, Suitor After Bustelli, Cherub 135.00

Occupied Japan is the mark used on pieces of pottery and porcelain made
during the American Occupation of Japan after World War II.
Collectors are now buying these pieces. The items were made for export to
the United States.
Occupied Japan, Ashtray, Indian Chief 7.50
Occupied Japan, Bottle, Snuff, Ivory, Hand-Painted, Signed 40.00
Occupied Japan, Box, Bleeding, Silver On Copper, Red Dragons, Footed 12.00
Occupied Japan, Box, Jewelry, Metal 8.00
Occupied Japan, Box, Jewelry, Musical, Piano Shape, Silver Plate 16.00
Occupied Japan, Box, Lovebirds On Lid, Marked Goldcastle, Japan 4.50
Occupied Japan, Clock, Wall, Eikeisha 35.00
Occupied Japan, Clown 7.00
Occupied Japan, Coaster Set, Boxed 7.00
Occupied Japan, Cup & Saucer 4.00
Occupied Japan, Cup & Saucer, Capo-Di-Monte Style .... Illus 6.50
Occupied Japan, Cup & Saucer, Demitasse, Turquoise, Pink & Gold, Footed 8.50
Occupied Japan, Cup & Saucer, Floral, Gold Banding, Kyoto 3.00
Occupied Japan, Cup & Saucer, Flowers, Orange, Pink, & Blue, Marked S.G.K. 4.00
Occupied Japan, Cup & Saucer, White Ground, Pink Bands, Gold Inside 10.00
Occupied Japan, Figurine, Angel Pulling 2 Wheeled Cart, Bisque 15.00
Occupied Japan, Figurine, Colonial Boy, 10 1/2 In.High 5.00
Occupied Japan, Figurine, Colonial Lady, 5 In.High 3.50
Occupied Japan, Figurine, Colonial Man & Woman, 7 1/2 In., Pair .... 8.00 To 10.00
Occupied Japan, Figurine, Colonial Man, 5 In.High 3.50
Occupied Japan, Figurine, Dancing Girl, Hand-Painted, Marked, 10 1/2 In.High 7.00
Occupied Japan, Figurine, Girl, Dancing, Lacy Dress 3.00
Occupied Japan, Figurine, Man, Girl, Chair, Piano, Pair 8.00
Occupied Japan, Figurine, Maruyamo, Lady & Man, 4 In. 15.00

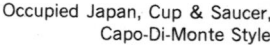

Occupied Japan, Cup & Saucer,
Capo-Di-Monte Style

Occupied Japan, **Figurine**, Nymph Sits Beside Pink Lily, Green, Wooden	5.75
Occupied Japan, **Figurine**, Peasant Lady, Bisque, 7 In.	3.50
Occupied Japan, **Figurine**, Rabbit, Plays Instrument, Pink, Five Pieces	10.00
Occupied Japan, **Figurine**, Santa, Paper & Felt Clothes, Stand Up, 7 In.	7.00
Occupied Japan, **Lighter**, Table Model, Metal	3.50
Occupied Japan, **Planter**, Wall, Two Figures With Gold Watering Cans	10.00
Occupied Japan, **Plaque**, Boy, Bisque	4.00
Occupied Japan, **Plate**, Painted, 5 In.	4.00
Occupied Japan, **Plate**, Scene, Hand-Painted	6.50
Occupied Japan, **Sugar & Creamer**	8.00
Occupied Japan, **Sugar**, Hand-Painted Geisha Girls, Gold, Marked	5.50
Occupied Japan, **Tape Measure**, Lady With Hat	18.50
Occupied Japan, **Tea Set**, Child's, Miniature, Florals, 15 Piece	9.50
Occupied Japan, **Tea Set**, Floral, 22 Piece	40.00
Occupied Japan, **Tea Set**, Floral, White, 9 Piece	16.50
Occupied Japan, **Tea Set**, Garden Scene, 15 Piece	45.00
Occupied Japan, **Tea Set**, Iris Motif, Gold, 3 Piece	33.50
Occupied Japan, **Teapot**, Brown	4.00
Occupied Japan, **Teapot**, Tomato	5.00
Occupied Japan, **Toothpick**, Indian With Bow	4.00
Occupied Japan, **Tray**, Black Lacquer, Gold Decorated, 5 X 10 In.	15.00
Occupied Japan, **Vase**, Hand-Painted, Double Handled, Signed, Hokuzo 29, Pair	38.00
Occupied Japan, **Vase**, Metal Base, Red Lacquer Ware, Maruni	20.00

Ohr pottery was made by George E.Ohr in Biloxi, Mississippi between 1883 and 1918. The pieces were made of very thin clay and were twisted, folded and dented into odd, graceful shapes.

G. E. OHR, BILOXI.

Ohr Pottery, **Hat**, Green, Marked	35.00
Ohr Pottery, **Mug**, Puzzle, Brown Glaze	95.00

Old Ivory China was made in Silesia, Germany, at the end of the nineteenth century. It is often marked with a crown and the word Silesia. The pattern numbers appear on the base of each piece.

Old Ivory, **Berry Set**, No.84, 7 Piece	75.00
Old Ivory, **Berry Set**, No.202, Brown & Turquoise Flowers, 7 Piece	55.00
Old Ivory, **Bowl & Plate**, Chantilly, 10 & 8 1/2 In.	32.00
Old Ivory, **Bowl**, Chantilly, Pink & Yellow Roses, 10 1/4 In.Diameter	28.00
Old Ivory, **Bowl**, No.10, Clairon, Oval, 6 1/2 X 5 In.	15.00
Old Ivory, **Bowl**, No.12	14.00
Old Ivory, **Bowl**, No.27, Silesia	35.00
Old Ivory, **Bowl**, No.84	32.00
Old Ivory, **Bowl.No.200**	35.00
Old Ivory, **Bowl**, 6 3/4 In.	12.00
Old Ivory, **Bowl**, Oatmeal	16.50
Old Ivory, **Celery**, No.16	40.00
Old Ivory, **Celery**, No.67, Ohme, Silesia Mark	28.50
Old Ivory, **Chocolate Pot**, Roses, Satin Finish, Signed	65.00
Old Ivory, **Chocolate Set**, No.15, 11 Piece	150.00
Old Ivory, **Creamer & Underplate**, No.16	40.00
Old Ivory, **Creamer**, No.16	24.00
Old Ivory, **Cup & Saucer**, Chocolate, No.16	22.00
Old Ivory, **Cup & Saucer**, Chocolate, No.75	23.00
Old Ivory, **Cup & Saucer**, No.84	35.00
Old Ivory, **Cup & Saucer**, No.200	28.00
Old Ivory, **Dessert**, No.200	8.00
Old Ivory, **Jar**, Cracker, No.73	125.00
Old Ivory, **Pepper Shaker**, No.84	22.00
Old Ivory, **Pickle**, Thistles, Silesia, 9 1/4 In.Long	9.00
Old Ivory, **Plate**, Bread & Butter, No.200	9.00
Old Ivory, **Plate**, Cake, No.11, Open Handles	37.50
Old Ivory, **Plate**, Cake, No.15	32.50
Old Ivory, **Plate**, Cake, Yellow Roses	32.00
Old Ivory, **Plate**, Chop, No.7	115.00
Old Ivory, **Plate**, Chop, No.15	85.00
Old Ivory, **Plate**, Dinner, Germany, Lavender Violets, Impressed N	30.00
Old Ivory, **Plate**, Luncheon, Germany, Pink & White Thistles, Gold	20.00

Old Ivory, Plate, Luncheon, No.200	16.00
Old Ivory, Plate, No.11, 6 In.	15.00
Old Ivory, Plate, No.15, Silesia, 7 1/2 In.	24.00
Old Ivory, Plate, No.15, 6 1/4 In.	15.00
Old Ivory, Plate, No.15, 7 In.	22.50
Old Ivory, Plate, No.28, Silesia, 6 In.	10.50
Old Ivory, Plate, No.75, Ohme, Silesia Mark, 9 3/4 In.	40.00
Old Ivory, Plate, No.82, Ohme, Silesia Mark, 7 3/4 In.	18.00
Old Ivory, Plate, No.82, White, Rose, 9 In.	55.00
Old Ivory, Plate, No.84, 7 1/2 In.	18.50
Old Ivory, Plate, No.84, 7 3/4 In.	27.50
Old Ivory, Platter, No.16, 11 1/2 In.Long	40.00
Old Ivory, Relish, No.10	26.00
Old Ivory, Relish, No.16, 8 1/2 X 4 3/4 In.	20.00
Old Ivory, Salt & Pepper, No.84	35.00
Old Ivory, Sauce, No.7, 5 In.Diameter	11.50
Old Ivory, Sauce, No.16, 5 In.Diameter	11.00
Old Ivory, Sauce, No.84, Set Of 6	50.00
Old Ivory, Saucer, No.15, Silesia	6.00
Old Ivory, Saucer, No.73, Silesia	6.00
Old Ivory, Sugar & Creamer, Daisy Design	65.00
Old Ivory, Sugar & Creamer, No.200	85.00
Old Ivory, Table Set, No.10, 16 Piece	300.00
Old Ivory, Teapot, No.200	85.00
Old Ivory, Tray, No.16, Roses, Oval, Silesia, 11 1/2 X 8 1/4 In.	45.00
Old Ivory, Tureen, Vegetable, Covered, No.84	165.00

Onion, originally named 'bulb Pattern' is a white ware decorated with cobalt blue. Although it is commonly associated with Meissen, other companies made the pattern in the latter part of the nineteenth century.

Onion, Bowl, Cereal, Design Inside & Outside	10.00
Onion, Bowl, Lacy Border, Oval, Crossed Swords, Meissen	55.00
Onion, Bowl, Meissen, Germany, 6 In.Square	22.00
Onion, Bowl, Vegetable, Signed Furnivals, England	25.00
Onion, Box, Salt, Wooden Lid, Meissen	40.00
Onion, Box, Sugar, Hinged Clasp, Four Feet, Meissen	150.00
Onion, Butter, Scrolled Circle Mark, Meissen	65.00
Onion, Cake Set, Open Handled Plate, Augustus Rex, Meissen, 7 Piece	135.00
Onion, Creamer, Applied Leaves & 3 Feet, Meissen, Crossed Swords Mark	35.00
Onion, Cup & Saucer	15.00
Onion, Eggcup, Blue, Crossed Swords Mark	10.50
Onion, Eggcup, Meissen	7.50
Onion, Gravy Boat & Attached Tray, Covered, Meissen, Germany	37.50
Onion, Horseradish Set, Covered, Meissen, 2 Piece	15.00
Onion, Hot Plate, Metal Base, Handles, Meissen	33.00
Onion, Invalid Feeder, Boat Shape, Germany	14.00
Onion, Knife & Fork, Meissen	30.00
Onion, Knife Rest, Meissen, Crossed Swords Mark	35.00
Onion, Ladle, Turned Wooden Handle	21.00
Onion, Masher, Pink, German	12.50
Onion, Match Holder, Striker Plate On Base	10.00
Onion, Mug, Flared Top, Germany	12.50
Onion, Mustard Set, Covered, Meissen, 2 Piece	18.50
Onion, Mustard, Spoon	10.00
Onion, Pitcher, Meissen, 3 1/4 In.	10.00
Onion, Plate, Blue, Lattice Edge, 8 1/4 In.	28.00
Onion, Plate, Crossed Swords Mark, Meissen	24.00
Onion, Plate, Deep, England, 9 1/2 In., Set Of 4	35.00
Onion, Plate, Lacy Rim, Oval Mark, Meissen, Blue, 7 3/8 In.	12.00
Onion, Plate, Lacy Rim, Oval Mark, Meissen, Blue, 9 3/4 In.	22.00
Onion, Plate, Lattice Edge, Meissen, 7 1/8 In.	12.00
Onion, Plate, Meissen, 7 1/2 In.	13.00
Onion, Plate, Replica By Allerton, 1912, 9 In.	14.50
Onion, Plate, Scalloped Border, C.1883, Crossed Swords Mark, Meissen	22.00
Onion, Plate, Scalloped, Meissen, 7 3/4 In.Diameter	12.00
Onion, Platter, Sectioned, Meissen, 9 X 11 In.	140.00

Onion, Rolling Pin .... 16.50 To 40.00
Onion, Skimmer, Pink, German 12.50
Onion, Soup, Meissen, Crossed Swords Mark 12.00
Onion, Strainer, Tea, Blue, Wooden Handle 9.50
Onion, Teapot, Rose Finial, Crossed Swords Mark, Meissen 85.00
Onion, Tray, Serving, Crossed Swords Mark, Meissen, 12 X 17 In. 95.00

Opalescent Glass is translucent Glass that has the bluish-white tones of
the opal gemstone. It is often found in pressed glassware made in Victorian
times. Some dealers use the terms opaline and opalescent for any of the
bluish-white translucent wares.

Opalescent, Basket, Blue, Opalescent Handle, Victorian, Marked, Patented 25.00
Opalescent, Basket, Blue, Scalloped, Ruffled, Clear Thorn Handle, 8 In. 57.50
Opalescent, Basket, Honeycomb, Blue To White, Blown 50.00
Opalescent, Basket, White, Made In 1908 .... 22.00
Opalescent, Bowl, Berry, Swag, Blue 45.00
Opalescent, Bowl, Blue, Beaded Flower Rosette, 3 Footed 24.00
Opalescent, Bowl, Blue, Beaded Stars, Footed 16.50
Opalescent, Bowl, Blue, Many Loops, 7 1/2 In. 22.00
Opalescent, Bowl, Blue, Pearl Flowers, Footed, 6 1/2 In. 34.00
Opalescent, Bowl, Blue, Ribbed, 9 In. 13.50
Opalescent, Bowl, Blue, Six Ruffled Points, 5 1/4 In. 14.00
Opalescent, Bowl, Cactus, Footed 30.00
Opalescent, Bowl, Cattails & Water Lilies, Amethyst, 9 In. 42.50
Opalescent, Bowl, Finger, Ribbed, Fluted 28.00
Opalescent, Bowl, Flora, Blue, Fluted 30.00
Opalescent, Bowl, Fluted, Footed, Green, 8 3/4 In.Diameter 25.00
Opalescent, Bowl, Fruit, Green, Footed, Ruffled 18.00
Opalescent, Bowl, Green, Dewdrops, Pleated Edge, 8 1/2 In. 22.50
Opalescent, Bowl, Petals & Fan, Peach, 6 In. 17.50
Opalescent, Bowl, Ruffled, Green, White, Footed, 9 In.Diameter 18.00
Opalescent, Bowl, Stipple, Peach 25.00
Opalescent, Butter Pat, Hobnail 6.00
Opalescent, Celery, Fiery Rim, Flora 32.00
Opalescent, Celery, 1, 000-Eye 55.00
Opalescent, Compote, Jelly, White, Tokyo Pattern 18.50
Opalescent, Creamer, Intaglio, White, Northwood 29.00
Opalescent, Creamer, 1, 000-Eye .... 38.00 To 40.00
Opalescent, Dish, Candy, Green, Sea Spray Pattern, Handle, Triangular 18.50
Opalescent, Epergne, Blue, 4 Hanging Baskets, 9 1/2 In.High 65.00
Opalescent, Epergne, Four Lilies, Rigaree, Ruffled Bowl, Green 185.00
Opalescent, Ewer, Blue To Opalescent Stripes, Applied Pink Floral, Fluted 48.00
Opalescent, Ewer, White To Apricot, Crimped, Applied Crystal Handles, Pair 95.00
Opalescent, Goblet, Colonial Pattern, Fiery 300.00
Opalescent, Ice Cream Set, Blue, Hobnail, Square Plates & Tray, 7 Piece 89.00
Opalescent, Muffineer, Coin Spot, Blue 55.00
Opalescent, Muffineer, Daisy & Fern, Blue 55.00
Opalescent, Muffineer, Ribbed, Crisscross, Clear .... 30.00 To 35.00
Opalescent, Mug, Child's, Painted Floral, Blown, Applied Handle 16.00
Opalescent, Mug, Heron & Peacock, Flowers 16.75
Opalescent, Pitcher, Blue, Wild Bouquet 65.00
Opalescent, Pitcher, Coin Spot 27.00
Opalescent, Pitcher, Coin Spot, Crimped Rim, Bulbous, 9 1/2 In.High 65.00
Opalescent, Pitcher, Water, Blue, Coin Spot, Ruffled, Clear Reeded Handle 45.00
Opalescent, Pitcher, Water, Coin Spot, Bulbous, Ruffle Top, 10 In. 38.50
Opalescent, Pitcher, Water, Pink & White Swirls, Canary Handle, Ruffled Top 85.00
Opalescent, Pitcher, 1, 000-Eye, Green, Opaline Handle, Czechoslovakia 35.00
Opalescent, Rose Bowl, Green, Beaded Drape, Footed 27.00
Opalescent, Salt & Pepper, Ribbed, Melon Sections With Diamond Stripes 20.00
Opalescent, Salt Dip, Wreathed Shell, White, Albany Glass, Footed 35.00
Opalescent, Salt Shaker, Swag Brackets 12.75
Opalescent, Sauce, Pink, Threaded, Ruffled 18.50
Opalescent, Spooner, 1, 000-Eye 30.00
Opalescent, Sugar, Gothic Arch, C.1840 .... *Illus* 250.00
Opalescent, Swan, Pink, Ribbed Body, Clear Applied Neck, Duncan Miller, 6 In. 21.50
Opalescent, Syrup, Blue, Swirl With Coin Dot 75.00

Opalescent, Sugar, Gothic Arch, C.1840
See Page 378

Opalescent, Syrup, Hand-Painted Flowers, Pewter Top	45.00
Opalescent, Toothpick, Blue, Oval Bulbous Body	48.50
Opalescent, Toothpick, Hobnail, Footed	75.00
Opalescent, Toothpick, Ribbed, Melon Sections With Diamond Stripes	28.00
Opalescent, Tumbler, Coin Spot	18.50
Opalescent, Vase, Blue Stripes, Swirls, Crimped & Flared Rim, Clear Edge	35.00
Opalescent, Vase, Blue, Clear Blue Bottom & Feet, 9 In.	35.00
Opalescent, Vase, Blue. Silver Wash Top, England, 1900, 9 3/4 In.High, Pair	65.00
Opalescent, Vase, Green, Ribbed With Opalescent Swirl, 11 In.High, Pair	40.00
Opalescent, Vase, Swirl, Flare Top, Ruffle Edge, Pink, 5 In.Tall	16.50
Opalescent, Water Set, White Swirl, Blown, Applied Handle, 5 Piece	65.00

Opaline Glass, or Opal Glass, was made in white, apple green, and other colors. The glass had a matte surface and a lack of transparency. It was often gilded or painted. It was a popular mid-nineteenth century European glassware.

Opaline, Basket, Rose Pink, Clear Twisted Handle	55.00
Opaline, Bottle, Perfume, White, Grapes, Leaves, Slender Neck, France, Pair	25.00
Opaline, Bottle, Scent, Gold Enameling, C.1850	90.00
Opaline, Bottle, Toilet, Pink, Yellow Enamel Scroll, Clear Stopper	20.00
Opaline, Bottle, White, Gold Decoration, Tulip Shape Top, French, Stopper	98.00
Opaline, Bowl, Basket Weave, Yellow, Fluted Corners, Pearl Style Edges	35.00
Opaline, Bowl, Deep Blue, Fluted Top, Flowers In Relief, Enamel Bow	35.00
Opaline, Box, Blue, Enameling, Brass Feet, France	68.50
Opaline, Box, Dresser, Covered, Green Bush, Pink Blossoms	47.50
Opaline, Centerpiece, Blue, Enamel Raised Birds, Floral, Beading, Pedestal	125.00
Opaline, Cruet, Pink	14.50
Opaline, Cruet, Pink, Quilted	17.50
Opaline, Dish, Hen Cover, Basket-Weaved Sides, Scalloped, Scotland	35.00
Opaline, Jar, Powder, Covered, Apple Green	22.00
Opaline, Muffineer, Silver Plated Top	27.50
Opaline, Perfume, Green, Gold Decoration	45.00
Opaline, Ring Tree, Pink, Yellow Enamel Scroll, Clear Center Post	20.00
Opaline, Toothpick, Pink	15.00
Opaline, Vase, Blue At Base To White At Top, Scalloped, French, 5 3/4 In.	40.00
Opaline, Vase, Blue, Enamel Decoration	45.00
Opaline, Vase, Bulbous, Flaring Top, Smoky Amethyst, 10 In.High, Pair	42.50
Opaline, Vase, Deep Blue, Fluted Top, Flower Inside In Relief, 6 1/2 In.	35.00
Opaline, Vase, French Blue, Bulbous Bottom, Long Neck, 5 1/2 In.High, Pair	55.00
Opaline, Vase, Gold Stars, 3 1/4 In.High	37.50
Opaline, Vase, Lavender, C.1920, 10 In.High, Pair	35.00
Opaline, Vase, Pink, Flared Top, France	35.00
Opaline, Vase, Purple Flowers & Snowballs, Signed, 5 In., Pair	30.00
Opera Glasses, Brass, Black Paint	11.00
Opera Glasses, For Vest Pocket, Marked Lemaire, Paris, Leather Case	15.00
Opera Glasses, French, Chevalier, Paris, Leatherette Covering	12.00
Opera Glasses, Lemaire, Mother-Of-Pearl, Brass, Leather Case	22.50 To 35.00
Opera Glasses, Marked Chevalier, Paris, No Case	10.00
Opera Glasses, Mother-Of-Pearl, Gold Color, Case, France	22.50

Opera Glasses, Mother-Of-Pearl, Gold Frame, Signed L.E.Fils Paris, Case	39.50
Opera Glasses, Mother-Of-Pearl, Silver Handle, Memaire, Paris	15.00
Organ, see Music, Organ	
Ormolu, Candlestick, Charles X, Bacchic Trophies, Palm Leaves, C.1890, Pair	110.00
Ormolu, Candlestick, Victorian, Drop Hung Corona, White Marble Base, 1850	60.00
Ormolu, Figurine, Minstrel & Mandolin, Lady & Lyre, C.1850, Pair	350.00
Ormolu, Light, Wall, Cut Glass, 2 Drop Hung Candle Branches, Pair	140.00
Ormolu, Ornament, Desk, Russian, Malachite Veneer, 2 Candle Arms, Dagger, 1850	250.00
Ormolu, Ornament, Desk, Russian, Pendulum Clock, Malachite Veneer, C.1850	350.00
Ormolu, Urn, Empire, Oviform, Enamel Classical Sacrifices, C.1820, Pair	775.00
Ormolu, Vase, Bloodstone, Boat Shape, Carved, Pierced Rim, C.1850	550.00
Ormolu, Vase, Louis XVI Style, Ovoid, Silver Metal, White Marble, Pair	225.00
Orphan Annie, Doll, Rag, Name On Dress, 17 1/2 In.	18.00
Orphan Annie, Mug	9.50
Orphan Annie, Mug, Beetleware	14.00
Orphan Annie, Mug, Ovaltine, 1933	19.00
Orphan Annie, Mug, Shaker, Ovaltine	3.50 To 14.00
Orphan Annie, Pin, Decoder, Dated 1935	10.00
Orphan Annie, Stove	6.00
Orphan Annie, Tea Set, Porcelain, 13 Piece	30.00
Orphan Annie, Tumbler, Orphan Annie & Sandy, Ovaltine, Beetleware	12.50
Orphan Annie, Watch, New Haven Clock And Watch Co., 1934	90.00
Orphan Annie, Watch, Wrist	35.00
Orphan Annie, Whistle, Three Way, Mystic, 1939	15.00
Orrefors, Bowl, Blue, Scalloped, 10 1/4 In.	30.00
Orrefors, Candleholder, Blue, Paperweight, Pair	15.00
Orrefors, Vase, Carved Nude, Signed Vicki Lindstrand, Hexagon, Round Base	38.00
Orrefors, Vase, Cranberry, 7 In.High	10.00
Orrefors, Vase, Crystal, Etched Design, Swedish, 5 In.	25.00
Orrefors, Vase, Paperweight, Clear Crystal, Interior Resembles Bamboo Stalk	19.00

Owens Pottery was made in Zanesville, Ohio, from 1891 to 1928. The first Art Pottery was made after 1896. Utopian Ware, Cyrano, Navarre, Feroza, and Henri Deux were made. Pieces were usually marked with a form of the name Owens. About 1907 the firm began to make tile and gave up the art pottery wares.

OWENS UTOPIAN

Owens, Bottle, Punch, Utopian, Orange Flower On Brown	50.00
Owens, Bottle, Punch, Utopian, 3 Sided, Yellow Wild Rose Decoration, 6 1/2 In.	75.00
Owens, Jug, Utopian, Brown Glaze, Ear Of Corn Decoration, Artist I.S.	67.50
Owens, Lamp Base, Pebbly Black Matte Finish, Floral, Sudanese, 7 3/4 In.High	52.00
Owens, Mug, Brown Glaze, Decorated, 5 In.	37.50
Owens, Mug, Left Handed, Red Cherries, Green Leaves, Artist F., Marked	55.00
Owens, Mug, Utopian, Berries, High Glaze, Artist S.T., 7 In.	75.00
Owens, Pitcher, Utopian, Dark Brown To Light Green, Branches, Leaves, Floral	100.00
Owens, Pitcher, 6 In. *Illus*	68.00
Owens, Tankard, Cherries, Leaves, Brown, 12 1/2 In.Tall	95.00
Owens, Tankard, Flowers, Relief, Artist Initial, 11 In.	135.00
Owens, Vase, Pansies, 10 1/2 In.	45.00
Owens, Vase, Utopian, Brown Glaze, Clovers, Artist H.E., 6 In.High	40.00
Owens, Vase, Utopian, Cat Design, Signed A.M.T., 5 In.High	285.00
Owens, Vase, Utopian, Leaves, Brown, Green, 9 In.Tall	45.00
Oyster Plate, American, Union Porcelain Works, N.Y., 1881	30.00
Oyster Plate, Austria, Pastel Flowers, Set Of 6	100.00
Oyster Plate, Brown *Illus*	40.00
Oyster Plate, Brown Decoration On Five Areas, Gold Scalloped Rim	12.00
Oyster Plate, Five Impressions Among A Seal, Shells, Seaweed, Limoges, 1885	48.00
Oyster Plate, Five Places, Sauce In Center, 22k Raised Roman Gold, Limoges	26.50
Oyster Plate, Floral Design	12.50
Oyster Plate, Pink & Aqua, 9 In.	12.50
Oyster Plate, Pink Roses, Purple Flowers, Embossed, Gold Trim, Set Of 4	52.00
Oyster Plate, Shell Design, Flowers, Pink Purple Ground	15.00
Oyster Plate, Shell, Lobster Design, Pink, Marked U.P.W.	25.00
Oyster Plate, Six Shells, Pink, Yellow, Blue, Brown, Scalloped Rim, Porcelain	12.00
Oyster Plate, Swirl Inserts, Rosebuds, Gold Border, CFM GDM FRANCE	17.50
Oyster Plate, White, Brown Trim, Germany, Weiman	10.00
Oyster Plate, White, Gold, Medailles D'Or, Chas.Pilivayt & Co., Paris	22.50

Owens, Pitcher, 6 In.
See Page 380

Oyster Plate, Brown
See Page 380

Oyster Plate, White, Small Flowers, Gold, Marked Leonard, Vienna	25.00
Painting, see also Picture, Print	
Painting, Diorama, Schooner Rachel, English Flag, Pier, Frame	125.00
Painting, Miniature, Boy, American, C.1820, 2 5/8 In.	200.00
Painting, Miniature, Boy, English, Blue Ground, C.1800, 1 1/2 In.	100.00
Painting, Miniature, Gentleman, American, C.1790, 2 In.	70.00
Painting, Miniature, Gentleman, Continental, C.1750, 1 3/4 In.	70.00
Painting, Miniature, Gentleman, English, Blue Enamel, C.1720, 1 3/4 In.	150.00
Painting, Miniature, Gentleman, English, Blue Enamel, C.1750, 3 1/8 In.	230.00
Painting, Miniature, Gentleman, English, C.1820, 2 7/8 In.	120.00
Painting, Miniature, Gentleman, George Engleheart, English, 1750, 2 1/4 In.	150.00
Painting, Miniature, Gentleman, Gray Brown Ground, 4 In.	90.00
Painting, Miniature, Gentleman, Signed J.S., 2 3/4 In.	160.00
Painting, Miniature, George Washington, American, C.1790, 2 1/2 In.	700.00
Painting, Miniature, Lady, English, Gray Ground, C.1820, 1 1/4 In.	100.00
Painting, Miniature, Lady, French, Opalescent Enamel, C.1890, 2 3/4 In.	170.00
Painting, Miniature, Lady, George Engleheart, English, 1750, 2 1/4 In.	375.00
Painting, Miniature, Lady, Signed A.B., American, C.1840, 2 5/8 In.	70.00
Painting, Miniature, Lady, Signed Besch, French, 3 1/2 In.	170.00
Painting, Miniature, Lady, Signed Vavart, French, 3 1/2 In.	180.00
Painting, Miniature, Lady, Sky Ground, English, C.1825, 2 7/8 In.	120.00
Painting, Miniature, Officer, English, C.1790, 2 1/8 In.	120.00
Painting, Miniature, On Ivory, Gentleman, C.1750 *Illus*	325.00
Painting, Miniature, On Ivory, Girl, C.1780	125.00
Painting, Miniature, On Ivory, Mother & Child, Signed Le Brun	55.00
Painting, Miniature, On Ivory, Portrait, Boy In Period Costume	50.00
Painting, Miniature, On Ivory, Portrait, Lady, Gold Liner, Frame	60.00
Painting, Miniature, On Ivory, Washington, American, 1790 *Illus*	375.00
Painting, Miniature, Thomas Gray, English, 3 1/8 In.	70.00
Painting, Miniature, Young Man, C.1840, 2 1/8 In.	50.00
Painting, Miniature, Young Man, English, Gouache & Oil, C.1820, 2 7/8 In.	120.00

Painting, Miniature,
On Ivory, Gentleman,
C.1750

Painting, Miniature,
On Ivory, Washington,
American, 1790

Painting, **Miniature**, Young Man, Red Lacquer Plaque, C.1850, 4 1/8 In.	110.00
Painting, **Miniature**, Young Officer, English, C.1820, 2 1/8 In.	100.00
Painting, **Miniature**, Young Officer, Opalescent Ground, C.1820, 2 3/4 In.	110.00
Painting, **Oil On Artist's Board**, Alaska, Leonard M.Davis, 1864	84.50
Painting, **Oil On Canvas**, Indian Tepees, Signed Mason, C.1890, 16 X 10 In.	75.00
Painting, **Oil On Wood**, Port Scene, English Sailing Vessel, 30 X 40 In.	150.00
Painting, **Oil**, California Landscape, By Handson Puthuff, Frame	175.00
Painting, **Oil**, Coastal Scene, Signed H.P.Smith, Frame, 20 X 30 In.	475.00
Painting, **Oil**, Landscape, W.Linton, Frame, 21 1/2 X 30 In.	450.00
Painting, **Oil**, Marine Shipwreck, Signed W.Sontag, Jr., Frame, 12 X 21 In.	350.00
Painting, **Oil**, Seascape, James Gale Tyler, Frame, 10 1/2 X 24 In.	300.00
Painting, **Oil**, Seascape, Signed N.White, Gold Frame, Pair	95.00
Painting, **Oil**, Vase With Flowers, By Carl Schmidt, Frame	50.00
Painting, **On Celluloid**, Disney's Sleepy, Frame, 9 X 12 In.	40.00
Painting, **On Celluloid**, Scene From The Practical Pig, Frame, 16 X 18 In.	50.00
Painting, **On Ivory**, Blond Girl, Gold Wash Frame, 3 X 2 1/2 In.	50.00
Painting, **On Ivory**, Lady In Robes, Wooden Frame, 4 1/2 X 5 In.	85.00
Painting, **On Ivory**, Lady Jodrell, Dated 1818	250.00
Painting, **On Ivory**, Lady, Robed, Wooden Frame, 4 1/2 X 5 In.	85.00
Painting, **On Ivory**, Lady, Signed Gainsborough	200.00
Painting, **On Ivory**, Napoleon, Signed Peler, Walnut Frame, 3 1/4 X 2 3/4 In.	145.00
Painting, **On Ivory**, Portrait, Young Woman, Signed	35.00
Painting, **On Porcelain**, Boy, Bavarian Dress, Franz Till, Frame, Pair	650.00
Painting, **On Porcelain**, Girl Dressed In Furs, 5 3/4 X 7 1/2 In.Oval	375.00
Painting, **On Porcelain**, Girl, Flowers In Hair, White Dress, E.N.Wing, Frame	250.00
Painting, **On Porcelain**, Girl, Frame, Dated 1882, Signed, 20 1/2 X 10 1/4 In.	750.00
Painting, **On Porcelain**, Girl, Ornate Wooden Frame, 6 1/2 X 5 In.	375.00
Painting, **On Porcelain**, Girl, Purple Flowers In Hair, By E.N.Wing, Frame	150.00
Painting, **On Porcelain**, Girl, White Robe, Red Shawl Over Shoulder, 4 X 5 In.	135.00
Painting, **On Porcelain**, Lady, Rococo Frame	39.50
Painting, **On Porcelain**, Lady, Signed Bachrach, Leather Easel Case, 3 1/2 In.	95.00
Painting, **On Porcelain**, Little Boy, Signed Re No.107 On Back	300.00
Painting, **On Porcelain**, Madonna & Child, Signed Wagner, 4 X 6 In.Long	275.00
Painting, **On Porcelain**, Nude Holds Torch, Mat, Frame, 9 3/4 X 10 1/2 In.	185.00
Painting, **On Porcelain**, Ophelia, Frame, 13 X 16 In.	425.00
Painting, **On Porcelain**, Portrait, Girl Furs, Velvet, Oval, 5 3/4 X 7 1/2 In.	375.00
Painting, **On Porcelain**, Psyche, Frame, 5 X 7 1/2 In.	395.00
Painting, **On Porcelain**, Queen Louise, Gold Frame, 3 In.Wide X 3 1/2 In.Long	75.00
Painting, **On Porcelain**, Royal Lady, Signed Limore, 5 X 7 In.	175.00
Painting, **On Porcelain**, Three Stages Of Life, By E.N.Wing, Frame	185.00
Painting, **On Porcelain**, Woman, Blonde Hair, Artist Santtag, Mat, Gilt Frame	185.00
Painting, **On Porcelain**, Woman, Gold Frame, 12 X 8 1/2 In.	495.00
Painting, **On Porcelain**, Woman, Lying On Pillow, Signed Jager, Frame, 6 X 8 In	300.00
Painting, **On Porcelain**, Women, Old, Middle Age, Young, E.N.Wing, Frame, 11 In.	285.00
Painting, **On Silk**, Chinese Scroll, Sung Dynasty, Restored	75.00
Painting, **On Tin**, Brunette, Rose In Hair, Signed Pratt, Vienna	30.00
Painting, **On Velvet**, Indian Chief, C.1898, 22 X 32 1/2 In.	150.00
Painting, **Portrait**, Pastels, By J.Baldry	300.00
Painting, **Primitive**, Child, England, C.1845	500.00
Painting, **Reverse On Glass**, Oriental Woman, China, C.1850, 18 X 24 In.	135.00
Painting, **Reverse On Glass**, Oriental Woman, China, Frame, 18 X 24 In.	186.00
Painting, **Theorem**, On Velvet, American, C.1840 *Illus*	375.00
Painting, **Watercolor & Chalk**, Persian Cat, Agnes Tait, Frame	85.00
Painting, **Watercolor**, Bird On Branch, Bird In Flight, China, Frame, Pair	65.00
Painting, **Watercolor**, British Square Rigged Merchant, Henry T.Dawson, 1811	74.50
Painting, **Watercolor**, In Memoriam, American, 1805 *Illus*	375.00
Painting, **Watercolor**, Mosswork, American, C.1840 *Illus*	150.00
Painting, **Watercolor**, Royal Yacht & Cruisers For Cherbourg, Padday, 1890	59.50
Painting, **Watercolor**, Stream Leaving Woodland, By H.Winthrop Pierce	200.00
Painting, **Watercolor**, Woman, Chair, James M.Flugg, Dated 1911, 14 X 16 In.	125.00

Pairpoint Corporation was a silver and glass firm founded in New Bedford, Massachusetts, in 1880.

Pairpoint, **Basket**, Enameled Pansy Decoration On White Interior, Silver	
Pairpoint, **Basket**, Fruit, Quadruple Plate, Dated Nov.28, 1893, Scroll Feet	20.00
Pairpoint, **Basket**, Fruit, Quadruple Plate, Lacy Embossed Feet & Handle	16.00

Painting, Theorem, On Velvet,
American, C.1840
See Page 382

Painting, Watercolor, In Memoriam,
American, 1805
See Page 382

Painting, Watercolor, Mosswork, American, C.1840
See Page 382

Pairpoint, Bowl, Amethyst, Large Size	45.00
Pairpoint, Candelabrum, Roses, Scrolls, Frame In Center, 5-Light, Silver	58.50
Pairpoint, Candlestick, Art Nouveau, Signed	25.00
Pairpoint, Candlestick, Trapped Air Bubble, Purple, 9 In.	75.00
Pairpoint, Chamberstick, Paperweight, Loop Handle, Pink Decoration	25.00
Pairpoint, Champagne, Melrose, 7 In.High	20.00
Pairpoint, Compote, Amethyst, Copper Wheel Engraved, Vintage	85.00
Pairpoint, Compote, Clear, Bubble Stem, Marked, 12 In.Diameter	145.00
Pairpoint, Compote, Cobalt Blue, Clear Twisted Stem, Blue Base	48.00
Pairpoint, Compote, Green Bowl, Clear Bubble Ball In Stem	135.00
Pairpoint, Compote, Pedestal, Buckingham, 4 In.High	65.00
Pairpoint, Cornucopia, Ruby, Bubble Ball Base, 9 In.	55.00
Pairpoint, Creamer, Stripes, White, Applied Handle, Signed, 4 In.High	22.50
Pairpoint, Epergne, Single Trumpet Vase, Saucer, Feet, Clear & Amethyst	48.00
Pairpoint, Jar, Cookie, Signed & Numbered	175.00
Pairpoint, Lamp, Black Shade, Yellow & Pink, Blown-Out Floral, Butterflies	495.00
Pairpoint, Lamp, Boudoir, Bell Shape Shade, Scene In Pastels, Brass Base	150.00
Pairpoint, Lamp, Butterflies & Flowers, 16 1/2 In.High	425.00
Pairpoint, Lamp, Candlestick, Butterflies, Signed, 17 In.High, Pair	400.00
Pairpoint, Lamp, Desert, Oasis, Palms, Pyramids, Camels, Artist W.Macy, 22 In.	350.00
Pairpoint, Lamp, Dragonfly, Blown-Out Flowers, Pink, Signed, 8 In.Shade	225.00
Pairpoint, Lamp, Large Puffy Rose, Signed	900.00
Pairpoint, Lamp, Pink, Blown-Out Flowers & Butterflies, 16 In.High	550.00
Pairpoint, Lamp, Red Shade, Black Painted Scene, Light Blue Water, Signed	200.00
Pairpoint, Lamp, Scenic, Shade & Base Signed, 16 In.Diameter Shade	425.00
Pairpoint, Lamp, Table, Grecian Scene, Signed, 16 In.High	425.00
Pairpoint, Lamp, Table, Iris Decorated Shade, Art Nouveau Base, 21 In.High	450.00
Pairpoint, Lamp, Table, Orchard Scene, Signed, 20 In.Diameter, 24 In.High	450.00
Pairpoint, Paperweight, Crystal Swan, Bubbles, Pedestal, Label	25.00
Pairpoint, Perfume, Controlled Bubbles, Stopper, Clear, 5 1/2 In.	35.00
Pairpoint, Pitcher, Silver Plate, Ornate Border	13.00
Pairpoint, Plate, Engraved, Tulips & Butterflies, 10 In.	65.00
Pairpoint, Sugar & Creamer, Silver, Art Nouveau	35.00
Pairpoint, Sugar, Creamer, & Waste Bowl, Embossed Floral, Silver Plate	35.00
Pairpoint, Swan, Clear Crystal	18.00
Pairpoint, Syrup, Quadruple Plate	23.00
Pairpoint, Tea Set, Flower Design, Footed, Engraved, 7 Piece	350.00
Pairpoint, Urn, Covered, Clarina Cutting	28.00
Pairpoint, Vase, Engraved Floral, Swags, Leaves, Cranberry Trim At Top	125.00
Pairpoint, Vase, Red, Paperweight Base, Horn Of Plenty, Ruffled Top	58.00
Pairpoint, Vase, Yellow, Grapes, Controlled Bubble Clear Paperweight Base	65.00
Pairpoint, Wine, Flambo, Black & Red, Tall Stem	55.00
Palmer Cox, Brownie, Tin Plate, Abc Border, Brownies Washing Dishes, 1896	35.00
Paper, Almanac, Ayer's American, 1859	1.50
Paper, Almanac, Ayer's American, 1861	1.50
Paper, Almanac, Ayer's American, 1866	1.50
Paper, Almanac, Ayer's American, 1889	1.50
Paper, Almanac, Ayer's American, 1924	1.50
Paper, Almanac, Farmer's, 1867	1.00
Paper, Almanac, Farmer's, 1900 To 1972, Each	1.00
Paper, Almanac, Hazeltine's, 1883, Miniature	3.00
Paper, Almanac, Piso's, 1897, Miniature	3.00
Paper, Calendar, 1893, 16 Scenes From Life Of Columbus, By Louis Prang	25.00
Paper, Calendar, 1899, Spanish War Heroes, Advertises Fairbank's Fairy Soap	8.00
Paper, Catalogue, Chas.Williams, Winter, 1927	10.00
Paper, Catalogue, Johnson Smith & Co., 1931	7.00
Paper, Catalogue, Montgomery Ward, Winter, 1944	7.00
Paper, Catalogue, Montgomery Ward, 1925	25.00
Paper, Catalogue, National Cloak & Suit, Summer, 1927	8.00
Paper, Catalogue, Sears Roebuck & Co., 1908	3.95
Paper, Catalogue, Sears Roebuck & Co., 1910	15.00
Paper, Catalogue, Sears Roebuck & Co., 1916	50.00
Paper, Catalogue, Sears Roebuck & Co., 1929	8.00
Paper, Catalogue, Sears Roebuck & Co.1937	8.00
Paper, Catalogue, Sears Roebuck & Co., 1939	4.00
Paper, Catalogue, Sears Roebuck & Co., 1940	8.00

Paper, Catalogue, Sears Roebuck & Co., 1946 .... 3.50
Paper, Catalogue, Sears Roebuck & Co., 1948 .... 7.00
Paper, Comic Book, Cisco Kid, 1941 .... 1.50
Paper, Scrapbook, Christies, American Girl, 20 Black & White & 15 Color 20.00
Paper, Scrapbook, Fisher Bachelor Belles, 1909, 20 Color Pictures 25.00
Paperweight, Aartmahn In Center, Colored Pieces Of Glass, 3 1/4 In. 35.00
Paperweight, Advertising, Bell Telephone, Cobalt .... 25.00 To 29.00
Paperweight, Advertising, Bell Telephone, New York, Blue Glass 28.00
Paperweight, Advertising, Bulldog, Merriam Segars, Iron 18.50
Paperweight, Advertising, Doorknob, Old Union Glass Co., Mass., Dated 1880 .... 20.00
Paperweight, Advertising, Fat Man, Your Warm Friend Thatcher, Iron 12.50
Paperweight, Advertising, Figural, Tree Trunk, Delta Lumber Co., Iron 9.95
Paperweight, Advertising, Jester's Head, Marked Boston Terra-Cotta Co. 34.50
Paperweight, Advertising, Lincoln, Car Emblem On Marble 20.00
Paperweight, Advertising, Lincoln, Hexagon, Bronze 12.50
Paperweight, Advertising, Lion On Base, Strand Baking Co., Iron 8.50
Paperweight, Advertising, Merchant Truck Line, Brass 7.50
Paperweight, Advertising, National Cash Register, Iron 65.00
Paperweight, Advertising, S.P.Shotter & Co., Savannah, Ga., 2 Negro Children 17.50
Paperweight, Advertising, Three Feet, Brass 4.50
Paperweight, Advertising, Union Glass Co., Dated 1880, Red, White, & Blue 35.00
Paperweight, Advertising, Valvoline Motor Oil, Glass 7.50
Paperweight, Advertising, Wagon Horses, Transfer Company 12.00
Paperweight, Apple, Blue & Clear, Blue Stem, Applied Leaf 15.00
Paperweight, Baccarat, see Baccarat, Paperweight
Paperweight, Banford, Snake, Blue Ground, Flowers 95.00
Paperweight, Barney Google Riding Spark Plug, Lead 3.00
Paperweight, Bennington, Spaniel, Graniteware 125.00
Paperweight, Bird & Flowers, Blown, Multiflower Base, C.T.Schulze 22.50
Paperweight, Blown, Swirled Color Base 25.00
Paperweight, Blue Flower, Lattice Ground, Cut Faceted Top 230.00
Paperweight, Buttons, Floral Design In Center 5.00
Paperweight, Cameo Shell, Carved Lady's Profile 55.00
Paperweight, Capitol, Albany, N.Y., Clear Glass, 4 1/4 X 2 3/4 In. 3.95
Paperweight, Centennial, West Virginia 35.00
Paperweight, Chicago Exposition, 1893, Picture Of Building 9.50
Paperweight, Chicken, Snow Globe 3.75
Paperweight, Choko, Flat Floral Bouquet 100.00
Paperweight, Choko, Lizard 200.00
Paperweight, Choko, Snake 150.00
Paperweight, Clichy, Basket Of White & Blue Staves, Millefiori .... 350.00 To 800.00
Paperweight, Clichy, Benjamin Franklin, Sulfide, Blue Ground 775.00
Paperweight, Clichy, Blue Florette, Millefiori Roses, Canes .... 200.00 To 250.00
Paperweight, Clichy, Central Pink & Green Rose, Cogwheel Canes, 1 3/4 In. 225.00
Paperweight, Clichy, Chequer Type, Florettes, Pink & White Mottled Ground 120.00
Paperweight, Clichy, Dicentra, Pink Flowers, Green Leaves, Star Cut Base 1750.00
Paperweight, Clichy, Florette, One Coral & White Pastry Mold Cane 70.00
Paperweight, Clichy, Florette, White Ground, Faceted, Canes 400.00
Paperweight, Clichy, Green & Pink Rose, Turquoise Ground, Florettes 450.00
Paperweight, Clichy, Green Pastry Mold Cane, Swirling Staves .... 150.00 To 200.00
Paperweight, Clichy, Mauve Florette, Millefiori Canes, Faceted 300.00
Paperweight, Clichy, Miniature, Green, White, & Red Florette, Blue Ground 130.00
Paperweight, Clichy, Mushroom, Concentric Millefiori Canes, Faceted 400.00
Paperweight, Clichy, Open Concentric, Mold Canes, Pink Rose Like Centers 220.00
Paperweight, Clichy, Pastry Mold Cane, Millefiori Florettes 80.00
Paperweight, Clichy, Pink & Green Rose, Millefiori Canes, Loops, Clear 175.00
Paperweight, Clichy, Pink & White Rose, Green, Millefiori Florettes 100.00
Paperweight, Clichy, Posy Of 3 Florettes, White, Mauve, & Red, Waffle Base 175.00
Paperweight, Clichy, Posy, Pastry Canes, Green Leaves, 1 3/4 In. 235.00
Paperweight, Clichy, Purple & Yellow Pansy, Clear Ground, Green Leaves 375.00
Paperweight, Clichy, Red, White, & Blue Florette, Pink Ground, Canes 250.00
Paperweight, Clichy, Swirl, 2 13/16 In.Diameter .... Illus 1800.00
Paperweight, Clichy, Three Rows Of Canes, White Ground, Floret 250.00
Paperweight, Clichy, Two Roses, Clear, Millefiori Scattered Floret 200.00
Paperweight, Clichy, White, Red, & Blue Florette, White Latticinio Ground 850.00
Paperweight, Clichy, White, Red, & Blue, Pastry Mold Cane, Swirling Staves 175.00

Paperweight, Clichy, Swirl,
2 13/16 In.Diameter
See Page 385

Paperweight, **Crown Design**, Etched, Vase Top, 8 In.High	75.00
Paperweight, **D'Albret**, Christopher Columbus, Sulfide, Blue Ground	50.00
Paperweight, **D'Albret**, Da Vinci	62.00
Paperweight, **D'Albret**, Da Vinci, Overlay	160.00
Paperweight, **D'Albret**, F.D.Roosevelt, Sulfide	62.00
Paperweight, **D'Albret**, F.D.Roosevelt, Sulfide, Overlay	160.00
Paperweight, **D'Albret**, Hemingway, Sulfide	62.00
Paperweight, **D'Albret**, Hemingway, Sulfide, Overlay	160.00
Paperweight, **D'Albret**, John J.Kennedy, Overlay	160.00
Paperweight, **D'Albret**, King Of Sweden, Sulfide, Blue Ground	50.00
Paperweight, **D'Albret**, MacArthur, Sulfide	62.00
Paperweight, **D'Albret**, MacArthur, Sulfide, Overlay	160.00
Paperweight, **D'Albret**, Mark Twain, Sulfide, Blue Green Ground	47.50 To 62.00
Paperweight, **D'Albret**, Mark Twain, Sulfide, Overlay	160.00
Paperweight, **D'Albret**, Mr.& Mrs.John F.Kennedy, Sulfide, Green Ground	35.00
Paperweight, **D'Albret**, Paul Revere, Sulfide	62.00
Paperweight, **D'Albret**, Paul Revere, Sulfide, Overlay	160.00
Paperweight, **D'Albret**, Prince Charles, Sulfide	62.00
Paperweight, **D'Albret**, Prince Charles, Sulfide, Overlay	160.00
Paperweight, **D'Albret**, Robert Kennedy, Sulfide, Overlay	160.00
Paperweight, **D'Albret**, Schweitzer, Sulfide, Overlay	140.00 To 160.00
Paperweight, **D'Albret**, Schweitzer, Sulfide	62.00
Paperweight, **Dahlia & Leaves**, China, C.1900	62.50
Paperweight, **Dog**, Metal	4.50
Paperweight, **Dog**, Sitting Puppy, St.Louis, Cast Iron	2.25
Paperweight, **Dog**, Sitting, Frosted, 5 1/8 In.High	45.00
Paperweight, **Erlacher**, Intaglio Bird, Nest	300.00
Paperweight, **Figural**, Replica Of Old Well, Cast Iron	30.00
Paperweight, **Figural**, Scarab	25.00
Paperweight, **Figural**, Snail, Colored Center, Spatter Glass	15.50
Paperweight, **Figural**, Stack Of Gold Coins, Railway Congress, May, 1905, Brass	4.75
Paperweight, **Fish**, Swimming, Seaweed, Dome, Clear	17.50
Paperweight, **General Douglas Macarthur**, Snow	30.00
Paperweight, **General Lafayette**, Sulfide, Clear Ground	200.00
Paperweight, **General Pershing**, Dated 1917, 4 In.Diameter	20.00 To 22.00
Paperweight, **Hacker**, John F.Kennedy, Speckled Ground	20.00
Paperweight, **Hacker**, Lizard, Flat, Sand Ground, Signed	350.00
Paperweight, **Hamon**, Rose, Hand-Cut	21.00
Paperweight, **J.F.Kennedy**, Sulfide, Cobalt Ground, Waffle Base	35.00
Paperweight, **Kaziun**, Purple Ground, Yellow Pansy	450.00
Paperweight, **Kaziun**, Turtle Silhouette, Pink, Blue, White, Black, 2 1/2 In.	360.00
Paperweight, **Last Supper**, Signed M	22.00 To 27.50
Paperweight, **Libbey Glass Co.**, Columbian Exposition, 1893, Liberty Bell	20.00
Paperweight, **Liberty Bell**, Blue Glass, 3 1/2 In.High	25.00
Paperweight, **Lighthouse**, Snow	20.00
Paperweight, **Lindsey**, No.404, General Pershing, Gold Paint	24.00
Paperweight, **Lion**, Reclining, Frosted	48.00
Paperweight, **Maine State Building**, 1893	9.00
Paperweight, **Masonic Emblem**, Blue	16.50

Paperweight, **Masonic**, Shrine Emblem, Red	16.50
Paperweight, **McKinley**, Brass	10.00
Paperweight, **Millefiori**, Candy Canes	35.00
Paperweight, **Millefiori**, Dated 1825	70.00
Paperweight, **Millefiori**, 2 Doves, 1 Goat, 1 Chicken	310.00
Paperweight, **Millville**, Canary Rose, Green Leaves, Clear Ground, Footed	275.00
Paperweight, **Millville**, Mushroom, Teardrop Center, Red, Green, Blue, 3 1/4 In.	195.00
Paperweight, **Millville**, Ship, Blue Waves, Red Flag, Faceted Ground	650.00
Paperweight, **Miniature**, Chinese, Butterfly In Center	3.25
Paperweight, **Miniature**, Chinese, Millefiori Cane, 1 In.Across	1.50
Paperweight, **Miniature**, Chinese, Red Rose In Center, 1 1/2 In.Across	7.00
Paperweight, **Multicolored**, Flowers, Blown, Blue Base, C.1870	59.00
Paperweight, **Multicolored**, Flowers, 1 Clear Stamen	22.50
Paperweight, **Murano**, Rose Petals Float Over A Ribbed Goldstone Crown	37.50
Paperweight, **Mutt & Jeff**, Mirror Base, Round, Boston	8.50
Paperweight, **Napoleon III**, Etched, Faceted, Amber Flashed, 7 Windows	100.00
Paperweight, **New England**, Apple, Green Stem, Clear Foot	325.00
Paperweight, **New England**, Clematis, Pink & White Jasper Bround	190.00
Paperweight, **New England**, Clematis, White Latticinio, White Florette	180.00
Paperweight, **New England**, Concentric Canes, Stars, Tubes	290.00
Paperweight, **New England**, Pear & 2 Cherries, Faceted, Brown Twig	375.00
Paperweight, **New England**, Pear, Yellow To Russet, Clear Foot	400.00
Paperweight, **New England**, Pears & Cherries, White Latticinio ....80.00 To	140.00
Paperweight, **New England**, Pink Double Clematis, Blue & White Jasper	175.00
Paperweight, **New England**, Pink Double Clematis, Clear Ground, Leaves	250.00
Paperweight, **New England**, Pink Double Clematis, Red, White, & Blue Jasper	200.00
Paperweight, **New England**, Pink Double Clematis, White Latticinio Ground	150.00
Paperweight, **New England**, Scrambled Canes	110.00
Paperweight, **New England**, Scrambled, 2 3/4 In.	75.00
Paperweight, **New England**, Twist & Cane, Multicolored	125.00
Paperweight, **Notre Dame**, Metal, Marble Base, 3 In.High	5.00
Paperweight, **Old South Church**, Boston, Glass	3.95
Paperweight, **Pairpoint**, Flattened Spiral In Opaque White, Clear	70.00
Paperweight, **Pairpoint**, Pear Shape, Airtrap Bubbles, Ruby Stem	35.00
Paperweight, **Pairpoint**, White Spirals, Clear	65.00
Paperweight, **Palace Fine Arts**, P.P.I.E., San Francisco, 1915, 3 In.Square	10.50
Paperweight, **Pan American Exposition**, 1901	8.50
Paperweight, **Perthshire**, Crown, Latticinio, Blue & Red Canes	55.00
Paperweight, **Perthshire**, Green Faceted Overlay, Signed & Dated	145.00
Paperweight, **Perthshire**, Miniature, Closed Concentric Canes, Blue Ground	20.00
Paperweight, **Perthshire**, Spoked Concentric, Canes, Pink, Green, Blue, Yellow	30.00
Paperweight, **Pestle**, Opaque White Ground, Blue, Green, Rose, Black Spatter	60.00
Paperweight, **Photographs Of Fairies**, Cascade, Brown & White, Glass, Oblong	7.00
Paperweight, **Pink & White Weedflower**, Cane Florette Center, Jasper Ground	300.00
Paperweight, **Plymouth Rock**, Inscribed On Beveled Edge	85.00
Paperweight, **Plymouth Rock**, 1876, 3 1/2 In.	25.00
Paperweight, **Royale**, 1970	180.00
Paperweight, **Royale**, 1971	200.00
Paperweight, **Royale**, 1972	270.00
Paperweight, **Sandwich**, Blue & White Twists, Canes	90.00
Paperweight, **Sandwich Glass**, Blue Double Clematis, Clear .... 125.00 To	170.00
Paperweight, **Sandwich Glass**, Blue, Red, & White Weedflower, Clear	200.00
Paperweight, **Sandwich Glass**, Dahlia & Leaves On White Jasper, Canes Center	200.00
Paperweight, **Sandwich Glass**, Morning Glory, Blue & White Jasper Ground	300.00
Paperweight, **Sandwich**, Fruit Center, Latticinio Ground	400.00
Paperweight, **Sandwich**, Multicolored Scrambled Canes	65.00
Paperweight, **Sandwich**, Poinsettia	210.00
Paperweight, **Sandwich Glass**, Red Double Clematis, Clear	200.00
Paperweight, **Sandwich**, Scrambled	70.00
Paperweight, **Sandwich Glass**, Yellow Double Clematis, White Latticinio	225.00
Paperweight, **Scene**, Man, Cascade, N.H., Upright, Pair	15.00
Paperweight, **Semiround Glass**, Indian Picture, Gainesville, Texas	5.00
Paperweight, **Six Petal Pink Dahlia**, Green Stem, Leaves, White Matte	55.00
Paperweight, **Snake**, Green, White Ground	300.00
Paperweight, **Soldiers' Home**, Marion, Ind., C.1890, 3 1/2 In. .... 65.00 To	75.00
Paperweight, **Somerville**, Chipped Ground, Blue, White, Black, Dated 1884	80.00

Paperweight, St.Clair, Bell, Marked 15.00
Paperweight, St.Clair, Crown, Blue & White Flower On Top 15.00
Paperweight, St.Louis, Bird, Amber, Signed 165.00
Paperweight, St.Louis, Blue & White Pinwheel, 1971 .... 140.00
Paperweight, St.Louis, Blue Dahlia, White Latticinio Ground, Faceted 450.00
Paperweight, St.Louis, Blue Double Clematis, White Latticinio, Faceted 250.00
Paperweight, St.Louis, Blue, White, & Red Bouquet, White Latticinio Spiral 1050.00
Paperweight, St.Louis, Bouquet Of 4 Florettes, Flat, Diamond Cut Base 250.00
Paperweight, St.Louis, Bouquet Of 7 Florettes, White Latticinio Strands 450.00
Paperweight, St.Louis, Bouquet, Blue Clematis, White & Pink, Double Overlay 600.00
Paperweight, St.Louis, Carpet Ground, 1972 .... 170.00
Paperweight, St.Louis, Carpet Ground, 2 1/2 In.Diameter .... *Illus* 2000.00
Paperweight, St.Louis, Carpet Ground, 2 1/2 In.Diameter .... *Illus* 2200.00
Paperweight, St.Louis, Concentric Canes In Pink, Blue, & Mauve, Jasper 90.00

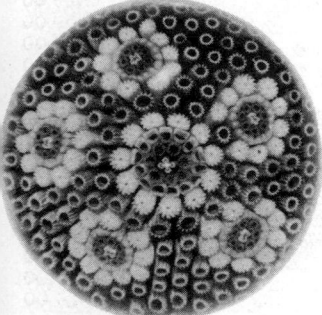
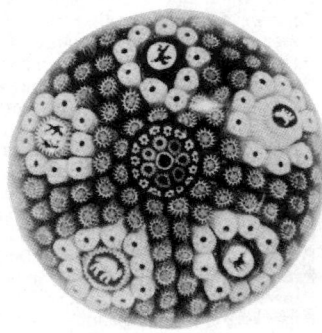

Paperweight, St.Louis,   Paperweight, St.Louis,
Carpet Ground, 2 1/2 In.Diameter   Carpet Ground, 2 1/2 In.Diameter

Paperweight, St.Louis, Concentric Millefiori Canes, Florettes, 1848 .... 1350.00
Paperweight, St.Louis, Concentric Rows Of Canes, Florette, Blue, White, Ruby 125.00
Paperweight, St.Louis, Crown, Florette, Twisted Latticinio Threads, Ribbons 550.00
Paperweight, St.Louis, Crown, Green Florette, White Latticinio Strands 750.00
Paperweight, St.Louis, Doily 170.00
Paperweight, St.Louis, Double Clematis, Leaves, Latticinio Ground, 3 In. 750.00
Paperweight, St.Louis, Five Clusters Of Green & White Canes, Pink Ground 1400.00
Paperweight, St.Louis, Fuchsia, Orange Twig, Star Cut Base 700.00
Paperweight, St.Louis, Green Florette, Millefiori Canes, Faceted 275.00
Paperweight, St.Louis, Hand Cooler, Bouquet Of 6 Red, Blue, & White Floral 450.00
Paperweight, St.Louis, Hand Cooler, Twisted Latticinio & Ribbons 125.00
Paperweight, St.Louis, Marbrie, Magnum 200.00
Paperweight, St.Louis, Mauve Dahlia, Clear, Star Cut Base 400.00
Paperweight, St.Louis, Millefiori Star, 1971 .... 120.00
Paperweight, St.Louis, Millefiori With Lace, 1972 .... 190.00
Paperweight, St.Louis, Miniature, Cerise Canes, Blue, Coral, White 130.00
Paperweight, St.Louis, Mushroom, Clear, Concentric Canes, Latticinio, 1848 .... 1600.00
Paperweight, St.Louis, Mushroom, White Overlay 210.00
Paperweight, St.Louis, Mushroom, 1970, Black & White Overlay 160.00
Paperweight, St.Louis, Mushroom, 1970, White Overlay .... 160.00 To 210.00
Paperweight, St.Louis, Pansy, Mauve, Green Stalk 100.00
Paperweight, St.Louis, Pears & Cherries, White Latticinio, Gree .... 300.00 To 500.00
Paperweight, St.Louis, Pink Clematis Bouquet, White Latticinio Spiral 1050.00
Paperweight, St.Louis, Pink Dahlia, Faceted, Green Leaves 600.00
Paperweight, St.Louis, Pink Dahlia, Ocher, White, & Blue Canes, Star Cut Base 900.00
Paperweight, St.Louis, Pink Veined Dahlia, White Latticinio Ground, Faceted 550.00
Paperweight, St.Louis, Pinwheel, 1971, Blue & White 140.00
Paperweight, St.Louis, Pinwheel, 1971, Five Colors 140.00
Paperweight, St.Louis, Pistachio Flower, 1970 .... 140.00
Paperweight, St.Louis, Pistachio Flower, 1971 .... 170.00
Paperweight, St.Louis, Queen Elizabeth II, Sulfide, 7 Windows, Green, White 225.00
Paperweight, St.Louis, Red Clematis Bouquet, Blue Ground, Flat, Star Cut 550.00

Paperweight, St.Louis, Red Flower, Faceted 140.00
Paperweight, St.Louis, Red, White, & Green Florette, Millefiori Canes 150.00
Paperweight, St.Louis, Star Silhouetted Canes, Millefiori Florettes 225.00
Paperweight, Strathearn, Canes On Lace Crown, Faceted, Signed, Dated Canes 25.00
Paperweight, Sugar Bag, Says Boston Banes, Cuba, Bronze, 5 In.High 30.00
Paperweight, The Big Well, Greensburg, Kansas, Color 8.50
Paperweight, The Cairn, Penn's Hill, Quincy, Mass., Glass 3.95
Paperweight, Two Birds Sitting On Branch, Chinese, Square 25.00
Paperweight, Union Station, Portland, Me., Pictures Horse & Wagon 10.00
Paperweight, U.S.Battleship Maine, 1893 .... 9.00
Paperweight, Van Fleet, President Mansfield, Drug, Tenn., Amethyst 7.50
Paperweight, Vaseline Egg, Revel Cut, Black Pottery Base, Flint Dome 135.00
Paperweight, White, Red & Pink Pebbles, White Band Through Center 25.00
Paperweight, Whitefriars, Florette, Millefiori, Canes, White, Blue, & Red 50.00
Paperweight, Whittemore, Christmas Stocking, Candy Cane, Leaves 350.00
Paperweight, Whittemore, Forget-Me-Nots, Blue On Wine, Flat Dome, Faceted 325.00
Paperweight, Whittemore, Iowa Wild Rose, Green Ground, Faceted 400.00
Paperweight, Whittemore, Lady Slipper, Minnesota State Flower 350.00
Paperweight, Whittemore, Pink Rose & Bud On Stem, Cobalt Ground, Domed 300.00
Paperweight, Whittemore, Shaded Blue Rose, Green Leaves, Pedestal 145.00
Paperweight, Whittemore, Tilted White Rose, Pedestal 145.00
Paperweight, Whittemore, Upright Shaded Blue Rose, Pedestal 120.00
Paperweight, Whittemore, White Calla Lily, Green Leaves, Cobalt, Flat Dome 300.00
Paperweight, Ysart, Bouquet Tied With Ribbon, Twisted Latticinio Ground 190.00
Paperweight, Ysart, Butterfly On Twisted Latticinio Swirled Ground 190.00
Paperweight, Ysart, Complex Flower, Radial Cane Border, Jasper Cushion 190.00
Paperweight, Ysart, Flower In Basket 190.00
Paperweight, Ysart, Large Flower With Leaves 190.00
Paperweight, Ysart, Single Swimming Fish 300.00
Paperweight, Ysart, Snake 450.00

Papier-Mache is a decorative form made from paper mixed with glue, chalk, and other ingredients, then molded and baked. It becomes very hard and can be decorated. Boxes, trays, and furniture were made of Papier-Mache. Some of the early nineteenth century pieces were decorated with mother-of-pearl.

Papier-Mache, see also Furniture
Papier-Mache, Box, Allover Oriental Scenes, Blue Lined, 13 In.Diameter 35.00
Papier-Mache, Box, Collar 45.00
Papier-Mache, Box, Pencil, Baseball Team Picture 25.00
Papier-Mache, Caddy, Dresser, Venetian Scenes Painted 45.00
Papier-Mache, Casket, Russian, Lacquer, Ivan & Bride, Rectangular, C.1850 .... 150.00
Papier-Mache, Cup & Saucer, Demitasse, Black, Gold Lining, Japan, Set Of 6 .... 10.00
Papier-Mache, Egg, Easter, Filled With Cotton Chickens 15.00
Papier-Mache, Figurine, Magi Guide, Christmas, Wooden Stand, C.1810 .... 175.00
Papier-Mache, Mask, Death, President Buchanan, Painted 280.00
Papier-Mache, Plate, Mother-Of-Pearl Inlay, Scalloped Edge, 10 In. 27.00
Papier-Mache, Snuffbox, Black Enamel, Pewter Inlaid Bands, Cartouche 12.50
Papier-Mache, Snuffbox, Black Finish, Inlaid Silver Decoration On Edge 21.00
Papier-Mache, Snuffbox, Black, Silver Inlay On Top, Made In France 45.00
Papier-Mache, Snuffbox, Inlaid Lid 12.50
Papier-Mache, Snuffbox, Painting Of Couple In Peasant Costumes 27.50
Papier-Mache, Snuffbox, Painting Of Lafayette On Cover 45.00
Papier-Mache, Snuffbox, Primitive Painting 27.50
Papier-Mache, Snuffbox, Shell Shape, Red On Black, Marbleized Effect 18.00
Papier-Mache, Snuffbox, Transfer Of U.S.Naval Engagement, C.1815 .... 400.00
Papier-Mache, Tea Caddy, Pair Pewter Covered Canisters 198.00
Papier-Mache, Tray, Mounted As Table, Flower & Bird Decorations 70.00
Papier-Mache, Tray, Scalloped Edge, Gold, Painted Flowers, Handle 8.50
Papier-Mache, Tray, Victorian, Oval, Black, Simulated Tortoiseshell, C.1890 .... 150.00

Parian is a fine-grained, hard-paste porcelain named for the marble it resembles. It was first made in England in 1846 and gained in favor in the United States about 1860. Figures, tea sets, vases, and other items were made of Parian at many English and American factories.

Parian, Box, Blue, White, Dead Game Birds On Lid, 4 In.Oval 32.50
Parian, Box, Trinket, Embossed, 2 X 4 In. 35.00

Parian, Box, Trinket, Gold Color Band, Raised Cherubs On Dome Lid, Hinged 50.00
Parian, Bust, Bismarck, Meissen Mark, Bought At World's Fair, 1893, 16 In. 275.00
Parian, Bust, Diana & Apollo, China Base, 5 In.High, Pair 10.00
Parian, Bust, Napoleon, 6 In.High 62.50
Parian, Creamer, Figural, Cow, White 22.50
Parian, Creamer, Narrow Reeding Around Body, Small Size 20.00
Parian, Dish & Underplate, Candy, White Raised Grapes & Leaves On Pink 97.50
Parian, Dish & Underplate, Sweetmeat, Covered 52.00
Parian, Figurine, Baby Writing In Book Held On His Knee, 5 In. 20.00
Parian, Figurine, Blacksmith With Girl, Germany, 7 In.High 42.50
Parian, Figurine, Boy Pouring Water From Vase, Duck At Base, Sevres, 1875 .... 195.00
Parian, Figurine, Boy, Period Costume, Holds Dog, 7 1/2 In. 22.50
Parian, Figurine, Bunny, 1 In.High 4.00
Parian, Figurine, Bust Of Disraeli 44.00
Parian, Figurine, Child, Ruffled Cap, Cross & Heart Necklace, White, 8 In. 32.00
Parian, Figurine, Cow With Calf 32.50
Parian, Figurine, Dog, 1 In.High 4.00
Parian, Figurine, Draped Woman, Holds Tortoiseshell Musical Instrument 75.00
Parian, Figurine, Girl Plays Harp, Kneels On Pillow, Tassels At Corners 25.00
Parian, Figurine, Girl, Standing, Holds Lamb, 5 In. 22.50
Parian, Figurine, Greek Slave, Minton, 1848 .... 150.00
Parian, Figurine, Jupiter Bull Swimming With Europa, Minton, 1881 .... 185.00
Parian, Figurine, Mary, Queen Of Scots, 6 1/4 In. 35.00
Parian, Figurine, Ruth, Oval Base, White, 13 In.High 65.00
Parian, Figurine, Shakespeare, Standing, Elbow On Stack Of Books, 9 In. 42.50
Parian, Figurine, Shakespeare, Unglazed, 6 In.High 22.50
Parian, Jar, Honey, Basket Weave, Bees, Leaves, Twig Handle, Plate, Copeland 35.50
Parian, Match Holder, Standing, Girl Leans On Urn, Germany 25.00
Parian, Mug, Pink Stained Ground, White Dancing Figures, Presentation Seal 97.50
Parian, Pitcher, Babes In The Woods, 7 In. 55.00
Parian, Pitcher, Prince Albert, Coat Of Arms, England, 9 In. 245.00
Parian, Pitcher, White Ground, White Acanthus Leaves, Blue Panels, 4 In. 18.00
Parian, Sconce, Classic Scroll, Bow Front Plateau, Pair 58.00
Parian, Syrup, Bird & Nest Pattern, Pewter Lid 55.00
Parian, Syrup, Raised Pattern, Birds & Foliage, Hinged Pewter Lid 18.00
Parian, Syrup, Three Branch Design, Pewter Cover, Brown 46.00
Parian, Vase, Grape Design, White 25.00
Parian, Vase, Grapes & Ivy, 7 1/2 In.High 50.00
Parian, Vase, Hand Holds Vase, Crimped Top, White & Blue Green Flowers 22.00
Parian, Vase, Hand Holds Vase, Tulip, Raised Forget-Me-Nots, 8 In.High 20.00
Parian, Vase, Raised Lions' Heads, Flowers, & Leaves, C.1845, 4 1/2 In.High 62.00
Paris, Cup & Saucer, After Dinner, Lavender, Classical Medallions, C.1800 .... 35.00
Paris, Plaque, Pink & White Roses, Blue Morning Glories On Claret, C.1830 .... 260.00

*Pate de Verre is an ancient technique in which glass is made by blending
and refining powdered glass of different colors into molds. The process was
revived by French glassmakers, especially Galle, around the end of the
nineteenth century.*

Pate De Verre, Ashtray, Blue, Gold & Black Bees At Ends, Walter, Berge 395.00
Pate De Verre, Ashtray, Deep Blue, Diamond Shape, Signed Walter, Berge 395.00
Pate De Verre, Bowl, Gray, Amethyst Poppies, G.Argy Rousseau 375.00
Pate De Verre, Bowl, Roses, Stems, Leaves, Flared Edge, 2 1/2 In.Diameter 165.00
Pate De Verre, Box, Turquoise, Red Berries, Beetles, A.Walter, Nancy 600.00
Pate De Verre, Figurine, Dolphin, Green, Signed A.Walter, Nancy, 3 In.Long 250.00
Pate De Verre, Figurine, Frog, A.Walter, 2 In. 285.00
Pate De Verre, Figurine, Monkey, Sitting Near Tree Stump, Light Amber, Green 375.00
Pate De Verre, Figurine, Moth, Yellow, Green, Orange, & Brown Body, Floral 295.00
Pate De Verre, Figurine, Seminude Dancer, A.Walter, Nancy, & Jean Descomps 1800.00
Pate De Verre, Inkwell, On Disc, Pen Recess, Tree Trunk, Bee, Twig, Berries 525.00
Pate De Verre, Liquor, Flower Design, Blue, Amethyst, Signed, 2 In.High 110.00
Pate De Verre, Mask, Napoleon 395.00
Pate De Verre, Paperweight, Large Insect On Top, Signed Walter 350.00
Pate De Verre, Paperweight, Mouse Shape, Signed, 5 1/2 In.Diameter 450.00
Pate De Verre, Plaque, Nude, Flowing Hair, Kneels At Tree, Artist A.Finol 575.00
Pate De Verre, Sconce, Wall, Peacock On Yellow Sunburst, 3 Panels, Signed R 150.00
Pate De Verre, Vase, Baby Robin, Blue, Green, Signed, 4 In.High, 5 In.Long 550.00

Pate De Verre, Vase, Bulbous, Spiders & Webs On Milky, G.Argy Rousseau 450.00
Pate De Verre, Vase, Clear, Blue Flowers Form Arches, 3 In. 250.00
Pate De Verre, Vase, Gray, Red Poppies, G.Argy Rousseau, 7 In.High 395.00

*Pate Sur Pate means paste on paste. The design was made by painting
layers of slip (which see) on the piece until a relief decoration was formed.
The method was developed at the Sevres Factory in France about 1850.
It became even more famous at the English Minton Factory about 1870.*
Pate Sur Pate, Box, Butter, Meissen, 4 In.Diameter 1350.00
Pate Sur Pate, Box, Covered, Raised Figures Of Man & Lady 85.00
Pate Sur Pate, Box, Powder, Nymph Plays Flute, Branch, Flowers, Bird 125.00
Pate Sur Pate, Fernery, Fern Decoration, Granger, Ball Feet, Pair 300.00
Pate Sur Pate, Plaque, Reclining Nudes, Swan, Foliage, Tree Border, Scalloped 175.00
Pate Sur Pate, Vase, Brown, White Floral, Butterflies, Signed G.Jones & Sons 125.00
Pate Sur Pate, Vase, Cobalt, Enamel Cupids Riding Moon, Gold Trim 75.00
Pate Sur Pate, Vase, Green, Mauve Medallion Of Dancing Graces, 7 In.High 80.00
Pate Sur Pate, Vase, Raised Winged Angels On Cloud, Embossed, Gold Handles 45.00
Patent Model, Adding Machine, M.O.Dolson, Dec.9, 1884 .... 35.00
Patent Model, Animal Trap, N.B.Lucas, April 11, 1848 .... 60.00
Patent Model, Artificial Arm, Condell, July 11, 1865 .... 225.00
Patent Model, Beer Cooler, J.Herget, Sept.11, 1866 .... 30.00
Patent Model, Carpet Sweeper, John Kauper, Aug.3, 1875 .... 20.00
Patent Model, Clothes Wringer, J.M.Mcmaster, Sept.17, 1867 .... 50.00
Patent Model, Electric Railway Signal, Warner & O'Dell, Aug.20, 1872 .... 90.00
Patent Model, Fence Posts, G.Swenson, May 30, 1879 .... 45.00
Patent Model, Fruit Jar, G.Williams, Nov.13, 1866 .... 20.00
Patent Model, Gas Meter, Castro D.Burton, Jul.29, 1873 .... 55.00
Patent Model, Horse Collar, D.J.Robinson, May 7, 1867 .... 30.00
Patent Model, Horseshoe, J.Brackett, Mar.21, 1871 .... 80.00
Patent Model, Life Preserving Float, G.W.Hamilton, Mar.16, 1858 .... 35.00
Patent Model, Mining Pan, John A.Brock, Apr.23, 1861 .... 20.00
Patent Model, Rotary Engine, Robert Hughes, June 5, 1866 .... 330.00
Patent Model, Sewing Machine, S.W.Miller, June 8, 1869 .... 70.00
Patent Model, Steam Generator, M.Foreman, Oct.16, 1866 .... 45.00
Patent Model, Submarine Telescopic Lantern, H.Thompson, Feb.16, 1869 .... 30.00
Patent Model, Sugar Cube Press, Albert De La Montagnie, Sept.5, 1876 .... 350.00
Patent Model, Thermometer, J.P.F.Huddleston, Jan.22, 1878 .... 30.00
Patent Model, Washing Machine, John Keane, Nov.7, 1865 .... 20.00
Patent Model, Water Purifier & Cooler, J.A.Casey, May 18, 1869 .... 40.00
Patent Model, Wood Carving Machine, I.Hall, Mar.10, 1868 .... 60.00

*Peachblow Glass originated about 1883 at Hobbs, Brockunier and Company
of Wheeling, West Virginia. It is a glass that shades from yellow to
peach. It was lined in white. New England Peachblow is a one-layer
glass with a lining shading from red to white. Mt.Washington Peachblow
shades from pink to blue. Reproductions of peachblow have been made, but they
are of poor quality and can be detected.*
Peachblow, see also Gunderson, Peachblow
Peachblow, Bobeche, Pink To White, New England, Pair 95.00
Peachblow, Bobeche, Rose Pink To White At Base, Frilled, Ruffled 65.00
Peachblow, Bowl, Berry, New Martinsville, Pink, Pink To Custard Interior 55.00
Peachblow, Bowl, New Martinsville, Ribbed, Scalloped, 5 In. 125.00
Peachblow, Bowl, New Martinsville, Ruffled, Small Size 95.00
Peachblow, Bowl, New Martinsville, Ruffled, 4 1/2 In.Square 125.00
Peachblow, Bowl, New Martinsville, Ruffled, 5 In. 80.00
Peachblow, Bowl, Vase, Mt.Washington, Pink To Pale Blue, Berry Pontil, Footed 1050.00
Peachblow, Bride's Basket, Martinsville, Silver Frame, Footed, 15 In.High 165.00
Peachblow, Bride's Basket, New Martinsville 185.00
Peachblow, Bride's Bowl, Cream To Pink, Scalloped Edge, 10 In.Diameter 79.00
Peachblow, Bride's Bowl, New Martinsville, Pink, Yellow Inside, Ribbed 87.50
Peachblow, Bride's Bowl, New Martinsville, Sunglow, 11 In.Diameter 145.00
Peachblow, Bride's Bowl, Wheeling, Rose Beige, Caramel, Yellow, Pink Lining 155.00
Peachblow, Candleholder, Compote Shape, Cranberry Ruffles, Pleated, Footed 125.00
Peachblow, Celery, New England 352.00
Peachblow, Cologne, Webb, Floral Enamel, Clear Stopper 155.00
Peachblow, Cologne, Webb, Floral Enamel, White Opaque Stopper, Marked 165.00

Peachblow, **Creamer**, Sandwich, Ashes Of Roses, Daisies, Violets, Silver Top 155.00
Peachblow, **Creamer**, Wheeling, Mahogany To Yellow, Amber Handle .... 575.00 To 695.00
Peachblow, **Cruet**, Wheeling, Amber Handle & Stopper 600.00
Peachblow, **Cruet**, Wheeling, Teardrop Stopper 650.00
Peachblow, **Cruet**, Yellow To Deep Red, Not Cased, Yellow Stopper, Petals 150.00
Peachblow, **Cup**, Punch, New England, Deep Pink Shading, White Handle 225.00
Peachblow, **Cup**, Punch, Wheeling, Deep Color 245.00
Peachblow, **Cup**, Punch, Wheeling, Light Color 235.00
Peachblow, **Darner**, New England, Souvenir, World's Fair, 1893, Handle 95.00
Peachblow, **Decanter**, Wheeling, Fuchsia, Rope Handle, Acid Finish, 9 1/2 In. 1050.00
Peachblow, **Ewer**, Enamel Flowers, 9 In.High, Pair 195.00
Peachblow, **Mustard**, Wheeling 150.00
Peachblow, **Mustard**, Wheeling, Fuchsia To Yellow, 3 3/4 In.High 195.00
Peachblow, **Pear**, New England, Open End Stem 85.00
Peachblow, **Pear**, New England, Open End Stem, Glossy 225.00
Peachblow, **Perfume**, Webb, Red To Pink, Gold Design 547.00
Peachblow, **Pitcher**, Cherry To White, Finely Ribbed, Clear Handle, Overlay 185.00
Peachblow, **Pitcher**, New England, Dark Rose To White, White Handle 215.00
Peachblow, **Pitcher**, Water, Webb, Scalloped Petal Top, Clear Ribbed Handle 275.00
Peachblow, **Rose Bowl**, England, C.1870 .... 55.00
Peachblow, **Rose Bowl**, Libbey, Ribbed, Turned Down Top, C.1893 .... 225.00
Peachblow, **Rose Bowl**, Libbey, 'World's Fair, 1893, ' Acid Finish 235.00
Peachblow, **Rose Bowl**, New England, 'World's Fair, 1893, ' Gold Inscribed 325.00
Peachblow, **Rose Bowl**, Petal Shape Top, Crimped, Cased, Pedestal Metal Stand 125.00
Peachblow, **Rose Bowl**, Sandwich, Crimped Top, 3 In. 155.00
Peachblow, **Salt & Pepper**, Diamond-Quilted, Cased, Acid 48.00
Peachblow, **Salt & Pepper**, Florette Pattern 75.00
Peachblow, **Salt & Pepper**, New England, Acorn, Brass Tops 85.00
Peachblow, **Salt Shaker**, Wild Rose, New England 175.00
Peachblow, **Salt**, New Martinsville 60.00
Peachblow, **Sugar**, Two Handled, Acid Finish 50.00
Peachblow, **Toothpick**, Square Top, Raspberry Color Extends To Base 225.00
Peachblow, **Tumbler**, New England, Raspberry .... 225.00 To 250.00
Peachblow, **Tumbler**, New England, Raspberry Halfway Down 260.00
Peachblow, **Tumbler**, Sandwich, Light Raspberry To White At Top, Glossy 185.00
Peachblow, **Tumbler**, Wheeling, Fuchsia To Yellow, Glossy 275.00
Peachblow, **Tumbler**, Wheeling, Mahogany 350.00
Peachblow, **Tumbler**, White Lining 150.00
Peachblow, **Vase**, New England, Bulbous, White Cased, 9 In.High 350.00
Peachblow, **Vase**, New England, Lily Trumpet, 7 In.High 425.00
Peachblow, **Vase**, New England, Lily, Three Petals, Acid Finish, 7 3/4 In.High 450.00
Peachblow, **Vase**, New England, Pinched Sides, Ruffled Square Top 450.00
Peachblow, **Vase**, New England, Trumpet, 7 In.High 425.00
Peachblow, **Vase**, New Martinsville, Caramel Iridescent Inside, Acid Finish 170.00
Peachblow, **Vase**, New Martinsville, Pink, Caramel Lining 220.00
Peachblow, **Vase**, Sandwich, Ashes Of Roses, Dusky Pink, Frosted Feet, Acid 185.00
Peachblow, **Vase**, Sandwich, Diamond-Quilted, Applied Rigaree, 7 1/2 In.High 60.00
Peachblow, **Vase**, Sandwich, Pink To White, Crimped, Acid Finish, Frosted Feet 165.00
Peachblow, **Vase**, Sandwich, Pink To White, Dusky Pink Inside, Acid Finish 40.00
Peachblow, **Vase**, Sandwich, Ruffled Top, Footed, 6 In.High 175.00
Peachblow, **Vase**, Sandwich, Yellow Daisy, Amber Leaves & Ruffle, Overlay 160.00
Peachblow, **Vase**, Swirl, Pink, Applied Frosted Binding Around Top, Acid 240.00
Peachblow, **Vase**, Webb Type, 11 In.High .... *Illus* 500.00
Peachblow, **Vase**, Webb, Cherry Red To White At Base, Creamy Lining 110.00
Peachblow, **Vase**, Webb, Coralene 392.00
Peachblow, **Vase**, Webb, Tree Branch, Bird, Gold Design 125.00
Peachblow, **Vase**, Wheeling, Acid Finish 425.00
Peachblow, **Vase**, Wheeling, Mahogany To Fuchsia To Yellow, Slender Neck 525.00
Peachblow, **Vase**, Wheeling, Mahogany To Yellow, Teardrop, 8 3/4 In.High 550.00
Peachblow, **Vase**, Wheeling, Yellow To Mahogany, Gourd Shape, 7 1/2 In.High 750.00
Pearl, **Bottle**, Snuff, Flattened Ovate, Applied Medallions 40.00
Pearl, **Bottle**, Snuff, Flattened Shield Shape, Carved Lady 60.00
Pearl, **Bottle**, Snuff, Flattened, Carved Eighteen Lohan 60.00
Pearl, **Carving Set**, Universal, Embossed Silver Ferrules, Movable Guard 25.00
Pearl, **Knife**, Fruit, Landers Frary, & Clark, Sterling, Set Of 6 .... 47.50
Pearl, **Knife**, Fruit, Sterling Bands, H On Blade, Paul Harvey, Portsmouth, 6 .... 35.00

Peachblow, Vase, Webb Type, 11 In.High
See Page 392

Pearl, Knife, Landers, Frary, & Clark, Aetna Works, Set Of 6	100.00
Pearl, Knife, Sterling Ferrule, 6	25.00
Pearl, Manicure & Toilet Set, 8 Pieces In Leather Case	26.00
Pearl, Napkin Ring	7.50
Pearl, Pen, Case	7.50
Pearl, Pencil, Mechanical, Gold, 1871	11.00
Pearl, Plaque, Last Supper, Hand-Carved, Oval, Pierced Design	155.00
Pearl, Steak Set, Sterling Bands, Plated Tines & Blades, 12 Piece	125.00

Peking Glass is a Chinese Cameo Glass of the eighteenth and nineteenth centuries.

Peking Glass, Ashtray, White, Enameled Mounts	29.00
Peking Glass, Bottle, Snuff, Flask, Enameled Reserves On Blue, Metal Stopper	70.00
Peking Glass, Bottle, Snuff, Flask, Ruby Red, Carved Horses, Ring Handles	25.00
Peking Glass, Bottle, Snuff, Flattened Flask, Enameled Reserves On Pink	50.00
Peking Glass, Bottle, Snuff, Flattened Flask, Snowflake, Green Overlay	60.00
Peking Glass, Bottle, Snuff, Oviform, Enameled Reserved On Boue, Ch'len Lung	60.00
Peking Glass, Bottle, Snuff, Red, Gray, & Green Veining, Jade Stopper	55.00
Peking Glass, Bowl, Blue, On Stand, 5 1/2 In.	65.00
Peking Glass, Bowl, Cameo, Red Birds & Leaves, 8 In.	150.00
Peking Glass, Bowl, Cameo, White, Green Cherries & Leaves, 6 3/4 In., Pair	300.00
Peking Glass, Bowl, Green & White Cameo, Carved Birds On Prunus Branch	120.00
Peking Glass, Bowl, Oval, Yellow, Bracket Feet, Stand, C.1820	175.00
Peking Glass, Bowl, Raspberry, Transparent, 4 In.	30.00
Peking Glass, Bowl, Red, Carved Lotus Blossoms, Vines, 8 In., Pair	300.00
Peking Glass, Bowl, Ruby Red, Carved Lotus Blossoms & Leaves, Ring Foot	170.00
Peking Glass, Bowl, Transparent Raspberry Color, 6 In.Diameter	70.00
Peking Glass, Cup, Floral Carving, Footed, Yellow, Pair	150.00
Peking Glass, Cup, Green, In Hand Rolled Silver Holder	38.00
Peking Glass, Lamp, White, Raspberry, Three Scenes, Prunus Blossoms, Birds	185.00
Peking Glass, Plate, Green, 7 3/4 In.	29.00
Peking Glass, Plate, Turquoise, Full Pontil Bottom, 10 1/2 In.Diameter	55.00
Peking Glass, Rose Bowl, Pink, Plain	47.50
Peking Glass, Vase, Cameo, White Ground, Turquoise Sea Gulls, People, 10 In.	235.00
Peking Glass, Vase, Cameo, Yellow, Red Overlay, Foo Dogs, C.1850, Pair	675.00
Peking Glass, Vase, Cylindrical, Carved Bird & Peonies, Red & White, Pair	400.00
Peking Glass, Vase, Fisherman, Boat, Trees, Carved Teak Stand, Pair	500.00
Peking Glass, Vase, Green To White, 7 1/2 In.High	200.00
Peking Glass, Vase, Ovoid, Corn Sheaves & Birds In Green On White, Pair	400.00

Peloton Glass is European glass with small threads of colored glass rolled onto the surface of clear or colored glass. It is sometimes called spaghetti or shredded coconut glass.

Peloton Glass, Bowl, Finger, Turquoise, Coconut	95.00
Peloton Glass, Pitcher, Water, Clear, Enamel Flower Sprays, Threading	185.00
Peloton Glass, Vase, Fan Shape, Orchid Pink, Blue, Yellow, White, Crimped Top	255.00
Pen, see Store, Pen	

Peters & Reed, Vase, Stippled Brown, Green Sprig Decoration, 13 In.High 55.00

Pewter is a metal alloy of tin and lead. Some of the Pewter made after
about 1840 has a slightly different composition and is called Britannia
metal.

Pewter, Ashtray, Heart, Spade, Club, Diamond, By Poole, Set Of 4	7.75
Pewter, Basin, American, C.1800, 1 3/4 In.High, 6 1/2 In.Across Top	125.00
Pewter, Basin, American, 6 1/2 In.Diameter	65.00
Pewter, Basin, American, 8 In.Diameter	85.00
Pewter, Basin, Gershom Jones, Providence, R.I., C.1785, 8 In.	345.00
Pewter, Basin, S.Maxwell, London Pewter Exported To U.S., 10 1/4 In.	130.00
Pewter, Basin, Signed Boardman, 7 7/8 In.Diameter	200.00
Pewter, Basket, Art Nouveau Raised Design, Moth, Tulips, Kayserzinn	45.00
Pewter, Basket, Pilgrim	10.00
Pewter, Bowl, Baptismal, American, C.1825	175.00
Pewter, Bowl, England, Hammered, 4 1/4 In.Diameter	4.25
Pewter, Bowl, English, Townsend & Compton London, C.1800, 11 In.Diameter	125.00
Pewter, Bowl, English, Townsend, 10 1/2 In.	70.00
Pewter, Bowl, Flagg & Homan	45.00
Pewter, Bowl, G.Lightner, Baltimore, 10 1/4 In.	280.00
Pewter, Bowl, Kayserzinn, Two Birds On Cherry Tree Branch, Cherry Clusters	22.00
Pewter, Bowl, Marked Genuine Pewter, 8 In.Diameter, 2 1/4 In.High	20.00
Pewter, Bowl, Marked Nekrassoff, Hand Hammered, Handles, 9 1/4 In.Diameter	9.75
Pewter, Bowl, Marked Nekrassoff, 4 7/8 In.Diameter, 1 1/2 In.Deep	5.75
Pewter, Bowl, Scroll Design On Handles, 8 In.	25.00
Pewter, Bowl, Vegetable, Kayserzinn, Mark 4099, Sunflower & Blossom Design	50.00
Pewter, Box, China, 5 In.Diameter	20.00
Pewter, Box, Patch, Butterfly Shape, Wings Lift, Chinese Touch Marks	30.00
Pewter, Box, Timber, Hinged	35.00
Pewter, Butter, England, Ornate Decoration, Blue Bristol Liner	40.00
Pewter, Candleholder, American, Pine Tree Touchmark, Handled Reflector	85.00
Pewter, Candleholder, Denmark, Pair	65.00
Pewter, Candlestick, Bulbous Base, 17th Century	260.00
Pewter, Candlestick, Continental, Incised Guilloche Molding, Pair	60.00
Pewter, Candlestick, Marked Genuine Pewter, Double Arms, Pair	18.00
Pewter, Candlestick, Marked Windsor Pewter, J.E.Inings Bros., Mfg.Co., Pair	25.00
Pewter, Candlestick, Queen Anne, 7 In., Pair	225.00
Pewter, Candlestick, 3 In., Pair	32.50
Pewter, Canister, Eight Sides, Screw Top, Oval Handle, Chased, 12 In.High	80.00
Pewter, Castor Set, Signed R.Dunham, Glass Bottles, Pewter Tops	135.00
Pewter, Chalice, Flared Top, Footed, 5 1/2 In.High, Pair	170.00
Pewter, Charger, Burford & Green, C.1750, 15 In.Diameter	125.00
Pewter, Charger, English, Townson & Compton, 13 In.Diameter	70.00
Pewter, Charger, English, 18th Century, 16 1/2 In.Diameter .... 100.00 To 250.00
Pewter, Charger, F.Basset, New York, No.24, 13 1/2 In.Diameter	450.00
Pewter, Charger, 18th Century, 18 In.Diameter	150.00
Pewter, Coffeepot, Boardman, 12 In.	160.00
Pewter, Coffeepot, Britannia, C.1850, 11 In. High .... *Illus*	75.00
Pewter, Coffeepot, English, M.Simon, Pat.1868	65.00
Pewter, Coffeepot, H.B.Ward, Lighthouse	165.00
Pewter, Coffeepot, Marked R.Dunham, Reeded Spout, Delicate Floral Finial	100.00
Pewter, Coffeepot, Porter, Westbrook	180.00
Pewter Coffeepot, Signed R.Dunham .... 80.00 To 85.00
Pewter, Coffeepot, Wm.Calder, Providence, R.I., C.1825, 8 3/4 In.	225.00
Pewter, Compote, Flagg & Homan, Scalloped & Fluted Bowl, 6 In.	22.00
Pewter, Compote, Marked Flagg & Homan, C.1842, 4 X 5 1/2 In.Diameter	27.50
Pewter, Compote, Marked India 183e, 8 In.Diameter, 4 In.Tall	12.00
Pewter, Cooler, Wine, Tudric, England, Inverted Bell Shape, 3 Applied Handles	130.00
Pewter, Cordial, Stirrup, Fox Head	15.00
Pewter, Creamer, Marked Roundhead Pewter, Made In England, 3 3/4 In.High	18.50
Pewter, Creamer, Reed & Barton, Panels, Rococo Handle & Feet	32.00
Pewter, Cup, Collapsible, Issued To Civil War Soldier, Tin Case	10.00
Pewter, Cup, Collapsible, Tin Case	4.75
Pewter, Cup, Loving, Marked Bell & Co., Belfast, Double Handles, 4 1/2 In.	95.00
Pewter, Cup, Stirrup, Fox Head, Monogrammed	27.00
Pewter, Figurine, Birds On Tree Branch, Grapes, Leaves, 8 X 10 In.High	150.00

Pewter, Flagon, Dome Cover, Pear Shape, 18th Century, 10 In.High 70.00
Pewter, Flagon, German, Spherical Thumbpiece, S Curved Handle, C.1730 .... 225.00
Pewter, Flask, Glass, Screw Stopper, C.1866 .... 5.95
Pewter, Foot Warmer, France 45.00
Pewter, Funnel 15.00
Pewter, Goblet, Marked Federal Solid Pewter, 6 1/2 In.High 21.00
Pewter, Goblet, White, Handmade, 4 Oz., 5 1/4 In.High 10.00
Pewter, Incense Burner, French, 6 1/2 In.High 12.00
Pewter, Inkwell, Colishaw, Boston, Hinged Lid, Quill Type, Insert 40.00
Pewter, Inkwell, English, 2 1/4 In.High, 3 1/4 In.Diameter 35.00
Pewter, Inkwell, Hinged Lid, Round, 3 1/4 In.Diameter 15.00
Pewter, Inkwell, Insert, Quill Holes, 3 1/4 In.Diameter 35.00
Pewter, Inkwell, L.H.Vaughan, Taunton, Mass., Eagle With Shield Touchmark 14.75
Pewter, Jar, Covered, Ming, Chai Ching, Octagonal, Bronze Inlaid Vignettes 550.00
Pewter, Jar, Tobacco, Signed Insico, Scroll Footed, C.1920 .... 29.00
Pewter, Ladle, Black Wooden Handle, 16 1/2 In.Long 20.00
Pewter, Lamp Filler, Oil, Handle, Capped Spout 12.00
Pewter, Lamp, Camphene, Sparking, Handle, 3 1/2 In.High 50.00
Pewter, Lamp, Engraved Cherubs, Blue Swirl Shade, 20 In.High 250.00
Pewter, Lamp, Student, Wide Shade, One Arm, Green 135.00
Pewter, Lamp, Whale Oil, Ring Handle 80.00

Pewter, Coffeepot. Britannia, C.1850, 11 In. High
See Page 394

Pewter, Matchbox, English, Hinged, For Long Matches 32.50
Pewter, Matchbox, Engraved Figure Of Golfer 17.00
Pewter, Measure, C.1840, Set Of 8 .... 180.00
Pewter, Measure, England, 1/4 Gill 17.50
Pewter, Measure, England, 1 3/4 Pint, Wooden Thumbrest & Lid, Wicker Handle 65.00
Pewter, Measure, French, Covered, 2 Liters To 1/10th, C.1850, 5 .... 80.00
Pewter, Measure, French, Liter, 2 Demiliters, 2 Double Deciliters, C.1850, 5 .... 70.00
Pewter, Measure, James Yates, England, 1/2 Pint, C.1850 .... 50.00
Pewter, Measure, James Yates, England, Pint 40.00
Pewter, Measure, James Yates, England, Pint, C.1850 .... 55.00
Pewter, Measure, Scottish, D.Gourley & Son, 7 In.High 175.00
Pewter, Measure, Signed Yates Birch & Co., Gill 42.00
Pewter, Measure, 1/4 Gill, Handled 12.50
Pewter, Mold, Chocolate, Nine Animals, 7 1/8 X 5 1/2 In. 25.00
Pewter, Mold, Chocolate, Owl, 4 1/2 X 3 In. 15.00
Pewter, Mold, Easter Egg, Embossed With Flower & Easter Greeting 15.00
Pewter, Mold, Hard Candy, Three Camels, 6 1/8 X 2 1/4 In. 25.00
Pewter, Mold, Hard Candy, Three Jenny Lind Faces, 6 3/4 X 2 1/2 In. 25.00
Pewter, Mold, Ice Cream, Airplane 12.00
Pewter, Mold, Ice Cream, American Eagle 25.00
Pewter, Mold, Ice Cream, Apple 10.00
Pewter, Mold, Ice Cream, Apple, E.& Co. 13.00
Pewter, Mold, Ice Cream, Ascension Balloon, Ribbed 28.50
Pewter, Mold, Ice Cream, Banana 13.00
Pewter, Mold, Ice Cream, Banjo, S.& Co. 13.00
Pewter, Mold, Ice Cream, Basket .... 10.00 To 13.00
Pewter, Mold, Ice Cream, Basket, Three Part 10.00
Pewter, Mold, Ice Cream, Bell 10.00

Pewter, Mold, Ice Cream, Bell With Cupid	12.00
Pewter, Mold, Ice Cream, Bird's Nest	10.00
Pewter, Mold, Ice Cream, Boy On Bike	20.00
Pewter, Mold, Ice Cream, Bunch Of Grapes	13.00
Pewter, Mold, Ice Cream, Cat	25.00
Pewter, Mold, Ice Cream, Champagne Bottle, E.& Co.	14.00
Pewter, Mold, Ice Cream, Cherries	10.00
Pewter, Mold, Ice Cream, Chicken, T.Mills, & Bro.	13.00
Pewter, Mold, Ice Cream, Chicks & Eggs	15.00
Pewter, Mold, Ice Cream, Christmas Wreath	14.00
Pewter, Mold, Ice Cream, Cradle	10.00
Pewter, Mold, Ice Cream, Cross, Knight Templar	10.00
Pewter, Mold, Ice Cream, Cupid	13.00
Pewter, Mold, Ice Cream, Cupid On Rabbit	15.00
Pewter, Mold, Ice Cream, Cupid With Anvil	10.00
Pewter, Mold, Ice Cream, Diamond Shape, E.& Co.	13.00
Pewter, Mold, Ice Cream, Eagle, Spread Wings	22.00
Pewter, Mold, Ice Cream, Ear Of Corn	12.00
Pewter, Mold, Ice Cream, Easter Lily, Three Piece	13.00
Pewter, Mold, Ice Cream, Elephant	14.00
Pewter, Mold, Ice Cream, Engagement Ring	10.00
Pewter, Mold, Ice Cream, Engraved Wedding Ring, E.& Co.	13.00
Pewter, Mold, Ice Cream, Flat Spade	10.00
Pewter, Mold, Ice Cream, Football	10.00
Pewter, Mold, Ice Cream, Hamburg, 3 In.	6.00
Pewter, Mold, Ice Cream, Hatchet, George Washington Bust	20.00
Pewter, Mold, Ice Cream, Hatchet, Initials G.W.	12.00
Pewter, Mold, Ice Cream, Heart	10.00
Pewter, Mold, Ice Cream, Heart, Cupid	12.00
Pewter, Mold, Ice Cream, Heart, E.& Co.	13.00
Pewter, Mold, Ice Cream, Heart, Lady's Head & Four Leaf Clover	17.00
Pewter, Mold, Ice Cream, Hen	10.00
Pewter, Mold, Ice Cream, Lemon	9.00
Pewter, Mold, Ice Cream, Musk Melon, D.& Co.	13.00
Pewter, Mold, Ice Cream, Peach	10.00 To 13.00
Pewter, Mold, Ice Cream, Poppy	13.00
Pewter, Mold, Ice Cream, Question Mark, Marked S. & Co.	16.50
Pewter, Mold, Ice Cream, Rabbit	12.00
Pewter, Mold, Ice Cream, Rabbit, German, 5 X 10 1/2 In.	12.00
Pewter, Mold, Ice Cream, Rabbit, Sitting, 4 In.High	9.00
Pewter, Mold, Ice Cream, Rabbit, 6 1/2 In.High	12.00
Pewter, Mold, Ice Cream, Rooster	15.00
Pewter, Mold, Ice Cream, Rooster, No.6184, U.S.A., 7 X 11 In.	12.00
Pewter, Mold, Ice Cream, Rose, American Beauty	10.00
Pewter, Mold, Ice Cream, Rosebud	10.00
Pewter, Mold, Ice Cream, Santa	15.00
Pewter, Mold, Ice Cream, Santa, Dated 1890	15.00
Pewter, Mold, Ice Cream, Shamrock	10.00
Pewter, Mold, Ice Cream, Slice Of Watermelon	10.00
Pewter, Mold, Ice Cream, Slipper	10.00
Pewter, Mold, Ice Cream, Spade Shape, E.& Co.	23.00
Pewter, Mold, Ice Cream, Squirrel	14.00
Pewter, Mold, Ice Cream, Star Medallion	10.00
Pewter, Mold, Ice Cream, Statue Of Liberty, E & Co., N.Y., 24 In.High	215.00
Pewter, Mold, Ice Cream, Strawberry Basket	13.00
Pewter, Mold, Ice Cream, Sweet Pea	10.00
Pewter, Mold, Ice Cream, Tiger Lily	1200.
Pewter, Mold, Ice Cream, Tulip Shape	12.50
Pewter, Mold, Ice Cream, Turkey	12.00
Pewter, Mold, Ice Cream, Turkey, Roast	10.00
Pewter, Mold, Ice Cream, Two Doves	12.50
Pewter, Mold, Ice Cream, Two Santas, 7 In.Wide, 7 1/4 In.High	45.00
Pewter, Mold, Ice Cream, Umbrella	10.00
Pewter, Mold, Ice Cream, Wishbone	10.00
Pewter, Mold, Ice Cream, Witches Kettle Dated 1889	12.00
Pewter, Mold, Ice Cream, Yule Log	10.00

Pewter, Muffineer, England, Bulbous Base, Long Neck, Screw Cap, Footed 21.00
Pewter, Mug, British Touchmarks, Inscribed Name, Glass Bottom, 3 5/8 In. 28.00
Pewter, Mug, C.1820, Pint 65.00
Pewter, Mug, C.1820, Quart 95.00
Pewter, Mug, C.1840, 1/2 Pint 35.00
Pewter, Mug, English, Pint 35.00
Pewter, Mug, George IV, Glass Bottom, Dated 1850 .... 85.00
Pewter, Mug, Glass Bottom, Engraved Thayer Club 1907-8 .... 12.75
Pewter, Mug, James Yates, Tulip Shape, Double Handle, Engraved, Pint, C.1820 .... 45.00
Pewter, Mug, Reed & Barton, 1898, Glass Bottom, Bronze Medallion, Whist Club 24.50
Pewter, Mug, Scroll Handle, Dated April, 1891, Glass Bottom, 4 In.High 35.00
Pewter, Mustard Stein, Ornate Open Sides, Blue Violet Insert, Hinged Lid 35.00
Pewter, Mustard, Blue Glass Liner 22.00
Pewter, Night-Light, Alcohol, Resembles A Lamp Post, Weighted Base 45.00
Pewter, Pitcher, American, Hinged Lid, Finial, 6 In.High 95.00
Pewter, Pitcher, Cider, R.Dunham, 6 1/2 In.High 250.00
Pewter, Pitcher, R.Dunham, Portland, Me., C.1840, 6 1/2 In.High 325.00
Pewter, Pitcher, Signed Shanghai, China, Raised Dragon, 6 In.High 30.00
Pewter, Pitcher, Water, Covered, William McQuilkin, 10 1/2 In.High 420.00
Pewter, Pitcher, Water, Kayserzinn, Horned Mythological Head, Floral 125.00
Pewter, Plate, American, Sam Danforth, 7 7/8 In. 235.00
Pewter, Plate, Boardman & Co., 9 1/4 In.Diameter 180.00
Pewter, Plate, Boardman & Hart, New York, Two Eagles In Ovals, 9 1/2 In. 230.00
Pewter, Plate, Coat Of Arms, C.1840, 9 1/4 In.Diameter 75.00
Pewter, Plate, Crown & Flower Touchmarks, 8 1/2 In.Diameter 35.00
Pewter, Plate, English Touchmarks, 9 In. 35.00
Pewter, Plate, English, C.1830 .... 72.50
Pewter, Plate, English, Dated 1785 .... 45.00
Pewter, Plate, English, Dated 1814 .... 45.00
Pewter, Plate, English, 8 In. 170.00
Pewter, Plate, German, 8 1/2 In., Set Of 4 .... 40.00
Pewter, Plate, Harbeson, Philadelphia, 7 3/4 In. 190.00
Pewter, Plate, Henry Will, New York, 8 3/4 In.Diameter 600.00
Pewter, Plate, Kayserzinn, Raised Flowers, Dragonfly, 8 1/2 In. 60.00
Pewter, Plate, Marked Berges, Rolled Edge, 5 In. 15.00
Pewter, Plate, Marked Berges, 5 1/2 In. 15.00
Pewter, Plate, Marked Genuine Pewter, 6 1/2 In. 15.00
Pewter, Plate, Reed & Barton, No.1671, 5 1/4 In. 13.50
Pewter, Plate, Samuel Ellis, English, C.1760, 9 3/4 In. 110.00
Pewter, Plate, Stephen Barnes, Conn., C.1791-1800, 8 3/4 In.Diameter 310.00
Pewter, Plate, T.Danforth, Phila., Two Circles With Eagle & T.D., 9 1/4 In. 320.00
Pewter, Plate, Thomas Badger, Boston, 8 1/4 In.Diameter 220.00
Pewter, Plate, Wm.Danforth, Conn., 11 1/4 In.Diameter 190.00
Pewter, Platter, Kayserzinn, Marked 4345, Running Deer Design, 22 In.Long 55.00
Pewter, Platter, Kayserzinn, Woodcocks Amid Vegetables, 16 X 10 In. 65.00
Pewter, Platter, Thomas Badger, C.1790, 12 1/4 In.Diameter 375.00
Pewter, Porringer, Boardman & Co., New York, 5 In.Diameter 360.00
Pewter, Porringer, Marked Pewter 06252, Handles, 5 In.Diameter 25.00
Pewter, Porringer, Marked T.D.& S.B., Openwork Handle 155.00
Pewter, Porringer, Stede, 2 1/2 In. 15.00
Pewter, Porringer, Stede, 5 3/4 In.Diameter 15.00
Pewter, Pot, Wine, Overall Punched Design, 6 1/2 In.High 55.00
Pewter, Salt & Pepper, Signed W.B.Mfg.Co., Mayflower Pewter, Handle 14.00
Pewter, Salt Dip, Viking Ship .... 7.50 To 8.50
Pewter, Salt, Master, C.1840, Pair 15.00
Pewter, Seal, Embossed Dog Heads On Top, Vase Shape, Initial, 3 1/2 In. 65.00
Pewter, Server, Coffee, Holland, Methavia, Footed, Brass Holder 195.00
Pewter, Shoe, Britannia, Victorian, Laced, 5 1/2 In. 19.00
Pewter, Snuffbox, Hinged Lid, Embossed Floral, Spoon 38.00
Pewter, Snuffbox, Marked J.& D.W., Rectangular, 2 X 2 7/8 In. 38.00
Pewter, Spigot, Cider, Pocket Size, 4 In., Leather Case 12.50
Pewter, Spoon, Dutch, Ornately Molded, Cherubs At Top Of Bowl, Set Of 5 .... 30.00
Pewter, Spoon, Soup, 8 In.Long 5.00
Pewter, Stein, Germany, Hinged Lid, 12 In.High 135.00
Pewter, Stein, Hinged Cover, 6 In.High 45.00
Pewter, Stein, Signed English Pewter, Spring Cover, Flower Design, 8 In.High 30.00

Pewter, Sugar & Creamer, Marked Arundel Pewter, C.W.F.& Sons, Ltd. 25.00
Pewter, Sugar & Creamer, Marked Brewster 100.00
Pewter, Sugar & Creamer, Marked Concord 19.50
Pewter, Sugar, Creamer, & Tray 16.50
Pewter, Sugar, Sellew & Co., Two Handled, Acorn Finial, C.1840, 7 In.High 375.00
Pewter, Sugar, Signed Sheldon & Feitman, Albany 125.00
Pewter, Syrup, Marked Insico, Hinged Cover, Numbered 34.00
Pewter, Tablespoon, Marked John Yates, C.1835 .... 15.00
Pewter, Tankard, Continental, Wrigglework Decoration, Engraved, Dated 1802 .... 90.00
Pewter, Tankard, Covered, Boardman & Co., N.Y., 9 1/4 In. 700.00
Pewter, Tankard, Covered, Kayserzinn, Inscribed To A Painter, Dated 1896 .... 175.00
Pewter, Tankard, Dublin, Harp Mark, Pint 45.00
Pewter, Tankard, French, Boulanget, C.1838, 1/2 Liter 40.00
Pewter, Tankard, French, C.1838, Liter 45.00
Pewter, Tankard, James Yates, Victorian, 1/2 Pint 57.00
Pewter, Tankard, Signed Yates, Pint 65.00
Pewter, Tea Caddy, Chinese, Globe Shape, 6 In.High 65.00
Pewter, Tea Set, Child's, 3 Piece 5.00
Pewter, Tea Set, Hutton Sheffield, Harold Stabler, C.1930, 4 Piece 225.00
Pewter, Tea Set, Rattan Handles, 3 Concentric Stepped Circles, 3 Piece 80.00
Pewter, Tea Set, Soo Chow Province, Floral Engraving, Jade Handles, 9 Piece 125.00
Pewter, Teapot, Acorn Finial 45.00
Pewter, Teapot, American, Putnam, 11 In.High 240.00
Pewter, Teapot, Chinese, Jade & Rose Quartz Inserts 150.00
Pewter, Teapot, Chinese, Jade Insert In Handle, Jade Finial, Hexagonal 65.00
Pewter, Teapot, Chinese, Signed Hsein Feng, Fish, Green Stone Eyes, 1851 .... 100.00
Pewter, Teapot, Dixon & Sons, Small Size 37.50
Pewter, Teapot, Filigree, 4 Footed Base, Bud & Leaf Decoration, No.6500-6 .... 75.00
Pewter, Teapot, H.B.Ward, Wallingford, Conn., 8 In.High 165.00
Pewter, Teapot, H.Yale, Conn., S-Scroll Handle, Tapering, C.1830 .... 100.00
Pewter, Teapot, James Dixon & Sons, Wooden Handle 52.50
Pewter, Teapot, Lewis & Co., American 175.00
Pewter, Teapot, Marked China, Quilted Look, Onyx Handle & Finial 35.00
Pewter, Teapot, Marked James Dixon & Sons, Pear Shape, Footed, 10 1/2 In. 55.00
Pewter, Teapot, Marked Reed & Barton, Mass., No.3690, 10 Panels, Hinged 40.00
Pewter, Teapot, Putnam, 6 1/2 In. .... *Illus* 225.00
Pewter, Teapot, Reed & Barton, Fleur-De-Lis, Footed, Wooden Handle & Finial 35.00
Pewter, Teapot, Reed & Barton, Melon Ribbed, Scroll Feet, Flower Finial, 1845 .... 48.00
Pewter, Teapot, Reed & Barton, Octagonal, Scrolling Wooden Handle, C.1840 .... 80.00
Pewter, Teapot, Rosewell Gleason, Pear Shape, Footed 185.00
Pewter, Teapot, Signed Dover Stamp Co., Copper Bottom, Acorn Finial 55.00
Pewter, Teapot, Signed James Dixon, Melon Ribbed, Acorn Finial 63.00
Pewter, Teaspoon, C.Parker & Co. 12.00
Pewter, Tray, Bread, Rice, 12 In. 9.00
Pewter, Tray, Kayserzinn, Nude Figure, Flowing Hair, Shell Shape 75.00
Pewter, Tray, Kayserzinn, Oblong 40.00
Pewter, Urn, Twin Handles, 5 1/2 In.High 9.50
Pewter, Vase, Liberty & Co., England, Bullet Shape, Hammered Devices, Pair 150.00
Pewter, Vase, Marked Concord Pewter, 9 1/2 In.High 27.50
Pewter, Vase, Marked Solid Pewter, 8 In. 15.00

Pewter, Teapot, Putnam, 6 1/2 In.

Pewter, Whistle, Bird 4.75
Pewter, Whistle, Dog Figure, 1 5/8 In.Long 2.75
Pewter, Whistle, Hole At Top For Chain, 1 7/8 In.Long 2.75
Pewter, Wine Taster, French 55.00
Pewter, Wine, 5 In.High 2.00

Phoenix Glass Company was founded in 1880 in Pennsylvania. The firm made commercial products such as lampshades, bottles, glassware. Collectors today are interested in the sculptured glassware made by the company from the 1930s until the mid-1950s.

Phoenix, Bowl, Blue, Diving Girl, Sculptured 85.00
Phoenix, Bowl, Custard Color, Three Dimensional Design, Round 52.00
Phoenix, Bowl, Flowers, Red, Blue, 11 In.Wide 25.00
Phoenix, Bowl, Frolicking Nudes, Pink, 10 In. 45.00
Phoenix, Centerpiece, Alabaster White, Birds & Berries, Acid 65.00
Phoenix, Globe, Stalactite, Opalescent Ribbed, 8 In.Long, 3 In.Opening 22.50
Phoenix, Lamp Base, Blue, Rust, Green, White Ground, Base Lights 38.00
Phoenix, Lamp Base, Coral Berries, Green Leaves, No Fittings, 9 1/2 In. 17.00
Phoenix, Plate, Nude Frolicking Figure, Clear, 10 In. 40.00
Phoenix, Tumbler, Embossed Fruit In Pink Brilliantine, Footed, Set Of 4 ...... 65.00
Phoenix, Tumbler, Frosted, Lavender, Fruit Decoration, Cone Shape, Footed 16.00
Phoenix, Tumbler, Lavender, Unsigned, Set Of 4 .... 35.00
Phoenix, Vase, Amethyst Praying Mantis On Lavender, Oval 65.00
Phoenix, Vase, Aqua Birds In Tree Branches On Custard, Rectangular 32.00
Phoenix, Vase, Aquamarine Birds & Leaves On Cream, 6 In.High 40.00
Phoenix, Vase, Art Nouveau Girl On Custard, Sculptured, 10 In.High 45.00
Phoenix, Vase, Beige Katydids On White Satin, Coreopolis 45.00
Phoenix, Vase, Bell Shape, Molded White Lily Of The Valley On Blue, 7 In. 48.00
Phoenix, Vase, Birds, Grapes, & Vines On Custard, 10 1/4 In.High 67.50
Phoenix, Vase, Bittersweet On White, 10 In.High 60.00
Phoenix, Vase, Blue Bluebells On White 45.00
Phoenix, Vase, Blue Dragonfly On White 45.00
Phoenix, Vase, Blue Leaves & Fruit On Custard, 6 In.High 55.00
Phoenix, Vase, Blue Vines, Leaves, & Fruit On Opaque Custard 40.00
Phoenix, Vase, Brown Owls & Green Stems On Custard, 6 In.High 45.00
Phoenix, Vase, Brown Pinecones & Green Leaves On White, 6 3/4 In.High 22.50
Phoenix, Vase, Chrysanthemums, White Blown Out Centers, Red Ground, 5 In. 45.00
Phoenix, Vase, Cockatoos & Tan Twigs On White, 9 1/2 In.High 58.00
Phoenix, Vase, Crystal Grasshoppers On Blue, 8 In.High 40.00
Phoenix, Vase, Dancing Girls With Scarves, White Figures On Blue, 12 In. 78.00
Phoenix, Vase, Dancing Nudes, Metal Ornamentation Top & Bottom .... 75.00 To 95.00
Phoenix, Vase, Dogwood Blossoms On Coffee, 11 In.High 50.00
Phoenix, Vase, Fish, Amethyst, 9 In.High 45.00
Phoenix, Vase, Freesia On Light Blue, Frosted White, Oval Top, Round Base 65.00
Phoenix, Vase, Geese On Custard, Pillow 100.00
Phoenix, Vase, Grasshoppers On Green, Brilliantine 37.50
Phoenix, Vase, Grasshoppers, Brilliantine, Freesia Type, Crystal 28.00
Phoenix, Vase, Head Of Woman On Each Side, Sticker, 10 1/2 In.High 50.00
Phoenix, Vase, Hummingbird & Floral Decoration, Amethyst 35.00
Phoenix, Vase, Hummingbirds & Flowers On Green, 5 1/4 In.High 85.00
Phoenix, Vase, Madonna, White & Pastel Green Ground, 10 1/2 In.High 65.00
Phoenix, Vase, Mother-Of-Pearl, Blue Shading, Acid Finish 115.00
Phoenix, Vase, Nudes On Black Amethyst, Triangular, 8 1/2 In.High 25.00
Phoenix, Vase, Orange Bittersweet & Blue Leaves On White, 10 In.High 65.00
Phoenix, Vase, Owls On Blue, Sticker 45.00
Phoenix, Vase, Peach Floral & Green Stems On White, Satinized 70.00
Phoenix, Vase, Praying Mantis On Green 45.00
Phoenix, Vase, Praying Mantis On Green, 8 1/2 In.High 30.00
Phoenix, Vase, Red Mums, White Centers, Label, 4 3/4 In.High 50.00
Phoenix, Vase, Starflower On Amber 20.00
Phoenix, Vase, White Flying Geese On Blue 85.00
Phoenix, Vase, White Luster Flowers On Pink 85.00
Phoenix, Vase, White Wild Rose On Peach 52.50
Phoenix, Vase, Yellow Plums & Green Leaves On White, 4 In.High 35.00
    Phonograph, see Music, Phonograph
Photography, Album, Japan, 34 Photographs Of Towns & Temples, 1900s 35.00

Photography, **Album**, Leather, Brass Binding, 6 X 5 2 1/2 In. 6.00
Photography, **Album**, Leather, Dated 1892, 50 Photographs Of Holmes Family 14.00
Photography, **Album**, Stereo, Nazi, Occupation Views, Hitler, Hoffmann 59.50
Photography, **Ambrotype**, Dog Wearing Glasses & Smoking Pipe 32.00
Photography, **Ambrotype**, Sixth Plate, Man, Oval Liner 18.00
Photography, **Camera & Graphoscope**, Patent In The Entire World, Dec.'92 .... 125.00
Photography, **Camera**, Box, Kewpie, Sears, Roebuck & Co., 3 6/4 X 5 1/2 In. 65.00
Photography, **Camera**, Brownie Jr., Folding Autographic, Instruction Book 15.00
Photography, **Camera**, Brownie, No.3, 1912 .... 8.00
Photography, **Camera**, Cooke F 2.9 Lens, Graflex 90.00
Photography, **Camera**, Eastman Kodak, 50th Anniversary, 1880-1930 .... 25.00
Photography, **Camera**, Folding, Autographic, Kodak, No.2 .... 14.00
Photography, **Camera**, Folding, Cartridge Premo, Kodak, No.2a, Box 9.00
Photography, **Camera**, Folding, Cirkut Back, Tripod Head, No Gears, Century 125.00
Photography, **Camera**, Folding, Plate, Red Bellows, Korona, C.1900 .... 40.00
Photography, **Camera**, Folding, Pocket, Eastman Kodak, C.1906 .... 28.00
Photography, **Camera**, Folding, Premo Model, Plates, Kodak 30.00
Photography, **Camera**, Hawkeye, Box, 1906 .... 20.00
Photography, **Camera**, Hawkeye, Eastman Kodak, Vest Pocket, No.3832, C.1917 .... 20.00
Photography, **Camera**, Magazine, Spring Advance, Circa 1905, Conley 60.00
Photography, **Camera**, Motion Picture, Bell & Howell, Model 10 .... 35.00
Photography, **Camera**, Rolleiflex, Tessar Lenses 50.00
Photography, **Camera**, Self Developing, See & Made By Photo-See Corp. 12.00
Photography, **Camera**, Telescopic, Cherry Wood Box, C.1880 .... 75.00
Photography, **Carte De Visite**, A.Lincoln 14.00
Photography, **Carte De Visite**, U.S.Grant 14.00
Photography, **Daguerreotype Case**, Black, Man 8.00
Photography, **Daguerreotype Case**, Black, Young Couple, C.1860 .... 15.00
Photography, **Daguerreotype Case**, Brown, Screw Type, 2 In.Diameter 30.00
Photography, **Daguerreotype Case**, Civil War Soldier, Red Velvet Lined 12.00
Photography, **Daguerreotype Case**, Gutta-Percha, Angel Carrying Babies 45.00
Phogography, **Daguerreotype Case**, Gutta-Percha, Apple Picker 39.00
Photography, **Daguerreotype Case**, Gutta-Percha, Apple Picker, Brown 35.00
Photography, **Daguerreotype Case**, Gutta-Percha, Beehive, Black 25.00
Photography, **Daguerreotype Case**, Gutta-Percha, Black, Baby, Advertising, ... 35.00
Photography, **Daguerreotype Case**, Gutta-Percha, Black, Fruit, Signed Smith 18.00
Photography, **Daguerreotype Case**, Gutta-Percha, Black, Oval 14.75
Photography, **Daguerreotype Case**, Gutta-Percha, Bobby Shafto 50.00
Photography, **Daguerreotype Case**, Gutta-Percha, Brown, July 4 & 11, 1858 .... 60.00
Photography, **Daguerreotype Case**, Gutta-Percha, Children Chasing Butterfly 25.00
Photography, **Daguerreotype Case**, Gutta-Percha, Civil War Soldier, Color 27.50
Photography, **Daguerreotype Case**, Gutta-Percha, Dancing Girl, Floral Border 28.00
Photography, **Daguerreotype Case**, Gutta-Percha, Daniel In The Lion's Den 100.00
Photography, **Daguerreotype Case**, Gutta-Percha, Faithful Hound 45.00
Photography, **Daguerreotype Case**, Gutta-Percha, Fireman 39.50
Photography, **Daguerreotype Case**, Gutta-Percha, Fireman Saving Child 100.00
Photography, **Daguerreotype Case**, Gutta-Percha, Fireman, Kimball & Cooper 55.00
Photography, **Daguerreotype Case**, Gutta-Percha, Floral & Leaf, Lady Inside 11.00
Photography, **Daguerreotype Case**, Gutta-Percha, Fruit, Floral, Jewels 48.00
Photography, **Daguerreotype Case**, Gutta-Percha, Geometric 27.50
Photography, **Daguerreotype Case**, Gutta-Percha, Gypsy 55.00
Photography, **Daguerreotype Case**, Gutta-Percha, Hunter & Fallen Deer 90.00
Photography, **Daguerreotype Case**, Gutta-Percha, Littlefield Parson's Lady 50.00
Photography, **Daguerreotype Case**, Gutta-Percha, Lord's Prayer, R.Paine 75.00
Photography, **Daguerreotype Case**, Gutta-Percha, Man 15.00
Photography, **Daguerreotype Case**, Gutta-Percha, Mary Had A Little Lamb 25.00
Photography, **Daguerreotype Case**, Gutta-Percha, Patent 1868 .... 9.75
Photography, **Daguerreotype Case**, Gutta-Percha, Quarter Plate, Major Andre 45.00
Photography, **Daguerreotype Case**, Gutta-Percha, Raised Design, Velvet 42.50
Photography, **Daguerreotype Case**, Gutta-Percha, Rebecca At The Well 50.00
Photography, **Daguerreotype Case**, Gutta-Percha, Rebel Soldier In Uniform 32.50
Photography, **Daguerreotype Case**, Gutta-Percha, The Blind Beggar 45.00
Photography, **Daguerreotype Case**, Gutta-Percha, The Chess Players 45.00
Photography, **Daguerreotype Case**, Gutta-Percha, The Clipper Ship & Fort 100.00
Photography, **Daguerreotype Case**, Gutta-Percha, The Vision Of Ezekiel 175.00
Photography, **Daguerreotype Case**, Gutta-Percha, Washington Monument, F.Goll 125.00

Photography, Daguerreotype Case, Gutta-Percha, Wedding Couple, 5 X 4 In. 35.00
Photography, Daguerreotype Case, Gutta-Percha, Young Woman, Oval 9.00
Photography, Daguerreotype Case, Gutta-Percha, 3 In. 35.00
Photography, Daguerreotype Case, Leather, Embossed, Velvet Lined 18.00
Photography, Daguerreotype Case, Leather, Floral, Grandma, White Bonnet 12.50
Photography, Daguerreotype Case, Leather, Quarter Plate, Seated Woman 20.00
Photography, Daguerreotype Case, Leather, Tintype In Gold Frame, Embossed, 4 .... 28.50
Photography, Daguerreotype Case, Man In Dress Of 1850s, Leatherette 10.00
Photography, Daguerreotype Case, Mother-Of-Pearl Inlay 35.00
Photography, Daguerreotype Case, Mother-Of-Pearl, French, Floral 30.00
Photography, Daguerreotype Case, Octagonal, 3 In. .... *Illus* 35.00
Photography, Daguerreotype Case, Papier-Mache, Embossed, Ambrotype Of Man 6.00
Photography, Daguerreotype Case, Papier-Mache, Embossed, Women, Silver 6.50
Photography, Daguerreotype Case, Papier-Mache, Maroon, Young Lady 4.50
Photography, Daguerreotype, Child In Pantalettes, Holds Ribboned Hat 12.00
Photography, Daguerreotype, Civil War Confederate Soldier 40.00
Photography, Daguerreotype, Civil War Soldier 15.00
Photography, Daguerreotype, Mournful Young Woman, Gold Locket, White Dress 10.00
Photography, Daguerreotype, Old Woman In Bonnet, Small Boy 10.00
Photography, Daguerreotype, Old Woman, Glasses, Black Dress, Lace Bonnet 20.00
Photography, Daguerreotype, Quarter Plate, Husband & Wife, Full Length 30.00
Photography, Daguerreotype, Quarter Plate, White Family Of Ga., Set Of 3 .... 75.00
Photography, Daguerreotype, Sixth Plate, Dead Baby Holding Rattle 22.50
Photography, Daguerreotype, Sixth Plate, Dead Man, Profile 18.00
Photography, Daguerreotype, Sixth Plate, Painting Of Woman, Leather Case 30.00
Photography, Daguerreotype, Sixth Plate, Quaker Woman 10.00
Photography, Daguerreotype, Sixth Plate, Steel Engraving Of Gentleman 22.00
Photography, Daguerreotype, Sixth Plate, Woman In Sailboat, Leather Case 20.00
Photography, Daguerreotype, Sixth Plate, Woman, Gold Brooch, Impressed Dots 15.00
Photography, Daguerreotype, Sixth Plate, Young Man, Gold Embossed Leather 23.00
Photography, Daguerreotype, Sixth Plate, 2 Sisters, Floral Leather, Pretlove 12.00
Photography, Daguerreotype, Two Sisters Dressed For Winter 15.00
Photography, Daguerreotype, Young Couple 14.00
Photography, Daguerreotype, Young Man In High Hat 20.00
Photography, Daguerreotype, Young Woman, Signed Plumbe 30.00
Photography, Magic Lantern 25.00
Photography, Magic Lantern Slide, Advertising Roman's Bread, Verses, 4 .... 4.95
Photography, Magic Lantern Slide, Old Japan, Oak Dovetailed Case, 100 .... 39.00
Photography, Magic Lantern Slide, 8 .... 3.50

Photography, Daguerreotype Case, Octagonal, 3 In.

Photography, Magic Lantern, Venus Em-Co Usa, 24 Slides 55.00
Photography, Magic Lantern, 21 Slides, Boxed 58.00
Photography, Movie Projector, Lindstrom, 2 Reels Mickey Mouse Film 45.00
Photography, Movie Projector, 35mm, Keystone 40.00
Photography, Photograph, American Militia Group, Rhode Island, Dated 1870 .... 17.50
Photography, Photograph, American Militia, Keystone Cop, R.I., C.1890 .... 9.50
Photography, Photograph, Blacksmiths & Horses, P.Shay Horseshoer, C.1880 .... 7.50
Photography, Photograph, Chief Engineer Of Fire Dept.St.Louis, Mo., C.1904 .... 22.50
Photography, Photograph, Civil War General N.P.Banks, 1894 .... 12.50
Photography, Photograph, Civil War Union Infantry Company, Gilt Frame 29.50
Photography, Photograph, Concord, N.H., Volunteer Fire Dept., C.1880 .... 12.50
Photography, Photograph, Finger Lakes Steamer, Kate Morgan, Oval 7.00
Photography, Photograph, Horse-Drawn Fire Engine, Steam Pump, Vermont 8.00
Photography, Photograph, Locomotives Taken In The 1930s, 135 .... 9.75
Photography, Photograph, Portsmouth Baseball Club, C.1890 .... 7.50
Photography, Photograph, Shenandoah Zeppelin After It Fell, Ohio, 1925 .... 4.00

Photography, Photograph, Spanish American War Soldiers	7.50
Photography, Photograph, Spanish American War U.S.Infantry Soldiers	7.50
Photography, Photograph, T.Roosevelt, Autographed, Harris & Ewing, 1912	75.00
Photography, Photograph, The Monarch Of Boston & Lowell Railroad, C.1870	12.50
Photography, Photograph, U.S.Flagship San Francisco, Officers, 1895	6.00
Photography, Photograph, U.S.S.Comfort, Brown, 12 X 20 In.	4.00
Photography, Projector For Postcards, Electric	20.00
Photography, Stereo, see Stereo	
Photography, Tintype, G.A.R.Veteran, Bearded, Standing, C.1880	9.50
Photography, Tintype, Soldier, Civil War	25.00
Piano Baby, see Bisque, Piano Baby	
Piano, see Music, Piano	

Pickard China was started in 1898 by Wilder Pickard. Hand-painted china was a featured product. The firm is still working in Antioch, Illinois.

Pickard, Berry Set, Tulips, Artist Arno, 10 In., 7 Piece	135.00
Pickard, Bonbon, Allover Floral, Etched, Gold, Two Handles	30.00
Pickard, Bowl, Acorns, Artist-Signed, C.1905	75.00
Pickard, Bowl, Allover Gold With Raised Floral, Scalloped Rim, Marked	20.00
Pickard, Bowl, Fruit, Easter Lily, Artist Blazek, 1898	95.00
Pickard, Bowl, Fruit, Poppies, 1905	70.00
Pickard, Bowl, Handles, Luster, Signed Landon, 1912, 4 1/2 In.Diameter	18.00
Pickard, Bowl, Nuts On Bottom & Sides, Artist-Signed, 5 1/2 In.	30.00
Pickard, Bowl, Poinsettias, Leaves, Gold, Hand-Painted, 10 In.	35.00
Pickard, Bowl, Poppies, Daisies, Artist Gasper, Gold Around Edges, Ruffled	42.00
Pickard, Bowl, Signed Blazek, Yellow Exterior, Easter Lilies, 1898	78.00
Pickard, Bowl, Stylized Design, Gold Inside, 4 In.	25.00
Pickard, Bowl, Violets, Leaves, Coin Gold, Low Foot, 8 In.Diameter	38.00
Pickard, Bowl, White Background, Edges Pink And Lavender, Signed	25.00
Pickard, Butter Pat, Floral, 1938 Mark	10.00
Pickard, Butter Pat, Violets, Purple, Signed	8.25
Pickard, Candlestick, Pink & Blue Designs, Gold, 1912, 6 1/8 In.High, Pair	32.00
Pickard, Celery, Pink Blossoms, Gold, 13 In.Long	30.00
Pickard, Celery, Scenic, Artist-Signed	40.00
Pickard, Chocolate Pot, Blue Luster, Gold Etched Floral, Spout & Handle	48.00
Pickard, Coffee Set, Aura, Argenta Linear Design, Artist Hess, 3 Piece	135.00
Pickard, Compote, Gold, Etched	20.00
Pickard, Creamer, Allover Gold Decoration, Marked, 4 1/2 In.High	12.50
Pickard, Creamer, Allover Gold With Raised Floral, Marked 3 X 4 In.Base	15.00
Pickard, Creamer, Gold	27.50
Pickard, Creamer, Hand-Painted Violets, Gold, 4 In.High	12.00
Pickard, Cup & Saucer, Fruit, Blue, Gold, Artist-Signed	5.50
Pickard, Dish, Candy, Allover Gold Stipple Floral, Pierced Handles	12.00
Pickard, Dish, Candy, Covered, Allover Gold Decoration, Iridescent Inside	24.00
Pickard, Dish, Candy, Etched Gold, Open Handles	16.00
Pickard, Dish, Candy, Floral, Pierced Handles, 6 3/4 In.Diameter	14.00
Pickard, Dish, Candy, Stippled Gold, Three Sections, Center Handle	35.00
Pickard, Dish, Candy, 2 Hand-Painted Floral Groups, Gold Leaf & 1912 Mark	7.50
Pickard, Hatpin Holder, Allover Stipple Gold Floral	25.00
Pickard, Hatpin Holder, Floral, C.1925	25.00
Pickard, Jar & Underplate, Jam, Aura Argenta Linear Design	85.00
Pickard, Jar, Cracker, Hand-Painted, Gold, Poppy, Marked W.A.Pickard	35.00
Pickard, Muffineer, White, Gold Trim, Black Band	10.00
Pickard, Mug, Grapes, Red, Green, Gold, Signed, Handle	48.50
Pickard, Mug, Hand-Painted Poppies, Green Leaves, Gold Trim, Signed LOL	85.00
Pickard, Mug, Purple Grapes, Gold, Signed O.Goess	150.00
Pickard, Pitcher, Art Nouveau Type Forest Scene, Signed Heaney, Round Mark	110.00
Pickard, Pitcher, Celtic Pattern, 6 Sided, Green, Signed, 10 In.High	115.00
Pickard, Pitcher, Cider, Multicolor Enamel Floral Band, Artist E.Tolpin	70.00
Pickard, Pitcher, Cider, Signed Yeschek, 8 3/4 X 6 1/4 In.	165.00
Pickard, Pitcher, Milk, Gold & Floral Border, Art Deco Design On Body	75.00
Pickard, Pitcher, Pastel Ground, Multicolored Violets, Gold Trim, 4 1/2 In.	24.00
Pickard, Pitcher, Roseland, By Marker, 6 In.	155.00
Pickard, Pitcher, Scene, River, Trees, Wild Rose Shrubs, Gold Rim & Handle	115.00
Pickard, Pitcher, Water, Helmet Shape, Golden Pheasant	145.00

Pickard, Plate, Art Nouveau Painting Of Green Flowers, Cobalt Trim 28.50
Pickard, Plate, Cake, Orange, Yellow Poppies, Open Handle, Gifford, 1905 .... 38.50
Pickard, Plate, Cake, Pink, Yellow, & Lavender Florals, Gold Bows, 1912 .... 28.00
Pickard, Plate, Cake, Signed James, Dutch Scenes On Bisque, 11 In.Diameter 50.00
Pickard, Plate, Floral Designs, 6 In.Diameter 6.00
Pickard, Plate, Forest Scene & Daisies, Signed Heaney, Round Mark 45.00
Pickard, Plate, Fruit & Floral Border, Gold, Two Handles, Signed, 10 In. 37.50
Pickard, Plate, Gold Acid Etched Design, Signed, 5 1/2 In. 12.00
Pickard, Plate, Green, Century Of Progress Scene, 1937, Hand-Painted 15.00
Pickard, Plate, Green, Gold, Floral Center 50.00
Pickard, Plate, Jonquils On Green To Yellow, Artist E.Gibson, 1898-1904 .... 42.00
Pickard, Plate, Maple Leaves, Blue Flowers, Gold, Hand-Painted, 7 3/4 In. 18.00
Pickard, Plate, Nasturtium Decoration, Artist F.James, 1898 .... 28.00
Pickard, Plate, Pastel Floral, Gold Work, Pierced Handles, 7 3/4 In. 28.00
Pickard, Plate, Pink Rose Decor, 1912, 6 3/4 In.Diameter 8.00
Pickard, Plate, Pink Rose Decor, 1912, 8 3/8 In.Diameter 14.00
Pickard, Plate, Purple Iris, By Lind, Irregular Edge, 9 In. 45.00
Pickard, Plate, Ravens Wood, Strutting Turkey, 10 1/2 In. 10.00
Pickard, Plate, Roseland, By Marker, 11 In. 155.00
Pickard, Plate, Scalloped Edge, Signed 14.00
Pickard, Plate, Service, Gold Designs & Bands, 10 3/4 In.Diameter, Set Of 6 .... 115.00
Pickard, Plate, Signed Arile, 1905, Strawberries & Blossoms, 8 7/8 In. 38.00
Pickard, Plate, Signed Blaha, Scalloped, Beaded Gold Border, Currants 52.00
Pickard, Plate, Signed Hawes, 1905, Violets & Ferns, 8 7/8 In.Diameter 38.00
Pickard, Plate, Signed May, 1912, Violets & Foliage, Scalloped, 8 1/2 In. 35.00
Pickard, Plate, Tulips, Signed, Marked, Gold, Pink, 8 1/2 In.Diameter 25.00
Pickard, Plate, White, Gold, Floral Border, Rosenthal Blank, 10 In. 12.50
Pickard, Relish, Dutch Girl, Vellum Finish, C.1905 .... 38.00
Pickard, Relish, Gold Floral & Wheat, Signed Artist Vobor, 1905 .... 35.00
Pickard, Relish, Gold Urns, Pink & Green Decoration, 1912 .... 28.00
Pickard, Relish, Nuts, By Vokral, 1907 .... 65.00
Pickard, Salt & Pepper, Allover Gold With Raised Floral, Marked, 3 3/8 In. 25.00
Pickard, Salt & Pepper, Floral 14.00
Pickard, Salt & Pepper, Gold Etched, 4 In. 11.00
Pickard, Salt & Pepper, Gold, Acid Etched Scrolling, Signed 14.00
Pickard, Salt & Pepper, Hand-Painted Flowers, Gold, Mark 18.00
Pickard, Salt & Pepper, Pink Rose Decoration, 1912, Pair 20.00
Pickard, Sugar & Creamer, Aura Argenta Linear, Marked 95.00
Pickard, Sugar & Creamer, Blue, Floral, Pagoda Shape, Artist-Signed 68.00
Pickard, Sugar & Creamer, Cover, Pastel, Blue & Purple Flowers, Artist M.P. 70.00
Pickard, Sugar & Creamer, Cream & Gold, Violets, Artist Fisher 70.00
Pickard, Sugar & Creamer, Etched Gold Design, Acid, Signed 40.00
Pickard, Sugar & Creamer, Floral, Gold 35.00
Pickard, Sugar & Creamer, Floral, Gold Handles, Signed Beutich 48.00
Pickard, Sugar & Creamer, Gold Decorated, Basket Shape 32.00
Pickard, Sugar & Creamer, Gold Etched, Ball Footed, Marked 22.50
Pickard, Sugar & Creamer, Gold Roses & Foliage On Cream 30.00
Pickard, Sugar & Creamer, Gold, Etched Floral & Leaf Decoration, Signed 42.50
Pickard, Sugar & Creamer, Hand-Painted Fruit, Gold Trim, Signed 55.00
Pickard, Sugar & Creamer, Pastel Ground, Red & Blue Floral, Limoges Blank 70.00
Pickard, Sugar & Creamer, Pedestaled, Artist Schoneck 150.00
Pickard, Sugar & Creamer, Purple Violets, Gold Border, Handles 55.00
Pickard, Sugar & Creamer, Roses, Gold Scrollwork, Black Outline, Gold Trim 22.00
Pickard, Sugar, Creamer, & Plate, Gold & Black Designs 35.00
Pickard, Tea Set, Allover Gold Stippled Floral, 4 Piece 85.00
Pickard, Tea Tile, Gold Urns, Pink & Green Decor, 1912, 7 In.Diameter 18.00
Pickard, Teapot, Pink Iridescent, Gold Design, Pink Floral, Artist Lind 70.00
Pickard, Teapot, Signed Alex, Dutch Scenes On Bisque 50.00
Pickard, Tray, Dresser, Scalloped, Blue Forget-Me-Nots, Artist L.Mac 57.50
Pickard, Tray, Oblong, Allover Gold With Raised Floral, Marked, 8 1/2 In. 25.00
Pickard, Tray, Round, Allover Gold With Raised Floral, Marked, 7 In. 20.00
Pickard, Vase, Allover Gold With Raised Floral, Marked, 5 3/4 In.High 20.00
Pickard, Vase, Allover Stipple Floral, Gold Ground, Green Lining, 7 3/8 In. 18.00
Pickard, Vase, Arbor Scene, Gold Trim, Handle, Artist-Signed, 10 1/4 In. 75.00
Pickard, Tray, Arbor Scene, Signed E.Challinor, 10 In.High 75.00
Pickard, Vase, Blue Luster, Gold Pistol Handles, Scalloped Top & Base, 1905 .... 42.00

Pickard, Vase, Brown Ground, Floral, Artist H.Reury, 10 In. 120.00
Pickard, Vase, Floral, Green Interior, 1930-38 Mark, 7 3/8 In. 18.00
Pickard, Vase, Gold, Embossed, Green Lining, 7 1/2 In. 39.00
Pickard, Vase, Gold, Signed, 3 In.High 6.00
Pickard, Vase, Peonies, Gold Scalloped Rim And Base 165.00
Pickard, Vase, Red & Yellow Tulips On White, Artist Schonek, Gold, Marked 85.00
Pickard, Vase, Signed Fisher, Tulip Decoration, Handled, 8 1/2 In.High 67.50
Pickard, Vase, Signed L.M., 1905, Violet Decoration On Cream, Gold Handles 58.00
Pickard, Vase, Square, Forest Scene On Tapestry, Signed E.Challinor, Marked 135.00
   Picture, see also Print, Painting
Picture, Charcoal Drawing By Rose O'Neill, Frame, 12 X 17 In. 175.00
Picture, Color On Rice Paper, Cloth Making, Woman Spinning, Weaving, Pair 85.00
Picture, Color On Rice Paper, Couple, Mandarin & Consort, Pair 50.00
Picture, Cutout, Birds, People, Flowers, Pa.Dutch, July 4, 1854, Color 270.00
Picture, Embroidery, Washington Memorial, Watercolor On Silk Ground, 1800 .... 1400.00
Picture, Embroidery, Wool & Silk, Naval Battle, H.C.Grant, Framed 37.50
   Picture, Frame, see Furniture, Frame
Picture, Needlework, Couple & Garden Statue, George II, Framed, C.1750 .... 190.00
Picture, Needlework, Couple Strolling With Dog, George II, Framed, C.1750 .... 250.00
Picture, Needlework, Figures In Garden Beside Pond, Charles II, C.1650 .... 90.00
Picture, Needlework, Monarch On Throne, Charles II, Gold, Blue, C.1650 .... 275.00
Picture, Needlework, Shepherd & Domestic Animals, George II, Framed, 1750 .... 140.00
Picture, Needlework, Young Handmaidens, Unicorn, Lion, Victorian, C.1890 .... 160.00
Picture, Needlework, Young Man Playing Flute, George II, Framed, C.1750 .... 150.00
Picture, Paper Diorama, 5 1/2 X 4 1/2 In. .... Illus   10.00
Picture, Relief, Crucifixion, Ivory, Polychrome, Spanish, Framed, C.1650 .... 250.00
Picture, Silhouette, Aaron Burr, Frame, 4 X 4 7/8 In. 300.00
Picture, Silhouette, August Eduart, Frame 12.50
Picture, Silhouette, Bust Of Man, Ink, 1820, Bird's-Eye Maple Frame, 7 X 8 In 60.00
Picture, Silhouette, 11 In. .... Illus   110.00

Picture, Paper Diorama, 5 1/2 X 4 1/2 In.   Picture, Silhouette, 11 In.

Picture, Silk Embroidery, Cherub Masks & Floral Drapery, Italian, C.1750 .... 90.00
Picture, Silk Embroidery, Chinese, Peacocks, Framed 85.00
Picture, Silk Embroidery, Panoply Of Flags Of All Nations, Photograph 37.50
Picture, Silk Needlework, Spring & Summer Flowers, George III, 1850, Pair 100.00
Picture, Silk Needlework, Victorian, Vase Of Flowers, Painted, Gilt Frame 70.00
Picture, Silk Needlework, Young Woman In Landscape, George III, Oval, 1750 .... 170.00
Picture, Tinsel, Basket Of Flowers With Spread Eagle, Flag, Framed 100.00
Picture, Tinsel, Basket Of Flowers, Gold Leaf Frame 30.00
Picture, Wax, The Corsican Mother Of Buonaparte, Letizia Ramolino, C.1810 .... 54.50
Picture, Waxed Busts, Colonial Lady & Gentleman, Maple Shadow Frame, Pair 60.00
   Pigeon Blood, see Ruby, Cranberry
   Pink Slag, see Slag
Pipe, Glass, Amber Tip 15.00
   Pipe, Meerschaum, see Meerschaum, Pipe
Pipe, Opium, Brass & Bamboo, 31 In.Long 15.00
Pipe, Russian, Miniature, Gold, Rhodonite, & Ivory, Cyrillic N.I., C.1900 .... 300.00

Pipe, Uncle Sam, Clay	5.00
Pipe, Wooden, Primitive Face, Hand Carved, 5 1/2 In.Long	15.00
Plate, see under special types such as ABC, Calendar, Christmas	

Plique a Jour is an enameling process. The enamel was laid between thin raised metal lines and heated. The finished piece has transparent enamel held between the thin metal wires.

Plated Amberina, Bowl, 8 In.Diameter	3240.00
Plated Silver, see Silver Plate	
Plique A Jour, Bowl, Flower Design, Silver Mounts, 4 1/2 In.Diameter	195.00
Plique A Jour, Bowl, Flowers, 4 1/2 In.Diameter	130.00
Plique A Jour, Bowl, Maple Leaves, 4 3/4 In.Diameter	195.00
Plique A Jour, Buttonhook	85.00
Plique A Jour, Figurine, Viking Ship, 3 X 2 In.	195.00
Plique A Jour, Pendant, Abstract Jugendstil Design, Baroque Pearls, Silver	150.00
Plique A Jour, Spoon, Geometric Designs, Ruby, Mint Green, Blue, Emerald, Pink	75.00
Plique A Jour, Spoon, Large	90.00
Plique A Jour, Spoon, Multicolor Transparent Enamel Panes In Handle, Metal	60.00
Plique A Jour, Vase, Angel Fish, Siamese, Seaweed, Bubbles, 5 1/2 In.High	280.00
Plique A Jour, Vase, Blue, Plum Tree, Yellow Flowers, 5 In.	220.00
Plique A Jour, Vase, Floral, 7 In.High	225.00
Plique A Jour, Vase, Flower Design, 7 In.High	210.00
Plique A Jour, Vase, Green Ground, Allover Floral, 7 In.High	220.00
Plique A Jour, Vase, Green Ground, Floral, Silver Base & Rims, 5 In.High	170.00
Plique A Jour, Vase, Mums & Dahlias On Green, 6 In.High	135.00
Plique A Jour, Vase, Silver Mountings, 7 In.High	245.00
Political Campaign, Ashtray, 'Under Our Flag We Do Have A Choice, 1952'	5.00
Political Campaign, Bookmark, Eisenhower & Stevenson, 1956, Silk, Color	25.00
Political Campaign, Broadside, Anti-Lincoln, 1864, Read Chicago Platform	34.50
Political Campaign, Button, Cox & Roosevelt	20.00
Political Campaign, Button, Eisenhower, Flasher	2.50
Political Campaign, Button, 'For President, John W.Davis, 1924'	55.00
Political Campaign, Button, Goldwater, 1964, Hanging Pendant & Elephant	.85
Political Campaign, Button, Kennedy, Johnson, Pictures, 2 1/2 In.	3.00
Political Campaign, Button, Pictorial, Blue, Roosevelt, 1940, 1 1/2 In.	2.50
Political Campaign, Button, Pictorial, Roosevelt, 1941	10.50
Political Campaign, Button, Pictorial, Teddy Roosevelt, Multi-Color	10.50
Political Campaign, Button, Pictorial, Thomas E.Dewey	3.00
Political Campaign, Button, Pictorial, Willkie, 1 1/2 In.	3.50
Political Campaign, Button, Pictures Theo.Roosevelt, 'Rough Rider'	15.00
Political Campaign, Button, Robert Kennedy, 'Vote For Our Next President'	.75
Political Campaign, Button, Roosevelt, 1940, 'No Third Term'	2.50
Political Campaign, Button, Roosevelt, 1940, 'No Third Term, Uncle Sam'	10.00
Political Campaign, Button, 'Thomas E.Dewey For President, ' 3 1/2 In.	8.00
Political Campaign, Button, 'Vandenberg For President, 1936'	8.00
Political Campaign, Button, 'Win With Wilson, ' Color, 1 1/4 In.	10.50
Political Campaign, Button, 'Wm.H.Taft For President, ' Bar Pin, 3 1/2 In.	18.00
Political Campaign, Cigar Cutter, Pocket, 'Theo.Roosevelt, Bullmoose Party'	37.50
Political Campaign, Cowboy Hat, Johnson, Metal, L.B.J.On Hat	2.00
Political Campaign, Cup, McKinley, Covered	39.00
Political Campaign, Doll, George Wallace	25.00
Political Campaign, Doll, Humphrey	25.00
Political Campaign, Doll, McGovern	25.00
Political Campaign, Doll, Nixon	25.00
Political Campaign, Doll, Shirley Chisholm	25.00
Political Campaign, Figurine, Elephant, 'Ike, ' Donkey, 'Dem, ' Yellow, Pair	10.00
Political Campaign, Flag, Harrison, 1840, Silk, 'Hero Of Tippecanoe'	295.00
Political Campaign, Fob, Taft & Sherman, Brass Tag	12.00
Political Campaign, Game, Anti-Nixon, Nose Ringer, 1968, Wood	5.00
Political Campaign, Handkerchief, 'More Beer, Less Taxes, Repeal 18th'	7.00
Political Campaign, Hat, 1865, Iron	15.00
Political Campaign, Jugate, Chafin & Watkins	50.00
Political Campaign, Jugate, Coolidge & Dawes	13.00
Political Campaign, Jugate, Kennedy & Johnson, 2 1/2 In.	3.00
Political Campaign, Jugate, McGovern & Eagleton, 1 3/4 In.	1.00
Political Campaign, Jugate, McGovern & Eagleton, 3 1/2 In.	3.00

Political Campaign, Jugate, Parker & Davis 20.00
Political Campaign, Jugate, Stevenson & Kefauver, 3 1/2 In. 10.00
Political Campaign, Jugate, Wilson & Marshall 15.00
Political Campaign, Knife, McGovern & Eagleton 2.00
Political Campaign, Knife, McGovern & Shriver 2.00
Political Campaign, Knife, Nixon & Agnew 2.00
Political Campaign, Matchbook, Wendell Willkie, Pictorial 5.00
Political Campaign, Medal, 'Hoover For President, 1928, ' Picture, Bronze 12.50
Political Campaign, Medal, John Kennedy, Metal, Design Of U.S.& J.F. 2.50
Political Campaign, Medal, John Kennedy, Rocking Chair 2.00
Political Campaign, Medal, Lafollette, Wheeler, Double Picture, Bronze 15.00
Political Campaign, Medal, Texas Star, L.B.J.On Star 2.25
Political Campaign, Mug, McKinley 20.00
Political Campaign, Mug, Shield With F.D.R.'s Head, 'The New Deal, ' Yellow 8.50
Political Campaign, Napkin, Landon, 1936, Picture .... .85
Political Campaign, Pass, Guest, Democratic National Convention, 1932 .... 7.50
Political Campaign, Pencil, 'Al Smith For President, ' Wooden 10.00
Political Campaign, Pennant, F.D.Roosevelt, Felt, Purple, Ship, Name 10.00
Political Campaign, Plate, Tin, Taft-Sherman, 1908, Pictures 35.00
Political Campaign, Plate, William J.Bryan & Smith, 7 1/2 In. 75.00
Political Campaign, Poster, Pro-Lincoln, 'A Traitor's Peace, ' 1864 .... 59.50
Political Campaign, Potholder, John Kennedy 3.00
Political Campaign, Ribbon, Pictures Harrison, Morton, Flag, 'Protection' 25.00
Political Campaign, Silk Square, McKinley & Roosevelt, Portraits, Eagle 29.50
Political Campaign, Sticker, Window, F.D.R. 2.50
Political Campaign, Stickpin, Benjamin Harrison 6.50
Political Campaign, Suspenders, 'Willkie For President, ' Red, White, Blue 47.50
Political Campaign, Thimble, Coolidge & Dawes, Aluminum, Blue Band 4.00
Political Campaign, Ticket, Republican National Convention, 1904 .... 8.00
Political Campaign, Ticket, Republican National Convention, 1908 .... 5.50
Political Campaign, Tie, Thos.E.Dewey's Picture, Maroon, Silk 12.00
Political Campaign, Token, Breckenridge & Lane, 1860, Ferrotype 50.00
Political Campaign, Tray, 'Keep Roosevelt In The White House, ' Tin 35.00
Political Campaign, Tumbler, Juice, Sherman, Taft 15.00
Political Campaign, Tumbler, 'McKinley, Our Next President, ' Etched 12.00
Political Campaign, Tumbler, McKinley, Etched Portrait .... 8.00 To 12.00
Political Campaign, Tumbler, Taft, Sherman, Etched Busts, Flag, Shield, Wreath 23.50
Political Campaign, Tumbler, William H.Taft & James S. Sheehan 39.00
Political Campaign, Tumbler, 1932 Democrat Convention, Slogan, Donkey 15.00
Political Campaign, Watch Fob, William H.Taft, Brass 20.00

Pomona Glass is clear with a soft amber border decorated with pale blue or rose-colored flowers and leaves. The colors are very, very pale. The background of the glass is covered with a network of fine lines. It was made from 1885 to 1888 by the New England Glass Company.

Pomona, Bowl, Berry, First Grind, 9 In.Diameter 361.00
Pomona, Bowl, Finger, Cornflowers, Inverted Thumbprint, New England 110.00
Pomona, Bowl, Finger, Ruffled Top, New England, First Grind 65.00
Pomona, Bowl, Pansy & Butterfly, Scalloped Base & Rim, Second Grind, 10 In. 295.00
Pomona, Castor, Pickle, Inverted Thumbprint, Cornflowers 235.00
Pomona, Celery, Acorns And Leaves, Inverted Thumbprint, Second Grind 160.00
Pomona, Celery, Amber Scalloped Rim, Second Grind 55.00
Pomona, Cup, Punch, Allover Hand Etching, First Grind 97.00
Pomona, Cup, Punch, Applied Handle, Amber 75.00
Pomona, Cup, Punch, Blue Butterfly & Pansy, New England 125.00
Pomona, Cup, Punch, Diamond-Quilted, Amber Border & Handle, First Grind 92.50
Pomona, Cup, Punch, Diamond-Quilted, Amber Top & Handle, New England 40.00
Pomona, Cup, Punch, Inverted Thumbprint, Amber Rim & Handle, First Grind 75.00
Pomona, Cup, Punch, New England, First Grind .... 78.00 To 90.00
Pomona, Lampshade, Enameled Birds, Embossed 3 Handled Amber Base 145.00
Pomona, Pitcher, Blue Cornflower, Amber Stain, Square Mouth, Three Way Pour 250.00
Pomona, Pitcher, Butterfly & Pansy, New England, 1885, First Grind 950.00
Pomona, Pitcher, Lemonade, Diamond-Quilted, First Grind, New England 110.00
Pomona, Pitcher, Pale Amber Top, Bulbous, Second Grind, 5 1/2 In. 76.00
Pomona, Pitcher, Water, Cornflower Design, Bulbous, New England 475.00
Pomona, Pitcher, Water, Inverted Thumbprint 125.00

Pomona, Pitcher, Water, Inverted Thumbprint, Fern, Daisy, Tulip, Amber Band 175.00
Pomona, Rose Bowl, Amber Stain, Scalloped Top, Three Feet 60.00
Pomona, Rose Bowl, Cornflower, Inverted Thumbprint, Amber, Blue, Second Grind 325.00
Pomona, Toothpick, Diamond Pattern, Tricorn Top, Second Grind 95.00
Pomona, Toothpick, Enameled Daisies, Amber Band, Midwest ....67.50 To 75.00
Pomona, Toothpick, Inverted Thumbprint, Tricorner Top, Second Grind 125.00
Pomona, Toothpick, Square Mouth, Enameled Flowers 135.00
Pomona, Toothpick, Tricorner, Amber Border, Second Grind 125.00
Pomona, Toothpick, Tricorner, First Grind 175.00
Pomona, Tumbler, Acanthus Leaf Decoration, First Grind 135.00
Pomona, Tumbler, Blue Cornflower, Amber Stain, Second Grind ....80.00 To 85.00
Pomona, Tumbler, Butterfly & Pansy, Amber 145.00
Pomona, Tumbler, Cornflower, Blue & Amber 110.00
Pomona, Tumbler, Cornflower, First Grind 125.00
Pomona, Tumbler, Diamond-Quilted, Acanthus Leaf, First Grind, New England 125.00
Pomona, Tumbler, Diamond-Quilted, Cornflowers, Second Grind, New England 110.00
Pomona, Tumbler, Fish & Plant Pattern, Midwestern 120.00
Pomona, Tumbler, Inverted Thumbprint, First Grind 55.00
Pomona, Tumbler, Lemonade, Diamond Pattern, First Grind 95.00
Pomona, Tumbler, Pansy And Butterfly, Second Grind 165.00
Pomona, Vase, Crimped Top, Second Grind, 5 1/4 In. 190.00
Pomona, Vase, Raspberries & Leaves, 5 In.High 40.00
Pomona, Vase, Rigaree On Neck, Ruffled Top, 6 1/4 In. 95.00
Pomona, Vase, Ruffled Top, Amber Foot, 6 1/4 In.High 95.00
    Pontypool, see Tole
Popeye, Charm, From Cracker Jack 3.00
Popeye, Pencil, Mechanical, 10 In.Long 5.00
Popeye, Statue, Popeye & Wimpy, 1940s, Pair 25.00
Popeye, Watch 55.00
    Porcelain, see also, Copeland, Nippon, RS Prussia, etc.
Porcelain, Ashtray With Pipe, German, Scalloped 7.00
Porcelain, Berry Set, German Mark, Fruit Pattern, 7 Piece 40.00
Porcelain, Berry Set, German, Yellow Roses, 10 Piece 15.00
Porcelain, Berry Set, Germany, Purple & Green Grapes, Embossing, 5 Piece 25.00
Porcelain, Boot, White, Raised Decoration, Gold, 4 1/4 In.High 7.50
Porcelain, Bowl & Pitcher, Gold Drapery, Angel Wings, Leaves 55.00
Porcelain, Bowl & Underplate, Finger, French, Inlay, Green, Gold 195.00
Porcelain, Bowl, Covered, German, Handles, White, Pink Roses, Pair 130.00
Porcelain, Bowl, France, Angel, Hand-Painted 15.00
Porcelain, Bowl, Frantz & Heinberg Benn, Floral Cat-O'-Nine-Tails, Gold 6.00
Porcelain, Bowl, Italian, Leaf, Mottamedeh Design, Pair 150.00
Porcelain, Bowl, Oval Design, Red, Reticular, Gold Trim 75.00
Porcelain, Bowl, Russian, Imperial, Monogram Of Catherine The Great, 1762 .... 70.00
Porcelain, Bowl, Russian, Youssoupov Service, C.1800 .... Illus 625.00
Porcelain, Box, Boy Fishing, Enamel, Signed Veuve Perrin, 2 1/2 X 3 X 1 1/4 .... 85.00
Porcelain, Box, Patch, Oriental Mark, Yellow, Pink & Blue Flowers 35.00
Porcelain, Box, Patch, Portrait Of Man & Woman, Blue, Round 45.00
Porcelain, Box, Patch, Queen Louise On Cover, Round 45.00
Porcelain, Box, Pin, M.Z.Austria, Queen Louise Portrait On Blue, Marked 18.00
Porcelain, Box, Russian, Letter Form, Imperial, Hinged, St.Petersburg, 1750 .... 675.00

Porcelain, Bowl, Russian, Youssoupov Service, C.1800

Porcelain, **Box**, Salt, Germany, Blue With White Windmill	14.50
Porcelain, **Box**, Sardine, Covered, Thistle, Leaves, Gold, Brown	37.50
Porcelain, **Box**, Sweetmeat, France, White, Blue Floral, Bird, Tree, C.1779	65.00
Porcelain, **Butter**, Covered, Insert, Sprays Of Pink Roses, Embossed	7.00
Porcelain, **Cachepot**, French, Bucket Style, Orange, Center Rose Garland, Pair	80.00
Porcelain, **Cake Set**, Royal Koya, Japan, Ladies, Pagodas, 7 Piece	20.00
Porcelain, **Celery**, Three Crown, Pink Poppies, Pearlized, Embossed	8.00
Porcelain, **Chocolate Set**, Chinese, Green & Tan, Scene On White, 11 Piece	35.00
Porcelain, **Chocolate Set**, Germany, Hand-Painted Red Roses, M.W.Co., 9 Piece	57.00
Porcelain, **Creamer**, Austria, Moose, Marked, 4 1/2 In.High	15.00
Porcelain, **Creamer**, Czechoslovakia, Moose, 4 1/2 In.High	9.00
Porcelain, **Creamer**, Czechoslovakia, Orange, Stagecoach Crossing Bridge	8.00
Porcelain, **Creamer**, Czechoslovakia, Sitting Cow, Orange & Black	10.00
Porcelain, **Creamer**, Germany, Hand-Painted Roses	8.50
Porcelain, **Cup & Saucer**, Chain Of States, C.1850 *Illus*	30.00
Porcelain, **Cup & Saucer**, Demitasse, Carlsbad, Austria, Pink & White, Gold	6.00
Porcelain, **Cup & Saucer**, Demitasse, G.& W.Mayers, Melbourne, Pat.Marked	5.00
Porcelain, **Cup & Saucer**, Maling, English, Farmer's, Oriental Scene	18.00
Porcelain, **Cup & Saucer**, Russian, Kornilov Decorated, C.1850	70.00
Porcelain, **Cup & Saucer**, Russian, Kuznetzov Decorated, C.1850, Set Of 5	175.00
Porcelain, **Cup**, Blue, Made In Siam, Set Of 6	125.00
Porcelain, **Dish**, Candy, Vienna, Austria, Octagonal, Embossed Pink Feather	10.00
Porcelain, **Dish**, Feeding, French, Gold Trim, Cat's Head Stopper, Marked	18.00
Porcelain, **Dish**, Lobster, Marked Austria, Divided	38.50
Porcelain, **Dish**, Lobster, Marked C.T.Germany, Gold Decoration, 11 X 14 In.	39.00
Porcelain, **Dish**, Oyster, Marked Weimar, Germany, Blue & White, Delft Type	7.50
Porcelain, **Dish**, Sardine, Covered, Victoria, Austria, Sardine Handle, Florals	9.00
Porcelain, **Dish**, Sardine, Ribbed, Embossed Sardine On Cover	15.00
Porcelain, **Dish**, Sardine, Victoria, Austria, Applied Black Sardine Handle	12.00
Porcelain, **Doorknob**, Black, Pair	2.00
Porcelain, **Dresser Set**, England, Roses, 5 Piece	22.50
Porcelain, **Dresser Set**, Signed Forsbeck, Hand-Painted, 5 Piece	85.00
Porcelain, **Dresser Set**, 4 Piece	42.50

Porcelain, Cup & Saucer,
Chain Of States, C.1850

Porcelain, Figurine, Boy, Girl, 6 In., Pair
See Page 409

Porcelain, **Egg**, Easter, Russian, Annunciation, Biblical Symbols, C.1850 .... 100.00
Porcelain, **Egg**, Easter, Russian, Last Supper, Biblical Symbols, C.1850 .... 150.00
Porcelain, **Egg**, Easter, Russian, Resurrection, Biblical Symbols, C.1850 .... 100.00
Porcelain, **Eggcup**, Orchid Design, 3 In.High 4.50
Porcelain, **Eggcup**, Train Shape, Chicken Conductor, Whistle On End, C.1880 .... 27.00
Porcelain, **Figurine**, Bluebird, Crown & H-S Mark, Long Beak, 3 1/2 In. 10.00
Porcelain, **Figurine**, Boy, Girl, 6 In., Pair .... *Illus* 50.00
Porcelain, **Figurine**, Cat, Calico, Sitting, Green Eyes, 12 In.High 160.00
Porcelain, **Figurine**, Dog, Danish, Great Dane, 10 1/2 In.High 135.00
Porcelain, **Figurine**, Dogs, Danish, Pointer & Puppies, 11 1/2 In.High 135.00
Porcelain, **Figurine**, Dutch Boy, Germany, Brown Pants, Blue Hat, Standing 4.00
Porcelain, **Figurine**, Elephant, Allover Gold Leaf, 4 X 6 1/2 In.Long, Pair 45.00
Porcelain, **Figurine**, Female, Lenci, Italy, Stylized, Nude To Waist, 1931 .... 75.00
Porcelain, **Figurine**, Finch, Hutschenreuther, Blue, Orange, Bug, 4 In.High 32.00
Porcelain, **Figurine**, French Poodle, By Doris Dawson, Alton, England 35.00
Porcelain, **Figurine**, Girl With Basket, Boy With Wheat, Sitzendorf, 1850, Pair 95.00
Porcelain, **Figurine**, Lady On Madame Recamier Sofa, German, 9 1/2 In. 60.00
Porcelain, **Figurine**, Madame Holding Candle, Marked Germany, White, Gold 10.00
Porcelain, **Figurine**, Maiden, French, Yellow Gown, Blue Scarf, Signed Almera 50.00
Porcelain, **Figurine**, Oriental Man & Woman, China, 3 1/2 In.High, Pair 10.00
Porcelain, **Figurine**, Peasant Woman, Russia, Bandana, Long Dress, Blue Flowers 60.00
Porcelain, **Figurine**, Pig, French, Jacket, Gold Cup, Pair 30.00
Porcelain, **Figurine**, Russian Wolfhound, Borzoi, Vienna, Lying, 12 X 7 In. 80.00
Porcelain, **Figurine**, Swan, Signed Von Schierholz, Germany, Applied Roses 28.00
Porcelain, **Figurine**, Trout, Mounted On Rough Hewn Boulder Of Crystal 155.00
Porcelain, **Figurine**, Two Pink Pigs In Green Basket, Germany 14.50
Porcelain, **Figurine**, Wagner, Sitting In Chair 30.00
Porcelain, **Figurine**, Whippet, Vienna, 10 In.Long 60.00
Porcelain, **Fish Set**, Carlsbad, Orange Border, Oval Platter, 17 Piece 150.00
Porcelain, **Flower Frog**, Germany, Dancing Nude, 9 In., Marked 15.00
Porcelain, **Hair Receiver**, Clover, Blue, Gold, Pink, White, Hand-Painted 22.50
Porcelain, **Hair Receiver**, Oriental Mark, Heavy Decoration 17.50
Porcelain, **Hair Receiver**, M.Z.Austria, Footed, Blue Flowers, Gold Scrolls 15.00
Porcelain, **Hair Receiver**, MW Germany Mark, Roses 8.00
Porcelain, **Hair Receiver**, Pink Roses, Gold, Extended Base Holds Lid 15.00
Porcelain, **Hair Receiver**, Roses, Raised Design, Pink, Gold, Square 12.50
Porcelain, **Hair Receiver**, Roses, Violets, Pink, Red, Gold, Blue 13.00
Porcelain, **Hatpin Holder**, Austrian, Floral 10.00
Porcelain, **Hatpin Holder**, Bird On Tree Stump, C.1880 .... 27.00
Porcelain, **Hatpin Holder**, German, Rose Design, 4 In.High 12.50
Porcelain, **Hatpin Holder**, Hand-Painted Purple Violets, Gold 12.50
Porcelain, **Hatpin Holder**, Leaf Motif, Hand-Painted, With Three Hatpins 16.00
Porcelain, **Hatpin Holder**, Rose Design, Hand-Painted 18.00
Porcelain, **Holder**, Placecard, Germany, Flowers 5.50
Porcelain, **Humidor**, Dark Blue Green, Dog With Pipe In Mouth 40.00
Porcelain, **Invalid Feeder** 15.00
Porcelain, **Invalid Feeder**, Germany, White, Raised White Flowers 8.00
Porcelain, **Jar**, Cracker, English, Floral, Cobalt & Gold, Silver Top, Marked 35.00
Porcelain, **Jar**, Cracker, German, Pink Roses, Embossed 16.00
Porcelain, **Jar**, Cracker, Weimer, Germany, Pink & Red Roses On White, Gold 22.50
Porcelain, **Jar**, Ginger, Covered, Storks & Clouds Decoration, Blue & White 175.00
Porcelain, **Jar**, Mustard, Germany, Bear, Removable Head, Place For Spoon 18.00
Porcelain, **Jug**, Saki, Chinese, Russet On White, Lady, Floral, Signed 18.50
Porcelain, **Match Holder**, Black Boot, White & Tan Puppy Lying On Foot 15.00
Porcelain, **Match Holder**, Touring Car, Red Devil In Back Seat, Green 8.50
Porcelain, **Milk & Mush Set**, Loneton, Blue Flowers On White, Gold, C.1850 .... 35.00
Porcelain, **Mirror**, Hand, Violets, Hand-Painted 10.00
Porcelain, **Muffineer**, Chinese Design, Orange, Green, White, Gold, Squatty 19.00
Porcelain, **Mug**, Child's, Carousel Horse 4.00
Porcelain, **Mug**, Child's, Germany, Embossed, Pink Luster Border, Merry Xmas 7.00
Porcelain, **Mug**, German, Green With Gold Luster 15.00
    Porcelain, **Napkin Ring**, see also Napkin Ring
Porcelain, **Nappy**, M.Z.Austria, Violets On Cream, Gold Handle, Scalloped 13.00
Porcelain, **Opener**, Letter, Germany, Blue & White, Brass Handle 6.00
    Porcelain, **Oyster Plate**, see Oyster Plate
Porcelain, **Parlor Set**, Japan, Miniature, Hand-Painted, 6 Piece 25.00

Porcelain, **Perfume**, Lady Shape, Red, White, & Blue, 3 1/2 In.High 5.00
Porcelain, **Pig**, German, Pink, Green Purse, Gold Clasp 15.00
Porcelain, **Pincushion**, Japan, Woman On Whiskbroom, 4 In. 7.00
Porcelain, **Pitcher**, Classical Figures, Leaf Design, 8 In.High 40.00
Porcelain, **Pitcher**, Germany, Strawberries, Green Stem Handle, Signed In Red 25.00
Porcelain, **Pitcher**, Marked T.& R.Boote, Classical Figures, Blue, C.1850 .... 40.00
Porcelain, **Pitcher**, Petunia Design, 2 Quart 15.00
Porcelain, **Plaque**, Signed & Dated I.Holzmann, 1878, Reclining Nude, Gold 485.00
Porcelain, **Plaque**, Victoria, Austria, Birds On Branches Of Roses, 13 In. 58.00
Porcelain, **Plate**, Acke, Germany, Fruit, 'Give Us This Day' In Gold, 11 In. 10.00
Porcelain, **Plate**, Austria, Gold Triangle With Leaf, Star Center, 8 1/2 In. 5.75
Porcelain, **Plate**, Austrian, Signed Raymonds, Roses 22.00
Porcelain, **Plate**, Blue Violets, Gold Trim, Two Handles 16.00
Porcelain, **Plate**, Cake, Austria, Gold Handles, Floral & Foliage 6.00
Porcelain, **Plate**, Cake, German, Hand-Painted Pink & White Wild Roses 6.00
Porcelain, **Plate**, Cake, German, Purple Crocus, Handles, Signed 9.00
Porcelain, **Plate**, Cake, Wedding Ring Pattern, Gold Handles, 9 1/2 In. 12.00
Porcelain, **Plate**, 'China Collector' 55.00
Porcelain, **Plate**, Dinner, French, Flower Center, Black Scroll & Gold Edge 14.50
Porcelain, **Plate**, Easter Scene, Embossed Rim, Easter Greetings, 7 In. 10.00
Porcelain, **Plate**, Empire China, Venetian Couple & Gondola, 9 3/4 In. 14.00
Porcelain, **Plate**, English, Gold Scalloped Edge, Cosmos Design, 8 1/2 In. 30.00
Porcelain, **Plate**, Fish, Fondeville, England, Underwater Fish Scene, Maroon 10.00
Porcelain, **Plate**, French, Flowered Wreath & Crab Center, Fish Border 8.75
Porcelain, **Plate**, French, Gold Edge, Fruit & Flower Design, 8 1/4 In. 5.75
Porcelain, **Plate**, Fruit, Open Lattice Edge, 7 In., Set Of 6 .... 40.00
Porcelain, **Plate**, German, Signed Genicond, Water Lilies, Luster Ground 12.00
Porcelain, **Plate**, Germany, Signed Brousillon, Hand-Painted Asters, Pierced 10.00
Porcelain, **Plate**, Hand-Painted Pink Sweet Peas 17.00
Porcelain, **Plate**, Hand-Painted Sea Gulls, White, Brown, & Yellow 6.00
Porcelain, **Plate**, Hanging, Signed Coronet, 2 Women & Baskets, Artist Leo 95.00
Porcelain, **Plate**, Karlsbad, Austria, Hand-Painted Poppies, Gold Leaves 14.00
Porcelain, **Plate**, M.Z.Austria, Hand-Painted Apples, 7 3/4 In.Diameter 6.00
Porcelain, **Plate**, M.Z.Austria, Hanging, Roses, Tinted Ground 11.00
Porcelain, **Plate**, M.Z.Austria, Narcissus On Blue Resist Ground 10.00
Porcelain, **Plate**, M.Z.Austria, Pink Floral, Embossed Scalloped Edge 8.00
Porcelain, **Plate**, Marked Germany, White, Pink Roses, Gold Band, 8 1/2 In. 10.00
Porcelain, **Plate**, Marked Luettenberg, Germany, Fruit, Peaches, Gold 20.00
Porcelain, **Plate**, Marked Milan, U & H, Gaudy Design 21.00
Porcelain, **Plate**, Pancake, Sebring, Ohio, Pewter Dede & Dome 9.00
Porcelain, **Plate**, Prussia, Rampant Lion Mark, Ferns, Flowers, Tinted Ground 10.00
Porcelain, **Plate**, Russian, Imperial, Catherine Great Monogram, C.1762 .... 80.00
Porcelain, **Plate**, Russian, Imperial, White, Gilt, Nicholas I Period, 1825 .... 90.00
Porcelain, **Plate**, Signed C.Penet, Hand-Painted Pink & Red Roses, 9 In. 13.50
Porcelain, **Plate**, Signed R.K.Beck, Scenes Of Deer, 12 Sided, Gold Rim 16.00
Porcelain, **Plate**, Vienna Under Crown, Lady Sitting In Tree, Gold 16.00
Porcelain, **Plate**, Weimar, Germany, Hand-Painted Blackberry Groupings, 1911 .... 8.00
Porcelain, **Plate**, Weimar, Germany, Hand-Painted Floral, Nuts, On Cream, Gold 12.00
Porcelain, **Platter**, French, Rose Spray Center, Gold Border, 10 X 27 In. 14.00
Porcelain, **Platter**, Russian, Imperial, C.1810 .... *Illus* 350.00
Porcelain, **Ring Tree**, Hand, Sleeve Cuff, Gold Bracelet, Saucer Base, Floral 37.50
Porcelain, **Rolling Pin**, German, Forget-Me-Nots 25.00
Porcelain, **Salt**, French, Footed, Enamel, Animals At Top 25.00
Porcelain, **Shoe**, Applied Flowers 18.00
Porcelain, **Shoe**, Flowers On Heel, Top & Across Toe, 5 In.Long 9.00
Porcelain, **Shoe**, High, Real Shoe Lace, Brown, 5 1/2 In.Long 15.00
Porcelain, **Shoe**, Man's Oxford, Green, Lacing .... 10.00 To 12.50
Porcelain, **Shoe**, Man's, Eyelets, Laces, Green And Tan 15.00
Porcelain, **Shoe**, Man's, High Laced, Yellow, Gold 12.00
Porcelain, **Shoe**, White, Pale Green Interior, 6 1/2 In.Long 16.00
Porcelain, **Shoe**, Woman's Portrait On Toe, 7 In.Long 20.00
Porcelain, **Slipper**, Pink, Embossed Blue & Gold Floral, Gold Leaves, 4 In. 7.00
Porcelain, **Strainer**, Tea, Floral 16.00
Porcelain, **Sugar & Creamer**, German, Square, Browns, Gold Floral & Trim 10.00
Porcelain, **Sugar & Creamer**, Marked S.Gold Luster 20.00
Porcelain, **Sugar & Creamer**, Signed E.S.Germany, Birds On Tree, Black Edge 10.50

Porcelain, **Sugar & Creamer**, Signed Prussia, Hand-Painted Flowers, Grapes 32.50
Porcelain, **Swan**, Germany, Applied Pink Roses & Blue Forget-Me-Nots 26.00
Porcelain, **Syrup**, M.Z.Austria, Individual, Covered, Pink & White Florals 10.00
Porcelain, **Tazza**, Russian, Imperial, White, Scalloped, Gilt, Nicholas I, C.1825 .... 250.00
Porcelain, **Tea Caddy**, Cameo Medallion Center, Woman Holds Branch 85.00
Porcelain, **Tea Caddy**, Green, Gold Top, Pink & Blue Flowers 28.50
Porcelain, **Tea Set**, Bohemian, Cobalt & Gold Bands, Court Figures, 9 Piece 97.50
Porcelain, **Teapot**, Wemyss, T.Good & Co., Black Rooster, 'Bon Jour, ' 1880 .... 50.00
Porcelain, **Tieback**, Pink & Gold, Pair 17.00
Porcelain, **Toast Rack**, Poppies, Gold Trim, Holds Four Slices 15.00
Porcelain, **Toast Rack**, White, 5 Dolphin Dividers 17.50
Porcelain, **Toothpick**, Germany, White Pig & 3 Babies, Green Nest 16.00
Porcelain, **Tray**, Dresser, M.Z.Austria, Roses, Garlands, Green Tint On Rim 10.00
Porcelain, **Vase**, Austria, Buildings On Waterfront, Gold Beading, Crown Mark 50.00
Porcelain, **Vase**, German, Rainbow Luster, Iris, 2 Marks 17.50
Porcelain, **Vase**, Japan, Hawthorn Pattern On Blue Fishscale, White Motif 58.00
Porcelain, **Vase**, Overlay, White To Clear, Gold Design, 9 In.High, Pair 250.00
Porcelain, **Vase**, Signed Jorgenson, Bouquets Of Pink Roses On Blue, Gold 30.00
Porcelain, **Vase**, Victorian, White, Medallion Of Roman Soldier, Handles 22.00
Porcelain, **Washstand Set**, Blue, Pink Rose Border, 2 Piece 62.00
Porcelain, **Washstand Set**, English, White, Pink & Gold Design, 2 Piece 75.00
Porcelain, **Washstand Set**, White, Embossed Leaves, Gold Drapery, 2 Piece 50.00
Porcelain, **Wine**, Teutonic Pattern, By Cox, Footed, Set Of 4 .... 28.00
Portrait, **Bowl**, Girl, Flowing Hair, Embossed Floral, Gold, Scalloped, Austria 45.00
Portrait, **Box**, Jewel, Man & Lady, Blue, Gold Trim, Porcelain, Signed 215.00
Portrait, **Butter Pat**, Lady, Large Hat, French 25.00
Portrait, **Butter Pat**, Victorian Lady, Gold Brushed Edges 16.00
Portrait, **Plate**, Blue, Gold, Royal Austria .... *Illus* 65.00

Porcelain, Plate, 'China Collector'
See Page 410

Portrait, Plate,
Blue, Gold, Royal Austria

Porcelain, Platter, Russian, Imperial, C.1810
See Page 410

Portrait, **Plate**, Brunette, Gold Tracery On Brown, Beehive, 9 1/2 In. 45.00
Portrait, **Plate**, Brunette, Pink Rose In Hair, Cobalt With Gold, Austria 38.00
Portrait, **Plate**, Classical, Man Playing Lute, Gold, Imperial Crown, Austria 35.00
Portrait, **Plate**, Colonial Man & Woman, Flower Band, Bavaria 10.00
Portrait, **Plate**, Dark Haired Lovely Lady, 12 3/4 In., Signed Amicita 35.00
Portrait, **Plate**, George Washington, Bust After G.Stuart, Sepia, England 7.00

Portrait, Plate, Girl With Roses, Openwork Rim, 7 1/2 In. 17.50
Portrait, Plate, Girl With Strawberries, Openwork Rim, 7 1/2 In. 17.50
Portrait, Plate, Head & Shoulders, Brunette, Gold Tracery, Beehive 95.00
Portrait, Plate, Indian, Marked E.S.Germany 68.00
Portrait, Plate, Jack Dempsey, Autographed 14.00
Portrait, Plate, Lady & Man In Garden, Gold Trim 15.00
Portrait, Plate, Lady On Swing, Man Playing Stringed Instrument, F.Stahl 45.00
Portrait, Plate, Lady, Blue & Gold Border, Copyright 1907, Meek Co., Tin 12.00
Portrait, Plate, Lady, Gold, Porcelain, 9 In. 20.00
Portrait, Plate, Man With Sword, Signed J.B.Velvet Frame 400.00
Portrait, Plate, Monk, Drawing Beer, Gold, O.S.L.St.Killian, Germany 55.00
Portrait, Plate, Napoleon 20.00
Portrait, Plate, Napoleon, Green Ground, Star Scalloped, Brown & Gold Edge 45.00
Portrait, Plate, Queen Louise, Gold Tracery, Floral, Lattices, ZS Mark 24.00
Portrait, Plate, Queen Louise, White Ground, Gold Design At Edge, 7 1/2 In. 25.00
Portrait, Plate, Queen Victoria, Year Of Jubilee, 1887, Scalloped 69.00
Portrait, Plate, Schubert, Brown & Cream, 8 In. 4.00
Portrait, Plate, Vignettes Of Cherubs, Royal Blue & Gold, Royal Vienna 70.00
Portrait, Plate, Woman Holds Cherry Blossom Branch, B.T.Co., Germany 20.00
Portrait, Slipper, Lady's, Queen Louise, Apricot To Pink, Gold Scrolls 24.50
Portrait, Tray, Pin, Pink, Brunette, Austria 24.00
Portrait, Vase, Gentleman In Period Costume, Austria, 4 In. 30.00
Portrait, Vase, Maiden At Well Scene, Two Handles, Gold Trim, 12 1/2 In. 55.00
Portrait, Vase, Medallion, Lady, Gold, Turquoise, Cobalt, Austria, Beehive Mark 60.00
Portrait, Vase, Queen Louise, Full Figure, Germany, 8 In. 32.50
Portrait, Vase, Signed Ferd, Vienna, Pair 500.00

Postcards were first legally permitted in Austria on October 1, 1869.
The United States passed postal regulations allowing the card in 1873.
Most of the picture postcards collected today date from 1910.

Postcard, see Album

Postcard, American Seaplane, 1919 .... 3.00
Postcard, Army Comics, Pack Of 39 .... 5.25
Postcard, Assorted, 503 In Album 27.00
Postcard, Atlantic City Series 442, View .... .50
Postcard, Chief Flat Iron, Sioux 1.75
Postcard, Chief Red Cloud .... .75
Postcard, Coffin Flower & Figure, Seminude, 5 .... 7.00
Postcard, Cracker Jack Bears, No.3 .... 2.00
Postcard, Decoration Day, Fred Lounsbury 1.50
Postcard, Ellen Clapsaddle 1.00
Postcard, Fire Department, Horse Drawn, Pair 3.00
Postcard, German Flag, Valentine Artotype .... .75
Postcard, Girls Undressing For Wein Series 1760, Set Of 5 .... 2.50
Postcard, Halloween Precautions, E.Nash .... .50
Postcard, Holidays, Cats, Rabbits, Chickens, Dogs, Santas, 20 .... 25.00
Postcard, Indian Chief, Big Man, 1903 .... 4.00
Postcard, Katzenjammer Kids, Mechanical, 1906 .... 4.00
Postcard, Kewpies, Set Of 12 .... 4.00
Postcard, Leather, Set Of 12 .... 12.00
Postcard, Lincoln's Birthday, E.Nash 2.00
Postcard, Lord's Prayer, Embossed, Color, C.1900, Set Of 8 .... 15.00
Postcard, Love Tribunes, R.Tuck .... .50
Postcard, Memorial Day Series 1.00
Postcard, Missouri Bldg., 1904 St.Louis World's Fair 2.50
Postcard, Moxie, Billy B.Van, The Bish, In 'The Rainbow Girl' 5.00
Postcard, Moxie, Man Sitting On Box, Labeled Drink Moxie 5.00
Postcard, Moxie, Meditation 5.00
Postcard, Mt.Vesuvius Erupts 1.00
Postcard, Niagara Engine Co., Providence, R.I., Horse, Fire Engine 2.00
Postcard, Pen & Ink Prints Of Famous American Steam Locomotives, Set Of 9 ...... 1.50
Postcard, Pride Of The Navies, 1907 Jamestown Exposition 1.50
Postcard, Red Wing, Minnesota, 1907, Lot Of 39 .... 13.50
Postcard, San Francisco Fire, Unused, Set Of 7 .... 7.00
Postcard, Santa With Doll & Toys, Hallowe'En, Tuck, 3 .... 6.00
Postcard, Santa, Embossed, E.Nash 1.00

Postcard, St.Patrick's Day, Embossed, 1909, 6	7.00
Postcard, Steamer Lapland	.50
Postcard, Thanksgiving, Christmas, New Year, Embossed, Circa 1900, 12	2.50
Postcard, The Clermont, 1909, Hudson-Fulton Exposition	2.50
Postcard, Transcontinental Railroad Centennial Limited Edition, 1969, 50	5.00
Postcard, Tuck Rembrandtesque Series 914	1.00
Postcard, U.S.Battleship Wisconsin	.50
Postcard, Utopian Yarn	.50
Postcard, View Of 1906 San Francisco Quake, Lot Of 8	3.75
Postcard, 1905-1920, 200	15.00
Postcard, 4th Of July, Fred Lounsbury, Series 2020-1	1.50
Pot Lid, Natchez Riverboat Scene	32.00
Pot Lid, Uncle Toby, 5 In.Diameter	50.00
Pottery, see also Buffalo Pottery, Staffordshire, Wedgwood, etc.	
Pottery, Basket, White, Applied Grapes & Leaves, Marked Italy, 4 In.High	10.00
Pottery, Birdhouse, Brick Clay, Shape Of Cabin With Chimney	225.00
Pottery, Bowl, Crock, Gray, Daisy Design, 10 In.	6.00
Pottery, Bowl, Miniature, Cream, Brown Splotching	30.00
Pottery, Chamberstick, Miniature, Brown Glaze, Swank Potteries	50.00
Pottery, Crock, Miniature, Blue Decoration, Signed C.S., Double Eared, Swank	240.00
Pottery, Crock, Miniature, Signed C.S., Swank Potteries	40.00
Pottery, Crock, Pickle, Miniature, Blue Decoration, Signed C.S., Swank	160.00
Pottery, Dish, Child's, 'Baby's Plate'In Gold, Hand-Painted Dogs & Crow	9.00
Pottery, Dog, Sitting, Glazed, Brown With Green Splotches, 6 1/2 In.High	95.00
Pottery, Ewer, Incised Blossoms In Multicolor, 24 In.High	100.00
Pottery, Figurine, Animal, Miniature, Glazed, Swank Potteries	35.00
Pottery, Figurine, Sitting Dog, Miniature, Blue Decoration, Swank Potteries	200.00
Pottery, Flowerpot, Miniature, Signed C.S., Swank Potteries	50.00
Pottery, Holder, Wall, Bouquet, S.Bell, Raised Bird & Flower Decoration	350.00
Pottery, Jug, Blue Under Glaze, M.Friedlander & Bro., Hazleton, Pa., Gallon	15.00
Pottery, Jug, Iron Bail, Wooden Handle, 10 In.High	8.00
Pottery, Jug, Miniature, Signed A.B.S., 1887, Swank Potteries	50.00
Pottery, Mold, Candle, 12 Tube, Pine Frame	300.00
Pottery, Mug, Brown Shading, Raised Figures, Strap Handle, Frog Inside	115.00
Pottery, Mug, Gesundheit, Brown, 5 In.High	15.00
Pottery, Pitcher, Miniature, Blue Decoration, Signed C.S., Swank Potteries	200.00
Pottery, Spittoon, Miniature, Blue Decoration, Signed A.S., April 6, 1874	240.00
Pottery, Spittoon, Miniature, Blue Decoration, Signed C.S., Swank Potteries	110.00
Pottery, Urn, Czechoslovakia, Side Handles, Black On Brown & White	4.00
Pottery, Urn, Yellow Glazed, Arabellos Form Double Scroll Handles, Pair	275.00
Pottery, Vase, Green, Matte Finish, Waco, 6 In.High	12.50
Pottery, Vase, Italian, Shape Of Pineapple, 15 In.High	80.00
Pottery, Vessel, Hopi Indian, Brown, Bear, Geometric Designs	325.00
Pottery, Wine Jug, Tan Ground, One Brown Leaf, Marked Seto-Ware, Circa 1850	20.00
Powder Horn, see Weapon, Powder Horn	

Pratt Ware means two different things. It was an early Staffordshire Pottery, cream-colored with colored decorations, made by Felix Pratt during the late eighteenth century. There was also Pratt Ware made with transfer designs during the mid-nineteenth century.

PRATT FENTON.

Pratt, Bowl, Ann Hathaway House, Ordered For Kerrs China Hall, Phila.	16.00
Pratt, Creamer & Bowl, Matte, Black, White, Chariot Scene	40.00
Pratt, Cup & Saucer, Magenta Border	35.00
Pratt, Cup & Saucer, Transfer, Fortune Teller Outside Inn.Aqua Ground	30.00
Pratt, Jar, Blue, Brown Figures, Boar Hunt	12.00
Pratt, Jar, Covered, The Village Wedding, Dated Jan.1857	50.00
Pratt, Jug, Turquoise, Shell Collage, Pewter Lid	75.00
Pratt, Pitcher, Black Greek Style Decoration, Orange & White, Dated 1861	80.00
Pratt, Pitcher, Black, White Grecian Figures, 4 1/4 In.High	27.50
Pratt, Pitcher, Cherubs In Vineyard	24.00
Pratt, Pitcher, Mischievous	85.00
Pratt, Pitcher, The Greeks, Greek Key Border, Fenton, 6 In.	125.00
Pratt, Plate, Battle Of The Nile, Basket Weave Border, 9 1/4 In.	25.00
Pratt, Plate, Halt By The Wayside, P.Wouvermann, White Border, Pratt Fenton	25.00
Pratt, Plate, Market Scene, Center Turquoise Border, Gold Trim, C.1840	47.50
Pratt, Plate, Red Bull Inn, Golden Brown Border	27.50

Pratt, Plate, Roman Ruins Center, Orange Border	45.00
Pratt, Plate, Street Scene, People, Church, Orange Border	45.00
Pratt, Pot & Cover, Old Jack, Fenton, 3 In.Diameter	85.00
Pratt, Pot Lid, Advertising Oriental Toothpaste, C.1850, 3 In.	24.00
Pratt, Pot Lid, 'Alas, Poor Bruin, ' 3 1/4 In.	45.00
Pratt, Pot Lid, Cavaliers, Fenton, C.1855, 4 3/4 In.Diameter	75.00
Pratt, Pot Lid, J.B.Thorn, Chemist, London, John A Tarrant, N.Y., U.S.Agent	15.00
Pratt, Pot Lid, Mastiff & Whippet, Browns, 4 In.Diameter	75.00
Pratt, Pot Lid, Picture Of Men & Women Having Picnic	37.50
Pratt, Pot Lid, Six People At Picnic	45.00
Pratt, Pot Lid, 'The Best Card'	48.50
Pratt, Pot Lid, The Rivals, Fenton	150.00
Pratt, Pot Lid, The Village Wedding	35.00
Pratt, Pot Lid, Uncle Toby	48.50
Pratt, Pot, Mustard, Underglaze Lithograph Transfer, Yellow, Black, Blue, 1850	24.00
Pratt, Stein, Hunting Scene, Pewter & Hand-Painted Lid, 8 In.	85.00 To 95.00
Pratt, Tea Caddy, Baracenoni Figures, C.1780, Fenton	250.00
Presidential China, Cup & Saucer, Demitasse, Benjamin Harrison, Set Of 6	5750.00
Presidential China, Plate, Cake, Benjamin Harrison Service, Set Of 6	5000.00
Presidential China, Plate, Dessert, Benjamin Harrison Service, Set Of 6	4250.00
Presidential China, Plate, Dinner, Benjamin Harrison Service, Set Of 6	5900.00
Presidential China, Plate, Soup, Lincoln, 9 1/2 In.	*Illus* 4500.00

Presidential China, Plate, Soup, Lincoln, 9 1/2 In.

Pressed glass was first made in the United States in the 1820s after the invention of pressed-glass machines. Hundreds of patterns of pressed glass were made in complete table settings. Although the Boston and Sandwich works was the most famous of the pressed glass factories, there were about sixteen other factories making pressed glass from 1830 to 1850, and still more from 1850 to 1900, when pressed glass reached its greatest popularity. It is now being widely reproduced.

Pressed Glass, see also Cosmos, Croesus, etc.

Pressed Glass, Ale, Mephistopheles, German, Gold Bands	30.00
Pressed Glass, Ale, Waffle & Thumbprint, Flint	45.00
Pressed Glass, Banana Boat, Delaware, Cranberry, Gold	43.00
Pressed Glass, Banana Boat, Delaware, Rose, Gold, 11 1/2 In.Long	45.00 To 49.00
Pressed Glass, Banana Boat, Pan Thistle, 9 1/2 In.	12.50
Pressed Glass, Banana Stand, Bull's-Eye	85.00
Pressed Glass, Banana Stand, Zipper, Miniature	12.75
Pressed Glass, Basket, Oblong, 7 1/2 In.	12.00
Pressed Glass, Bathtub, Daisy & Button, Golden Amber, Sietz	67.50
Pressed Glass, Berry Set, Bar & Diamond, Pedestal Base, 7 Piece	30.00
Pressed Glass, Berry Set, Bars & Buttons, 5 Piece	20.00
Pressed Glass, Berry Set, Child's, Lacy Daisy, 7 Piece	55.00
Pressed Glass, Berry Set, Daisy & Button With V Ornament, Clear, 7 Piece	75.00
Pressed Glass, Berry Set, Diamond Lace, Sun Purple, 4 Piece	25.00
Pressed Glass, Berry Set, Portland, Gold, 7 Piece	38.00
Pressed Glass, Bottle, Bar, Paneled, Flint, Quart	18.00
Pressed Glass, Bottle, Bar, Prism & Sawtooth, Flint, Quart	27.00

Pressed Glass, Bottle, Bitters, Thumbprint	42.50
Pressed Glass, Bottle, Waffle & Thumbprint, 11 In.High	45.00
Pressed Glass, Bottle, Water, Deer & Thumbprint	30.00
Pressed Glass, Bottle, Wine, Waffle, Square, Stopper	8.50
Pressed Glass, Bowl, Alabama, Clear, 8 In.Diameter	15.00
Pressed Glass, Bowl, Atlas, Covered, 8 In.Diameter	37.50
Pressed Glass, Bowl, Banana, Intaglio Sunflower, Pedestal, 7 1/2 In.High	16.00
Pressed Glass, Bowl, Banded Raindrop, Oblong, 9 1/2 X 6 X 2 In.	16.50
Pressed Glass, Bowl, Beaded Swirl With Disc Bands, Yellow Band, Cranberry	15.00
Pressed Glass, Bowl, Bellflower, Single Vine, Footed, Scalloped Top, Flint	65.00
Pressed Glass, Bowl, Berry, Delaware, Green, Gold	22.00
Pressed Glass, Bowl, Berry, Horseshoe	12.00
Pressed Glass, Bowl, Berry, Manhattan, 9 In.	12.00
Pressed Glass, Bowl, Berry, Michigan	8.00
Pressed Glass, Bowl, Berry, Moon Star, 9 In.Diameter	15.00
Pressed Glass, Bowl, Berry, Paneled Daisy	9.00
Pressed Glass, Bowl, Berry, Pleat & Panel	9.00 To 14.00
Pressed Glass, Bowl, Berry, Plume	11.00
Pressed Glass, Bowl, Berry, Priscilla	16.00
Pressed Glass, Bowl, Berry, Shell & Tassel, Oblong	18.00
Pressed Glass, Bowl, Bird & Strawberry, Oblong	30.00
Pressed Glass, Bowl, Blue Mirror, Oval, 7 X 4 3/4 In.	16.50
Pressed Glass, Bowl, Broad Loop, Flint, Footed, 8 1/2 In.Diameter	12.00
Pressed Glass, Bowl, Bull's-Eye & Fan, 10 In.Diameter, 3 3/4 In.High	12.00
Pressed Glass, Bowl, Colorado, Clear, Footed, 6 In.Diameter	6.00
Pressed Glass, Bowl, Cupid's Hunt, Covered	36.50
Pressed Glass, Bowl, Cut Leaf Flower, 4 In.Deep, 8 1/2 In.Wide	40.00
Pressed Glass, Bowl, Daisy & Button With Crossbar	30.00
Pressed Glass, Bowl, Daisy & Button, Amber Buttons, Flat Bottomed	47.50
Pressed Glass, Bowl, Daisy & Button, Amber, Bathtub Shape, 9 In.Long	45.00
Pressed Glass, Bowl, Daisy & Button, Blue, 9 1/2 In.Diameter	30.00
Pressed Glass, Bowl, Daisy & Button, Clear, Clover Leaf, 9 1/2 In.	10.00
Pressed Glass, Bowl, Delaware, Green, 8 In.Diameter	30.00 To 35.00
Pressed Glass, Bowl, Delaware, Rose, 8 In.	35.00
Pressed Glass, Bowl, Dewdrop & Star, 6 In.	9.50
Pressed Glass, Bowl, Double Beetle Band, Blue, Findlay	48.50
Pressed Glass, Bowl, Feather, 6 1/4 X 9 1/2 In.	10.00
Pressed Glass, Bowl, Finger, Frosted Artichoke	14.00
Pressed Glass, Bowl, Finger, Tree Of Life	5.00
Pressed Glass, Bowl, Flattened Hobnail, Two Rows, C.1885, 5 1/2 In.Diameter	15.00
Pressed Glass, Bowl, Fleur-De-Lis & Drape, Footed	11.00
Pressed Glass, Bowl, Fluted, Leaf In Oval, 9 In.	12.50
Pressed Glass, Bowl, Fruit, Inverted Thumbprint, Amber, Metal Base & Lid	95.00
Pressed Glass, Bowl, Hartley, Footed	12.50
Pressed Glass, Bowl, Horn Of Plenty, Flint, Footed, 8 In.Diameter	32.00
Pressed Glass, Bowl, Jacob's Ladder, Oval, 9 In.	8.50
Pressed Glass, Bowl, Manhattan, 8 1/2 In.Diameter	7.00
Pressed Glass, Bowl, Maple Leaf, Clear, Oval	15.00
Pressed Glass, Bowl, Maple Leaf, Log Feet, Frosted	15.00
Pressed Glass, Bowl, Narcissus, 8 In.	18.00
Pressed Glass, Bowl, Opal Hobnail, Ribbon Top, 6 In.Diameter	14.00
Pressed Glass, Bowl, Oregon, Oval, 9 1/4 X 6 3/4 In.	16.50
Pressed Glass, Bowl, Peacock And Grape, Spatula Footed, 7 1/2 In.	35.00
Pressed Glass, Bowl, Pineapple & Fan, Emerald Green, 8 In.	45.00
Pressed Glass, Bowl, Pineapple Fan, Bee Mark, 7 In.	20.00
Pressed Glass, Bowl, Pinwheels, 7 In. Sq.	15.00
Pressed Glass, Bowl, Pleat & Panel, Flat, 8 In.	22.50
Pressed Glass, Bowl, Punch, Child's, Feather Arches	15.00
Pressed Glass, Bowl, Punch, Child's, Halley's Comet, 4 1/2 In.High	15.00
Pressed Glass, Bowl, Punch, Child's, Whirligig	15.00 To 25.00
Pressed Glass, Bowl, Punch, Child's, Whirling Star	22.50
Pressed Glass, Bowl, Punch, Tulip & Honeycomb, Miniature	14.00
Pressed Glass, Bowl, Queen Anne, Oval, Open, 9 X 13 In.	32.50
Pressed Glass, Bowl, Rose Sprig, Footed, 10 In.Diameter	22.00
Pressed Glass, Bowl, Ruffles & Rings, Opalescent, 8 In., Flint	25.00
Pressed Glass, Bowl, Star And File, 7 In.	15.00

Pressed Glass, Bowl, Thistle, 6 1/2 In. 10.00
Pressed Glass, Bowl, Tokyo, Blue, Opalescent, Jefferson Glass Co., C.1899 .... 40.00
Pressed Glass, Bowl, Torpedo, 8 In.Diameter 9.00
Pressed Glass, Bowl, Torpedo, 9 In.Diameter 10.00
Pressed Glass, Bowl, Tree Of Life, 8 In.Diameter 8.00
Pressed Glass, Bowl, Waste, Banded Portland 16.50
Pressed Glass, Bowl, Waste, Frosted Ribbon 28.50
Pressed Glass, Bowl, Water Lily, Ruffled Edge, 10 In. 15.00
Pressed Glass, Bowl, Whirling Star, Flattened Diamonds, Flint, 11 1/2 In. 125.00
Pressed Glass, Bowl, Wildflower, Blue, Square, Large 25.00
Pressed Glass, Bowl, Yoked Loop, Flint, 8 In.Diameter 12.00
Pressed Glass, Box, Whiskbroom, Daisy & Button, Blue, 7 X 5 In. 32.50
Pressed Glass, Bride's Basket, Frosted Waffle, Miniature, Metal Holder 15.00
Pressed Glass, Bucket, Ice, Block & Fan 35.00
Pressed Glass, Bust, Dewey 42.50
Pressed Glass, Butter Chip, Daisy & Button, Square 7.50
Pressed Glass, Butter, Anthemion 7.50
Pressed Glass, Butter, Anthemion, Covered 29.50
Pressed Glass, Butter, Backward S, Blue, Covered, Gold 65.00
Pressed Glass, Butter, Baltimore Pear, Covered 28.00
Pressed Glass, Butter, Beaded Grape Medallion 10.00
Pressed Glass, Butter, Block & Fan 35.00
Pressed Glass, Butter, Bowtie, Covered 32.50
Pressed Glass, Butter, Cable 67.50
Pressed Glass, Butter, Carolina, Covered 17.50
Pressed Glass, Butter, Child's, Grapevine, Covered, 3 3/4 In.Diameter 5.00
Pressed Glass, Butter, Child's Nursery Rhyme Cover .... 48.50 To 55.00
Pressed Glass, Butter, Child's, Oval Star Cover 16.00
Pressed Glass, Butter, Classic, Open Log, Covered, Footed 125.00
Pressed Glass, Butter, Colorado, Blue, Gold 33.00
Pressed Glass, Butter, Colorado, Green 59.50
Pressed Glass, Butter, Cranberry, Gold 75.00
Pressed Glass, Butter, Cube & Fan, Covered 16.50
Pressed Glass, Butter, Dakota, Clear, Covered 27.50
Pressed Glass, Butter, Delaware, Green, Gold 48.00
Pressed Glass, Butter, Etched Bearded Man, Covered 20.00
Pressed Glass, Butter, Etched Button Band, Covered 25.00
Pressed Glass, Butter, Fans With Crossbars, Covered, Red Flashed 58.00
Pressed Glass, Butter, Feather, Covered 25.00
Pressed Glass, Butter, Fleur-De-Lis, Emerald Green, Covered, Greentown 35.00
Pressed Glass, Butter, Flowerpot 12.50
Pressed Glass, Butter, Frosted Circle 35.00
Pressed Glass, Butter, Frosted Lion, Crouching Lion Finial 49.50
Pressed Glass, Butter, Goodluck, Covered 65.00
Pressed Glass, Butter, Grape & Festoon, Covered, Acorn Finial 25.00
Pressed Glass, Butter, Herringbone, Green, Covered 28.50
Pressed Glass, Butter, Horseshoe, Covered 22.50
Pressed Glass, Butter, Ivanhoe Findley, Clear 25.00
Pressed Glass, Butter, Lace, Pink, Covered, 12 In.Long 8.00
Pressed Glass, Butter, Leaf Medallion, Purple, Covered, Gold 45.00
Pressed Glass, Butter, Liberty Bell 65.00
Pressed Glass, Butter, Loop & Dart With Round Ornament, Covered 27.00
Pressed Glass, Butter, Loop & Jewel 7.50
Pressed Glass, Butter, Lorne 35.00
Pressed Glass, Butter, Lorne, Covered 17.50
Pressed Glass, Butter, Lotus 12.50
Pressed Glass, Butter, Lotus With Serpent, Covered 40.00
Pressed Glass, Butter, Michigan, Covered, Pink Flashed, Gold 45.00
Pressed Glass, Butter, Mitered Prisms, Covered 25.00
Pressed Glass, Butter, New Jersey, Covered 32.50
Pressed Glass, Butter, Oaken Bucket 10.00
Pressed Glass, Butter, Oregon & Beaded Oval, Covered 27.50
Pressed Glass, Butter, Paneled Grape Band 30.00
Pressed Glass, Butter, Paneled Thistle, Covered 22.50
Pressed Glass, Butter, Paneled Wheat, Covered 22.50
Pressed Glass, Butter, Pennsylvania, Covered 22.00

Pressed Glass, Butter, Princess Feather 35.00
Pressed Glass, Butter, Priscilla, Covered 34.50
Pressed Glass, Butter, Queen Victoria 24.00
Pressed Glass, Butter, Rosette, Palm 25.00
Pressed Glass, Butter, Royal .... *Illus* 35.00

Pressed Glass, Butter, Royal

Pressed Glass, Butter, Royal Oak, Frosted, Clear, Covered 29.50
Pressed Glass, Butter, Snail, Covered 32.00
Pressed Glass, Butter, Stars & Bars 3.75
Pressed Glass, Butter, Stippled Medallion, Covered, Flint 23.50
Pressed Glass, Butter, Tokyo, Blue, Opalescent, Covered, Jefferson Co., C.1899 .... 65.00
Pressed Glass, Butter, Tulip & Honeycomb, Covered, Miniature 10.00
Pressed Glass, Butter, Tulip, Covered, Miniature, Oval 12.00
Pressed Glass, Butter, Viking, Covered 35.00
Pressed Glass, Butter, Westward Ho, Covered 45.00
Pressed Glass, Butter, Willow Oak 7.50
Pressed Glass, Cake Stand, Ball & Swirl, 9 1/4 In. 22.50
Pressed Glass, Cake Stand, Barley 25.00
Pressed Glass, Cake Stand, Beaded Band, 8 In. 18.50
Pressed Glass, Cake Stand, Bird & Strawberry, Clear 25.00
Pressed Glass, Cake Stand, Buckle With Star, 10 1/4 In. 29.50
Pressed Glass, Cake Stand, Cathedral, Amber 40.00
Pressed Glass, Cake Stand, Circle, Frosted, 9 1/2 In. 32.50
Pressed Glass, Cake Stand, Cord Drapery, 6 In.High 30.00
Pressed Glass, Cake Stand, Cottage, 9 X 6 1/2 In. 16.50
Pressed Glass, Cake Stand, Daisy & Cane 8.00
Pressed Glass, Cake Stand, Dakota, 10 In.Diameter 18.50
Pressed Glass, Cake Stand, Dewdrop, 9 1/2 In.Diameter 19.00
Pressed Glass, Cake Stand, Feather, 8 In.Diameter 13.00
Pressed Glass, Cake Stand, Festoon, 9 In. 15.00
Pressed Glass, Cake Stand, Garden Pink, 9 1/2 In. 10.50
Pressed Glass, Cake Stand, Good Luck, 8 X 6 1/2 In. 35.00
Pressed Glass, Cake Stand, Hanover, Amber, 10 1/2 In. 42.50
Pressed Glass, Cake Stand, Hex & Block, 9 In. 21.50
Pressed Glass, Cake Stand, Horseshoe, 9 In. 21.50
Pressed Glass, Cake Stand, Horseshoe, 10 In. 32.50
Pressed Glass, Cake Stand, Inverted Thumbprint, Amber, 9 3/4 In. 30.00
Pressed Glass, Cake Stand, Jersey Swirl, 10 In. 29.50
Pressed Glass, Cake Stand, Melrose 29.50
Pressed Glass, Cake Stand, Multiple Fruits, 10 1/2 In. 35.00
Pressed Glass, Cake Stand, Nailhead, 8 3/4 In. 11.50
Pressed Glass, Cake Stand, Paneled Forget-Me-Not, 10 In. 27.50
Pressed Glass, Cake Stand, Pinwheels 18.50
Pressed Glass, Cake Stand, Pleat & Panel, 9 In. 25.00
Pressed Glass, Cake Stand, Pleat & Panel, 10 In. 27.50
Pressed Glass, Cake Stand, Portland, 10 In. Diameter 28.50
Pressed Glass, Cake Stand, Pressed Diamond, Blue, 10 In. 45.00
Pressed Glass, Cake Stand, Priscilla, 9 1/2 In. 28.50
Pressed Glass, Cake Stand, Ribbon, Clear, 8 1/2 In. 24.00
Pressed Glass, Cake Stand, Ribbon, Clear, 10 In. 20.00

Pressed Glass, Cake Stand, Rope Band, 8 1/2 In.	12.50
Pressed Glass, Cake Stand, Rosette & Pinwheel	15.00
Pressed Glass, Cake Stand, Rosette With Palms, 9 1/2 In.	16.00
Pressed Glass, Cake Stand, Scroll With Star, Miniature, Fluted Rim	22.50
Pressed Glass, Cake Stand, Shell & Tassel, Pedestal	18.00
Pressed Glass, Cake Stand, Shoshone	22.50
Pressed Glass, Cake Stand, Stippled Forget-Me-Not, Small Size	13.00
Pressed Glass, Cake Stand, Sunburst	15.00
Pressed Glass, Cake Stand, U.S.Coin Glass, Dollars & Quarters, 7 In.High	295.00
Pressed Glass, Cake Stand, U.S.Coin, 10 In.Diameter, 6 1/4 In.Tall	295.00
Pressed Glass, Cake Stand, Utah, 8 1/2 In.	23.50
Pressed Glass, Cake Stand, Valencia Waffle, 10 In.	27.50
Pressed Glass, Cake Stand, Water Lily	17.50
Pressed Glass, Cake Stand, Willow Oak, Clear, 10 In.Diameter	12.50
Pressed Glass, Cake Stand, Wyoming	22.50
Pressed Glass, Candleholder, Frosted Figure, Clear Top	90.00
Pressed Glass, Candlestick, Lacy, Clear, 9 In.Tall, Pair	30.00
Pressed Glass, Candlestick, Owl Figure, 1 Candle	11.00
Pressed Glass, Candlestick, Wedding Bell, Pair	14.00
Pressed Glass, Candlestick, Wedding Ring	13.00
Pressed Glass, Carafe, Whiskey, Beaded Loop	13.00
Pressed Glass, Celery, Aetna 300	8.00
Pressed Glass, Celery, Arched Grape	16.00
Pressed Glass, Celery, Ashburton	41.00
Pressed Glass, Celery, Beaded Grape, Green, Rectangular	27.50
Pressed Glass, Celery, Bevel Diamond, Star	16.50
Pressed Glass, Celery, Blackberry	24.00
Pressed Glass, Celery, Block	8.00
Pressed Glass, Celery, Block & Fan	15.00
Pressed Glass, Celery, Cabbage Rose	45.00
Pressed Glass, Celery, Cable	95.00
Pressed Glass, Celery, Canadian	30.00
Pressed Glass, Celery, Chandelier	19.50
Pressed Glass, Celery, Classic, Open Log, Footed	87.50
Pressed Glass, Celery, Currant	27.50
Pressed Glass, Celery, Curtain, 7 1/2 In.High	7.00
Pressed Glass, Celery, Cut Log	17.00
Pressed Glass, Celery, Daisy & Button	22.50
Pressed Glass, Celery, Daisy & Button, Amberette	32.00
Pressed Glass, Celery, Daisy & Button, Canoe Shape, 14 In.Long	18.50
Pressed Glass, Celery, Daisy & Button, With Thumbprint, Clear, 8 In.	18.50
Pressed Glass, Celery, Dakota	18.00
Pressed Glass, Celery, Delaware, Green	35.00
Pressed Glass, Celery, Diagonal Band	8.50
Pressed Glass, Celery, Diamond & Star, Beveled	10.00
Pressed Glass, Celery, Diamond & Sunburst, Footed	17.75
Pressed Glass, Celery, Diamond Point, Flint, Pedestal Base	65.00
Pressed Glass, Celery, Double Daisy	25.00
Pressed Glass, Celery, Double Fan, Findlay	12.00
Pressed Glass, Celery, Egyptian	32.50
Pressed Glass, Celery, Etched Eagle, Frosted	29.50
Pressed Glass, Celery, Etched Snail	22.50
Pressed Glass, Celery, Etched Three Faces	85.00
Pressed Glass, Celery, Feather	18.50
Pressed Glass, Celery, Fern & Daisy	6.00
Pressed Glass, Celery, Frosted Flower Band	38.00
Pressed Glass, Celery, Frosted Ribbon	35.00
Pressed Glass, Celery, Garfield Drape	27.50
Pressed Glass, Celery, Good Luck	20.00
Pressed Glass, Celery, Hidalgo, Frosted	17.50
Pressed Glass, Celery, Hobnail With Fan, Clear, Thumbprint Base	18.50
Pressed Glass, Celery, Holly Band *Illus*	20.00
Pressed Glass, Celery, Horn Of Plenty, Flint 82.50 To 97.50	
Pressed Glass, Celery, Inverted Thumbprint, Ruby, 4 In.Ruby Band, 6 In.High	20.00
Pressed Glass, Celery, Jacobs Ladder	20.00
Pressed Glass, Celery, Jewel Band	11.00

Pressed Glass, Celery, Holly Band
See Page 418

Pressed Glass, Celery, Lattice .... 12.00 To 15.00
Pressed Glass, Celery, Lion 22.50
Pressed Glass, Celery, Loop & Dart 25.00
Pressed Glass, Celery, Manhattan 15.00
Pressed Glass, Celery, Marquisette 17.00
Pressed Glass, Celery, Mascotte 18.50
Pressed Glass, Celery, Michigan 12.00
Pressed Glass, Celery, Oak Leaf Band 21.50
Pressed Glass, Celery, Palm Leaf, Fan, 6 1/2 In.High 11.00
Pressed Glass, Celery, Pan Thistle, Two Handles 18.00
Pressed Glass, Celery, Pavonia 14.50
Pressed Glass, Celery, Picket 30.00
Pressed Glass, Celery, Pillow Encircled 14.00
Pressed Glass, Celery, Pillow Encircled, Findlay 12.00
Pressed Glass, Celery, Pittsburgh Pillar, Knob Stem 100.00
Pressed Glass, Celery, Pleat & Panel, Clear 16.50
Pressed Glass, Celery, Plume 12.00
Pressed Glass, Celery, Plume, Vertical 18.00
Pressed Glass, Celery, Portland 11.00
Pressed Glass, Celery, Prayer Rug, Flint 20.00
Pressed Glass, Celery, Princess Feather 20.00
Pressed Glass, Celery, Prism Arc 15.00
Pressed Glass, Celery, Prism Band 14.00
Pressed Glass, Celery, Quaker Lady 25.00
Pressed Glass, Celery, Quartered Block 10.00
Pressed Glass, Celery, Ribbon, Panel, Clear 9.00
Pressed Glass, Celery, Rose & Celery Stalk 17.50
Pressed Glass, Celery, Rose Sprig 15.00
Pressed Glass, Celery, Rosette & Palm 18.50
Pressed Glass, Celery, Ruby Thumbprint 35.00
Pressed Glass, Celery, Ruby Thumbprint, Scalloped Rim 45.00
Pressed Glass, Celery, Sawtooth & Tulip, Flint 29.00
Pressed Glass, Celery, Scallop Top, Clear, Flint 50.00
Pressed Glass, Celery, Seneca Loop 12.50
Pressed Glass, Celery, Sheaf & Block 8.00
Pressed Glass, Celery, Shell & Tassel, Round 24.00
Pressed Glass, Celery, Spirea Band 13.75
Pressed Glass, Celery, Sprig 25.00
Pressed Glass, Celery, Star & Oval, Frosted 12.00
Pressed Glass, Celery, Star And File, Handles 15.00
Pressed Glass, Celery, Sunk Daisy 10.00
Pressed Glass, Celery, Texas Blue-Bell 15.00
Pressed Glass, Celery, Thumbprint .... 45.00 To 150.00
Pressed Glass, Celery, Tropical Villa 24.00
Pressed Glass, Celery, Tulip & Sawtooth, 10 In.Tall 24.00
Pressed Glass, Celery, Two Panel, Blue 37.50
Pressed Glass, Celery, U.S.Coin, 1892 Quarters 140.00

Pressed Glass, **Celery**, Vernon Honeycomb	36.00
Pressed Glass, **Celery**, Waffle, 9 In.High, Flint	42.00
Pressed Glass, **Celery**, Washboard, Green	14.00
Pressed Glass, **Celery**, Zipper	17.50
Pressed Glass, **Celery**, 1, 000-Eye	15.00
Pressed Glass, **Celery**, 1, 000-Eye, Amber	37.50
Pressed Glass, **Celery**, 1, 000-Eye, 3 Balls Near Base	20.00
Pressed Glass, **Center Bowl**, Strawberry, 8 1/2 In.	20.00
Pressed Glass, **Champagne**, Almond Thumbprint	30.00
Pressed Glass, **Champagne**, Ashburton	30.00
Pressed Glass, **Champagne**, Ashburton, Flint	22.50
Pressed Glass, **Champagne**, Belted Worcester	20.00
Pressed Glass, **Champagne**, Colonial, Teardrop Stem	12.00
Pressed Glass, **Champagne**, Fine Rib	37.50
Pressed Glass, **Champagne**, Gothic	65.00
Pressed Glass, **Champagne**, Priscilla	25.00
Pressed Glass, **Champagne**, Ripple	10.00
Pressed Glass, **Champagne**, Sawtooth, Bulb Stem, Flint	24.00
Pressed Glass, **Champagne**, U.S.Coin Glass, Frosted, 1/2 Dimes, Stemmed, Flared	300.00
Pressed Glass, **Champagne**, Waffle & Thumbprint, Cut, Stemmed	45.00
Pressed Glass, **Champagne**, Waffle, Flint	48.00
Pressed Glass, **Claret**, Ashburton	45.00
Pressed Glass, **Cologne**, Maiden's Blush	35.00
Pressed Glass, **Compote**, Arched Leaf, Footed, Low, Flint, 8 1/4 In.	27.50
Pressed Glass, **Compote**, Atlanta Lion, Open, Scalloped Top, Square Stem	22.00
Pressed Glass, **Compote**, Atlas, Scalloped	75.00
Pressed Glass, **Compote**, Austrian	15.00
Pressed Glass, **Compote**, Aztec, Clear, Footed	14.00
Pressed Glass, **Compote**, Ball & Swirl, Open, 5 In.High	13.00
Pressed Glass, **Compote**, Barberry, Cover, On Low Standard	35.00
Pressed Glass, **Compote**, Barberry, Open, 8 In.Diameter	25.00
Pressed Glass, **Compote**, Barley, Cover	40.00
Pressed Glass, **Compote**, Bellflower, Flint, Open, 8 In.	55.00
Pressed Glass, **Compote**, Bellflower, Flint, 8 In.High	42.00
Pressed Glass, **Compote**, Bellflower, Footed, Flint, Scalloped	50.00
Pressed Glass, **Compote**, Bellflower, Single Vine, Low Stand, Flint	40.00
Pressed Glass, **Compote**, Bellflower, 5 1/4 In.High	65.00
Pressed Glass, **Compote**, Bellflower, 7 In.Diameter	43.00
Pressed Glass, **Compote**, Bethlehem Star, Lid, Small Size	12.00
Pressed Glass, **Compote**, Blaze, Wafer Applied Pedestal, Flint	38.00
Pressed Glass, **Compote**, Block & Bar, Open, Scalloped Top, Low Standard, Flint	27.50
Pressed Glass, **Compote**, Block, Old Water Construction, Flint	42.00
Pressed Glass, **Compote**, Broadflute, 9 In.	20.00
Pressed Glass, **Compote**, Cabbage Rose, Cover, 8 1/2 In.Diameter	47.50
Pressed Glass, **Compote**, Cable, Open, Low Standard, 8 In., Flint	28.00
Pressed Glass, **Compote**, Cameo, Clear, 4 In.High, 8 In.Diameter	12.00
Pressed Glass, **Compote**, Cameo, Open, Low Pedestal	18.00
Pressed Glass, **Compote**, Canadian	16.00
Pressed Glass, **Compote**, Canadian, Covered, 9 In.High	55.00
Pressed Glass, **Compote**, Canadian, Covered, 11 In.High, 7 In.Diameter	38.50
Pressed Glass, **Compote**, Candy, Loops With Dewdrops, 5 In.Diameter	18.50
Pressed Glass, **Compote**, Cape Cod	45.00
Pressed Glass, **Compote**, Cape Cod, Covered	58.00
Pressed Glass, **Compote**, Cathedral Amber, Flared Rim	37.50
Pressed Glass, **Compote**, Cathedral, Amber	15.00
Pressed Glass, **Compote**, Chicken, Footed, Covered	45.00
Pressed Glass, **Compote**, Classic, Covered, 7 1/2 In.Diameter	85.00
Pressed Glass, **Compote**, Classic, 6 1/2 In.High	65.00
Pressed Glass, **Compote**, Crystal Wedding	20.00
Pressed Glass, **Compote**, Crystal Wedding, Covered, 13 In.High	60.00
Pressed Glass, **Compote**, Daisy & Button With Crossbars, Amber, 8 In.Diameter	45.00
Pressed Glass, **Compote**, Daisy & Button With Crossbars, Clear, 7 1/2 In.High	14.00
Pressed Glass, **Compote**, Daisy & Button, Clear	32.00
Pressed Glass, **Compote**, Dakota, 9 In.	22.00
Pressed Glass, **Compote**, Diagonal Band, 7 In.Diameter, 7 1/2 In.High	25.00
Pressed Glass, **Compote**, Diamond Medallion, Footed, Low	8.00

Pressed Glass, Compote, Diamond Medallion, 6 In.High 10.00
Pressed Glass, Compote, Diamond Point Disc, 9 In. 25.00
Pressed Glass, Compote, Diamond Point, Scalloped, 6 In. 9.00
Pressed Glass, Compote, Diamond Thumbprint, Low Footed 27.50
Pressed Glass, Compote, Diamond Thumbprint, 8 In.High 150.00
Pressed Glass, Compote, Dolphin, Pittsburgh Petticoat, White, Peacock Blue 197.00
Pressed Glass, Compote, Dolphin, Pittsburgh, 8 In. .... *Illus* 95.00
Pressed Glass, Compote, Double Ribbon, Frosted, Covered 48.50
Pressed Glass, Compote, Drapery, 8 In. 12.50
Pressed Glass, Compote, Duchess Loop, Flint 15.00
Pressed Glass, Compote, Etched Dakota, Flared Lip, 8 In.Diameter 22.50
Pressed Glass, Compote, Feather, Footed, 4 1/2 In.High 12.00
Pressed Glass, Compote, Fine Rib, Covered, 8 In.High 59.00
Pressed Glass, Compote, Fleur-De-Lis Drape, Green 18.50
Pressed Glass, Compote, Frosted Lion, Covered, Crouching Lion Finial, Oval 49.50
Pressed Glass, Compote, Frosted Roses, Crystal, Gold, 8 In.High 10.00
Pressed Glass, Compote, Fruit, Reverse Torpedo 29.00
Pressed Glass, Compote, Garfield Drape, Covered, High Standard 35.00
Pressed Glass, Compote, Grape Band, Covered, 8 In.Diameter 22.50

Pressed Glass, Compote, Dolphin, Pittsburgh, 8 In.

Pressed Glass, Compote, Hamilton, 5 X 7 In. 35.00
Pressed Glass, Compote, Hamilton, 8 1/4 X 8 1/4 In. 45.00
Pressed Glass, Compote, Hawaiian Lei, 8 In.Diameter, 7 In.High 16.50
Pressed Glass, Compote, Hickman, 7 3/4 In. 14.00
Pressed Glass, Compote, Honeycomb 9.75
Pressed Glass, Compote, Horn Of Plenty, Flint, 7 In.High 95.00
Pressed Glass, Compote, Horn Of Plenty, 7 X 7 In. 45.00
Pressed Glass, Compote, Huckle 8.00
Pressed Glass, Compote, Hundred Leaved Ivy 12.50
Pressed Glass, Compote, Ivanhoe, 7 1/4 In. 16.00
Pressed Glass, Compote, Jacob's Ladder, 7 1/2 In.High 23.50
Pressed Glass, Compote, Jelly, Beaded Grape, Emerald Green 21.00
Pressed Glass, Compote, Jelly, Circled Scroll, White Opalescent 17.50
Pressed Glass, Compote, Jelly, Maine, Covered 25.00
Pressed Glass, Compote, Jelly, Priscilla 17.50
Pressed Glass, Compote, Jelly, Priscilla, Covered 20.00
Pressed Glass, Compote, Jelly, Shell, White Opalescent, Footed 18.00
Pressed Glass, Compote, Jelly, Shrine Pattern 35.00
Pressed Glass, Compote, Jersey Swirl, Scalloped Edge, 8 In.Diameter 22.50
Pressed Glass, Compote, Jeweled Moon & Star, 8 1/2 In.High 28.50
Pressed Glass, Compote, King Crown 18.00
Pressed Glass, Compote, Late Buckle, Footed, Covered 25.00
Pressed Glass, Compote, Leaf & Flower, Ruffled Edge 45.00
Pressed Glass, Compote, Lily Of The Valley 30.00
Pressed Glass, Compote, Lincoln Drape, 5 1/4 In.High, 8 In.Wide 38.00
Pressed Glass, Compote, Maryland 9.75
Pressed Glass, Compote, Minerva, Footed, 7 In.Diameter 12.00

Pressed Glass, Compote, Miter Diamond, Footed, 9 In.High, 10 In.Diameter 28.00
Pressed Glass, Compote, Moon & Star 20.00
Pressed Glass, Compote, Moon & Star, Blue, Covered, 7 1/2 In.High 40.00
Pressed Glass, Compote, Moon & Star, Clear, Covered, Pedestal, 10 In.High 47.50
Pressed Glass, Compote, New England Pineapple, Flint 56.00
Pressed Glass, Compote, New England Pineapple, Flint, 7 X 8 1/2 In. 80.00
Pressed Glass, Compote, New England Pineapple, 5 X 7 1/2 In. 35.00
Pressed Glass, Compote, New England Pineapple, 9 1/2 X 8 1/2 In. 56.00
Pressed Glass, Compote, New Jersey, 5 In. 12.50
Pressed Glass, Compote, Opal Intaglio 16.50
Pressed Glass, Compote, Open Rose, Low 20.00
Pressed Glass, Compote, Panel & Cord Band 25.00
Pressed Glass, Compote, Paneled Thistle, Footed, Flint 50.00
Pressed Glass, Compote, Picket, High Standard, 7 In. 18.00
Pressed Glass, Compote, Pineapple, Flint, 8 X 5 In. 44.00
Pressed Glass, Compote, Plum 16.00
Pressed Glass, Compote, Pressed Block, Flint 55.00
Pressed Glass, Compote, Rayed Flower, Covered, 9 In.High 25.00
Pressed Glass, Compote, Rib Ivy, 8 In.High 35.00
Pressed Glass, Compote, Ribbon, 7 In.Diameter, 6 1/2 In.High 38.50
Pressed Glass, Compote, Roman Rosette 17.50
Pressed Glass, Compote, Rose In Snow, 4 1/2 In.High 50.00
Pressed Glass, Compote, Rosette 9.50
Pressed Glass, Compote, Sawtooth Variant, Flint 28.50
Pressed Glass, Compote, Sawtooth, Flint 42.00
Pressed Glass, Compote, Sawtooth, Flint, 3 1/2 In.High 35.00
Pressed Glass, Compote, Sawtooth, Flint, 5 In.High, 7 In.Diameter 18.00
Pressed Glass, Compote, Sheaf & Diamond 9.00
Pressed Glass, Compote, Shell & Tassel 32.00
Pressed Glass, Compote, Shell & Tassel, High Standard, 7 3/4 In. 22.00
Pressed Glass, Compote, Shell & Tassel, Square, 8 In.High 32.00
Pressed Glass, Compote, Strawberry & Cable, Covered 25.00
Pressed Glass, Compote, Swan, 8 In.High 45.00
Pressed Glass, Compote, Sweetmeat, Westward Ho, Covered, 4 In.High 37.50
Pressed Glass, Compote, Teaberry Gum, Clear, Footed 12.50
Pressed Glass, Compote, Three Panel, Clear, 4 In.High, 7 1/4 In.Diameter 8.50
Pressed Glass, Compote, Thumbprint, Amber, Ruffled Top 7.00
Pressed Glass, Compote, Thumbprint, Covered, Flint, 7 In.High 50.00
Pressed Glass, Compote, Tokyo, Blue, Opalescent, Jefferson Glass Co., C.1899 .... 42.00
Pressed Glass, Compote, Torpedo & Fan 17.00
Pressed Glass, Compote, Tree Of Life, Clear, Hand Holding Stem, 8 In. 35.00
Pressed Glass, Compote, Tree Of Life, Covered 45.00
Pressed Glass, Compote, Tree Of Life, Hand, Frosted Stem, Base, 8 1/2 In. 26.00
Pressed Glass, Compote, Tree Of Life, Hand, Pittsburgh, High 35.00
Pressed Glass, Compote, Tree Of Life, Pittsburgh 52.00
Pressed Glass, Compote, Tree Of Life, Portland, Patent P G & Co. 55.00
Pressed Glass, Compote, Tree Of Life, 9 In. .... *Illus* 65.00
Pressed Glass, Compote, U.S.Coin, Covered, 11 1/2 In.High 450.00
Pressed Glass, Compote, U.S.Coin, Frosted Dimes & Quarters 250.00
Pressed Glass, Compote, U.S.Coin, Frosted Dimes & Quarters, 8 In.Diameter 250.00
Pressed Glass, Compote, U.S.Coin, Half Dollars, Covered, 12 In.High 450.00
Pressed Glass, Compote, Westward Ho, Covered, 11 In.High 105.00
Pressed Glass, Compote, Westward Ho, Covered, 16 In.High, 9 In.Diameter 165.00
Pressed Glass, Compote, Westward Ho, 8 In.Diameter 45.00
Pressed Glass, Compote, Wheat & Barley 13.50
Pressed Glass, Compote, Wildflower, Blue 32.00
Pressed Glass, Compote, Willow Oak, 8 1/4 In.Diameter, 7 In.High 18.50
Pressed Glass, Compote, Wisconsin 22.50
Pressed Glass, Compote, 1, 000-Eye, Amber, Square 55.00
Pressed Glass, Condiment Set, Daisy & Button, Amber, Ring Handled Holder 72.50
Pressed Glass, Cordial, Ashburton 35.00
Pressed Glass, Cordial, Ashburton Cut 25.00
Pressed Glass, Cordial, Crochet Band 5.00
Pressed Glass, Cordial, Diamond Point 8.75
Pressed Glass, Cordial, Dutchess Loop 10.00
Pressed Glass, Cordial, Feather ....28.75 To 50.00

Pressed Glass, **Cordial**, Fine Cut And Block	34.50
Pressed Glass, **Cordial**, Hand	30.00
Pressed Glass, **Cordial**, Hearts Of Loch Lomond	8.50
Pressed Glass, **Cordial**, Huber	20.00
Pressed Glass, **Cordial**, Paneled Grape	7.50
Pressed Glass, **Cordial**, Quartered Block	7.50
Pressed Glass, **Cordial**, Ruby Thumbprint	20.00
Pressed Glass, **Cordial**, Sawtooth, Stemmed, Flint, 4 1/2 In.High	25.00

Pressed Glass, **Creamer & Sugar, see Pressed Glass, Sugar & Creamer**

Pressed Glass, **Creamer**, Acorn, Applied Handle	30.00
Pressed Glass, **Creamer**, Arched Ovals	9.00
Pressed Glass, **Creamer**, Baltimore Pear	17.00
Pressed Glass, **Creamer**, Barberry	15.00 To 16.50
Pressed Glass, **Creamer**, Barberry, Oval Berries	20.00
Pressed Glass, **Creamer**, Barred Forget-Me-Not	18.00
Pressed Glass, **Creamer**, Bars & Button	10.00
Pressed Glass, **Creamer**, Beaded Tulip	22.00
Pressed Glass, **Creamer**, Blackberry	22.00
Pressed Glass, **Creamer**, Block & Bar	40.00
Pressed Glass, **Creamer**, Block & Bar, Flint	52.00
Pressed Glass, **Creamer**, Block & Circle	17.50
Pressed Glass, **Creamer**, Block & Fan	30.00
Pressed Glass, **Creamer**, Bowtie	22.50
Pressed Glass, **Creamer**, Broken Column	22.50
Pressed Glass, **Creamer**, Bryce	12.00
Pressed Glass, **Creamer**, Cable & Ring	80.00
Pressed Glass, **Creamer**, Canadian	25.00
Pressed Glass, **Creamer**, Candlewick	10.00
Pressed Glass, **Creamer**, Cape Cod	28.00
Pressed Glass, **Creamer**, Cats Eye & Block, Small	15.00
Pressed Glass, **Creamer**, Centennial Shield	30.00
Pressed Glass, **Creamer**, Center Medallion	12.50
Pressed Glass, **Creamer**, Chain & Shield	16.00
Pressed Glass, **Creamer**, Charleston Swirl	8.50
Pressed Glass, **Creamer**, Child's, Blue	16.00
Pressed Glass, **Creamer**, Child's, Grape With Ovals, 1 3/4 In.High	10.00
Pressed Glass, **Creamer**, Child's, Green	16.00
Pressed Glass, **Creamer**, Child's, Hearts In Stippled Band, 1 3/4 In.High	10.00
Pressed Glass, **Creamer**, Clover, 3 1/2 In. *Illus*	12.00
Pressed Glass, **Creamer**, Colorado, Green, Gold, Large	35.00
Pressed Glass, **Creamer**, Cut Long	12.50

Pressed Glass,
Compote, Tree Of Life, 9 In.
See Page 422

Pressed Glass,
Creamer, Inverted Fern, 6 In.
See Page 424

Pressed Glass,
Creamer, Clover, 3 1/2 In

Pressed Glass, Creamer, Delaware, Cranberry, Gold	35.00 To 45.00
Pressed Glass, Creamer, Diamond Band	6.25
Pressed Glass, Creamer, Diamond Thumbprint, 6 1/2 In.High	95.00
Pressed Glass, Creamer, Diamonds In Diamond	12.00
Pressed Glass, Creamer, Double Doughnut	11.00
Pressed Glass, Creamer, Double Doughnut, Handles, Two Pouring Spouts	45.00
Pressed Glass, Creamer, Double Pinwheel, Gold Band	8.00
Pressed Glass, Creamer, Drapery	15.00
Pressed Glass, Creamer, Edgerton	6.25
Pressed Glass, Creamer, Etched Dakota	25.00
Pressed Glass, Creamer, Etched Sunk Teardrop	7.50
Pressed Glass, Creamer, Fan Band	10.00
Pressed Glass, Creamer, Festoon	15.50
Pressed Glass, Creamer, Flamingo Habitat, Applied Handle	24.50
Pressed Glass, Creamer, Fleur-De-Lis & Drape, Emerald	20.00
Pressed Glass, Creamer, Fluted Scrolls, Opalescent	32.50
Pressed Glass, Creamer, Frosted Circle	30.00
Pressed Glass, Creamer, Galloway	12.00
Pressed Glass, Creamer, Garden, Pink	7.00
Pressed Glass, Creamer, Garfield Drape	30.00
Pressed Glass, Creamer, Gibson Girl	40.00
Pressed Glass, Creamer, Good Luck	16.00
Pressed Glass, Creamer, Grand	15.00
Pressed Glass, Creamer, Grated Diamond & Sunburst	10.50
Pressed Glass, Creamer, Heart & Thumbprint, Small	10.00
Pressed Glass, Creamer, Herringbone	10.00
Pressed Glass, Creamer, Horn Of Plenty, Flint, 5 1/4 In.High	252.00
Pressed Glass, Creamer, Horn Of Plenty, Flint, 6 3/4 In.High	135.00
Pressed Glass, Creamer, Horn Of Plenty, 6 In.	125.00
Pressed Glass, Creamer, Hummingbird	28.00
Pressed Glass, Creamer, Inverted Fern, 6 In. *Illus*	55.00
Pressed Glass, Creamer, Jacob's Ladder	16.50 To 18.00
Pressed Glass, Creamer, King's Crown	19.00
Pressed Glass, Creamer, Knife & Fork, Clear	6.00
Pressed Glass, Creamer, Lattice	13.50
Pressed Glass, Creamer, Liberty Bell	72.00
Pressed Glass, Creamer, Loop & Pillar, 3 In.High	6.50
Pressed Glass, Creamer, Loop And Jewel	7.50
Pressed Glass, Creamer, Lotus	18.00
Pressed Glass, Creamer, Michigan, Large Size	20.00
Pressed Glass, Creamer, Minerva	20.00
Pressed Glass, Creamer, Open Rose	47.50
Pressed Glass, Creamer, Open Rose, Applied Handle	28.00
Pressed Glass, Creamer, Oval Thumbprint, Column	8.00
Pressed Glass, Creamer, Palmette, Applied Handle	25.00
Pressed Glass, Creamer, Paneled Acorn Band, Applied Handle	22.50
Pressed Glass, Creamer, Paneled Zipper	16.75
Pressed Glass, Creamer, Pineapple & Fan	17.50
Pressed Glass, Creamer, Popcorn	20.00
Pressed Glass, Creamer, Powder & Shot	25.00
Pressed Glass, Creamer, Princess Feather	25.00
Pressed Glass, Creamer, Raspberry & Grape	26.50
Pressed Glass, Creamer, Ribbed Opalescent	25.00
Pressed Glass, Creamer, Ribbed Palm, Flint	65.00
Pressed Glass, Creamer, Ribbon	16.50 To 25.00
Pressed Glass, Creamer, Ribbon Candy	22.00
Pressed Glass, Creamer, Roman Rosette	18.50
Pressed Glass, Creamer, Romeo	7.50
Pressed Glass, Creamer, Rose In Snow	22.50
Pressed Glass, Creamer, Ruby Thumbprint, Bulbous, Large Size	48.00
Pressed Glass, Creamer, Sandwich, Overshot, 4 In.	19.50
Pressed Glass, Creamer, Selby	17.50
Pressed Glass, Creamer, Spirea Band	12.50
Pressed Glass, Creamer, Stippled Star	25.00
Pressed Glass, Creamer, Stork, Clear	20.00
Pressed Glass, Creamer, Strawberry, 5 1/2 In. *Illus*	50.00

Pressed Glass, Creamer, Sunburst 6.52
Pressed Glass, Creamer, Teardrop & Tassel 11.00
Pressed Glass, Creamer, Texas 10.50
Pressed Glass, Creamer, Texas, Small 12.00
Pressed Glass, Creamer, Three Flowers 10.00
Pressed Glass, Creamer, Three Panel 12.50
Pressed Glass, Creamer, Tokyo, Blue, Opalescent, Jefferson Glass Co., C.1899 .... 30.00
Pressed Glass, Creamer, Viking 20.00
Pressed Glass, Creamer, Virginia 17.50
Pressed Glass, Creamer, Washington Centennial 42.50
Pressed Glass, Creamer, Willow Aok .... 12.50 to 20.00
Pressed Glass, Creamer, Willow Oak, Blue, 5 In.High 30.00
Pressed Glass, Creamer, Windflower 15.00
Pressed Glass, Creamer, 101, 5 In.High 15.00
    Pressed Glass, Cruet, see also Cruet
Pressed Glass, Cruet, Cord Drapery, Clear, Stopper, Greentown 38.50
Pressed Glass, Cruet, Daisy & Button, Paneled 6.50
Pressed Glass, Cruet, Dewey, Green, Stopper 48.00
Pressed Glass, Cruet, Etched Dakota, Matching Stopper 55.00
Pressed Glass, Cruet, Frisco 18.50
Pressed Glass, Cruet, Herringbone, Emerald Green, Applied Handle, Stopper 55.00
Pressed Glass, Cruet, Hobstars, Fan Shape Floral, Stopper, Hand Blown 12.00
Pressed Glass, Cruet, Inverted Baby Thumbprint, Sapphire, Applied Handle 68.00
Pressed Glass, Cruet, Paneled Thistle, Faceted 22.00
Pressed Glass, Cruet, Panels, Pontil, Aqua Cast, Pointed Stopper 11.00
Pressed Glass, Cruet, Pioneer, Ruby Flashed, Clear Stopper 28.50
Pressed Glass, Cruet, Zipper, Faceted Stopper 10.00
Pressed Glass, Cruet, 1, OOO-Eye 15.00
Pressed Glass, Cup & Saucer, Basket Weave, Amber 15.00
Pressed Glass, Cup & Saucer, Candlewick 12.50
Pressed Glass, Cup & Saucer, Child's, Wee Branches 35.00
Pressed Glass, Cup & Saucer, Colorado, Green, Footed 18.00
Pressed Glass, Cup & Saucer, Fleur-De-Lis & Drape 12.00
Pressed Glass, Cup & Saucer, Grape & Vine, Clear, Miniature 16.00
Pressed Glass, Cup & Saucer, Lion's Head, Child's 28.00
Pressed Glass, Cup & Saucer, Rose Medallion, Demitasse 18.00
Pressed Glass, Cup Plate, Henry Clay, Flint 15.00
Pressed Glass, Cup Plate, Lacy, Peacock Blue 245.00
Pressed Glass, Cup, Beaded Arch Panels, Handled 8.50
Pressed Glass, Cup, Grape & Festoon .... Illus 18.00

Pressed Glass,
Creamer,
Strawberry,
5 1/2 In.
See Page 424

Pressed Glass, Cup, Grape & Festoon

Pressed Glass, Cup, Lacy Medallion, Green 12.00
Pressed Glass, Cup, Punch, Bird & Strawberry 11.00
Pressed Glass, Cup, Punch, Colonial 11.00
Pressed Glass, Cup, Punch, Colorado, Green 15.00
Pressed Glass, Cup, Punch, Cordova 7.00
Pressed Glass, Cup, Punch, Diamond Ridge, C.1901 .... 4.00
Pressed Glass, Cup, Punch, Fancy Loop 12.00
Pressed Glass, Cup, Punch, Flower Design, Blue, Delaware 40.00

Pressed Glass, **Cup**, Punch, Galloway	4.50
Pressed Glass, **Cup**, Punch, King's Crown	9.00
Pressed Glass, **Cup**, Punch, Pennsylvania	4.00
Pressed Glass, **Cup**, Punch, Star In Bull's-Eye, Gold	8.50
Pressed Glass, **Cup**, Ruby Thumbprint	25.00
Pressed Glass, **Decanter**, Bull's-Eye & Fleur-De-Lis, Pint	45.00
Pressed Glass, **Decanter**, Cable, Bar Lip	75.00
Pressed Glass, **Decanter**, Horn Of Plenty, Flint, Diamond Point Stopper, Quart	125.00
Pressed Glass, **Decanter**, Horn Of Plenty, Patented Stopper, Pint	60.00
Pressed Glass, **Decanter**, Pittsburgh Pillar, Bar, Cobalt Blue Stripes	50.00
Pressed Glass, **Decanter**, Waffle & Thumbprint, Flint	42.50
Pressed Glass, **Decanter**, Wine, Overshot, Hollow Stopper, 10 In.	75.00
Pressed Glass, **Dish, Butter**, see Pressed Glass, Butter	
Pressed Glass, **Dish**, Candy, Greentown Pattern No.11, Ruby Flashed, Handled	20.00
Pressed Glass, **Dish**, Candy, Lincoln Drape	75.00
Pressed Glass, **Dish**, Candy, New England Pineapple	165.00
Pressed Glass, **Dish**, Honey, Bees & Beehives, Square	65.00
Pressed Glass, **Dish**, Honey, Buckle, Flint	4.75
Pressed Glass, **Dish**, Honey, Horn Plenty, Flint	14.00
Pressed Glass, **Dish**, Honey, Jacob's Ladder, Set Of 6	37.50
Pressed Glass, **Dish**, Mint, Fans With Crossbars, Red Flashed, Handled	16.50
Pressed Glass, **Dish**, Swan Cover, Knobbed Basket-Weaved Base, Clear	57.50
Pressed Glass, **Eggcup**, Argus, Flint	12.00 To 15.00
Pressed Glass, **Eggcup**, Ashburton, Flint	15.00 To 18.00
Pressed Glass, **Eggcup**, Banded Buckle	16.50
Pressed Glass, **Eggcup**, Barberry	12.50 To 14.00
Pressed Glass, **Eggcup**, Beaded Grape Medallion	22.00
Pressed Glass, **Eggcup**, Bellflower, Flared	22.50
Pressed Glass, **Eggcup**, Bellflower, Flint	24.00
Pressed Glass, **Eggcup**, Bellflower, Single Vine	32.00
Pressed Glass, **Eggcup**, Bleeding Heart	22.00
Pressed Glass, **Eggcup**, Buckle	12.75 To 16.50
Pressed Glass, **Eggcup**, Bull's-Eye And Bar	75.00
Pressed Glass, **Eggcup**, Cable	25.00 To 32.00
Pressed Glass, **Eggcup**, Daisy & Button, Set Of 6	38.50
Pressed Glass, **Eggcup**, Diamond Point, Flint	24.00
Pressed Glass, **Eggcup**, Divided Hearts, Flint	35.00
Pressed Glass, **Eggcup**, Eureka	15.00
Pressed Glass, **Eggcup**, Fine Rib	32.50
Pressed Glass, **Eggcup**, Flute	9.00
Pressed Glass, **Eggcup**, Gothic	26.50
Pressed Glass, **Eggcup**, Grape	3.50
Pressed Glass, **Eggcup**, Hairpin, Flint	15.00
Pressed Glass, **Eggcup**, Hairpin, Sandwich	18.00
Pressed Glass, **Eggcup**, Hamilton	24.50
Pressed Glass, **Eggcup**, Hamilton With Clear Leaf, Flint	19.00 To 28.00
Pressed Glass, **Eggcup**, Holly	45.00
Pressed Glass, **Eggcup**, Honeycomb	5.00
Pressed Glass, **Eggcup**, Horn Of Plenty, Flint	24.00 To 28.00
Pressed Glass, **Eggcup**, Huber, Flint	12.00
Pressed Glass, **Eggcup**, Inverted Fern, Flint	15.00 To 20.00
Pressed Glass, **Eggcup**, Loop & Dart	12.50 To 16.00
Pressed Glass, **Eggcup**, Loop & Dart, Double	14.50
Pressed Glass, **Eggcup**, Loop & Dart With Diamond Ornament	13.50
Pressed Glass, **Eggcup**, New England Pineapple, Flint	20.00 To 34.50
Pressed Glass, **Eggcup**, Open Rose	13.50
Pressed Glass, **Eggcup**, Powder And Shot	34.50
Pressed Glass, **Eggcup**, Pressed Leaf	7.50
Pressed Glass, **Eggcup**, Pressed Leaf, Flint	15.00
Pressed Glass, **Eggcup**, Ribbed Ivy, Flint	22.50 To 30.25
Pressed Glass, **Eggcup**, Ribbed Palm	22.50
Pressed Glass, **Eggcup**, Ripple	6.00 To 9.00
Pressed Glass, **Eggcup**, Sawtooth	16.00
Pressed Glass, **Eggcup**, Scalloped Lines	6.00
Pressed Glass, **Eggcup**, Scalloped Tape	15.00
Pressed Glass, **Eggcup**, Stippled Loop & Dart With Diamond	12.00

Pressed Glass, **Eggcup**, Stippled Medallion 15.00
Pressed Glass, **Eggcup**, Umbilicated Sawtooth 17.00
Pressed Glass, **Eggcup**, Viking 18.00
Pressed Glass, **Eggcup**, Waffle & Thumbprint, Flint .... 19.50 To 28.00
Pressed Glass, **Eggcup**, Washington 50.00
Pressed Glass, **Flowerpot**, Jewel Band 20.00
Pressed Glass, **Goblet**, Almond Thumbprint, Flint .... 18.00 To 30.00
Pressed Glass, **Goblet**, Arched Grape .... 8.00 To 13.50
Pressed Glass, **Goblet**, Argosy, Flint 19.50
Pressed Glass, **Goblet**, Argus, Bulb Stem, Flint 40.00
Pressed Glass, **Goblet**, Argus, Flint 21.50
Pressed Glass, **Goblet**, Art 25.00
Pressed Glass, **Goblet**, Ashburton, Flint 21.50
Pressed Glass, **Goblet**, Ashburton, Semi-Square, Flint 21.50
Pressed Glass, **Goblet**, Balder 8.00
Pressed Glass, **Goblet**, Banded Prism Bar 10.00
Pressed Glass, **Goblet**, Barberry 8.50
Pressed Glass, **Goblet**, Barley 14.50
Pressed Glass, **Goblet**, Barred Forget-Me-Not 12.50
Pressed Glass, **Goblet**, Barred Hobnail 10.50
Pressed Glass, **Goblet**, Barrel 32.00
Pressed Glass, **Goblet**, Barrel Honeycomb, Flint 15.00
Pressed Glass, **Goblet**, Basket Weave, Amber 18.50
Pressed Glass, **Goblet**, Bead & Scroll 10.00
Pressed Glass, **Goblet**, Beaded Acorn Medallion .... 14.50 To 16.50
Pressed Glass, **Goblet**, Beaded Chain 9.00
Pressed Glass, **Goblet**, Beaded Grape, Emerald Green 6.00
Pressed Glass, **Goblet**, Beaded Oval With Scroll 15.00
Pressed Glass, **Goblet**, Beaded Rosette 13.50
Pressed Glass, **Goblet**, Bellflower, Coarse Rib, Flint 27.50
Pressed Glass, **Goblet**, Bellflower, Flint .... 21.50 To 32.00
Pressed Glass, **Goblet**, Belted Worcester, Flint 20.00
Pressed Glass, **Goblet**, Bessimer Flute, Flint 12.00
Pressed Glass, **Goblet**, Bigler, Flared, Flint 22.00
Pressed Glass, **Goblet**, Bigler, Flint .... 15.00 To 22.00
Pressed Glass, **Goblet**, Billiken Flute 6.00
Pressed Glass, **Goblet**, Birch Leaf 11.00
Pressed Glass, **Goblet**, Bleeding Heart 9.50
Pressed Glass, **Goblet**, Block & Fan 24.50
Pressed Glass, **Goblet**, Block & Pleat 9.00
Pressed Glass, **Goblet**, Block & Triple Bar 18.00
Pressed Glass, **Goblet**, Bordered Ellipse 11.00
Pressed Glass, **Goblet**, Bradford Blackberry 40.00
Pressed Glass, **Goblet**, Bradford Grape, Flint 65.00
Pressed Glass, **Goblet**, Broken Column, Clear 16.00
Pressed Glass, **Goblet**, Brooklyn Flute, Flint 20.00
Pressed Glass, **Goblet**, Buckle, Flint .... 20.00 To 22.00
Pressed Glass, **Goblet**, Budded Ivy 12.50
Pressed Glass, **Goblet**, Bull's-Eye & Daisy, Gold 10.00
Pressed Glass, **Goblet**, Bull's-Eye & Daisy, Pine Eyes 15.00
Pressed Glass, **Goblet**, Bull's-Eye & Diamond Point, Flint 75.00
Pressed Glass, **Goblet**, Bull's-Eye & Fleur-De-Lis, Flint .... 49.50 To 55.00
Pressed Glass, **Goblet**, Bull's-Eye, Flint 32.50
Pressed Glass, **Goblet**, Bumble Bee Honeycomb, Flint 18.50
Pressed Glass, **Goblet**, Buttermilk, Pressed Leaf 12.00
Pressed Glass, **Goblet**, Buttermilk, Ribbed Palm, Flint 18.00
Pressed Glass, **Goblet**, Cable, Flint .... 37.50 To 60.00
Pressed Glass, **Goblet**, Camel Caravan, Etched 35.00
Pressed Glass, **Goblet**, Canadian .... 22.50 To 25.00
Pressed Glass, **Goblet**, Cane, Clear 14.00
Pressed Glass, **Goblet**, Cannonball 16.50
Pressed Glass, **Goblet**, Cardinal Bird .... 20.00 To 25.00
Pressed Glass, **Goblet**, Cathedral, Amber 42.00
Pressed Glass, **Goblet**, Cavitt 9.50
Pressed Glass, **Goblet**, Centennial 40.00
Pressed Glass, **Goblet**, Chain 9.75

Pressed Glass, Goblet, Chain & Star Band 9.50
Pressed Glass, Goblet, Chilson, Flint 110.00
Pressed Glass, Goblet, Choked Ashburton, Flint 29.50
Pressed Glass, Goblet, Classic 95.00
Pressed Glass, Goblet, Colonial, Teardrop Stem 13.00
Pressed Glass, Goblet, Colossus 14.00
Pressed Glass, Goblet, Comet, Flint 49.50
Pressed Glass, Goblet, Coral Gables 9.00
Pressed Glass, Goblet, Cord & Tassel 16.00
Pressed Glass, Goblet, Cord Rosettes 18.50
Pressed Glass, Goblet, Crazy Patch 11.00
Pressed Glass, Goblet, Crescent & Fan 14.00
Pressed Glass, Goblet, Crossed Pressed Leaf 12.50
Pressed Glass, Goblet, Crowsfoot 17.00
Pressed Glass, Goblet, Crystal, Flint 16.00
Pressed Glass, Goblet, Cube 7.50
Pressed Glass, Goblet, Cupid And Venus 45.00
Pressed Glass, Goblet, Currier & Ives 18.00
Pressed Glass, Goblet, Curtain Tieback 7.50
Pressed Glass, Goblet, Dahlia, Etched 20.00
Pressed Glass, Goblet, Daisy & Block 11.50
Pressed Glass, Goblet, Daisy & Button With Amber Panels 18.00
Pressed Glass, Goblet, Daisy & Button With Crossbar .... *Illus* 12.00
Pressed Glass, Goblet, Daisy & Button With Excelsior, Amber 20.00
Pressed Glass, Goblet, Daisy & Button With Rimmed Ovals 9.00
Pressed Glass, Goblet, Daisy & Button With Thumbprint, Vaseline 14.50
Pressed Glass, Goblet, Daisy & Button, Amberette 32.00
Pressed Glass, Goblet, Dakota 14.00
Pressed Glass, Goblet, Dakota, Etched 20.00

Pressed Glass, Goblet, Daisy & Button With Crossbar

Pressed Glass, Goblet, Darling Grape 12.50
Pressed Glass, Goblet, Deer & Dog 35.00
Pressed Glass, Goblet, Deer & Dog, U Shape, Etched 38.00
Pressed Glass, Goblet, Deer & Pine Tree .... 17.50 To 25.00
Pressed Glass, Goblet, Dewdrop 13.50
Pressed Glass, Goblet, Dewdrop With Star 9.50
Pressed Glass, Goblet, Diagonal Band .... 9.00 To 12.50
Pressed Glass, Goblet, Diagonal Block Band 12.50
Pressed Glass, Goblet, Diamond & Sunburst 7.50
Pressed Glass, Goblet, Diamond Band 7.50
Pressed Glass, Goblet, Diamond Cut With Leaf 13.50
Pressed Glass, Goblet, Diamond Medallion 18.00
Pressed Glass, Goblet, Diamond Point 10.00
Pressed Glass, Goblet, Diamond Point, Flint .... 20.00 To 35.00
Pressed Glass, Goblet, Diedre 6.75
Pressed Glass, Goblet, Dodged Block & Fan 8.72
Pressed Glass, Goblet, Dodo, Flint 25.00
Pressed Glass, Goblet, Double Beetle Band 10.50
Pressed Glass, Goblet, Double Daisy 17.50

Pressed Glass, Goblet, Double Frosted Ribbon		215.0
Pressed Glass, Goblet, Double Loop & Dart		9.00
Pressed Glass, Goblet, Double Spear		9.50
Pressed Glass, Goblet, Drapery With Stars		8.50
Pressed Glass, Goblet, Duke		8.00
Pressed Glass, Goblet, Early Paneled Grape Band, Flint		20.00
Pressed Glass, Goblet, Early Thumbprint, Flint		40.00
Pressed Glass, Goblet, Eastern Star		9.50
Pressed Glass, Goblet, Egyptian		25.00
Pressed Glass, Goblet, Ellipse		10.00
Pressed Glass, Goblet, Etched Dahlia		13.50
Pressed Glass, Goblet, Etched Dakota		22.00
Pressed Glass, Goblet, Etched Flamingo		17.00
Pressed Glass, Goblet, Etched Mascotte		19.00
Pressed Glass, Goblet, Etched Pavonia		26.50
Pressed Glass, Goblet, Etched Ring & Block		14.00
Pressed Glass, Goblet, Etched Spirea Band		18.00
Pressed Glass, Goblet, Eureka, Flint		17.00
Pressed Glass, Goblet, Excelsior With Maltese Cross, Flint		35.00
Pressed Glass, Goblet, Excelsior, Flint		32.50
Pressed Glass, Goblet, Fan & Diamond		8.50
Pressed Glass, Goblet, Feather		25.00
Pressed Glass, Goblet, Fine Diamond Point, Flint		20.00
Pressed Glass, Goblet, Fine Rib With Cut Ovals, Three Rows, Flint		195.00
Pressed Glass, Goblet, Fine Rib, Flint	25.00 To	35.00
Pressed Glass, Goblet, Finecut & Block, Clear		16.50
Pressed Glass, Goblet, Fishscale		20.00
Pressed Glass, Goblet, Flamingo, Habitat		21.00
Pressed Glass, Goblet, Flattened Sawtooth With Panels, Flint		27.50
Pressed Glass, Goblet, Fleur-De-Lis		12.50
Pressed Glass, Goblet, Flying Stork, Etched		20.00
Pressed Glass, Goblet, Forget-Me-Not Scroll	9.00 To	12.00
Pressed Glass, Goblet, Frosted Leaf, Flint		55.00
Pressed Glass, Goblet, Frosted Leaf, Single Vine		26.50
Pressed Glass, Goblet, G.A.R., 9-27-87		20.00
Pressed Glass, Goblet, Garfield Drape	16.00 To	20.00
Pressed Glass, Goblet, Giant Prism, Flint		45.00
Pressed Glass, Goblet, Good Luck, Knob Stem		22.50
Pressed Glass, Goblet, Gooseberry		16.00
Pressed Glass, Goblet, Gothic, Flint		38.00
Pressed Glass, Goblet, Grand		11.50
Pressed Glass, Goblet, Grape & Festoon		18.00
Pressed Glass, Goblet, Grape Festoon, Clear With Stippled Leaf		9.50
Pressed Glass, Goblet, Grape With Thumbprint Band		8.50
Pressed Glass, Goblet, Grogan		8.50
Pressed Glass, Goblet, Hairpin & Thumbprint, Flint	25.00 To	38.00
Pressed Glass, Goblet, Hamilton, Flint	24.50 To	28.00
Pressed Glass, Goblet, Hanover	11.50 To	13.50
Pressed Glass, Goblet, Hartley		16.50
Pressed Glass, Goblet, Hawaiian Pineapple, Flint		55.00
Pressed Glass, Goblet, Heart & Thumbprint, Gold		28.50
Pressed Glass, Goblet, Herringbone		10.00
Pressed Glass, Goblet, Herringbone Band		7.00
Pressed Glass, Goblet, Herringbone, Iris, Clear, Footed		2.00
Pressed Glass, Goblet, Hidalgo, Clear		10.00
Pressed Glass, Goblet, Hill & Dale		6.00
Pressed Glass, Goblet, Hinoto, Flint		37.00
Pressed Glass, Goblet, Hobnail, Moonstone, Opalescent		6.50
Pressed Glass, Goblet, Honeycomb		8.00
Pressed Glass, Goblet, Hops Band		8.50
Pressed Glass, Goblet, Horn Of Plenty, Flint	35.00 To	39.00
Pressed Glass, Goblet, Horn Of Plenty, Flint, 6 In.		36.00
Pressed Glass, Goblet, Horn Of Plenty, Knob Stem	35.00 To	70.00
Pressed Glass, Goblet, Horseshoe, Plain Stem		16.50
Pressed Glass, Goblet, Horseshoe, Stem Shaped Like A Horseshoe		32.50
Pressed Glass, Goblet, Huber, Flaring, Flint		14.00

Pressed Glass, Goblet, Huber, Flint 10.00
Pressed Glass, Goblet, Inverted Fern 20.00
Pressed Glass, Goblet, Inverted Fern, Flint .... 22.00 To 30.00
Pressed Glass, Goblet, Inverted Palm, Flint 22.50
Pressed Glass, Goblet, Inverted Thumbprint, Blue 17.50
Pressed Glass, Goblet, Isis 7.50
Pressed Glass, Goblet, Lakewood 7.50
Pressed Glass, Goblet, Laredo Honeycomb 6.00
Pressed Glass, Goblet, Late Sawtooth 18.50
Pressed Glass, Goblet, Leaf & Dart .... 12.50 To 15.00
Pressed Glass, Goblet, Lincoln Drape, Flint .... 40.00 To 45.00
Pressed Glass, Goblet, Lion, Etched 39.00
Pressed Glass, Goblet, Loop & Dart .... 9.50 To 16.50
Pressed Glass, Goblet, Loop & Dart With Round Ornaments, Flint 14.00
Pressed Glass, Goblet, Loop & Dewdrop 14.50
Pressed Glass, Goblet, Loop & Honeycomb 13.00
Pressed Glass, Goblet, Loop & Moose-Eye, Flint 19.50
Pressed Glass, Goblet, Loop With Dewdrops .... 14.50 To 16.00
Pressed Glass, Goblet, Lotus 18.00
Pressed Glass, Goblet, Magnet & Grape 15.00
Pressed Glass, Goblet, Magnet & Grape With Frosted Leaf, Flint 35.00
Pressed Glass, Goblet, Manhattan 6.00
Pressed Glass, Goblet, Maple Leaf 17.50
Pressed Glass, Goblet, Marquisette .... 10.00 To 12.00
Pressed Glass, Goblet, Mascotte, Etched 18.00
Pressed Glass, Goblet, Master Argus, Flint 45.00
Pressed Glass, Goblet, Michigan .... 9.00 To 19.50
Pressed Glass, Goblet, Milady's Work Basket 8.50
Pressed Glass, Goblet, Milton 15.75
Pressed Glass, Goblet, Minnesota 16.50
Pressed Glass, Goblet, Mirror, Flint 18.00
Pressed Glass, Goblet, Mitered Frieze, Findlay 15.00
Pressed Glass, Goblet, Moon & Star 30.00
Pressed Glass, Goblet, Moon & Star, Blue, 6 In.High 10.00
Pressed Glass, Goblet, Moon & Stork .... *Illus* 75.00
Pressed Glass, Goblet, Morning Glory, Flint 200.00
Pressed Glass, Goblet, Naturalistic Blackberry 16.00
Pressed Glass, Goblet, New England Pineapple, Flint 30.00
Pressed Glass, Goblet, Nicotiana, Etched 16.00
Pressed Glass, Goblet, Oak Leaf Band .... 12.50 To 20.00
Pressed Glass, Goblet, Open Cryptic 9.00
Pressed Glass, Goblet, Open Plaid 7.50
Pressed Glass, Goblet, Open Rose 14.00
Pressed Glass, Goblet, Oriental Fan 18.00
Pressed Glass, Goblet, Oval Miter 10.00
Pressed Glass, Goblet, Paisley, Amethyst Eyes 17.50
Pressed Glass, Goblet, Palmette 11.00
Pressed Glass, Goblet, Panel Cane 11.00
Pressed Glass, Goblet, Panel Diamond & Flower 11.50
Pressed Glass, Goblet, Panel Sawtooth, Flint 35.00
Pressed Glass, Goblet, Paneled Cane .... 7.50 To 11.00
Pressed Glass, Goblet, Paneled Diamond Point 17.00
Pressed Glass, Goblet, Paneled Grape 9.50
Pressed Glass, Goblet, Paneled Jewels, Clear, Findlay 13.50
Pressed Glass, Goblet, Paneled Oval, Flint 38.00
Pressed Glass, Goblet, Paneled Sage 40.00
Pressed Glass, Goblet, Paneled Sunflower 13.50
Pressed Glass, Goblet, Parrot .... 16.50 To 22.00
Pressed Glass, Goblet, Pavonia, Pineapple Stem 21.50
Pressed Glass, Goblet, Peacock Feather 15.00
Pressed Glass, Goblet, Pecorah 6.00
Pressed Glass, Goblet, Pennsylvania 10.50
Pressed Glass, Goblet, Pequot 12.50
Pressed Glass, Goblet, Philadelphia Centennial 45.00
Pressed Glass, Goblet, Picket Fence 25.00
Pressed Glass, Goblet, Pillar & Bull's-Eye, Flint 30.00

Pressed Glass, Goblet, Pineapple, Amber, New England 45.00
Pressed Glass, Goblet, Pineapple, Flint, New England 28.50
Pressed Glass, Goblet, Pleat & Panel 9.00
Pressed Glass, Goblet, Plume .... 12.50 To 18.50
Pressed Glass, Goblet, Popcorn With Raised Ears 27.50
Pressed Glass, Goblet, Pressed Leaf, Flint 16.00
Pressed Glass, Goblet, Princess Feather 18.75
Pressed Glass, Goblet, Prism & Sawtooth, Flint 25.00
Pressed Glass, Goblet, Prism Banded Top 5.50
Pressed Glass, Goblet, Prism, Flint 14.00
Pressed Glass, Goblet, Prisms With Loops 8.00
Pressed Glass, Goblet, Queen 10.00
Pressed Glass, Goblet, Queen, Blue 22.00
Pressed Glass, Goblet, Rail Fence 18.25
Pressed Glass, Goblet, Recessed Ovals 9.00
Pressed Glass, Goblet, Ribbed Ivy, Flint .... 25.00 To 37.50
Pressed Glass, Goblet, Ribbed Palm, Flint 22.50
Pressed Glass, Goblet, Ribbed Pineapple, Flint 29.00
Pressed Glass, Goblet, Ribbon .... 18.00 To 24.00
Pressed Glass, Goblet, Ribbon, Clear 18.50
Pressed Glass, Goblet, Rising Sun, Gold 10.00
Pressed Glass, Goblet, Roman Key, Frosted, Flint 28.00
Pressed Glass, Goblet, Roman Rosette 26.00
Pressed Glass, Goblet, Rose Leaves 9.00
Pressed Glass, Goblet, Rose Sprig .... *Illus* 18.50

Pressed Glass,
Goblet, Moon & Stork
See Page 430

Pressed Glass,
Goblet, Rose Sprig

Pressed Glass, Goblet,
Wildflower, Vaseline
See Page 432

Pressed Glass, Goblet, Rosette 18.00
Pressed Glass, Goblet, Rosette And Palms 12.50
Pressed Glass, Goblet, Sandwich Hairpin, Flint 20.00
Pressed Glass, Goblet, Sawtooth 7.50
Pressed Glass, Goblet, Scarab, Flint 75.00
Pressed Glass, Goblet, Scroll 8.25
Pressed Glass, Goblet, Sedan .... 7.00 To 9.50
Pressed Glass, Goblet, Seneca Loop .... 8.00 To 12.00
Pressed Glass, Goblet, Shell & Tassel .... 16.50 To 25.00
Pressed Glass, Goblet, Sheraton .... 8.50 To 12.50
Pressed Glass, Goblet, Short Loops 5.00
Pressed Glass, Goblet, Smocking, Flint 40.00
Pressed Glass, Goblet, Snail 25.00
Pressed Glass, Goblet, Snake Drape 8.50
Pressed Glass, Goblet, Snakeskin & Dot .... 9.00 To 15.00
Pressed Glass, Goblet, Snow Band 7.50
Pressed Glass, Goblet, Spaulding 8.00
Pressed Glass, Goblet, Spirea Band, Amber 18.50
Pressed Glass, Goblet, Spirea Band, Blue 25.00
Pressed Glass, Goblet, Spirea Band, Clear 6.00

Pressed Glass, Goblet, Spirea Band, Etched	6.00
Pressed Glass, Goblet, Sprig	14.00 To 18.50
Pressed Glass, Goblet, Star Band, Basworth, Gold	9.00
Pressed Glass, Goblet, Star Whirl	12.50
Pressed Glass, Goblet, Starburst	8.00
Pressed Glass, Goblet, Starflower Band	5.00
Pressed Glass, Goblet, State Pattern, 6 1/2 In.High	14.00
Pressed Glass, Goblet, Stippled Bowl	10.50
Pressed Glass, Goblet, Stippled Grape And Festoon, Clear Leaf	12.50
Pressed Glass, Goblet, Stippled Medallion, Flint	25.00
Pressed Glass, Goblet, Strawberry	11.50
Pressed Glass, Goblet, Tandem Bicycle	13.50
Pressed Glass, Goblet, Teasel	12.50
Pressed Glass, Goblet, The States	16.50
Pressed Glass, Goblet, Three Face	35.00
Pressed Glass, Goblet, Tile Band	15.00
Pressed Glass, Goblet, Tree Of Life, Signed, PG, Company	40.00
Pressed Glass, Goblet, Triple Triangle, Flashed	25.00
Pressed Glass, Goblet, Triple Triangle, Ruby	35.00
Pressed Glass, Goblet, Tulip, Ribs, Flint	32.00
Pressed Glass, Goblet, Two Panel	13.50
Pressed Glass, Goblet, Two Tigers, Etched	40.00
Pressed Glass, Goblet, U.S.Coin, Dimes	225.00
Pressed Glass, Goblet, Valencia Waffle	12.50
Pressed Glass, Goblet, Vernon Honeycomb, Flint	18.00
Pressed Glass, Goblet, Waffle & Thumbprint, Flint	38.00
Pressed Glass, Goblet, Washington, Flint	60.00
Pressed Glass, Goblet, Westward Ho	22.50 To 55.00
Pressed Glass, Goblet, Wildflower, Clear	15.00
Pressed Glass, Goblet, Wildflower, Green	12.00
Pressed Glass, Goblet, Wildflower, Vaseline *Illus*	22.00
Pressed Glass, Goblet, Willow Oak	16.00
Pressed Glass, Goblet, Willow Oak, Amber	27.50
Pressed Glass, Goblet, Willow Oak, Blue	28.50
Pressed Glass, Goblet, Windflower	14.00
Pressed Glass, Goblet, Yoked Loop	14.00
Pressed Glass, Goblet, Yoked Loop, Flint	18.00 To 27.50
Pressed Glass, Goblet, Zipper	13.50
Pressed Glass, Goblet, 101	19.50
Pressed Glass, Goblet, 1, 000-Eye, Amber	24.00
Pressed Glass, Goblet, 1, 000-Eye, Clear	20.00
Pressed Glass, Hat, Daisy & Button, Blue	15.00
Pressed Glass, Hat, Daisy & Button, Clear	12.50
Pressed Glass, Honey, Cable	12.50
Pressed Glass, Honey, Horn Of Plenty	12.50
Pressed Glass, Ice Bucket, Block & Fan	35.00
Pressed Glass, Jar, Honey, Thumbprint	12.50
Pressed Glass, Jar, Jam, Bowite, Covered	25.00
Pressed Glass, Jar, Marmalade, Frosted Lion, Lion Finial	48.00 To 57.50
Pressed Glass, Jar, Marmalade, Westward Ho	30.00
Pressed Glass, Jar, Pickle Castor, Portland, Clear, Silver Plated Cover	14.00
Pressed Glass, Jar, Pomade, Argus, Covered, Barrel Shape	24.00
Pressed Glass, Jar, Pomade, Sawtooth, Covered	22.50
Pressed Glass, Jardiniere, Thousand Face, 5 X 5 In.	15.00
Pressed Glass, Juice, Colonial	8.00
Pressed Glass, Juice, Etched 4 Bears In Forest, Clear	12.50
Pressed Glass, Juice, Pennsylvania	4.50
Pressed Glass, Kettle, Daisy & Button, Canary	15.00
Pressed Glass, Lamp, Cord And Tassel	25.00
Pressed Glass, Lamp, Horn Of Plenty	125.00
Pressed Glass, Lamp, Oil, Pedestal, Puffy Panels, Beading, Burner, Chimney	27.50
Pressed Glass, Lamp, U.S.Coin	250.00
Pressed Glass, Match Holder, Picket Fence	22.00
Pressed Glass, Muffineer, Cabbage Rose, Aqua	75.00
Pressed Glass, Muffineer, Clear, English Hallmarked Sterling Top	47.50
Pressed Glass, Muffineer, Guttate Drape, Pink Cased In White	85.00

Pressed Glass, Muffineer, Hickman	21.00
Pressed Glass, Muffineer, Horseshoe, Amber	28.00
Pressed Glass, Muffineer, Ribbed, Blue, Green	32.50
Pressed Glass, Muffineer, Thumbprint, Opalescent, White, Top	55.00
Pressed Glass, Mug, Bird & Harp	15.00
Pressed Glass, Mug, By Jingo, 3 In.High	18.00
Pressed Glass, Mug, Cat's-Eye & Block	9.25
Pressed Glass, Mug, Child's, Beaded Ovals, Gold	4.00
Pressed Glass, Mug, Child's, Bird & Dog, Clear	9.00
Pressed Glass, Mug, Child's, Grape Pattern, Covered	12.50
Pressed Glass, Mug, Crystal, Applied Handle, Flint	35.00
Pressed Glass, Mug, Cut Long, 3 In.	12.50
Pressed Glass, Mug, Daisy & Button, Blue	14.00
Pressed Glass, Mug, Drum, Gold	13.50
Pressed Glass, Mug, Garfield, Memorial, Miniature	40.00
Pressed Glass, Mug, Gooseberry	21.00
Pressed Glass, Mug, Loganberry, Blue, Miniature	16.00
Pressed Glass, Mug, McKinley, Covered	29.50
Pressed Glass, Mug, McKinley, Memorial	18.00
Pressed Glass, Mug, Michigan, Ruby Flashed Top	12.50
Pressed Glass, Mug, New Hampshire, Handled	9.00
Pressed Glass, Mug, Paneled Cane, Blue	12.50
Pressed Glass, Mug, Pittsburgh, White Opal Swirls, Clear, Applied Handle	40.00
Pressed Glass, Mug, Prince Of Wales Plumes	9.25
Pressed Glass, Mug, Robin & Wheat, Blue	22.00
Pressed Glass, Mug, Rose In Snow	13.00
Pressed Glass, Mug, Rose In Snow, 'In Fond Remembrance'	13.00
Pressed Glass, Mug, Serenade, Blue, Greentown, 5 In.	48.00
Pressed Glass, Mug, Shaving, St.Louis Panel	7.50
Pressed Glass, Mug, Sleepy Eye, Signed, 4 3/8 In.High	27.00
Pressed Glass, Mug, Sweetheart & Cherries	18.00
Pressed Glass, Mug, Toddy, Jewel & Dewdrop, Handled	9.00
Pressed Glass, Mug, Troubadour, Green, Greentown, 5 In.	48.00
Pressed Glass, Mug, Wheat & Barley, Blue	22.50
Pressed Glass, Mug, Wheat & Bird, Amber	22.00
Pressed Glass, Mug, Windmill Scene	25.00
Pressed Glass, Mug, 1, 000-Eye, Amber	16.50
Pressed Glass, Nappy, Colorado, Green, Three Sided, Footed	14.00
Pressed Glass, Nappy, Cut Log	15.00
Pressed Glass, Nappy, Cut Log, Handled	6.00
Pressed Glass, Nappy, Daisy & Button With V Ornament	8.50
Pressed Glass, Nappy, Maiden's Blush, Handle	22.00
Pressed Glass, Nappy, Paneled Thistle, 5 1/2 In.	14.50
Pressed Glass, Perfume, Panel & Star, Clear, Stopper	10.00
Pressed Glass, Pickle, Beaded Dewdrop	14.50
Pressed Glass, Pickle, Beaded Dewdrop, 8 1/4 X 4 In.	15.00
Pressed Glass, Pickle, Egyptian	6.00
Pressed Glass, Pickle, Horseshoe, Oval Shape	12.50
Pressed Glass, Pickle, Michigan, Gold Trim	10.00
Pressed Glass, Pitcher, Actress *Illus*	45.00
Pressed Glass, Pitcher, Cane, Variant, Scalloped Top, 6 1/2 In.High	15.00
Pressed Glass, Pitcher, Chain & Shell *Illus*	16.00
Pressed Glass, Pitcher, Currier & Ives, Tin Lid	22.50
Pressed Glass, Pitcher, Curtain Tieback, 8 1/2 In.High	16.00
Pressed Glass, Pitcher, Daisy & Button With Crossbar, Amber	35.00
Pressed Glass, Pitcher, Deer Alert	55.00
Pressed Glass, Pitcher, Diagonal Band, Clear, 8 In.High	14.00
Pressed Glass, Pitcher, Diamond & Sunburst	18.50
Pressed Glass, Pitcher, Excelsior	167.00
Pressed Glass, Pitcher, Festoon	29.50
Pressed Glass, Pitcher, Flowerpot	45.00
Pressed Glass, Pitcher, Horseshoe Curve	16.50
Pressed Glass, Pitcher, Jewel & Dewdrop, Kansas	24.50
Pressed Glass, Pitcher, Lemonade, Paneled Grape	25.00
Pressed Glass, Pitcher, Milk, Daisy & Button With V Ornament, Amber	37.50
Pressed Glass, Pitcher, Milk, Egg In Sand	18.00

Pressed Glass,
Pitcher, Actress
See Page 433

Pressed Glass,
Pitcher, Chain & Shell
See Page 433

Pressed Glass,
Pitcher, Primrose, 7 In.

Pressed Glass, Pitcher, Milk, Finecut & Block, Clear, Footed	16.00
Pressed Glass, Pitcher, Milk, Fishscale	17.50
Pressed Glass, Pitcher, Milk, Fleur-De-Lis & Drape, Green	29.50
Pressed Glass, Pitcher, Milk, Garfield Drape, Applied Handle	29.00
Pressed Glass, Pitcher, Milk, Loop & Fan	12.00
Pressed Glass, Pitcher, Milk, Pressed Diamond, Amber	19.00
Pressed Glass, Pitcher, Milk, Reeded Waffle	15.00
Pressed Glass, Pitcher, Milk, Rosette	25.00
Pressed Glass, Pitcher, Milk, Star Medallion	12.50 To 14.00
Pressed Glass, Pitcher, Milk, U.S.Coin, Half Dollars, 8 3/8 In.High	425.00
Pressed Glass, Pitcher, Milk, Water Lily	12.00
Pressed Glass, Pitcher, Milk, Wheat & Barley, Clear	14.50
Pressed Glass, Pitcher, Paneled Dewdrop	18.50
Pressed Glass, Pitcher, Pittsburgh, Clear, Miniature, Tooled Lip	45.00
Pressed Glass, Pitcher, Pressed Leaf, Applied Handle	58.00
Pressed Glass, Pitcher, Primrose, 7 In. *Illus*	22.00
Pressed Glass, Pitcher, Shell & Jewel	22.50
Pressed Glass, Pitcher, Sleepy Eye, 7 1/2 In.High, 2 Quart	39.00
Pressed Glass, Pitcher, Two Panel, Blue, 6 In.High	25.00
Pressed Glass, Pitcher, Water, Beaded Dewdrop	23.50
Pressed Glass, Pitcher, Water, Beaded Loop	14.00
Pressed Glass, Pitcher, Water, Bellflower, Double Vine	225.00
Pressed Glass, Pitcher, Water, Block & Fan, Mold Flaws	13.00
Pressed Glass, Pitcher, Water, Broken Column	40.00
Pressed Glass, Pitcher, Water, Canadian	65.00
Pressed Glass, Pitcher, Water, Carolina, Footed, White Enamel Trim	32.50
Pressed Glass, Pitcher, Water, Cathedral, Gold	14.50
Pressed Glass, Pitcher, Water, Classic, Collared Base	110.00
Pressed Glass, Pitcher, Water, Classic, Log Feet	150.00
Pressed Glass, Pitcher, Water, Colonial	18.00
Pressed Glass, Pitcher, Water, Cordova	20.00
Pressed Glass, Pitcher, Water, Cottage, Amber	75.00
Pressed Glass, Pitcher, Water, Currier & Ives	38.00
Pressed Glass, Pitcher, Water, Delaware, Cranberry, Gold	90.00
Pressed Glass, Pitcher, Water, Delaware, Green *Illus*	60.00
Pressed Glass, Pitcher, Water, Dewey	30.00 To 60.00
Pressed Glass, Pitcher, Water, Drapery, Applied Handle	35.00
Pressed Glass, Pitcher, Water, Etched Pavonia	27.00 To 29.50
Pressed Glass, Pitcher, Water, Etched Regal Block	20.00
Pressed Glass, Pitcher, Water, Feather	20.00 To 22.00
Pressed Glass, Pitcher, Water, Frosted Lion	52.00
Pressed Glass, Pitcher, Water, Fruit Cornucopia	22.00
Pressed Glass, Pitcher, Water, Garfield Drape, Applied Handle	35.00
Pressed Glass, Pitcher, Water, Grasshopper Without Insect	33.00
Pressed Glass, Pitcher, Water, Huckle, Emerald	24.00
Pressed Glass, Pitcher, Water, Jewel & Dewdrop	25.00

Pressed Glass, Pitcher, Water, Leaf & Dart, Bulbous	32.00
Pressed Glass, Pitcher, Water, Leaf & Flower, Golden Amber	40.00
Pressed Glass, Pitcher, Water, Lotus With Serpent	35.00
Pressed Glass, Pitcher, Water, Medallion, Apple Green	48.00
Pressed Glass, Pitcher, Water, Minerva	35.00
Pressed Glass, Pitcher, Water, Paneled Diamond Point	15.00
Pressed Glass, Pitcher, Water, Paneled Forget-Me-Not	17.50
Pressed Glass, Pitcher, Water, Pavonia	16.00
Pressed Glass, Pitcher, Water, Pittsburgh, Footed, Applied Handle, Rings	210.00
Pressed Glass, Pitcher, Water, Portland	18.50
Pressed Glass, Pitcher, Water, Psyche & Cupid, Pedestal	50.00
Pressed Glass, Pitcher, Water, Sedan	12.00
Pressed Glass, Pitcher, Water, Shell & Jewel	13.50 To 18.00
Pressed Glass, Pitcher, Water, Shrine	25.00
Pressed Glass, Pitcher, Water, Stippled Grape & Festoon	45.00
Pressed Glass, Pitcher, Water, Sunk Diamond & Lattice	15.00
Pressed Glass, Pitcher, Water, Two Panel, Clear	20.00
Pressed Glass, Pitcher, Water, Viking	58.50
Pressed Glass, Pitcher, Water, Water Lily	25.00
Pressed Glass, Pitcher, Water, Wildflower	25.00
Pressed Glass, Pitcher, Water, Wildflower, Blue	20.00
Pressed Glass, Pitcher, Water, Wistarburg Type, Pink & White Loopings	400.00
Pressed Glass, Pitcher, Water, Zipper	15.00
Pressed Glass, Pitcher, Westward Ho	125.00
Pressed Glass, Plate, Baltimore Pear	10.00
Pressed Glass, Plate, Barberry, 6 In.	10.00
Pressed Glass, Plate, Block & Fan, 10 In.	8.75

Pressed Glass, Pitcher,
Water, Delaware, Green
See Page 434

Pressed Glass, Plate, Bread, Last Supper
See Page 436

Pressed Glass, Plate, Bread, Arched Leaf	18.00
Pressed Glass, Plate, Bread, Baby	45.00
Pressed Glass, Plate, Bread, Barley	15.00
Pressed Glass, Plate, Bread, Beaded Loop	16.00
Pressed Glass, Plate, Bread, Bent Leaf	14.00
Pressed Glass, Plate, Bread, Bunker Hill	45.00
Pressed Glass, Plate, Bread, Canadian, 7 In.	25.00
Pressed Glass, Plate, Bread, Canadian, 8 In.	25.00
Pressed Glass, Plate, Bread, Canadian, 10 In.	33.00
Pressed Glass, Plate, Bread, Cannon Ball	20.00
Pressed Glass, Plate, Bread, Centennial, Philadelphia	55.00
Pressed Glass, Plate, Bread, Chain & Shield	32.00
Pressed Glass, Plate, Bread, Chain & Shield, Amber	15.00
Pressed Glass, Plate, Bread, Chain, Blue	30.00
Pressed Glass, Plate, Bread, Chain, 13 1/2 In.	26.50
Pressed Glass, Plate, Bread, Classic Warrior	75.00 To 95.00
Pressed Glass, Plate, Bread, Commemorative, Bunker Hill	45.00

Pressed Glass, Plate, Bread, Cord & Panel	5.00
Pressed Glass, Plate, Bread, Cupid & Venus	16.00
Pressed Glass, Plate, Bread, Cupid's Hunt	48.00
Pressed Glass, Plate, Bread, Daisy & Button With Crossbar	16.00
Pressed Glass, Plate, Bread, Deer & Pine Tree	21.00 To 32.00
Pressed Glass, Plate, Bread, Dewdrop With Sheaf Of Wheat	22.00
Pressed Glass, Plate, Bread, Diagonal Band, Clear	14.00
Pressed Glass, Plate, Bread, Diamond Point & Flute	9.50
Pressed Glass, Plate, Bread, Doric	22.00
Pressed Glass, Plate, Bread, Double Frosted Ribbon	28.00
Pressed Glass, Plate, Bread, Egg In Sand	16.00
Pressed Glass, Plate, Bread, Eureka	21.50
Pressed Glass, Plate, Bread, Faith, Hope, & Charity	40.00
Pressed Glass, Plate, Bread, Flowerpot, 'In God We Trust'	20.00
Pressed Glass, Plate, Bread, Frosted Fruit, Raised Rim Shell Ornaments	45.00
Pressed Glass, Plate, Bread, Frosted Lion, Polished Rim	35.00
Pressed Glass, Plate, Bread, Frosted Ribbon	25.00
Pressed Glass, Plate, Bread, Frosted Stork	59.00
Pressed Glass, Plate, Bread, Garfield Memorial, Clear	22.00 To 35.00
Pressed Glass, Plate, Bread, Garfield, Flint	57.50
Pressed Glass, Plate, Bread, Garfield, Frosted, 101 Border	59.00
Pressed Glass, Plate, Bread, Gibson Girl, Light Blue	30.00
Pressed Glass, Plate, Bread, 'Give Us This Day, Etc., ' Amber, Anchor Handles	35.00
Pressed Glass, Plate, Bread, 'Give Us This Day, Etc., ' Eagle, Oval, 12 X 9 In	25.00
Pressed Glass, Plate, Bread, Golden Rule	35.00
Pressed Glass, Plate, Bread, Good Luck	25.00
Pressed Glass, Plate, Bread, Grant Peace, Maple Leaf Border, Amber	39.00
Pressed Glass, Plate, Bread, Grant Peace, Maple Leaf Border, Green	39.00
Pressed Glass, Plate, Bread, Horseshoe	25.00
Pressed Glass, Plate, Bread, Iowa City, Frosted, 2 Cranes	49.00
Pressed Glass, Plate, Bread, Iowa City, Frosted, 3 Cranes	55.00
Pressed Glass, Plate, Bread, Jewel & Dewdrop	35.00
Pressed Glass, Plate, Bread, Last Supper	*Illus* 45.00
Pressed Glass, Plate, Bread, Liberty Bell, Signers	52.00
Pressed Glass, Plate, Bread, Liberty Bell, States, 8 In.	45.00
Pressed Glass, Plate, Bread, Lotus, 'Give Us This Day, Etc., ' Bark Handles	35.00
Pressed Glass, Plate, Bread, Maple Leaf	18.00
Pressed Glass, Plate, Bread, Mayflower	16.00
Pressed Glass, Plate, Bread, McCormick Reaper	55.00
Pressed Glass, Plate, Bread, McKinley	20.00
Pressed Glass, Plate, Bread, Medallion, Open Rim	12.00
Pressed Glass, Plate, Bread, Memorial, McKinley	35.00
Pressed Glass, Plate, Bread, Niagara Falls	95.00
Pressed Glass, Plate, Bread, Pleat & Panel	20.00 To 25.00
Pressed Glass, Plate, Bread, Pope Leo XIII	22.00 To 25.00
Pressed Glass, Plate, Bread, Post	15.00
Pressed Glass, Plate, Bread, Rock Of Ages, Clear	48.00
Pressed Glass, Plate, Bread, Rock Of Ages, Opaque White Inlay Center	115.00
Pressed Glass, Plate, Bread, Roman Rosette	29.00
Pressed Glass, Plate, Bread, Rosette Medallion	12.50
Pressed Glass, Plate, Bread, Royal	47.00
Pressed Glass, Plate, Bread, Saxon	12.00 To 24.00
Pressed Glass, Plate, Bread, Scroll With Flowers	22.00
Pressed Glass, Plate, Bread, Sheaf Of Wheat	14.00
Pressed Glass, Plate, Bread, Sheaf Of Wheat Center, 'Give Us This Day, Etc.'	15.00
Pressed Glass, Plate, Bread, Spirea, 8 X 11 In.	12.50
Pressed Glass, Plate, Bread, Stippled Forget-Me-Not, Kitten Center	49.00
Pressed Glass, Plate, Bread, Sunburst	17.50
Pressed Glass, Plate, Bread, Teddy Roosevelt, Frosted	55.00
Pressed Glass, Plate, Bread, Three Presidents, Lincoln, Grant, & Washington	25.00
Pressed Glass, Plate, Bread, Troy, Maltese Crosses On Rim	16.50
Pressed Glass, Plate, Bread, U.S.Coin, 10 X 7 In.	275.00
Pressed Glass, Plate, Bread, Upset, Frosted, 11 In.	48.00
Pressed Glass, Plate, Bread, Washington Centennial, Portrait	85.00
Pressed Glass, Plate, Bread, 101, 'Be Industrious'	59.00
Pressed Glass, Plate, Broken Column, Red Flashed	35.00

Pressed Glass, Plate, Bryce, 8 1/4 In.	10.00
Pressed Glass, Plate, Cake, Bird & Strawberry	24.00
Pressed Glass, Plate, Cake, Chain & Star, Portland, 11 In.	25.00
Pressed Glass, Plate, Cake, Daisy & Button, 10 In., Flat	13.50
Pressed Glass, Plate, Cake, Harp, Pedestal Base	10.00
Pressed Glass, Plate, Cake, U.S.Coin, Dollars Around Top, Quarters In Stand	275.00
Pressed Glass, Plate, Canadian, 6 In.	15.00
Pressed Glass, Plate, Child's, Hey Diddle Diddle, Clear, 6 1/4 In.	18.00
Pressed Glass, Plate, Child's, Seesaw Margery Daw, Clear, 3 Part, 9 In.	18.00
Pressed Glass, Plate, Child's, Seesaw Margery Daw, Green, 8 1/4 In.	16.00
Pressed Glass, Plate, Classic, Warrior	87.50
Pressed Glass, Plate, Daisy & Button, Amber, 7 In.	15.00
Pressed Glass, Plate, Dewey, 101 Border, 6 In.	10.50
Pressed Glass, Plate, Diagonal Band With Fan, 8 In.	16.50
Pressed Glass, Plate, Diamond Medallion, 10 In.	8.50
Pressed Glass, Plate, Drapery, 6 In.	10.00
Pressed Glass, Plate, Eagle & Fleur-De-Lis, Milk White, 1903, 7 1/4 In.	20.00
Pressed Glass, Plate, Elaine, 101 Border, Iowa City	59.00
Pressed Glass, Plate, Eyewinker, 8 In.	18.75
Pressed Glass, Plate, Field Marshall Roberts, Boer War, 1900, 10 In.	20.00
Pressed Glass, Plate, Fleur-De-Lis & Drape, 10 1/4 In.	8.75
Pressed Glass, Plate, Florida Palm, 9 1/4 In.	8.75
Pressed Glass, Plate, Garfield Star Border, Frosted Center, 6 In.	24.00
Pressed Glass, Plate, Garfield Star, Flint	22.50
Pressed Glass, Plate, Gladstone, 'For The Millions'	20.00
Pressed Glass, Plate, Huckle, 7 1/2 In.Diameter	8.00
Pressed Glass, Plate, Jacob's Ladder, 6 1/2 In.	12.00
Pressed Glass, Plate, Jersey Swirl, 10 In.Diameter	15.00 To 18.00
Pressed Glass, Plate, Late Thistle, 10 1/2 In.	13.50
Pressed Glass, Plate, Lattice, 6 1/4 In.	5.00
Pressed Glass, Plate, Liberty Bell, 6 In.	51.00
Pressed Glass, Plate, Liberty Bell, 8 In.	57.50
Pressed Glass, Plate, Liberty Bell, 10 In.	55.00
Pressed Glass, Plate, Mikado Fan, 7 1/4 In.	6.00
Pressed Glass, Plate, Paneled Thistle, 10 In.	18.00
Pressed Glass, Plate, Pittsburgh, 6 In.Diameter, Flint	27.50
Pressed Glass, Plate, Pleat & Panel, 5 In.Diameter	25.00
Pressed Glass, Plate, Pleat & Panel, 6 In.Square	9.00
Pressed Glass, Plate, Primrose, Amber, 7 In.	16.00
Pressed Glass, Plate, Primrose, 9 In.	10.00
Pressed Glass, Plate, Princess Feather, 6 In.	15.00
Pressed Glass, Plate, Priscilla	27.50
Pressed Glass, Plate, Prism Arc	7.50
Pressed Glass, Plate, Puck, Dog, Rabbit Series, Scene 3	45.00
Pressed Glass, Plate, Raindrop, Amber, 10 In.	15.00
Pressed Glass, Plate, Ribbon, 8 1/2 In.Diameter	13.50
Pressed Glass, Plate, Ripple, 5 In.	7.50
Pressed Glass, Plate, Roman Cross, 7 1/2 In.	5.00
Pressed Glass, Plate, Rose In Snow, 6 In.Diameter	12.00
Pressed Glass, Plate, Rose In Snow, 9 In.Diameter	18.50
Pressed Glass, Plate, Royal Lace, Cobalt Blue, 6 In.	4.00
Pressed Glass, Plate, Royal Oak, Clear, 11 1/2 In.	25.00
Pressed Glass, Plate, Sawtooth & Star, 10 1/4 In.	7.50
Pressed Glass, Plate, Scalloped Lines, 6 1/4 In.	8.75
Pressed Glass, Plate, Single Band Wedding Ring	9.00
Pressed Glass, Plate, Snakeskin & Dot, 4 1/2 In.	7.50
Pressed Glass, Plate, Three Mold, 6 In., McKearin G 11-22	50.00
Pressed Glass, Plate, Tokyo, Blue, Opalescent, Jefferson Glass Co., C.1899	30.00
Pressed Glass, Plate, Victoria Jubilee, 1837-1887, Amber	20.00
Pressed Glass, Plate, Waffle, Flint, 6 In.	12.00
Pressed Glass, Plate, Wildflower, Blue, 9 3/4 In.	21.50
Pressed Glass, Plate, Willow Oak, 9 In.Diameter	13.50
Pressed Glass, Plate, 101, 7 In.	10.25
Pressed Glass, Platter, Beehive, 'Be Industrious, ' Iowa City	55.00
Pressed Glass, Platter, Heroes Of Bunker Hill	32.00
Pressed Glass, Platter, Independence Hall	44.00

Pressed Glass, **Platter**, Liberty Bell, Round, Handled, Signed With Colonies 85.00
Pressed Glass, **Platter**, Liberty Bell, Signers 65.00
Pressed Glass, **Platter**, McKinley Memorial 36.00
Pressed Glass, **Platter**, Philadelphia Centennial, Oval, 9 1/2 X 14 In. 35.00
Pressed Glass, **Platter**, Pinafore 29.00
Pressed Glass, **Platter**, Raindrop, Blue 29.00
Pressed Glass, **Platter**, Roman Rosette, Oval, 11 X 9 In. 24.50
Pressed Glass, **Punch Set**, Honeycomb, Clear, 7 Piece 48.00
Pressed Glass, **Punch Set**, Manhattan, 14 Piece 150.00
Pressed Glass, **Punch Set**, Nearcut, Marked, 14 Piece 75.00
Pressed Glass, **Punch Set**, Tulip, Miniature, 5 Piece 27.50
Pressed Glass, **Relish**, Barley 15.00
Pressed Glass, **Relish**, Barred Forget-Me-Not 15.00
Pressed Glass, **Relish**, Broken Column, Red, Notched 38.50
Pressed Glass, **Relish**, Daisy & Button, Clear, 10 In.Long 10.00
Pressed Glass, **Relish**, Daisy & Button, Clear, 14 In.Long 15.00
Pressed Glass, **Relish**, Good Luck 12.00
Pressed Glass, **Relish**, Hickman 8.50
Pressed Glass, **Relish**, Horsemint, Oval 5.00
Pressed Glass, **Relish**, Ivy In Snow 4.50
Pressed Glass, **Relish**, Jacob's Ladder 12.00
Pressed Glass, **Relish**, Jewel & Dewdrop, Oval 12.00
Pressed Glass, **Relish**, Minerva 16.00
Pressed Glass, **Relish**, Paneled Forget-Me-Not 6.50
Pressed Glass, **Relish**, Plume, Oval, Flat 12.75
Pressed Glass, **Relish**, Rose Sprig, Blue 24.50
Pressed Glass, **Relish**, Spirea Band, Amber, Handle, 5 X 7 1/2 In. 15.00
Pressed Glass, **Relish**, Thumbprint, Flint 22.50
Pressed Glass, **Relish**, Tree Of Life 12.00
Pressed Glass, **Relish**, 1, 000-Eye 15.00
Pressed Glass, **Rose Bowl**, Cube & Fan, 5 In. 7.50
Pressed Glass, **Rose Bowl**, Fluted Scrolls, Opalescent, Flint 42.00
Pressed Glass, **Rose Bowl**, Frosted Artichoke 48.50
Pressed Glass, **Rose Bowl**, Heart & Thumbprint, 4 X 2 In. 12.00
Pressed Glass, **Rose Bowl**, Starred Scroll, 4 In.High 12.50
Pressed Glass, **Salt & Pepper**, Delaware, Green .... *Illus* 55.00
Pressed Glass, **Salt & Pepper**, Diamond Point & Punty 25.00
Pressed Glass, **Salt & Pepper**, Flattened Hobnail, Clear, 4 1/2 In.High 8.50
Pressed Glass, **Salt & Pepper**, Horseshoe, Amber 20.00
Pressed Glass, **Salt & Pepper**, Intaglio Swirl, White Opaque 20.00
Pressed Glass, **Salt & Pepper**, Leaf & Flower, Clear & Frosted 18.00
Pressed Glass, **Salt & Pepper**, Pineapple, Blue 28.00
Pressed Glass, **Salt & Pepper**, Waffle, Blue, Tops 30.00
Pressed Glass, **Salt Dip**, Jersey Swirl 5.50
Pressed Glass, **Salt Dip**, Post 7.00
Pressed Glass, **Salt Dip**, Scalloped Rim, Green, Round .... .50
Pressed Glass, **Salt Dip**, Swan, Green, Open Top .... .50
Pressed Glass, **Salt**, Bull's-Eye, Panels, Flint, 4 In.High 27.50
Pressed Glass, **Salt**, Button & Block, Amber 10.50
Pressed Glass, **Salt**, Chair, Daisy & Button, Spoon 30.00

Pressed Glass, Salt & Pepper, Delaware, Green

Pressed Glass, Salt, Dolphin, Opalescent, Footed, Double, Ribbed Shells 38.50
Pressed Glass, Salt, Hexagon, Oval Panel, Clear, Pedestal, Flint 12.00
Pressed Glass, Salt, Master, Atlas 7.50
Pressed Glass, Salt, Master, Bail & Swirl 3.75
Pressed Glass, Salt, Master, Barberry 12.50
Pressed Glass, Salt, Master, Bleeding Heart Oval 22.50
Pressed Glass, Salt, Master, Buckle 15.00
Pressed Glass, Salt, Master, Buckle, Footed, Scalloped Rim 18.00
Pressed Glass, Salt, Master, Bull's-Eye With Fleur-De-Lis 25.00
Pressed Glass, Salt, Master, Cable 30.00
Pressed Glass, Salt, Master, Daisy & Button 15.00
Pressed Glass, Salt, Master, Daisy & Button, Amber 20.00
Pressed Glass, Salt, Master, Daisy & Button, Apple Green 100.00
Pressed Glass, Salt, Master, Grasshopper 12.50
Pressed Glass, Salt, Master, Leaf & Dart 12.50
Pressed Glass, Salt, Master, Lily Of The Valley 15.00
Pressed Glass, Salt, Master, Loop & Dart 12.50
Pressed Glass, Salt, Master, New England Pineapple 30.00
Pressed Glass, Salt, Master, Oak Wreath 12.50
Pressed Glass, Salt, Master, Open Rose 15.00
Pressed Glass, Salt, Master, Paneled Thistle 8.50
Pressed Glass, Salt, Master, Pressed Leaf, Footed, Scalloped Rim 14.50
Pressed Glass, Salt, Master, Ribbed Ivy 25.00
Pressed Glass, Salt, Master, Ribbed Palm, Footed, Scalloped Rim, Flint 25.00
Pressed Glass, Salt, Master, Sawtooth, Clear 6.00
Pressed Glass, Salt, Master, Tidy 12.50
Pressed Glass, Salt, Master, Tulip With Sawtooth, Footed, Pointed Rim 18.00
Pressed Glass, Salt, Master, Valencia Waffle 8.00
Pressed Glass, Salt, Master, Waffle & Thumbprint 17.50
Pressed Glass, Salt, Master, Washington 25.00
Pressed Glass, Salt, Master, 1, 000-Eye, Banded, Blue 24.50
Pressed Glass, Salt, Pittsburgh, Blue, Anchor Base 220.00
Pressed Glass, Salt, Punty & Diamond 16.00
Pressed Glass, Salt, Sawtooth, Covered 29.50
Pressed Glass, Saltshaker, Banded Portland, Gold Flashed 12.00
Pressed Glass, Saltshaker, Beaded Fan 8.00
Pressed Glass, Saltshaker, Christmas Barrel, Pearl 20.00
Pressed Glass, Saltshaker, Chrysanthemum Base, Cranberry Swirl 25.00
Pressed Glass, Saltshaker, Climbing Rose, Pair 10.50
Pressed Glass, Saltshaker, Colonial 6.50
Pressed Glass, Saltshaker, Concave Grape 9.50
Pressed Glass, Saltshaker, Cord & Tassel, Pair 15.00
Pressed Glass, Saltshaker, Corn 12.50
Pressed Glass, Saltshaker, Geneva, Clear, Greentown 15.00
Pressed Glass, Saltshaker, Grape Four Leaf, Pair 20.00
Pressed Glass, Saltshaker, Jeweled Moon & Star 20.00
Pressed Glass, Saltshaker, King's Crown 8.00
Pressed Glass, Saltshaker, Kokomo 5.50
Pressed Glass, Saltshaker, Overlapping Shells, Pale Green 14.00
Pressed Glass, Saltshaker, Paneled Fishbone 6.50
Pressed Glass, Saltshaker, Ribbon Band, Pale Pink 25.00
Pressed Glass, Saltshaker, Roman Rosette 7.00
Pressed Glass, Saltshaker, Rosette Row 8.50
Pressed Glass, Saltshaker, Shag, Clear, Pair 18.00
Pressed Glass, Saltshaker, Sunken Teardrop 3.00
Pressed Glass, Saltshaker, Virginia .... 7.00 To 8.50
Pressed Glass, Saltshaker, Wheel Of Fortune 9.00
Pressed Glass, Saltshaker, Zipper Block, Red Flashed 9.00
Pressed Glass, Sauce, Actress, Footed 8.50
Pressed Glass, Sauce, Ashburton, Flint 5.00
Pressed Glass, Sauce, Atlanta, Square 12.50
Pressed Glass, Sauce, Austrian, 4 1/2 In. 12.50
Pressed Glass, Sauce, Barberry, Footed .... 4.00 To 7.50
Pressed Glass, Sauce, Barley 4.00
Pressed Glass, Sauce, Beaded Band 3.00
Pressed Glass, Sauce, Beaded Grape, Emerald Green .... 8.00 To 12.50

Pressed Glass, Sauce, Bellflower	8.00
Pressed Glass, Sauce, Bellflower, Single Vine, Flint	15.00
Pressed Glass, Sauce, Bleeding Heart	5.00
Pressed Glass, Sauce, Block & Fan	3.50
Pressed Glass, Sauce, Block & Star, Amber	6.50
Pressed Glass, Sauce, Bull's-Eye And Diamond Point	12.50
Pressed Glass, Sauce, Cabbage Rose, 4 1/8 In.	7.50
Pressed Glass, Sauce, Cable, Flint	6.50 To 7.50
Pressed Glass, Sauce, Canadian, Footed, 4 In.	10.50
Pressed Glass, Sauce, Chain & Star	5.00 To 5.75
Pressed Glass, Sauce, Crossed Disks	3.50
Pressed Glass, Sauce, Crystal Wedding	5.00
Pressed Glass, Sauce, Cupid & Venus, Footed, 3 1/2 In.	5.00 To 6.50
Pressed Glass, Sauce, Dahlia, 4 1/2 In.	5.00
Pressed Glass, Sauce, Daisy & Button With Crossbar, Amber	8.50 To 9.00
Pressed Glass, Sauce, Daisy & Button, Amberette, 4 In.Diameter	11.00
Pressed Glass, Sauce, Dakota, Footed	6.00
Pressed Glass, Sauce, Delaware, Gold, Boat Shape	12.00
Pressed Glass, Sauce, Delaware, Rose	11.00
Pressed Glass, Sauce, Diamond & Thumbprint, Flint	9.00 To 14.00
Pressed Glass, Sauce, Diamond Point	7.00
Pressed Glass, Sauce, Dickensen	4.50
Pressed Glass, Sauce, Double Spear, 4 1/2 In.	3.75
Pressed Glass, Sauce, Etched Dakota, Footed	12.00
Pressed Glass, Sauce, Feather	5.00
Pressed Glass, Sauce, Feather, Flat	4.00
Pressed Glass, Sauce, Festoon, 4 In.	3.75 To 4.50
Pressed Glass, Sauce, Fringed Drape	6.50
Pressed Glass, Sauce, Frosted Artichoke	12.00
Pressed Glass, Sauce, Frosted Lion, Footed	15.00
Pressed Glass, Sauce, Gothic	10.00
Pressed Glass, Sauce, Grape, Gold	6.50
Pressed Glass, Sauce, Hairpin	7.00
Pressed Glass, Sauce, Hamilton	8.00
Pressed Glass, Sauce, Herringbone, Emerald Green	8.00
Pressed Glass, Sauce, Hobbs Block, Amber, Three Cornered	12.00
Pressed Glass, Sauce, Horn Of Plenty, Flint	6.00 To 10.00
Pressed Glass, Sauce, Horn Of Plenty, Flint, 4 3/8 In.	12.50
Pressed Glass, Sauce, Horseshoe	5.00
Pressed Glass, Sauce, Horseshoe, Footed, 4 1/2 In.	7.00
Pressed Glass, Sauce, Jewel & Dewdrop, Flared Sides	6.50
Pressed Glass, Sauce, Jewel & Dewdrop, Rounded Sides	7.00
Pressed Glass, Sauce, Kentucky, Footed	9.50
Pressed Glass, Sauce, Liberty Bell, Footed	17.50
Pressed Glass, Sauce, Lincoln Drape	10.00
Pressed Glass, Sauce, Lion & Baboon, 4 In.	12.50
Pressed Glass, Sauce, Loop & Dart	3.00 To 5.00
Pressed Glass, Sauce, Magnet & Grape With Stippled Leaf	4.00
Pressed Glass, Sauce, Magnet & Grape, Flat	12.50
Pressed Glass, Sauce, Manhattan, Flat, Gold Scallops, 4 3/8 In.	4.00
Pressed Glass, Sauce, Maple Leaf, Frosted, 5 In.Diameter	6.00
Pressed Glass, Sauce, Maple Leaf, 5 In.Diameter	4.50
Pressed Glass, Sauce, Marsh, Pink	3.50
Pressed Glass, Sauce, Minerva, Footed	10.00
Pressed Glass, Sauce, New England Pineapple	10.00
Pressed Glass, Sauce, New Jersey	4.50
Pressed Glass, Sauce, Paddlewheel	9.50
Pressed Glass, Sauce, Panel Cherry, 4 1/4 In.	3.75
Pressed Glass, Sauce, Paneled Daisy, Footed	9.00
Pressed Glass, Sauce, Picket	5.00 To 7.50
Pressed Glass, Sauce, Picket, Handled	7.00
Pressed Glass, Sauce, Pineapple & Fan, Emerald Green	15.00
Pressed Glass, Sauce, Pleat & Panel, Square, Footed	9.50
Pressed Glass, Sauce, Plume	4.25 To 8.00
Pressed Glass, Sauce, Plume, Ruby Edge, 4 1/2 In.	8.75
Pressed Glass, Sauce, Pressed Leaf	4.00

Pressed Glass, Sauce, Reversed Torpedo 4.00
Pressed Glass, Sauce, Ribbed Acorn 10.00
Pressed Glass, Sauce, Ribbed Grape 9.00
Pressed Glass, Sauce, Ribbed Ivy 10.00
Pressed Glass, Sauce, Rose In Snow, Flat, 4 In. 4.00
Pressed Glass, Sauce, Rose In Snow, Footed 9.00
Pressed Glass, Sauce, Sedan, Flat .... 2.50 To 2.70
Pressed Glass, Sauce, Shell & Jewel 4.50
Pressed Glass, Sauce, Shell & Tassel, Square, Handled, 4 In. 4.90
Pressed Glass, Sauce, Shoehone 6.00
Pressed Glass, Sauce, Shrine, Flat 8.50
Pressed Glass, Sauce, Spirea Band, Amber 6.00
Pressed Glass, Sauce, Star Rosette 2.50
Pressed Glass, Sauce, Two Panel, Clear, Footed 3.50
Pressed Glass, Sauce, U.S.Coin, Frosted Quarters .... 60.00 To 85.00
Pressed Glass, Sauce, Waffle & Fan, Footed 3.50
Pressed Glass, Sauce, Waffle, Flint 4.00
Pressed Glass, Sauce, Washington 8.00
Pressed Glass, Sauce, Westward Ho, Footed, 4 In.Diameter 18.50
Pressed Glass, Sauce, Wildflower, Vaseline, Square 7.50
Pressed Glass, Server, Sandwich, Grape, Amber 30.00
Pressed Glass, Shade, Crosscut Diamond, Amberina, Conical, 5 1/4 In. 17.50
Pressed Glass, Sherbet, Dakota, Footed 7.50
Pressed Glass, Sherbet, Egyptian, Footed 8.00
Pressed Glass, Shoe, Daisy & Button, Blue, Dated, Pair 75.00
Pressed Glass, Shoe, Daisy & Button, Blue, Striker On Bottom, Bow 16.00
Pressed Glass, Shoe, Daisy & Button, Blue, Striker On Bottom, 3-Lace 14.00
Pressed Glass, Shoe, Daisy & Button, Clear, Dated, Oxford 25.00
Pressed Glass, Slipper, Daisy & Button, Amethyst 7.50
Pressed Glass, Slipper, Daisy & Button, Blue 15.00
Pressed Glass, Slipper, Frosted, White, Bow, Marked Gillinder 30.00
Pressed Glass, Spill, Harp, Gold, 5 In. .... *Illus* 75.00
Pressed Glass, Spill, Horn Of Plenty 35.00
Pressed Glass, Spill, Sandwich Star, Flint 35.00
Pressed Glass, Spittoon, Button Arches, 6 1/2 In. .... *Illus* 35.00
Pressed Glass, Spooner, Almond Thumbprint, Flint 22.00
Pressed Glass, Spooner, Barley, Beaded 14.50
Pressed Glass, Spooner, Beaded Acorn Medallion 15.00
Pressed Glass, Spooner, Beaded Grape Medallion 12.00
Pressed Glass, Spooner, Bellflower, Flint .... 16.00 To 28.00
Pressed Glass, Spooner, Bellflower, Single Vine, Scalloped Top, Flint 38.00
Pressed Glass, Spooner, Bowtie, Scalloped Rim 18.00
Pressed Glass, Spooner, Broken Column .... 17.50 To 19.00
Pressed Glass, Spooner, Bryce 11.00
Pressed Glass, Spooner, Buckle .... 14.00 To 15.00
Pressed Glass, Spooner, Cabbage Rose 20.00
Pressed Glass, Spooner, Cable 12.50
Pressed Glass, Spooner, Cable, Flint 20.00
Pressed Glass, Spooner, Cardinal Bird 15.00
Pressed Glass, Spooner, Cathedral .... 11.00 To 16.50

Pressed Glass,
Spill, Harp,
Gold, 5 In.

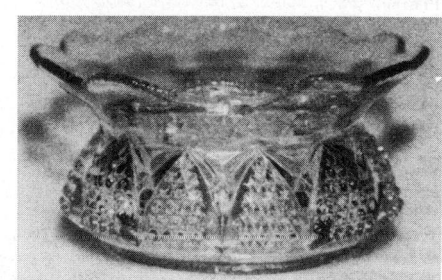

Pressed Glass, Spittoon, Button Arches, 6 1/2 In.

Pressed Glass, Spooner, Cathedral, Blue 35.00
Pressed Glass, Spooner, Child's, Blue 16.00
Pressed Glass, Spooner, Child's, Colonial, Clear 12.00
Pressed Glass, Spooner, Colorado, Green, Gold, Footed 24.00
Pressed Glass, Spooner, Colossus 12.00
Pressed Glass, Spooner, Cord & Tassel 15.00
Pressed Glass, Spooner, Crow's-Foot .... 10.00 To 15.00
Pressed Glass, Spooner, Crystal Wedding, Frosted 30.00
Pressed Glass, Spooner, Cupid & Venus 23.00
Pressed Glass, Spooner, Daisy & Button With Crossbar 12.50
Pressed Glass, Spooner, Delaware, Cranberry, Gold 35.00
Pressed Glass, Spooner, Diagonal Band 12.00
Pressed Glass, Spooner, Diamond Band, Clear 7.00
Pressed Glass, Spooner, Diamond Band With Fan 14.00
Pressed Glass, Spooner, Diamond Panel, Flat 10.00
Pressed Glass, Spooner, Diamonds & Crossbars 5.50
Pressed Glass, Spooner, Diamonds In Diamonds 18.00
Pressed Glass, Spooner, Fandango 36.00
Pressed Glass, Spooner, Frosted Circle 18.00
Pressed Glass, Spooner, Garfield Drape 16.00
Pressed Glass, Spooner, Grape & Festoon 9.00
Pressed Glass, Spooner, Grape & Festoon With Stippled Leaf 9.00
Pressed Glass, Spooner, Grape Medallion With Beaded Band 8.50
Pressed Glass, Spooner, Hamilton, Flint 16.50
Pressed Glass, Spooner, Hairpin Loop, Rayed Base, Flint 15.00
Pressed Glass, Spooner, Herringbone 8.00
Pressed Glass, Spooner, Hobnail & Big Diamond 10.50
Pressed Glass, Spooner, Honeycomb 16.50
Pressed Glass, Spooner, Hops Band 7.00
Pressed Glass, Spooner, Horn Of Plenty, Flint .... 26.00 To 34.00
Pressed Glass, Spooner, Inverted Fern 35.00
Pressed Glass, Spooner, Jacob's Ladder 10.00
Pressed Glass, Spooner, King's Crown 27.50
Pressed Glass, Spooner, Lattice, Flint 15.00
Pressed Glass, Spooner, Lily Of The Valley 19.50
Pressed Glass, Spooner, Lincoln Drape 35.00
Pressed Glass, Spooner, Lippman 8.25
Pressed Glass, Spooner, Loop & Dart, Red 13.50
Pressed Glass, Spooner, Loop & Dart, Round Ornament 10.00
Pressed Glass, Spooner, Manhattan 10.00
Pressed Glass, Spooner, Mascotte 10.00
Pressed Glass, Spooner, Massachusetts 13.00
Pressed Glass, Spooner, Paneled Daisy 12.50
Pressed Glass, Spooner, Paneled Forget-Me-Not 12.50
Pressed Glass, Spooner, Pennsylvania 10.00
Pressed Glass, Spooner, Pineapple, Ribbed, Flint 16.00
Pressed Glass, Spooner, Pleat & Panel .... 7.00 To 15.00
Pressed Glass, Spooner, Plume .... 9.00 To 15.00
Pressed Glass, Spooner, Pointed Jewel, Clear 15.00
Pressed Glass, Spooner, Powder & Shot 9.00
Pressed Glass, Spooner, Powder & Shot, Flint 28.00
Pressed Glass, Spooner, Princess Feather .... 10.00 To 18.50
Pressed Glass, Spooner, Prism, Flint 15.00
Pressed Glass, Spooner, Prisms With Diamond Point 11.00
Pressed Glass, Spooner, Red Block .... 25.00 To 30.00
Pressed Glass, Spooner, Ribbed Ivy, Flint 36.50
Pressed Glass, Spooner, Ribbon 10.00
Pressed Glass, Spooner, Ribbon, Clear 8.00
Pressed Glass, Spooner, Royal Crystal, Ruby 20.00
Pressed Glass, Spooner, Ruby Thumbprint .... 28.00 To 35.00
Pressed Glass, Spooner, Sawtooth 6.50
Pressed Glass, Spooner, Seneca Loop .... 12.00 To 20.00
Pressed Glass, Spooner, Sheraton, Clear 8.00
Pressed Glass, Spooner, Star & File 15.00
Pressed Glass, Spooner, Star Band 8.00
Pressed Glass, Spooner, Stars & Bars 8.00

Pressed Glass, Spooner, Stippled Grape & Festoon 11.00
Pressed Glass, Spooner, Stippled Ivy 7.50
Pressed Glass, Spooner, Stippled Panel & Band 7.50
Pressed Glass, Spooner, Stippled Peppers 13.50
Pressed Glass, Spooner, Stippled Sandburr 8.75
Pressed Glass, Spooner, Strawberry .... 10.00 To 18.00
Pressed Glass, Spooner, Thistle 18.00
Pressed Glass, Spooner, Three Panel 18.00
Pressed Glass, Spooner, Tokyo, Blue, Opalescent, Jefferson Glass Co., C.1899 .... 30.00
Pressed Glass, Spooner, Torpedo 13.50
Pressed Glass, Spooner, Tree Of Life 75.00
Pressed Glass, Spooner, Tulip & Sawtooth 18.50
Pressed Glass, Spooner, U.S.Coin, Clear 85.00
Pressed Glass, Spooner, U.S.Coin, Frosted Half Dollars, C.1892 .... 95.00
Pressed Glass, Spooner, Umbilicated Sawtooth, Flint 16.00
Pressed Glass, Spooner, Virginia 17.50
Pressed Glass, Spooner, Washboard 5.00
Pressed Glass, Spooner, Wildflower, Blue, Footed 15.00
Pressed Glass, Spooner, Yuma Loop 6.75
Pressed Glass, Spooner, Yuma Loop, Footed 10.00
Pressed Glass, Spooner, 101 .... 9.00
Pressed Glass, Sugar & Creamer, Azalea, Covered Sugar 15.00
Pressed Glass, Sugar & Creamer, Child's, Little Sweetheart 27.50
Pressed Glass, Sugar & Creamer, Cut Leaf Flower, Star Of David On Bottom 35.00
Pressed Glass, Sugar & Creamer, Garfield Drape 27.50
Pressed Glass, Sugar & Creamer, Intaglio Jewel 24.00
Pressed Glass, Sugar & Creamer, Maple Leaf, Covered 68.00
Pressed Glass, Sugar & Creamer, Paneled Daisy & Button, Narcissus, Clear 25.00
Pressed Glass, Sugar & Creamer, Paneled Dewdrop, Covered Sugar 40.00
Pressed Glass, Sugar & Creamer, Portland, Individual 12.50
Pressed Glass, Sugar & Creamer, Smocking, Covered, Flint 145.00
Pressed Glass, Sugar & Creamer, Thistle, Near Cut 24.00
Pressed Glass, Sugar & Creamer, Westward Ho 150.00
Pressed Glass, Sugar & Creamer, Wildflower, Amber, Footed 50.00
Pressed Glass, Sugar, Art, Covered 30.00
Pressed Glass, Sugar, Baltimore Pear 23.00
Pressed Glass, Sugar, Barley, Covered 20.00
Pressed Glass, Sugar, Basket Weave, Clear, Covered 14.00
Pressed Glass, Sugar, Beaded Arch Panels, Covered 14.00
Pressed Glass, Sugar, Beaded Grape Medallion, Covered 38.00
Pressed Glass, Sugar, Beaded Grape 11.00
Pressed Glass, Sugar, Beaded Grape, Covered, Square 16.00
Pressed Glass, Sugar, Beautiful Lady, Covered 16.50
Pressed Glass, Sugar, Bellflower, Flint 35.00
Pressed Glass, Sugar, Block & Circle, Covered 15.00
Pressed Glass, Sugar, Broken Arches, Frosted & Clear, Covered 30.00
Pressed Glass, Sugar, Bull's-Eye & Daisy, Gold 28.00
Pressed Glass, Sugar, Bull's-Eye Variant, Clear, Hexagonal, Flint 30.00
Pressed Glass, Sugar, Bull's-Eye, Flint 52.50
Pressed Glass, Sugar, Button Arches, Covered 14.00
Pressed Glass, Sugar, Cabbage Rose, Covered 12.00
Pressed Glass, Sugar, Cable & Ring, Flint .... 25.00 To 45.00
Pressed Glass, Sugar, Cane Medallion, Covered 13.50
Pressed Glass, Sugar, Chain, Covered 28.00
Pressed Glass, Sugar, Church Window 23.00
Pressed Glass, Sugar, Classic, Log Feet .... 40.00 To 110.00
Pressed Glass, Sugar, Colorado, Green, Covered, Footed 52.00
Pressed Glass, Sugar, Colossus, Covered 15.00
Pressed Glass, Sugar, Crescent & Fan, Covered 14.00
Pressed Glass, Sugar, Cube With Fan, Covered 16.50
Pressed Glass, Sugar, Daisy & Button With Thumbprint, Clear, Covered 21.00
Pressed Glass, Sugar, Delaware, Cranberry, Covered, Gold 50.00
Pressed Glass, Sugar, Delaware, Rose 35.00
Pressed Glass, Sugar, Diamond Point 61.00
Pressed Glass, Sugar, Diamond Point Discs, Covered 18.50
Pressed Glass, Sugar, Diamond Thumbprint, Covered, Flint 65.00

Pressed Glass, Sugar, Egg In Sand, Covered	15.00
Pressed Glass, Sugar, Egyptian, Covered	55.00
Pressed Glass, Sugar, Esther, Clear	8.50
Pressed Glass, Sugar, Etched Dakota, Covered	29.50 To 35.00
Pressed Glass, Sugar, Etched Gooseberries	20.00
Pressed Glass, Sugar, Etched Mascotte, Covered	23.00
Pressed Glass, Sugar, Etched Wheel & Comma, Covered	15.00
Pressed Glass, Sugar, Excelsior, Covered, Flint	55.00
Pressed Glass, Sugar, Fan & Block	5.98
Pressed Glass, Sugar, Feather Swirl	16.50
Pressèd Glass, Sugar, Feather, Covered	13.50
Pressed Glass, Sugar, Fleur-De-Lis With Tassel	16.50
Pressed Glass, Sugar, Fleur-De-Lis, Arched _Illus_	7.00
Pressed Glass, Sugar, Floral Diamond, Covered	15.00
Pressed Glass, Sugar, Flute With Cane, Covered, Handled	11.00
Pressed Glass, Sugar, Four Petal, Covered	37.50
Pressed Glass, Sugar, Four Petal, Round Top, Flint	50.00
Pressed Glass, Sugar, Frosted Circle	35.00
Pressed Glass, Sugar, Frosted Circle, Covered	47.00
Pressed Glass, Sugar, Frosted Lion, Collared Base	18.50 To 20.00
Pressed Glass, Sugar, Frosted Lion, Covered	20.00
Pressed Glass, Sugar, Frosted Lion, Crouching Lion Finial	49.50
Pressed Glass, Sugar, Galloway, Covered	19.00
Pressed Glass, Sugar, Gibson Girl, Covered	55.00
Pressed Glass, Sugar, Heart & Thumbprint, Gold	6.50
Pressed Glass, Sugar, Hinoto, Covered, Flint	40.00
Pressed Glass, Sugar, Horn Of Plenty	27.50 To 35.00
Pressed Glass, Sugar, Ihmsen, Opaque White, Covered, Flint	460.00
Pressed Glass, Sugar, Inverted Fern, Covered, Flint	45.00
Pressed Glass, Sugar, Inverted Fern, Flint	38.00
Pressed Glass, Sugar, Inverted Strawberry, Covered	28.00
Pressed Glass, Sugar, Lacy Daisy, Covered	14.00
Pressed Glass, Sugar, Late Thistle, Covered, 2 Handles	13.00
Pressed Glass, Sugar, Lattice, Covered	19.50
Pressed Glass, Sugar, Leaf & Dart	9.00
Pressed Glass, Sugar, Leaf & Dart, Covered	22.50
Pressed Glass, Sugar, Liberty Bell	65.00
Pressed Glass, Sugar, Loop & Fan	8.00
Pressed Glass, Sugar, Louisiana, Covered	27.50
Pressed Glass, Sugar, Manhattan	10.00
Pressed Glass, Sugar, Marquisette	12.00
Pressed Glass, Sugar, Michigan, Covered, Large Size	35.00
Pressed Glass, Sugar, Minerva	24.00
Pressed Glass, Sugar, New England Pineapple, Covered	55.00
Pressed Glass, Sugar, Orange Peel Band	8.50
Pressed Glass, Sugar, Palm Leaf, Covered	13.50
Pressed Glass, Sugar, Palm, Flint	35.00
Pressed Glass, Sugar, Palmette, Covered	28.00
Pressed Glass, Sugar, Paneled Bull's-Eye, Clear, Hexagonal, Flint	37.50
Pressed Glass, Sugar, Pavonia, Etched Maple Leaf, Covered	27.00
Pressed Glass, Sugar, Picket, Covered	27.50
Pressed Glass, Sugar, Pittsburgh, Cobalt Blue, Paneled, Covered, Footed, Flint	230.00
Pressed Glass, Sugar, Portland, Covered	22.50
Pressed Glass, Sugar, Powder & Shot	30.00
Pressed Glass, Sugar, Princess Feather	34.00
Pressed Glass, Sugar, Princess Feather, Covered	35.00
Pressed Glass, Sugar, Priscilla	20.00
Pressed Glass, Sugar, Psyche & Cupid	30.00
Pressed Glass, Sugar, Rain & Dewdrops, Covered	27.50
Pressed Glass, Sugar, Red Block, Covered	35.00
Pressed Glass, Sugar, Reeded Waffle	10.00
Pressed Glass, Sugar, Ribbed Palm, Flint	20.00
Pressed Glass, Sugar, Ruby Thumbprint	35.00
Pressed Glass, Sugar, Starflower, Covered _Illus_	22.00
Pressed Glass, Sugar, Stippled Grape & Festoon	11.00
Pressed Glass, Sugar, Swirled Star, Covered	30.00

Pressed Glass, Sugar, Starflower, Covered
See Page 444

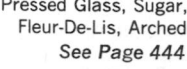

Pressed Glass, Sugar,
Fleur-De-Lis, Arched
See Page 444

Pressed Glass, Sugar, The States 22.50
Pressed Glass, Sugar, Thumbprint 57.50
Pressed Glass, Sugar, Tokyo, Blue, Opalescent, Jefferson Glass Co., C.1899 .... 30.00
Pressed Glass, Sugar, Tong, Flint 39.50
Pressed Glass, Sugar, Triple Triangle, Flashed, Handles 19.50
Pressed Glass, Sugar, Tulip & Honeycomb, Miniature .... 6.50 To 15.00
Pressed Glass, Sugar, Virginia, Covered 17.50
Pressed Glass, Sugar, Wheat & Barley, Clear, Covered, 8 In. 22.50
Pressed Glass, Sugar, Willow Oak 25.00
Pressed Glass, Sugar, Zipper 10.00
Pressed Glass, Sweetmeat, Westward-Ho 175.00
Pressed Glass, Syrup, Alabama 25.00
Pressed Glass, Syrup, Apple Green, Rosettes, Paneled, Diamond Band, 1871 .... 68.00
Pressed Glass, Syrup, Baccarat Type Swirl 20.00
Pressed Glass, Syrup, Banded Buckle, Silver Spring Lid, Applied Handle 55.00
Pressed Glass, Syrup, Button Arches, Red Flashed, Pewter Lid 68.50
Pressed Glass, Syrup, Clear, Applied Handle, Pewter Top 28.75
Pressed Glass, Syrup, Cord & Tassel 25.00
Pressed Glass, Syrup, Diamond Point Band Top & Bottom, Clear Center 18.00
Pressed Glass, Syrup, Frosted Lion, Patent July 16, 1872 .... 75.00
Pressed Glass, Syrup, Heart & Thumbprint, Spout, Pewter Lid 40.00
Pressed Glass, Syrup, Jewel & Dewdrop, Silver Plate Spring Lid 65.00
Pressed Glass, Syrup, Lens & Star, Clear, Top 17.50
Pressed Glass, Syrup, Michigan, Pewter Top 25.00
Pressed Glass, Syrup, Paneled Cherry, Glass Cover 18.00
Pressed Glass, Syrup, Sapphire Blue, Pewter Top 75.00
Pressed Glass, Syrup, Tepee, 4 In.High 11.00
Pressed Glass, Syrup, Torpedo, Ruby Stain 34.00
Pressed Glass, Syrup, Torpedo, 7 In.High 21.00
Pressed Glass, Syrup, Tunis Pattern, Pewter Top 14.00
Pressed Glass, Table Set, Child's, Pewter Candlestick, 4 Piece 19.00
Pressed Glass, Table Set, Delaware, Rose, Gold, 4 Piece 260.00
Pressed Glass, Table Set, Diamond Medallion, 3 Piece 57.00
Pressed Glass, Table Set, Paneled Heather, 4 Piece 77.00
Pressed Glass, Tankard, Tokyo, Blue, Jefferson Glass Co., C.1899 .... 70.00
Pressed Glass, Taster, Fine Rib 13.00
Pressed Glass, Tazza, Tokyo, Blue, Opalescent, Jefferson Glass Co., C.1899 .... 38.00
Pressed Glass, Toothpick, Colorado, Blue, Gold 18.50
Pressed Glass, Toothpick, Colorado, Green, Gold, Lewis & Clark Expedition 18.00
Pressed Glass, Toothpick, Daisy & Button, Clear, Hat Shape 10.50
Pressed Glass, Toothpick, Delaware, Rose, Gold 45.00
Pressed Glass, Toothpick, Etched Thumbprint, Ruby 22.50
Pressed Glass, Toothpick, Fans With Crossbars, Ruby Flashed, Pointed Rim 16.50
Pressed Glass, Toothpick, Frosted Daisy & Button, Uncle Sam Hat 10.00
Pressed Glass, Toothpick, Frosted U.S.Coin 95.00
Pressed Glass, Toothpick, Galloway 10.00

Pressed Glass, Toothpick, Illinois	10.50
Pressed Glass, Toothpick, Long Buttress	8.50
Pressed Glass, Toothpick, Michigan, Milk White	30.00
Pressed Glass, Toothpick, Monkey & Stump	18.00
Pressed Glass, Toothpick, Quartered Block	9.50
Pressed Glass, Toothpick, Red Flashed, 'Export Expo, 1899, '	8.00
Pressed Glass, Toothpick, Solomon's Bell	45.00
Pressed Glass, Toothpick, Stippled Cradle	25.00
Pressed Glass, Toothpick, Swirl & Panel	8.00
Pressed Glass, Toothpick, Texas	17.50
Pressed Glass, Toothpick, Thistle	6.00
Pressed Glass, Toothpick, Virginia, Clear	15.00
Pressed Glass, Tray, Bread, see Pressed Glass, Plate, Bread	
Pressed Glass, Tray, Condiment, Double Circle, 6 In.Diameter	10.00
Pressed Glass, Tray, Condiment, Heart & Thumbprint, Green	15.00
Pressed Glass, Tray, Currier & Ives, Mule	39.75
Pressed Glass, Tray, Daisy & Button, Bull's-Eye Border, Blue, 16 X 9 1/2 In.	100.00
Pressed Glass, Tray, Deer & Pine, Oblong, 13 X 7 3/4 In.	29.50
Pressed Glass, Tray, Garfield Drape	45.00
Pressed Glass, Tray, Grant, Patriot Soldier	25.00
Pressed Glass, Tray, Maple Leaf, Canary, 10 1/2 In.Diameter	28.00
Pressed Glass, Tray, Pillows Encircled, Ruby Flashed, Oval	22.00
Pressed Glass, Tray, Pin, Delaware, Rose, Gold	16.00
Pressed Glass, Tray, Valencia Waffle, Amber	20.00
Pressed Glass, Tray, Water, Basket Weave, Vaseline	25.00
Pressed Glass, Tray, Water, Currier & Ives	45.00
Pressed Glass, Tray, Water, Fern & Berry	55.00
Pressed Glass, Tray, Water, Fishscale, Round	22.50
Pressed Glass, Tray, Water, Horseshoe, Double Horseshoe Handles	55.00
Pressed Glass, Tray, Water, State House	49.50
Pressed Glass, Tray, Water, Wildflower, Blue, 11 X 13 In.	32.50
Pressed Glass, Tray, Water, 1, 000-Eye, 11 3/4 X 14 In.	40.00
Pressed Glass, Tray, Wildflower, Blue, 9 1/2 In.Square	24.50
Pressed Glass, Tub, The States, 4 1/4 In.	8.50
Pressed Glass, Tumbler, Atlantic	4.00
Pressed Glass, Tumbler, Banded Grape, Thumbprint Base	24.50
Pressed Glass, Tumbler, Broken Column	30.00
Pressed Glass, Tumbler, Bull's-Eye, Flint	27.00 To 49.00
Pressed Glass, Tumbler, Cable, Footed	125.00
Pressed Glass, Tumbler, Cane	11.00
Pressed Glass, Tumbler, Cranberry Stripe Swirl, Opalescent	65.00
Pressed Glass, Tumbler, Currier & Ives	15.00
Pressed Glass, Tumbler, Daisy & Button, Amber	18.00
Pressed Glass, Tumbler, Daisy, Oval Panel	4.50
Pressed Glass, Tumbler, Dakota, Ruby Flashed	22.50 To 28.00
Pressed Glass, Tumbler, Delaware, Green, Gold	25.00
Pressed Glass, Tumbler, Dew & Raindrop	10.00
Pressed Glass, Tumbler, Dewey	18.00
Pressed Glass, Tumbler, Diamond Point, Flint	40.00
Pressed Glass, Tumbler, Diamond Thumbprint, Flint	69.50
Pressed Glass, Tumbler, Etched Pavonia	11.00 To 12.75
Pressed Glass, Tumbler, Etched Thumbprint, Ruby	22.50
Pressed Glass, Tumbler, Excelsior, Flint	15.00
Pressed Glass, Tumbler, Excelsior, Flint, Footed	45.00
Pressed Glass, Tumbler, Festoon	12.50
Pressed Glass, Tumbler, Flute, Flint	9.00
Pressed Glass, Tumbler, Giant Prism With Thumbprint Band, Flint	48.00
Pressed Glass, Tumbler, Grape	10.00
Pressed Glass, Tumbler, Heart & Band, Ruby Flashed	16.00
Pressed Glass, Tumbler, Hobnail	4.50 To 10.00
Pressed Glass, Tumbler, Honeycomb, Blue, Daisy & Button Base	8.00
Pressed Glass, Tumbler, Horn Of Plenty	75.00
Pressed Glass, Tumbler, Horseshoe	6.00
Pressed Glass, Tumbler, Knobby Bull's-Eye	12.00
Pressed Glass, Tumbler, Loop And Fans	9.50
Pressed Glass, Tumbler, Michigan	9.50 To 15.00

Pressed Glass, Tumbler, Michigan, Gold 11.00
Pressed Glass, Tumbler, Ohio, Amber, Fluted Swirl 230.00
Pressed Glass, Tumbler, Paneled 44, Silver Decorated 18.00
Pressed Glass, Tumbler, Pavonia, Ruby Flashed 26.00
Pressed Glass, Tumbler, Peacock Feather 18.50
Pressed Glass, Tumbler, Pennsylvania, Gold 10.00
Pressed Glass, Tumbler, Portland 6.50
Pressed Glass, Tumbler, Prism & Crescent, Flint 38.00
Pressed Glass, Tumbler, Red Block 19.50
Pressed Glass, Tumbler, Ruby Thumbprint, Ruby Flashed 26.00
Pressed Glass, Tumbler, Sawtooth, Flint 14.00
Pressed Glass, Tumbler, Shell & Jewel, Blue 15.00
Pressed Glass, Tumbler, Spiked Argus, Flint 39.00
Pressed Glass, Tumbler, Sunburst, Ruby Flashed 26.00
Pressed Glass, Tumbler, Three Fruit, Frosted 7.50
Pressed Glass, Tumbler, Three Stony 12.00
Pressed Glass, Tumbler, Torpedo, Ruby Top 18.50
Pressed Glass, Tumbler, U.S.Coin ....95.00 To 175.00
Pressed Glass, Tumbler, U.S.Coin, American Dollar In Base, Dated 1879 .... 100.00
Pressed Glass, Tumbler, Water, Currier & Ives, Footed 24.00
Pressed Glass, Tumbler, Whiskey, Horn Of Plenty, Flint, 3 In.High 62.50
Pressed Glass, Tumbler, 1, 000-Eye 9.00
Pressed Glass, Vanity Set, Smoked, 3 Piece 25.00
Pressed Glass, Vase, Ashburton, Flint, 8 In.High 25.00
Pressed Glass, Vase, Banded Portland, 6 In.High 5.00
Pressed Glass, Vase, Beaded Dewdrop, Trumpet, 8 In.High 16.50
   Pressed Glass, Vase, Celery, see Pressed Glass, Celery
Pressed Glass, Vase, Centennial, Camphor, 7 In. .... *Illus* 18.00
Pressed Glass, Vase, Colorado, Cobalt, Gold, Footed 47.50
Pressed Glass, Vase, Electric Blue, Flowers And Leaves Fused To Glass 150.00
Pressed Glass, Vase, Fan & Diamond, Clear, 6 1/2 In.High 14.00
Pressed Glass, Vase, Galloway, 11 1/2 In.High 11.50
Pressed Glass, Vase, Michigan 12.00
Pressed Glass, Vase, Sawtooth, Flowers, Birds, Square, 10 In.High 55.00
Pressed Glass, Water Set, Grape & Gothic, Green, Gold, 5 Piece 900.00
Pressed Glass, Water, Set, Rayed Flower, Painted Flowers, 7 Piece 46.00
Pressed Glass, Whiskey Taster, Beaded Swirl, Handled 12.00
Pressed Glass, Whiskey Taster, Colorado, Green, 'Mary' 7.50
Pressed Glass, Whiskey Taster, Fine Rib 15.00
Pressed Glass, Whiskey, Ashburton Banded 12.50
Pressed Glass, Whiskey, Honeycomb, Handle 15.00
Pressed Glass, Whiskey, Ribbed Ivy 45.00
Pressed Glass, Whiskey, Way Colonial 45.00
Pressed Glass, Wine, Almond Thumbprint 25.00
Pressed Glass, Wine, Apple Green, Two Panel 26.50
Pressed Glass, Wine, Argus 27.50
Pressed Glass, Wine, Argus Cut 17.50
Pressed Glass, Wine, Ashburton 22.50

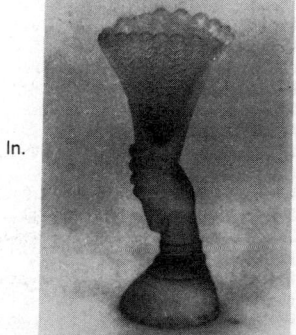

Pressed Glass, Vase, Centennial, Camphor, 7 In.

Pressed Glass, Wine, Ashburton, Claret	37.50
Pressed Glass, Wine, Aurora	10.00
Pressed Glass, Wine, Balder, Gold	7.50
Pressed Glass, Wine, Banded Buckle	17.50
Pressed Glass, Wine, Bellflower, Fine Rib, Single Vine	20.00
Pressed Glass, Wine, Belted Worcester	12.50
Pressed Glass, Wine, Bird & Strawberry	25.00 To 28.50
Pressed Glass, Wine, Buckle & Star	12.50
Pressed Glass, Wine, Bull's-Eye	45.00
Pressed Glass, Wine, Bull's-Eye, Red, Clear	14.00
Pressed Glass, Wine, Button Arches, Ruby	24.50
Pressed Glass, Wine, Cabbage Rose	28.50
Pressed Glass, Wine, Chain & Star	10.00
Pressed Glass, Wine, Clear Diagonal Band	8.00
Pressed Glass, Wine, Cord & Tassel	13.50 To 16.00
Pressed Glass, Wine, Cut Log	12.50 To 16.50
Pressed Glass, Wine, Cut Log, Stemmed	10.00
Pressed Glass, Wine, Daisy & Button, With Narcissus	12.50
Pressed Glass, Wine, Dakota	15.00
Pressed Glass, Wine, Diamond & Sunburst	6.00
Pressed Glass, Wine, Diamond Point, Flint	22.50 To 25.00
Pressed Glass, Wine, Diamond-Quilted	8.75
Pressed Glass, Wine, Double Beetle Band	7.50
Pressed Glass, Wine, Etched Atlas	18.50
Pressed Glass, Wine, Etched Bottoms Up, Clear, Green Knob, 4 In.High	3.85
Pressed Glass, Wine, Etched Dakota	15.00
Pressed Glass, Wine, Etched Ruby Thumbprint	20.00
Pressed Glass, Wine, Feather	15.00
Pressed Glass, Wine, Feather, Banded Top	18.50
Pressed Glass, Wine, Feather, Nearcut, Gold	8.00
Pressed Glass, Wine, Feather, Straight Top	12.50
Pressed Glass, Wine, Fern & Berry	24.00
Pressed Glass, Wine, Fine Rib	27.50
Pressed Glass, Wine, Finecut & Panel, Amber	18.00
Pressed Glass, Wine, Finecut & Panel, Vaseline	19.50
Pressed Glass, Wine, Good Luck	95.00
Pressed Glass, Wine, Halley's Comet	10.00
Pressed Glass, Wine, Hamilton, Flint	35.00
Pressed Glass, Wine, Heart & Thumbprint, Green	14.00
Pressed Glass, Wine, Honeycomb Pillar	6.00
Pressed Glass, Wine, Horn Of Plenty	35.00
Pressed Glass, Wine, Horsemint	6.00
Pressed Glass, Wine, Huber	10.00
Pressed Glass, Wine, Iowa City	13.50
Pressed Glass, Wine, Ivy In Snow	22.50
Pressed Glass, Wine, Jacob's Ladder	18.50
Pressed Glass, Wine, Jeweled Moon & Star	40.00
Pressed Glass, Wine, King's Crown	5.00
Pressed Glass, Wine, Liberty	9.00
Pressed Glass, Wine, Loop & Dart, Clear	12.25
Pressed Glass, Wine, Loop & Moose Eye	22.50
Pressed Glass, Wine, Milton	12.50
Pressed Glass, Wine, Mirror, Flint	22.00
Pressed Glass, Wine, Moon & Star	11.25
Pressed Glass, Wine, Nailhead	12.50
Pressed Glass, Wine, Paneled Dewdrop	8.00 To 10.00
Pressed Glass, Wine, Paneled Thistle With Bee	12.50
Pressed Glass, Wine, Paneled Zipper	5.00
Pressed Glass, Wine, Parrot & Fan	35.00
Pressed Glass, Wine, Pennsylvania	9.50
Pressed Glass, Wine, Pineapple & Fan	6.50
Pressed Glass, Wine, Red Block, Ruby	22.00
Pressed Glass, Wine, Ribbed Palm	32.50
Pressed Glass, Wine, Rose Sprig	18.50
Pressed Glass, Wine, Sawtooth	5.00
Pressed Glass, Wine, Sequoia	12.50

Pressed Glass, Wine, Shrine, 1908	49.50
Pressed Glass, Wine, Star Whorl	6.00
Pressed Glass, Wine, Stars & Stripes	6.00
Pressed Glass, Wine, Stippled Fleur-De-Lis, Amber	15.00
Pressed Glass, Wine, Tulip And Sawtooth	19.50
Pressed Glass, Wine, Two Panel, Amber	20.00
Pressed Glass, Wine, U.S.Coin, Frosted, Stemmed, 4 1/4 In.High	265.00
Pressed Glass, Wine, Waffle	25.00
Pressed Glass, Wine, Waffle, Flint	42.00
Pressed Glass, Wine, 1, 000-Eye	8.75
Print, A Dangerous Cripple, Charles Russel, Brown & Bigelow, 1914, Color	2.00
Print, A Home In The Country, Summer, Spence, N.Y., C.1850, Color	54.50
Print, A Little Bit Of Heaven, Bessie Pease Gutmann, Gilt Frame	27.50
Print, A Little Dream, Dated 1932	4.50
Print, Actor In Soga Play, Kunimasa Ga, 1800, Oban	2750.00
Print, Aiken, Doing It Somehow, 1881, 9 3/4 X 6 1/4 In.	25.00
Print, Aiken, Down Leap Done, 1818, 8 3/4 X 6 1/2 In.	25.00
Print, Aiken, Westminster Pit, Dog & Monkey Fight, 1823, 7 1/4 X 4 1/2 In.	30.00
Print, Alphonse Mucha, Cafe Martin Menu, 1903, Lithograph, Color	110.00 To 150.00
Print, Alphonse Mucha, L'Automne, Lithograph, Color	650.00
Print, Alphonse Mucha, La Trappistine, 1898, Lithograph, Color	400.00
Print, Alphonse Mucha, Lance Parfum 'Rodo, ' Lithograph, _Color_	175.00
Print, Alphonse Mucha, Oesterreich Auf Der Weltausstellung, 1900	425.00
Print, Alphonse Mucha, Salambo, 1896, Lithograph, Color	110.00
Print, Alphonse Mucha, Salome, 1897, Lithograph, Color, 13 X 9 In.	40.00
Print, Alphonse Mucha, Springtime, 1900, Lithograph, Color	550.00
Print, Alphonse Mucha, Verola, Paul, Rama, A Dramatic Poem, 1898	110.00
Print, Alphonse Mucha, Zdenka Cerny, Bohemian Violoncellist, 1913	150.00
Print, America, C.& T.Stampa & Co., England, 1804, Color _Illus_	170.00
Print, Andersonville Prison, Sinclair, Philadelphia, 1864, Black & White	24.50
Print, Asao Tamejuro In Edo, Shunko Ga, 1789, Hosoban	350.00
Print, Audubon, American Bison, 1845, Lithograph, Hand-Colored	375.00
Print, Audubon, American Sparrow Hawk, 1834, Engraving & Aquatint, Colored	650.00
Print, Audubon, Barred Owl, 1830, Engraving & Aquatint, Hand-Colored	950.00
Print, Audubon, Belted Kingfisher, 1836, Engraving & Aquatint, Hand-Colored	850.00
Print, Audubon, Blue Jay, 1830, Engraving & Aquatint, Hand-Colored	1100.00
Print, Audubon, Broad-Winged Hawk, 1830, Engraving & Aquatint, Hand-Colored	550.00
Print, Audubon, Great American Cock, Wild Turkey, 1828 _Illus_	9000.00
Print, Audubon, Grizzly Bear, 1848, Lithograph, Hand-Colored	250.00
Print, Audubon, Marsh Hawk, 1873, Engraving & Aquatint, Hand-Colored	625.00
Print, Audubon, Meadow Lark, 1832, Engraving & Aquatint, Hand-Colored	850.00
Print, Audubon, Ocelot, 1846, J.T.Bowen, Philadelphia _Illus_	475.00
Print, Audubon, Red-Breasted Nuthatch, 1836, Etching & Aquatint, Colored	275.00
Print, Audubon, Red-Shouldered Hawk, 1828, Engraving & Aquatint, Colored	825.00
Print, Audubon, Rocky Mountain Goat, 1847, Lithograph, Hand-Colored	300.00
Print, Audubon, The Cougar, 1851, Lithograph, Bowen Edition	20.00
Print, Audubon, Tyrant Flycatcher, 1830, Engraving & Aquatint, Hand-Colored	275.00
Print, Audubon, White-Headed Eagle, 1836, Havell, London _Illus_	2100.00
Print, Awakening, Bessie Pease Gutmann, Gilt Frame	27.50
Print, Babes In The Woods, Jessie Wilcox Smith, Walnut Frame, 10 X 13 In.	14.50
Print, Bagged In France, Hercules Powder Co., 1918, Lithograph, Color	19.50
Print, Battle In Missouri, Boston Chemical Printing Co., Linen, Woodcut	47.50
Print, Battle Of Chapultepec, S.Walker, C.1845, 6 7/8 X 4 3/4 In.	25.00
Print, Battle Of Palo Alto, S.Walker, C.1845, 6 7/8 X 4 3/4 In.	25.00
Print, Boston, Robert Havell, 1841, English	1200.00
Print, Camp Rightwood-Col.H.S.Briggs, J.Dunavan, 1861, Black & White	17.50
Print, Cavalrymen, Horses, Schrievogel, 1899, Lithograph, Uncolored, Frame	32.00
Print, Child Looking At Broken Wheelbarrow, Maude Humphrey, 11 X 8 In.	38.00
Print, Coheleach, Cardinals, Signed	100.00
Print, Coheleach, Kirtland's Warbler	25.00
Print, Colossi Of Memnon, 1849, Lithograph, Hand-Colored	40.00
Print, Courtesan Kasugano Of Taka-Ya, Utamaro Hitsu, 1799, Oban	2300.00
Print, Courtesan, Lover In Bed, Utamaro Ga, 1788, Aiban	650.00
Print, Cupid Asleep & Cupid Awake, M.B.Parkinson, 1897, Double Oval Frame	4.00
Print, Currier & Ives, see Currier & Ives	
Print, Currier, see Currier	

Print, **Dolce Far Niente**, B.Vautier, Arnz & Co., Dusseldork, Lithograph 65.00
Print, **Eight Views Of Kanazawa**, Musahi Province By Night, Tsutaya, 1857 .... 8000.00
Print, **English Hunting Scene**, John Leech, C.1850, Matte, 6 X 4 In. 3.75
Print, **Erotic**, Man & 2 Females Lifting Skirts, Risso & Brown, 1810, British 64.50
Print, **Etai Bridge**, Hiroshige Ga, 1857, Oban 175.00
Print, **Ferry At Yoroi In Snowstorm**, Hiroshige Ga, 1863, Oban 120.00
Print, **Fishing**, E.P.L.Restein, Copyright 1878, Phila., Carved Frame 19.00
Print, **Flowers**, Birds, Japan, 13 X 8 3/4 In. 1.00
Print, **Fruit Cluster**, T.L.Prevost, Pair 20.00
Print, **Fuji Across Asakusa**, Hiroshige Ga, 1857, Oban 1000.00
Print, **George Washington**, Amos Doolittle, 1794 .... *Illus* 3300.00

Print, America, C.& T.Stampa & Co., England, 1804, Color
See Page 449

Print, Audubon, Ocelot, 1846, J.T.Bowen, Philadelphia
See Page 449

Print, Audubon, White-Headed Eagle, 1836, Havell, London
See Page 449

Print, Audubon,
Great American Cock,
Wild Turkey, 1828
See Page 449

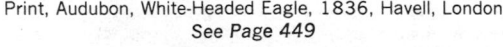

Print, **Girl Touching Blossoms**, Paul Berthon, Lithograph, Color, Signed .... *Color* 80.00
Print, **Go Tiheki Shiraishi Banashi**, Kiyonaga Ga, Kiyonaga Ga, 1785, Chuban 475.00
Print, **Godey**, Ladies & Child Whipping Cat, Tinted, April 1870, Frame 18.00
Print, **Going For The Bird**, E.P.L.Restein, Copyright 1878, Carved Frame 19.00
Print, **Great Conflagration In San Francisco**, Justh & Quirot, 1851 .... 425.00

Print, George Washington, Amos Doolittle, 1794
See Page 450

Print, **Handsome Dan**, Yale's Bulldog, Signed A.B.Graves 13.00
Print, **Heisha Restringing Samisen**, Kiyomine Ga, 1807, Oban 950.00
Print, **Heron Maiden**, Ippitsusai Buncho Ga, 1770, Hosoban 2200.00
Print, **Hunter**, Dog, Farmer, Artist A.B.Frost, 1903, 19 X 24 In. 12.50
Print, **Ichikawa Omezo & Matsuo**, Kunimasa Ga, 1800, Oban 1900.00
Print, **Jeff's Last Shift**, Georgia, Bufford, Boston, 1865, Black & White 27.50
Print, **Kellogg**, Child Saved By St. Bernard Dog, Frame 24.00
Print, **Kellogg**, Great Naval Expedition, 1861, 9 1/2 X 13 In. 125.00
Print, **Kellogg**, Jefferson Davis In Military Uniform, Lithograph, Color 22.50
Print, **Kellogg**, Lincoln At Home, Oak Frame, 16 1/2 X 12 1/2 In. 35.00
Print, **Kellogg**, Little Mother, Walnut Frame, 12 X 14 In. 24.50
Print, **Kellogg**, Little William, Frame 24.00
Print, **Kellogg**, Married, 1846 .... 18.00
Print, **Kellogg**, The Dancing Lesson, Color 20.00
Print, **Kellogg**, The Morning Prayer, Pine Frame, 10 X 14 In. 18.00
Print, **Kellogg**, The Old Husband, The Young Wife, The Gay Lieutenant 45.00
Print, **Kellogg**, To My Fair Friend, Bouquet Of Flowers 19.00
Print, **Kibayashi Asahina & Oiso No Tora**, Ekigi Ga, 1806, Surimono 100.00
Print, **Kikunojo I As Oiso No Tora**, Signed Torii Kiyonobu Hitsu, 1737, Color 900.00
Print, **Kingfishers**, Morning Glories, Water Lilies, Zen Hokusai I-Itsu, 1848 .... 170.00
Print, **Konya-Cho In Kanda**, Hiroshige Ga, 1857, Oban 475.00
Print, **Kurz & Allison**, Battle Of Chattanooga, Dated 1888, Color 22.50
Print, **Kurz & Allison**, Battle Of Fort Donelson, Dated 1887, Color 24.50
Print, **Kurz & Allison**, Battle Of Kennesaw Mountain, Dated 1891 .... 24.50
Print, **Kurz & Allison**, Battle Of Opequan, Va., Dated 1893, Color 22.50
Print, **Kurz & Allison**, Battle Of Tippecanoe, 1889, 18 X 25 In. 100.00
Print, **Kurz & Allison**, Chicago In Early Days, 1893 .... 150.00
Print, **Le Livre De Magda**, Paul Berthon, Lithograph, Color, 22 1/4 X 15 In. 80.00
Print, **Les Boules De Neige**, Paul Berthon, Lithograph, Color, Signed 100.00
Print, **Lincoln During Civil War**, T.Nast 7.50
Print, **Look At Mama**, J.Bailie, Lithograph, Hand-Colored, Frame, 20 X 16 In. 18.50
Print, **Map**, America, Jan Jansson, 1644 .... 350.00
Print, **Map**, Asia Minor, Claudius Ptolemy, 1513, 15 X 21 .... 200.00
Print, **Map**, Connecticut, F.Lucas, C.1822 .... 41.00
Print, **Map**, East & West Florida, T.Jefferys, 1775, 19 X 48 1/2 In. 285.00
Print, **Map**, Massachusetts, F.Lucas, C.1822 .... 41.00
Print, **Map**, New York & Environs, 1867, H.Peters, Engraved By R.Kupfer, Frame 35.00
Print, **Map**, New York, 1859, Grover & Bakers Sewing Machine, Roller 25.00
Print, **Map**, Rhode Island, F.Lucas, C.1822 .... 41.00
Print, **Map**, Seat Of The War, W.Schaus, N.Y.C., 1861, 30 X 36 In. 150.00
Print, **Map**, State Of Vermont, H.F.Walling, Albert D.Hager, C.1859 .... 250.00
Print, **Map**, The Great Lakes, J.N.Belling, Paris, 1757, 7 1/2 X 11 1/2 In. 75.00
Print, **Map**, The Southern Dominions Of The United States, London, 1794 .... 225.00
Print, **Map**, Vermont, F.Lucas, C.1822 .... 41.00
Print, **Map**, Virginia, Captain John Smith, 1628 .... 750.00
Print, **Market Plate At Cambridge**, Rowlandson, 1801, 9 3/4 X 6 In. 45.00

Print, **Matsumoto Koshiro As Amakawaya Gihei,** Shunsho Ga, 1780, Hosoban 200.00
Print, **Maxfield Parrish,** A Perfect Day, Frame, 11 1/2 X 8 1/2 In. 17.50
Print, **Maxfield Parrish,** Aladdin, Frame 21.00
Print, **Maxfield Parrish,** Centaurs, Frame 21.00
Print, **Maxfield Parrish,** Contentment, 7 X 10 In. 10.00
Print, **Maxfield Parrish,** Daybreak, Frame, 6 1/2 X 4 1/2 In. 18.00
Print, **Maxfield Parrish,** Daybreak, Frame, 12 X 19 In. 25.00
Print, **Maxfield Parrish,** Daybreak, Frame, 17 1/2 X 10 In. 25.00
Print, **Maxfield Parrish,** Daybreak, Gold Embossed Frame, 18 X 10 1/2 In. 32.50
Print, **Maxfield Parrish,** Dicky Bird, Frame .... 32.50 To 38.00
Print, **Maxfield Parrish,** Edison Mazda, Frame 22.00
Print, **Maxfield Parrish,** Girl In Canyon, Frame 27.50
Print, **Maxfield Parrish,** Land Of Make Believe, 8 X 11 In. 10.00
Print, **Maxfield Parrish,** Landscape, Sepia, Signed In Pencil 25.00
Print, **Maxfield Parrish,** Lights Of Home, Frame, 13 X 16 In. 20.00
Print, **Maxfield Parrish,** Pandora, 1908, 9 1/4 X 11 1/2 In. 10.00
Print, **Maxfield Parrish,** Reveries, 7 X 11 In. 10.00
Print, **Maxfield Parrish,** Stars, Nude Woman Looking Up At Sky, Frame 29.00
Print, **Maxfield Parrish,** The Lute Players, Frame, 16 X 13 In. 14.00
Print, **Maxfield Parrish,** Waterfall, 6 X 8 In. 8.00
Print, **Maxfield Parrish,** Ye Royall Recepcioun, 8 X 11 In. 6.00
Print, **May Day In The City,** A.Fredericks, Woodcut, Harper's, 1859 .... 20.00
Print, **Meadow Grass,** Alice Brown, Lithograph, Metal Frame 35.00
Print, **Merchant Kamiya Jihei & Geisha,** Utamaro Hitsu, 1898, Oban 3400.00
Print, **Miss Muffet's Birthday Party,** Maude Humphrey, C.1908 .... 25.00
Print, **Mountains & Streams On Kiso Highway,** Tsutaya, 1857, Oban 7000.00
Print, **Nakumura Noshio I As Courtesan,** Shuncho Zu, C.1770, Hosoban 1700.00
Print, **Nakamura Noshio I As Oiso No Tora,** Shunsho Ga, 1775, Hosoban 275.00
Print, **Napoleon In Coronation Robes,** G.Cruikshank, 1826, Engraved, Color 45.00
Print, **Normandie,** A.M.Cassandre, 1935, Lithograph, Color 150.00
Print, **Panorama Of Chicago,** G.W.Melville, 1897, 12 1/2 X 15 1/2 In. 325.00
Print, **Parade Of Grand Army Of Republic,** Keystone Co., Phila., 1892, Color 19.50
Print, **Paris,** A.M.Cassandre, Lithograph, Color, 38 X 23 1/2 In. 400.00
Print, **Prang,** Kenesaw, Civil War Battle, 21 1/2 X 15 In. 50.00
Print, **Prang,** Spottsylvania, Civil War Battle, 21 1/2 X 15 In. 50.00
Print, **Presidents Of The United States,** Baillie, N.Y., 1844, Hand-Colored 24.50
Print, **Queen Victoria's Yacht,** George Baxter, 1853, Frame 58.00
Print, **Remington,** Caught In A Circle, Copyright 1908, Oak Frame, 23 X 18 In. 22.00
Print, **Remington,** Done In The Open, C.1902, Large Folio 69.00
Print, **Remington,** Done In The Open, 1903, 16 X 11 In. 5.00
Print, **Remington,** Evening On A Canadian Lake, Unframed Mat 19.50
Print, **Remington,** Indians In Canoe, 1907, 9 X 13 In. 5.00
Print, **Remington,** Portfolio Entitled Eight New Paints, P.F.Collier 200.00
Print, **Remington,** The Advance, 1903, 16 X 11 In. 5.00
Print, **Remington,** The Moose, Dated 1908, Mahogany Frame, 10 1/2 X 15 In. 65.00
Print, **Remington,** The Parley, 1903, 16 X 11 In. 5.00
Print, **Remington,** The Round Up, 1903, 16 X 11 In. 5.00
Print, **Rockwell,** Doctor Takes Boy's Temperature, Advertisement 25.00
Print, **Roland Clark,** Open Water, F.Lowe Derry Dale, 1943 .... 300.00
Print, **Ruins Of Marco Agrippa,** G.B.Piranesi, Etching, Frame 199.00
Print, **Sagebrush Sport,** Charles Russel, Brown & Bigelow, 1914, Color 2.00
Print, **San Francisco Mountain,** Sarony & Co., N.Y., 1853, Lithograph, Frame 70.00
Print, **Sarony & Major,** Napoleon Sanguinary Battle, 9 3/4 X 6 In. 20.00
Print, **Sawamura Harugoro,** Signed Torii Kiyonobu Hitsu, 1746, Hand-Colored 900.00
Print, **Segawa Kikuouo I,** Signed Eshi Torii Kiyomasu Hitsu, 1737, Colored 1800.00
Print, **Single Handed,** Charles Russel, Brown & Bigelow, 1914, Color 2.00
Print, **Snow On Imado Bridge Near Matsuchiyama,** Hiroshige Ga, 1862, Oban 200.00
Print, **Springtime Of Life,** Copyright 1908, Cambell Art Co., Frame 7.00
Print, **Sumida River Beyond Ommaya Embankment,** Hiroshige Ga, 1857, Oban 375.00
Print, **Sumida River,** Hiroshige Ga, 1856, Oban 200.00
Print, **Surrender Of Cornwallis,** Baillie 35.00
Print, **Sympathy,** J.Knowles Hare, Etching 25.00
Print, **Taken From Flora's Feast,** Walter Crane, Published 1889, Frame 15.00
Print, **Taylor & His Battles,** Ensigns & Thayer, N.Y., Dated 1847, Color 39.50
Print, **The Alamo,** F.O.Putnam, 1925 .... 4.50
Print, **The American Gentleman,** Carpenter, Frame 12.50

Print, The Baths Of Trajan, Piranesi, Paris Edition Of 1836	200.00
Print, The Fallowfield Hunt, Cecil Aldin, 10 1/2 X 6 1/2 In., Set Of 5	40.00
Print, The Medicine Man, Carpenter, Frame	12.50
Print, The New School, T.G.Dutton, 1855, Lithograph, Color	160.00
Print, The President Of The U.S., Sowle & Shaw, N.Y., 1845, Lithograph, Color	32.50
Print, The War In The West, Thomas Nast, Woodcut, Harper's, 1863	50.00
Print, The Yellow Book, Aubrey Beardsley, Oct., 1894, Lithograph	60.00
Print, Three Bulls In Field, Rosa Bonheur, Dated, 1885, Oak Frame	35.00
Print, U.S.Steam Frigate Roanoke, T.Bonar, N.Y., Lithograph, Built 1852	24.50
Print, Uchi River, Suijin Woods, & Sekiya, Hiroshige Ga, 1857, Oban	275.00
Print, Wallace Nutting, A Bit Of Sewing, Frame	28.00
Print, Wallace Nutting, A Canopied Road, Signed, Frame	13.00
Print, Wallace Nutting, A Guardian Of The Road, Frame, 13 X 11 In.	15.00
Print, Wallace Nutting, An Alstead Drive, Matte, Frame, 14 X 18 In.	12.00
Print, Wallace Nutting, Blossom Bend, Frame, Glass	17.00
Print, Wallace Nutting, Bridesmaid Procession, 13 1/2 X 21 1/2 In.	13.00
Print, Wallace Nutting, Coming Out Of Rosa, Frame	6.00
Print, Wallace Nutting, Concord Banks, Frame, 14 X 16 In.	16.00
Print, Wallace Nutting, Elm Birch Arch, Gold Leaf Embossed Frame	18.50
Print, Wallace Nutting, Enticing Water, 17 X 14 In.	12.00
Print, Wallace Nutting, Grafton Windings, Apple Orchard, Mahogany Frame	14.00
Print, Wallace Nutting, Hollyhock Cottage, Frame, 21 3/4 In.	21.00
Print, Wallace Nutting, Interior, Colonial Ladies	20.00
Print, Wallace Nutting, Into The Woodland, Signed, Frame	13.00
Print, Wallace Nutting, Many Happy Returns, Signed, Frame, 13 In.	12.00
Print, Wallace Nutting, Nethercote, Cottage Midst Flower Garden	7.50
Print, Wallace Nutting, Newmarket Belle, Frame, 16 X 23 In.	25.00
Print, Wallace Nutting, Orchard Scene, 8 1/2 X 12 1/2 In.	7.50
Print, Wallace Nutting, Over The Crest, Frame, 15 X 10 In.	12.00
Print, Wallace Nutting, Scotland, Frame, 16 X 12 In.	15.00
Print, Wallace Nutting, The Call Of The Road, Frame, Glass	15.00
Print, Wallace Nutting, The Lincoln Drive, Signed, Color, 7 1/2 X 9 1/2 In.	10.00
Print, Wallace Nutting, The Peigola Amalfi, Copyright 1904, Mat, Frame	16.00
Print, Wedding Scene, Harrison Fisher, Gilt Carved Frame	20.00
Print, Welcome Home Boys, Edward V.Brewer, Dated 1919, Frame	18.50
Print, Whirlpool At Naruta In Awa Province, Hiroshige Hitsu, 1855, Oban	2200.00
Print, Winslow Homer, Merry Christmas & Happy New Year, 1859, Woodcut	70.00
Print, Winslow Homer, Pay Day In The Army, 1863, Woodcut, Harper's	75.00
Print, Winslow Homer, Winter Quarters In Camp, 1863, Woodcut, Harper's	50.00
Print, Winter In The Country, Haskell & Allen, 1877, 9 X 12 1/2 In.	150.00
Print, Woman In Summer Robe, Utamaro Hitsu, C.1881, Oban	5200.00
Print, Yoko-E Album Sheet, Keisai, 1796	150.00
Purple Slag, see Slag	
Quartz, Figurine, Chinese Goddess, Pink, 7 In.High	250.00
Quartz, Figurine, Lovebirds, Smoky, Gray Blue, 4 1/2 In.Long, Pair	160.00
Quartz, Figurine, Squirrel, Green, 3 In.High	117.50
Quartz, Figurine, Woman, Rose, Standing, High Topknot, Holding Lantern, Cat	575.00
Quartz, Vase, Amethystine, Silver Gilt, Louis XVI Style, Carved, C.1900	270.00

Quezal Glass was made from 1901 to 1920 by Martin Bach, Sr. He made **Queza**
iridescent glass of the same type as Tiffany.

Quezal, Bowl, Blue, Bronze, Red, Purple, Crimped Edge, Ribbed Sides, 6 In.	175.00
Quezal, Bowl, Gold & Cerise, Stretch Border, Multicolor Bands, 6 1/2 In.	225.00
Quezal, Bowl, Gold, Rainbow Iridescent, 12 In.	295.00
Quezal, Bowl, Nut, Ribbed Sides, Turned Edge Top, Gold Iridescent, Set Of 4	325.00
Quezal, Candlestick, Green, Not Signed, 9 1/2 In., Pair	85.00
Quezal, Lamp Shade, Corset Shape, Wide Ribs, Morning Glory, 4 1/4 In.	78.00
Quezal, Lamp Shade, Desk, Ribbed, Gold, Iridescent, Flares, Signed	165.00
Quezal, Lamp, Calcite & Green Feather, Gold Lining, Bronze Base, 13 In.	175.00
Quezal, Lamp, Desk, Bell Shape Shade, Gold, Harp Footed Base, Onyx Motif	95.00
Quezal, Lamp, Three Lilies, Signed	495.00
Quezal, Rose Bowl, Panels, Embossed Circles, Yellow Opalescent, Green Cast	69.50
Quezal, Rose Bowl, Red Highlights, Footed	225.00
Quezal, Salt Dip, Ribbed, Gold Iridescent, Stand Up Collar, Signed	80.00
Quezal, Salt, Iridescent, Open, Signed	65.00
Quezal, Salt, Master, Gold & Purple Iridescent, Signed	155.00

Quezal, Salt, Ribbed Body, Signed	75.00
Quezal, Shade, Bell Shape, Gold Iridescent, Gold Feathers, Green Outline	49.00
Quezal, Shade, Electric, Gold, Signed, Set Of 3	75.00
Quezal, Shade, Feather Design, White On Gold, Blue Iridescent	60.00
Quezal, Shade, Feather Design, White On Gold, Yellow Iridescent, Signed	39.00
Quezal, Shade, Gas, Signed, Green Feather Design Outside, Gold Inside, Pair	90.00
Quezal, Shade, Gold Iridescent, King Tut Design, 5 3/4 In.	65.00
Quezal, Shade, Gold, Ribbed, Signed, 5 1/2 In.Long	30.00
Quezal, Shade, Green & Gold Iridescence, Autumn Leaves, Threading	35.00
Quezal, Shade, Lamp, Corset Shape, Scalloped, Ribs, Iridescent, Blue Top Edge	68.00
Quezal, Shade, Lily Light, Green Gold, Green Feathers, Signed, Set Of 3	425.00
Quezal, Shade, Lily, Gold Iridescent, Signed	135.00
Quezal, Shade, Lily, Green Feather, Gold Iridescent Inside, Signed, 5 In.	165.00
Quezal, Shade, Lily, Green Gold Ground, Green Feathers, Signed, Set Of 3	400.00
Quezal, Shade, Opalescent Luster, Orange Lined, Leaves, Vines, 5 In., Pair	59.00
Quezal, Shade, Pale Green Feathers Outlined In Gold On White	37.50
Quezal, Shade, Ribbed Bell, Gold & Calcite, Signed	30.00
Quezal, Shade, Ribs, Blue Scallops, Corseted Below Top, 4 1/4 In.High	75.00
Quezal, Shade, Signed, Rose, Green, Blue, Gold	35.00
Quezal, Shade, Zipper Pattern	67.00
Quezal, Vase, Burnished Coin Gold, Yellow Feathers, Signed	750.00
Quezal, Vase, Fluted Edge, Green, White, Gold, 8 In.Tall	375.00
Quezal, Vase, Gold Aurene Liner, Green Feather On White, Signed	875.00
Quezal, Vase, Gold Aurene Liner, Signed, 8 3/4 In.	875.00
Quezal, Vase, Gold Iridescent, Signed, 3 In.High	200.00
Quezal, Vase, Gold Iridescent, 1 1/2 In.High	139.50
Quezal, Vase, Green, Crest Waves, Platinum Feathers, Gold Outline, 4 In.High	625.00
Quezal, Vase, Pulled Feather, Stretched Interior, Signed	360.00
Quezal, Vase, Rainbow Color, Stretched Edges, Fluted	295.00
Quezal, Vase, Sterling Overlay, Gold, Iridescent, Red Highlights, 5 1/2 In.	395.00
Quezal, Vase, Trumpet, Gold, Signed, 8 1/2 In.High	175.00
Quilt, see Textile, Quilt	

*Quimper Pottery was made in Finistere, France, after 1900. Most of the
pieces found today were made during the twentieth century. A Quimper
factory has worked in France since the eighteenth century.*

Quimper, Basket, Handled, 3 X 4 In.	17.50
Quimper, Bowl, Salad, Lady, Flowers, Vine, Scallop Edge, Green, Blue, Red, Signed	15.00
Quimper, Box, Candy, Covered, Dutch Man On Blue	55.00
Quimper, Box, Covered, Two Incised Deer, Signed	75.00
Quimper, Butter Tub, Covered, Blue Floral	10.00
Quimper, Butter Tub, Woman, Floral	18.00
Quimper, Butter, Covered, Round, Henriot	30.00
Quimper, Candlestick, Boy & Girl With Pots On Heads, Signed, Pair	34.00
Quimper, Coffeepot, Signed, 9 1/2 In.High	65.00
Quimper, Creamer, Man, Flowers, Signed	10.00
Quimper, Creamer, White Ground, Man Figure	12.00
Quimper, Cup & Saucer, Portrait Of Man In Cup, Floral, Hexagon	14.50
Quimper, Cup & Saucer, Yellow, Green, Red, People, Flowers	19.50
Quimper, Dish, Dresser, Heart Shape, Peasants	10.00
Quimper, Dish, Heart Shape, Signed	6.00
Quimper, Inkwell, Man On Front, Marked Henriot, France, 3 3/4 In.Long	28.00
Quimper, Jug, Water, Signed	22.50
Quimper, Knife Rest, Floral	16.00
Quimper, Knife Rest, Woman, Flowers, Signed Henriot, Set Of 4	20.00
Quimper, Pitcher, Yellow, Man, 8 1/2 In.	27.50
Quimper, Plate, Breton Man, Yellow Border, Marked Henriot Quimper	11.00
Quimper, Plate, Center Portrait, Girl, Border, Octagon	12.50
Quimper, Plate, Peasant Boy & Fishing Pole, Blue, Orange & Green On White	8.00
Quimper, Plate, Peasant Smokes Pipe, Irregular Shape Rim, Signed, 9 1/2 In.	20.00
Quimper, Plate, Peasant, 11 In.Diameter	10.00
Quimper, Porringer, Man In Green, Yellow, Blue, White Ground, Double Handle	12.00
Quimper, Porringer, Peasant, Signed Henriot, Dated '86, Pierced For Hanging	15.00
Quimper, Porringer, Yellow, Peasant Decoration	10.00
Quimper, Porringer, 2 Handled	10.00
Quimper, Pot, Watering, Signed, 6 In.High	42.00

Quimper, **Salt**, Footed 6.00
Quimper, **Salt**, Open, Two Swans Join Salts 16.50
Quimper, **Sugar & Creamer**, Peasant Figures On Yellow, Covered Sugar 15.00
Quimper, **Sugar**, Yellow Ground, Girl, Boy, Floral 28.00
Quimper, **Syrup**, Covered, Man, Woman, Pair 25.00
Quimper, **Teapot**, Celadon Green Dragon Handle & Spout, Fleur-De-Lis Finial 125.00
Quimper, **Tray**, Yellow, Peasant Decoration, 5 3/4 X 9 In. 12.50
Quimper, **Vase**, Embossed Brittany, Maidens In Native Dress, Artist-Signed 55.00
Radio, A.C.Dayton, Battery, Wooden Case, Serial No.H.P.1097 .... 37.00
Radio, Charley McCarthy, Figures Of Charley 195.00
Radio, Craft, Shortwave, 1930 .... 3.00
Radio, Crosely, Gembox, Battery, Dynocone Speaker 60.00
Radio, Emerson, Metal Figure Of Mickey Mouse On Speaker, 1935 .... 65.00
Radio, Freed-Eisemann, Battery, Model NR5 .... 50.00
Radio, Radiola, Super Hetrodyne, Battery, Horn Speaker, Loop Antenna 100.00
Radio, Silvertone, Neutrodyne, Battery 37.50
Radio, Table, Spartan, Michigan, Mirrored Glass, Chrome, & Bakelite, C.1930 .... 200.00
Railroad, Badge, Conductor's Cap, Boston & Maine, Brass 10.00
Railroad, Badge, Conductor's, Santa Fe, Brass 5.00
Railroad, Boiler Plate, Locomotive, B6SB, Brass 75.00
Railroad, Book, Employee's Book Of Ready Reference, 1904 .... 5.00
Railroad, Bowl, New Haven, Silver 9.50
Railroad, Bowl, Salad, Milwaukee, Traveler, Pink, Porcelain 28.00
Railroad, Box, Conductor's, Tole, Black, Gold Red Trim, Lettering 20.00
Railroad, Box, Timetable, Southern Pacific, Tin 8.00
Railroad, Cards, Playing, Chesapeake & Ohio, Dated 1897 .... 14.00
Railroad, Cards, Playing, Illinois Central 5.00
Railroad, Cards, Playing, Pennsylvania, Pinochle, Gold Keystone 3.50
Railroad, Cards, Playing, Pullman Company, Pinochle, Double P On Backs 3.50
Railroad, Cards, Playing, Santa Fe, Boxed 5.50
Railroad, Cards, Playing, South Pacific 5.00
Railroad, Cards, Playing, Milwaukee, Bridge, Emblem 3.50
Railroad, Coffeepot, Individual, Pennsylvania, Silver, 14 Oz. .... 25.00 To 37.50
Railroad, Creamer, B.& O.R.R., 100 Year Issue 11.00
Railroad, Cup & Saucer, Demitasse, Milwaukee, Traveler, Pink 25.00
Railroad, Cup, Marked LVRR, Tin 10.00
Railroad, Date Nail, Square, Indent, No.1 .... 2.25
Railroad, Date Nail, Square, Indent, No.2 .... 2.25
Railroad, Date Nail, Square, Indent, No.3 .... 2.25
Railroad, Date Nail, Square, Indent, No.4 .... 2.25
Railroad, Date Nail, Square, Raised, No.22 .... .55
Railroad, Date Nail, Square, Raised, No.23 .... .55
Railroad, Date Nail, Square, Raised, No.24 .... .55
Railroad, Date Nail, 1923-1942, Complete Set 10.00
Railroad, Guide, Official, 1886 .... 50.00
Railroad, Key, Coach, Pullman, Brass 7.50
Railroad, Key, Switch, Adlake, Canadian National 4.00
Railroad, Key, Switch, Frisco 6.50
Railroad, Key, Switch, Long Island & Norfolk 6.50
Railroad, Key, Switch, Pennsylvania 6.50
Railroad, Key, Switch, Soo Line 6.50
Railroad, Key, Switch, Southern Pacific 6.50
Railroad, Lamp, Carbide 17.50
Railroad, Lamp, Coach, Kerosene, Hanging, Double Armed, Brass, 1880s 395.00
Railroad, Lamp, Coach, Kerosene, White Enamel Shade, Spring Mount Bracket 30.00
     Railroad, Lantern, see also Lantern, Railroad
Railroad, Lantern, Caboose, Dressel, Kerosene, Marked 45.00
Railroad, Lantern, Caboose, Marked S.RY.Adlake, Pat.1913 .... 16.50
Railroad, Lantern, Dietz, New York Central, Clear Globe 10.00
Railroad, Lantern, Dietz, New York Central, Red Globe 25.00
Railroad, Lantern, Dietz, Vesta, N.Y.Central, N.Y.C.Lines On Globe 14.00
Railroad, Lantern, Globe, Handlan, Red, 4 3/4 In. 5.00
Railroad, Lantern, Globe, Red, A.T.& S.F., Etched, Short 8.00
Railroad, Lantern, Marked C.P.R., Switch, H.L.P.Piper, Nov.12, 1910 .... 37.00
Railroad, Lantern, Pennsylvania R.R., Clear Globe 20.00
Railroad, Lantern, Switch, Dressel, Kerosene, Marked 30.00

Railroad, Lantern, Switchman's, Baltimore & Ohio, Kerosene, Red Globe 17.75
Railroad, Lantern, Vesta, N.Y.O.& W.Marked On Frame, Clear Globe 25.00
Railroad, Lock & Chain, A.T. & S.F. 9.50
Railroad, Lock & Key, Mo.Pac., Brass 16.00
Railroad, Lock & Key, Switch 25.00
Railroad, Lock, Coach, Brass 20.00
Railroad, Lock, O.& LC.R.R., Dated 1853, Brass 8.50
Railroad, Lock, Switch, B.& O. 6.00
Railroad, Lock, Switch, B.& O., Brass 18.00
Railroad, Lock, Switch, D.L.& W., Brass Keyhole Trapdoor, Iron 12.00
Railroad, Lock, Switch, N.& W., Brass 18.00
Railroad, Magazine, The Railroad Telegrapher, 1920 .... 2.50
Railroad, Martini Set, Union Pacific Railroad In Shield, 4 Piece 25.00
Railroad, Medal, Santa Fe Centennial, 100 Year 3.00
Railroad, Menu, Denver Zephyr Chuckwagon 5.00
Railroad, Menu, Dinner, California Zephyr 5.00
Railroad, Oil Can, Cone Top, Bail, N.Y.C.& Hudson River, Tin, 11 In.High 10.00
Railroad, Oiler, Engine, Erie, Long Spout 10.00
Railroad, Plate, Baltimore & Ohio, Dark Blue, White, Wood & Son, Burselm 150.00
Railroad, Plate, Baltimore & Ohio, Train Scene, Dark Blue, 6 1/2 In. 18.00
Railroad, Plate, Bread, Seaboard, Silver, Oval, Scalloped Rim 25.00
Railroad, Plate, Bread, Transcontinental, Pressed Glass 69.00
Railroad, Plate, Dinner, Baltimore & Ohio, Dated 1827-1927 .... 11.00
Railroad, Plate, Dinner, Union Pacific Streamliner, 10 1/2 In. 12.00
Railroad, Platter, C.& N.W.R.R., Wild Rose Pattern, Oval, Porcelain 25.00
Railroad, Platter, Marked, PRR, Oval 10.00
Railroad, Platter, Meat, Oval, Silver, 12 In. 22.50
Railroad, Platter, Roger's Seaweed & Shell Border, Naval Battle, Chesapeake 350.00
Railroad, Pot, Mustard, Covered, Santa Fe, Indian Mimbreno, Porcelain 15.00
Railroad, Punch, Ticket, Brass, Colt Trade Mark, Patent 1870 .... 49.50
Railroad, Punch, Ticket, Iron, Nickel Plated 10.00
Railroad, Rack, Luggage, Marked C.& A.R.R., Cherubs Blowing Horns On Ends 45.00
Railroad, Spittoon, C.P.R.Iron 20.00
Railroad, Spittoon, Metal, Marked Pullman 20.00
Railroad, Syrup & Attached Underplate, Hinged Lid, Silver 37.50
Railroad, Teapot, White Porcelain, Silver Handle & Lid 25.00
Railroad, Ticket, Issued By B&o, N.W.Va.R.R., Dated 1865 .... 10.00
Railroad, Tongs, Sugar, Atlantic Coastline, Silver 6.50
Railroad, Wagon, Railway Express 50.00
Railroad, Watch, Ball Watch Co., Commercial Standard, Silveroid, Size 18 .... 45.00
Railroad, Watch, Ball, Official, 23 Jewel 95.00
Railroad, Watch, Bunn, Masonic Emblem, 21 Jewel, 60 Hour 110.00
Railroad, Watch, Elgin, Silveroid Case, Engraved Engine, 1884 .... 39.50
Railroad, Watch, Illinois, Bunn, 21 Jewel, Double Hour Hand 75.00
Railroad, Whistle, Steam Locomotive 125.00
    Rainbow, see Satin Glass

    *The Red Wing Pottery of Red Wing, Minnesota, was a firm started in
    1878. It was not until the 1920s that art pottery was made. It closed in
    1967. Rumrill pottery was made for George Rumrill by the Red Wing
    Pottery Company and other firms. It was sold in the 1930s.*
Red Wing, Vase, Belle Kogan, 8 1/2 In.High 30.00

    *Redware is a hard red stoneware that originated in the late 1600s and
    continues to be made. The term is also used to describe any common clay
    pottery that is reddish in color.*
Redware, Bottle, Field, Barrel Shape, Rings 45.00
Redware, Bowl, Decorated, 9 In. 30.00
Redware, Bowl, Loaf, Martha Danil, Crimped Edge, 10 1/2 X 8 In. 262.50
Redware, Bowl, Miniature, Flare Sides, Reeded Rim 40.00
Redware, Bowl, Mottled Glaze, Inscribed I.F.1769, 12 1/2 In.Diameter 900.00
Redware, Bowl, Shallow, Cream, Brown, Green, C.1800, 10 1/4 In.Diameter 350.00
Redware, Bowl, Shallow, Glazed, John W.Bell, Waynesboro, Pa. 70.00
Redware, Bowl, Shaving, Yellow Orange Glaze, Michael Mour, 1830 .... 190.00
Redware, Bowl, Slip Decorated, Oval, Crimped Edge, 10 1/2 X 16 In. 210.00
Redware, Bowl, Yellow Slip Decoration, Rectangular, Pa., 11 1/2 X 15 In. 190.00

Redware, **Cup**, Miniature, Splotched, Lipped	35.00
Redware, **Figurine**, Bird On Perch, Glazed, 4 1/2 In.High	110.00
Redware, **Figurine**, Dog On Base, John Bell, Splotched	90.00
Redware, **Figurine**, Dog On Base, Sleeping, Glazed	55.00
Redware, **Figurine**, Hen On Nest, Whistle Splotched Decoration	275.00
Redware, **Inkwell**, Brown, Yellow	80.00
Redware, **Inkwell**, Quill Penholder, Mottled Glaze, Friedrich Diek, 1788	475.00
Redware, **Jar**, Covered, Sgraffito Of Tulips, Hearts, Hex Signs & Date 1822	2500.00
Redware, **Jar**, Pennsylvania, Puzzle, Incised Decoration, J.Warehem, 1825	375.00
Redware, **Jar**, Tooled Open Handles, Incised Decoration, 7 In.High	45.00
Redware, **Jug**, Handled, Glazed Inside, Pennsylvania, 5 In.High	20.00
Redware, **Jug**, Puzzle, Sgraffito Of Tulip & Bird, James Green, Oct.14, 1828	475.00
Redware, **Mold**, Cake, Pennsylvania Dutch, 5 1/2 In., Pair	100.00
Redware, **Mold**, Pudding	15.00
Redware, **Mold**, Pudding, Plum, Handle, Large Size	47.50
Redware, **Mug**, Glazed	75.00
Redware, **Mug**, Shaving, Flat Strap Decorated Handle, Raised Cream Circles	200.00
Redware, **Pitcher**, Dark Spots Outside, Glazed Inside, 4 1/2 In.High	75.00
Redware, **Pitcher**, Glazed, Three Pouring Slots	110.00
Redware, **Pitcher**, Gray Glaze, Blue Sponge	150.00
Redware, **Pitcher**, Miniature, Bulbous	55.00
Redware, **Pitcher**, Splotched Decoration, Tool Work	80.00
Redware, **Pitcher**, Strap Handle, Mottled Decoration, 6 1/4 In.High	60.00
Redware, **Plate**, Pie, Tree, Tulips, Bird, & Fish, Sgraffito, Crimped Edge	400.00
Redware, **Plate**, Pie, 10 In.	7.00
Redware, **Plate**, Slip Decoration Of Yellow Conventional Design, Tooled Edge	130.00
Redware, **Pot**, Bean	6.00 To 12.00
Redware, **Pot**, Bean, Brown Glaze	15.00
Redware, **Salt**, Footed, Glazed	50.00
Redware, **Salt**, Master, Red & Brown, Glaze	38.00
Redware, **Salt**, Splotched Decoration, Glazed	60.00
Redware, **Sugar**, Brown Glaze, Bulbous, Open	60.00
Redware, **Sugar**, Covered, Eight Sided, Fine Glazing	70.00
Redware, **Sugar**, Covered, Open Handles, Raised Flowers & Leaves, Baecher, Va.	350.00
Redware, **Sugar**, Covered, Open Handles, 5 In.Diameter	50.00
Redware, **Sugar**, Covered, Queen Anne, Oval	10.00
Redware, **Sugar**, Covered, Splotched, Ring Handle	50.00
Redware, **Sugar**, Covered, Yellow Glaze, Dark Brown Splotches, Handles	120.00
Redware, **Sugar**, Slip Decoration Of Ovals In Cream & Green, 2 Handles	250.00
Redware, **Teapot**, Enameled Bird & Prunus Blossoms, C.1790, China	60.00
Redware, **Teapot**, Raised Bead Decoration, Small Size	5.00
Redware, **Tile**, Table, Sgraffito, Tulip, Birds, Hearts, Jacob Kretzer, 1812	750.00
Richard, **Vase**, Allover Purple Flowers, Lavender, Blue, & Camphor, Signed	165.00
Richard, **Vase**, Cameo, Cylindrical, Green Leaves On Milky, Singed, 7 In.High	100.00
Richard, **Vase**, Grapevine Design On Orange & Yellow, Signed, 6 In.High	145.00
Richard, **Vase**, Holly, Berries, Blue, Green, Yellow, Signed, 4 In.Tall	105.00
Richard, **Vase**, Scenic, Black & Green, Handled, Signed, France	250.00
Richard, **Vase**, Scenic, Crimped Top, Signed, 8 1/2 In.	200.00
Richard, **Vase**, Tree Landscape On Gold Opaque, Cameo, Signed	150.00

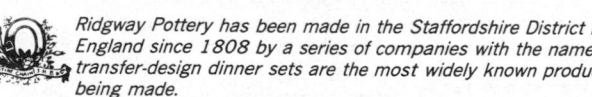

Ridgway Pottery has been made in the Staffordshire District in England since 1808 by a series of companies with the name Ridgway. The transfer-design dinner sets are the most widely known product. They are still being made.

Ridgway, **Bowl**, Coaching Days, Scenes Of Three Inns, 7 In.	30.00
Ridgway, **Bowl**, Covered, Old Derby, Handled, Finial, C.1860	35.00
Ridgway, **Bowl**, Fruit, Light Green, Coaching Days & Ways, Silver Rim	15.00
Ridgway, **Bowl**, Vegetable, Blue Willow, Finial, 10 In.Square	35.00
Ridgway, **Butter Pat**, Gaudy Willow	9.50
Ridgway, **Creamer**, Fresh Team, Changing Horses, Caramel & Silver	16.00 To 28.00
Ridgway, **Creamer**, Heads Of Two Girls	17.50
Ridgway, **Creamer**, Lonsdale, Flow Blue	18.00
Ridgway, **Cup & Saucer**, Blue Willow	8.50
Ridgway, **Cup & Saucer**, Coaching Days & Ways, Caramel, Silver Luster Trim	28.00
Ridgway, **Cup & Saucer**, Pink, Oriental	25.00
Ridgway, **Cup & Saucer**, Seaweed, Black & Gray Transfer, Handleless, 1848	25.00

Ridgway, **Cup**, Blue Willow 3.00
Ridgway, **Dish**, Coaching Days, Paying Toll, Leaf Shape 29.00
Ridgway, **Jug**, Tavern Scene, Rider In Forest, Salt Glaze, 1835 .... 75.00
Ridgway, **Mug**, Coaching Days 18.50
Ridgway, **Mug**, Coaching Days & Ways, Changing Horses, Silver Rim .... 19.00 To 27.50
Ridgway, **Pitcher**, Apostle, Brown, 9 In.High 60.00
Ridgway, **Pitcher**, Coaching Days, Caramel, Silver Luster Trim, Bulbous 24.00
Ridgway, **Pitcher**, Hound Handle, Deer, Game Decoration, Light Tan 40.00
Ridgway, **Pitcher**, Knights, Blue Gray, Stoneware, Dated 1840 .... 85.00 To 95.00
Ridgway, **Pitcher**, Tavern Scene, Salt Glaze, October 1, 1835 .... 95.00
Ridgway, **Pitcher**, Water, Scenic Designs, Brown, 10 In.High 60.00
Ridgway, **Pitcher**, White, Bell Shaped Floral, Yellow, Pink, Salt Glaze, 1850 .... 80.00
Ridgway, **Plaque**, Coaching Days & Ways, The Broken Trace, Pierced, 11 In. 75.00
Ridgway, **Plaque**, Portrait, St.James Beauty, Bartolozzi, 1783, 11 X 8 1/2 In. 65.00
Ridgway, **Plate**, Brown, Large White Cat, 7 In. 17.00
Ridgway, **Plate**, Coaching Days & Ways, Brown, Black Figures, Silver Rim 28.00
Ridgway, **Plate**, Euphrates, Dark Blue, C.1830, 9 1/2 In. 15.55
Ridgway, **Plate**, Fairmount Gardens, 9 In. 10.00
Ridgway, **Plate**, Monk's Bridge, Artist-Signed, Pierced To Hang .... 12.00 To 15.00
Ridgway, **Plate**, Oriental, Blue, 10 In. 10.00
Ridgway, **Plate**, Oriental, 8 7/8 In. 6.00
Ridgway, **Plate**, Oriental, 9 In. 17.00
Ridgway, **Plate**, Pomerania, Pink, Staffordshire, C.1835, 8 In. 10.00
Ridgway, **Plate**, Portrait, George & Martha Washington, Flow Blue, 10 In. 67.50
Ridgway, **Plate**, Portrait, Robert Burns, Brown Glaze 20.00
Ridgway, **Plate**, Portrait, Robert Burns, Mocha Color, 9 1/2 In.Diameter 65.00
Ridgway, **Plate**, Seaweed, Black & Gray Transfer, Dated 1848 .... 15.00
Ridgway, **Plate**, Tam O'shanter & Souter Johnny, 9 In. 22.50
Ridgway, **Plate**, Turkey, Scalloped, Embossed Edge, Floral Border, 10 In. 30.00
Ridgway, **Platter**, Arundel, Enameled Floral, 14 In. 9.00
Ridgway, **Platter**, Penna.Hospital, Beauties Of America Series, 18 1/2 In. 395.00
Ridgway, **Relish**, Coaching Days, Paying Toll, Yellow, Silver Luster Rim 20.00
Ridgway, **Soup**, Blue Willow 4.50
Ridgway, **Soup**, Devonshire, Brown & White Transfer, C.1884 .... 2.50
Ridgway, **Sugar & Creamer**, Coaching Days & Ways, Caramel, Silver Luster Trim 39.00
Ridgway, **Teapot**, Bird & Tree, Pewter Top 45.00
Ridgway, **Teapot**, Coaching Days & Ways, Caramel & Silver Luster Trim 49.00
Ridgway, **Tile**, Columbus Cathedral, Havana, Brown Glaze, Silver Luster Trim 14.50
Ridgway, **Tray**, Coaching Ways & Days, Luster Rim, 12 1/2 In.Diameter 52.00
Ridgway, **Tray**, Taking Up The Mails, 12 1/2 In.Diameter 55.00
Ridgway, **Tureen Set**, Historical Blue, Beauties Of America, 6 In., 3 Piece 300.00
Rock Crystal, **Holder**, Place Card, Chrysanthemum On Leaves, Square Base, Pair 17.50
Rock Crystal, **Tankard**, Silver Mounted, Enameled Landscape, Viennese, C.1850 .... 400.00
Rock Crystal, **Tazza**, Silver Mounted, Enameled Masks & Floral, Viennese, 1850 .... 450.00
Rockingham Type, **Flower Frog**, Flower Shape, Glazed 15.00
Rockingham Type, **Pitcher**, Water, Raised Swan On Lily Pads 55.00
Rockingham Type, **Pot**, Bean, Covered, Brown Mottled, Handle, 2 1/2 In. 12.50

Rockingham in the United States is a brown glazed pottery with a
tortoiseshell-like glaze. It was made from 1840 to 1900 by many American
potteries. The mottled brown Rockingham wares were first made in England
at the Rockingham Factory. Other wares were also made by the English
firm.

Rockingham, **Beaker**, Oval, 9 X 7 1/2 X 2 1/4 In. 36.00
Rockingham, **Bottle**, Figural, Boot, Side Laces, Glaze, 7 In.High 42.00
Rockingham, **Bowl**, Landscape, Marked Manufacturers To The King, 1823 .... 25.00
Rockingham, **Compote**, Landscape Center, Leaf Border, Base, C.1820, Pair 125.00
Rockingham, **Creamer**, Cobalt, Pink Flowers, Gold Trim, C.1800 .... 25.00
Rockingham, **Creamer**, Cow, Plinth, Saddle, 5 1/4 In.High 100.00
Rockingham, **Dish**, Pie, Mottled, Brown & Tan, 11 In.Diameter 12.50
Rockingham, **Figurine**, Pig, Brown, 7 In.Long 35.00
Rockingham, **Mug**, Panels 75.00
Rockingham, **Pan**, Milk, Mottled, 12 In.Diameter, 2 3/4 In.Deep 48.50
Rockingham, **Pitcher**, Mottled, Figures, Goat, Acanthus Leaf Handle, 1850 .... 48.00
Rockingham, **Spittoon** 9.00
Rockingham, **Teapot**, Classic Shape, Brown Glaze, 11 In.High 68.00

Rockingham, Tea Set, Gold, Gray, C.1820, 13 Piece 150.00
Rohn, Figurine, Coolie 700.00
Rohn, Figurine, Crow Indian 800.00
Rohn, Figurine, Gypsy 1450.00
Rohn, Figurine, Riverboat Captain 1000.00
Rohn, Figurine, Trail Hand 1200.00

 Rookwood Pottery was made in Cincinnati, Ohio, from 1880 to 1960. All of this art pottery is marked, most with the famous flame mark. The R is reversed and placed back to back with the letter P. Flames surround the letters.

Rookwood, Ashtray, Dark Red, Heart Shape, 5 In. 15.00
Rookwood, Ashtray, Frog, Apple Green, Dated 1934 .... 37.50
Rookwood, Ashtray, Magenta Rook Perched On Edge, 1951 .... 45.00
Rookwood, Bonbon, Orange Red Ground, Floral, Handle, Footed, 1892, Artist C.S. 140.00
Rookwood, Bookend, Baby Sits On Floor, Back To Books, Brown, 1921, Pair 45.00
Rookwood, Bookend, Beige, Brown, Marked, Pair 95.00
Rookwood, Bookend, Blue, Dated 1919, 5 1/2 In.High, Pair 85.00
Rookwood, Bookend, Figural, Elephant, Green, 1923, 5 In.High, Pair 80.00
Rookwood, Bookend, Ivory, Signed McDonald, 1938, Pair 55.00
Rookwood, Bowl & Frog, Matte Finish, 1921 .... 30.00
Rookwood, Bowl, Bird & Bamboo Motif, Yellow, Dated 1885 .... 165.00
Rookwood, Bowl, Bird In Flight Decoration, Scalloped, 1883, Artist N.J.H. 140.00
Rookwood, Bowl, Blue Matte Glaze, No.2027, 1923 .... 25.00
Rookwood, Bowl, Cobalt Drip Exterior, Floral Interior, Signed L.E., 1924 .... 125.00
Rookwood, Bowl, Dark Blue, Grapes, Vines, & Leaves, No.2168, 1924 .... 45.00
Rookwood, Bowl, Fish Around Upper Section, 1921, 7 In. 24.00
Rookwood, Bowl, Floral, Edith R.Felten, 1901, 2 1/2 In.High 75.00
Rookwood, Bowl, Gray To Brown, Red Flowers, Signed Sara Sax, 1922 .... 75.00
Rookwood, Bowl, Green, Six Berry Sections On Bowl, Ribbed, Flower Frog, 1914 .... 35.00
Rookwood, Bowl, Incised Center, Dark Blue To Tan, 1912, Chas.S.Todd 48.00
Rookwood, Bowl, Light Brown Glaze, Daisies, Signed C.S., 1892, Handles, 4 In. 105.00
Rookwood, Bowl, Mottled Blue, 1921, Shallow, Frog, 7 In.Diameter 35.00
Rookwood, Bowl, Peach, Ivory, White Chrysanthemums, Signed A.M.V., 1887 .... 110.00
Rookwood, Bowl, Rook Head Design, X Mark, Albert Pons, 3 X 3 In. 30.00
Rookwood, Candleholder, Blue Green, Fish Scale, Roses, No.2473, 1920, Pair 15.00
Rookwood, Candlestick, Blue, Triangular Shape, Seahorses On Corners, 1927 .... 17.50
Rookwood, Candlestick, Blue, 1920 .... 16.00
Rookwood, Candlestick, Green To Yellow, Art Deco Floral, 1900, 6 3/4 In.High 22.00
Rookwood, Candlestick, Pink Leaves On Base, 1924, Low, Pair .... 17.00 To 18.00
Rookwood, Centerpiece, Ovoid, 2 Female Figures, Aqua, Louise Abel, 1926 .... 125.00
Rookwood, Chamberstick, Flower Form, Lavender Water Lily, 1930 .... 23.00
Rookwood, Chamberstick, Lily Bud Candle Cup, Water Lily Saucer, 1927, 5 In. 30.00
Rookwood, Creamer, Brown Glaze, Orange Flowers In Relief, 1893, S.E.Coyne 95.00
Rookwood, Creamer, Butterfly Handle, Floral By Elizabeth N.Lincoln, 1894 .... 150.00
Rookwood, Cup & Saucer, Child's, Flower Design, Signed, Dated 1888 .... 150.00
Rookwood, Cup, Portrait Of Dutch Gentleman, Matthew A.Daly, 3 Handled 180.00
Rookwood, Ewer, Allover Trees, Signed H.H., 1883, 4 7/8 In.High 175.00
Rookwood, Ewer, Carnation Design, Bulbous, Yellow, Handle, Signed, 11 In. 195.00
Rookwood, Ewer, Christmas Rose Under Glaze, Harriet E.Wilcox, 1894 .... 125.00
Rookwood, Ewer, Dark Brown To Tan, Sally Coyne, 1894 .... 175.00
Rookwood, Ewer, Gold, Green Nasturtiums, Signed C.A.B., 7 Flames, 1893 .... 125.00
Rookwood, Ewer, Handle, Brown Glaze, Artist S.E.C., 1894, 9 1/2 In.High 165.00
Rookwood, Ewer, Squat, Left Handed, Yellow Floral, By L.Fry, 1889 .... 195.00
Rookwood, Ewer, Standard Glaze, Trefoil Top, Leaves, E.R.F., 1898, 5 1/2 In. 175.00
Rookwood, Figurine, Doe, Oblong Base, White, Louise Abel, 1937 .... 35.00
Rookwood, Figurine, Dog, Tan Glaze, 1946, 5 In. 27.00
Rookwood, Figurine, Duck, Blue & Green, Wax Matte Glaze, 1931 .... 37.50
Rookwood, Figurine, Duck, Cream Color, Dated 1933, 3 In.Long, 3/4 In.High 20.00
Rookwood, Figurine, Elephant, Stands On Pedestal, Blue Gray, 1919, 4 3/4 In. 50.00
Rookwood, Figurine, Girl In White, Seated, Signed Louise Abel, Dated 1934 .... 45.00
Rookwood, Figurine, Nude, Blue, Signed L.Able, A In Circle, 1927 .... 38.50
Rookwood, Figurine, St.Francis, Signed Clotilda Zanetta, 1947 .... 37.50
Rookwood, Flask, Pilgrim, Thistle & Bamboo, Albert Valentien, 1885 .... 265.00
Rookwood, Flower Frog, Blue, 2 1/4 In.Across 10.00
Rookwood, Flower Frog, Pan With Turtle, Amelia B.Sprague, 1921, 7 In.High 62.00

Rookwood, Holder, Flower, Green Glaze, Signed, Dated 1922, 7 In.High 55.00
Rookwood, Humidor, Cigarettes Among Leaves & Flowers, Artist P.R., 1901 .... 295.00
Rookwood, Jar, Rose Petal, Covered, Teal Blue Matte Finish, 1909, Signed 45.00
Rookwood, Jardiniere, Green, 47 C.Z.Stamped On Bottom, 8 In.High 35.00
Rookwood, Jug, Brown Glaze, Currants & Leaves, Handle, Signed R.F., 1898 .... 125.00
Rookwood, Jug, Corn, Signed E.C.L., 1901, 6 In.High 200.00
Rookwood, Jug, Covered, Blown-Out Dragonfly, Matte, A.P., 1907 .... 175.00
Rookwood, Jug, Flowers, Leaves, Brown, Green, Orange Glaze, Signed L.N.L., 1896 ...... 145.00
Rookwood, Jug, Gray, Russet, Gold Fleck, Swallow, Foliage, ARV, 1884 .... 235.00
Rookwood, Lamp Base, Egyptian Girl Holds Pot, Green, 1921, 11 In., Pair 100.00
Rookwood, Lamp Base, Orange Nasturtiums, Baluster Shape, Grace Young, 1899 .... 145.00
Rookwood, Lamp, Table, Oil, Yellow Ball Shade, Clear Chimney, HEW 1897 .... 475.00
Rookwood, Letter Holder, Blueberry & Leaf, Footed, Signed H.A., 1901 .... 135.00
Rookwood, Mug, Copy Of 1880 Cooperage Mug, Label, Dated 1963 & 1880, 7 In. 18.00
Rookwood, Mug, Corn Design, Blue To Green, Dated 1906 .... 75.00
Rookwood, Mug, Green Matte, Raised Greek Key Design, C.1906 .... 22.50
Rookwood, Paperweight, Crow On Base, Dark Green Matte Glaze, No.1623, 1930 ...... 25.00
Rookwood, Pitcher, Glossy Green, 1947, 3 In. 25.00
Rookwood, Pitcher, Gold Chestnut Color, Feathery Pollen Sprays, Wilcox, 1888 .... 175.00
Rookwood, Pitcher, Green Blue, 1941, 4 In.High 15.00
Rookwood, Planter, Green, Yellow Chrysanthemums, Kataro Shirayamadani, 1887 .... 195.00
Rookwood, Planter, Rosy Pink, Hexagon, Three Small Handles, 1930 .... 18.00
Rookwood, Plate, Blue Sailing Pirate Ships, 1886, 8 1/2 In. .... 15.00 To 32.00
Rookwood, Plate, White, Blue Sailboats, 10 In. 40.00
Rookwood, Plate, 12 Sided, 3 Sailing Ships, 1926, 6 1/2 In. 22.50
Rookwood, Sugar, Covered, Brown Glaze, Floral, Butterfly Handles, 1891 .... 75.00
Rookwood, Tea Caddy, Covered, Yellow Matte, Dated 1929, 4 In.High, 3 Piece 22.50
Rookwood, Tile, Basket Of Flowers, Butterflies, Footed, 1929 .... 25.00
Rookwood, Tile, Blue & Yellow Design, Marked, 6 In. 28.50
Rookwood, Tile, Three White Geese Feeding At Water Edge, 1925, 5 3/4 In.Sq. 30.00
Rookwood, Tray, Nude Woman Figure, White, Oval, 1934, 4 1/4 X 3 In. 20.00
Rookwood, Tray, Nude Woman, White Glaze, 1929 .... 27.50
Rookwood, Tray, Wild Roses On Cream, Artist-Signed, 1891 .... 48.00
Rookwood, Vase, Aqua Matte, Squared Grecian Type Handles 15.00
Rookwood, Vase, Arthur P.Conant, 1916, Off White, Blue, Floral Border 109.00
Rookwood, Vase, Autumn Leaves, LNL, 1901, 6 1/2 In.High 135.00
Rookwood, Vase, Autumn Leaves, Two Handles, CFB, 1903, 7 1/2 In. High 150.00
Rookwood, Vase, Blossom & Leaf Design, Yellow, Signed, Dated 1888, 5 1/2 In. 185.00
Rookwood, Vase, Blue Currants, Iris Glaze By Van Horne, 1911 .... 135.00
Rookwood, Vase, Blue Green Ground, Dated 1916, 5 In. 22.00
Rookwood, Vase, Blue Matte, 1919 .... 15.00
Rookwood, Vase, Blue, Molded Fish, 1937 .... 21.50
Rookwood, Vase, Blue, Yellow Lining, Geometric Pattern, Handles, 1922 .... 395.00
Rookwood, Vase, Blue, 1927, 10 In.High· 17.00
Rookwood, Vase, Brown High Glaze, Yellow Floral Spray, Artist-Signed, 7 In. 165.00
Rookwood, Vase, Brown Lava Flow Over Mottled Tan, Incised Floral, L.N.L. 35.00
Rookwood, Vase, Brown To Yellow, Orange And Yellow Violets, 1893, L.N.L. 95.00
Rookwood, Vase, Brown With Flowers, 7 In.Signed 165.00
Rookwood, Vase, Bud, Dark Blue, Grecian Style, Square Handles, 1913, 6 1/2 In. 45.00
Rookwood, Vase, Bulbous, Frieze Of Sharks, Green, Signed, Dated 1921 .... 90.00
Rookwood, Vase, Burgundy, Border Design, Glossy, Sara Sax, 1919 .... 65.00
Rookwood, Vase, Butterflies, Purple To Mauve, Dated 1913, 6 1/2 In. 50.00
Rookwood, Vase, Butterflies, White Enameled Ground, Martin Rettig, Artist 120.00
Rookwood, Vase, Caramel Crackle, Matte, Blossoms Around Collar, 1925 .... 50.00
Rookwood, Vase, Carrie Steinle, 1903, Floral, High Glaze, 4 1/2 In. 85.00
Rookwood, Vase, Chain Handle, Pastel Iris, Pink Beige Ground 75.00
Rookwood, Vase, Cherry Blossoms On Rose Blue, Kataro Shirayamadani 185.00
Rookwood, Vase, Cream, Pastel Floral, Green Leaves, L.A., 1926 .... 75.00 To 85.00
Rookwood, Vase, Dark Green & Blue, Edward Diers, 1918, 11 1/4 In.High 250.00
Rookwood, Vase, Dark Green Matte, Incised Floral, W.E.H., 1910 .... 45.00
Rookwood, Vase, Embossed, Brown, Blue, White, & Gold, Signed, 1929 .... 85.00
Rookwood, Vase, Fall Leaves, Signed LNL, 6 1/2 In.High 135.00
Rookwood, Vase, Falling Leaves, Two Handles, Signed C.F.B., 7 1/2 In.High 150.00
Rookwood, Vase, Fan Shape, Dark Blue, 1954, 8 In. 17.50
Rookwood, Vase, Floral, L.N.L., 1901, 6 In.High 100.00
Rookwood, Vase, Floral, Signed J.Z., 1903, 6 1/2 In.High 80.00

Rookwood, Vase, Floral, 1904, 4 1/2 In. 97.00
Rookwood, Vase, Flower & Moss Design, Signed L.N.Lincoln, 7 In.High 45.00
Rookwood, Vase, Flower Design, Blue Vellum, Signed C.J.M., Dated 1915 .... 75.00
Rookwood, Vase, Flower Design, Signed K.L.M.1892, Footed, 4 In.High 110.00
Rookwood, Vase, Four-Leaf Clovers, Panels, Pink To Purple, 1927 .... 26.50 To 35.00
Rookwood, Vase, Glossy Yellow Floral, Relief Pattern, 1946, 6 In. 25.00
Rookwood, Vase, Gold, Blackbird, Black Branches, Pebbly, Matt Daly, 1886 .... 295.00
Rookwood, Vase, Goldstone, Brown Glaze, 1932, 6308-C 275.00
Rookwood, Vase, Green, Floral, MHM, 6 In. 58.00
Rookwood, Vase, Green, Incised, Art Nouveau, 1902, 4 In.High 40.00
Rookwood, Vase, Green, Raised Oak Leaves, Acorns, No.2590 .... 55.00
Rookwood, Vase, Green, Relief Floral, Yellow Outline, Dated 1915, 7 1/4 In. 45.00
Rookwood, Vase, Green, Trees, Scenic, Signed Lenore Asbury, 1912 .... 170.00
Rookwood, Vase, Holly Decoration, Signed Lincoln, 1902, 6 In.High 95.00
Rookwood, Vase, Iris, Beige & Rust Oak Leaves On Royal Blue To Ivory 155.00
Rookwood, Vase, Iris, Floral, K.Van Horne, 1910, Drilled For Lamp 85.00
Rookwood, Vase, Iris, Pink To Gray, Rose Morning Glories, Signed, Dated 1903 .... 110.00
Rookwood, Vase, Iris, White Flowers, I.B., 1904, 5 1/2 In.High 165.00
Rookwood, Vase, Ivory, Vellum Finish, 15 Flames, 7 In. 18.00
Rookwood, Vase, J.Zettel, 1892, 3 3/4 In.High 95.00
Rookwood, Vase, Jardiniere Type, Embossed Pussy Willows, Marked Starkville 38.00
Rookwood, Vase, Jeweled Porcelain, Geometric Decoration, Signed W.E.H., 1920 .... 65.00
Rookwood, Vase, Jonquils In Relief On Gray To Violet, No.1712, 1922 .... 45.00
Rookwood, Vase, L.E.L., 1902, Glaze, Floral, 4 1/2 In. 85.00
Rookwood, Vase, Leaf & Berry Design, Green, Tan, Signed C.S.Todd, 11 In.High 65.00
Rookwood, Vase, Light Blue, 1915, 4 1/2 In. 37.50
Rookwood, Vase, Lily Design, Green, Signed C.A.G., Dated 1900, 6 1/2 In. 125.00
Rookwood, Vase, Madonna And Child, Blue Matte, 5 In.Commemorative, 1934 .... 22.50
Rookwood, Vase, Maroon, Geometric, Matte Finish, Dated 1908 .... 24.50
Rookwood, Vase, Matte Glaze, Dark Blue, No.1813, 7 1/4 In.High 30.00
Rookwood, Vase, Mauve, Floral Relief, Flame Mark, 1930, 6 In. 27.50
Rookwood, Vase, Molded Matte Dragonfly, Tan Ground, Dated 1922, 7 In. 25.00
Rookwood, Vase, Mottled Blue, Signed & Dated 1920, 7 In.High 20.00
Rookwood, Vase, Mottled Dark Blue Green Matte Glaze, Dated 1931 .... 25.00
Rookwood, Vase, Mulberry Pattern, High Glaze Beige Ground, Signed, 5 1/2 In. 30.00
Rookwood, Vase, Narcissus, Ivory To Blue Ground, 1903, J.Zettel 195.00
Rookwood, Vase, Octagon Shape, 3 Handles, Matte Glaze, Green, No.2671, 1923 ...... 30.00
Rookwood, Vase, Painted Matte Glaze, Signed K.Shirayamadani 1938, 7 In.High 155.00
Rookwood, Vase, Painted Matte Glaze, Signed M.H.M.1926, 5 1/2 In.High 110.00
Rookwood, Vase, Panels, Brown Tones, Dated 1950, 4 1/2 In.High 14.00
Rookwood, Vase, Pansy Decoration, Handled, H.R.Strafer, 1890, Shape No.461 .... 195.00
Rookwood, Vase, Pink, Green, Signed Wilhelmine Rehm, 1931, 4 In. 85.00
Rookwood, Vase, Pink, Raised Daisies, 1930, 5 1/2 In. 21.00
Rookwood, Vase, Plum Brown, Wax Matte, 1922, Art Deco, 6 1/2 In. 37.00
Rookwood, Vase, Powder Blue & Gray, Dogwood At Top, Dated 1927 .... 40.00
Rookwood, Vase, Reverse Cone, Pedestal, Turquoise, Blue Inside, No.2734, 1924 .... 46.00
Rookwood, Vase, Reverse Cone, Pedestal, White, Blue Inside, No.2733, 1924 .... 38.00
Rookwood, Vase, Roses, Stems, Mauve Bottom, White Neck, Lorinda Epply, 1928 .... 65.00
Rookwood, Vase, Row Of Rooks, 1917, 5 1/2 In. 45.00
Rookwood, Vase, Scenic, Lake, Trees, Lenore Asbury, 1920 .... 140.00
Rookwood, Vase, Signed C.C.L, 1906, 5 In. 105.00
Rookwood, Vase, Silver Overlay, Signed Matthew A.Daly .... *Illus* 1800.00
Rookwood, Vase, Swirling Leaves, Handled, C.F.B., 1903, 7 In.High 125.00
Rookwood, Vase, Swirling Leaves, L.N.L., 1901, 6 1/4 In.High 100.00
Rookwood, Vase, Spice Bag Shape With Drawstring, Floral, Sprague, 1888 .... 125.00
Rookwood, Vase, Swirling Leaves, 6 1/4 In.High, 1901, L.N.L. 100.00
Rookwood, Vase, Turquoise, Matte Finish, 1936, 4 1/2 In. 18.50
Rookwood, Vase, Vellum, Autumn Landscape & House, Fred Rothenbusch, 1923 .... 165.00
Rookwood, Vase, Vellum, Cream Ground, Pastel Floral, Artist M.N., 1895, 7 In. 95.00
Rookwood, Vase, Vellum, Dandelion Design, Green, Yellow, Signed, 5 1/2 In. 95.00
Rookwood, Vase, Vellum, Dogwood Blossoms, E.N.L., 1907, 8 1/2 In.High 98.50
Rookwood, Vase, Vellum, Forest & Water Scene, Signed F.Rothenbusch, 1912 .... 130.00
Rookwood, Vase, Vellum, Green & Pink Floral, Signed LNL, 1912 .... 110.00
Rookwood, Vase, Vellum, Lorinda Epply, 1907, 7 In. 62.50
Rookwood, Vase, Vellum, Mauve Ground, Grapes, Artist-Signed, 1908 .... 58.00
Rookwood, Vase, Vellum, Ovoid, Gray Ground, Pink Roses, Rothenbusch, 1914 .... 70.00

Rookwood, Vase, Silver Overlay, Signed Matthew A.Daly
See Page 461

Rookwood, Vase, Vellum, Parchment, Sycamores, E.O.W., 1912, 6 1/2 In.High	125.00
Rookwood, Vase, Vellum, Pink, Blue, Scenic, Signed L.A., 9 1/2 In.High	215.00
Rookwood, Vase, Wax Matte, Artist M.H.M., Purple Floral On Green, 5 1/2 In.	50.00
Rookwood, Vase, Windmill, Sea, Gray, Cream, Signed L.E., Dated 1910, 6 1/4 In.	175.00
Rookwood, Vase, Yellow Green, Cattails In Relief, Marked 14 Flames, 5 In.	8.50
Rookwood, Vase, Yellow Tulip On Brown, Sally Toohey, 1902	145.00
Rookwood, Wall Pocket, Cicada, Pale Green, C.1915, 8 1/2 In.Long	57.00

Rosaline Glass is a rose-colored jade glass that was made by the Steuben Glass Works in Corning, New York.

Rosaline, Bowl, Flip, Signed Fleur-De-Lis & Steuben, 14 In.Diameter	145.00

Rose Bowls were popular during the 1880s. Rose petals were kept in the open bowl to add fragrance to a room. The glass bowls were made with crimped tops, which kept the petals inside. Many types of Victorian Art Glass were made into rose bowls.

Rose Bowl, see also under special types of Art Glass

Rose Bowl, Citrine, Dimpled, Overshot Striped	35.00
Rose Bowl, Collared, Alabaster, Black Jade Prunts & Spiral Threading	27.50
Rose Bowl, Cranberry Shades, Royal Ivy, Frosted, Clear Leaves	84.00
Rose Bowl, Emerald Green, Fluted Top, Gold Enamel Trim	16.00
Rose Bowl, Fiery Red Orange, Clear Base, Signed, Dated	20.00
Rose Bowl, Green, Transparent, Blue & White Fused On Glass Spattering	35.00
Rose Bowl, Porcelain, Hand-Painted Floral, Gold Trim, Footed	14.00
Rose Bowl, Red Flashed, Block & Star, Scalloped Rim	18.75
Rose Canton, Butter Pat, Enameled Butterflies	10.00
Rose Canton, Cup & Saucer	26.00
Rose Canton, Cup & Saucer, Demitasse	18.00
Rose Canton, Plate, 10 In.	35.00
Rose Canton, Teapot, Floral, Insects, Wrapped Wire Handle	55.00
Rose Canton, Teapot, Flowers & Birds	58.00
Rose Canton, Teapot, People, Flowers, Birds, Wire Handle, 6 1/2 In.	70.00
Rose Canton, Teapot, Two Panels, One Has People, Other Birds, 19th Century	45.00
Rose Canton, Vase, Double Gourd, Unmarked, 9 In.High	135.00

Rose Medallion China was made in China during the nineteenth and twentieth centuries. It is a distinctive design picturing people, flowers, birds, and butterflies. They are colored in greens, pinks, and other colors.

Rose Medallion, Basket, Reticulated, 4 In.High X 10 1/2 In.Long	250.00
Rose Medallion, Bouillon & Saucer, Covered	20.00
Rose Medallion, Bowl, Flanged, 7 1/4 In.	35.00
Rose Medallion, Bowl, Floral & Family Group Medallions	100.00
Rose Medallion, Bowl, Four Panels, C.1840, 8 3/4 In.	85.00
Rose Medallion, Bowl, Four Panels, People, Birds, Butterflies, Shallow	90.00
Rose Medallion, Bowl, Green & Rose Floral, 11 3/4 In.Diameter	175.00

Rose Medallion, Bowl, Lipped Edge, 24 In.Diameter .... 450.00 To 500.00
Rose Medallion, Bowl, Lotus, Alternating Panels, Scenic, Floral Inside & Out 285.00
Rose Medallion, Bowl, Panels Inside & Outside, Made In China, 4 1/2 In. 25.00
Rose Medallion, Bowl, Panels, Figures, Celadon, Lipped, 1820, 18 1/2 In. 275.00
Rose Medallion, Bowl, Panels, Painted Figures, Peonies, Lipped, 1850, 16 In. 250.00
Rose Medallion, Bowl, Punch, Panels, Figures, Birds, 1860, 12 In. 200.00
Rose Medallion, Bowl, Punch, 11 In.Diameter 140.00
Rose Medallion, Bowl, Punch, 12 In.Diameter 225.00
Rose Medallion, Bowl, Punch, 13 In.Diameter 300.00
Rose Medallion, Bowl, Punch, 14 In.Diameter 235.00
Rose Medallion, Bowl, Punch, 14 1/2 In.Diameter 450.00
Rose Medallion, Bowl, 5 3/4 In.Diameter 35.00
Rose Medallion, Bowl, 6 1/4 In.Diameter 55.00
Rose Medallion, Bowl, 7 In.Diameter 75.00
Rose Medallion, Bowl, 8 3/4 In.Diameter 125.00
Rose Medallion, Bowl, 10 In.Diameter 195.00
Rose Medallion, Bowl, 11 In.Diameter .... 135.00 To 235.00
Rose Medallion, Bowl, 12 In.Diameter 125.00
Rose Medallion, Box, Covered, Foo Dog Finial, Reserves, Duel Scene, Floral 90.00
Rose Medallion, Box, Covered, 3 In.Square 15.00
Rose Medallion, Box, Covered, 3 3/4 In.Diameter 65.00
Rose Medallion, Candlestick, Marked China, 6 1/4 In.High, Pair 55.00
Rose Medallion, Candlestick, 9 1/4 In.High, Pair 185.00
Rose Medallion, Candlestick, 10 1/4 In.High, Pair 195.00
Rose Medallion, Cup & Saucer .... 25.00 To 35.00
Rose Medallion, Cup & Saucer, Demitasse 16.00
Rose Medallion, Cup & Saucer, Demitasse, Quadrangular 25.00
Rose Medallion, Cup & Saucer, Set Of 6 .... 150.00
Rose Medallion, Cup Stand, Open Ring 28.00
Rose Medallion, Cup, Handleless, Set Of 4 .... 15.00
Rose Medallion, Dish, Curry, 1 1/2 In.Foot, 14 1/2 In. 325.00
Rose Medallion, Dish, Soap, Covered, Drain, Base, C.1820 .... 125.00
Rose Medallion, Dish, Soap, 3 Parts 115.00
Rose Medallion, Gravy Boat 70.00
Rose Medallion, Holder, Paintbrush, Flowers, People, & Butterflies 55.00
Rose Medallion, Lamp Base 250.00
Rose Medallion, Mug, Strap Handle .... 70.00 To 75.00
Rose Medallion, Pitcher, C.1840, 7 In.High 585.00
Rose Medallion, Pitcher, 3 In.High 10.00
Rose Medallion, Pitcher, 8 In.High 198.00
Rose Medallion, Plate, C.1820, 8 1/2 In., Pair 55.00
Rose Medallion, Plate, No Mark, 8 1/4 In. 20.00
Rose Medallion, Plate, Pierced Border, Oval, 9 In. 28.00
Rose Medallion, Plate, Reticulated, 8 1/2 In., Pair 68.00
Rose Medallion, Plate, Unsigned, 7 1/4 In. 16.00
Rose Medallion, Plate, 6 In. 15.00
Rose Medallion, Plate, 9 1/2 In. 245.00
Rose Medallion, Plate, 9 7/8 In. 55.00
Rose Medallion, Plate, 10 In. 28.50
Rose Medallion, Plate, 11 In. 35.00
Rose Medallion, Platter, Floral, Bird, People 125.00
Rose Medallion, Platter, Oval, Gilt Ground, Birds, Flowering Peonies, C.1825 .... 110.00
Rose Medallion, Platter, Raised Scalloped Edge, 12 3/4 In. 125.00
Rose Medallion, Platter, 10 In. 55.00
Rose Medallion, Spill, Enameled, C.1850, 4 1/4 In.High 98.00
Rose Medallion, Sugar & Creamer 35.00
Rose Medallion, Tea Set, Handleless Cups, Tea Caddy & Basket, 5 Piece 135.00
Rose Medallion, Teapot 165.00
Rose Medallion, Teapot, Cylinder Shape, 3 3/4 In.High 95.00
Rose Medallion, Teapot, In Basket, Brass Lock, 5 In. 65.00
Rose Medallion, Teapot, Panels, People, Roses, Butterflies, Straw Bail 50.00
Rose Medallion, Teapot, Wicker Handle 65.00
Rose Medallion, Teapot, 5 In.High, 5 In.Diameter 110.00
Rose Medallion, Tray, Orange Peel Glaze, 8 1/2 In.Long 120.00
Rose Medallion, Urn, Panels, Mandarin Figures, Birds, Lion Mask Handles 85.00
Rose Medallion, Vase, Birds, Peonies, Dog Finial On Cover, 14 1/2 In. 225.00

Rose Medallion, Vase, China, 10 In.High, Pair 250.00
Rose Medallion, Vase, Chinese Figurines, Temple Dogs, Crackleware, 9 In. 115.00
Rose Medallion, Vase, C.1820, 6 1/2 In.High, Pair 175.00
Rose Medallion, Vase, Four Figures On Front, Birds, Floral On Back 110.00
Rose Medallion, Vase, Long Neck, Ball Shape, Marked, 7 In.High 40.00
Rose Medallion, Vase, Panels, Birds, Floral, Butterfly, People, 4 3/4 In., Pair 65.00
Rose Medallion, Vase, 8 In., Pair 150.00
Rose O'Neill, see Kewpie

Rose Tapestry Porcelain was made by the Royal Bayreuth Factory of
Germany during the late nineteenth century. The surface of the ware feels
like cloth.

Rose Tapestry, Basket, Gold Handle, Pedestal, Royal Bayreuth, Blue Mark 210.00
Rose Tapestry, Basket, Openwork Base Decoration, Royal Bayreuth 165.00
Rose Tapestry, Bowl, Cereal, Rose Design, Pink, Signed, Blue Mark 100.00
Rose Tapestry, Bowl, Royal Bayreuth, Blue Mark, 10 1/2 In.Diameter 350.00
Rose Tapestry, Box, Pin, Courting Scene, Rococo Costumes, Royal Bayreuth 120.00
Rose Tapestry, Box, Pin, Covered, Oblong 125.00
Rose Tapestry, Box, Powder, Colonial, Royal Bayreuth, Blue Mark 155.00
Rose Tapestry, Box, Powder, Covered, Footed, Gold 95.00
Rose Tapestry, Box, Powder, Footed, Royal Bayreuth 100.00
Rose Tapestry, Box, Powder, Pink & Yellow Roses, Domed Cover, Royal Bayreuth 325.00
Rose Tapestry, Candleholder, Saucer Type, Handle, Pink Roses, Royal Bayreuth 65.00
Rose Tapestry, Creamer, Blue Mark, Royal Bayreuth 150.00
Rose Tapestry, Creamer, Cavaliers, Signed Dixon, Royal Bayreuth 115.00
Rose Tapestry, Creamer, Cylindrical, Graceful Lip, Royal Bayreuth 95.00
Rose Tapestry, Creamer, Goats, Royal Bayreuth, Blue Mark 70.00
Rose Tapestry, Creamer, Gold Trim, Royal Bayreuth 100.00
Rose Tapestry, Creamer, Pinched Spout, Blue Mark ....90.00 To 135.00
Rose Tapestry, Creamer, Pink & Yellow Roses, Gold Handle .... 110.00 To 120.00
Rose Tapestry, Creamer, Pink Roses, Gold Trim, Pinched Lip, Blue Mark 155.00
Rose Tapestry, Creamer, Portrait, Lady, Horse, Royal Bayreuth, Blue Mark 85.00
Rose Tapestry, Creamer, Rose Color Roses, Blue Mark, Royal Bayreuth 125.00
Rose Tapestry, Creamer, Three Color Roses, Pinched Spout ....85.00 To 115.00
Rose Tapestry, Dish, Pin, Leaf Shape, Blue Mark .... 60.00 To 87.00
Rose Tapestry, Dresser Set, Pink Roses, Royal Bayreuth, Blue Mark, 3 Piece 295.00
Rose Tapestry, Flowerpot Liner, Royal Bayreuth, Marked 105.00
Rose Tapestry, Hair Receiver, Chartreuse Ground, Pink & Yellow Roses 115.00
Rose Tapestry, Hair Receiver, Colonial, Royal Bayreuth, Blue Mark 155.00
Rose Tapestry, Hair Receiver, Footed, Royal Bayreuth, Blue Mark 87.50
Rose Tapestry, Hair Receiver, Pink & Yellow Roses, Footed, Blue Mark 105.00
Rose Tapestry, Hair Receiver, Roses, Daisies, Footed, Royal Bayreuth, Mark 135.00
Rose Tapestry, Hair Receiver, Swans On Water, Footed, Royal Bayreuth 135.00
Rose Tapestry, Hatpin Holder, Openwork Base, Royal Bayreuth .... 120.00 To 165.00
Rose Tapestry, Hatpin Holder, Pink Roses 125.00
Rose Tapestry, Hatpin Holder, Royal Bayreuth, Blue Mark .... 115.00 To 135.00
Rose Tapestry, Pitcher, Pinched Spout, Gold Handle, Blue Mark, 4 1/4 In.High 135.00
Rose Tapestry, Pitcher, Pink & Yellow Roses, Gold Handle, Royal Bayreuth 125.00
Rose Tapestry, Pitcher, Royal Bayreuth, Blue Mark 125.00
Rose Tapestry, Pitcher, Sheep On Hillside, Royal Bayreuth ....98.00 To 115.00
Rose Tapestry, Planter, Gold Handles, Porcelain Insert, Royal Bayreuth, Mark 85.00
Rose Tapestry, Planter, No Insert, Royal Bayreuth, Blue Mark, 3 In. 125.00
Rose Tapestry, Planter, Pink, Yellow & White Roses, Handles, Royal Bayreuth 165.00
Rose Tapestry, Planter, Three Color Roses, No Insert, Royal Bayreuth, Mark 85.00
Rose Tapestry, Plate, Gold Trim, Royal Bayreuth, 7 1/2 In. 150.00
Rose Tapestry, Plate, Lady & Horse, 9 1/2 In. 155.00
Rose Tapestry, Plate, Royal Bayreuth, Blue Mark, 6 In.Diameter 65.00
Rose Tapestry, Plate, Royal Bayreuth, Blue Mark, 7 1/4 In. 90.00
Rose Tapestry, Plate, Scalloped Shells, Colored Roses, Royal Bayreuth 75.00
Rose Tapestry, Plate, Shell Rim, Royal Bayreuth, Blue Mark, 6 In. 60.00
Rose Tapestry, Plate, Three Color Roses, Green Ground, Ferns, Royal Bayreuth 60.00
Rose Tapestry, Relish 100.00
Rose Tapestry, Relish, Royal Bayreuth, Blue Mark 165.00
Rose Tapestry, Salt & Pepper, Royal Bayreuth, Blue Mark 250.00
Rose Tapestry, Shoe, Lacing Eyelets, Pointed Toe, High Heel, Royal Bayreuth 165.00
Rose Tapestry, Shoe, Lady's, Unmarked Royal Bayreuth 85.00

Rose Tapestry, Sugar & Creamer, Three Color Roses, Gold Handle .... 225.00 To 250.00
Rose Tapestry, Sugar, Covered, Two Handles, Royal Bayreuth 110.00
Rose Tapestry, Toothpick, Footed, Two Handles, Royal Bayreuth 155.00
Rose Tapestry, Toothpick, Scenic, Royal Bayreuth, Blue Mark 185.00
Rose Tapestry, Tray, Celery, Three Color Roses, Open Handles, Royal Bayreuth 165.00
Rose Tapestry, Tray, Dresser, Blue Mark, 10 X 7 1/2 In. .... 145.00 To 160.00
Rose Tapestry, Tumbler, Pavillion, Deer, Lake, Woods, Blue Mark 90.00
Rose Tapestry, Vase, Bulbous, Narrow Neck, Blue Mark, Royal Bayreuth 100.00
Rose Tapestry, Vase, Deer, Castle, Blue Mark, Royal Bayreuth 90.00
Rose Tapestry, Vase, Girl With Muff, Signed Koff, Royal Bayreuth, 3 1/2 In. 115.00
Rose Tapestry, Vase, La Aria, Two Cavaliers On Front, 4 In.High 150.00
Rose Tapestry, Vase, Pheasant, Royal Bayreuth, Blue Mark, 2 1/2 In. 110.00
Rose Tapestry, Vase, Portrait, Royal Bayreuth, Blue Mark, 4 In.High 115.00
Rose Tapestry, Vase, Portrait, Royal Bayreuth, 7 In. 240.00
Rose Tapestry, Vase, Portrait, Two Handles, Royal Bayreuth, 10 In. 345.00
Rose Tapestry, Vase, Royal Bayreuth, Blue Mark, 4 In.High .... 75.00 To 90.00
Rose Tapestry, Vase, Royal Bayreuth, Blue Mark, 5 1/4 In.High 150.00
Rose Tapestry, Vase, Scenic, People In Garden, Impressed 3600 On Base 225.00
Rose Tapestry, Vase, Three Color Roses, Royal Bayreuth, Blue Mark, 9 In. 185.00
Rose Tapestry, Vase, Victorian Lady In Garden, 3 1/2 In. 100.00
Rosenburg, Vase, Art Nouveau, 16 In.High .... Illus 400.00

*Rosenthal Porcelain was established in Sels, Bavaria, in 1880. The
German factory still continues to make fine-quality tableware and figurines.*

MARKE

Rosenburg, Vase, Art Nouveau, 16 In.High

Rosenthal, Bowl, Covered, Green Hydrangea, Artist-Signed 47.50
Rosenthal, Condiment Set, Dragon Design, Orange, 4 Piece 35.00
Rosenthal, Creamer, Brown Shades, Hand-Painted Roses 5.00
Rosenthal, Cup & Saucer, Bouillon, Gold Trim, Premier, Made For Ovington 7.50
Rosenthal, Cup & Saucer, Demitasse, Sterling Holder 16.50
Rosenthal, Figurine, Chicken, Artist Signature Impressed, 3 1/2 In., Pair 12.00
Rosenthal, Figurine, Dancer, White & Gold, C.1905, 8 In. 75.00
Rosenthal, Figurine, Dog, Pointer, Signed F.Diller, 11 In. 140.00
Rosenthal, Figurine, Moor, Colorful Costume, Artist-Signed, 7 3/4 In.High 60.00
Rosenthal, Figurine, Young Nubian, Colorful Costume, Artist-Signed 60.00
Rosenthal, Hatpin Holder, White, Pink Roses 13.50
Rosenthal, Mortar & Pestle, Porcelain, Bavaria, 1 3/8 X 2 1/2 In.Diameter 5.95
Rosenthal, Mug, Gold Handle, Rim, Base, & Crest On Cream 12.00
Rosenthal, Plate, Cherries & Foliage, Scalloped Rim, 8 5/8 In. 6.00
Rosenthal, Plate, Dessert, Grape Design, Artist-Signed, Gold Rim 9.50
Rosenthal, Plate, Grape Design, Purple, Blue, 8 1/2 In.Diameter 18.00
Rosenthal, Plate, Ivory Center, Floral, Maroon Border With Gold Scrolls 75.00
Rosenthal, Plate, King's Rose, Bavarian, 11 In. 24.50
Rosenthal, Plate, Luncheon, Gold Band, Bird, Floral, Ovington Bros., Set Of 6 .... 130.00
Rosenthal, Plate, Mexican Children, Burgundy & Gold Band, 6 In. 8.50

Rosenthal, Plate, Portrait, Cobalt & Gold Border 30.00
Rosenthal, Plate, Portrait, Woman In Window, Blue, Green, Marked 35.00
Rosenthal, Plate, Three Large Roses, Pale Green Leaves, Vine Border 16.50
Rosenthal, Plate, White, Vines, Peacock Border, Selb Bavaria, 10 1/2 In., 10 .... 50.00
Rosenthal, Server, Pink, White, & Green Roses On Pink, Signed Liningston 14.50
Rosenthal, Sugar & Creamer, Green, Red, Pink, Lavender, Black, Gold Background 30.00
Rosenthal, Vase, Artist Gibbon, Mark, 7 In.High 35.00
Rosenthal, Vase, Gold Luster, Girls Blowing Bubbles, Silhouette, Teak Stand 50.00
Rosenthal, Vase, Hand-Painted Red Poppies With Gold Border, 9 In. 27.50
Rosenthal, Vase, Silver Deposit, Purple Band, Selb Bavaria 72.00

ROZ≈NE WARE   *Roseville Pottery Company was established in 1891 in Zanesville, Ohio.* ~~Roseville~~
       Many types of pottery were made, including flower vases.
Roseville, Ashtray, Turquoise, Roses, Handle 7.00
Roseville, Basket, Blue, Embossed Cream Lilies .... 11.00 To 20.00
Roseville, Basket, Blue, Water Lily, 12 In.High 37.00
Roseville, Basket, Green, Embossed Floral, Cosmos, U.S.A. 18.00
Roseville, Bookend, Blue, Pinecone, Pair 15.00
Roseville, Bookend, Open Book, Lilies, Tan, Olive, Cream, & Yellow, No.16, Pair 25.00
Roseville, Bowl Vase, Wisteria, Two Handles, 6 1/2 X 5 1/2 In. 15.00
Roseville, Bowl, Bleeding Heart Sprays, Blue Ground, Two Handles, 4 1/2 In. 9.50
Roseville, Bowl, Bleeding Hearts On Blue, 3 1/2 In.High 9.50
Roseville, Bowl, Blue, Iris, 3 In. 8.00
Roseville, Bowl, Blue, Lily, No.655 .... 8.00
Roseville, Bowl, Brown, Yellow, Fuchsia, 4 In. 10.00
Roseville, Bowl, Centerpiece, Tan, Embossed Roses, Handles, 13 In. 13.00
Roseville, Bowl, Clematis Design, Blue, White, 6 In. 12.00
Roseville, Bowl, Clematis, Green, Two Handle, 9 In.Diameter 15.00
Roseville, Bowl, Console, Turquoise, Pink, Foxglove, 10 In. 20.00
Roseville, Bowl, Corinthian, 6 1/2 In.Diameter 12.50
Roseville, Bowl, Dark Mottled Green, Gold, Paper Label, 6 1/2 In. 5.00
Roseville, Bowl, Embossed Yellow Floral, Green Leaves, Handle 19.50
Roseville, Bowl, Floral Panels, Brown, Rust, 7 1/2 In. 18.50
Roseville, Bowl, Freesia, Signed, 3 1/2 In. 17.50
Roseville, Bowl, Fruit, Metallic Green, Carnelian, RV Mark 22.50
Roseville, Bowl, Green, Snowberry, 4 In. 8.00
Roseville, Bowl, Green, Zephyr Lily, Oval, Handled, 10 In. 15.00
Roseville, Bowl, Magnolia, Double Handles, Marked, 3 1/4 In. 12.00
Roseville, Bowl, Mostique, Geometric Design, Gray Ground, 8 In. 12.50
Roseville, Bowl, Mostique, Yellow Spear Heads On Green Stem, 7 In. 10.00
Roseville, Bowl, Oval, Carnelian, Slate Blue, Earlike Handles, RV Mark 16.50
Roseville, Bowl, Pink, Apple Blossoms, Tan Branches, Scalloped Rim, Handles 10.00
Roseville, Bowl, Pink, Green, Columbine, 3 In. 8.00
Roseville, Bowl, Poppy, Yellow Flowers, Green, Open Handles 14.00
Roseville, Bowl, Red Flowers, Vine, 6 1/2 In. 10.00
Roseville, Bowl, Tan To Purple, Hyacinth Sprays, Two Handles 19.50
Roseville, Bowl, Two Handled, Lava, Pink And Lavender 9.00
Roseville, Cachepot, Donatello, Figures All Around, 3 In.High 15.00
Roseville, Candleholder, Apple Blossoms, Rose Color, Pair 8.00
Roseville, Candleholder, Blue, Lily Pattern, Marked, 2 1/2 In.High, Pair 10.00
Roseville, Candleholder, Blue, Turquoise, Zephyr Lily, 2 In. 5.00
Roseville, Candleholder, Water Lilies, Pair 15.00
Roseville, Candlestick, Three Holders, Yellow, Embossed Violets, Pair 16.50
Roseville, Conch, Green, Pink, Water Lily, Footed, 9 1/2 In.Long 16.00
Roseville, Console Set, Handled Bowl, Flowers, Scalloped, Pair Candlesticks 28.00
Roseville, Cornucopia, Blue, Foxglove, 8 In. 15.00
Roseville, Cornucopia, Pink Peony 12.50
Roseville, Creamer, Lilies, 3 In. 4.00
Roseville, Cup & Saucer, Floral, Gold, Hughes 25.00
Roseville, Ewer, Blue, Roses, 6 In. 12.50
Roseville, Ewer, Brown Ground, Clematis, 10 1/2 In.High 22.50
Roseville, Ewer, Brown Ground, Lily 22.50
Roseville, Ewer, Brown Ground, Snowberry 22.50
Roseville, Ewer, Pink & Yellow Lilies On Green, Openwork On Neck, Pair 50.00
Roseville, Flower Frog, Brown & Green, 4 1/2 In. 4.00
Roseville, Flower Frog, 7 1/2 In. 8.50

Roseville, Jar, Cookie, Blue, White Water Lily	28.00
Roseville, Jar, Cookie, Magnolias	30.00
Roseville, Jardiniere, Ball Shape, Yellow, Tan, Brown, White Floral	18.00
Roseville, Jardiniere, Donatello, 9 X 7 In.	20.00
Roseville, Jardiniere, Green, Green Blue Flowers, 9 In.	23.00
Roseville, Jug, Dull Brown, Bittersweet, Yellow Freesias	22.50
Roseville, Mug, Pink Ground, Peonies	18.00
Roseville, Pitcher, Blue, Columbine, 7 In.	15.00
Roseville, Pitcher, Pinecone	22.00
Roseville, Pitcher, Rockingham Type Glaze, 8 In.	12.50
Roseville, Planter, Brown, Green, Holly, 3 X 6 In.	6.00
Roseville, Planter, Green Ground, Floral, Two Handles, 4 1/2 In.Diameter	5.95
Roseville, Planter, Hanging, Aqua, Pink, Foxgloves	10.00
Roseville, Planter, Rose & Green, Yellow Flowers, Handle, 7 In.Long	5.95
Roseville, Red Basket, 6 In.	10.00
Roseville, Sign, 7 In. .... *Illus*	35.00

Roseville, Sign, 7 In.

Roseville, Tea Set, Green, Yellow & Pink Lilies, 3 Piece	48.00
Roseville, Tea Set, Nile Green With Pink & Bisque Magnolias, 3 Piece	50.00
Roseville, Tea Set, Yellow & Green Floral, 3 Piece	49.00
Roseville, Umbrella Stand, Dogwood, C.1916	55.00
Roseville, Urn, Pinecone, Twig Handles, Orange, Brown, Roseville, U.S.A.	10.00
Roseville, Vase, Bleeding Heart, Handles	8.00
Roseville, Vase, Bleeding Heart, Hexagon Top, Two Handles, 4 1/2 In.High	12.50
Roseville, Vase, Bleeding Hearts, 4 In.	15.50
Roseville, Vase, Blue, Branches, White Berries, Two Handles, 6 In.High	5.95
Roseville, Vase, Blue, Handles, 12 In.High	12.00
Roseville, Vase, Blue, Sprig Yellow Flowers, Conch Shell Shape, 6 In.	14.00
Roseville, Vase, Blue, Thornapple, 6 In.	9.00
Roseville, Vase, Blue, Twig, White Berries, Two Handles, 2 In.High	20.00
Roseville, Vase, Blue, Yellow Floral, Side Handles, 7 1/4 In.High	7.95
Roseville, Vase, Brown & Green Pinecones On Blue, 7 1/2 In.High	8.50
Roseville, Vase, Brown Lily, No.140, 12 In.	18.00
Roseville, Vase, Brown Shades, White Iris, 6 1/4 In.	12.50
Roseville, Vase, Brown, Green, Columbine, 6 In.	10.00
Roseville, Vase, Brown, Orange, Open Handles, Roseville, U.S.A.	15.00
Roseville, Vase, Bud, Blue, Snowberry, 7 In.	10.00
Roseville, Vase, Columbine, 5 In.High	20.00
Roseville, Vase, Cornucopia, Foxglove, Blue, No.197, 6 In.High	12.00
Roseville, Vase, Cylinder, Dawn, Green With White, Handles, Pedestal	8.50
Roseville, Vase, Donatello, RV Mark, 3 In.High	19.00
Roseville, Vase, Donatello, 10 In.High	25.00
Roseville, Vase, Donatello, 11 1/2 In.High, 6 In.Diameter	40.00
Roseville, Vase, Double, Connecting Lattice, Marked R.V.	14.00
Roseville, Vase, Double, Rose Design, White	12.50
Roseville, Vase, Fan, Carnelian, Green, Pedestal, RV Mark	12.50
Roseville, Vase, Florentine, Marked RV, 6 1/2 In.	15.00
Roseville, Vase, Flower Design, Brown, Corset Shape, 7 3/4 In.Tall	55.00
Roseville, Vase, Foxglove, Double Handles, 4 1/2 In.High, Pair	12.00
Roseville, Vase, Fuchsia, Squatty, Two Handles, 4 In.	6.50

Roseville, Vase, Gardenia, Blue Ground, 7 1/2 In.High 10.00
Roseville, Vase, Glazed Yellow, Blue, Brown, Tulip, 8 In. 10.00
Roseville, Vase, Green Ground, Pink Clematis, Handled, 10 1/2 In. 19.00
Roseville, Vase, Green Ground, Pink Flowers, Two Handles, 8 1/2 In. 20.00
Roseville, Vase, Green Leaf Swags, Small Roses, Crackled Cream, 8 1/2 In. 11.00
Roseville, Vase, Green, Bud Type Top, Bulbous Bottom, Two Handles, Pair 18.00
Roseville, Vase, Green Leaves & Grapes On Green, 4 In.High 9.00
Roseville, Vase, Green, Orange, White Blossoms, Two Handles, 5 In. 6.00
Roseville, Vase, Hanging, Donatello, Signed 25.00
Roseville, Vase, Holly, Green Matte Glaze, Two Handles 8.00
Roseville, Vase, Magnolia, 8 In.High 10.00
Roseville, Vase, Monticello, Handled 20.00
Roseville, Vase, Mostique, Geometric Pattern 17.50
Roseville, Vase, Mottled Green, Palm Tree, Brown Base, 9 In. 12.00
Roseville, Vase, Pansies On Brown, Bulbous, Handles, Footed, 7 1/4 In.High 75.00
Roseville, Vase, Pinecone, Autumn Shades, Twig Handles, 15 In. 38.50
Roseville, Vase, Pinecone, Green Matte, Twig Handles, Marked 40.00
Roseville, Vase, Pinecone, Two Handles, 5 X 6 In. 14.00
Roseville, Vase, Pink & Blue Mottled 12.00
Roseville, Vase, Pink, Bleeding Heart, 6 In. 8.00
Roseville, Vase, Pink, Yellow Floral, Double Handles, 7 In.High 15.00
Roseville, Vase, Poppy, Two Handles, 6 X 7 In. 12.00
Roseville, Vase, Rose & Bud, Green, Pink, Tan, Bulbous, Marked 8.50
Roseville, Vase, Rosecraft Hexagon, Orange Bleeding Heart On Green Matte 30.00
Roseville, Vase, Rozanne, Yellow & Brown Flowers On Green & Brown, Signed 95.00
Roseville, Vase, Rust Snowberry On Green, Handles, 7 1/2 In.High 15.00
Roseville, Vase, Shaded Rose, Snowberry, Two Handles, Bulbous, 5 In.High 10.00
Roseville, Vase, Slim Neck, Yellow Flower, Artist V.Adams, 10 In. 80.00
Roseville, Vase, Sunflower, Green, Yellow, Handles, 4 1/2 In.High 18.00
Roseville, Vase, Trumpet, Brown, Chartreuse, & Blue, Embossed Floral, 12 In. 16.50
Roseville, Vase, Urn Shape, Fuchsia, 7 In.High 8.00
Roseville, Vase, Wall Pocket, Donatello, Unmarked, 9 3/4 In.High 22.00
Roseville, Vase, Wall, Florentine, 8 1/2 In., Pair 18.00
Roseville, Vase, Water Lily, Rose & Green, Handles, 4 1/2 In. 5.00
Roseville, Vase, Wisteria, Cone Shape, Gold Sticker, 8 1/4 In., Pair 60.00
Roy Rogers, Mug, Plastic 6.00
Roy Rogers, Wash Mitt, Colored 5.00
Royal Austria, Hatpin Holder, Dark To Light Green, Violets, Closed Top 22.50
Royal Austria, Nappy, Leaf Shape, Lavender Luster, Gold Handle, Ruffled 14.50
Royal Austria, Plate, Bluebirds, Roses, Gold Rim, C.1890, Artist Stumpp, 6 .... 45.00

Royal Bayreuth Porcelain was made in Germany during the late
nineteenth and twentieth centuries. Many types of wares were made.
Royal Bayreuth, see also Snow Baby, Rose Tapestry,
Sunbonnet Babies
Royal Bayreuth, Ashtray, Arab & Horse, Blue Mark .... 30.00 To 32.00
Royal Bayreuth, Ashtray, Black Corinthian 35.00
Royal Bayreuth, Ashtray, Cavaliers, Signed Dixon, Three Corners, Blue Mark 32.00
Royal Bayreuth, Ashtray, Devil & Cards, Green Mark .... 39.00 To 40.00
Royal Bayreuth, Ashtray, Devil, Red, Signed, Blue Mark 50.00
Royal Bayreuth, Ashtray, Frog Shape, Purple, Blue Mark 35.00
Royal Bayreuth, Ashtray, Little Boy Blue, Square 36.00
Royal Bayreuth, Ashtray, Monkey Lying Down, Blue Mark 80.00
Royal Bayreuth, Ashtray, Santa Claus, Blue Mark .... 110.00 To 115.00
Royal Bayreuth, Bowl & Underplate, Lobster, Green, Oval, Blue Mark 35.00
Royal Bayreuth, Bowl, Center, Tomato, Raised Green Leaf Base 48.00
Royal Bayreuth, Bowl, Conch Shell, Mother-Of-Pearl Finish, Blue Mark 24.00
Royal Bayreuth, Bowl, Heart Shape, Hunter On Horse, Dogs, Handled, Blue Mark 22.50
Royal Bayreuth, Bowl, Heart Shape, Little Jack Horner, Blue Mar .... 47.50 To 49.00
Royal Bayreuth, Bowl, Large Roses, 11 In. 50.00
Royal Bayreuth, Bowl, Little Jack Horner, Blue Mark, Footed 65.00
Royal Bayreuth, Bowl, Little Jack Horner, Verse, Round, Blue Mark 20.00
Royal Bayreuth, Bowl, Lobster, Blue Mark 35.00
Royal Bayreuth, Box, Covered, Bopeep, Green 75.00
Royal Bayreuth, Box, Covered, Devil & Cards 45.00
Royal Bayreuth, Box, Covered, Hunter On Horse, Oval 35.00

Royal Bayreuth, Box, Covered, Hunting Scene, Oblong, Blue Mark 25.00
Royal Bayreuth, Box, Lift Cover, The Hunt, Gray Green Ground 67.00
Royal Bayreuth, Candleholder & Match Holder, Clown, Blue Mark 125.00
Royal Bayreuth, Candleholder, Black Corinthian, Grecian Figures, Pair 50.00
Royal Bayreuth, Candleholder, Horse, Rider, Lady & Cart 35.00
Royal Bayreuth, Candlestick, Corinthian, Black, Blue Mark, 5 1/4 In., Pair 65.00
Royal Bayreuth, Candlestick, Moose Face, Antlers Form Front, Handle In Back 100.00
Royal Bayreuth, Candlestick, Scene Of Castle & Mountains, Yellow & Green 22.50
Royal Bayreuth, Candlestick, Scene, The Reals, Hooded, Blue Mark 65.00
Royal Bayreuth, Candlestick, White, Gold Trim, Green Mark, 6 1/2 In., Pair 20.00
Royal Bayreuth, Candlestick, 6 In. .... *Illus* 80.00

Royal Bayreuth, Candlestick, 6 In.

Royal Bayreuth, Celery, Goosegirl, Cutout Handles, Signed, Blue Mark 47.00
Royal Bayreuth, Chamberstick, Attached Saucer Base, Girl, Geese 65.00
Royal Bayreuth, Chocolate Pot, Tankard, Girl & Dog, Blue Mark 115.00
Royal Bayreuth, Compote, Boy, Two Donkeys, Scene, Blue Mark .... 39.00 To 42.00
Royal Bayreuth, Creamer & Underplate, Lobster & Lettuce, Green Mark 40.00
Royal Bayreuth, Creamer, Alligator, Blue Mark .... 32.50 To 75.00
Royal Bayreuth, Creamer, Black Bull, Blue Mark 50.00
Royal Bayreuth, Creamer, Black Cat .... 50.00 To 75.00
Royal Bayreuth, Creamer, Black Crow, Blue Mark, 5 In.High .... 45.00 To 50.00
Royal Bayreuth, Creamer, Blue To Pink, Yellow Roses, Gold, Bulbous 35.00
Royal Bayreuth, Creamer, Brittany Girls, Double Handle, Blue Mark, 4 In.High 45.00
Royal Bayreuth Creamer, Brown & Gray Bull, Blue Mark 45.00
Royal Bayreuth, Creamer, Bull's Head, Brown, Orange, White Horns, Blue Mark 40.00
Royal Bayreuth, Creamer, Chambered Shell, Lobster Handle, Blue Mark 37.50
Royal Bayreuth, Creamer, Clown, Pearlized 95.00
Royal Bayreuth, Creamer, Clown, Red Suit, Blue Mark 65.00
Royal Bayreuth, Creamer, Conch Shell, Blue Mark .... 25.00 To 47.00
Royal Bayreuth, Creamer, Conch Shell, Mother-Of-Pearl .... 40.00 To 65.00
Royal Bayreuth, Creamer, Corset Shape, Jack & Jill, Rhyme Around Top 62.00
Royal Bayreuth, Creamer, Cow, Gray, Beige, White, Blue Mark 55.00
Royal Bayreuth, Creamer, Cow, Red, White Horns, Blue Mark 48.00
Royal Bayreuth, Creamer, Crow And Bull 50.00
Royal Bayreuth, Creamer, Devil & Cards, Blue Mark .... 45.00 To 68.00
Royal Bayreuth, Creamer, Dog, Begging, Blue Mark 75.00
Royal Bayreuth, Creamer, Dog, Blue Mark 95.00
Royal Bayreuth, Creamer, Donkey & Boy, Blue Mark 48.00
Royal Bayreuth, Creamer, Duck, Blue Mark 65.00
Royal Bayreuth, Creamer, Eagle .... 60.00 To 78.00
Royal Bayreuth, Creamer, Elk, Gray To Brown, Antlers, Blue Mark .... 29.00 To 37.50
Royal Bayreuth, Creamer, Frog, Red, Yellow Eyes, Green Handle, Blue Mark 75.00
Royal Bayreuth, Creamer, Goosegirl 78.00
Royal Bayreuth, Creamer, Goats, Blue Mark .... 42.50 To 58.00
Royal Bayreuth, Creamer, Hunt Scene, Blue Mark 75.00
Royal Bayreuth, Creamer, Hunting Scene, Groomed Lady, Three Pointers 58.00
Royal Bayreuth, Creamer, Ladybug, Blue Mark 72.00

Royal Bayreuth, Creamer, Lemon, Blue Mark 55.00
Royal Bayreuth, Creamer, Little Boy Blue 55.00
Royal Bayreuth, Creamer, Little Miss Muffet, Double Handles, Blue Mark 55.00
Royal Bayreuth, Creamer, Lobster, Blue Mark .... 34.00 To 85.00
Royal Bayreuth, Creamer, Lobster, St.Andrew's, Blue Mark, 4 In.High 30.00
Royal Bayreuth, Creamer, Long-Haired Goats, Blue Mark 42.50
Royal Bayreuth, Creamer, Man, Horse, Farmhouse, Blue Mark, 5 1/2 In.High 48.00
Royal Bayreuth, Creamer, Milkmaid, Blue Mark 160.00
Royal Bayreuth, Creamer, Monkey 25.00
Royal Bayreuth, Creamer, Monkey With Open Mouth, Blue Mark 95.00
Royal Bayreuth, Creamer, Moose, Black, Red Horns, Inscribed Portland, Maine 45.00
Royal Bayreuth, Creamer, Moose, Blue Mark .... 16.00 To 45.00
Royal Bayreuth, Creamer, Murex, Green Mark 35.00
Royal Bayreuth, Creamer, Murex, Marked Atlantic City, Pearlized, Blue Mark 27.00
Royal Bayreuth, Creamer, Musicians On Dark Brown, Blue Mark, 3 1/2 In. 37.50
Royal Bayreuth, Creamer, Orange, Roman Figures, Blue Mark 22.50
Royal Bayreuth, Creamer, Pansy, Blue Mark .... 42.00 To 95.00
Royal Bayreuth, Creamer, Pansy, Purple, Blue Mark 135.00
Royal Bayreuth, Creamer, Pearl Grape 65.00
Royal Bayreuth, Creamer, Poppy, Pink 70.00
Royal Bayreuth, Creamer, Poppy, Red, Stem Handle, Blue Mark .... 50.00 To 65.00
Royal Bayreuth, Creamer, Ram's Head, Blue Mark 64.00
Royal Bayreuth, Creamer, Rooster 65.00
Royal Bayreuth, Creamer, Rose Shape, Yellow & Pink, Blue Mark 125.00
Royal Bayreuth, Creamer, Scenic, Man & Turkeys, Mountains, Blue Mark 37.00
Royal Bayreuth, Creamer, Scenic, Sailing Ship, Choppy Waters, Gold Border 45.00
Royal Bayreuth, Creamer, Shell, Coral Handle, Blue Mark .... 26.50 To 37.50
Royal Bayreuth, Creamer, Tomato, Blue Mark .... 26.50 To 37.00
Royal Bayreuth, Creamer, Water Buffalo, Green Mark .... 45.00 To 53.00
Royal Bayreuth, Cup & Saucer, Boy Standing Between Two Donkeys 35.00
Royal Bayreuth, Cup & Saucer, Demitasse, Aster, Blue Mark 25.00
Royal Bayreuth, Cup & Saucer, Red Devil, Cards, & Dice, Green Mark 59.00
Royal Bayreuth, Cup, Demitasse, Devil & Dice 29.00
Royal Bayreuth, Cup, Elk, Stirrup, Blue Mark 95.00
Royal Bayreuth, Cup, Loving, Animal Scene, Triple Handle, Blue Mark 40.00
Royal Bayreuth, Cup, Pansy Shape, Purple, Footed 70.00
Royal Bayreuth, Dish, Children Playing Ring Around The Rosie, Heart Shape 50.00
Royal Bayreuth, Dish, Feeding, Child's, Bopeep 27.00
Royal Bayreuth, Dish, Lobster, Red, Brown Tinges, Blue Mark .... 48.00 To 115.00
Royal Bayreuth, Feeding Set, Child's, Little Boy Blue, 3 Piece 90.00
Royal Bayreuth, Figurine, Apple, Red, Blue Mark 40.00
Royal Bayreuth, Figurine, Black Crow, Blue Mark 45.00
Royal Bayreuth, Figurine, Girls, One With Umbrella, One With Basket, Pair 45.00
Royal Bayreuth, Figurine, Water Buffalo, Mouth Open, Blue Mark 55.00
Royal Bayreuth, Hair Receiver, Japanese Chrysanthemum, Green Mark 110.00
Royal Bayreuth, Hatpin Holder, Green Iridescent, Handle On Base, Flared Top 85.00
Royal Bayreuth, Hatpin Holder, White Rose Sprays, Gilt Embossing, Blue Mark 47.50
Royal Bayreuth, Hatpin Holder, White Roses, Blue Mark, 4 In.High 50.00
Royal Bayreuth, Humidor, Elk, Covered, Blue Mark 125.00
Royal Bayreuth, Humidor, Moose, Cover, Blue Mark 145.00
Royal Bayreuth, Jar, Cracker, Double Headed, Cover, Blue Mark 135.00
Royal Bayreuth, Jar, Cracker, Red Poppy, Blue Mark, Cover 150.00
Royal Bayreuth, Jug, Stag & Doe, Blue Mark, 4 In.Tall 35.00
Royal Bayreuth, Match Holder, Clown, Hanging, Embossed Deponiery, Blue Mark 85.00
Royal Bayreuth, Match Holder, Clown, Red, Hanging 65.00
Royal Bayreuth, Match Holder, Devil & Cards, Hanging 65.00
Royal Bayreuth, Match Holder, Devil & Cards, Wall, Blue Mark 70.00
Royal Bayreuth, Match Holder, Red Devil, Tricorner, Blue Mark 48.00
Royal Bayreuth, Mug, Devil And Cards, Mark Reads Koniglper Tettau, Germany 35.00
Royal Bayreuth, Mug, Elk, 4 1/2 In.High 75.00
Royal Bayreuth, Mug, Red Devil & Cards, 4 3/4 In.High 75.00
Royal Bayreuth, Mustard Pot, Tomato, Blue Mark 18.00
Royal Bayreuth, Mustard Pot, Tomato, 3 1/2 In.High 25.00
Royal Bayreuth, Mustard Set, Grape, Covered, Iridescent, Blue Mark, 2 Piece 60.00
Royal Bayreuth, Mustard Set, Tomato & Leaf, Covered, Blue Mark, 3 Piece 45.00
Royal Bayreuth, Mustard Set, Tomato, Covered, 2 Piece 35.00

Royal Bayreuth, Pipe, Man With Plumed Hat, Blue Mark	45.00
Royal Bayreuth, Pitcher & Underplate, Conch Shell, Pearlized, 4 In.High	50.00
Royal Bayreuth, Pitcher, Apple Cover, Blue Mark	55.00
Royal Bayreuth, Pitcher, Art Nouveau	195.00
Royal Bayreuth, Pitcher, Black Cat, Marked, 5 1/2 In.	65.00
Royal Bayreuth, Pitcher, Brittany Girl	36.50
Royal Bayreuth, Pitcher, Cavaliers Toasting, Green, 3 3/4 In.Tall	42.50
Royal Bayreuth, Pitcher, Clown	98.00
Royal Bayreuth, Pitcher, Conch, Pearlized, Blue Mark	55.00
Royal Bayreuth, Pitcher, Corinthian, Blue Mark, 7 In.High	57.50
Royal Bayreuth, Pitcher, Corinthian, Black, Grecian Figures, 3 3/4 In.High	68.00
Royal Bayreuth, Pitcher, Corinthian, Yellow, Blue Mark, 4 1/2 In.High	25.00
Royal Bayreuth, Pitcher, Cows, Scenic, 5 1/2 In.	55.00
Royal Bayreuth, Pitcher, Crow	85.00
Royal Bayreuth, Pitcher, Deer Scene, Blue Mark	35.00
Royal Bayreuth, Pitcher, Devil & Cards, Green Mark, 8 In.High	165.00
Royal Bayreuth, Pitcher, Devil & Cards, Inscribed Bermuda, Green Mark	155.00
Royal Bayreuth, Pitcher, Devil & Cards, 4 3/4 In., Green Mark	70.00
Royal Bayreuth, Pitcher, Gibson Girls, Green, Blue Mark	48.00
Royal Bayreuth, Pitcher, Girl Sitting On Log, Holding Doll	100.00
Royal Bayreuth, Pitcher, Hunt Scene, Two Handles, Marked	60.00
Royal Bayreuth, Pitcher, Hunting Scene, Blue Mark, 4 In.	20.00
Royal Bayreuth, Pitcher, Lobster, Green Handle, Blue Mark	40.00
Royal Bayreuth, Pitcher, Milk, Green & Rose	62.00
Royal Bayreuth, Pitcher, Milk, Man Fishing, Green, Blue, Blue Mar	52.50 To 85.00
Royal Bayreuth, Pitcher, Milk, Scene, Man Fishing, Bulbous, Blue Mark	57.50
Royal Bayreuth, Pitcher, Orange, Green Leaves, White Flower, Blue Mark	57.50
Royal Bayreuth, Pitcher, Pansy, Blue Mark	85.00 To 125.00
Royal Bayreuth, Pitcher, Pansy, Figural, Blue Mark	95.00
Royal Bayreuth, Pitcher, Parrot, Marked	62.00
Royal Bayreuth, Pitcher, Peasant Musicians, Blue Mark, 3 3/4 In.High	55.00
Royal Bayreuth, Pitcher, Peasant, Turkeys, Gold Handle, 3 1/2 In.	45.00
Royal Bayreuth, Pitcher, Poppy Shape, Stem Handle, Red, Green, Marked, 6 In.	135.00
Royal Bayreuth, Pitcher, Roses, Blue Mark	32.00
Royal Bayreuth, Pitcher, Sailing Ships, Blue Mark, 4 1/4 In.	45.00
Royal Bayreuth, Pitcher, Scenic, Boy, Donkeys, 2 1/4 In.High	48.50
Royal Bayreuth, Pitcher, Scenic, Cows	55.00
Royal Bayreuth, Pitcher, Yellow, Three Cows In Top Band, 4 1/2 In.	48.00
Royal Bayreuth, Pitcher, Yellow, Three Goats In Top Band, 4 In.	38.00
Royal Bayreuth, Planter, Pastel Colors, White & Yellow Roses, Gold Trim	37.00
Royal Bayreuth, Plaque, Arabian Rider In Desert, Tapestry, Blue Mark	240.00
Royal Bayreuth, Plate, Arab & Horse, 7 1/2 In.Diameter	42.50
Royal Bayreuth, Plate, Boy With Donkeys, Blue Mark, 9 1/2 In.	47.00
Royal Bayreuth, Plate, Cake, Rosemont, Blue Mark, Set Of 4	20.00
Royal Bayreuth, Plate, Dutch Boy & Girl, Blue Mark, 7 1/2 In.Diameter	37.50
Royal Bayreuth, Plate, Dutch Children, 6 In., Pair	50.00
Royal Bayreuth, Plate, Floral Center, Yellow Border, Marked German U.S.Zone	10.00
Royal Bayreuth, Plate, Girl With Dog, 4 3/8 In.	15.00
Royal Bayreuth, Plate, Hunter With Dog, Flying Geese, Blue Mark	48.00
Royal Bayreuth, Plate, Hunting Scene, Blue Mark, 7 In.	27.00
Royal Bayreuth, Plate, Jack & Jill, Blue Mark	50.00
Royal Bayreuth, Plate, Jack In The Beanstalk, 6 In.	35.00
Royal Bayreuth, Plate, Leaf, Handle, 7 In., Blue Mark	20.00
Royal Bayreuth, Plate, Leaf, Yellow Blossoms, Ring Handle, Green Mark	15.00
Royal Bayreuth, Plate, Little Bopeep, 7 1/2 In.	34.00
Royal Bayreuth, Plate, Man Seated On Ground Holding 2 Horses, 9 In.	65.00
Royal Bayreuth, Plate, Poppy, Blue Mark	35.00
Royal Bayreuth, Plate, Red Roses, Violets, 10 1/2 In.	35.00
Royal Bayreuth, Plate, Tomato, Blue Mark	40.00
Royal Bayreuth, Plate, Yellow & Red Roses On Shaded, H.Matthes	14.00 To 15.00
Royal Bayreuth, Platter, Pink Rose In Center And In Corners, Scrolled Band	25.00
Royal Bayreuth, Salt & Pepper, Fish, Unmarked	28.00
Royal Bayreuth, Salt & Pepper, Grape, Blue Mark	55.00
Royal Bayreuth, Salt & Pepper, Tomato, Blue Mark	30.00
Royal Bayreuth, Sauceboat, Tomato Shape, Blue Mark	32.50
Royal Bayreuth, Service For Twelve, Candy Stripe Pattern, 93 Piece	375.00

Royal Bayreuth, Sugar & Creamer, Corinthian, Blue Mark 75.00
Royal Bayreuth, Sugar & Creamer, Devil & Cards, Covered, Blue Mark 68.00
Royal Bayreuth, Sugar & Creamer, Elk, Elk Handles 75.00
Royal Bayreuth, Sugar & Creamer, Lobster .... 65.00 To 80.00
Royal Bayreuth, Sugar & Creamer, Mother-Of-Pearl, Blue Mark 60.00
Royal Bayreuth, Sugar & Creamer, Pheasant, Blue Mark 75.00
Royal Bayreuth, Sugar & Creamer, Poppies, Blue Mark 55.00
Royal Bayreuth, Sugar & Creamer, Strawberry, Covered, Blue Mark .... 110.00 To 120.00
Royal Bayreuth, Sugar & Creamer, Tomato, Footed Leaf Bases, Blue Mark, 4 In. 65.00
Royal Bayreuth, Sugar & Creamer, Tomato, Leaf Bases 35.00
Royal Bayreuth, Sugar, Corinthian, Blue Mark 30.00
Royal Bayreuth, Sugar, Covered, Cauliflower 42.50
Royal Bayreuth, Sugar, Pearlized Grapes, Covered 35.00
Royal Bayreuth, Sugar, Tomato, Covered, Blue Mark 22.50
Royal Bayreuth, Sugar, Tomato, Cover, Green Mark 22.50
Royal Bayreuth, Table Set, Purple Grapes, Green Leaves, 3 Piece 90.00
Royal Bayreuth, Tankard, Pink Rose, Gold, Cream To Green, 11 1/2 In.High 55.00
Royal Bayreuth, Tankard, Scenic, Man, Horse, Pasture, Farm, Blue Mark 32.00
Royal Bayreuth, Tea Set, Tomato, Blue Mark, 3 Piece 85.00
Royal Bayreuth, Teapot, Allover Flower Sprig Design, White, Gold, 4 In.High 18.00
Royal Bayreuth, Teapot, Orange Shape, Blue Mark 115.00
Royal Bayreuth, Tomato On Leaf, Blue Mark, 4 In. 25.00
Royal Bayreuth, Tomato On Lettuce Leaf, Covered, Dated 1910, Blue Mark 15.00
Royal Bayreuth, Tomato, Covered 23.00
Royal Bayreuth, Tomato, Covered, Marked 20.00
Royal Bayreuth, Toothpick, Devil & Cards, Green Mark 57.00
Royal Bayreuth, Toothpick, Moose Head, Blue Mark 50.00
Royal Bayreuth, Toothpick, Sportsman Scene 75.00
Royal Bayreuth, Toothpick, White Figure, Gold, Black & White Figure Band 33.00
Royal Bayreuth, Tray, Dresser, Goose Girl, Gold, Blue Mark 87.50
Royal Bayreuth, Tray, Dresser, Man Fishing From Boat, Blue Mark 75.00
Royal Bayreuth, Tray, Flower, Leaf Design, Raised, Green, Ring Handle, 7 In. 12.50
Royal Bayreuth, Tray, Pin, Devil & Cards 125.00
Royal Bayreuth, Tray, Pin, Flowers, Tomato Leaf, Blue Mark, Green, Pink 27.00
Royal Bayreuth, Tray, Pin, Santa Claus, Blue Mark 110.00
Royal Bayreuth, Tray, Red Devil & Cards, Oval, 7 In.Diameter 68.00
Royal Bayreuth, Tray, Santa Claus, Blue Mark, 4 X 5 In. 110.00
Royal Bayreuth, Tumbler, White Ground, Green, Gold, Rust Design, Set Of 4 .... 75.00
Royal Bayreuth, Urn, Sunset, Handled, 3 In.High, Pair 80.00
Royal Bayreuth, Vase, Apple Green, Pastoral Scene Top Border, Blue Mark 62.00
Royal Bayreuth, Vase, Brittany Girl, 4 1/4 In. 50.00
Royal Bayreuth, Vase, Castle Scene, 4 In.High 110.00
Royal Bayreuth, Vase, Cobalt, Gold, Portrait, Band Roses, Narrow Neck, 6 In. 55.00
Royal Bayreuth, Vase, Cow Scene, 8 1/2 In.High 65.00
Royal Bayreuth, Vase, Cows In Pasture, 6 In.High 15.00
Royal Bayreuth, Vase, Cream, Pink Roses, Gold Trim, Footed, Handles, 4 1/2 In. 30.00
Royal Bayreuth, Vase, Fishermen In Boat, Flying Birds, Blue Mark, 4 1/4 In. 45.00
Royal Bayreuth, Vase, Goosegirl, Blue Mark, 7 1/2 In.High 90.00
Royal Bayreuth, Vase, Green Ground, Winged Nymph Sitting On Rock, Footed 50.00
Royal Bayreuth, Vase, Green, Stagecoach Scene Border, Blue Mark 42.50
Royal Bayreuth, Vase, Hounds & Moose, 8 1/2 In.High 65.00
Royal Bayreuth, Vase, Musical Cavaliers, Artist Dixon, Handles, Marked 42.50
Royal Bayreuth, Vase, Musicians, Silver Rim, Two Handles, 3 1/4 In. 37.50
Royal Bayreuth, Vase, Orange & Yellow Shades, Ship, Trees, Blue Mark, 3 In. 20.00
Royal Bayreuth, Vase, Pink, Pastel Green Polar Bears, Blue Mark, 8 1/4 In. 37.50
Royal Bayreuth, Vase, Red Corinthian, Classical Figures, Two Handles, 5 In. 58.00
Royal Bayreuth, Vase, Roses, Pearlized, Blue Mark, 6 In. 20.00
Royal Bayreuth, Vase, Scene, Man & Dog Hunting Quail, 6 In. 49.00
Royal Bayreuth, Vase, Scenic, Inn, Hunters, Horses, Dogs, Blue Mark, 8 1/2 In. 55.00
Royal Bayreuth, Vase, Swans On Lake, Blue Mark, 3 1/2 In. 27.50
Royal Bayreuth, Vase, Tan, Green, Rose, Sheep Scene, Silver Band, Footed 28.00
Royal Bayreuth, Vase, Wall, Lady, Flowing Hair, Gown 48.00
Royal Bayreuth, Vase, Woman On Horse, Strolling Couple, Clouds, 4 5/8 In. 38.00
Royal Bayreuth, Vase, Yellow, Hunt Scene, Blue Mark, 5 In. 30.00

Royal Bonn is the nineteenth century tradename for the Bonn china manufactory established in 1755 at Bonn, Germany. A general line of porcelain dishes was made.

Royal Bonn, Bowl, Centerpiece, Pink & White Panels, Apron Base, 8 1/2 In.	22.50
Royal Bonn, Bowl, Chrysanthemum, Blue	12.50
Royal Bonn, Bowl, Dome Cover, Multicolor Indian Tree On White	18.00
Royal Bonn, Cake Set, Deep Blue On White, Castle Mark, 5 Piece	35.00
Royal Bonn, Cheese, Pink & White, Circular Cover	12.50
Royal Bonn, Clock, Woodland Scene, Deer, Signed La Roda, Chime, Ansonia	200.00
Royal Bonn, Dish, Bone, Rosenguirland, Blue & Gold, Set Of 4	15.00
Royal Bonn, Plate, Windmill Scene, 10 1/2 In.	25.00
Royal Bonn, Soup, Wild Rose, Set Of 8	32.00
Royal Bonn, Vase, Blue Green Ground, Yellow, Pink & Blue Roses, Ball Shape	40.00
Royal Bonn, Vase, Blue, Gold, Yellow, Long Stem, 20 In.High	47.50
Royal Bonn, Vase, Floral, Gold, Two Handles, Art Nouveau, Germany, 11 In.	35.00
Royal Bonn, Vase, Flower Design, Yellow, Pink, Gold Trim, 13 1/2 In.High	50.00
Royal Bonn, Vase, Lady, Flowing Hair, Art Nouveau, 10 1/2 In.	125.00
Royal Bonn, Vase, Multicolored Designs, Candlestick Type Top, Art Nouveau	145.00
Royal Bonn, Vase, Overall Floral In Green Shades, Gold Trim, 8 In.	27.50
Royal Bonn, Vase, Pink Ground, Pink & Purple Pansies, No.605423f On Bottom	30.00
Royal Bonn, Vase, Portrait, Art Nouveau, Artist A.Wiehaz, Gold, 12 1/2 In.	98.00
Royal Bonn, Vase, Portrait, Lady, Flowing Hair, Signed, 2 Handle, Footed, Gold	125.00
Royal Bonn, Vase, Portrait, Signed H.Wicharz	95.00
Royal Bonn, Vase, Red & Yellow Roses, Green Leaves, 7 In.High	29.50
Royal Bonn, Vase, Yellow & Pink Roses, Artist Signed, 11 In.	54.00
Royal Cauldon, Bowl, Floral, Windsor Castle Scene Inside, C.1900	65.00

Royal Copenhagen Porcelain and Pottery has been made in Denmark since 1772. It is still being made. One of their most famous wares is the Christmas Plate Series.

DENMARK

Royal Copenhagen, see also Collector plate

Royal Copenhagan, Cup & Saucer, Onion Type Pattern, Signed	12.50
Royal Copenhagen, Bowl, Little Mermaid, 8 1/2 In.	70.00
Royal Copenhagen, Box, Covered, Raised Nude & Swan, 3 1/2 In.Square	8.75
Royal Copenhagen, Coffeepot, Blue Floral On White Underglaze	24.00
Royal Copenhagen, Compote, Poppy Pattern, Footed	70.00
Royal Copenhagen, Creamer, Onion Flower	18.00
Royal Copenhagen, Cup & Saucer, Wild Flowers, No.2162 & 3 Blue Lines	17.50
Royal Copenhagen, Dish, Blue, Fluted, 10 In.	12.50
Royal Copenhagen, Figurine, Boy & Calf, 6 1/2 In.	135.00
Royal Copenhagen, Figurine, Boy Whittling, 7 1/8 In.	125.00
Royal Copenhagen, Figurine, German Shepherd, Lying, Head Raised	82.00
Royal Copenhagen, Figurine, Goosegirl, 7 In.High	50.00
Royal Copenhagen, Figurine, Goosegirl, 9 1/4 In.High	120.00
Royal Copenhagen, Figurine, Little Mermaid, Signed Udda Boulin, 1923	85.00
Royal Copenhagen, Figurine, Man & Woman Peasants, 17 X 10 1/2 In.	475.00
Royal Copenhagen, Figurine, Peasant Girl, Signed Alex Loch, 11 In.	94.00
Royal Copenhagen, Figurine, Sandman, Boy, Umbrella, 6 1/4 In.	60.00
Royal Copenhagen, Figurine, Scottish Terrier, Artist Signed, 4 In.High	22.00
Royal Copenhagen, Jar, Snuff, White Pottery	10.00
Royal Copenhagen, Pitcher, Milk, Onion Flower, Blue, White	12.00
Royal Copenhagen, Plate, Mermaid In Wintertime	75.00
Royal Copenhagen, Rose Bowl, Nasturtiums & Leaves, 4 1/2 In.	40.00
Royal Copenhagen, Sugar & Creamer, Blue, Scalloped, Square Handles	20.00
Royal Copenhagen, Vase, Silver Deposit, Female Head On Front & Back	65.00

Royal Crown Derby Company LTD. was established in England in 1876.

Royal Crown Derby, see also Crown Derby

Royal Crown Derby, Bowl, Pink, Yellow & Blue Florals, Embossed Floral Rim	40.00
Royal Crown Derby, Box, Horse's Head On Top, White, Gold, 1933	37.50
Royal Crown Derby, Cup & Saucer, Demitasse, White, Orange Birds & Trees	12.00
Royal Crown Derby, Figurine, Eagle, 5 In.Wing Spread	65.00
Royal Crown Derby, Figurine, Pheasant, Applied Flowers On Base, 12 In.	175.00
Royal Crown Derby, Jar, Tea, Covered, Octagon, Heavy Decoration, Gold	28.00
Royal Crown Derby, Plate, Birds, Flowers, Blue & Gold Border, 1875 Mark	27.00
Royal Crown Derby, Plate, Wall, Embossed Grapes & Floral, Gold Rim	16.50
Royal Crown Derby, Tea Strainer, Derby Posies, Made In England	6.00

Royal Crown Derby, Teapot, White Ground, Green Chelsea Birds In Trees, Gold 85.00
Royal Crown Derby, Vase, Pink, Encrusted Gold Floral, 13 In.High 225.00

Royal Doulton was the name used on pottery made after 1902. The Doulton
Factory was founded in 1815. Their wares are still being made.
Royal Doulton, see also Doulton
Royal Doulton, Beaker, Hamlet, Shakespeare Series, 4 In.High 22.00
Royal Doulton, Beaker, Juliet, Shakespeare Series, 4 In.High 22.00
Royal Doulton, Bookend, Darby & Joan, 5 1/2 In.High, Pair 75.00
Royal Doulton, Bookend, Lady Patricia, Sweet Anne, Blue Green Mounts, Pair 65.00
Royal Doulton, Bottle, Zorro, England .... 35.00 To 50.00
Royal Doulton, Bowl, Berry, Dickens, Barnaby Rudge 20.00
Royal Doulton, Bowl, Cream Ground, Green Scenery Inside & Outside Of Rim 30.00
Royal Doulton, Bowl, Flambe, 10 In.Diameter .... *Illus* 350.00
Royal Doulton, Bowl, Punch, Dickensware, 10 In. 75.00
Royal Doulton, Bowl, Queen Elizabeth I At Old Moreton, Dark Colors 25.00
Royal Doulton, Bowl, Santa Claus, Bunnykins, 4 In. 10.00

Royal Doulton, Bowl, Flambe, 10 In.Diameter

Royal Doulton, Bowl, Shakespearean Series, Anne Page, Footed 50.00
Royal Doulton, Bust, Judge, A Mark, 2 1/2 In.High 10.00
Royal Doulton, Bust, Mr.Pickwick, 2 1/2 In.Tall 15.00
Royal Doulton, Candlestick, Brown, Yellow, Decorator's Initials, Pair 88.00
Royal Doulton, Charger, Dog Chasing Rabbits, Blue & White, 1890 .... 62.50
Royal Doulton, Compote, Covered, Coaching Scene On Top & Sides 60.00
Royal Doulton, Creamer, Dickensware, The Artful Dodger 38.50
Royal Doulton, Creamer, Jester, 3 In.High 11.00
Royal Doulton, Creamer, Sampler Series, 4 In.High 22.50
Royal Doulton, Creamer, Sir Roger De Coverley 27.50
Royal Doulton, Cup & Saucer, Coaching Days .... 15.00 To 22.00
Royal Doulton, Cup & Saucer, Gaffers 22.50
Royal Doulton, Cup & Saucer, Rouge Flambe 40.00
Royal Doulton, Cup & Saucer, Shakespeare Series 24.00
Royal Doulton, Dish, Country Scene, Open Handles, Octagon, 6 3/4 In. 34.50
Royal Doulton, Dish, Feeding, Bopeep 22.50
Royal Doulton, Dish, Fruit, Coaching Days, Silver Plate Stand 38.00
Royal Doulton, Ewer, Blue Top & Bottom, 8 Panels Of Floral, Marked 35.00
Royal Doulton, Feeding Set, Bunnykins, 3 Piece 21.00
Royal Doulton, Figurine, Artful Dodger 10.00
Royal Doulton, Figurine, Autumn Breezes, 8 In.High 45.00
Royal Doulton, Figurine, Balloon Seller 40.00
Royal Doulton, Figurine, Bedtime 10.00
Royal Doulton, Figurine, Bess 55.00
Royal Doulton, Figurine, Biddy Penny Farthing 25.00
Royal Doulton, Figurine, Blythe Morning, 1948 .... 38.00
Royal Doulton, Figurine, Bopeep, C.1938 .... 37.50
Royal Doulton, Figurine, Bulldog, In World War I Uniform, Pair 125.00
Royal Doulton, Figurine, Captain Cuttle 10.00
Royal Doulton, Figurine, Christmas Morn, Marked 34.50
Royal Doulton, Figurine, Christmas Morn, 7 In. 75.00
Royal Doulton, Figurine, Columbine & Harlequin, Pair 80.00

Royal Doulton, Figurine, Daffy-Down-Dilly, Marked 65.00
Royal Doulton, Figurine, Delight 25.00
Royal Doulton, Figurine, Doberman Pinscher, 6 In.High 18.50
Royal Doulton, Figurine, Dog, Rouge Flambe 75.00
Royal Doulton, Figurine, Duck, Squatting, Flambe, 3 1/2 In.Long 18.00
Royal Doulton, Figurine, Elephant, Flambe, 7 1/2 In.Long 70.00
Royal Doulton, Figurine, Fox, Crouched, Flambe, Signed, 5 1/4 In.Long 42.50
Royal Doulton, Figurine, Fox, Sitting, Flambe, 5 In.High 25.00
Royal Doulton, Figurine, Horse & Colt, 15 In. 135.00
Royal Doulton, Figurine, Humidor With Ivory Cameo 89.00
Royal Doulton, Figurine, Lavinia, 5 1/2 In.High .... 25.00 To 28.00
Royal Doulton, Figurine, Lily, 5 In.High 37.50
Royal Doulton, Figurine, Lily, 5 1/2 In. 40.00
Royal Doulton, Figurine, Lisa, Matte Finish 37.00
Royal Doulton, Figurine, Medicant 75.00
Royal Doulton, Figurine, Miss Demure, 8 In.High 40.00
Royal Doulton, Figurine, Mrs.Bartel 10.00
Royal Doulton, Figurine, Paisley Shawl, 4 In.High .... 45.00 To 48.00
Royal Doulton, Figurine, Patricia, Blonde Hair, Green, Pink, Lavender 115.00
Royal Doulton, Figurine, Patricia, C.1937, 4 In.High 45.00
Royal Doulton, Figurine, Peggy, Lady In Hoop Skirt Dress 28.50
Royal Doulton, Figurine, Peggy, 5 In.High 48.00
Royal Doulton, Figurine, Penguin On Rock, Flambe, Artist-Signed, 6 In. 40.00
Royal Doulton, Figurine, Penguin, Flambe, Artist Noke, 5 1/2 In. 45.00
Royal Doulton, Figurine, Penguin, Rouge Flambe, 6 In.High 47.50
Royal Doulton, Figurine, Poodle, 6 X 6 In. 15.00
Royal Doulton, Figurine, Rabbit, Flambe, Marked, 3 In.High 32.00
Royal Doulton, Figurine, Rhoda, Girl In Bonnet, Shawl, Full Skirt Dress 150.00
Royal Doulton, Figurine, Rose, 5 In.High 22.00
Royal Doulton, Figurine, Sea Harvest, Mint 32.50
Royal Doulton, Figurine, Sitting English Bulldog, Union Jack On Back 22.50
Royal Doulton, Figurine, Sweet & Twenty 75.00
Royal Doulton, Figurine, Sweet Anne 55.00
Royal Doulton, Figurine, The Bride 48.50
Royal Doulton, Figurine, The Bridesmaid 25.00
Royal Doulton, Figurine, The Ermine Coat .... 45.00 To 55.00
Royal Doulton, Figurine, The Parson's Daughter, Dated 1917 .... 57.50
Royal Doulton, Figurine, The Rag Doll, Girl With Doll In Red, C.1953 .... 30.00
Royal Doulton, Figurine, This Little Piggie 25.00
Royal Doulton, Figurine, Tiny Tim, Dicken's Series, 4 In.High .... 10.00 To 19.00
Royal Doulton, Figurine, Top Of Hill 40.00
Royal Doulton, Figurine, Uriah Heep 10.00
Royal Doulton, Figurine, Woodland Dance 40.00
Royal Doulton, Hatpin Holder, Bill Sykes, Dickensware, 5 1/2 In. 23.00
Royal Doulton, Jar, Tobacco, Coaching Scene, Silver Plate Rim, Finial 35.00
Royal Doulton, Jar, Tobacco, Covered, Rip Van Winkle Scene, Marked 47.50
Royal Doulton, Jar, Tobacco, Mister Pickwick Proposes A Toast, Scene, Noke 125.00
Royal Doulton, Jardiniere, Flow Blue, Child With Doll Under A Tree 200.00
Royal Doulton, Jug, Dewar's, Scotsman, Brown 45.00
Royal Doulton, Jug, Sir Roger De Coverley, Two Ladies 24.00
Royal Doulton, Jug, Whiskey, Ship, Highland, Registry Mark 25.00
Royal Doulton, Mug, Aramis, D Series, 4 In. 15.00
Royal Doulton, Mug, Child's, Captain Hook, 3 1/2 In.High 18.50
Royal Doulton, Mug, China, Pickwick, 'A' Mark 50.00
Royal Doulton, Mug, Crusader Figures On Green, 5 3/8 In. 25.00
Royal Doulton, Pitcher, Blue, Green, Farm Scene, 7 1/2 In. 30.00
Royal Doulton, Pitcher, Brown Tones, Motto, Stoneware, 6 1/2 In.High 19.00
Royal Doulton, Pitcher, Dickensware, Barkis, 5 In. 22.50
Royal Doulton, Pitcher, Dickensware, Mr.Pickwick, 7 1/4 In. 35.00
Royal Doulton, Pitcher, Eglinton Tournament, Blue, White, 1902 .... 45.00 To 65.00
Royal Doulton, Pitcher, Eglinton Tournament, Flow Blue, 4 In. 25.00
Royal Doulton, Pitcher, Mr.Squeers, Signed Noke, Dickensware, 7 1/4 In. 45.00
Royal Doulton, Pitcher, Pickwick Paper Design, Square Shape, 5 1/2 In. 55.00
Royal Doulton, Pitcher, Raised Dickens' Figures, Rectangular, 6 In. 30.00
Royal Doulton, Pitcher, Rustic Cottages, Trees, 4 1/2 In. 12.00
Royal Doulton, Pitcher, Sairey Gamp, Dickensware, 7 In. 30.00

Royal Doulton, Pitcher, Tan, Old Bob Ye Guard, 8 In. .... *Illus* 30.00
Royal Doulton, Pitcher, The Fat Boy, Dickensware 25.00
Royal Doulton, Pitcher, The Gleaners, 6 In. 85.00
Royal Doulton, Pitcher, Tony Weller, Side Handle, Green Mark, 7 In.High 67.00
Royal Doulton, Pitcher, Watchman, What Of The Night, 7 1/2 In.High 25.00
Royal Doulton, Pitcher, Welsh Country Scene, 3 1/4 In.High 24.50
Royal Doulton, Plate, Arundel Castle, Buff To Yellow Border .... 22.00 To 37.50
Royal Doulton, Plate, Battle Of Trafalgar, 10 1/2 In. .... 20.00 To 31.00
Royal Doulton, Plate, Bermuda Scene, Blue, White, 10 In. 22.50
Royal Doulton, Plate, Bunnykin, Rabbits Mailing Letters, 7 1/2 In. 12.50

Royal Doulton, Pitcher, Tan, Old Bob Ye Guard, 8 In.

Royal Doulton, Plate, Canterbury Pilgrims, Dates 1335-1399, 10 1/2 In. 18.00
Royal Doulton, Plate, Circus, 7 In. 16.00
Royal Doulton, Plate, Coaching Days 10.00
Royal Doulton, Plate, Coaching Scene, 10 1/2 In. 24.00
Royal Doulton, Plate, Cream, Brown, Glazed Dog, Proverb, 10 In. 40.00
Royal Doulton, Plate, Dickens, 10 1/2 In. 22.00
Royal Doulton, Plate, Dinner, Black Enamel & Floral On Orange, Hexagonal, 8 .... 550.00
Royal Doulton, Plate, Dinner, Sairey Gamp, Dickensware 25.00
Royal Doulton, Plate, Don Quixote 27.50
Royal Doulton, Plate, Fagin, Dickensware, Signed Noke, 8 1/2 In. 24.00
Royal Doulton, Plate, Falstaff, 10 3/4 In. 21.00
Royal Doulton, Plate, Hamlet, 9 In. 20.00
Royal Doulton, Plate, Harvest Landscape, Castle In Background, 10 1/2 In. 25.00
Royal Doulton, Plate, Hereford Cattle, Green & White, 10 In. 15.00
Royal Doulton, Plate, Highland Cattle, Blue With White, 10 3/4 In. .,............... 15.00
Royal Doulton, Plate, Horses, Covered Wagon Scene 14.00
Royal Doulton, Plate, Jackdaw Of Rheims, Chaucer Canterbury Pilgrim 45.00
Royal Doulton, Plate, Little Nell, Dickensware, 10 In. 24.00
Royal Doulton, Plate, Little Tommy Tucker, Girls, Boy, 9 In. 20.00
Royal Doulton, Plate, Logging Scene, Six-Horse Hitch, 10 1/2 In. 20.00
Royal Doulton, Plate, Murray River Gums, 10 1/4 In. 22.00
Royal Doulton, Plate, Nursery Rhyme, 'There Was A Little Man' 15.00
Royal Doulton, Plate, Orlando 20.00
Royal Doulton, Plate, Pheasant In Natural Setting, 9 1/2 In., Set Of 6 .... 25.00
Royal Doulton, Plate, Portia, Shakespeare Series, 6 1/2 In. 16.00
Royal Doulton, Plate, Robert Burns, 10 1/2 In. .... 15.00 To 22.00
Royal Doulton, Plate, Royal Mail Scene, 10 1/2 In. 24.00
Royal Doulton, Plate, Rustic English Scene, 10 1/2 In. 20.00
Royal Doulton, Plate, Sam Weller, Dickensware, 8 In.Square 45.00
Royal Doulton, Plate, Scenic, Farmhouse, Woods, 10 1/2 In. 18.00
Royal Doulton, Plate, Shakespeare, 10 1/2 In. .... 22.00 To 25.00
Royal Doulton, Plate, Sheep In Meadow, 10 1/2 In. 19.00
Royal Doulton, Plate, Squire, 10 1/4 In. 28.00
Royal Doulton, Plate, Tea, Gaffers, Dickensware, Pair 17.00
Royal Doulton, Plate, The Admiral, 10 1/2 In. .... 22.00 To 27.50
Royal Doulton, Plate, The Bookworm 27.50
Royal Doulton, Plate, The Doctor, Black & White Border .... 22.00 To 25.00
Royal Doulton, Plate, The Falconer, 10 3/8 In. 39.00
Royal Doulton, Plate, The Hunting Man 27.50
Royal Doulton, Plate, The Mayor 27.50

Royal Doulton, Plate, The Parson, Black & White Border 25.00
Royal Doulton, Plate, Tomorrow Will Be Friday, Monk Fishing, Signed Noke 30.00
Royal Doulton, Plate, Tower Of London 15.00
Royal Doulton, Plate, Turkeys, Blue, 10 In. 16.00
Royal Doulton, Plate, Wall, Fox Hunt Scene, 1890, 10 In. 30.00
Royal Doulton, Plate, White, Cream Border, Gold Trim, Gold Wreaths, Baskets 22.50
Royal Doulton, Plate, Witch, Greek Key Border, Black & Orange 23.00
Royal Doulton, Plate, Wolsey, Shakespeare Series, 6 1/2 In. 16.00
Royal Doulton, Platter, Blue, Nature Scene, Deer, Marked Kang He, 18 In.Long 30.00
Royal Doulton, Platter, Sutherland, 13 In.Long, 10 In.Wide 10.00
Royal Doulton, Punch Bowl, Footed, Coaching 75.00
Royal Doulton, Sugar & Creamer, Brown & Tan, Applied Sporting Figures, 1904 .... 42.50
Royal Doulton, Sugar & Creamer, Caramel With Black Farm Horse Scene 37.00
Royal Doulton, Sugar & Creamer, Falconry, Burslem 45.00
Royal Doulton, Sugar, Covered, Portia, Shakespeare Series 25.00
Royal Doulton, Sugar, Titamian 15.50
Royal Doulton, Syrup, Blue, White Flowers, Hinged Pewter Cover 35.00
Royal Doulton, Table Set, Old Trevethan, Covered Sugar, 3 Piece 26.00
Royal Doulton, Tankard, Blue, White, Flowers, England, 14 3/4 In.High 78.00
Royal Doulton, Tankard, Columbian Exposition, 1892, Embossed Ship 45.00
Royal Doulton, Teapot, Jackdaw Of Rheims 50.00
Royal Doulton, Teapot, Mr.Micawber, Dickensware 35.00
Royal Doulton, Teapot, Square, Beige, Green, Brown, English Shop Scene 28.00
Royal Doulton, Teapot, Tan, Brown, Transfer, 5 1/2 In. .... *Illus* 25.00

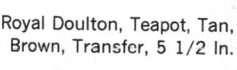

Royal Doulton, Teapot, Tan,
Brown, Transfer, 5 1/2 In.

Royal Doulton, Toby Mug.Santa, Dickensware, 2 3/4 In.High 14.00
Royal Doulton, Toby Mug, Alfred Jingle, Dickensware, 6 In.High 35.00
Royal Doulton, Toby Mug, Auld Mac, Register Number, 6 1/4 In.High 45.00
Royal Doulton, Toby Mug, Auld Mac, 3 In.High 12.50
Royal Doulton, Toby Mug, Auld Mac, 3 1/4 In.High 20.00
Royal Doulton, Toby Mug, Auld Mac, 3 1/2 In. 15.00
Royal Doulton, Toby Mug, Auld Mac, 6 1/2 In. 35.00
Royal Doulton, Toby Mug, Captain Henry Morgan 22.00
Royal Doulton, Toby Mug, Cardinal, 2 1/2 In. 15.00
Royal Doulton, Toby Mug, Cardinal, 3 In.High 27.00
Royal Doulton, Toby Mug, Carpenter & Walrus 27.50
Royal Doulton, Toby Mug, Cavalier, 3 1/2 In.High 19.00
Royal Doulton, Toby Mug, Churchill, 5 1/2 In.High 32.00
Royal Doulton, Toby Mug, Churchill, 8 1/2 In.High 47.50
Royal Doulton, Toby Mug, Dick Turpin, Miniature .... 10.00 To 12.50
Royal Doulton, Toby Mug, Dutch Ladies, Dickensware, 2 1/2 In.High 14.00
Royal Doulton, Toby Mug, Fagin, Dickensware, 6 In.High 35.00
Royal Doulton, Toby Mug, Falconer, 4 In. 15.00
Royal Doulton, Toby Mug, Falstaff, 4 In.High 22.00
Royal Doulton, Toby Mug, Farmer John 50.00
Royal Doulton, Toby Mug, Farmer John, Green Mark 30.00
Royal Doulton, Toby Mug, Fat Boy, Dickensware, 4 In.High 24.00
Royal Doulton, Toby Mug, Fat Boy, 1 1/4 In. 30.00
Royal Doulton, Toby Mug, Fat Boy, 3 1/2 In. 25.00
Royal Doulton, Toby Mug, Gaoler, 3 1/2 In. 10.00
Royal Doulton, Toby Mug, Gone Away, Fox Handle, 9 In.High 35.00

Royal Doulton, Toby Mug, Granny, 3 1/2 In. 15.00
Royal Doulton, Toby Mug, Izaak Walton, Quotation, Noke .... 27.50 To 45.00
Royal Doulton, Toby Mug, James John, 2 1/2 In. 27.50
Royal Doulton, Toby Mug, Jester, A Mark, 3 In. 21.50
Royal Doulton, Toby Mug, Jester, 7 In. 75.00
Royal Doulton, Toby Mug, John Barleycorn, Old Lad, 7 In. .... 40.00 To 42.50
Royal Doulton, Toby Mug, John Barleycorn, 3 In. 22.00
Royal Doulton, Toby Mug, Lawyer, 2 1/2 In.High 15.00
Royal Doulton, Toby Mug, Long John Silver .... 17.50 To 27.50
Royal Doulton, Toby Mug, Monty 34.00
Royal Doulton, Toby Mug, Mr.Micawbar, Blue Mark, 3 In. 15.00
Royal Doulton, Toby Mug, Mr.Micawber, Miniature 22.00
Royal Doulton, Toby Mug, Mr.Micawber, 2 In. 15.00
Royal Doulton, Toby Mug, Mr.Pickwick, 2 1/4 In. 12.50
Royal Doulton, Toby Mug, Old Charley, 1 1/4 In. 32.50
Royal Doulton, Toby Mug, Old Charley, 2 1/4 In. 13.00
Royal Doulton, Toby Mug, Old Charley, 2 1/2 In. 15.00
Royal Doulton, Toby Mug, Old King Cole, 3 1/4 In. 35.00
Royal Doulton, Toby Mug, Paddy, 1 1/4 In. 30.00
Royal Doulton, Toby Mug, Paddy, 3 1/4 In. 20.00
Royal Doulton, Toby Mug, Parson Brown, 3 In.High .... 25.50 To 27.00
Royal Doulton, Toby Mug, Pied Piper 15.00
Royal Doulton, Toby Mug, Poacher, 4 In. 15.00
Royal Doulton, Toby Mug, Potter 73.00
Royal Doulton, Toby Mug, Regency Beau, 4 In.High 22.00
Royal Doulton, Toby Mug, Rip Van Winkle, 3 1/2 In. 18.00
Royal Doulton, Toby Mug, Robin Hood, A Mark, 2 1/2 In.High 29.50
Royal Doulton, Toby Mug, Sairey Gamp, 1 1/4 In. 30.00
Royal Doulton, Toby Mug, Sairey Gamp, 2 1/4 In. 12.00
Royal Doulton, Toby Mug, Sairey Gamp, 2 3/4 In. 20.00
Royal Doulton, Toby Mug, Sairey Gamp, 3 1/4 In.High 11.50
Royal Doulton, Toby Mug, Sairey Gamp, 3 1/2 In.High 22.50
Royal Doulton, Toby Mug, Sairey Gamp, 6 1/4 In. 45.00
Royal Doulton, Toby Mug, Sairey Gamp, 6 3/8 In. 32.50
Royal Doulton, Toby Mug, Sam Weller, A Mark, 3 In. 21.50
Royal Doulton, Toby Mug, Sam Weller, Large Size, A Mark 45.00
Royal Doulton, Toby Mug, Sam Weller, 1 1/4 In.High 30.00
Royal Doulton, Toby Mug, Serjeant Buzfuz 25.00
Royal Doulton, Toby Mug, Simon Legree 15.00
Royal Doulton, Toby Mug, Simon The Cellarer .... 25.00 To 40.00
Royal Doulton, Toby Mug, St.George, 4 In. 15.00
Royal Doulton, Toby Mug, St.George, 7 In. 20.00
Royal Doulton, Toby Mug, Titanium, 2 Terrier Dog's Heads On Gray, Signed 55.00
Royal Doulton, Toby Mug, Toby Philpot 20.00
Royal Doulton, Toby Mug, Toby Philpot, 2 1/2 In. 15.00
Royal Doulton, Toby Mug, Tony Weller, A Mark, 3 In. 21.50
Royal Doulton, Toby Mug, Winston Churchill 47.50
Royal Doulton, Toby Mug, Winston Churchill, Full Figure, 9 In. 40.00
Royal Doulton, Toothpick, Farmhouse Scene, Square Mouth, England, Signed 25.00
Royal Doulton, Tray, Deer Scene, Handled, 1910, 5 X 11 In. 20.00
Royal Doulton, Tray, Rustic England, Farmhouse Scene, Registry Mark 38.50
Royal Doulton, Tumbler, Embossed Hunting Scenes, Sterling Rim 50.00
Royal Doulton, Urn, Figures & Verse, Izaak Walton Ware, Handles, Signed Noke 48.00
Royal Doulton, Urn, Three Musketeers, Two Handles, 10 In.High 350.00
Royal Doulton, Vase, Bill Sykes, Dickensware, 3 In. 22.00
Royal Doulton, Vase, Blue, Tan Decoration Around Top, 9 In. 85.00
Royal Doulton, Vase, Blue, Tan, Brown Vine, Blue Flowers, 12 In., Pair 125.00
Royal Doulton, Vase, Coaching Days, 6 In.High 24.00
Royal Doulton, Vase, Dickensware, Barkis 39.00
Royal Doulton, Vase, Faces & Garlands 25.00
Royal Doulton, Vase, Flambe, Red, Black Desert Scene, Camels, Arabs, 5 In. 100.00
Royal Doulton, Vase, Flow Blue, Child Holds Little Brother, Handles, 8 In. 75.00
Royal Doulton, Vase, Flow Blue, Girl With Balloon, 7 In. 75.00
Royal Doulton, Vase, Flow Blue, Panels, Child, Tree Stump, Doll, Frog, 14 In. 185.00
Royal Doulton, Vase, Gibson Girl Type Figures, Marked England, 9 In., Pair 100.00
Royal Doulton, Vase, Gray Green & Dark Blue, Faces, Festoons, 9 In., Pair 33.00

Royal Doulton, Vase, Green Gray, Impressed Leaves, 7 1/2 In., Pair 115.00
Royal Doulton, Vase, Ladies' Faces & Swags, Blue, Green, Brown, England, Pair 40.00
Royal Doulton, Vase, Little Nell 30.00
Royal Doulton, Vase, Old Peggotty, Large, Handled, Dickensware 37.50
Royal Doulton, Vase, Pink & Blue Mottle, Raised Floral, Leaves, 1929 .... 20.00
Royal Doulton, Vase, Raised Flowers, 4 In. 15.00
Royal Doulton, Vase, Red & Gray Floral, Majolica, 8 In. 30.00
Royal Doulton, Vase, Red, Veined Designs, Rouge Flambe, 8 In. 38.00
Royal Doulton, Vase, Rook With Hat Decoration, 7 In.High 175.00
Royal Doulton, Vase, Rouge Flambe, Woodcut, Boy, Gun, Dog, C.1920 .... 75.00
Royal Doulton, Vase, Scene, Woods & House, Rouge Flambe, 7 1/2 In. 115.00
Royal Doulton, Vase, Silicon, Incised Gold Leaves & Berries On Blue, 1884 .... 40.00
Royal Doulton, Vase, Stagecoach, Hunting Scene, 4 1/2 In.High 25.00
Royal Doulton, Vase, Stick, House, Trees, Flowers, Scene, Rouge Flambe, 1920 .... 65.00
Royal Doulton, Vase, Stoneware, Tan, Gray, Blue, Green, 8 1/2 In., Pair 80.00

*Royal Dux is a Czechoslovakian pottery made at the turn of the twentieth
century. Unfortunately reproductions are now appearing on the market.*

Royal Dux, Basket, Creamy Satin Ground, Basket Weave Pattern, Cherries 45.00
Royal Dux, Figurine, Arab On Camel, Boy On Ground Attends Supplies 325.00
Royal Dux, Figurine, Bird, Cream Color, Gold Beak, Gold Claws, Pedestal 48.00
Royal Dux, Figurine, Bohemian, Lady In Greek Dress, Gold Trim, Red Dux Mark 95.00
Royal Dux, Figurine, Boy & Dog, Green, White, Pink Triangle Mark 195.00
Royal Dux, Figurine, Boy Driving Ox & Cow In Harness, Mark 135.00
Royal Dux, Figurine, Boy Holds Basket, Pink Triangle Mark On Base, 11 In. 85.00
Royal Dux, Figurine, Boy With Jugs, Pink Triangle Mark, 9 1/2 In. 58.00
Royal Dux, Figurine, Brown Hunting Dogs, 18 In.Base 42.00
Royal Dux, Figurine, Cockatoo, White, Pink Crest, On Flower Bough, 15 In.High 110.00
Royal Dux, Figurine, Donkey, Beige, Tan, Green, Matte, Pink Triangle Mark 78.00
Royal Dux, Figurine, Draped Nude, Art Deco, 9 1/4 In.High 55.00
Royal Dux, Figurine, Lady, Grecian Draped, Holds Basket, Mark, 11 In. 95.00
Royal Dux, Figurine, Lion, Stalking, On Oval Base, 7 In.High, 15 In.Long 150.00
Royal Dux, Figurine, Man, Basket, Smoking Pie, Lavender, Gold, Signed, Mark 135.00
Royal Dux, Figurine, Man, Woman, Decorating Jugs, Bohemia, Pair 295.00
Royal Dux, Figurine, Nude, 11 1/2 In. 275.00
Royal Dux, Figurine, 'Pax Et Labor, ' Blacksmith, Child, Mother, 9 1/2 In. 335.00
Royal Dux, Figurine, Setter With Game Bird In Mouth, Marked .... 125.00 To 250.00
Royal Dux, Figurine, Shepherd Boy With Dog, 23 In.High, Mark 195.00
Royal Dux, Figurine, Woman With Two Baskets, Bohemia, Pink Triangle Mark 100.00
Royal Dux, Figurine, Woman, Seated, Sheep, Baskets At Her Side, Bohemia 195.00
Royal Dux, Hatpin Holder, Floral, Art Nouveau 15.00
Royal Dux, Mirror, Art Nouveau, Woman In Pond, Removing Shoes, 13 X 9 In. 215.00
Royal Dux, Vase, Art Nouveau, Pink Seal 48.00
Royal Dux, Vase, Beige, Green, Gold, Berries, Floral, Two Handles, 13 In. 95.00
Royal Dux, Vase, Dark Blue, Gold Grape & Leaf Decoration, 11 In. 65.00
Royal Dux, Vase, Green, Art Nouveau Woman's Face On Front, 8 1/2 In. 60.00
Royal Dux, Vase, Maiden Perched At Side, Twig Handle, Applied Fruit, 6 In. 70.00
Royal Dux, Vase, Matte Finish, Beige, Figure Of Girl Each Side, Mark 98.00
Royal Dux, Vase, Nude Girl, Flowers, Gold Design On Handles, 19 In. 110.00
Royal Dux, Vase, Panel, Girl Holds Vase, Portrait, Sepia Scenery, Pair 150.00
Royal Dux, Vase, Shepherd, Girl, Sheep, Beige Ground, Burnished Gold, Pair 440.00
Royal Dux, Vase, Yellow, Floral, Mark, 11 1/4 In. 55.00

*Royal Flemish Glass was made during the late 1880s in New Bedford,
Massachusetts, by the Mt.Washington Glass Works. It is a colored
satin glass decorated in dark colors with gold designs.*

Royal Flemish, Box, 6 1/2 In.Wide, 3 In.High .... *Illus* 1800.00
Royal Flemish, Sweetmeat, Turtle On Cover, Signed 550.00

*Royal Rudolstadt, a German faience factory, was established in Thuringia,
Germany in 1721. Hardpaste porcelain was made by E.Bohne after 1854.
Late nineteenth and early twentieth century pieces are most commonly found
today. The later mark is a shield with the letters RW inside superceded by
a Crown and the words Royal Rudolstadt.*

Royal Rudolstadt, see also Kewpie
Royal Rudolstadt, Basket, Leaves Form Bowl, Twig Handle, Floral, Gold Legs 38.00

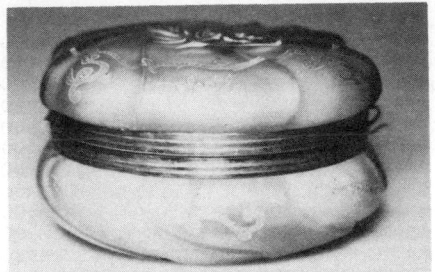

Royal Flemish, Box, 6 1/2 In.Wide, 3 In.High
See Page 479

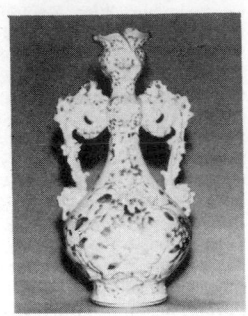

Royal Rudolstadt, Vase, 12 In.

Royal Rudolstadt, Berry Set, Cream Satin, Red Poppies, C.1885, 7 Piece	125.00
Royal Rudolstadt, Bowl, Hand-Painted Roses, Signed Franz	42.50
Royal Rudolstadt, Box, Powder, Covered, Pink, Yellow, White Roses, Gold Band	15.00
Royal Rudolstadt, Cake Set, Poppy Design, Yellow, Green, 5 Piece	68.00
Royal Rudolstadt, Celery, Pink Roses, Gold Rim, 12 In.	35.00
Royal Rudolstadt, Chocolate Set, Hand-Painted Poppies, 13 Piece	90.00
Royal Rudolstadt, Creamer, Yellow Roses, Gold Trim, Lid, Signed J.Kahn	25.00
Royal Rudolstadt, Cup & Saucer, Gold, Marked, Footed	22.00
Royal Rudolstadt, Cup & Saucer, Happy Fats	22.00
Royal Rudolstadt, Ewer, Creamy Rough Finish, Large Gold Flower, Blue Beads	58.00
Royal Rudolstadt, Ewer, Hand-Painted Floral Decoration, Bird	40.00
Royal Rudolstadt, Figurine, Girl, Holds Doll, Muff, Pastel Colors, 10 In.	75.00
Royal Rudolstadt, Hatpin Holder, White & Green, Purple Violets	35.00
Royal Rudolstadt, Lamp Base, Cream, Ribbed, Floral, Pink, Blue, Gold, 7 1/2 In.	45.00
Royal Rudolstadt, Nappy, Pastel Blue, Poppies, Gold, Open Handled	21.50
Royal Rudolstadt, Piano Baby, Blue Dress, Gold Beading, Finger Mended, 8 In.	90.00
Royal Rudolstadt, Plate, Black & White Bust Of Gen.Grant, Gold Border	15.00
Royal Rudolstadt, Plate, Blue & Yellow Pansies, Signed, 8 1/2 In.	9.00
Royal Rudolstadt, Plate, Cake, Floral, Gold Rim, Octagon, Perforated Handles	25.00
Royal Rudolstadt, Plate, Cake, Orange Roses, Green Leaves, Open Handles	24.00
Royal Rudolstadt, Plate, Happy Fats, 5 3/8 In., Set Of 4	18.00
Royal Rudolstadt, Plate, Lilies, Artist-Signed, Thuringia, 8 1/2 In.	14.00
Royal Rudolstadt, Plate, Lilies, Thuringia, Artist-Signed, 8 1/2 In.	14.00
Royal Rudolstadt, Plate, Pink & Green Poppies, Gold Etched Wheat Sprays	18.00
Royal Rudolstadt, Plate, Pink & Green Poppies, Gold Wheat Sprays, Gold Band	20.00
Royal Rudolstadt, Plate, Portrait, General Grant	15.00
Royal Rudolstadt, Plate, Rose, Gold Center Design, Gold Embossed Rim	16.00
Royal Rudolstadt, Plate, Roses, 7 3/4 In.	11.50
Royal Rudolstadt, Plate, Three Poppies, Shaded Ground, 8 1/2 In.	18.00
Royal Rudolstadt, Plate, Three Poppies, White To Salmon Ground, 8 1/2 In.	18.00
Royal Rudolstadt, Plate, Three Poppies, 8 1/2 In.	18.00
Royal Rudolstadt, Plate, Violets, Purple, White, Gold Trim, Marked	15.00
Royal Rudolstadt, Plate, Yellow, Pink Roses, 13 In.	24.00
Royal Rudolstadt, Saucer, Happy Fats	18.00
Royal Rudolstadt, Sugar & Creamer, Oval Shape, Pale Roses, Lavender Band	15.00
Royal Rudolstadt, Syrup & Underplate, Hand-Painted Roses & Mums, Signed	25.00
Royal Rudolstadt, Tray, Celery, Yellow, Tan, Gold, White Roses, 13 X 5 In.	18.00
Royal Rudolstadt, Vase, Beige, Pink & Yellow Floral, Latticework, Pair	150.00
Royal Rudolstadt, Vase, Couple In 18th Century Costume, 9 In.	280.00
Royal Rudolstadt, Vase, Cream Color, Fern, Flying Bird, Gold, 8 In.	35.00
Royal Rudolstadt, Vase, Floral & Animal's Head On Cream, 3 Footed, Pair	150.00
Royal Rudolstadt, Vase, Floral On Cream, Scalloped, Two Gold Handles	18.00
Royal Rudolstadt, Vase, Flower Design, Multicolored, Round, Germany, 11 In.	55.00
Royal Rudolstadt, Vase, Painted Iris, Purple, Green, & Yellow, Signed, 10 In.	40.00
Royal Rudolstadt, Vase, Puce & Avocado Ground, Orange Lilac Floral	22.50
Royal Rudolstadt, Vase, 12 In. *Illus*	95.00

*Royal Vienna was established in Vienna by Claude Innocentius du
Paquier in 1719. The factory closed in 1865. Since then, various German*

and Austrian factories have reproduced Royal Vienna wares, complete with the original 'Beehive' mark.

Royal Vienna, **Chocolate Pot**, Girls, Men, Cupids, Gold Beading, Gold Floral	90.00
Royal Vienna, **Clock**, Medallion, Panels, Birds, Gilt, Steel Face, 13 In.High	350.00
Royal Vienna, **Coffeepot**, Panels, Women, Cupid, Courting Lovers, Two Cups	265.00
Royal Vienna, **Creamer**, Wild Rose Sprays, White Daisies, Green & Gold Border	12.50
Royal Vienna, **Cup & Saucer**, Classic Scene, Gold Trim, Marked	60.00
Royal Vienna, **Cup & Saucer**, Scene With Figures, Cobalt Blue, Gold, Signed	75.00
Royal Vienna, **Dish & Saucer**, Paneled Scene On Yellow, Gold Filigree	75.00
Royal Vienna, **Ewer**, Plum Ground, Panels Of Classical Figures	600.00
Royal Vienna, **Figurine**, Fox, Bronze, Marked Geschutz, 4 In.Tall	85.00
Royal Vienna, **Figurine**, Woman At Dressing Table, Holds Flower	145.00
Royal Vienna, **Jar**, Cookie, Girls Cavorting Together, Signed Kauffmann	95.00
Royal Vienna, **Pincushion**, Camel, Bronze, 3 1/2 In.High	85.00
Royal Vienna, **Pincushion**, Kitten, Bronze, 4 1/2 In.High	95.00
Royal Vienna, **Pitcher**, Brown Ground, Red & Blue Floral, 5 1/2 In.	45.00
Royal Vienna, **Plate**, Game, Duck, Beehive Mark	35.00
Royal Vienna, **Plate**, Portrait, Amicitia, Gold Beehive, Gold Tracery	45.00
Royal Vienna, **Plate**, Portrait, Brunette, Gold Tracings, Brown Ground	40.00
Royal Vienna, **Plate**, Portrait, Cobalt Blue, White, Gold, 9 3/4 In.Diameter	57.50
Royal Vienna, **Plate**, Portrait, Floral & Gold Border, By Wagner, Frame	275.00
Royal Vienna, **Plate**, Portrait, Girl, Brown Hair, Beehive Mark, 10 In.	115.00
Royal Vienna, **Plate**, Portrait, Girl, Pink Gown, Pastel Ground, Signed Wagner	275.00
Royal Vienna, **Plate**, Portrait, Girl, White Dress, Gold Crusted Border	165.00
Royal Vienna, **Plate**, Portrait, Lady With Dove, Cobalt Border, Beehive	350.00
Royal Vienna, **Plate**, Portrait, Lovers In Woodland Scene, Beehive Mark	12.00
Royal Vienna, **Plate**, Portrait, Profile Of Ruth, Beehive Mark, Signed Wagner	135.00
Royal Vienna, **Plate**, Portrait, Woman, Bien-Etre, Signed Wagner, Beehive Mark	85.00
Royal Vienna, **Plate**, Portrait, Young Girl, Jeweled Border	185.00
Royal Vienna, **Plate**, Red, Yellow & Pink Roses, Gold Trim, Artist Lefevre	22.00
Royal Vienna, **Plate**, Scenic, Cupid & Girl, Yellow Ground, Blue & Gold Border	150.00
Royal Vienna, **Plate**, Scenic, Red Reserves In Border, Encrusted Gold Dots	35.00
Royal Vienna, **Stein**, Classical Panels, Blue Beehive Mark, Underglaze, 6 In.	95.00
Royal Vienna, **Stein**, Cobalt, Raised Gold, Portrait Of Cavalier, Beehive Mark	550.00
Royal Vienna, **Tankard**, Classical Sacrifice Scene On Gilt, C.1850	600.00
Royal Vienna, **Urn**, Geometric Design, Signed, Green, Yellow, Gold, 14 In.Tall	95.00
Royal Vienna, **Urn**, Pedestal Base, 17 In.	175.00
Royal Vienna, **Vase**, Cobalt, Gold Tracery, Vines, Floral, Scenic Medallion	45.00
Royal Vienna, **Vase**, Cobalt, Gold, & White, 2 Bathers, Insert, Signed A.F.	90.00
Royal Vienna, **Vase**, Ewer, Floral & Gilt, 10 1/2 In.	58.00
Royal Vienna, **Vase**, Full Figures Obverse, Cupids Reverse, Blue, Gold, Neumann	450.00
Royal Vienna, **Vase**, Girl, Jeweled, Gold, Red, Signed Wagner, 4 1/2 In.Tall	150.00
Royal Vienna, **Vase**, Kauffmann Scene, Gold, 2 Handles, 4 Feet, Beehive Mark	57.50
Royal Vienna, **Vase**, Miniature, 2 1/2 In.High, Pair	22.00
Royal Vienna, **Vase**, Portrait, Cobalt Ground, Fish Mouth, 4 1/2 In.	135.00
Royal Vienna, **Vase**, Portrait, Lady, Signed Ferd, Pair	565.00
Royal Vienna, **Vase**, Portrait, Queen Louise	98.00
Royal Vienna, **Vase**, Portraits Front & Back, Maroon, Green, Gold, Two Handles	40.00
Royal Vienna, **Vase**, Scenic, Maroon, Gold, Flat Oval, Blue Mark, 13 In.	125.00
Royal Vienna, **Vase**, Transfers Of Roman Figures, Coralene Type Beading	85.00

Royal Worcester Porcelain was made in the later period of Worcester Pottery which was originally established in 1751. The Royal Worcester tradename has been used by the Worcester Royal Porcelain Company, Ltd.since 1862.

Royal Worcester, see also Worcester

Royal Worcester, **Basket**, Basket Weave, Two Roses, Dated 1912, 3 1/2 In.Long	30.00
Royal Worcester, **Basket**, Covered, Footed, Pink, Rose, Yellow Flowers	115.00
Royal Worcester, **Basket**, Ivory To Apricot, Basket Weave, Gold Trim, 1899	45.00
Royal Worcester, **Bowl**, Basket Weave, Floral Inside, Open Gold Handles	125.00
Royal Worcester, **Bowl**, Creamy Satin, Basket Weave, Floral Inside, Handles	115.00
Royal Worcester, **Bowl**, Ivory, Floral, Gold Trim, 10 X 2 1/2 In.High	65.00
Royal Worcester, **Bowl**. Scalloped & Ribbed Sides, Hand-Painted Florals, Gold	135.00
Royal Worcester, **Bowl**, Shell, Cream Ground, Gold Design, 4 In.	20.00
Royal Worcester, **Box**, Covered, Floral On Satiny Beige, Purple Mark, Round	35.00
Royal Worcester, **Box**, Patch, Covered, Hand-Painted Floral, 1918	25.00

Royal Worcester, Butter & Attached Underplate, Brass Cover, Enamel Floral	55.00
Royal Worcester, Candlesnuffer, Figural, Monk Reading Book, 4 3/4 In.	95.00
Royal Worcester, Candlesnuffer, Figural, Oriental Lady Eats From Bowl	95.00
Royal Worcester, Candlesnuffer, Nun, Purple Mark	55.00
Royal Worcester, Candlesnuffer, Robin Hood's Hat Shape, Feather, 3 In.	55.00
Royal Worcester, Candlesnuffer, Sleeping Man Head With Nightcap, Handle	40.00
Royal Worcester, Compote, Ribbed With Three Dolphins	135.00
Royal Worcester, Compote, Turquoise, Floral Panel, Scrolls, Swags	275.00
Royal Worcester, Creamer, Figural, Form Of Green Leaves, Leaf Handle	23.00
Royal Worcester, Creamer, Floral Decoration, Gold Trim	45.00
Royal Worcester, Creamer, Pink & Yellow Roses On Beige, Gold, Purple Mark	42.00
Royal Worcester, Cup & Saucer, Anne Hathaway Cottage, Gold Scalloped Edges	22.00
Royal Worcester, Cup & Saucer, Cream, Floral	32.00
Royal Worcester, Cup & Saucer, Demitasse, Dunrobin Pattern	10.00
Royal Worcester, Cup & Saucer, Demitasse, Enamel, Coin Gold Floral	20.00
Royal Worcester, Cup & Saucer, Demitasse, Medallions, Gold Motif, Reliefs	28.00
Royal Worcester, Cup & Saucer, Demitasse, Pink, Gold Lined, Jewel Decoration	35.00
Royal Worcester, Cup & Saucer, Demitasse, Rosemary Pattern, Set Of 8	160.00
Royal Worcester, Dresser Set, 10 Piece	150.00
Royal Worcester, Ewer, Cream Ground, Enamel Floral, Gold Handles, 1888	90.00
Royal Worcester, Ewer, Enamel Pansies, Gold Encrusted, Serpent, 9 In.High	250.00
Royal Worcester, Ewer, Flower Design, Cream, 4 1/4 In.	40.00
Royal Worcester, Ewer, Flowers, White And Pink, Gold Pedestal	165.00
Royal Worcester, Ewer, Gold Decoration, Purple Crown Signature, 10 In.High	150.00
Royal Worcester, Figurine, Asian Man, Purple, Incised Mark, C.1877	75.00
Royal Worcester, Figurine, August, Girl On Rock, Modeled By F.G.Doughty	75.00
Royal Worcester, Figurine, Baby, Crawls, Blue Dress, Modeled By F.G.Doughty	72.00
Royal Worcester, Figurine, Girl Leaning On Fountain, Gold And Green	195.00
Royal Worcester, Figurine, Grandmother's Dress, Red Dress, 6 1/2 In.High	60.00
Royal Worcester, Figurine, June, Lady In Blue Dress, C.1940, 4 In.High	50.00
Royal Worcester, Figurine, June, Lady In Blue Dress, Williams & Bray	45.00
Royal Worcester, Figurine, Man Drinking, Woman Leaning, Signed, 1895, Pair	375.00
Royal Worcester, Figurine, Man In Black Hat, Register Mark 1876, 5 In.	98.00
Royal Worcester, Figurine, Mother Machree, 6 1/2 In.F.Doughty	75.00
Royal Worcester, Figurine, Penelope	225.00
Royal Worcester, Figurine, Saturday's Child, Girl Knitting, Cat, 5 1/2 In.	50.00
Royal Worcester, Figurine, Scotland, Girl In Green Skirt, Orange Blouse	60.00
Royal Worcester, Figurine, Sunday's Child, Boy, 4 1/2 In.High	55.00
Royal Worcester, Figurine, Snake Charmer Plays Flute, Blue Turban	55.00
Royal Worcester, Figurine, The Parakeet, Boy Holds Bird	80.00
Royal Worcester, Figurine, Woman, Holding Gold Tambourine, Marked	225.00
Royal Worcester, Flower Holder, Beige Ground, Gold Trim, Pedestal	70.00
Royal Worcester, Flower Holder, Green Leaves, White Floral, Circa 1905	45.00
Royal Worcester, Flower Holder, White Top, Green Base, Glazed, 1905	45.00
Royal Worcester, Jar & Underplate, Biscuit, Melon Rib, Floral, Gold Trim	135.00
Royal Worcester, Jar & Underplate, Cracker, Floral, Purple Mark	135.00
Royal Worcester, Jar, Biscuit, Melon Rib, Raised Gold Leaves, Silver Mount	60.00
Royal Worcester, Jar, Covered, Cream, Floral, 7 In.	95.00
Royal Worcester, Jar, Figural, Bust Of Cat Cover, White, Blue Ribbon On Neck	125.00
Royal Worcester, Jar, Rose, Brown To Cream, Red Roses, Pierced Lid, 1909	95.00
Royal Worcester, Jardiniere, Cream Color, Gilt Enamel, Purple Mark, 1891	98.00
Royal Worcester, Jug, Cream Color, Allover Floral, Gold, Purple Mark	135.00
Royal Worcester, Jug, Milk, Floral, England, Dated 1896	45.00
Royal Worcester, Jug, Wine, Allover Floral On Cream, Gold, C.1887	135.00
Royal Worcester, Jug, Wine, Cream, Floral, Gold Decoration, Purple Mark	138.00
Royal Worcester, Muffineer, Cream Ground, Raised Leaves, Gold, Dr.Locke Mark	30.00
Royal Worcester, Muffineer, Cream Ground, Raised Leaves, Gold, Silver Top	35.00
Royal Worcester, Muffineer, Relief Design On Rosy Beige, C.1862	64.00
Royal Worcester, Pitcher, Beige Satiny Ground, Gold Leaf, Floral, 9 1/2 In.	110.00
Royal Worcester, Pitcher, Cream Ground, Floral, Powder Horn Shape, 1887	85.00
Royal Worcester, Pitcher, Cream Ground, Vivid Floral, Gold Trim, 6 1/4 In.	73.00
Royal Worcester, Pitcher, Cream, Gold Outlined Florals, Signed H.L., 1889	85.00
Royal Worcester, Pitcher, Eggshell Finish, Floral, Gold Handle, 3 1/2 In.	45.00
Royal Worcester, Pitcher, Face Spout, Gold Handle, 3 1/2 In.High	57.50
Royal Worcester, Pitcher, Floral Sprays, Gold Handle, 14 X 6 In.High	69.00
Royal Worcester, Pitcher, Floral, Gold Handle, Green Mark, 5 1/2 In.	38.00

Royal Worcester, Pitcher, Flower Design, Gargoyle Handle, Beige, Purple Mark 65.00
Royal Worcester, Pitcher, Hand-Painted Flower, Gold Handle, Signed 65.00
Royal Worcester, Pitcher, Horn Shape, Cream, Gold Bands & Handle, Red Mark 40.00
Royal Worcester, Pitcher, Palm Leaf Design, 9 In. 60.00
Royal Worcester, Pitcher, White Porcelain, Purple Mark, 1884 .... 110.00
Royal Worcester, Pitcher, 5 1/2 In. .... *Illus* 135.00

Royal Worcester, Pitcher, 5 1/2 In.

Royal Worcester, Plate & Attached Stand, Cake, Blue Pagodas 60.00
Royal Worcester, Plate, Blue Flowers, Gold Stamens, C.1886, 8 1/8 In. 8.00
Royal Worcester, Plate, Cake, Anne Hathaway Cottage 28.00
Royal Worcester, Plate, Cake, Floral, Signed Twice 30.00
Royal Worcester, Plate, Chinese Pagoda Pattern, Gold Rim, C.1878, Set Of 6 .... 25.00
Royal Worcester, Plate, Cream Ground, Purple Iris, Signed, 6 3/4 In. 10.00
Royal Worcester, Plate, Flower Sprays, Pink, Yellow, & Red, England, W4160 .... 11.50
Royal Worcester, Plate, Pie, Anne Hathaway Cottage 10.00
Royal Worcester, Plate, Tan, Ivory Medallion, Scene, Artist Sedgley, 12 .... 180.00
Royal Worcester, Plate, The Grammar School, Stratford-On-Avon, 10 1/2 In. 15.00
Royal Worcester, Plate, Tiffany & Co., C.1910 .... 12.50
Royal Worcester, Plate, Tiny Blue Flowers, 6 In. ....
Royal Worcester, Platter, Gold Scalloped Edge, 16 X 1 1/2 In., Marked 125.00
Royal Worcester, Potpourri, Ivory To Green, Reticulated Cover, 1901 .... 47.50
Royal Worcester, Sugar & Creamer, Ivory, Gold, Shell Design, Dolphin Handles 85.00
Royal Worcester, Teapot, Flower Design, Green, Blue, Coral, Gold, 6 Cup Size 75.00
Royal Worcester, Teapot, Flowers, Gold Trim, Handle, Marked 85.00
Royal Worcester, Teapot, Individual, White Ground, Flower Swags, Gold, Mark 59.00
Royal Worcester, Teapot, Individual, White, Floral Swags, Gold, Registry Mark 68.50
Royal Worcester, Teapot, Panels, Blue, Gold, Orange Floral, Green Leaves 115.00
Royal Worcester, Teapot, Squat, Floral Decoration, Bamboo Handle 85.00
Royal Worcester, Toothpick, Tree Stump 24.50
Royal Worcester, Tray, Floral Center, Ornate, Raised Gold Floral Edge 60.00
Royal Worcester, Tray, Flowers, Leaves, Matte Finish, 4 3/4 In.Diameter 20.00
Royal Worcester, Tray, Gold Floral Edge, 10 1/2 X 7 1/2 In., Marked 60.00
Royal Worcester, Tureen, Soup, Hollyhocks, Elephant Head Handles, 1862 .... 75.00
Royal Worcester, Vase, Apricot, Gold, Floral, 3 1/4 In.High 38.50
Royal Worcester, Vase, Beige, Floral, Dated 1897, Ewer, Satin Finish, Pair 105.00
Royal Worcester, Vase, Cream, Brown Flying Bird, Castle, Trees, C.1867 .... 85.00
Royal Worcester, Vase, Cream, Floral, Autumn Colors, Gold Rim, 3 3/4 In. 35.00
Royal Worcester, Vase, Enamel Floral, Gold Trim, Pedestal Base, 10 1/2 In. 105.00
Royal Worcester, Vase, Floral, C.1887, Handles, 5 In. 68.00
Royal Worcester, Vase, Green, Bouquets, Tracery, Two Handles, Pedestal, 1894 ...... 85.00
Royal Worcester, Vase, Hand-Painted Flowers, 1900 .... 37.50
Royal Worcester, Vase, Little Owl In Pine Tree, Purple Mark, Artist-Signed 200.00
Royal Worcester, Vase, Openwork Top, Decorated, Royal China Works, 1801 .... 70.00
Royal Worcester, Vase, Orange, Birds' Feet On Base, Registry Mark, 7 In. 195.00
Royal Worcester, Vase, Peacock, Trees, Locke & Co., 3 In.High 65.00
Royal Worcester, Vase, Pitcher, Embossed Flowers, Cream Colors 125.00
Royal Worcester, Vase, Red, Yellow, Orange Flowers, C.1860, 5 3/4 In. 45.00
Royal Worcester, Vase, Reticulated, Raised Gold Leaves, Floral, 7 1/2 In. 145.00
Royal Worcester, Vase, Roses, Pink, Yellow And Blue, Gold Trim 85.00
Royal Worcester, Vase, Star Shape, Green, White, Pink Legs, 2 1/2 In.High 25.00
Royal Worcester, Vase, Tree Trunk Shape, Menu Holder, Cream, Frog, C.1805 .... 50.00

Roycroft products were made by the Roycrofter community of East Aurora, New York in the late nineteenth and early twentieth centuries. The community was founded by Elbert Hubbard. The products included furniture, metalware, leatherwork and jewelry.

Roycroft, Desk Set, Hammered Copper, Pen Tray, Calendar, & Inkwell	15.50
Roycroft, Vase, Tan High Glaze, Signed, 4 1/4 In.High	15.00

RS Germany Porcelain was made at the factory of Rheinhold Schlegelmilch after 1869 in Tillowitz, Germany. It was sold both decorated and undecorated.

RS Germany, see also RS Prussia

RS Germany, Basket, Flower Design, Orange, Brown, Blue Mark, 4 1/2 In.	22.00
RS Germany, Basket, Flowers, Butterfly Shape, Pearlized Iridescent, Gold	24.00
RS Germany, Basket, Pink Roses, Tan Ground, With Handle	27.50
RS Germany, Berry Set, Hydrangea Design, Coin Gold, Signed, 5 Piece	53.00
RS Germany, Berry Set, Roses, 5 Piece	35.00
RS Germany, Berry Set, Tea Roses On Gold & Tan, 5 Piece	45.00
RS Germany, Bowl & Underplate, Hand-Painted Flowers & Ivy, Yellow, Green	25.00
RS Germany, Bowl, Allover Gold Floral On Gold, Open Handles	18.00
RS Germany, Bowl, Berry, Cream Ground, Roses, Set Of 5	20.00
RS Germany, Bowl, Blue Gray Floral & Leaves On Green & Beige	20.00
RS Germany, Bowl, Cerise, Pink Tulips, Green Shading	5.00
RS Germany, Bowl, Embossed Edge, Flowers In Center, Gold Tracery	60.00
RS Germany, Bowl, Floral, 9 In.	28.00
RS Germany, Bowl, Footed, Garland Border, Gold, 4 Feet	16.50
RS Germany, Bowl, Gold Decoration Inside, Flowers, Marked Under Glaze	30.00
RS Germany, Bowl, Gold Ground, Coral Floral, Reinhold, Schlegelmilch	28.50
RS Germany, Bowl, Green Gray Ground, Blue Floral, Gold Trim, 9 1/2 In.	25.00
RS Germany, Bowl, Open Handled, Pink And White Tulips, Satin Finish	22.50
RS Germany, Bowl, Orange, Roses, Handle, 8 1/2 In.	16.50
RS Germany, Bowl, Red Ground, White & Black Floral, Tricorner	49.00
RS Germany, Bowl, Rose Design, Scalloped Edge, Green, 9 In.	22.50
RS Germany, Bowl, Scenic, House, Water Mill, Farm, 10 In.Diameter	35.00
RS Germany, Bowl, Shaded Surface, White Lilies, Petal Scallops	22.00
RS Germany, Bowl, White Floral, Green Border, 10 In.	28.00
RS Germany, Bowl, White Poppies, Blue & Gold Edge, Footed, Open Handles	30.00
RS Germany, Bowl, Yellow, Rose & White Irises On Beige To Brown, Marked	8.00
RS Germany, Bowl, Yellow Roses On Beige, Scalloped, Three Raised Handles	20.00
RS Germany, Box, Powder, Covered, Lilies	21.00
RS Germany, Box, Powder, Satin, Pink & Green Lilacs, Gold, Marked M.W.E.	18.00
RS Germany, Box, Powder, Tulips, Blue Wreath Mark	13.50
RS Germany, Cake Set, Rose Design, Pink, White, Red, Green, 5 Piece	55.00
RS Germany, Candlestick, Iridescent, Gold Pinecones, Gold Saucer Top, Pair	25.00
RS Germany, Celery, Allover Embossed Gold, Open Handle, 10 1/2 In.Long	23.50
RS Germany, Celery, Hand-Painted White Roses, Gold	16.50
RS Germany, Celery, Open Handles, Scalloped, Pink & White Floral, Green Mark	24.00
RS Germany, Celery, Orchids, Open Handles, Gold Border, 11 In.Long	22.50
RS Germany, Celery, Pierced Handles, Orange Roses On Beige & Blue	37.50
RS Germany, Celery, Tulips, Tillowitz, 11 In.	17.00
RS Germany, Chocolate Pot, Lavender, Peachy Poppy, Coupe Lines	27.50
RS Germany, Chocolate Pot, Rose Design, Tankard Shape, Individual, 6 In.Tall	22.50
RS Germany, Chocolate Set, Snowballs, Leaves, Gold Trim, 13 Piece	135.00
RS Germany, Compote, Orange Blossoms	19.00
RS Germany, Creamer, Calla Lily, Green Wreath, Footed	6.50
RS Germany, Creamer, Girl Silhouette Center, Yellow Ground, Silver Overlay	25.00
RS Germany, Creamer, Squatty, Green Shaded, Lavender Flowers	1.00
RS Germany, Creamer, White, Pink Roses, Gold	10.00
RS Germany, Creamer, White, Poppies, Bulbous	10.00
RS Germany, Cup & Saucer, Demitasse, Leaf Design, Light Green, Black Mark	13.50
RS Germany, Cup & Saucer, Demitasse, Roses	20.00
RS Germany, Cup & Saucer, Demitasse, Violets, Blue Mark & Star	25.00
RS Germany, Cup & Saucer, Green Ground, Pink Roses	10.00
RS Germany, Cup & Saucer, Poppies	34.00
RS Germany, Cup & Saucer, Roses	16.00
RS Germany, Cup & Saucer, White Roses, Coral Centers, Leaves	28.00
RS Germany, Dish, Cake, Rose Design, Handle, Gold Trim	12.50

RS Germany, **Dish**, Candy, Applied Strap Handles, Green Band & Block, Gold 10.00
RS Germany, **Dish**, Candy, Blue Forget-Me-Nots On Blue & Green 12.50
RS Germany, **Dish**, Candy, Orchid Flowers, Green, Hand-Painted, 6 1/4 In. 14.50
RS Germany, **Dish**, Cheese & Cracker, White Hydrangea, Bisque Finish 60.00
RS Germany, **Dish**, Double Decker, Green Ground, Orange, Rose, Yellow Floral 25.00
RS Germany, **Dish**, Double Decker, Rose Design, Pink, Blue, 4 1/2 In.Diameter 25.00
RS Germany, **Dish**, Lemon, Lemon Shape, Pink Floral On Green, Gold Handle 15.00
RS Germany, **Dish**, Nut, Purple Floral, Gold Border, Open Handle 16.50
RS Germany, **Dish**, Nut, White, Gold Border, Scallop, Footed, 3 1/4 In.Diameter 7.50
RS Germany, **Dish**, Olive, Hand-Painted Olives, Pink Ground, Openwork Handles 16.50
RS Germany, **Hair Receiver**, Hibiscus Design, White, Gold, Green 12.50
RS Germany, **Hair Receiver**, Shaded Green Ground, Pink Roses, Scalloped Edge 14.00
RS Germany, **Hair Receiver**, Wedding Band Pattern 9.50
RS Germany, **Hair Receiver**, White, White Roses, Pink Centers, Brown Leaves 18.00
RS Germany, **Hatpin Holder**, Blue Floral On Blue, Gold Top, Scalloped Top 20.00
RS Germany, **Hatpin Holder**, Calla Lily On White To Green .... 20.00 To 22.50
RS Germany, **Hatpin Holder**, Floral 22.00
RS Germany, **Hatpin Holder**, Floral Decoration 22.50
RS Germany, **Hatpin Holder**, Floral, 4 1/2 In.High 22.50
RS Germany, **Hatpin Holder**, Green Ground, White Lilies 24.00
RS Germany, **Hatpin Holder**, Green Ground, White Roses 22.50
RS Germany, **Hatpin Holder**, Hand-Painted Yellow Jonquils, Leaves, Gilt 25.00
RS Germany, **Hatpin Holder**, Lily Design, White, Green Wreath Mark 27.50
RS Germany, **Hatpin Holder**, Pink & White Roses, Blue Mark 21.50
RS Germany, **Hatpin Holder**, Poppies, Panels 17.75
RS Germany, **Hatpin Holder**, Rose Decoration 38.00
RS Germany, **Hatpin Holder**, Roses, Green Mark 28.00
RS Germany, **Hatpin Holder**, Tan & Cream, Red Poppies 22.50
RS Germany, **Hatpin Holder**, Tinted Roses, Panels, Irregular Gold Edge 23.50
RS Germany, **Hatpin Holder**, White, Gold Trim, Large 22.50
RS Germany, **Holder**, Ring, Covered, Tiny Pink Roses, Gold & Green Leaves 15.00
RS Germany, **Holder**, Toothbrush, Hanging, Green, Orange Poppies, Six Notches 20.00
RS Germany, **Inkwell**, Covered 20.00
RS Germany, **Inkwell**, Roses, Brown, Yellow 22.00
RS Germany, **Inkwell**, White, Undecorated, Hexagon Base, 3 In.Square 10.00
RS Germany, **Jar**, Biscuit, Calla Lilies On Green To Celadon, Gold 38.50
RS Germany, **Jar**, Cookie, Brushed Rust Ground, Rose Bouquets, Gold Trim 65.00
RS Germany, **Jar**, Cookie, Pink, Lavender, & Yellow Roses, Finial 80.00
RS Germany, **Jar**, Cracker, Carnation Design, Pink, Handle, Green Mark 38.00
RS Germany, **Jar**, Cracker, Covered, Cotton Plant Design, 2 Handles 37.50
RS Germany, **Jar**, Cracker, Leaf Design, Purple, Green, Handle, 6 1/2 In.High 90.00
RS Germany, **Jar**, Cracker, Roses, Two Handles 35.00
RS Germany, **Jar**, Powder, Floral 15.00
RS Germany, **Jar**, Powder, Pink Poppies, Gold, Green Mark 12.50
RS Germany, **Mug**, Shaving, Floral, Buds, Leaves 48.00
RS Germany, **Mug**, Shaving, Pink Blossom, Green Star 12.50
RS Germany, **Mustard Pot**, Covered, Yellow & Pink Roses On White To Green 17.00
RS Germany, **Mustard Pot**, Pink Peony & Snowball Motif, Ruffled Top 18.00
RS Germany, **Mustard Pot**, Roses, Wide Pink & Gold Border & Handle 16.50
RS Germany, **Mustard Set**, Lavender Pink Floral On Green, Scalloped, 2 Piece 18.50
RS Germany, **Nappy**, Cream To Tan, Roses, Buds, Gold, Handle 25.00
RS Germany, **Nappy**, Large Pink Roses, Green To Beige Ground, Tricorner 20.00
RS Germany, **Nappy**, Yellow Flowers, Luster Ground, Handle, Artist-Signed 14.00
RS Germany, **Perfume**, Cluster Of Pink Roses, Marigold Ground, Stopper 24.00
RS Germany, **Perfume**, Pink & White Roses On White To Green, 5 In.High 15.00
RS Germany, **Pitcher**, Milk, Green, White Lilies 23.00
RS Germany, **Plate**, Apple Blossoms, Satin Finish, 6 1/2 In., Set Of 3 .... 18.00
RS Germany, **Plate**, Cake, Grapes, Leaves, House, Purple, Yellow, Hand-Painted 14.00
RS Germany, **Plate**, Cake, Mother-Of-Pearl Finish, Apple Blossoms, Gold 32.00
RS Germany, **Plate**, Cake, Narcissus Flowers, Handled, Gold Border 28.00
RS Germany, **Plate**, Cake, Open Handles, Hand-Painted Poppies 40.00
RS Germany, **Plate**, Cake, Open Pink Roses, Shadow Leaves, Handle, 10 In. 15.00
RS Germany, **Plate**, Cake, Pierced Handles, Orchid Lilies 17.50
RS Germany, **Plate**, Cake, Pierced Handles, White Poppies, Green Mark 20.00
RS Germany, **Plate**, Cake, Pink Tulips, Green Ground, Gold Border, Open Handles 18.50
RS Germany, **Plate**, Cookie, Green, Double Gold Border, Dogwood, Open Handled 18.50

RS Germany, Plate, Hand-Painted Pink & Green Roses, Green Mark 15.00
RS Germany, Plate, Large White Peony, 7 1/2 In. 9.00
RS Germany, Plate, Peonies, Orange, 8 In. 16.00
RS Germany, Plate, Peonies, 6 1/2 In., Set Of 6 .... 40.00
RS Germany, Plate, Pink Iris, Blue Mark 9.50
RS Germany, Plate, Pink Poppies, Blue Mark, 8 1/4 In. 35.00
RS Germany, Plate, Pink Roses On Green & White, Open Handles 15.00
RS Germany, Plate, Pink Sweet Peas, Gold Border, Tracery, 8 In. 20.00
RS Germany, Plate, Raspberries & Florals, 8 3/8 In.Diameter 16.00
RS Germany, Plate, Raspberries, Forget-Me-Nots, Poppies 18.00
RS Germany, Plate, Roses, Scalloped Beaded Edge 7.50
RS Germany, Plate, Roses, 8 1/2 In. 22.50
RS Germany, Plate, Scenic, Hand-Painted, Shepherd Leading Sheep, Farm, Tree 22.50
RS Germany, Plate, White Tulips 18.50
RS Germany, Relish, Gold Floral, Ornate Handles 18.00
RS Germany, Relish, Lavender & Purple Flowers, Gold, Marked 16.00
RS Germany, Relish, Pink Roses, Tillowitz, 10 1/2 In. 19.00
RS Germany, Relish, Rose Design, Pink, Green, Open Handle, 9 1/2 In.Long 14.50
RS Germany, Ring Tree, Forget-Me-Nots At Base, Gold Tipped Branches 25.00
RS Germany, Rose Bowl, Carmine, Nasturtiums, Gold, Signed J.L.Black 17.50
RS Germany, Sauce, Flower Design, Purple, Green, Underplate, Blue Mark 8.00
RS Germany, Sauce, Lavender Floral On Green Ground, Scalloped 7.00
RS Germany, Sauce, Roses, Set Of 6 .... 25.00
RS Germany, Sugar & Creamer, Allover Gold, Marked Stouffer Studios 25.00
RS Germany, Sugar & Creamer, Green Shades, White Blossoms, Pink & Gold Trim 35.00
RS Germany, Sugar & Creamer, Ivory Ground, Magnolias, Gold Trim 55.00
RS Germany, Sugar & Creamer, Poinsettia Decoration 30.00
RS Germany, Sugar & Creamer, Roses, Tillowitz .... 19.00 To 29.00
RS Germany, Sugar & Creamer, Satinized Blue, Gold Trim 22.00
RS Germany, Sugar & Creamer, Shaded Beige Ground, Floral, Green Mark 28.50
RS Germany, Sugar, Beige Ground, Pink Roses, 8 In.Wide, 6 In.High 25.00
RS Germany, Sugar, Covered, Blue, Gold Flowers, Signed Sadie MacMillan 15.00
RS Germany, Syrup & Underplate, Overall Pink Roses 22.50
RS Germany, Syrup, Pale Green To White, White Hydrangea, Gold 25.00
RS Germany, Teapot, Roses, Green Mark 25.00
RS Germany, Toothpick, Green, Red & Pink Roses, Gold Handles, Green Mark 40.00
RS Germany, Toothpick, Opalescent, Gold Handles, Square 7.00
RS Germany, Toothpick, White, Three Gold Handles 20.00
RS Germany, Tray, Perfume, Floral, 7 X 12 In. 47.50
RS Germany, Tray, Pink Flowers, Beige Ground, Open Handles, 12 1/2 X 9 In. 22.50
RS Germany, Vase, Art Nouveau, Gold Border, Two Handles, Artist-Signed 16.50
RS Germany, Vase, Beige Ground, Orange, Orchid & White Floral, 3 1/4 In. 18.50
RS Germany, Vase, Blue Flowers On Cream, Dated 1912, 2 Handles, 5 1/2 In. 12.00
RS Germany, Vase, Gold Border, Two Gold Handles, Hand-Painted Design 18.50
RS Germany, Vase, Poppies, Bulbous, 3 1/4 In. 15.00

RS Prussia Porcelain was made at the factory of Rheinhold Schlegelmilch after 1869 in Tillowitz, Germany. The porcelain was sold decorated or undecorated.
RS Prussia, see also RS Germany
RS Prussia, Bell, Dinner, Iridescent, Green & Pink Floral, Unmarked 25.00
RS Prussia, Berry Set, Rose Clusters, White, Red Lion Marked, 7 Piece 45.00
RS Prussia, Bowl, Berry, Portrait, Lady's Head In Relief, Floral, Red Mark 125.00
RS Prussia, Bowl, Blue Embossed Forget-Me-Nots At Edge, Floral Center 55.00
RS Prussia, Bowl, Blue, Pink & White Roses, Green Leaves In Bottom, Red Mark 80.00
RS Prussia, Bowl, Boat Scene, Medallions, Winter Scenes, Gold Jeweling 275.00
RS Prussia, Bowl, Calla Lilies, Green, Beige, Gold, Satin Finish, Red Mark 85.00
RS Prussia, Bowl, Calla Lily, Open Ends, 10 In. 35.00
RS Prussia, Bowl, Carnations, Blue, Gold, Red Mark, 10 In.Diameter 50.00
RS Prussia, Bowl, Cookie, Satinized, Two Handles 45.00
RS Prussia, Bowl, Eggshell Porcelain, Fluted Oval Panels, Signed, Red Mark 125.00
RS Prussia, Bowl, Eight Indented Panels, Floral, Signed, Red Mark 70.00
RS Prussia, Bowl, Five Different Bust Portraits, Gold & Cobalt Rim 275.00
RS Prussia, Bowl, Floral, Clovers In Relief, Gold Outlines, Red Mark 69.50
RS Prussia, Bowl, Floral, Red Mark, 8 1/2 In. 75.00
RS Prussia, Bowl, Flowers In Bottom, Ivory Ground, Red Mark 65.00

RS Prussia, Bowl, Flowers, Lavender, Cobalt, Yellow, Scalloped Edge, Gold 85.00
RS Prussia, Bowl, Flowers, Light To Dark Green, Gold Trim, 11 In.Diameter 70.00
RS Prussia, Bowl, Flying Bluebirds, Open Handles, Red Mark 225.00
RS Prussia, Bowl, Four Season, Red Mark 375.00
RS Prussia, Bowl, Gold Trim, Red Roses 70.00
RS Prussia, Bowl, Green & Pink Decoration, Fluted Edges, 10 In. 100.00
RS Prussia, Bowl, Green Luster, Pink Roses, 10 In. 75.00
RS Prussia, Bowl, Green Medallions, Raised Tan Flower Pads, Rose Sprays 95.00
RS Prussia, Bowl, Green, Blue, Pink & Gold Luster, Water Lilies, Red Mark 85.00
RS Prussia, Bowl, Green, Tan, Pink, White, Lavender Floral In Center, 10 In. 75.00
RS Prussia, Bowl, Ice Cream, Rose Decoration 15.00
RS Prussia, Bowl, Ivory Surface, Gold Bands, Floral, Scallops, Ornate Handle 50.00
RS Prussia, Bowl, Jeweled, Beige Ground, Roses, 10 1/4 In. 88.50
RS Prussia, Bowl, Jeweled, Blue-Purple Luster, Roses & Fleur-De-Lis 95.00
RS Prussia, Bowl, Large Roses, Embossed Edge, Gold Trim, 10 1/2 In. 85.00
RS Prussia, Bowl, Lily Floral, Gold Sides, Red Mark 95.00
RS Prussia, Bowl, Medallions, Roses, Dogwood, Lilies Of The Valley, Gold 125.00
RS Prussia, Bowl, Oval, Autumn Colored 95.00
RS Prussia, Bowl, Pale Green, White, & Lavender Floral, Footed Square Base 68.00
RS Prussia, Bowl, Pastel Lavender And White Gardenias, Red Mark, 10 In. 75.00
RS Prussia, Bowl, Peacock Looks At Swan In Pond, Birds In Sky 65.00
RS Prussia, Bowl, Pheasant In Field, Swan, Red Mark, 5 1/2 In.Diameter 85.00
RS Prussia, Bowl, Pink & Green Floral, Raised Gold Iris Edge 45.00
RS Prussia, Bowl, Pink Roses, Green & Gold Rim, Scalloped, Footed, Red Mark 110.00
RS Prussia, Bowl, Pink Roses, Red Mark, 9 1/2 In. 78.50
RS Prussia, Bowl, Pink Roses, White Daisies, Beaded, Gold Edge, 10 1/2 In. 80.00
RS Prussia, Bowl, Pink, Poppy Center, Ornate Moulded Rim 59.00
RS Prussia, Bowl, Pond Lilies, Gilt Trim, 9 In. 75.00
RS Prussia, Bowl, Poppies 65.00
RS Prussia, Bowl, Purple, Iridescent, Center Roses, Pearlized Jewels, Footed 110.00
RS Prussia, Bowl, Reticulated Edge, Chrysanthemums On 6 Panels, Gold 35.00
RS Prussia, Bowl, Rose & Flower Design, Yellow, Pink, Red & Star Mark 75.00
RS Prussia, Bowl, Rose & Pink, Roses, Gold, Red Mark, 10 3/4 In. 85.00
RS Prussia, Bowl, Rose Bottom, Ruffled Edge, 12 Panels, Red Star Mark 65.00
RS Prussia, Bowl, Rose Design, Scalloped Edge, Pink, Red Mark, 10 In. 75.00
RS Prussia, Bowl, Salad, White, Raised Iris, Six Individual Bowls, Red Mark 150.00
RS Prussia, Bowl, Spring Season, Satinized, Red Mark 125.00
RS Prussia, Bowl, Spring Season, 5 1/2 In.Diameter, Red Mark 110.00
RS Prussia, Bowl, Star & Flower Design, Pink, White, Yellow, Red Mark & Star 75.00
RS Prussia, Bowl, Vegetable, Green, Lilies, Silver Resist Floral Border 70.00
RS Prussia, Bowl, White Lilies With Orange Centers, Scalloped, Red Mark 65.00
RS Prussia, Bowl, White, Pink Floral, Red Mark, 8 In.Diameter 37.50
RS Prussia, Bowl, White, Tan, Green, Gold, Red & White Roses, 10 1/2 In. 65.00
RS Prussia, Bowl, Yellow Ground, Pink Roses, Iris Border, Red Mark 60.00
RS Prussia, Box, Covered, Sheep Herder Scene 40.00
RS Prussia, Box, Portrait On Cover, Blown Iris Decoration 110.00
RS Prussia, Box, Powder, Roses, Green Leaves, Red Band Around Bottom, Red Top 70.00
RS Prussia, Celery, Art Nouveau Face In Orchid, Green Shadings 38.00
RS Prussia, Celery, Blue And Yellow Border, Pink Poppies, Red Mark 95.00
RS Prussia, Celery, Embossed Iris, Floral, Multicolor 55.00
RS Prussia, Celery, Floral Sprays, Scalloped Edge, Open Handle, Red Mark 65.00
RS Prussia, Celery, Open Handle, Roses & Daisies Center, Gold, Red Mark 42.00
RS Prussia, Celery, Pearlized, Pink Carnations, Scalloped, Red Mark 72.00
RS Prussia, Celery, Pink & Yellow Roses, Scalloped, Cutout Handles 85.00
RS Prussia, Celery, Pink Poppies, Scrolled Embossed Edge, Open Ends 70.00
RS Prussia, Celery, Red Roses, White Mums, Gold, Cutout Handles 95.00
RS Prussia, Celery, Scenic, Gold Trim, Red Mark, 12 In.Long 85.00
RS Prussia, Celery, Scenic, Water, Birds, Beaded Medallions, Red Mark 68.00
RS Prussia, Celery, Seven Large Roses, Red Mark 58.00
RS Prussia, Celery, Shepherd Scene, Red Mark, 12 1/2 In.Long 165.00
RS Prussia, Celery, Snowball & Rose Design, Green, Gold Border 65.00
RS Prussia, Celery, Water Lily Pond Scene, Gold Scrolls, Red Mark 53.00
RS Prussia, Celery, White Floral Nosegays, Gold Trim, Open Handles 65.00
RS Prussia, Chocolate Pot, Calla Lily, Red Mark 72.00
RS Prussia, Chocolate Pot, Corset Shape, Light To Dark Pink, Footed, 10 In. 160.00
RS Prussia, Chocolate Pot, Floral, Red Mark, 9 In.High 115.00

RS Prussia, **Chocolate Pot**, Footed, Gold, Embossed, Mauve Floral, Red Mark 110.00
RS Prussia, **Chocolate Pot**, Green Luster, Pink Roses, Red Mark 85.00
RS Prussia, **Chocolate Pot**, Panels, White Floral, Gold Centers, Green Tints 115.00
RS Prussia, **Chocolate Pot**, Pink, Orange Yellow Roses, Footed, Red Mark 70.00
RS Prussia, **Chocolate Pot**, Red Roses 95.00
RS Prussia, **Chocolate Pot**, Red, Iridescent, Large Pink Roses, Satinized 95.00
RS Prussia, **Chocolate Pot**, Red, Iridescent, Pink & Orange Roses, Red Mark 95.00
RS Prussia, **Chocolate Pot**, Rose Sprays & Gray Blue Decoration On White 165.00
RS Prussia, **Chocolate Pot**, Satinized, Red, Gold, Roses, Red Mark 110.00
RS Prussia, **Chocolate Pot**, Two Cups & Saucers, Green, White Lilies 150.00
RS Prussia, **Chocolate Pot**, White Daisies, Pink Poppies, Water, Red Mark 125.00
RS Prussia, **Chocolate Pot**, White Luster, Green, White Flowers, Gold Stems 110.00
RS Prussia, **Chocolate Set**, Dogwood Pattern, Red Mark, 9 Piece 175.00
RS Prussia, **Chocolate Set**, Dogwood Pattern, 12 Piece 150.00
RS Prussia, **Chocolate Set**, Green Luster, Lilies, Marked, 12 Piece 250.00
RS Prussia, **Chocolate Set**, Green Shades, White Floral, Gold, 9 Piece 285.00
RS Prussia, **Chocolate Set**, Pink Roses On Luster, Gilt, Red Mark, 9 Piece 150.00
RS Prussia, **Chocolate Set**, Poppy Decoration, Gold Beading, Red Mark, 9 Piece 185.00
RS Prussia, **Coffeepot**, Christmas Roses, Pine Needles, White 110.00
RS Prussia, **Compote**, Roses, Peach Color, Satin Finish, 8 1/2 In.Diameter 225.00
RS Prussia, **Creamer**, Ducks, Chickens, Red Mark 65.00
RS Prussia, **Creamer**, Green, White Chrysanthemums, Embossing, Beading 30.00
RS Prussia, **Creamer**, Orange Roses, Gold Trim, Footed 38.00
RS Prussia, **Creamer**, Pink Roses & Shadow Flowers, 2 Shades Of Green, Marked 32.00
RS Prussia, **Creamer**, Red Mark 28.00
RS Prussia, **Cup & Saucer**, Demitasse, Flowers, Ruffled Edge, 2 In. 30.00
RS Prussia, **Cup & Saucer**, Demitasse, Multicolor Floral 30.00
RS Prussia, **Cup & Saucer**, Demitasse, Pink & Gold Decoration, Roses, Red Mark 45.00
RS Prussia, **Cup & Saucer**, Green Ground, White Floral, Gold Edge, Footed 40.00
RS Prussia, **Cup & Saucer**, Holly & Berries, Miniature, Red Star Mark 75.00
RS Prussia, **Cup & Saucer**, Pink Shades, White Flowers 40.00
RS Prussia, **Cup**, Chocolate, Rose Decoration, Pink, White, Gold, Red Mark 20.00
RS Prussia, **Cup**, Chocolate, Roses, Pink, White, Gold Rim, Red & Star Mark 20.00
RS Prussia, **Cup**, Lavender & White, Scalloped Edge, Four Legs, Red Mark 12.50
RS Prussia, **Cup**, Mustache, Pink Roses, Red Mark 125.00
RS Prussia, **Cup**, Pink & Blue Forget-Me-Nots, Gold, Red Mark 10.00
RS Prussia, **Dish**, Candy, Open Handled, Round, Rose Decor 18.00
RS Prussia, **Dish**, Candy, Pink Shades, Yellow Roses, Gold Tracery, Handles 14.00
RS Prussia, **Dish**, Fruit, Carnations, Red Mark, Set Of 6 .... 35.00
RS Prussia, **Dish**, Mayonnaise, Satin Finish, Rose, Gold Trim, Red Mark 50.00
RS Prussia, **Dish**, Olive, Pink Roses, Gold, Cutout Handles 38.00
RS Prussia, **Fernery**, Fluted Edge, Liner, Red Mark 40.00
RS Prussia, **Fernery**, Footed, Marked, 3 1/2 X 6 1/2 In. 75.00
RS Prussia, **Fernery**, Pink & White Roses On Green, 3 In.High 85.00
RS Prussia, **Hair Receiver**, Cottage Scene, Footed, Oval 35.00
RS Prussia, **Hair Receiver**, Flower Design, Artist-Signed, Blue Mark, C.1861 .... 22.00
RS Prussia, **Hair Receiver**, Green Luster, Pink Roses, Red Mark 45.00
RS Prussia, **Hair Receiver**, Pearlized, Apple Blossoms, 2 Piece 75.00
RS Prussia, **Hair Receiver**, Pink Roses At Top & Base, Green Edges 40.00
RS Prussia, **Hatpin Holder & Jewel Box**, Red Roses, Gold, Signed 35.00
RS Prussia, **Hatpin Holder**, Red & Pink Roses 25.00
RS Prussia, **Hatpin Holder**, Roses, Two Open Handles, Red Mark .... 55.00 To 58.50
RS Prussia, **Hatpin Holder**, Shaded Green Ground, Pink Roses, Ribbed 75.00
RS Prussia, **Inkwell**, Glass Insert 45.00
RS Prussia, **Jar**, Cookie, Bunch Of Roses Front & Back, Small Roses At Top 85.00
RS Prussia, **Jar**, Cookie, Rose Design, Pink, Beige, 7 In.High 75.00
RS Prussia, **Jar**, Cracker, Buff Ground, Roses, Gold Trim, Red Mark 95.00
RS Prussia, **Jar**, Cracker, Bulbous Shoulder, Melon Ribbed, Red Mark 75.00
RS Prussia, **Jar**, Cracker, Footed, Scroll Handles, Pink Roses, Gilt, Marked 85.00
RS Prussia, **Jar**, Cracker, Greens, Tan, Pink Flowers, Gold Trim, Red Mark 90.00
RS Prussia, **Jar**, Cracker, Roses 75.00
RS Prussia, **Jar**, Cracker, Satinized Red & Pink Roses, White Ground, Fluted 70.00
RS Prussia, **Jar**, Cracker, Swan Design, Red Mark 80.00
RS Prussia, **Jar**, Cracker, White, Green, Gold, Signed C.K.W. 25.00
RS Prussia, **Jar**, Cracker, White, Pink Roses, Octagon, Red Mark 70.00
RS Prussia, **Muffineer**, Pearlized Green, White Firs, Gold Tracings, Mark 55.00

RS Prussia, **Muffineer**, Pink Floral On Green, Scalloped Top & Bottom 55.00
RS Prussia, **Muffineer**, Pink Roses On Green, Flared Base, Red Mark 60.00
RS Prussia, **Muffineer**, Two Handles 35.00
RS Prussia, **Muffineer**, White Floral, Gold, Blue Luster At Top 65.00
RS Prussia, **Muffineer**, White Flowers On Green, Scalloped Bottom 87.50
RS Prussia, **Mug**, Shaving, Beige, Pink & Yellow Flowers 70.00
RS Prussia, **Mug**, Shaving, Foliage, Roses, Yellow To Pink 60.00
RS Prussia, **Mug**, Shaving, Mirror, Red Mark 125.00
RS Prussia, **Mug**, Shaving, Pink Roses On Shaded Green, Red Mark 75.00
RS Prussia, **Mug**, Shaving, Rose Decoration, Insert, Beveled Mirror, Red Mark 135.00
RS Prussia, **Mug**, Shaving, Roses, Gold Trim, Soap Shelf, Footed, Red Mark 78.00
RS Prussia, **Mug**, Shaving, Roses, Insert, Beveled Mirror, Red Mark 110.00
RS Prussia, **Mustard Pot**, Lilies, Green Shades, Red Mark 38.50
RS Prussia, **Mustard Pot**, Pink Roses, Handled, Footed 35.00
RS Prussia, **Mustard Pot**, Scenic, Swans, Pond, Pine Trees, Unmarked 28.00
RS Prussia, **Mustard Pot**, Swans On Lake 23.00
RS Prussia, **Mustard Set**, Covered, 2 Piece 35.00
RS Prussia, **Pickle**, Floral 38.50
RS Prussia, **Pickle**, Red Mark 34.00
RS Prussia, **Pitcher**, Roses, Medallions, Green, White, Pink, Scalloped Top 195.00
RS Prussia, **Planter**, Roses, Red Mark, 8 1/4 In.Diameter 75.00
RS Prussia, **Plate**, Apples, Grapes, Cherries, Gold Trim, Scalloped, Red Mark 75.00
RS Prussia, **Plate**, Blackberries & Leaves, Green & Gold, Church Mark 17.50
RS Prussia, **Plate**, Blue Scalloped Border, Gold Trim, Flowers, Red Mark 63.00
RS Prussia, **Plate**, Bread, Rustic Scene, Old Mill, Water Wheel, Gold Beaded 55.00
RS Prussia, **Plate**, Bread, Windflower Design, Pink, Handle, 13 X 16 1/2 In. 80.00
RS Prussia, **Plate**, Cake, Gold Floral, Luster, Handle, Red Mark 59.00
RS Prussia, **Plate**, Cake, Large Roses, Satinized, Two Handles, Red Mark 110.00
RS Prussia, **Plate**, Cake, Open Handle, White Daisies, Pink Poppies, Water, Mark 70.00
RS Prussia, **Plate**, Cake, Orange Blossoms, Red Mark 38.00
RS Prussia, **Plate**, Cake, Pink Roses, Daisies, Scalloped Edge, Red Mark 50.00
RS Prussia, **Plate**, Cake, Pink Roses, White Daisies, Green Leaves, Red Mark 80.00
RS Prussia, **Plate**, Cake, Roses, Buds, Pink To Rose, Piecrust Edge, Red Mark 50.00
RS Prussia, **Plate**, Cake, Roses, Mums, Daisies, Cutout Handles, Pink, Green, Gold 70.00
RS Prussia, **Plate**, Cake, Roses, Violets, Baroque Edge, Perforated Handles 65.00
RS Prussia, **Plate**, Cake, Satinized, Red Roses, Open Handles, Red Mark 85.00
RS Prussia, **Plate**, Cake, Scene, Castles, Water, Boat, People, Handle, Signed 145.00
RS Prussia, **Plate**, Cake, White Floral Nosegay, Green Leaves, Scalloped Edge 85.00
RS Prussia, **Plate**, Cake, White Floral Nosegays, Open Handles, Gold Edge 80.00
RS Prussia, **Plate**, Chocolate Medallions, Gold Stems, Blue Water, Red Mark 63.00
RS Prussia, **Plate**, Five Medallion Portraits, Red Mark 195.00
RS Prussia, **Plate**, Flower Design, Green, White, Gold, Red Mark, 6 In. 17.00
RS Prussia, **Plate**, Flowers, Gold Rim, Raised Plumes, Red Mark, 11 In.Diameter 60.00
RS Prussia, **Plate**, Flowers, Medallions, Reliefs, Beading, Red Mark, 8 In. 95.00
RS Prussia, **Plate**, Green, White Floral, Gold, 10 In. 65.00
RS Prussia, **Plate**, Hanging, Three Roses & Foliage, Gold Border 12.00
RS Prussia, **Plate**, Orchid Design, Blue, Red Mark, Scallop, 8 In.Diameter 25.00
RS Prussia, **Plate**, Pastel Firs, Pearlized Beads, Embossed Edge, 8 1/2 In. 65.00
RS Prussia, **Plate**, Pink & White Dogwood, Signed Reinhold Schlegelmilch 40.00
RS Prussia, **Plate**, Pink Carnations On Blue Green To Cream Yellow, Red Mark 25.00
RS Prussia, **Plate**, Portrait, Winter Season, Raised & Figured, Gold Ground 400.00
RS Prussia, **Plate**, Red Roses, Satinized, 2 Handles, Red Mark 79.00
RS Prussia, **Plate**, Roses & Daisies, Coin Gold Trim, Red Mark, 7 1/2 In. 30.00
RS Prussia, **Plate**, Satin Finish, 8 1/2 In. 95.00
RS Prussia, **Plate**, Scenic, Boat, Sea, Mountains, 8 1/2 In. 195.00
RS Prussia, **Plate**, Seascape, Six-Medallion Edge, Red Mark, Open Handle 133.00
RS Prussia, **Plate**, Shaded Aqua, Pink Poppies, Red Mark, 8 1/2 In. 37.50
RS Prussia, **Plate**, Shaded Green Ground, Roses, Gold Scalloped Rim, Red Mark 47.50
RS Prussia, **Plate**, Ship Scene, Red Mark, 11 In. 150.00
RS Prussia, **Plate**, Six Petal Medallion, Floral, Gold, Red Mark 98.00
RS Prussia, **Plate**, Tan, Green, White, Gold, 7 In. 20.00
RS Prussia, **Platter**, Cake, Rose Decoration, Satinized, Open Handle, Red Mark 110.00
RS Prussia, **Platter**, Pearlized, Floral, Open Handles, Red Mark 90.00
RS Prussia, **Platter**, Satinized, Roses, Open Handles, 11 1/2 In.Diameter 85.00
RS Prussia, **Relish**, Pink Roses, Gold, Open Handles, Red Wreath With Star 24.50
RS Prussia, **Relish**, Poppies Reflected In Stream, Red Mark 25.00

RS Prussia, Relish, Rose Design, Pink, Green, Open Ends, Red & Star Mark 30.00
RS Prussia, Relish, Roses, Pink, Yellow, Handle, Red Mark, 12 X 6 In. 35.00
RS Prussia, Salt & Pepper, Pink Rose, Red Mark 65.00
RS Prussia, Sauce, Floral 17.50
RS Prussia, Sauce, Green Edges, Orchid, White & Gold Floral, Red Mark 15.00
RS Prussia, Sauce, Pansy Design, Yellow, Red Mark 28.50
RS Prussia, Sauce, Red Flowers, Shadings, Red Mark 12.00
RS Prussia, Sauce, White Dogwood, Green Leaves, Gold Beading Around Rim 30.00
RS Prussia, Sugar & Creamer .... *Illus* 250.00
RS Prussia, Sugar & Creamer, Chrysanthemums 85.00
RS Prussia, Sugar & Creamer, Chrysanthemums On Beige, Footed, Red Mark 85.00
RS Prussia, Sugar & Creamer, Cobalt 220.00
RS Prussia, Sugar & Creamer, Floral, Ornate Handles & Finial, No Mark 75.00
RS Prussia, Sugar & Creamer, Green With Gold, Red Mark 85.00

RS Prussia, Sugar & Creamer

RS Prussia, Teapot, Roses, 6 In.
See Page 491

RS Prussia, Sugar & Creamer, Magenta Floral, Satin Finish, Red Mark 80.00
RS Prussia, Sugar & Creamer, Panels, Pink Roses, Ornate Finial, Satin Finish 125.00
RS Prussia, Sugar & Creamer, Pansies, Red Mark, White, Pink, Green, Gold 95.00
RS Prussia, Sugar & Creamer, Pink & White Carnations 75.00
RS Prussia, Sugar & Creamer, Red Berries & White Floral On Green, Gold 72.50
RS Prussia, Sugar & Creamer, Satinized Red & Pink Roses, White Ground 45.00
RS Prussia, Sugar & Creamer, Scenic, Thatched Cottage, Cover 125.00
RS Prussia, Sugar & Creamer, Spring Season, Red Mark 425.00
RS Prussia, Sugar & Creamer, Violets, Ribbed, Red Mark 105.00
RS Prussia, Sugar, Covered, Castle Scene, Fluted Green Base, White Handles 59.00
RS Prussia, Sugar, Covered, Floral, Green, Yellow, Two Handles, Red Mark 45.00
RS Prussia, Sugar, Covered, Pearlized, Shades Of Green, White Floral, Gold 22.50
RS Prussia, Sugar, Covered, Pink Roses 30.00
RS Prussia, Sugar, Covered, Ribs, Yellow Orange Floral, Embossed, Ruffled 27.50
RS Prussia, Syrup, Covered, White & Peach Carnations, Red Mark 50.00
RS Prussia, Syrup, Melon Rib, Green Apple Blossoms, White Satin Finish 65.00
RS Prussia, Syrup, Pink & Yellow Roses, Gold, Aqua On Base, Double Handles 65.00
RS Prussia, Tankard, Cluster Grape Design, 13 1/2 In.High 245.00
RS Prussia, Tankard, Cream & Green Ground, Red, Pink & Yellow Floral, Gold 125.00
RS Prussia, Tankard, Floral, 11 1/2 In. 160.00
RS Prussia, Tankard, Satin Mother-Of-Pearl, Floral, Gold, Footed, Red Mark 195.00
RS Prussia, Tea Set, Demitasse, Pink Poppies, 13 Piece 285.00

RS Prussia, Teapot, Bisque With Sabre Finish, Pink & White Floral, Red Mark 80.00
RS Prussia, Teapot, Floral Decor, Pearlized Finish 59.00
RS Prussia, Teapot, Roses, 6 In. .... *Illus* 225.00
RS Prussia, Teapot, Rosy Beige To Light Brown, Pink & White Floral 80.00
RS Prussia, Toothpick, Floral, Red Mark 75.00
RS Prussia, Toothpick, Raised Gold Leaf Flowers, Pink Trim, Star Mark 22.00
RS Prussia, Toothpick, Red Roses, Red Mark 55.00
RS Prussia, Toothpick, Roses, Leaves, Scalloped Top & Bottom, Red Mark 65.00
RS Prussia, Toothpick, Roses, Two Handles, Six Feet 65.00
RS Prussia, Toothpick, Shaded Green, Pink Rose, 3 Handled 28.00
RS Prussia, Toothpick, Three Handles, Red Mark 55.00
RS Prussia, Tray, Dresser, Apricot Roses In Basket, Green Pearlized, Mark 75.00
RS Prussia, Tray, Dresser, Lilacs, Pink, Green, Gold, Red Mark, 11 X 8 In. 48.00
RS Prussia, Tray, Dresser, Old Red Mark, Roses 85.00
RS Prussia, Tray, Dresser, Red & Pink Roses, Buds, Leaves, Gold Trim 50.00
RS Prussia, Tray, Dresser, Snowballs, Raised Points, Gold Edge, Red Mark 82.50
RS Prussia, Tray, Dresser, White, Red & White Tulips, Schlegelmilch 55.00
RS Prussia, Tray, Dresser, Yellow Pink Roses 65.00
RS Prussia, Tray, Flowers, Open Handles, Red Mark, 13 1/4 In. 75.00
RS Prussia, Tray, Pearlized, Apple Blossoms, Scalloped, Pierced Ends 85.00
RS Prussia, Tray, Perfume, Mother-Of-Pearl Finish, Lilies-Of-The-Valley 75.00
RS Prussia, Tray, Pin, Green, Gold, Yellow Roses, Open End Handles 85.00
RS Prussia, Tray, Roses, Gold Border, Red Mark, 8 X 6 In. 20.00
RS Prussia, Tray, Round, Floral Decoration, Open Handles, Red Mark 75.00
RS Prussia, Vase, Angels, Butterflies, Egg Shape, Footed, Signed 18.00
RS Prussia, Vase, Cobalt, 6 1/2 In.High 145.00
RS Prussia, Vase, Crapshooters, Handles, Red Mark, 8 In.High 350.00
RS Prussia, Vase, Jeweled Top & Bottom, Medallions, Rose Garlands, Handles 95.00
RS Prussia, Vase, Jewels At Top, Openwork At Bottom, Green, Yellow, Floral 125.00
RS Prussia, Vase, Melon Boy & Crapshooter, Gold Handles, Red Mark 325.00
RS Prussia, Vase, Melon Boy, Dice Shooters, Gold Handles, Jeweled, Red Mark 350.00
RS Prussia, Vase, Melon Boy, Jewels, Handles, Red Mark, 10 1/2 In.High, Pair 600.00
RS Prussia, Vase, Mill Scene, Bulbous, Red Mark, 4 In. 165.00
RS Prussia, Vase, Swans, Boats, Scenery, Handles, Red Mark, 6 1/4 In. 85.00
RS Prussia, Vase, White Pearllike Jewels, Rose Garlands, Green Medallions 110.00
RS Tillowitz, Bowl, Pedestal, Yellow & Pink Roses On Beige To Orange 14.50
RS Tillowitz, Sauce, Yellow To Tan Ground, Pink & White Floral 4.25

Rubena Verde is a Victorian glassware that was shaded from red to green.
It was first made by Hobbs, Brockunier and Company of Wheeling, West
Virginia, about 1890.

Rubena Verde, Basket, Cranberry To Green 85.00
Rubena Verde, Bowl, Finger, Inverted Thumbprint 55.00
Rubena Verde, Bowl, Hobnail, Crimped Top, Mark, 2 In.High, 4 In.Across 65.00
Rubena Verde, Cruet, Inverted Thumbprint, Canary Handle & Stopper 120.00
Rubena Verde, Dome, Inverted Thumbprint 35.00
Rubena Verde, Epergne, Ruffled Bowl, Green, Cranberry, 10 In.High 175.00
Rubena Verde, Epergne, Single Trumpet Center Vase, Cranberry, Green 65.00
Rubena Verde, Jar, Jam, Ruffled Top, Petal Border, Footed, 4 1/2 In.High 45.00
Rubena Verde, Lemonade Set, Frosted, White & Gold Enamel, 6 Piece 75.00
Rubena Verde, Mug, Inverted Thumbprint, Applied Handle 65.00
Rubena Verde, Pitcher, Hobnail, Opalescent Hobs 175.00
Rubena Verde, Rose Bowl, C.1860 .... 60.00
Rubena Verde, Rose Bowl, Green To Opalescent To Ruby, Diamond-Quilted 47.50
Rubena Verde, Tumbler, Inverted Thumbprint 22.50
Rubena Verde, Vase, Double Tree Trunk, Leaf Base, 7 In. 40.00
Rubena Verde, Vase, Enameled Morning Glories, Forget-Me-Nots, Gold Leaves 85.00
Rubena Verde, Vase, Green Rigaree, 9 1/2 In. 35.00
Rubena Verde, Vase, Jack-In-The-Pulpit, Broken Pontil, 11 1/2 In.High 65.00
Rubena Verde, Vase, Jack-In-The-Pulpit, Flower Form Top, Paneled Body 45.00
Rubena Verde, Vase, Jack-In-The-Pulpit, Grape Tree, Silver Fox, 8 In. 175.00
Rubena Verde, Vase, Ruffled Top, Applied Six Petal Foot, 7 1/2 In.High 45.00
Rubena Verde, Vase, Vaseline At Base, Cranberry At Rim, Swirls, Ruffled 42.50

Rubena is a glassware that shades from red to clear. It was first made by
George Duncan and Sons of Pittsburgh, Pennsylvania, about 1885.

Rubena, Bobeche, Ruffled, Pair 15.00
Rubena, Bowl, Inverted Thumbprint, 4 1/2 In. 32.00
Rubena, Carafe, Deep Cranberry Shading To Clear, Underplate 45.00
Rubena, Carafe, 8 In.High 55.00
Rubena, Castor, Pickle, Thumbprint Insert, Ornate Footed Frame 110.00
Rubena, Celery, Inverted Thumbprint, Enamel, Flared, Crimped 95.00
Rubena, Compote, Honeycomb 100.00
Rubena, Cup, Punch, Reeded Handle, Dated 1908, Asbury Park, Name Vernon 18.50
Rubena, Ice Bucket, Enamel Decoration, Silver Bail 55.00
Rubena, Jar, Cookie, Cranberry Coloring, Silver Cover And Handle 70.00
Rubena, Jar, Cracker, Star Cut Base 68.00
Rubena, Muffineer 65.00
Rubena, Muffineer, Coin Spot, Opalescent, Brass Top 48.00
Rubena, Muffineer, Cut Glass 65.00
Rubena, Muffineer, Ribbed, Silver Top, English 28.50
Rubena, Pitcher, Milk, Cranberry To Clear, Overshot, Reed Handle 70.00
Rubena, Rose Bowl, Applied Flowers And Green Foliage 110.00
Rubena, Rose Bowl, Blown In 24 Rib Mold 46.00
Rubena, Rose Bowl, Swirled, Crimped Top 47.50
Rubena, Salt Shaker, Royal Ivy Pattern, Pair 35.00
Rubena, Syrup, Flower Design, Acid Etched 85.00
Rubena, Toothpick, Royal Ivy 30.00
Rubena, Toothpick, Royal Oak, Frosted To Clear 30.00
Rubena, Tumbler, Royal Ivy 35.00
Rubena, Tumbler, Royal Ivy, Cranberry 42.50
Rubena, Vase, Bud, Deep Floral Cutting 37.50
Rubena, Vase, Gold Design, Flair Top, 16 In.Tall, Pair 135.00
Rubena, Vase, Lily Shape, Ruffled Top, Enamel Floral, 8 In.High 65.00
Rubena, Wine, Enamel Floral, Gold Trim, Hand Blown 45.00

Ruby Glass is a dark red color. It was a Victorian and
twentieth-century ware. The name means many different types of red glass.

Ruby Glass, see also Cranberry Glass
Ruby Glass, Bell, To Margaret & Frank 40.00
Ruby Glass, Bowl, Center, Victorian, Silver Holder, Meriden, Oneida, N.Y. 26.00
Ruby Glass, Cordial, Thumbprint, Fern Etch 22.00
Ruby Glass, Creamer, Button & Arches, Etched Eagle, St.Paul, 1916 .... 17.50
Ruby Glass, Creamer, Gettysburg 10.00
Ruby Glass, Creamer, Thumbprint 17.50
Ruby Glass, Cruet, Beaded Swirl 40.00
Ruby Glass, Cup & Saucer, Thumbprint 28.75
Ruby Glass, Cup, Punch, Flashed & Clear Pattern 10.00
Ruby Glass, Cup, Punch, Handleless 9.00
Ruby Glass, Cup, Souvenir, Pan American Exposition, Buffalo, 1904, Flashed 7.50
Ruby Glass, Decanter, Frosted White Grape Pattern, Cut, Etched, C.1870 .... 38.00
Ruby Glass, Dish, Candy, Button Pattern, Lattice Rim 6.00
Ruby Glass, Dish, Leaf Pattern, Gold Highlights, 2 Section, Farberware Frame 22.00
Ruby Glass, Dish, Nut, Ornate Silver Holder, Handle, Footed, Tongs 39.50
Ruby Glass, Dish, Nut, Silver Holder, High Curved Feet 39.50
Ruby Glass, Goblet, Blocked Arches 22.50
Ruby Glass, Goblet, Etched Vintage, Knob Stem, Bohemian 45.00
Ruby Glass, Goblet, Thumbprint, Souvenir, Cedar Rapids, Iowa 18.50
Ruby Glass, Goblet, 5 In.Diameter, 7 In.High 25.00
Ruby Glass, Match Holder, World's Fair, King's Crown 18.00
Ruby Glass, Mug, Button Arches, Souvenir, Atlantic City, 1906, Flashed 12.50
Ruby Glass, Mug, Fleur-De-Lis 15.00
Ruby Glass, Mug, Souvenir, Atlantic City, Engraved, 1904, Flashed 14.00
Ruby Glass, Mug, Titusville, Pennsylvania 12.00
Ruby Glass, Perfume, Sterling Overlay 55.00
Ruby Glass, Pitcher, Bull's-Eye Pattern, 10 1/2 In.Tall 75.00
Ruby Glass, Pitcher, Etched, Bohemian, 2 In.High 15.00
Ruby Glass, Pitcher, Flashed, Button Arches, Ocean City, 1899, 3 1/2 In. 28.00
Ruby Glass, Pitcher, Gold, Pinched Sides, Clear Handle 85.00
Ruby Glass, Pitcher, Thumbprint, My Mother 1911, 4 1/2 In. 18.00
Ruby Glass, Pitcher, Water, Hobnail 50.00

Ruby Glass, Salt & Pepper, Button Arches, Souvenir 15.00
Ruby Glass, Saltshaker, Bird 19.00
Ruby Glass, Sauce, Serrated Block & Loop 9.50
Ruby Glass, Sauce, Thumbprint 10.00
Ruby Glass, Sauce, Waffle & Star 9.50
Ruby Glass, Shoe, Illinois State Fair, 1944 .... 15.00
Ruby Glass, Spooner, Button Arches, Frosted Band 18.50
Ruby Glass, Spooner, Thumbprint 5.00
Ruby Glass, Sugar, Etched Thumbprint 30.00
Ruby Glass, Swan, 12 X 8 In.Base, 10 In.High 30.00
Ruby Glass, Toothpick, Button Arches, Flashed, Souvenir Gettysburg 12.00
Ruby Glass, Toothpick, Thumbprint, Etched 22.00
Ruby Glass, Urn, Bubble Base, Pairpoint, 12 In. 45.00
Ruby Glass, Vase, Bud, 'Lulu 1906' In Gold, 6 In.High 22.50
Ruby Glass, Vase, Etched Daisies, Leaves, Flared Top, Bulbous Bottom.10 In. 50.00
Ruby Glass, Vase, Flower Form, Applied Vaseline Petals, Blown, 8 In. 45.00
Ruby Glass, Vase, Paperweight, Clear Base, 11 In. 30.00
Ruby Glass, Water Set, Button Arches With Frosted Band, 7 Piece 150.00
Ruby Glass, Wine, Knob Stem, Cut To Frosted Leaves, Berries, Bohemian 14.00
Rug, see Textile, Rug
Rumrill, Pitcher, Grecian Type, Shades Of Purple, Signed 15.00
Russian Enamel, Bowl, Blue, Flowers, White Touches, Gardner 95.00
Russian Enamel, Buckle, Hinged, Niello 40.00
Russian Enamel, Buckle, Multicolor, Held By Turquoise Dagger, Pinwheel 275.00
Russian Enamel, Case, Cigar, Scene, St.Basil Cathedral, Silver 150.00
Russian Enamel, Case, Cigarette, Niello, Marked T.K.84, Meshed Effect Finish 65.00
Russian Enamel, Cup, Vodka, Handle, Artist-Signed 195.00
Russian Enamel, Cup, Vodka, Turquoise, Black Enamel On Brass, 3 In.High 45.00
Russian Enamel, Perfume, Marked C.A., 4 In.High 475.00
Russian Enamel, Salt, Multicolor, Ball Feet 200.00
Russian Enamel, Tongs, Lemon Fork, Strainer, Spoon, Diamond, Spade, Club, Heart 950.00
Russian Lacquer, Box, Snuff, Painting Of Farm Girl With Water Pails, Gold 65.00
Sabino, Butterfly, Signed, 4 X 6 In. 82.00
Sabino, Figurine, Nude, Arm Extended, Flowing Gown, 8 1/2 In.High 85.00
Sabino, Vase, Blue, Red Loopings, 5 In. 137.50
Saddle, Lacquered Wood, Gold Decoration, Leather, Ornate, Japanese 135.00

Salopian Ware was made by the Caughley Factory of England during the eighteenth century. The early pieces were in blue and white with some colored decorations. Many of the pieces called Salopian are elaborate color-transfer decorated tablewares made during the late nineteenth century.

Salopian, Coffeepot, Cottage Pattern 300.00
Salopian, Cup & Saucer, Courtship Scene, Black Decoration 40.00
Salopian, Cup & Saucer, Handleless, Figures & Cottage 90.00
Salopian, Cup & Saucer, Handleless, Oak Leaves, Acorns, Floral 150.00
Salopian, Cup & Saucer, Urn Pattern, Brown Decoration 20.00
Salopian, Jug, Blue & White, Cabbage Leaf, Fisherman Pattern, C.1785, Pair 400.00
Salopian, Plate, Sheep & Eagle, Colored Border, 6 1/2 In.Diameter 120.00
Salopian, Plate, Toddy, Castle Scene, 5 1/2 In. 150.00
Salopian, Saucer, Flower Vase Design, Blue, Impressed Star Mark 32.00
Salopian, Saucer, Transfer Figures On Bridge, Gilding, C.1795 .... 15.00
Salopian, Sugar, Church Scene, Colored, Covered 110.00
Salt and Pepper, see Pressed Glass, Porcelain, etc.

Salt Glaze is a hard, shiny glaze that was developed for pottery during the eighteenth century. It is still being made.

Salt Glaze, Crock, Cobalt Leaf & Floral On Front, Cowden & Wilcox, 1 Gallon 32.50
Salt Glaze, Crock, Gray, Cobalt Leaf & Floral On Front, Sipe Sons, 1 Gallon 28.50
Salt Glaze, Jar, Preserving, Gray, Cobalt Bands On Front, 1 Gallon 23.50
Salt Glaze, Jug, Bacchus With Figural Pan Handle, Beige, Ridgway, C.1840 .... 88.00
Salt Glaze, Jug, Gray, Darrin & Richardson, Cobalt, Farrington Co., 2 Gallon 38.50
Salt Glaze, Jug, Milk, Pectin Shell, Staffordshire, 1740 .... *Illus* 375.00
Salt Glaze, Jug, Pewter Lid, English Registry Mark, 1873, 7 1/4 In.High 62.50
Salt Glaze, Mustard Pot, White, Embossed Drinking Scene, Pewter Mount 18.50
Salt Glaze, Pitcher, Blue, Wheat, Bowties, Bird On Lid, C.1890 .... 50.00
Salt Glaze, Pitcher, Embossed, 6 In. 55.00

Salt Glaze, Pitcher, Raised Medieval Horse, Captive In Forest, Gold Rim	40.00
Salt Glaze, Pitcher, Water, Gray Green, Cattails, Reeds	48.00
Salt Glaze, Pitcher, White, Brown, Grecian Designs, Argos Pattern, 1864	50.00
Salt Glaze, Pitcher, Wine, Gray, 2 Boy Cupids & Grapes, 1/2 Liter	22.50
Salt Glaze, Stein, 1/2 Liter, Titled Bier Halle, Pewter Top & Thumbpiece	25.00
Salt Glaze, Syrup, Pewter Top, Ribbon Mark	65.00
Salt Glaze, Teapot, Floral Vases, Masks, Square, C.1740, Staffordshire	70.00
Salt Glaze, Teapot, Pectin Shell, Staffordshire .... *Illus*	160.00
Salt Glaze, Teapot, Scratch Blue, C.1740 .... *Illus*	310.00
Samovar, Brass, 13 In.	34.50
Samovar, Brass, 16 In.	44.50
Samovar, Brass, 18 In.High, 18.In.Wide	40.00
Samovar, Burner, Whistle, Spigot, Brass, C.1920	22.00
Samovar, Openwork, Wooden Grips, Brass Handles, Dated 1872, Footed, Brass	145.00
Samovar, Replicas Of Medals Won At Trade Fairs, Eagle On Lid, Brass, Russia	375.00
Sampler, See Textile	

Samson and Company, a French firm specializing in the reproduction of collectible wares of many countries and periods, was founded in Paris in the early 19th century. Chelsea, Meissen, Famille Verte and Oriental Lowestoft are some of the wares that have been reproduced by the company. The company uses a variety of marks to distinguish its reproductions. It is still in operation.

Samson, Figurine, Bird, Leaves, C.1840, 9 1/4 In.High, Pair	225.00

Salt Glaze, Jug, Milk,
Pectin Shell,
Staffordshire, 1740
See *Page 493*

Salt Glaze, Teapot, Pectin Shell, Staffordshire

Salt Glaze, Teapot, Scratch Blue, C.1740

Samson, Figurine, Putti, France, C.1840, 7 1/2 In.High, Pair	195.00
Samson, Vase, Chelsea Style, Blue & Gold On White, Pierced Ormolu Base, Pair	350.00

Sandwich Glass is any one of the myriad types of glass made by the Boston and Sandwich Glass Works in Sandwich, Massachusetts, between 1825 and 1888. It is often very difficult to be sure whether a piece was really made at the Sandwich Factory because so many types were made there and similar pieces were made at other glass factories.

Sandwich Glass, see also Pressed Glass, etc.

Sandwich Glass, Basket, Brides, Emerald Green, Edge Ruffled, Mint	125.00

Sandwich Glass, **Basket**, Overshot, Swirl Rib, Ruffled, Thorn Handle 125.00
Sandwich Glass, **Bottle**, Scent, Amethyst, Screw Top 45.00
Sandwich Glass, **Bottle**, Scent, Peacock, Screw Top 50.00
Sandwich Glass, **Bottle**, Scent, Purple, Screw Top 50.00
Sandwich Glass, **Bowl**, Daisy With Peacock-Eye Border 17.50
Sandwich Glass, **Bowl**, Diamond Rosette Pattern, 6 1/2 In. 20.00
Sandwich Glass, **Bowl**, Finger, Frosted, Overshot, Melon Shape, Gold Band 45.00
Sandwich Glass, **Bowl**, Finger, Overshot, Flint 35.00
Sandwich Glass, **Bowl**, Lacy, Tulip & Acanthus Leaf Pattern 30.00
Sandwich Glass, **Bowl**, Lyre Center, 7 In. 20.00
Sandwich Glass, **Bowl**, Open Lacy Edge, 8 1/4 In. 16.50
Sandwich Glass, **Bowl**, Overshot, Large 49.00
Sandwich Glass, **Bowl**, Overshot, Portrait Of Woman, High Knob On Cover 115.00
Sandwich Glass, **Bowl**, Roman Rosette, 6 1/2 In.Deep 47.50
Sandwich Glass, **Bowl**, Tulip & Acanthus, 6 1/4 In.Diameter 55.00
Sandwich Glass, **Candlestick**, Blue & Clam 185.00
Sandwich Glass, **Candlestick**, Celeste Blue, Flint 125.00
Sandwich Glass, **Candlestick**, Clear, Pair 55.00
Sandwich Glass, **Candlestick**, Column, Clear, Joined By Wafer, 7 1/2 In.High 50.00
Sandwich Glass, **Candlestick**, Golden Amber, Hexagonal 87.00
Sandwich Glass, **Candlestick**, Step Base, Violet Blue, 6 3/4 In.High 150.00
Sandwich Glass, **Candlestick**, Vaseline With Touch Of Green, Marked, Pair 100.00
Sandwich Glass, **Candlestick**, Yellow, Hexagonal Base, 7 In.High, Pair 185.00
Sandwich Glass, **Christmas Light**, Diamond Quilt, Clear 9.00
Sandwich Glass, **Cologne**, Tortoiseshell Swirls, Turquoise, Graphite Pontil 150.00
Sandwich Glass, **Compote**, Bellflower, Flint, Scalloped 35.00
Sandwich Glass, **Compote**, Petal & Loop, Flint, 10 1/2 In.Diamete .... 78.00 To 85.00
Sandwich Glass, **Compote**, Smocking, Flint 75.00
Sandwich Glass, **Creamer**, Amethyst, Applied Handle, 3 Rows Of Rings 210.00
Sandwich Glass, **Creamer**, Miniature, Cobalt Blue, 2 1/4 In.High 25.00
Sandwich Glass, **Creamer**, Opalescent 260.00
Sandwich Glass, **Cruet**, Bull's-Eye 14.00
    Sandwich Glass, **Cup Plate**, see also Cup Plate
Sandwich Glass, **Cup Plate**, Bunker Hill Monument, Clear, McKearin 186, No.5 .... 25.00
Sandwich Glass, **Cup Plate**, Fiery Opalescent 35.00
Sandwich Glass, **Cup Plate**, Heart, Lacy 10.00
Sandwich Glass, **Cup Plate**, Lacy, Pinwheel Design, 3 1/2 In.Diameter 140.00
Sandwich Glass, **Cup Plate**, Lacy, Twelve Heart Border 11.00
Sandwich Glass, **Cup Plate**, Medallion Center, Fleur-De-Lis Border, Scalloped 25.00
Sandwich Glass, **Cup Plate**, Peacock Eye 18.50
Sandwich Glass, **Cup Plate**, Star & Forget-Me-Nots, Scalloped Edge 10.00
Sandwich Glass, **Cup Plate**, Three Feathers 35.00
Sandwich Glass, **Decanter**, Cut, Etched, Says Whiskey 110.00
Sandwich Glass, **Decanter**, Pontil 25.00
Sandwich Glass, **Dish**, Cake, Lacy, Beehive Pattern 75.00
Sandwich Glass, **Dish**, Honey, Dewdrop & Star 6.00
Sandwich Glass, **Dish**, Lion Cover, Lacy Nest 125.00
Sandwich Glass, **Eggcup**, Cobalt Blue, Candle Type 29.00
Sandwich Glass, **Figurine**, Bust Of Queen Victoria, Lacy 35.00
Sandwich Glass, **Goblet**, Comet, Flint, Set Of 6 .... 300.00
Sandwich Glass, **Hat**, Sunburst Motif, 1830, Blown, 3 Mold, 2 1/4 In.High 47.50
Sandwich Glass, **Inkwell & Tray**, Clear, Rectangular, Cover, Sander 90.00
Sandwich Glass, **Inkwell & Tray**, Green, Rectangular 35.00
Sandwich Glass, **Inkwell**, Dark Green, Elongated Oval Pattern, Spout 250.00
Sandwich Glass, **Jar & Underplate**, Mustard, Peacock's-Eye 150.00
Sandwich Glass, **Jar**, Jam, Cased, Dog's Head With Ruffled Collar Finial 62.50
Sandwich Glass, **Knob**, Furniture, Fiery Opalescent, Shaft, 1 3/4 In., Pair 22.00
    Sandwich Glass, **Lamp**, see also Lamp
Sandwich Glass, **Lamp**, Cobalt Cut To Clear Font, Opaline Base, Flint 225.00
Sandwich Glass, **Lamp**, Whale Oil, 9 In. .... *Illus* 85.00
Sandwich Glass, **Mustard Set**, Swirl Pattern, 2 Piece 27.50
-Sandwich Glass, **Paperweight**, See Paperweight, Sandwich ....
Sandwich Glass, **Pitcher**, Clear To Cranberry, Crystal Handle, Tankard Shape 75.00
Sandwich Glass, **Pitcher**, Clear, Overshot, Blown Ice Compartment, Reed Handle 175.00
Sandwich Glass, **Pitcher**, Cranberry, Overshot, Applied Reeded Handle 85.00
Sandwich Glass, **Pitcher**, Drapery 14.00

Sandwich Glass, Pitcher, Orchid & White Design, Green, 9 In.High	95.00
Sandwich Glass, Pitcher, Overshot, Bulbous, 5 3/4 In.High	45.00
Sandwich Glass, Pitcher, Overshot, Robin On Branch, Holly Berries, Leaves	145.00
Sandwich Glass, Pitcher, Overshot, Robin, Holly Berries, Leaves, 7 1/2 In.	120.00
Sandwich Glass, Pitcher, Overshot, Sapphire Blue, Applied Amber Handle, 8 In.	75.00
Sandwich Glass, Pitcher, Water, McKearin G I-29, Clear, Applied Handle	260.00
Sandwich Glass, Pitcher, Water, McKearin G V-17, Clear, Horn Of Plenty	310.00
Sandwich Glass, Plate, Beehive, Lacy, Flint, 9 1/2 In.	65.00
Sandwich Glass, Plate, Blue, Reverse Daisy & Roman Key, 6 1/2 In.	25.00
Sandwich Glass, Plate, Dolphin Pattern	12.50
Sandwich Glass, Plate, Double Vine, 10 1/2 In.	78.00
Sandwich Glass, Plate, Fan & Waffle Without Dots Between Fans	27.50
Sandwich Glass, Plate, Feather, 7 In.	16.00
Sandwich Glass, Plate, Hairpin, 6 In.	85.00 To 100.00
Sandwich Glass, Plate, Lacy, Clear, 6 In.	30.00
Sandwich Glass, Plate, Peacock's-Eye, Lacy, McKearin No.141, 5 1/4 In.	26.00
Sandwich Glass, Plate, Plait, Lacy, 8 In.	20.00
Sandwich Glass, Plate, Roman Rosette, Lacy, 5 1/2 In.	17.00
Sandwich Glass, Plate, Paneled Hobnail, Blue, Wire Card Basket, 4 1/4 In.	22.50
Sandwich Glass, Plate, Peacock Eye & Thistle, Lacy, 8 In.	87.50
Sandwich Glass, Plate, Plaid, 6 In.Diameter	46.00
Sandwich Glass, Plate, Plume Pattern, Blue, Lacy, 5 In.	65.00
Sandwich Glass, Salt & Pepper, Waffle, Clear, Octagon, Agitator	35.00
Sandwich Glass, Salt Shaker, Cranes & Cattails, Dana K.Alden, Boston, 1877	65.00
Sandwich Glass, Salt, Arched Design, Rectangular, Light Green	60.00
Sandwich Glass, Salt, Charioteer, Rectangular, Round Feet	20.00
Sandwich Glass, Salt, Clear, Footed	28.00
Sandwich Glass, Salt, Eagle & Tree, Rectangular, Round Feet	65.00
Sandwich Glass, Salt, Eagle, Stars, & Shield, Opalescent, Oblong, Footed	130.00
Sandwich Glass, Salt, Lacy, Green, Rectangular, Footed	60.00
Sandwich Glass, Salt, Master, Hexagon, Footed	27.50
Sandwich Glass, Salt, Master, Ribbed Palm	14.00

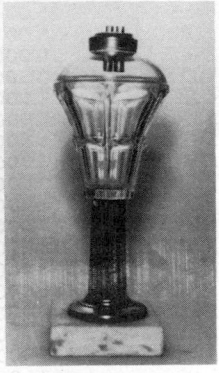

Sandwich Glass, Lamp, Whale Oil, 9 In.
See Page 495

Sandwich Glass, Vase, Vaseline, 9 In.
See Page 497

Sandwich Glass, Salt, Ribbed, Clear, Open, 3 In.Diameter	9.50
Sandwich Glass, Salt, Ship, Blue Opalescent, Marked	260.00
Sandwich Glass, Salt, Waffle, Amethyst, Rectangular	45.00
Sandwich Glass, Sauce, Peacock's-Eye, Lacy	18.00
Sandwich Glass, Slipper, Blue	30.00
Sandwich Glass, Smoke Bell	20.00
Sandwich Glass, Spillholder, Star	55.00
Sandwich Glass, Sugar, Cathedral & Arch Pattern, Vaseline, Covered	350.00
Sandwich Glass, Sugar, Cathedral, Opalescent, Footed	100.00
Sandwich Glass, Sugar, Ivy, Flint	38.00
Sandwich Glass, Sugar, Moon & Star	45.00
Sandwich Glass, Sugar, Ribbed Bellflower, Double Vine	25.00
Sandwich Glass, Sugar, Strawberry Rochelle	28.50
Sandwich Glass, Tieback, Amber, Pewter Shaft, Pair	35.00
Sandwich Glass, Tieback, Fiery Opalescent, Flint, Pewter Stem, 3 In., Pair	25.00

Sandwich Glass, Tieback, Lacy, Opalescent, Screws, 4 1/2 In.Diameter 25.00
Sandwich Glass, Tieback, Opalescent, Pewter Shaft, Pair .... 20.00 To 40.00
Sandwich Glass, Tieback, Opalescent, Pewter Shank, 2 1/2 In.Diameter, Pair 24.00
Sandwich Glass, Tieback, Opalescent, Pewter Shank, 3 In. 10.00
Sandwich Glass, Toddy, Roman Rosette, Lacy, Flint, 5 In. 24.00
Sandwich Glass, Tray, Gothic Arch, Lacy, Oblong, 7 X 5 1/2 In. 80.00
Sandwich Glass, Tray, Gothic, Oblong, 6 1/8 X 4 3/8 In. 25.00
Sandwich Glass, Tray, Gothic, Oblong, 7 X 5 1/8 In. 27.50
Sandwich Glass, Tray, Relish, White Oak Pattern, Conical Feet, C.1830 .... 50.00
Sandwich Glass, Tray, Scalloped Edge, Lacy, 4 3/4 X 6 1/2 In. 20.00
Sandwich Glass, Tumbler, Tree Of Life, Footed 15.00
Sandwich Glass, Vase, Elongated Loop, Vaseline, Footed 175.00
Sandwich Glass, Vase, Fireglow, Crackle, Acid Finish, 3 In.High 85.00
Sandwich Glass, Vase, Fireglow, Crackle, Peach Apricot, Acid, Pouch Shape 115.00
Sandwich Glass, Vase, Icicle, Amber, Clear Icicles, Applied Clear Rigaree 110.00
Sandwich Glass, Vase, Loop Pattern, Medium Green 240.00
Sandwich Glass, Vase, Vaseline, 9 In. .... Illus 250.00
Sandwich Glass, Whiskey Taster 25.00

Sarreguemines Pottery was first made in Lorraine, France, about 1770.
Most of the pieces found today date from the late nineteenth century.
Sarreguemines, Chamber Pot, White, Blue Floral, Marked Xenia Faienceries 23.00
Sarreguemines, Coffeepot, Floral, Gold Trim, C.1850 .... 45.00
Sarreguemines, Coffeepot, Pink, Purple & Yellow Roses, Branch Handle, C.1850 ... 45.00
Sarreguemines, Jar, Covered, Peasants In Field, Side Handles, 5 In. 9.00
Sarreguemines, Jug, Ewer, Pink Flowers 90.00
Sarreguemines, Plate, Chateau Series, Pierced For Hanging 10.00
Sarreguemines, Plate, Grapes, Leaves, Green Border, Majolica 32.50
Sarreguemines, Plate, Oyster, Pink To Tan, Green Border, Set Of 6 .... 72.00
Sarreguemines, Plate, Village Scene, Signed, 9 3/4 In.Diameter 9.50
Sarreguemines, Platter, Saucy Wenches, Signed, 11 X 16 In. 45.00

Satin Glass is a late nineteenth-century art glass. It has a dull finish
that is caused by a hydrofluoric acid vapor treatment. Satin Glass was made
in many colors and sometimes had applied decorations.
Satin Glass, Banana Boat, Pink, White Spatter, Camphor Glass Edge, Crimped 55.00
Satin Glass, Barrel, Cracker, Pink, Ball Shape, Silver Lid, Bail & Handle 95.00
Satin Glass, Basket, Rainbow, Pink, Blue Panels, Clear Handle, 7 In.Diameter 95.00
Satin Glass, Basket, Rainbow, Spangled With Mica, 7 In.Diameter 95.00
Satin Glass, Bottle, Barber, Rose Cased, Square Base, 7 In.High 35.00
Satin Glass, Bottle, Cologne, Pink, Silver Mounts 115.00
Satin Glass, Bottle, Scent, Rectangular, Gilt Prunus Blossoms On Green 120.00
Satin Glass, Bowl, Black, Separate Pedestal 20.00
Satin Glass, Bowl, End-Of-Day, Pink & White Panels, 3 1/2 In.High 70.00
Satin Glass, Bowl, Pink, Quilted, Silver Plate Lift Off Edge 110.00
Satin Glass, Bowl, Pink, White Casing, Maize Pattern, 7 In. 75.00
Satin Glass, Bowl, White, Fluted, One End Crimped Over, 12 In. 20.00
Satin Glass, Box, Pin, Mother-Of-Pearl, Covered 22.00
Satin Glass, Box, Pin, Mother-Of-Pearl, Diamond Shape 25.00
Satin Glass, Box, Powder, Yellow, Diamond, Silver Cover 185.00
Satin Glass, Bride's Basket, Salmon To Yellow, Enameled Blue Daisies, Gold 75.00
Satin Glass, Bride's Bowl, Mother-Of-Pearl, Herringbone Pattern 375.00
Satin Glass, Candleholder, Black, 8 1/4 In., Pair 18.00
Satin Glass, Carafe, Water, Raised Yellow Cosmos Flowers, Metal Neck 125.00
Satin Glass, Compote, Cranberry, Swirled, Crimped Edge, Brass Base 48.00
Satin Glass, Compote, Light Pink To Dark, Ruffled Edge, Brass Base, 6 In. 60.00
Satin Glass, Creamer, Blue, Raindrop Mother-Of-Pearl 150.00
Satin Glass, Creamer, Pink, Mother-Of-Pearl, Camphor Handle 100.00
Satin Glass, Creamer, Red 125.00
Satin Glass, Cruet, Apricot, Melon Rib, Squatty 165.00
Satin Glass, Cruet, Blue, Melon Rib, Squatty 165.00
Satin Glass, Cup, Nut, Mother-Of-Pearl, Rainbow, Sterling Rim 195.00
Satin Glass, Easter Egg, Daisies, Forget-Me-Nots, 6 In.Long 12.00
Satin Glass, Easter Egg, Forget-Me-Not Design, Blue, White, Hand-Painted 20.00
Satin Glass, Epergne, Quilted, White To Cranberry, Ruffled, Fluted 195.00
Satin Glass, Ewer, Apricot To White, White Lining, 5 In. 45.00

Satin Glass, Ewer, Apricot, Herringbone, White Enamel, Camphor Handle, 9 In.	240.00
Satin Glass, Ewer, Blue Decoration, 8 In.High, Pair	135.00
Satin Glass, Ewer, Blue, Cased, Applied Crystal Handle, Pair	150.00
Satin Glass, Ewer, Blue, Diamond Design, Applied Clear Handle, 8 In.High	135.00
Satin Glass, Ewer, Blue, Gold & White Flowers	57.00
Satin Glass, Ewer, Blue, Painted Birds, Foliage, Pair	85.00
Satin Glass, Ewer, Bulbous, Shaded White To Lemon, Gilt Decoration	140.00
Satin Glass, Ewer, Mother-Of-Pearl, Blue, Diamond-Quilted, Thorn Handle, 1890	165.00
Satin Glass, Ewer, Mother-Of-Pearl, Herringbone, Blue Shading, Gold Ferns	155.00
Satin Glass, Ewer, Mother-Of-Pearl, Pink, Frosted Rope Handle, Scalloped	200.00
Satin Glass, Ewer, Peach Color, Floral, Applied Thorn Handle	105.00
Satin Glass, Ewer, Pink Shades, Applied Camphor Handle, Harebells, Gold	45.00
Satin Glass, Ewer, Pink To Dark Pink, Applied Camphor Handle, Florals	45.00
Satin Glass, Ewer, Pink, Herringbone, Ribbon Top, Camphor Handle, 8 1/2 In.	190.00
Satin Glass, Ewer, Quilted, Coral, 8 In.	90.00
Satin Glass, Ewer, Shaded Blue, Overlay, Applied Thorn Handle, Floral Enamel	60.00
Satin Glass, Ewer, White, Bluebirds, Ball Shape Base, Applied Handle, Pair	125.00
Satin Glass, Jar, American Beauty Color, Mother-Of-Pearl, Covered, 8 1/2 In.	975.00
Satin Glass, Jar, Biscuit, White, Blue Scrollwork, Quarter Moons, Silver Lid	135.00
Satin Glass, Jar, Cracker, Beige, White Interior, Floral, Silver Plate Cover	75.00
Satin Glass, Jar, Cracker, Coralene Decoration	110.00
Satin Glass, Jar, Cracker, Cosmos, Melon Shape	165.00
Satin Glass, Jar, Jam, Lavender Coralene, Mother-Of-Pearl	695.00
Satin Glass, Jar, Powder, Red, Hand-Painted Flowers, Silver Lid	32.50
Satin Glass, Lamp Base, Red, Ornate Brass Fittings	69.00 To 95.00
Satin Glass, Lamp, Mother-Of-Pearl, Green, Quilted, Camphor Base, Chimney	150.00
Satin Glass, Lamp, Pink, Pleated Shade, Metal Base	55.00
Satin Glass, Lamp, Plume Pattern, Pink, 8 1/2 In.High	200.00
Satin Glass, Muffineer, Blue, Hand-Painted Floral	55.00
Satin Glass, Muffineer, White, Chrysanthemum Type Base, Flower, Leaves	55.00
Satin Glass, Pacifier, Baby's, Mother-Of-Pearl, Silver Band Whistle, Cat, Cow	12.50
Satin Glass, Paperweight, Lemon To White, Diamond-Quilted Mother-Of-Pearl	165.00
Satin Glass, Perfume, Blue, Decorated	19.00
Satin Glass, Pitcher, Diamond-Quilted Mother-Of-Pearl, 11 1/4 In.High	275.00
Satin Glass, Pitcher, Light Blue, Raindrop Pattern, Ruffled Rim, 5 In.	65.00
Satin Glass, Pitcher, Mother-Of-Pearl, Blue, White Handle, Marked Patent	750.00
Satin Glass, Pitcher, Mother-Of-Pearl, Coin Spot, Stripes, Camphor Handle	725.00
Satin Glass, Pitcher, Pink, Quilted, Applied Handle, Polished Pontil	250.00
Satin Glass, Pitcher, Yellow, Diamond-Quilted, Ruffled Top	325.00
Satin Glass, Rose Bowl & Candleholders, Black	55.00
Satin Glass, Rose Bowl, Blue Enamel Floral, Crimped Rim, 4 In.	75.00
Satin Glass, Rose Bowl, Blue Enameled, 4 In.Diameter	100.00
Satin Glass, Rose Bowl, Blue Shades, Crimped Top	70.00
Satin Glass, Rose Bowl, Blue Shades, Fluted Top	45.00
Satin Glass, Rose Bowl, Blue Shading, Pinched & Fluted Top	45.00
Satin Glass, Rose Bowl, Blue To Aqua, Pinched Top, 6 In.Diameter	150.00
Satin Glass, Rose Bowl, Blue, Crimped Rim, 5 In.High	42.50
Satin Glass, Rose Bowl, Blue, Crimped Top, Ground Pontil, 5 1/2 In.	65.00
Satin Glass, Rose Bowl, Blue, Enameled	95.00
Satin Glass, Rose Bowl, Blue, White Enamel Floral Decoration	125.00
Satin Glass, Rose Bowl, Cranberry, Flower Design, 3 In.High, 3 In.Diameter	48.00
Satin Glass, Rose Bowl, Deep Blue To Light Blue, Mold Blown Floral	105.00
Satin Glass, Rose Bowl, Deep Rose, Crimped Top, 4 1/2 In.High	90.00
Satin Glass, Rose Bowl, Diamond-Quilted Mother-Of-Pearl, Crimped Top	275.00
Satin Glass, Rose Bowl, Dusky Rose To Pink Blue, White Lining, 6 1/2 In.	115.00
Satin Glass, Rose Bowl, Green, Pink Floral, Hand Blown	30.00
Satin Glass, Rose Bowl, Light To Deep Blue, White Casing	60.00
Satin Glass, Rose Bowl, Lime To White, Fluted Rim	75.00
Satin Glass, Rose Bowl, Maroon To White, Cased, Crimped Rim, Metal Holder	125.00
Satin Glass, Rose Bowl, Opaque White, Crimped Top, 7 1/4 In.Diameter	45.00
Satin Glass, Rose Bowl, Persimmon Gold, Diamond-Quilted Mother-Of-Pearl	120.00
Satin Glass, Rose Bowl, Pink To Deep Rose At Top, White Lining	58.00
Satin Glass, Rose Bowl, Pink To Deep Rose, Shell & Seaweed, White Casing	87.50
Satin Glass, Rose Bowl, Pink, Cased White Inside, Crimped Top	25.00
Satin Glass, Rose Bowl, Pink, Crimped Top	55.00
Satin Glass, Rose Bowl, Pink, 'From Niagara Falls 1893' In Gold Leaf	125.00

Satin Glass, Rose Bowl, Pink, Shell Design 75.00
Satin Glass, Rose Bowl, Pink, White Casing, Camphor Gadrooning & Feet, Acid 300.00
Satin Glass, Rose Bowl, Red, Mother-Of-Pearl, Herringbone 160.00
Satin Glass, Rose Bowl, Rose Color, White Lining, Blown, 3 1/2 In.Tall 38.00
Satin Glass, Rose Bowl, Rose Shades, White Interior, Crimped Top, Enamel 95.00
Satin Glass, Rose Bowl, Rose To Pale Pink, White Cased 65.00
Satin Glass, Rose Bowl, Rose To Pink, Cherubs, Flowers, Scalloped Rim 140.00
Satin Glass, Rose Bowl, Rose To White, Mother-Of-Pearl, Coin Dot, Footed 240.00
Satin Glass, Rose Bowl, Shaded Rose, White Cased 46.00
Satin Glass, Rose Bowl, White To Yellow, Crimped Top, 4 In.Diameter 45.00
Satin Glass, Rose Bowl, Yellow To White, Orange & Green Enamel, Shell 95.00
Satin Glass, Rose Bowl, Yellow To White, Orange Scrollwork, Shell & Seaweed 175.00
Satin Glass, Rose Bowl, Yellow, Enameled, Flower Design 65.00
Satin Glass, Rose Bowl, Yellow, Mother-Of-Pearl, Applied Green Vines 165.00
Satin Glass, Rose Bowl, Yellow, Mother-Of-Pearl, Applied Leaves 150.00
Satin Glass, Rose Bowl, Yellow, White Casing, Blue & Gold Floral, Crimped 75.00
Satin Glass, Salt & Pepper, Pink, Green, Floral, Pewter Tops 25.00
Satin Glass, Salt & Pepper, White, Enamel Flowers 48.00
Satin Glass, Salt Shaker, Rose Color, Diamond-Quilted Mother-Of-Pearl 49.00
Satin Glass, Salt, Mother-Of-Pearl, Sterling Rim 195.00
Satin Glass, Shade, Electric Light, Orange, Hand-Painted Landscape, 5 1/2 In. 15.00
Satin Glass, Shade, Lamp, Red 95.00
Satin Glass, Sugar & Creamer, Pink, Diamond-Quilted, Puff 150.00
Satin Glass, Sugar & Creamer, Red, Quilted, Silver Tops 200.00
Satin Glass, Teething Ring, Baby's, Mother-Of-Pearl, Silver Bells 8.50
Satin Glass, Toothpick, Pink, Bulbous 45.00
Satin Glass, Tray, Pin, Black, Moose Trampling Wolf, Relief 16.00
Satin Glass, Tumbler, Blue To Clear, Mother-Of-Pearl, Herringbone, C.1890 .... 45.00
Satin Glass, Tumbler, Blue, Diamond-Quilted Mother-Of-Pearl 55.00
Satin Glass, Tumbler, Cranberry, Diamond-Quilted Mother-Of-Pearl 45.00
Satin Glass, Tumbler, Pink, Diamond-Quilted, White Interior .... 65.00 To 75.00
Satin Glass, Tumbler, Raspberry, Diamond-Quilted Mother-Of-Pearl 75.00
Satin Glass, Tumbler, Rose To White, Mother-Of-Pearl, Herringbone 85.00
Satin Glass, Tumbler, Water, Shaded Blue, Diamond-Quilted Mother-Of-Pearl 75.00
Satin Glass, Tumbler, Yellow, Mother-Of-Pearl, Peacock's-Eye, 4 In. 65.00
Satin Glass, Urn, Red To Chartreuse, Bead & Grape, 19 In.High, Pair 200.00
Satin Glass, Vase, Apricot To Pink Shade, Fluted Rim, 6 1/2 In. 65.00
Satin Glass, Vase, Apricot To Pink To White, Mother-Of-Pearl, White Casing 450.00
Satin Glass, Vase, Apricot, Red Enamel Floral, Green Leaves, 11 3/4 In. 250.00
Satin Glass, Vase, Aquamarine, Diamond-Quilted Mother-Of-Pearl, Pair 120.00
Satin Glass, Vase, Beige, Blue, Green, Mother-Of-Pearl .... Illus 250.00
Satin Glass, Vase, Black, Opaque, No Decoration, 7 1/2 In.High 65.00
Satin Glass, Vase, Blue Mother-Of-Pearl, Lavender Coralene, Red Jewels 695.00
Satin Glass, Vase, Blue Mother-Of-Pearl, Teardrop, Cased, 5 1/2 In.High 200.00
Satin Glass, Vase, Blue Raindrops, 5 1/2 In.High 175.00
Satin Glass, Vase, Blue Shades, Ovoid Body, Gold Coral Beading, 8 1/2 In. 400.00
Satin Glass, Vase, Blue To White, Raised Enamel Floral, Leaves, Stick Neck 70.00
Satin Glass, Vase, Blue, Diamond-Quilted Mother-Of-Pearl, Gold Floral 135.00
Satin Glass, Vase, Blue, Diamond-Quilted Mother-Of-Pearl, Scalloped, Ruffled 125.00
Satin Glass, Vase, Blue, Herringbone, Camphor Handles, 9 In. 180.00

Satin Glass, Vase, Beige, Blue, Green, Mother-Of-Pearl

Satin Glass, Vase, Blue, Melon Sectioned, Moss Roses, White Floral, Pair	125.00
Satin Glass, Vase, Blue, Overlay, Pink & Blue Enameled Floral, Gold, Pair	68.00
Satin Glass, Vase, Blue, Raindrop, Paneled Sides, Flared Top, Crimped Edge	225.00
Satin Glass, Vase, Blue, Rose, Swirled, Attributed Stevens & Williams, 8 In.	350.00
Satin Glass, Vase, Brown, Green Threading	60.00
Satin Glass, Vase, Cobalt, Silver Overlay Inlaid With 4 Cabochon Garnets	45.00
Satin Glass, Vase, Cream To Brown, Basket Weave, Ovoid, 5 3/4 In.High	175.00
Satin Glass, Vase, Cream To Brown, Ovoid, 5 3/4 In.High	175.00
Satin Glass, Vase, Cut Velvet, Blue Vertical Ribs, 5 In.	30.00
Satin Glass, Vase, Dark Red, Black Flecks, Cased, Corset Shape	32.50
Satin Glass, Vase, Flowers, Bluebird, Crimped Top, Hand-Painted, Footed	125.00
Satin Glass, Vase, Girl Holding Parrot & Thrush, Signed, Pair	185.00
Satin Glass, Vase, Jack-In-The-Pulpit, Orange, Gold, Yellow Butterflies	110.00
Satin Glass, Vase, Mother-Of-Pearl, Camphor Edge, 10 In.High	225.00
Satin Glass, Vase, Mother-Of-Pearl, Enameled, Pair .... *Illus*	575.00
Satin Glass, Vase, Mother-Of-Pearl, Purple Swirls, Gilded Ferns & Florals	475.00
Satin Glass, Vase, Mother-Of-Pearl, Silver Tree Trunk, Three Footed Holder	98.00
Satin Glass, Vase, Mother-Of-Pearl, Swirls In Red & Orange, Ovoid	250.00
Satin Glass, Vase, Mottled Pink & Clear, Pearl, Long Stem Flower, Ruffled	65.00

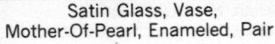

Satin Glass, Vase,
Mother-Of-Pearl, Enameled, Pair

Satsuma, Cup & Saucer
See Page 501

Satin Glass, Vase, Opaque White To Yellow, 14 1/2 In.High	185.00
Satin Glass, Vase, Opaque, Black, No Decoration, 7 1/2 In.High	65.00
Satin Glass, Vase, Ovoid, Enameled Peacock Design, 7 In.	185.00
Satin Glass, Vase, Oyster To Butterscotch, Mother-Of-Pearl, Herringbone	95.00
Satin Glass, Vase, Peach Shaded, Diamond-Quilted Mother-Of-Pearl	95.00
Satin Glass, Vase, Pink & Rose, Cased, Enameled Floral Decoration	60.00
Satin Glass, Vase, Pink Lilac, Apricot Lining, Enamel Floral & Leaves	100.00
Satin Glass, Vase, Pink Shading To White, Ruffled Top, 6 In., Pair	200.00
Satin Glass, Vase, Pink Shading, Ruffled Top, 7 In.High	85.00
Satin Glass, Vase, Pink, Cut Velvet, 8 In.High	210.00
Satin Glass, Vase, Pink, Diamond-Quilted Mother-Of-Pearl, Fluted Top	125.00
Satin Glass, Vase, Pink, Diamond-Quilted Mother-Of-Pearl, 6 In.High	120.00
Satin Glass, Vase, Pink, Marked P.F.K., Lavender Enameled Floral, Gold	125.00
Satin Glass, Vase, Pink, Melon Ribbed, Clear Satin Handle, 7 1/2 In., Tall	73.00
Satin Glass, Vase, Pink, Mother-Of-Pearl, Herringbone, Flared, Ruffled	115.00
Satin Glass, Vase, Rainbow Spatter, Cased, Pair, 6 1/2 In.High	200.00
Satin Glass, Vase, Rose To Pink, Diamond-Quilted Mother-Of-Pearl, Ruffled	110.00
Satin Glass, Vase, Rose To Pink, 17 In.High	125.00
Satin Glass, Vase, Rose, Pinched, Attributed To Stevens & Williams, 7 1/2 In.	325.00
Satin Glass, Vase, Stick, Apricot, Mother-Of-Pearl, 5 In.High	85.00
Satin Glass, Vase, Stick, Blue, Cut Velvet, Ribbed	115.00
Satin Glass, Vase, Stick, Blue, Raised Diamond-Quilted Mother-Of-Pearl, Pair	120.00
Satin Glass, Vase, Stick, Green, Cut Velvet, Ribbed	125.00
Satin Glass, Vase, White, Hand-Painted Daisy & Leaf, 10 In.High	25.00
Satin Glass, Vase, White, Yellow Top, 3 3/4 In.High	18.00
Satin Glass, Vase, Yellow To White, Clover Blossoms, Silver Standard, Pair	400.00
Satin Glass, Vase, Yellow To White, Gilt & Raised Lavender Enamel, Lined	90.00
Satin Glass, Vase, Yellow, Embossed Roses, Overlay, Bulbous	50.00

Satin Glass, Vase, Yellow, Mother-Of-Pearl, Raised Webs Of Coralene 165.00
Satin Glass, Vase, Yellow, Mother-Of-Pearl, Stretched Top, White Casing 110.00
Satin Glass, Vase, Yellow, Red Swirls, Attributed To Stevens & Williams 250.00

Satsuma is a Japanese Pottery with a distinctive creamy beige crackled
glaze. Most of the pieces were decorated with blue, red, green, orange, or gold.
Almost all the Satsuma found today was made after 1860. Japanese faces
are often a part of the decorative scheme.

Satsuma, Basket, Pink, White Floral, Men, Gold Outline, Scrolls, Fans, Handle 185.00
Satsuma, Bowl, Enamel, Hexagon, Warriors, 8 In. 135.00
Satsuma, Bowl, Flower Design, Gold, Orange, 2 In.High, 4 5/8 In.Diameter 85.00
Satsuma, Bowl, Interior Decoration, Medallion, Figural Scene, Hexagon 80.00
Satsuma, Bowl, Landscape, Birds, Mark, 3 1/2 In. 125.00
Satsuma, Bowl, People Center, Scenic Border, Scalloped 135.00
Satsuma, Box, Rouge, Imperial Mark 70.00
Satsuma, Candlestick, Wisteria, Pair 85.00
Satsuma, Candy, Oval, Blue On Gray, Raised Silver Sprays, 4 Legs 15.00
Satsuma, Creamer, Ivory, Allover Gold Mesh, Butterflies 40.00
Satsuma, Cruet, Men On One Side, Children On Reverse, Gold, Square Shape 75.00
Satsuma, Cup & Saucer .... *Illus* 68.00
Satsuma, Cup & Saucer, Demitasse, Thousand Flower Design 35.00
Satsuma, Cup & Saucer, Flower Design, People, Blue 40.00
Satsuma, Cup & Saucer, Millefiori Design, Autumn Shades 25.00
Satsuma, Cup & Saucer, People & Flower, Small 40.00
Satsuma, Cup & Saucer, Red Flowers, Green Leaves, Cream Background 30.00
Satsuma, Cup & Saucer, Translucent, Gold 8.50
Satsuma, Cup & Saucer, Wisteria Pattern, Black Border, C.1895 .... 15.00
Satsuma, Hatpin Holder, Bird 15.00
Satsuma, Hatpin Holder, Flowers, Bluebird 17.00
Satsuma, Incense Burner, Faces, Foo Dog Finial On Lid, Footed 77.00
Satsuma, Incense Burner, Wisteria Decoration 20.00
Satsuma, Jar, Covered, Heavy Gold Decoration, Soft Coloring, 5 In.High 55.00
Satsuma, Jar, Ginger, Warriors, 1893 .... 29.50
Satsuma, Jar, People One Side, Flower Reverse, Gold Foo Dog Handles, Finial 40.00
Satsuma, Lamp, Table, Thousand Faces Design, 24 In.High 225.00
Satsuma, Plate, Birds Of Paradise, Floral Ground, Border Key Design, 8 In. 90.00
Satsuma, Plate, Five Scenes Of People, 7 In. 55.00
Satsuma, Plate, Landscape Scene, Pink Wisteria, 9 1/2 In. 65.00
Satsuma, Plate, Millefiori, Autumn Shades 25.00
Satsuma, Salt & Pepper, Gold Design, Beading, Royal Satsuma 15.00
Satsuma, Salt Dip, Open, Allover Painting Of Men, 1 1/4 In.Diameter 10.00
Satsuma, Tea Set, Birds, Trees, 15 Piece 275.00
Satsuma, Teapot, Cream Ground, Men, Women, 3 1/2 In.High 30.00
Satsuma, Teapot, Miniature, People Having Tea, 2 1/2 In.High 175.00
Satsuma, Teapot, Red Flowers, Green Leaves, Cream Background 60.00
Satsuma, Teapot, Scenic, 3 In. 45.00
Satsuma, Teapot, Thousand Flower Pattern, Gold 60.00
Satsuma, Toothpick, Men, Women, Chilren 40.00
Satsuma, Toothpick, Purple Iris, Gold Leaves 32.00
Satsuma, Vase, Allover 1000 Flower Design, Cross In Circle Mark, 6 1/2 In. 95.00
Satsuma, Vase, Beige, Orange, Red, Blue, & Gold, Warriors, Signed, 18 In.High 65.00
Satsuma, Vase, Cobalt, Two Panels, Oriental Women, 6 In. 35.00
Satsuma, Vase, Decorated Panels, Cobalt, Gilt, 12 1/2 In., Pair 150.00
Satsuma, Vase, Emperor, Samurai Warrior Scenes On Ivory, 10 1/2 In. 95.00
Satsuma, Vase, Figures, 9 1/2 In.Tall, Pair 40.00
Satsuma, Vase, Floral Outlined In Gold, Oriental Signature 35.00
Satsuma, Vase, Foo Dog Base, 10 1/2 In. .... *Illus* 235.00
Satsuma, Vase, Gold, Costumed Natives, Stippled Design, Flare Rim 24.50
Satsuma, Vase, Heads Of Immortals, Gold Dragon, 9 In.High 110.00
Satsuma, Vase, Lamp, Brass, Electrified, 23 In.High 49.00
Satsuma, Vase, Lavender Wisteria Vines, Bulbous, 6 In., Pair 135.00
Satsuma, Vase, Men & Boy In Panel, Allover Decoration, 7 1/2 In.High 85.00
Satsuma, Vase, Men Fighting With Sticks, Cream Ground, 13 In.High, Pair 275.00
Satsuma, Vase, Miniature, Raised Enamel Oriental Figures, 4 In.High 10.00
Satsuma, Vase, Orange Ground, Ducks, Floral, Gilt, Green, Purple, Blue, Pair 250.00
Satsuma, Vase, Oriental Scene, Footed, 23 In.High, Pair 850.00

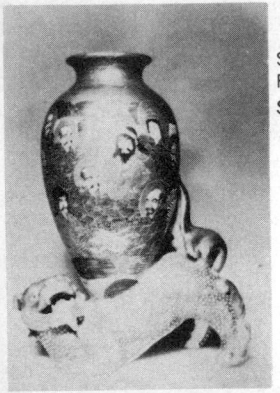

Satsuma, Vase,
Foo Dog Base, 10 1/2 In.
See Page 501

Satsuma, Vase, 6 In.

Satsuma, Vase, Raised Daisies, Beading, Golden Bamboo, Handles	25.00
Satsuma, Vase, Red Orange Figures, Raised Dots, 9 1/2 In.	35.00
Satsuma, Vase, Royal Blue Ground, Panels, Ladies, Child	42.00
Satsuma, Vase, Thousand Butterfly Pattern, Carved Stand, Miniature	35.00
Satsuma, Vase, Thousand Faces, Signed, 19 1/2 In.High	150.00
Satsuma, Vase, Thousand Flower Pattern, Wooden Stand, Marked, Pair	190.00
Satsuma, Vase, Thousand Priests Pattern, 6 In.High, Pair	125.00
Satsuma, Vase, Three Piece, 18th Century, 44 In.High	5000.00
Satsuma, Vase, Two Handled, Hand-Painted Flowers, 12 In.High	95.00
Satsuma, Vase, Warlords On Front, Two Dragon Handles, Unmarked, 11 In.	60.00
Satsuma, Vase, Warlords, Two Dragon Handles, 12 In.High	60.00
Satsuma, Vase, Warriors, Elephant's Head Handle, C.1840, 9 1/2 In.High, Pair	200.00
Satsuma, Vase, Wisteria, 6 1/4 In.	87.50
Satsuma, Vase, 6 In. *Illus*	175.00
Satsuma, Water Bucket, White Herons, Landscape, 13 1/4 In.High	165.00
Scale, Balance, Apothecary, Brass Pans, Five Weights, Gram, Germany, Box	28.00
Scale, Balance, Brandon, Patent 1867, 18 In.Long	35.00
Scale, Balance, Brass, Circa 1870, Doyle & Son, London	85.00
Scale, Balance, Iron, Tin Pan, Three Weights	27.50
Scale, Balance, Two Step Base, Large Pans, Onyx	80.00
Scale, Candy, Brass Pan, Dayton, 20 In.High	60.00
Scale, Candy, Superb, Brass Scoop, Pelanze Mfg. Co.	25.00
Scale, Chemist's, Precision, Beam, Glass & Mahogany Case, Made In London	78.00
Scale, Counter, Brass Dial, Decals, Soldier, U.S.Flag, Removable Tray	25.00
Scale, Cupid Holds Ring For Beam Which Holds Pans, Brass	45.00
Scale, Drug, Glass Case, 11 X 5 X 7 In.	48.00
Scale, Drug, Oak, Beveled Glass Lid, Marble & Oak Bottom, 13 X 7 X 7 In.	95.00
Scale, Fairbanks, Sliding Weight, Platform, Brass Beam, Iron	22.50
Scale, Hanging, Brass Face, Chatillon	7.00
Scale, Hanging, Brass Face, Embossed Tin Pan, Pelouze	27.50
Scale, Pharmaceutical, Drawer, Weights, Glass & Walnut Case	165.00
Scale, Postal, Black Iron & Brass, Stenciling, 1885, Separate Weights	85.00
Scale, Six Weights, Marked Eastman Kodak	35.00
Scale, Steel Yard, 50 Lb., Marked E.Collins, Iron	4.75
Scale, Store, Pelouze, Bronze Cast Base, Sliding Computing Beam, Scoop	27.00
Scale, Top Bar Across Standard, 10 1/2 In.Pans, 34 In.High, Brass	135.00

Schneider Glassworks was founded in 1903 at Epinay-sur-seine, France,
by Charles and Ernest Schneider. Art glass was made between 1903 and Schneider
1930. The company still produces clear crystal glass.

Schneider, Bowl, Bubbly Golden Yellow, Shallow, Signed, 8 1/2 In.	39.00
Schneider, Bowl, Yellow, Brown, Footed, Signed	140.00
Schneider, Compote, Blue, Brown, Tan, 8 1/2 In.Diameter, Signed	95.00
Schneider, Compote, Cobalt & Orange Mottle, 15 X 4 3/4 In.High	225.00
Schneider, Compote, Mottled Orange, Amethyst Base, Signed, 15 1/2 In Diam.	170.00
Schneider, Compote, Oxblood Red, Blue, Brown, Signed	115.00

Schneider, **Compote**, Purple, Lavender & White Mottle, Purple Glass Blobs 115.00
Schneider, **Compote**, Yellow & Black Mottle, Yellow Stem, Purple Mottle Base 95.00
Schneider, **Pitcher**, Applied Purple Teardrops, Applied Orange Handle 175.00
Schneider, **Tazza**, Orange Bowl, Controlled Bubbles, Amethyst Foot, 8 In. 95.00
Schneider, **Vase**, Baluster, Domed Foot, Yellow To Purple At Base, Signed 100.00
Schneider, **Vase**, Blue & Orange, Matte Finish, Art Nouveau, 15 1/2 In. 77.50
Schneider, **Vase**, Cameo, Cluthra Ground, Orange Flower, Deep Wine At Base 300.00
Schneider, **Vase**, Cherries, Iron Base, Flamelike Effect, 19 In.High 175.00
Schneider, **Vase**, Mottled Color, Art Nouveau Design, Signed, 16 In.High 135.00
Schneider, **Vase**, Mottled Purples & Lavenders, Amethyst Base, Signed, 13 In. 210.00
Schneider, **Vase**, Purple & White Marbelized, Signed, 14 In. 175.00

Scrimshaw is bone or ivory or whale's teeth carved by sailors and others for
entertainment during the sailing ship days. Some Scrimshaw was carved as
early as 1800.

Scrimshaw, **Antlers**, Penholder 17.50
Scrimshaw, **Bone**, Indian, Tlingit, Totemic Head, Protruding Tongue 1300.00
Scrimshaw, **Carved Oriental Lady**, Bone 30.00
Scrimshaw, **Chess Set**, Portable, Red & White Stained, Eliza Young, 1852 .... 325.00
Scrimshaw, **Cribbage Game**, Whale Tooth, Eskimo Scene, Circa 1940 .... 25.00
Scrimshaw, **Cup**, Carved Horn, British Huntsman, Dogs, Fox Hunt, C.1830 .... 37.50
Scrimshaw, **Dominoes**, 26 Pieces, Wooden Box 10.00
Scrimshaw, **Elephant Tusk**, Serpent, Palm Tree, Fish, Standing Beast, African 19.50
Scrimshaw, **Elephant Tusk**, Whaling Scene Of 1840s, New Bedford, Pair 125.00
Scrimshaw, **Horn**, Birds, 8 In., Pair 16.00
Scrimshaw, **Horn**, Civil War Soldiers, Sailor, Cannon, Ship, Union Forever, 1890 .... 75.00
Scrimshaw, **Pie Crimper**, Bird's-Eye Maple Handle, C.1860 .... 45.00
Scrimshaw, **Powder Horn**, Townscape & Portrait Medallion, Ezra Holmes, 1775 .... 1500.00
Scrimshaw, **Ruler**, Folding, 12 In. 10.00
Scrimshaw, **Sperm Whale's Inner Ear Drums**, Faces, Floral, Pair 54.50
Scrimshaw, **Sperm Whale's Tooth**, Whaling Scenes 32.50
Scrimshaw, **Tray**, Knife, Whaling Sailors, Drawer, Ivory Handle, C.1850 .... 125.00
Scrimshaw, **Tusk**, African Figures, Metallic Button Eyes, 14 In. 97.50
Scrimshaw, **Tusk**, Africans & Arabs, 9 In. 115.00
Scrimshaw, **Tusk**, Eskimo, Curved, Engraved Scene, Figures, Igloos, Seal Hunt 500.00
Scrimshaw, **Tusk**, Eskimo, Curved, Pierced, Engraved Figures 1900.00
Scrimshaw, **Walrus Tooth**, Cribbage Board, Fish & Seal Design, 9 1/2 In. 55.00
Scrimshaw, **Walrus Tusk**, Sailor & Sweetheart, 26 In.Long, C.1900s 300.00
Scrimshaw, **Weaving Shuttle** 10.00
Scrimshaw, **Whale Tooth**, Bust Of Lady, Pot Of Flowers Reverse, Colored 125.00
Scrimshaw, **Whale Tooth**, Eagle Head Shape, Flag, 5 In.Long, 19th Century 350.00
Scrimshaw, **Whale Tooth**, Engraved, Civil War Vessel, Says Peace & Union 165.00
Scrimshaw, **Whale Tooth**, Jugglers & Acrobats, 8 In. 105.00
Scrimshaw, **Whale Tooth**, Picture Of H.M.Bryant, Signed 40.00
Scrimshaw, **Whale Tooth**, Rigged Ship, Early New York City Street Scene 150.00
Scrimshaw, **Whale Tooth**, Schooner, Three Masted, Water Plumes Reverse 200.00
Scrimshaw, **Whale Tooth**, Washington On Horseback, Farmer, Flag, 7 In.Long 350.00
Scrimshaw, **Whalebone**, Carved Ship's Captain On Old Man Of The Sea 375.00
    Scuttle Mug, see Shaving Mug

Sevres Porcelain has been made in Sevres, France, since 1769. Many
copies of the famous ware have been made. The name originally referred to
the works of the Royal Factory. The name now includes any of the wares
made in the town of Sevres, France.

Sevres, **Bottle**, Rouge Scent, Panel, Cherub, Cone Shape 100.00
Sevres, **Bowl**, Basket Weave, Flowers Inside, Oval, Small Size, C.1793 .... 25.00
Sevres, **Box**, Bleu Celeste, Ormolu Feet, C.1780 .... 372.00
Sevres, **Box**, Cobalt, Gold Trim, Glaze, 1 1/4 X 2 1/2 In. 65.00
Sevres, **Box**, Covered, Round, Bouquets Of Flowers, Gold Scrolls, Signed 60.00
Sevres, **Box**, Egg Shape, Blue Floral Swags, Lavender Bows, Wreaths, Dore Rims 150.00
Sevres, **Box**, Patch, Blue, Gold, Hand-Painted Portrait, Flowers 38.50
Sevres, **Box**, Peacock Blue, Flowers, Gold, 3 1/2 X 2 3/4 X 2 In.High 45.00
Sevres, **Box**, Pink, C.1800, 4 X 6 In. 325.00
Sevres, **Box**, Romantic Scene, Blue, Gold Trim 90.00
Sevres, **Box**, Ruby, Flowers, Gold, Bronze Trim, 5 X 7 X 2 In.High 125.00
Sevres, **Box**, Stamp, Ruby, Flowers, Gold, Bronze Trim 45.00

Sevres, Box, Trinket, Transfer Scene, Allover Silver Overlay, 1846 Mark 150.00
Sevres, Clock, Blue Panels, Pink, Rose & Green Figures, 18 In.High 1000.00
Sevres, Clock, Blue, Gold Mounts & Ormolu, French Movement, C.1850 .... 1000.00
Sevres, Clock, Large Pink Panels, Fishing Theme, Ormolu 2000.00
Sevres, Cup & Saucer, Medallion, Cavaliers On Horses, Cobalt, Gold, 1846 .... 95.00
Sevres, Figurine, Bust Of Napoleon, Signed Canova, Parian, 5 In. 35.00
Sevres, Inkwell, Attached Tray, Pink, White, Blue Floral, Brass Ribbon & Bow 45.00
Sevres, Plate, Blue Rim, Gold Scrolls & Ferns, White, Cherubs, 1867 .... 95.00
Sevres, Plate, Chateau De Tuileries, Marked, 9 1/2 In. 55.00
Sevres, Plate, Cherubs, Bouquets, Floral Border, Signed Louis Philippe, 1846 .... 85.00
Sevres, Plate, Cluster Of Three Red Cherries, 6 In. 3.00
Sevres, Plate, Flowers In Center, Blue Border, 1874 Mark 40.00
Sevres, Plate, Lovers In Garden, Chateau St.Cloud, One Signed Debrie 100.00
Sevres, Plate, Pastoral Scenic, Signed Debrie, Gold Border, C.1846, Pair 150.00
Sevres, Plate, Portrait Of Madame Lamballe, Gold, Forget-Me-Nots 37.50
Sevres, Plate, Portrait, C.1850 .... 165.00
Sevres, Plate, Portrait, M'Elle Louise, Pink Border, 1779, 9 In. 165.00
Sevres, Plate, Portrait, M'Me De Genlis, Yellow Border, 1779, 9 In. 165.00
Sevres, Plate, Portrait, Mm.De Lamballe, Gold & Pink Edge, Signed Debrie 75.00
Sevres, Sugar, Birds, Wreaths, Gilt Decoration, Handle, 1834 .... 125.00
Sevres, Tea Set, Hand-Painted Cupids, Gold, 5 Piece 275.00
Sevres, Teapot & Sugar, Cherubs, Coin Gold, Signed Louis Philippe, 1846 .... 155.00
Sevres, Teapot, Portrait, C.1784, Signed 115.00
Sevres, Tray, Receiving, White, Conch Shape, Large 22.50
Sevres, Urn, Cobalt, Floral & Courting Couple, Covered, Signed Double L, Pair 295.00
Sevres, Urn, Girl Holds Urn, Cupid Holds Basket, Bronze Ormolu, Gold Beading 350.00
Sevres, Urn, Inverted Bell Shape, Domed Foot, Painted Frieze Of Fish, Signed 275.00
Sevres, Urn, Oriental Vignette, Royal Blue, Gold, Ornate Ormolu, Pair 450.00
Sevres, Urn, Painted Vignette, Brass Base, Finial On Lid, 7 In. 169.00
Sevres, Urn, Painting Of Boy On Steps With Dog, Porcelain, 8 In. 130.00
Sevres, Vase, Blue Black, Narrow Neck, No Decoration, Marked & Dated 1881 .... 60.00
Sevres, Vase, Mottled Green & Blue Glaze, Bronze Trim, C.1890, 6 1/2 In.High 80.00
Sevres, Vase, Panels, Louis XV & XVI Courts, Pink, Lid, 20 In., Pair 2200.00
Sevres, Vase, 17 1/2 In.High, Artist Signed Faiol 350.00

Sewer tile figures were made by workers in the sewer tile factories in the
Ohio area during the late 19th and early 20th centuries.

Sewer Tile, Dog, 9 In. .... *Illus*   85.00
Sewer Tile, Shoe, 5 1/2 In.Long .... *Illus*   28.00
Sewer Tile, Vase, Tree Stump, 16 In. 65.00
Sewing Tool, Basket, Peking Glass Rings, Chinese Coins, Wicker, Cover 10.00
Sewing Tool, Bird, Brass, Clamp 36.00
Sewing Tool, Bird, Brass, Double Cushion .... 32.00 To 35.00
Sewing Tool, Bird, Clamps On Table, Nickel Plate, No Pincushion 30.00
Sewing Tool, Bird, Dated Wings, Two Cushions 35.00
Sewing Tool, Bird, Double Cushion, Dated Feb.15, 1853, Brass 40.00
Sewing Tool, Bird, Embossed Brass, Orange Velvet Cushions 28.00
Sewing Tool, Bird, Ivory 7.00
Sewing Tool, Bird, Pincushion, Thread Box, Band, Carved Hearts, Penna. 45.00
Sewing Tool, Bird, Silver-Plated, One Cushion, Table Clamp 40.00
Sewing Tool, Bird, Sterling Silver 45.00
Sewing Tool, Bird, Two Green Cushions, Brass 28.50
Sewing Tool, Bird, Two Red Velvet Cushions, Dated 1853 .... 38.50
Sewing Tool, Bobbin, Mother-Of-Pearl, 3 In.Long 7.50
Sewing Tool, Bobbin, Whalebone, 2 1/3 In.Long 8.50
Sewing Tool, Bodkin, Ribbon, 14k Gold 12.00
Sewing Tool, Box, Brocaded, Ivory Sticks For Ribbon, Five Silver Bodkins 28.00
Sewing Tool, Box, Clark & Co. 12.50
Sewing Tool, Box, Leather, Victorian, Dome Top, Ball Feet, Snake Handle, 1890 .... 20.00
Sewing Tool, Box, Lithograph, Three Children Playing Bubbles, J & P Coats 14.00
Sewing Tool, Box, Walnut, Two Bands Of Inlaid Woods, 10 3/4 .... 23.00
Sewing Tool, Caddy, Spool Pegs, Revolving Turntables, Drawer, Iron Nails 50.00
Sewing Tool, Caddy, Seamstress's, Spool Pegs, Turntables, Drawer, Nails 50.00
Sewing Tool, Case, Needle, Carved Ivory 12.50
Sewing Tool, Case, Needle, English Silver, 2 1/2 In.Long 15.00
Sewing Tool, Clamp, Blade, Gauge To Cut Buttonholes, Iron, Dolphin 50.00

Sewing Tool, Clamp, Lady's Hand Form, Hand-Forged Steel, Pincushion, C.1750 .... 140.00
Sewing Tool, Clamp, Leaf, Hand-Forged Steel, Heart Shape, Pincushion, C.1750 .... 100.00
Sewing Tool, Clamp, Pincushion & Hook For Thimble, Steel 30.00
Sewing Tool, Crochet Hook, Sterling 3.75
Sewing Tool, Darner, Aqua Glass, Pontil, Blown 19.00
Sewing Tool, Darner, Black, Wooden 1.00
Sewing Tool, Darner, Cobalt, White Loopings, 6 In. 35.00
Sewing Tool, Darner, Glove, Sterling Silver 15.00
Sewing Tool, Darner, Nailsea Type 20.00
Sewing Tool, Darner, Sock, Sterling Silver Handle 6.50
Sewing Tool, Darning Egg, Wooden 2.50
Sewing Tool, Frame, Embroidery, Cherry, Turned, 2 Shoe Feet, C.1850 .... 400.00
Sewing Tool, Frame, Embroidery, Cherry, 1820, 15 1/4 In. .... Illus 200.00
Sewing Tool, Hem Measure, Silver Plate 8.00
Sewing Tool, Holder, Spool, Ivory Opening, Beeswax Finish, 6 1/2 In.High 30.00
Sewing Tool, Holder, Thimble & Spool, Egg Shape, 2 In.Long 25.00
Sewing Tool, Lace Bobbins, Glass Beads, Four Ivory, Five Wood, Lot Of 9 .... 55.00
Sewing Tool, Needle Box, Carved Ivory 5.00
Sewing Tool, Needle Case, Chased Work, English Silver 15.00
Sewing Tool, Needle Case, Chased Work, Ring At Ends, English Silver 22.50
Sewing Tool, Needle Case, Ring For Chain, English Silver, C.1890 .... 12.00
Sewing Tool, Pincushion & Brush Holder, High Heel Boot Of 1800s 11.50
Sewing Tool, Pincushion, Beaded Bird, 1899 .... 10.00
Sewing Tool, Pincushion, Bone, 3 1/2 In. .... Illus 45.00
Sewing Tool, Pincushion, Figural, Camel, English Silver, 2 In.High 45.00

Sewer Tile, Shoe, 5 1/2 In.Long
See Page 504

Sewer Tile, Dog, 9 In.
See Page 504

Sewing Tool, Frame,
Embroidery, Cherry,
c.1820, 15 1/4 In.

Sewing Tool,
Pincushion,
Bone, 3 1/2 In.

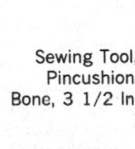

Sewing Tool, Pincushion, Lady's Shoe, Metal 3.75
Sewing Tool, Pincushion, Thread Holders, Sterling, James Tufts 25.00
Sewing Tool, Puncushion, Urn, 1 1/2 In. 7.50
Sewing Tool, Pincushion, Victorian, Beaded, 5 X 6 In. 5.00
Sewing Tool, Rug Hooker, Pat.1881 .... 3.00
Sewing Tool, Rule, Nickel Plated, Ladies Gem, Columbia Expo., 1893 .... 6.50
Sewing Tool, Scissors, Curved Edge, German Silver 6.25
Sewing Tool, Scissors, Embossed, Engraved, Silver, 5 In.Long 26.00
Sewing Tool, Scissors, Embroidery, Stork Shaped 9.00
Sewing Tool, Scissors, For Button Hole, Iron, Steel, Brass, Dated 1869 .... 8.50
Sewing Tool, Shears, Wrought Iron, Impressed Matkin, 18th Century, 8 1/2 In. 23.00
Sewing Tool, Sock Darner, Ruby, Cranberry & White Spatter On Clear, 9 In. 45.00
Sewing Tool, Tape Measure, Advertising, Lady's Picture, C.1900 .... 5.00
Sewing Tool, Tape Measure, Advertising, Lydia Pinkham, Picture 8.50
Sewing Tool, Tape Measure, Boat, Paddlewheel, Brass, Tape Inside, 1826 .... 65.00
Sewing Tool, Tape Measure, Indian, Celluloid, Japan 12.00
Sewing Tool, Tape Measure, Kangaroo, Baby In Pouch, Celluloid 14.50
Sewing Tool, Tape Measure, Metal Straw Hat, Slogan 20.00
Sewing Tool, Tape Measure, Pig, Brass 12.50
Sewing Tool, Tape Measure, Prince Of Wales, Celluloid Bust, 2 3/8 In.Tall 35.00
Sewing Tool, Tape Measure, Shape Of Half Moon Mandolin, C.1890 ....
Sewing Tool, Tape Measure, Victorian, Millhouse, Brass, Tape Inside 65.00
Sewing Tool, Tatting Shuttle, Horn 6.00
Sewing Tool, Tatting Shuttle, Scrimshaw 11.00
Sewing Tool, Tatting Shuttle, Sterling Silver 6.00
Sewing Tool, Thimble & Cage, Pierced, Repousse, Silver, Unger Bros., 1896 .... 39.00
Sewing Tool, Thimble & Thread In Nickel Case, Advertising, 1923 .... 6.00
Sewing Tool, Thimble Holder, Acorn, Hand Carved Ivory, Thimble, Needles 28.00
Sewing Tool, Thimble Holder, English Silver, Gold Gilt 45.00
Sewing Tool, Thimble Holder, Mother-Of-Pearl, Red Velvet Lined, C.1800 .... 38.00
Sewing Tool, Thimble Holder, Velvet Case With Handle 11.00
Sewing Tool, Thimble Holder, Wood Carving Of Woman With Sack On Back 28.00
Sewing Tool, Thimble, Advertising, Metal 2.50
Sewing Tool, Thimble, Band Of Raised Grapes, Place For Initials, Silver 15.50
Sewing Tool, Thimble, Blue Enamel Scene, German Silver 15.50
Sewing Tool, Thimble, Child's, Sterling Silver 9.50
Sewing Tool, Thimble, Cupids, Floral, Sterling Silver, Pat.1905 .... 6.00
Sewing Tool, Thimble, Diamond Faceted Rim, Narrow Band, Engraved Hearts, 10k 20.00
Sewing Tool, Thimble, Embossed Westward Ho Scene, Sterling Silver 17.50
Sewing Tool, Thimble, Floral Band, Sterling Silver 11.00
Sewing Tool, Thimble, Four Black Jade & Two Coral Stones, Italian Silver , ... 42.50
Sewing Tool, Thimble, Gold Band Of Heavy Scrollwork, English Silver 17.50
Sewing Tool, Thimble, Gold Band Of Raised Apple Blossoms, Sterling Silver 25.00
Sewing Tool, Thimble, Gold, Bridge, House, Sunset 35.00
Sewing Tool, Thimble, Gold, Early 19th Century 25.00
Sewing Tool, Thimble, Gold, Flower Design 20.00
Sewing Tool, Thimble, Gold, Flowers In Panels Around Base, English 28.50
Sewing Tool, Thimble, Gold, Landscape Scene At Top, Wooden Case, Rheinfell 35.00
Sewing Tool, Thimble, Gold, Ornate .... 30.00 To 35.00
Sewing Tool, Thimble, Gold, Scenes, Houses, Setting Sun, Engraved, Monogram 32.50
Sewing Tool, Thimble, Gold, Sunset, Buildings 28.50
Sewing Tool, Thimble, House, Sun, Trees, Sterling Silver 15.50
Sewing Tool, Thimble, Jade Top, Sterling Silver 18.00
Sewing Tool, Thimble, Milliner's, Sterling Silver 35.00
Sewing Tool, Thimble, Miniature, Silver 9.00
Sewing Tool, Thimble, Prudential Life Insurance Co. 3.00
Sewing Tool, Thimble, Scroll Design, Sterling Silver, Victorian 12.50
Sewing Tool, Thimble, Scrollwork, Silver & Gold 25.00
Sewing Tool, Thimble, Silver, Lily-Of-The-Valley Band 25.00
Sewing Tool, Thimble, Sterling Silver, Dated 1877, Basket Case 12.00
Sewing Tool, Thimble, Sterling Silver, Gold Band, Engraved Initial 25.00
Sewing Tool, Thimble, Sterling Silver, Mother-Of-Pearl Decoration 17.00
Sewing Tool, Thimble, Sterling Silver, Red Jeweled Band 25.00
Sewing Tool, Thimble, Sterling, Carved Gold Band 30.00
Sewing Tool, Thimble, Sterling, Fleur-De-Lis Band, Size 12 .... 6.50
Sewing Tool, Thimble, Sterling, Gold Trim, Size 10 .... 9.50

Sewing Tool, Thimble, Sterling, Ornate 4.50
Sewing Tool, Thimble, Sunset, Buildings, By Simons 12.00
Sewing Tool, Thimble, Village Scene Around Band 5.50
Sewing Tool, Thimble, Wide Pattern Gold Band, Sterling Silver 25.00
Sewing Tool, Thimble, 10K Gold, Engraved Geometric Design, Narrow Band 25.00
Sewing Tool, Thimble, 10K Gold, Plain Band 18.00
Sewing Tool, Thimble, 10K Gold, Raised, Carved Rim, Engraved Leaves 22.00
Sewing Tool, Thimble, 14K Gold, Carved Rim, Engraved Swirled Leaves 26.00
Sewing Tool, Thimble, 14K Gold, Carved Rim, Narrow Plain Band 25.00
Sewing Tool, Thimble, 14K Gold, Cherubs & Flowers Around Base 50.00
Sewing Tool, Thimble, 14K Gold, Diamonds, Rubies, & Sapphires In Center 89.00
Sewing Tool, Thimble, 14K Gold, Engraved, Embossed, Carved Acorn Case 42.00
Sewing Tool, Thread Holder, 8 Spool, Brass Plated Nickel & Iron, Marked 9.50
Sewing Tool, Vise, Depression At Top For Pins, Wood, Whalebone Trim 12.50
Sewing Tool, Yarn Winder, Pennsylvania 58.00
Shaker, Advertisement, Tamar Laxative, 9 X 11 In. ....75.00 To 140.00
Shaker, Auger, 4 In. 7.50
Shaker, Auger, 5 In. 15.00
Shaker, Bag, Flour, Shaker Mills, New Gloucester 230.00
Shaker, Bag, Laundry, Signed, M.A. 15.00
Shaker, Basin, Tin, Four Seamed, Signed, William Reynolds, 8 X 2 1/2 In. 40.00
Shaker, Basket, Garden, Round With Handle, 11 X 7 In. 85.00
Shaker, Basket, Garden, Round With Handle, 12 X 8 In. 75.00
Shaker, Basket, Garden, Round With Handles, 15 X 9 In. 60.00
Shaker, Basket, Handle, Signed Josiah Noyes, S.D.L., 16 X 12 1/2 X 5 In. 125.00
Shaker, Basket, Laundry Carrying, With Handle, 18 X 13 In. 80.00
Shaker, Basket, Laundry, Carrying, Handle, 13 X 18 X 9 In. 50.00
Shaker, Basket, Laundry, Signed Sarah Church, Handle, 14 X 19 X 8 In. 40.00
Shaker, Basket, Laundry, Two Handles, 12 X 17 In. 80.00
Shaker, Basket, Round, Two Handles, Signed, Anna Barnes 75.00
Shaker, Basket, Round, Two Handles, 14 1/2 X 6 In. 70.00
Shaker, Basket, Round, 17 X 10 In. 12.50
Shaker, Basket, Two Handles, 28 X 22 X 9 In. 40.00
Shaker, Basket, Wooden, Round, Handle, Old Blue, 12 1/2 X 9 1/2 In.Deep 35.00
Shaker, Board, Drying, With Bread Board Ends 55.00
Shaker, Board, Sleeve, 20 In.Long 15.00
Shaker, Board, Sleeve, 26 1/2 In.Long 20.00
Shaker, Bottle, Anodyne, North Family, Enfield, N.H., 4 In.High 44.00
Shaker, Bottle, Extract Valerian, Clear, 3 1/2 In.Tall 35.00
Shaker, Bottle, Shaker Hair Restorer, Amber, 8 In. Tall 100.00
Shaker, Bottle, Shaker Pickles, Aqua, 9 In.Tall 162.50
Shaker, Bottle, Syrup, No.1, Aqua, Canterbury, N.H., 8 In.Tall 45.00
Shaker, Box, Bonnet, Dovetailed, Carrying Handle, Old Red Paint, Paper Lined 200.00
Shaker, Box, Covered, Round, Old Blue Paint, 10 1/2 In. Diameter 100.00
Shaker, Box, Document, Dovetailed, Old Red, Alfred 125.00
Shaker, Box, Dough 85.00
Shaker, Box, Dovetailed, Made By Elder H.Green, 13 In.X 19 In.X 10 In. 125.00
Shaker, Box, Dresser, Round Open Fingered, Old Red Paint, 8 1/2 X 2 1/2 In. 125.00
Shaker, Box, Fingered, Covered, Cherry, Oval, Signed, 6 X 2 1/2 In. 150.00
Shaker, Box, Fingered, Covered, Cherry, Oval, Signed, 11 In.Diameter 200.00
Shaker, Box, Fingered, Covered, Oval, Red Paint, 6 X 9 In. 87.50
Shaker, Box, Fingered, Covered, Oval, Signed Alfred, 7 X 10 In. 112.50
Shaker, Box, Fingered, Covered, Oval, Signed Alfred, 8 1/2 X 12 In. 100.00
Shaker, Box, Fingered, Covered, Oval, Signed, 9 X 12 1/2 In. 100.00
Shaker, Box, Fingered, Covered, Oval, Signed, 9 1/2 X 3 In. 125.00
Shaker, Box, Fingered, Covered, Round, Signed Alfred, 6 1/4 In. 46.00
Shaker, Box, Large Wood, Old Yellow Paint, Turned Legs, Two Shaving Drawers 600.00
Shaker, Box, Lift Lid Blanket, Old Graining 262.50
Shaker, Box, Open, Used In Alfred Sewing Room, 10 1/2 X 6 3/4 In. 60.00
Shaker, Box, Pasteboard, Black, Lift Lid, Spools, Thread, 6 X 3 In., Alfred 32.50
Shaker, Box, Pine, Rectangular, Brass Carrying Handle, Blue Paint 100.00
Shaker, Box, Round, Cover, 7 1/2 X 4 1/2 In. 35.00
Shaker, Box, Seed, Shaker Label, 23 1/2 In.X 11 1/2 In.X 3 In.Deep 162.50
Shaker, Box, Sewing, Blanket Chest Style, Monogram, S.J.C. 375.00
Shaker, Box, Sewing, Pasteboard, Green And Red, Glass Top 27.50
Shaker, Box, Wood, Painted, With Turned Legs, 25 X 16 1/2 X 10 1/2 In. 100.00

Shaker, Box, Wood, 25 X 18 X 17 In. 137.50
Shaker, Brush, Clothes, Ribbed Top, 4 1/2 In.Long 20.00
Shaker, Brush, Clothes, Ribbed Top, 6 1/4 In. 10.00
Shaker, Brush, Dusting, 21 In. 10.00
Shaker, Bucket, Sap, Tin, Three Seamed, 12 X 9 In. ...... 20.00 To 27.50
Shaker, Bucket, Sap, Tin, 9 X 11 In. 20.00
Shaker, Bucket, Wooden, Red, With Bail Handle, 9 X 12 In. 30.00
Shaker, Bucket, Wooden, Round, With Handle, Old Blue, 12 1/2 X 9 1/2 In. 17.50
Shaker, Bucket, Wooden, Signed, M.H.C.December 25, 1915 ...... 30.00
Shaker, Can, Tin, Round, 'sage, ' Covered, S.D.L.Label ...... 55.00 To 85.00
Shaker, Can, Tin, Spice, Round, With Cover, 2 X 2 In. 35.00
Shaker, Carrier, Fingered, Cherry, Oval, With Handle, 10 3/4 X 8 In. 125.00
Shaker, Carrier, Handled, Footed, Hancock 125.00
Shaker, Carrier, Oval, Fingered, With Handle, 8 X 11 In.Signed S.D.L. 130.00
Shaker, Carrier, Wood, Dovetailed, Handle, 24 X 15 X 12 In.Deep, Canterbury 250.00
Shaker, Churn, Butter, Dasher, With Handle, 20 In. Tall 500.00
Shaker, Dipper, Tin, Long Handled, 13 In. 70.00
Shaker, Drawing, Spiritual, Framed, 27 1/2 X 21 1/2 In. 125.00
Shaker, Fan, Handle, Ivory, 7 In. 5.00
Shaker, Funnel, Tin, With Hangers, 4 1/2 In.Long, 3 1/2 In.Round 15.00
Shaker, Furniture, see Furniture
Shaker, Hammer, For Tin Knocking, 10 1/2 In., Alfred 3.00
Shaker, Hanger, Garment, Very Early Pine, Signed, Sarah Mace 250.00
Shaker, Hanger, Garment, With Original Braid, 15 3/4 In.Long 35.00
Shaker, Hanger, Garment, 16 In. 25.00
Shaker, Hanger, Gown, 19 1/2 In. 37.50
Shaker, Hetchel, For Splitting Flax, Handle, 11 1/2 In.Teeth, 11 In. 150.00
Shaker, Kerchief, Silk 15.00
Shaker, Kerchief, Silk And Wool, Sabbath Day Lake 35.00
Shaker, Lap Board, Cherry, 28 1/2 X 10 1/2 In. 25.00
Shaker, Lap Board, Measured, 21 1/2 X 14 1/2 In. 100.00
Shaker, Lap Board, Pine, Old Red With Breadboard Ends, 33 In.X 14 In. 135.00
Shaker, Lap Board, Pine, 16 X 17 In. 25.00
Shaker, Latch, Door, Early Thumb, Alfred ...... 40.00 To 50.00
Shaker, Mallet, Wooden, 12 In.Long 55.00
Shaker, Measure, Round, Covered, Alfred, 15 X 8 In.Eva M.Libby 80.00
Shaker, Measure, Round, Wooden, 7 1/2 X 4 In.Signed S.D.L. 55.00
Shaker, Measure, Round, Wooden, 9 1/4 X 5 In.Signed S.D.L. 65.00
Shaker, Measure, Round, 2 Deka, 20 Liter, Signed S.D.L. 100.00
Shaker, Measure, Round, 6 X 3 1/2 In. 15.00
Shaker, Measure, Round, 9 In.High X 14 1/2 In. 45.00
Shaker, Measure, Round, 10 Deka Liter, Signed S.D.L. 100.00
Shaker, Measure, Tin, Round, 6 1/4 X 4 3/4 In. 30.00
Shaker, Measure, Wooden, Round, 3 1/4 X 5 3/4 In. 35.00
Shaker, Measure, Wooden, Round, 5 3/4 X 3 1/2 In. 20.00
Shaker, Measure, Wooden, Round, 6 X 3 1/4 In., Signed S.D.L. 45.00
Shaker, Measure, Wooden, Round, 7 X 3 In. 32.50
Shaker, Measure, Wooden, Round, 7 1/2 X 4 In. 10.00
Shaker, Mug, Tin, 4 3/8 In. Tall 35.00
Shaker, Pegboard, 2 Pegs, 45 In. 50.00
Shaker, Pegboard, 4 Pegs, Alfred, 24 In. 85.00
Shaker, Pegboard, 4 Pegs, 47 In. 65.00
Shaker, Pegboard, 4 Pegs, 71 1/2 In. 65.00
Shaker, Pegboard, 6 Pegs, Alfred, 49 1/2 In. 100.00
Shaker, Pegboard, 8 Pegs, Alfred, 64 In. 70.00
Shaker, Pegboard, 18 Pegs, Alfred, 69 In. 100.00
Shaker, Photograph, Framed, Sabbathday Lake, By Delmar Wilson, 11 X 7 In. 50.00
Shaker, Pincushion, Blue Satin Upholstered, Emery Ball And Wax, 2 In. 15.00
Shaker, Pincushion, Round, Emery Ball & Wax, 2 In. ...... 5.00 To 65.00
Shaker, Pincushion, Round, Flowered, With Emery Ball And Handle, 2 In. 15.00
Shaker, Pincushion, Satin, Blue Patterned, 5 In.Round 25.00
Shaker, Pincushion, Satin, Green Patterned, 5 In. 15.00
Shaker, Pincushion, Satin, Round, Lavender, 5 In. 10.00
Shaker, Pincushion, Satin, Yellow Rose Pattern, 5 In.Round 15.00
Shaker, Pincushion, Thread Holder, Emery Ball & Wax, Blue 95.00
Shaker, Pincushion, Thread Holder, Emery Ball And Wax, Blue, Signed, S.D.L. 100.00

Shaker, Pincushion, Thread Holder, Pink Cloth, Signed S.D.L. 125.00
Shaker, Pincushion, Thread Holder, Pink Upholstery, Emery Ball, Wax, Signed 100.00
Shaker, Pincushion, Upholstered, Blue, 5 X 2 In. 125.00
Shaker, Pincushion, Yellow Satin Upholstery 12.50
Shaker, Pipe, Smoking, Mt.Lebanon 80.00
Shaker, Rack, Drying, Apple, 4 Feet X 2 Feet 35.00
Shaker, Rack, Drying, Herb, 6 Feet Tall X 31 In. 225.00
Shaker, Rack, Drying, Herb, 7 Feet X 31 In. 375.00
Shaker, Rack, Drying, Pill, Rectangular, 72 Points, 12 1/2 X 6 3/4 In. 100.00
Shaker, Rack, Laundry, Folding, 6 Ft.X 3 Ft. 115.00
Shaker, Rack, Pill Drying, Rectangular, 72 Points, 12 1/2 X 6 3/4 In. 70.00
Shaker, Robe, Lap, Used In Sleigh, Signed 175.00
Shaker, Rug, Whip, Canterbury, 24 In. 40.00
Shaker, Ruler, 6 In. 35.00
Shaker, Ruler, 6 In., Alfred 15.00
Shaker, Ruler, 12 In., Alfred 40.00
Shaker, Scarf, Heavy Linen Bureau, Seamed, Shaped Ends, 26 In.X 45 In. 25.00
Shaker, Scoop, Tin, With Handle 85.00
Shaker, Scribe, Primitive, 4 In. 17.50
Shaker, Sieve, Dovetailed, Rectangular, 18 In.X 10 3/4 In. 35.00
Shaker, Sign, 'Rules For Visitors, ' Framed, 13 X 17 In. 70.00
Shaker, Sled, Wood Carrying, 19 X 52 In. 50.00
Shaker, Spectacles 25.00
Shaker, Spinning Wheel, Large 375.00
Shaker, Spinning Wheel, Small Bobbin 325.00
Shaker, Stove, Wood, Canterbury 350.00
Shaker, Swift, Hancock, Old Yellow 175.00
Shaker, Tailor's Square, Wooden, 14 X 9 In. 70.00
Shaker, Tailoring Stock, 36 In., Alfred 189.50
Shaker, Teapot, Tin, Handled, 6 1/2 In.High 75.00
Shaker, Teapot, Tin, Spout And Handle, Hancock, 3 In.Tall 250.00
Shaker, Thread, One Hank, Shaker Made, Blue 27.50
Shaker, Towel, Linen, Bird's Eye, 24 X 33 In. 12.50
Shaker, Towel, Linen, 26 1/2 X 40 In. 10.00
Shaker, Tray, Dresser, Round, Wooden, 5 3/4 In. .... 17.50 To 25.00
Shaker, Tray, Wooden, Round, Marked, 'Meeting Room, '13 X 2 3/4 In. 55.00
Shaker, Tub, Apple Butter, Handle, Cover, Pine, Copper Nails, 8 In.High, Pair 40.00
Shaker, Tub, Wash, Wooden, Two Handled, 15 X 24 In. 130.00

Shaving Mugs were popular from 1860 to 1900. Many types were made,
including occupational mugs featuring pictures of the man's job. There were
scuttle mugs, silver-plated mugs, glass-lined mugs, and others.

Shaving Mug, Acorns & Oak Leaves, Dated 1870, White, Excelsior, Porcelain 14.75
Shaving Mug, Advertising Old Lavender By Wrisley, Brown 12.50
Shaving Mug, Advertising, Golden Knight Shaving Soap 8.00
Shaving Mug, Akro, White, Flat Cover .... 4.50 To 5.95
Shaving Mug, Arm Holding Hammer 40.00
Shaving Mug, Blue, Floral, Ironstone 14.00
Shaving Mug, Blue, Owl On Pine Branch, Half Moon, Broderick 27.50
Shaving Mug, Brush Holder On Handle, German Silver 10.00
Shaving Mug, Clear Paneled Glass 3.75
Shaving Mug, Cobalt Top, Soap Rest, Embossed White & Gold Leaves, Porcelain 15.00
Shaving Mug, Collar Base, Gold Band Top, Germany 6.00
Shaving Mug, Dark Red, Tan Trimmed, Embossed Fruit & Leaves 10.00
Shaving Mug, Deer Drinking, Forest 28.50
Shaving Mug, Desert Scene, Maharaja Riding Elephant, Palm Trees, Hills 25.00
Shaving Mug, Double, Advertising Wild Root, Porcelain, Metal Handle 35.00
Shaving Mug, Early Comic Strip Characters 25.00
Shaving Mug, Embossed Coat Of Arms, Advertising, Clear Glass 12.50
Shaving Mug, Embossed Ribbon & Bow, Blue & White Floral, Porcelain 24.00
Shaving Mug, Eye With Name, Also F.L.T. 40.00
Shaving Mug, Flowers, Numbered 12.00
Shaving Mug, German, Portrait, Pink Luster Rim 20.00
Shaving Mug, Gold Decorated, Name 35.00
Shaving Mug, Gold Name, W.C.Mccray, Indiana Governor, Scroll Of Gold Leaves 45.00
Shaving Mug, Golden Knight Shaving Soap, Ansehl, St.Louis, Clear 12.00

Shaving Mug, **High Stiff White Collar**, Gilt Detail Of Button & Edge	22.50
Shaving Mug, **Historical**, Centennial, 1867, Milk Glass, Double Compartment	55.00
Shaving Mug, **Horse's Head**, Gold Trim	27.50
Shaving Mug, **Horse's Head**, Horseshoe Around Neck, Flowers, Name	60.00
Shaving Mug, **Horse's Head**, Leaves, Pink Roses	18.00
Shaving Mug, **Ironstone**, White	4.00
Shaving Mug, **Leaves Form Base**, Lavender Hyacinth Bouquets, Soap Division	27.50
Shaving Mug, **Memory**, Green, Raised Floral, 'A Present' On Base	15.00
Shaving Mug, **Milk Glass Insert**, Tin Holder	12.50
Shaving Mug, **Morning Glories**, Beaded Rim, Left Handed, Germany	27.50
Shaving Mug, **Oak Leaves**, Acorns, Excelsior, Patent 1870	11.75
Shaving Mug, **Occupational**, Apothecary, Mortar & Pestle, Name	72.00
Shaving Mug, **Occupational**, Bartender	85.00
Shaving Mug, **Occupational**, Black & White Horses, Lightning, Name In Gold	50.00
Shaving Mug, **Occupational**, Blacksmith, Name In Gold Letters	70.00
Shaving Mug, **Occupational**, Blacksmith's Anvil	75.00
Shaving Mug, **Occupational**, Brewmaster	175.00
Shaving Mug, **Occupational**, Butcher	80.00
Shaving Mug, **Occupational**, Butcher, Bull, Eyes Staring, Butcher's Implements	85.00
Shaving Mug, **Occupational**, Butcher, Pink, White, Gold, Saw, Sharpener, Cleaver	115.00
Shaving Mug, **Occupational**, Cabinetmaker	185.00
Shaving Mug, **Occupational**, Carpenter	160.00
Shaving Mug, **Occupational**, Carpenter Tools	85.00
Shaving Mug, **Occupational**, Carpenter, Crossed Tools, Name	72.00
Shaving Mug, **Occupational**, Carpenter, Tools, Cincinnati, Gold Name	85.00
Shaving Mug, **Occupational**, Clergy, Church, Gold Wreath, Gold Name	95.00
Shaving Mug, **Occupational**, Coach, Horses, Rider, Ladies, Victorian Costumes	75.00
Shaving Mug, **Occupational**, Dentist, Sportsman, Hand-Painted	20.00
Shaving Mug, **Occupational**, Doctor, Examines Patient	150.00
Shaving Mug, **Occupational**, Druggist, Mortar & Pestle, Name	85.00
Shaving Mug, **Occupational**, Dry Goods Clerk	60.00
Shaving Mug, **Occupational**, Farmer, Year 1857, Name, Two Handles	58.00
Shaving Mug, **Occupational**, Fraternal, Knights Of Pythias	35.00
Shaving Mug, **Occupational**, Grist Mill	150.00 To 190.00
Shaving Mug, **Occupational**, Grocery Wagon & Horse, Name	75.00
Shaving Mug, **Occupational**, Harp, Winged Lady, Floral, Musician's Name	50.00
Shaving Mug, **Occupational**, Horse Drawn Drayage Wagon, Driver, Name Worn	90.00
Shaving Mug, **Occupational**, Horse, Gilt Sprays, Maroon Band, Name	60.00
Shaving Mug, **Occupational**, Horse, Standing, Name	90.00
Shaving Mug, **Occupational**, Hunter, Gun, Hound, Name, Limoges	95.00
Shaving Mug, **Occupational**, Hunting & Fishing, Personalized	49.00
Shaving Mug, **Occupational**, Judge	375.00
Shaving Mug, **Occupational**, Lumberyard Scene, Men, Team, Wagon, Lumber	65.00
Shaving Mug, **Occupational**, Man Driving Carriage	65.00
Shaving Mug, **Occupational**, Man In Buggy, Huge Wheels, Pulled By Horses, Name	95.00
Shaving Mug, **Occupational**, Modern Woodsmen Of America	35.00
Shaving Mug, **Occupational**, Mortar & Pestle, Gilt Wreath, Name	55.00
Shaving Mug, **Occupational**, Musical, Singer, Man Playing Accordion	65.00
Shaving Mug, **Occupational**, One Horse Sulky, Driver, Gold Name Worn, Limoges	67.50
Shaving Mug, **Occupational**, Painter, Pail & Brushes, Austria	75.00
Shaving Mug, **Occupational**, Pennsylvania State Senator	80.00
Shaving Mug, **Occupational**, Pocket Watch On Front, GDA, France	65.00
Shaving Mug, **Occupational**, Pointer Dog, Hunter's Equipment	75.00
Shaving Mug, **Occupational**, Policeman	95.00 To 135.00
Shaving Mug, **Occupational**, Steam Engine	85.00
Shaving Mug, **Occupational**, Train & Tender, Name In Gold, Limoges, Cloth Bag	95.00
Shaving Mug, **Odd Fellows**, Flowers, Leaves, Rose Border	19.75
Shaving Mug, **Odd Fellows**, Green Leaves, Floral, Rose Border, Red Striping	19.75
Shaving Mug, **Pairpoint Silver**, Lift Out Insert	25.00
Shaving Mug, **Pink & White Ground**, Yellow Rose, Green Leaves	15.00
Shaving Mug, **Pink Floral**	8.50
Shaving Mug, **Pink Luster**, Plain Medallion, Crow Foot Base	4.00
Shaving Mug, **Pink Luster**, Raised Gold, Brush Rest	11.00
Shaving Mug, **Pink**, Violets, Divided For Soap	25.00
Shaving Mug, **Portrait Of Man**	30.00
Shaving Mug, **Raised Floral**, Silver, Art Nouveau, Brush, Beaver Tail Bristles	55.00

Shaving Mug, Raised Indian's Head, Full Headdress, Brush, Bowl 115.00
Shaving Mug, Rose Design, White 14.50
Shaving Mug, Rose Design, Yellow 6.95
Shaving Mug, Roses On White, Gold Trim, Leuchtenburg, Made In Germany 15.00
Shaving Mug, Roses, Gold, Soap Shelf 10.00
Shaving Mug, Roses, Pale Matte Green Edge, Germany 18.50
Shaving Mug, Scattered Rose Sprays Allover Rim Base 8.00
Shaving Mug, Scuttle, Amethyst Color Lilies Of The Valley, Brush Rest 25.00
Shaving Mug, Scuttle, Bird On Branches, Brush Rest 25.00
Shaving Mug, Scuttle, Blue & Purple Flowers, Ironstone 15.00
Shaving Mug, Scuttle, Buff, Blue Trumpet Floral, Brown Leaves, Porcelain 18.00
Shaving Mug, Scuttle, Colored Bird 18.50
Shaving Mug, Scuttle, Corset Shape, Scalloped Top, Opalescent, Gold Trim 20.00
Shaving Mug, Scuttle, Figural, Oriental Man, Marked P M Bavaria 85.00
Shaving Mug, Scuttle, Floral, 'Dad' 20.00
Shaving Mug, Scuttle, Floral, 'Union Shaving Mug, Patent Sept.20, 1870' 24.00
Shaving Mug, Scuttle, Florals In Oil & Enamel On White 13.50
Shaving Mug, Scuttle, Flowers, Green, Rose, & Gold 28.00
Shaving Mug, Scuttle, Green Checkered Bands, Dated 1870, Ironstone 10.50
Shaving Mug, Scuttle, Made In Germany 7.50
Shaving Mug, Scuttle, Marked Union Shaving Mug, Pat.1870, White China 14.75
Shaving Mug, Scuttle, Panels, Pink Roses, Lavender Daisies, Blue Border 26.50
Shaving Mug, Scuttle, Pansies, Pink Flowers, Embossing, Gold Trim, Porcelain 18.00
Shaving Mug, Scuttle, Picture Of Steam Omnibus, James Kent, England 15.00
Shaving Mug, Scuttle, Pink & White Roses, James Kent, England 20.00
Shaving Mug, Scuttle, Pink, Gold Flowers 23.50
Shaving Mug, Scuttle, Roses 21.00
Shaving Mug, Scuttle, Swan Figural, Pink Poppies 18.00
Shaving Mug, Scuttle, Tan Ground, One Red Rose, Signed L.Damata 30.00
Shaving Mug, Scuttle, Tan, Blue Morning Glories, Brown Vine 16.00
Shaving Mug, Scuttle, Toby, One Side Clean Face, Other Side Needs Shave 25.00
Shaving Mug, Scuttle, Violets, Anchor Mark 20.00
Shaving Mug, Scuttle, White, Violets, Gold Border 24.00
Shaving Mug, Side Compartment, Strap Handle, Tin 17.50
Shaving Mug, Silver Plate, Brush With Beaver Tail Bristles 55.00
Shaving Mug, Silver Plate, Embossed Art Nouveau Flowers, 2 Piece 20.00
Shaving Mug, Silver Plate, Profile Of Two Ladies, Floral, Meriden 15.00
Shaving Mug, Silver Plate, Repousse Rim, Engraved, Brush Rest, Beaded Rim 18.00
Shaving Mug, Silver Plate, Stand With Beveled Mirror 14.00
Shaving Mug, Two Compartments, Tin, 4 1/4 In.High 20.00
Shaving Mug, White Porcelain, Soap Tray 9.95
Shaving Mug, White, Floral, Silk Lined Box 16.00
Shaving Mug, White, Multicolor Decoration, 'Love The Giver, ' 1 1/2 In. 12.00
Shaving Mug, White, Porcelain, Name Geo.C.Hagar In Gold 9.75
Shaving Mug, Wisteria Decoration, Porcelain, Pink Luster Top, Artist Signed 15.00
Shaving Mug, Yellow Luster, Flow Relief, Scalloped, Footed 30.00
Shawnee Pottery, Salt & Pepper, Cornware, 5 In.High 7.00
Shawnee, Teapot, Corn Covered 16.00
    Sheffield, see Silver, Sheffield
Ship, Barometer, Brass, Cylindrical, Steel Dial, Brass Gimbel Attachment 600.00
Ship, Binnacle, Compass Inside, Brass, 19th Century, 11 1/2 In.High 250.00
Ship, Block, Iron Hook, 3 Pullies, 14 Pounds 19.50
Ship, Block, Mast Head, Sailing, For Running Up Flags, Iron, Wood, Brass 32.50
Ship, Block, Metal Pulley, Iron Hook, 9 In. 11.50
Ship, Block, Rigging, Sailing, Iron Hook, Double Pullies, 12 Pounds 19.50
Ship, Block, Wooden, Single Pulley, 5 In. 7.50
Ship, Chronometer, Walnut Case, Hinged, Dovetailed, C.1800 .... 24.50
Ship, Dead-Eye, Wooden, Hand-Carved, 5 In.Diameter 8.50
Ship, Figurehead, Carved Wood, 19th Century, 59 In.High .... Illus 650.00
Ship, Foghorn, Tole, Round, Telescopic Opening, Van Tramp, Boston, 1867 .... 39.50
Ship, Foghorn, Windjammer, Chas.C.Hutchinson, Boston, Pump Handle 165.00
Ship, Light, Dated 1910, Red & Green Glass 22.50
Ship, Model, American, 3 Masted Square Rigged Merchant, C.1850, 15 In.High 375.00
Ship, Model, Builder's, Canoe, Half Model, Maple, 7 Sections, 15 In. 22.50
Ship, Model, Constitution, U.S.Frigate, Donald McNarry, 1963, 51 In.High 1100.00
Ship, Model, Prisoner Of War, 3 Masts, Red Ensign, C.1850 .... 275.00

Ship, Figurehead, Carved Wood, 19th Century, 59 In.High
See Page 511

Ship, Model, Signed Strom, 1884, 10 In.High, 15 In.Long	150.00
Ship, Navigation Item, Brass, Iron Gimbal Mount, Marine Compass Co., Mass.	24.50

Shirley Temple dishes, blue glassware, and any other souvenir-type objects with her name and picture are now collected.

Shirley Temple, Album, Song, Eight Songs, 15 Photos, 1935	12.50
Shirley Temple, Album, Song, 16 Pictures, Songs	16.00
Shirley Temple, Book, Jerome Beatty, 1935	6.00
Shirley Temple, Bowl, Cereal, Blue	10.00 To 14.50
Shirley Temple, Buggy, Doll's	65.00
Shirley Temple, Cards, Playing	3.95
Shirley Temple, Creamer	5.00 To 15.00
Shirley Temple, Doll, Bisque, German, 15 In.Tall	35.00
Shirley Temple, Doll, Bisque, German, 17 In.Tall	40.00
Shirley Temple, Doll, Composition, Dressed, Ideal, 18 In.Tall	48.00
Shirley Temple, Doll, Composition, Dressed, 16 In.Tall	65.00
Shirley Temple, Doll, Composition, Marked, 13 In.Tall	17.00 To 55.00
Shirley Temple, Doll, Composition, Wig, Dress, 21 In.	65.00
Shirley Temple, Doll, Composition, Wig, Signed	55.00
Shirley Temple, Doll, Pantaloons, Taffeta Dress, Bonnet, 24 In.Tall	100.00
Shirley Temple, Doll, Paper, Clothes	3.00
Shirley Temple, Doll, Paper, Clothes, Cut, 3	12.00
Shirley Temple, Doll, Paper, Dresses, 8 In.Tall	7.50
Shirley Temple, Doll, Sleep Eyes, Vinyl, Ideal, 14 In.	28.00
Shirley Temple, Doll, Vinyl, Dressed, 12 In.Tall	13.50
Shirley Temple, Doll, Vinyl, Flirty Eyes, Dressed, 1950s, 17 In.	18.95 To 28.00
Shirley Temple, Doll, Vinyl, Flirty Eyes, 18 In.	15.00
Shirley Temple, Doll, Vinyl, 15 In.Tall	15.00
Shirley Temple, Doll, Wee Willie Winkle Outfit, 1935, 18 In.	95.00
Shirley Temple, Doll, Wig, Pin, Ideal, 18 In.	42.50
Shirley Temple, Doll, Wig, Pin, 22 In.	55.00
Shirley Temple, Figurine, Chalk	15.00
Shirley Temple, Mirror, Picture, 1935	15.00
Shirley Temple, Mirror, Signed	9.50
Shirley Temple, Mug, Picture, Cobalt	8.00 To 14.00
Shirley Temple, Mug, Pitcher, Bowl, Cobalt, Pictures	35.00
Shirley Temple, Pen & Pencil	37.50
Shirley Temple, Photo, 8 X 10 In., Tinted, Advertising On Back	4.00
Shirley Temple, Pin, Picture And Signed	9.50
Shirley Temple, Pitcher, Blue Glass, Picture	5.00 To 15.00
Shirley Temple, Scrapbook, Blank, 1936, 9 X 12 In.	10.00
Shirley Temple, Sugar, Bisque Figurine	15.00
Shirley Temple, Trunk, Doll's	45.00
Silesia, Bowl, Roses In Center, 9 In.	15.00

Silesia, Bowl, White Grape Bunch, Autumn Leaves, Crimped, Ribbed Rim, Crown 12.00
Silesia, Bowl, White Ground, Pink Roses, Scalloped Border, Marked P.K. 15.00
Silesia, Cake Set, White Dogwood, Blue Green Shaded Edge, Tillowitz, 7 Piece 35.00
Silesia, Dish, Oval, Roses, Beaded, Open Handles, Marked P.K., 12 In. 13.00
Silesia, Hatpin Holder, Cream Ground, Blue Forget-Me-Nots, Gold Top 18.00
Silesia, Ice Cream Set, Green Forget-Me-Nots With Brown Gold, 11 Piece 55.00
Silesia, Pitcher, Water, Roses 35.00
Silesia, Plate, Cake, Handle, Black & Gold Border, Pink Roses, 4 Desserts 30.00
Silesia, Plate, Game, Quail & Teal, Drop Roses Around Medallions, Pair 48.00
Silesia, Plate, Game, Quail, Teal, Gold Scalloped Edge, Rose Border, Pair 38.00
Silesia, Plate, Hand-Painted Daisies, Foliage, Scalloped Embossed Edge 9.00
Silesia, Plate, Hand-Painted Yellow Orange Roses, Leaves & Vines 8.00
Silesia, Plate, Marked C.T.Altwasser, Hand-Painted Pink & White Roses, Gold 25.00
Silesia, Plate, Pink Blossoms, Foliage, 8 1/2 In. .... 10.00 To 12.00
Silesia, Plate, Pink To Black Ground, White Poppies, Mark, 6 In.Diameter 9.00
Silesia, Sugar & Creamer, Cream Color, Pink, Floral, Gold 35.00
Silesia, Sugar & Creamer, Gold Decoration, Purple Grapes, Footed 18.00
Silesia, Sugar & Creamer, Peacocks In Fruit Tree, Etched Gold Rim, Pickard 55.00
Silesia, Tile, Tea, Pink Roses 18.00
    Silhouette, see Picture, Silhouette

Silver Deposit Glass was made during the late nineteenth and early
twentieth centuries. Solid sterling silver was applied to the glass by a
chemical method so that a cutout design of silver metal appeared against a
clear or colored glass.
Silver Deposit, Bottle, Cologne, Stopper 12.00
Silver Deposit, Bottle, Crystal Stopper With Silver Top, 2 1/2 In. 11.00
Silver Deposit, Bowl, Flower, Red Orange, Czechoslovakia, 4 1/2 In. 18.50
Silver Deposit, Bowl, Fluted Panels, Fruits, 12 5/8 In.Diameter 18.00
Silver Deposit, Bowl, Fruit, Pair Candlesticks 35.00
Silver Deposit, Bowl, Giant Sawtooth Pattern, Silver Interior 17.00
Silver Deposit, Console Set, Pale Pink, Marked Sterling, 11 In.Bowl 10.00
Silver Deposit, Decanter, Wine, Blue, Stopper 25.00
Silver Deposit, Decanter, Wine, Green, Stopper 25.00
Silver Deposit, Dish, Candy, Tree Design, Silver Handles & Rim, Sectioned 30.00
Silver Deposit, Perfume, Floral, Ground Stopper, 4 1/2 In.High 35.00
Silver Deposit, Perfume, Numbered Stopper, 3 1/4 In.High 19.50
Silver Deposit, Perfume, Slender, 3 1/2 In. 14.00
Silver Deposit, Perfume, Squatty, 3 1/4 In. 10.50
Silver Deposit, Pitcher, Clear Glass, Applied Handle, Flowers & Leaves 19.50
Silver Deposit, Plate, Cake, Flowers, Leaves, Looped Handle In Center 15.00
Silver Deposit, Salt Open, Pedestal, Set Of 4 .... 15.00
Silver Deposit, Shot Glass 7.00
Silver Deposit, Sugar & Creamer, Vine Design .... 12.00 To 30.00
Silver Deposit, Tumbler, Thistle Design, Scotland, 5 In.High 12.00
Silver Deposit, Vase, Clear With Large Silver Roses, 10 In.High 12.00
Silver Deposit, Vase, Red Glass, Round, 10 1/2 In. 42.00
Silver Deposit, Vase, Yellow Ground, Flowers, Leaves, Berries, 3 1/2 In. 9.00
Silver Plate, Barrel, Cracker, Marked Aurora Co. 65.00
Silver Plate, Basket, Allover Embossing, Marked BMC 17.00
Silver Plate, Basket, Ball Design Along Rim, Braided Handle, Footed, Wilcox 20.00
Silver Plate, Basket, Engraved Birds & Floral, Handle 40.00
Silver Plate, Basket, For Calling Cards, Scene Of People, Trees, Relief 15.00
Silver Plate, Basket, Fruit, Pierced Openwork Sides, Pedestal Base 22.50
Silver Plate, Basket, Pierced Design, Hinged, Pierced Handle, Pairpoint 45.00
Silver Plate, Bell, Desk, Teacher's 4.00
Silver Plate, Box, Collar Button, Resilvered 9.50
Silver Plate, Box, Cuff Button, Rose Decoration 20.00
Silver Plate, Box, Hairpin, Covered, Footed 15.00
Silver Plate, Box, Jewel, Raised Figures, Cherubs, Flowers, Fountain 28.00
Silver Plate, Box, Snuff, Engine Turned, Monogram 22.50
Silver Plate, Box, Stamp, Pocket, Washington Two Cent Stamp In Relief 8.00
Silver Plate, Bride's Basket, Hinged Handle, Engraved Floral, Footed 10.00
Silver Plate, Brush, Clothes, Figure Of Lady On Top, Art Nouveau 5.00
Silver Plate, Butter, Benedict, Footed, 6 In.Diameter 11.00
Silver Plate, Butter, Covered, Victorian, Cut & Frosted Liner 28.00

Silver Plate, Butter, Cow Finial, Monogram, Carrie, Liner 22.50
Silver Plate, Butter, Ferns, Birds, Openwork Feet, Dome Cover 40.00
Silver Plate, Butter, Roll Top, Drain, Victorian 45.00
Silver Plate, Candelabra, 3-Light, Engraved Crest, Gadroon Borders, Pair 80.00
Silver Plate, Candleholder, Bird In Flight, Floral, James Tufts, 3 1/2 In. 115.00
Silver Plate, Candlesnuffer 24.50
Silver Plate, Candlestick, Italian Renaissance Style, 17 In., Pair 180.00
Silver Plate, Candlestick, Victorian Shape, Beaded Edge, 9 In. 9.00
    Silver Plate, Castor, see also Castor
Silver Plate, Castor, Pickle, Glass Insert, Tongs 55.00
Silver Plate, Chamberstick, Beaded Edge, Ring Handle, Meriden Co. 17.50
Silver Plate, Compote, Children, Draped, Playing Lyre, Reed & Barton 55.00
Silver Plate, Crumber, Quadruple, Handle, 7 X 3 In. 7.00
Silver Plate, Cup & Saucer, Floral, Tufts, Quadruple 35.00
Silver Plate, Cup & Saucer, Leaves, Art Nouveau, Quadruple, Wilcox 14.00
Silver Plate, Cup, Child's, Bopeep, Monogram 7.50
Silver Plate, Cup, Collapsible, Folding Handle, Gold Plate Inside, Pair, Case 15.00
Silver Plate, Dish, Candy, Hinged Cover, Clear Glass Insert 45.00
Silver Plate, Dish, Card, Heart Shape, Hummingbird On Top, Chased 22.50
Silver Plate, Dish, Filigree, James Tufts, Boston, 10 In. 28.00
Silver Plate, Dish, Meat, Oval, Crested Border, Gadroon Rim, Pair 140.00
Silver Plate, Dish, Shell, Blue Glass Liner 40.00
Silver Plate, Egg Warmer, Stand, Candle Cup, Eagle On Lid, Claw Feet 45.00
Silver Plate, Flask, Pocket, Round, Bust Of Man In Relief, Floral 24.00
Silver Plate, Frame, Raised Mums & Leaves, Round Insert, Oriental, 8 In.Sq. 20.00
Silver Plate, Holder, Relish, Cornucopia & Floral, Repousse, Derby 30.00
Silver Plate, Inkwell, Eagle, Glass Insert 25.00
Silver Plate, Inkwell, Hinged Lid, Glass Well, Simpson Hall Miller & Co. 32.00
Silver Plate, Knife Rest, Bird, Twisted Bar, Pair 35.00
Silver Plate, Knife Rest, British Register Mark 14.00
Silver Plate, Knife Rest, Butterfly Ends 16.00
Silver Plate, Knife Rest, Eagle 80.00
Silver Plate, Knife Rest, Jacks On Ends 6.50
Silver Plate, Knife Rest, Monkey 12.00
Silver Plate, Knife Rest, Pheasant 22.50
Silver Plate, Knife Rest, Rabbit 8.00
Silver Plate, Knife Rest, Rooster 12.00
Silver Plate, Knife Rest, Squirrel On Each End .... 16.00 To 18.50
Silver Plate, Knife Rest, Two Swans Hold Bar On Backs, 4 In. 30.00
Silver Plate, Knife Rest, Whippet 14.50
Silver Plate, Ladle, Art Deco Handle, Double Spout 12.50
Silver Plate, Ladle, Gravy, Mother-Of-Pearl Curved Handle 7.50
Silver Plate, Letter Holder, Pug Dog, Trellis, Grapes, Footed, Pairpoint 55.00
Silver Plate, Mirror, Hand, Art Nouveau Flowers, Beveled Glass, 4 In.Long 13.00
Silver Plate, Mug, Child's, Bopeep, Reed & Barton 18.00
    Silver Plate, Napkin Ring, see Napkin Ring
Silver Plate, Pen Tray, Scrolls, Flowers, Derby 9.00
Silver Plate, Pitcher, Thermos, Art Nouveau, Embossed Floral, 12 1/2 In.High 150.00
Silver Plate, Pitcher, Thermos, Victorian, 12 1/2 In.High 150.00
Silver Plate, Pitcher, Water, Engraved Floral, Beaded Rim & Base, Pairpoint 35.00
Silver Plate, Pitcher, Water, Homan's Quadruple, Engraved 1905 .... 10.00
Silver Plate, Planter, Filigree, Footed, Porcelain Insert, Pairpoint 16.00
Silver Plate, Punch Set, 1883 Rogers Bros., Resilvered, 15 Piece 175.00
Silver Plate, Salt Dip, Lions' Heads On Sides, Blue Glass Line .... 6.50 To 7.50
Silver Plate, Shaving Mug, Reed & Barton 18.50
Silver Plate, Shears, Grape, Handles In Leaves & Vines 22.50
Silver Plate, Shot Glass, Gold Wash, Germany, 4 Nesting 9.00
Silver Plate, Silent Butler, Engraved Lion, Acorn Knob, Teak Handle 20.00
Silver Plate, Silent Butler, Over Copper, Wooden Handle 15.00
    Silver Plate, Spoon, Souvenir, see Souvenir, Spoon
Silver Plate, Stand, Shaving, Mirror, Attached Porcelain Lined Mug 25.00
Silver Plate, String Holder, Repousse Ball, Three Ornate Feet 39.00
Silver Plate, Sugar & Creamer, Beaded Edge, Melon Rib, James Tufts 19.00
Silver Plate, Sugar & Creamer, C.1860 .... 39.00
Silver Plate, Sugar & Creamer, Floral Design, Footed 21.00
Silver Plate, Sugar & Creamer, Forbes & Co. 10.00

Silver Plate, Sugar & Creamer, On Copper, Paneling, Fluting, William Rogers 14.00
Silver Plate, Sugar & Spoon Holder, Bird Finial, Replated 50.00
Silver Plate, Syrup, Tray, Webster & Sons 35.00
Silver Plate, Tea Service, Queen Anne Design, 3 Piece 45.00
Silver Plate, Teakettle, Lampstand, George II Style, Rococo, Chased, Footed 170.00
Silver Plate, Teapot, Boat Shape, Sheffield, A.Goodman Co., Circa 1800 .... 125.00
Silver Plate, Teapot, Sugar, Creamer, Spooner, Butter, & Knife, Homan, Anchor 136.00
Silver Plate, Toast Rack, Four Ball Feet 17.50
Silver Plate, Toast Rack, Shape Of Swan, Marked E.P.N.S. 30.00
Silver Plate, Tongs, Asparagus, Claw Ends 3.50
Silver Plate, Toothpick, Cherub On Footed Cracked Egg, Derby Silver Co. 38.00
Silver Plate, Toothpick, Chick On Wishbone 17.00
Silver Plate, Toothpick, Chick, Egg, Wishbone 30.00
Silver Plate, Toothpick, Engraved Flowers, Ruffled Beaded Top 12.50
Silver Plate, Toothpick, Kate Greenaway Lady Beside Basket, Derby Silver 10.00
Silver Plate, Toothpick, Porcupine, Meriden Silver Co. 22.00
Silver Plate, Toothpick, Quadruple, P.Southington 6.50
Silver Plate, Toothpick, Take A Pick Engraved On Side, Embossed Floral 9.50
Silver Plate, Toothpick, Two Handles, Quadruple, Homan 14.00
Silver Plate, Tray, Bread & Roll, Engraved 10.00
Silver Plate, Tray, Bread, 'Daily Bread' 15.00
Silver Plate, Tray, Oblong, Embossed Rim, Handles, Meriden 45.00
Silver Plate, Tray, On Copper, Cable Edge, Dolphin Footed 10.00
Silver Plate, Tray, Serving, Engraved Border, Ribbon Bow Handles 18.00
Silver Plate, Tray, Victorian, On Copper, 16 1/2 X 11 1/2 In. 35.00
Silver Plate, Tureen, Soup, Flower Garlands, Handles, Derby Silver Co. 75.00
Silver Plate, Vase, Cobalt Glass Liner, Marked TW & S 16.00
Silver Plate, Vase, Ornate, Marked Derby S.P.Co., No.1301, 12 In.High 22.50
Silver, American, see also Silver, Tiffany
Silver, American, Basket, Cake, Boat Shape, 1860, New York, 19 Oz. 250.00
Silver, American, Bowl, Art Nouveau, Oval, Chased, Gorham, Martele, C.1900 .... 675.00
Silver, American, Bowl, Engraved Monogram Shield, Footed, James Black, 1790 .... 1400.00
Silver, American, Bowl, Floral, Paw Feet, Jones, Ball & Poor, Boston, 1840, 6 In 275.00
Silver, American, Bowl, Monteith, Pedestal, Canfield Bro.& Co., C.1870 .... 400.00
Silver, American, Brandy Warmer, C.1790, Coin 85.00
Silver, American, Butter Tub, Covered, Drain, Repousse, Kirk, C.1860, Coin 450.00
Silver, American, Can, Pear Shape, Livingston Crest, Myer Myers, C.1760 .... 4000.00
Silver, American, Can, Pear Shape, Monogram, Abraham Carlile, C.1795 .... 600.00
Silver, American, Can, Scroll Handle, 12 Sided, Bard & Lamont, C.1840 .... 200.00
Silver, American, Candelabra, Gilt, 4-Light, Howard & Co., N.Y., 1882, Pair 1900.00
Silver, American, Case, Calling Card, Coin, 3 5/8 In.High 12.75
Silver, American, Chalice, Repousse Strawberry & Leaves, Coin, 6 In.High 115.00
Silver, American, Coffee Set, Art Nouveau Lily Design, Pairpoint, 3 Piece 125.00
Silver, American, Coffeepot, Oval Vase, Engraved Birds & Unity, C.1800 .... 700.00
Silver, American, Coffeepot, Pear Shape, Chased, S.Kirk & Son, C.1850 .... 600.00
Silver, American, Coffeepot, Philadelphia, C.1815 .... *Illus* 3800.00
Silver, American, Compote, Greek Maiden Support, Ball, Black & Co., C.1880 .... 170.00
Silver, American, Creamer, Baluster Shape, Scroll Handle, C.1840, 6 3/4 In 120.00
Silver, American, Creamer, Helmet Shape, Engraved, Underhill & Vernon, C.1790 .... 350.00
Silver, American, Creamer, Oval Shape, Sayre & Richards, C.1810, 5 7/8 In. 225.00
Silver, American, Creamer, Pear Shape, Scroll Handle, Sanders Pitman, C.1755 .... 500.00
Silver, American, Creamer, Philadelphia, C.1780 .... *Illus* 525.00
Silver, American, Creamer, Rectangular, 4 Ball Feet, Shepherd & Boyd, C.1810 .... 80.00
Silver, American, Creamer, Vase Shape, Pedestal Base, William Ball, C.1785 .... 225.00
Silver, American, Cup, Bell Shape Bowl, Trumpet Base, Engraved, C.1860, Pair 130.00
Silver, American, Cup, California Coin, Pedestal, Gold Washed Interior 175.00
Silver, American, Cup, Campana, Engraved, Applied Stars, A.E.Warner, 1824 .... 160.00
Silver, American, Cup, Inverted Bell, 2 Handled, Simeon Soumaine, C.1730 .... 2800.00
Silver, American, Cup, Marked Wood & Hughes, Coin 60.00
Silver, American, Cup, Octagonal, Footed, Scroll Handle, Conrad Bard, C.1830 .... 130.00
Silver, American, Cup, Raised Design, Pedestal Base, Two Handles, Marked 1858 .... 49.75
Silver, American, Dredger, Pierced Cover, S-Scroll Handle, Jacob Hurd, C.1730 .... 1950.00
Silver, American, Eye Glasses, Granny, Marked, Coin 20.00
Silver, American, Fork & Spoon, Child's, Newell Harding & Co., Boston, 1850 .... 9.75
Silver, American, Fork, Luncheon, L.Forbes, St.Louis, Coin 25.00
Silver, American, Holder, Ramekin, Pierced Heart Design, Insert, Gorham, 12 .... 95.00

Silver, American, Coffeepot,
Philadelphia, C.1815
See Page 515

Silver, American, Creamer,
Philadelphia, C.1780
See Page 515

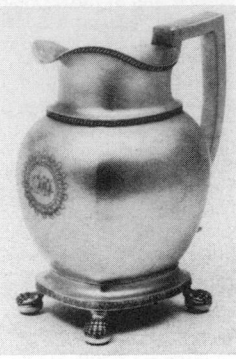

Silver, American, Pitcher,
Water, New York, C.1820

Silver, American, Jug, Milk, Embossed, Footed, Bailey & Co., Phila., C.1850	750.00
Silver, American, Knife Rest, Marled EBR On Back, 4 In.Long	14.00
Silver, American, Knife, Butter, Curved Blade, J.& W.L.Ward, Phila., 1839	15.00
Silver, American, Knife, Butter, Olive Pattern, Farrington & Hunnewell, Coin	9.95
Silver, American, Knife, Butter, Serving, Engraved, Samuel N.Smith, Mass., 1845	12.75
Silver, American, Knife, Butter, Serving, Fiddle Thread, Marked Pat, C.1850	9.95
Silver, American, Knife, Butter, Serving, Gale & Hayden, N.Y., 1848	12.75
Silver, American, Knife, Butter, Serving, Marked Coin Pat.1861	9.95
Silver, American, Knife, Butter, Serving, Raised Floral, Hine & Herzig, Coin	7.50
Silver, American, Knife, Butter, Serving, Shreve, Stanwood & Co., Boston, 1861	12.75
Silver, American, Knife, Cake, Embossed Floral & Scroll, B.Pitman Pure Coin	17.00
Silver, American, Knife, Fruit, Pocket, Marked T.& W., Coin	6.95
Silver, American, Knife, Pocket, Engraved, Two Blades, Initials, Coin	12.50
Silver, American, Knife, Pocket, Marked, Coin	25.00
Silver, American, Ladle, Beaded Edge, Marked Alexander Coffin Rosse, C.1812	150.00
Silver, American, Ladle, Belt & Buckle Design, Newell Harding & Co., Coin	26.75
Silver, American, Ladle, Gravy, Strawberry Pattern, Marked Pure Coin	28.00
Silver, American, Ladle, John Adams, Alexandria, Va., C.1800, 5 1/2 In., Coin	35.00
Silver, American, Ladle, Marked Geissler & Delang, Coin	70.00
Silver, American, Ladle, Mustard, Basket Of Flowers, J.Osgood, 1810	32.00
Silver, American, Ladle, Mustard, Fiddle, S.Huntington, Me., 1850, Coin	15.00
Silver, American, Ladle, Mustard, John Goodhue, Salem, Mass., C.1822, Coin	8.95
Silver, American, Ladle, Pierced, Applied Handle, Marked F.Ehrichson, 7 In.	25.00
Silver, American, Ladle, Punch, Gold Washed Bowl, Dated 1899, Gorham	60.00
Silver, American, Ladle, Sauce, Beaded Border, Coin	22.00
Silver, American, Ladle, Shell Bowl, E Mark, Coin	115.00
Silver, American, Ladle, Soup, Hanoverian, Engraved, Myer Myers, C.1750	675.00
Silver, American, Mug, Child's, By Thomas W.Radcliffe, Columbia, S.C., 1830	325.00
Silver, American, Mug, Child's, Engraved, Bigelow Kennard & Co., Boston, 1863	29.75
Silver, American, Mug, Repousse Floral & Leaves, Hamden Bros.& Co., 1853	135.00
Silver, American, Pickle, Engraved Monogram, Starr & Marcus, C.1876	80.00
Silver, American, Pitcher, Water, Baluster Form, Scroll & Fruit, C.1850	220.00
Silver, American, Pitcher, Water, Greek Krater Shape, S.Kirk & Son, C.1850	400.00
Silver, American, Pitcher, Water, New York, C.1820 Illus	600.00
Silver, American, Pitcher, Water, Pear Shape, Thomas Evans & Co., C.1860	300.00
Silver, American, Pitcher, Water, S.Kirk & Son, C.1885, 11 3/4 In.	525.00
Silver, American, Porringer, Bulbous, Engraved D.H.H., 1890, Keyhole Handle	750.00
Silver, American, Porringer, Engraved Keyhole Handle, George Baker, C.1840	300.00
Silver, American, Porringer, Keyhole Handle, John Andrew, C.1770, 5 1/2 In.	900.00
Silver, American, Porringer, Keyhole Handle, Jonathan Otis, C.1750	750.00
Silver, American, Porringer, Livingston Crest, Henricus Boelen, C.1730	3100.00
Silver, American, Salt Shovel, Master, Palmer & Bachelders, Boston, 1850, Coin	7.95
Silver, American, Salver, Round, Pierced Border, Floral, Shells, Starr, C.1890	350.00

Silver, American, Server, Butter, Crest, N.Harding, Boston, C.1845, Coin	10.00
Silver, American, Server, Pie, Engraved, Gorham & Co., Patent 1861, Coin	29.75
Silver, American, Slipper, High Heel, Gorham, 3 In.	18.50
Silver, American, Spectacles, Signed A.Smith, Coin	100.00
Silver, American, Spoon, Basting, Monogram, Signed J.Ward, Pair	90.00
Silver, American, Spoon, Berry, Beaded Border, Coin	20.00
Silver, American, Spoon, C.J.Wolf, Philadelphia, 1831	12.00
Silver, American, Spoon, C.J.Wyman, C.1810	8.50
Silver, American, Spoon, Demitasse, Gold Wash, Twisted Handle, Marked Coin	8.50
Silver, American, Spoon, Dessert, Fiddle, J.B.Akin, Danville, Ky., C.1820-1860	18.50
Silver, American, Spoon, Dessert, Hanoverian Pattern, Myer Myers, C.1760	275.00
Silver, American, Spoon, Dessert, Harriot, Williams, Coin	3.95
Silver, American, Spoon, Master Salt, Daniel Low, Salem, Mass., C.1835, Coin	7.95
Silver, American, Spoon, Master Salt, F.Curtis & Co., Conn., C.1845, Coin	7.95
Silver, American, Spoon, Master Salt, Jared Moore, N.Y., C.1825, Coin	7.95
Silver, American, Spoon, Master Salt, Marked Hall & Elton, Coin, Pair	15.00
Silver, American, Spoon, Master Salt, R.N.Dodge, Boston, 1850, Coin	7.95
Silver, American, Spoon, Monogram, Marked J.Hollister Pure Coin, Pair	45.00
Silver, American, Spoon, Mourning, R.Shepherd & W.Boyd, N.Y., C.1810	350.00
Silver, American, Spoon, N.& T.Foster, Newberryport, R.I., 1810	15.00
Silver, American, Spoon, Salt, Fiddleback, Gregg & Hayden, Va., 1840, Pair	40.00
Silver, American, Spoon, Serving, Beasoms & Reed, Portsmouth, N.H., Circa 1830	15.00
Silver, American, Spoon, Serving, Embossed Handle, Marked Coin, Leather Box	25.00
Silver, American, Spoon, Soup, Stanley & Ayer, C.1810 .... 9.00 To 12.00
Silver, American, Spoon, Sugar, Shovel, Engraved E.C.Smith, Root & Chaffe	9.50
Silver, American, Sugar Nip, Scissor, Shell Grips, Andrew Oliver, C.1760, Pair	170.00
Silver, American, Sugar Shell, Acorn & Oak Leaf, R.H.Dodge, 1850 .... 11.75 To 12.75
Silver, American, Sugar Shell, Farrington & Hunnewell, Boston, 1835	12.75
Silver, American, Sugar Shell, Palmer & Batchelder, Boston, 1840, Coin	12.00
Silver, American, Sugar Shell, Pinched In Fiddle, Gurney Bros., Coin	10.00
Silver, American, Sugar Shell, Pinched In Fiddle, H.L.Webster, Coin	10.00
Silver, American, Sugar Shell, Raised Tip, R.D.Dunbar, Worcester, C.1850	16.00
Silver, American, Sugar Shell, Shell Form, Marked Titcomb, Coin	15.00
Silver, American, Sugar Shell, Thread Pattern, Rogers & Son, Mass., 1850, Coin	12.75
Silver, American, Sugar Shell, Threaded, Rogers & Son, Mass., 1850, Coin	11.75
Silver, American, Sugar Shovel, Coin Silver, H.L.Sawyer, N.Y.C., 1840	12.75
Silver, American, Sugar, Covered, Oblong, 2 Handled, Joseph Shoemaker, C.1810	225.00
Silver, American, Sugar, Covered, Oval, Engraved, James Black, C.1810	650.00
Silver, American, Sugar, Covered, Oval, 2 Handled, Samuel Alexander, C.1800	225.00
Silver, American, Tablespoon, A.Parker, 1840	7.95
Silver, American, Tablespoon, Albert Jones, Greenfield, Mass., C.1820	12.50
Silver, American, Tablespoon, Coffin End, Thos.Emery, Boston, 1800, Coin	45.00
Silver, American, Tablespoon, Currie & Grott, Boston, 1836	12.75
Silver, American, Tablespoon, D.Gillis Leonard, Coin, Set Of 4	25.00
Silver, American, Tablespoon, E.Chubbuck, Lockport, N.Y., 1850	7.95
Silver, American, Tablespoon, Engraved Monogram, Joseph Lownes, C.1790, 6	180.00
Silver, American, Tablespoon, Engraved, J.B.Jones & Co., Boston, 1838, Coin	9.95
Silver, American, Tablespoon, Engraved, Joseph, Raynes, Lowell, Ma., 1835	11.75
Silver, American, Tablespoon, Family Name, Lincoln & Reed, C.1830, Coin, Pair	25.00
Silver, American, Tablespoon, Farrington & Hunnewell, Boston, 1835, Coin	9.95
Silver, American, Tablespoon, Fiddle & Thread, William Beebe, N.Y., 1850, Coin	15.00
Silver, American, Tablespoon, Fiddle Handle, Lincoln & Reed, C.1830, Coin	12.50
Silver, American, Tablespoon, Fiddle Handle, Palmer & Batchelder, 1840, Pair	22.00
Silver, American, Tablespoon, Fiddle Thread, Gale, Wood & Hughes, 1840	14.00
Silver, American, Tablespoon, Fiddle, Applied Handle, W.A.Williams, Va., 1809	36.00
Silver, American, Tablespoon, Fiddle, Engraved, Harvey Lewis, C.1820, 12	100.00
Silver, American, Tablespoon, Fiddleback, S.Kirk & Son, Baltimore, 1840, Pair	40.00
Silver, American, Tablespoon, Hanoverian, Engraved, Joseph Rogers, C.1760, 3	60.00
Silver, American, Tablespoon, Initial M, Stodder & Frobisher, Coin	9.95
Silver, American, Tablespoon, Initials, C.Bond, 1890, Coin	10.95
Silver, American, Tablespoon, Joseph Raynes, Lowell, Mass., C.1835, Coin	10.95
Silver, American, Tablespoon, M. & A., Utica, N.Y., 1840	11.75
Silver, American, Tablespoon, Monogram, Hallmark D Eagle & Head, Coin, Pair	18.00
Silver, American, Tablespoon, Old English, Engraved, J.& N.Richardson, 1870, 2	90.00
Silver, American, Tablespoon, Oval Tip, T.Perkins, Boston, Circa 1790, 6	300.00
Silver, American, Tablespoon, Paul Revere, Jr., C.1790	425.00

Silver, American, Tablespoon, Pelican In Bowl, Richard Humphreys, C.1790 .... 80.00
Silver, American, Tankard, Armorials, Livingston Manor, Myer Myers, C.1760 .... 3400.00
Silver, American, Tankard, Engraved, S-Scroll Handle, Samuel Vernon, C.1750 .... 4800.00
Silver, American, Tankard, S-Shape Handle, Molded Girdle & Foot, C.1760 .... 550.00
Silver, American, Tazza, Gilt Interior, Berries, W.Gale & Son, N.Y., 1863 .... 160.00
Silver, American, Tazza, Palm Tree Stem, Pheasant, Ball, Black & Co., C.1875 .... 170.00
Silver, American, Tea & Coffee Set, Engraved, Boston, C.1870, 7 Piece 825.00
Silver, American, Tea & Coffee Set, Laurel, Ball, Black & Co., C.1866, 5 Piece 1200.00
Silver, American, Tea & Coffee Set, 5 Pieces, Joseph Lownes, C.1810 .... 1800.00
Silver, American, Tea Caddy, Oval, Engraved, Swags, Garret Schnack, C.1790 .... 2350.00
Silver, American, Tea Set, Engraved Monogram, Joseph Lownes, C.1810, 3 Piece 900.00
Silver, American, Tea Set, Engraved, Chased, Harvey Lewis, C.1815, 3 Piece 1100.00
Silver, American, Tea Set, Inverted Pear Shape, S.Kirk & Son, C.1910, 4 Piece 1400.00
Silver, American, Tea Set, Oval, Acorns, William Thomson, C.1820, 4 Piece 825.00
Silver, American, Tea Set, Oval, Engraved, James Hamill, C.1820, 3 Piece 650.00
Silver, American, Tea Set, Oval, Swelling, W.G.Forbes, C.1800, 4 Piece 1200.00
Silver, American, Tea Set, Repousse, Hunting, S.Kirk & Son, C.1850, 5 Piece 1150.00
Silver, American, Tea Set, S.Kirk & Son, Md., C.1890 .... *Illus* 1200.00
Silver, American, Tea Set, Seasons Masks, Armorials, Gorham, 1872, 6 Piece 1800.00
Silver, American, Tea Set, William Thomson, N.Y., C.1830 .... *Illus* 1700.00
Silver, American, Teakettle & Lampstand, Oblong, 4 Paw Feet, Whiting, C.1910 .... 250.00
Silver, American, Teapot, Drum Shape, Engraved, Andrew Billings, C.1784 .... 2300.00
Silver, American, Teapot, Oblong, Chased, 4 Paw Feet, H.Reynolds, C.1830 .... 110.00
Silver, American, Teapot, Oval Vase, Engraved, Pedestal, William Seal, C.1800 .... 325.00
Silver, American, Teapot, Oval, Engraved, Floral, John Sayre, C.1800 .... 400.00
Silver, American, Teaspoon, A.F.Burbank & Co., Worcester, Ma., C.1850, Coin 3.95
Silver, American, Teaspoon, Andrew Billings, Fishkill, N.Y., Coin 22.50
Silver, American, Teaspoon, Applied Handle, Adam Lynn, Va., 1795-1835 .... 22.00
Silver, American, Teaspoon, Bigelow & Brothers, Set Of 6 .... 40.00
Silver, American, Teaspoon, C.L.Merry, Coin, Set Of 6 .... 25.00
Silver, American, Teaspoon, Coffin Handle, T.Bradbury, Newburyport, C.1815 .... 12.50
Silver, American, Teaspoon, Crest Handle, N.Harding, Boston, 1868, Set Of 8 .... 45.00
Silver, American, Teaspoon, D.Gillis Leonard, Coin, Set Of 6 .... 25.00
Silver, American, Teaspoon, Dugin, St.Louis, C.1825, Coin, Set Of 6 .... 48.00
Silver, American, Teaspoon, Engraved Monogram, Paul Revere, C.1790, 11 .... 2600.00
Silver, American, Teaspoon, Engraved Wrigglework, John David, C.1790, 6 .... 100.00
Silver, American, Teaspoon, Fiddle Handle, E.Whiton, Boston, C.1840, Coin 6.50
Silver, American, Teaspoon, Fiddle, J.Hollister, N.Y., C.1850, Pure Coin 7.50
Silver, American, Teaspoon, Fiddle, Raised Tip, J.Conning, Mobile 15.00
Silver, American, Teaspoon, Fiddleback, G.Russell, Phila., C.1835, Set Of 12 .... 150.00
Silver, American, Teaspoon, Harris & Stanwood, Boston, C.1835, Coin, Set Of 4 .... 19.75
Silver, American, Teaspoon, Initial, Marker's Mark H, 1815 .... 4.95
Silver, American, Teaspoon, Initials J.P.B., Boyden & Fenno, Coin 4.95
Silver, American, Teaspoon, Initials, Marked L.Phelps, Coin, Set Of 12 .... 65.00
Silver, American, Teaspoon, J.Fenno, Lowell, Ma., 1825 .... 4.95
Silver, American, Teaspoon, J.W.Beebe & Co., Coin, Set Of 6 .... 32.00
Silver, American, Teaspoon, James Parmele, Conn., C.1810, Coin 5.95
Silver, American, Teaspoon, Knife, Child's, Coin, Olive Pattern, Duhme, 1860 .... 45.00
Silver, American, Teaspoon, Lincoln, Foss, Coin 6.50
Silver, American, Teaspoon, McKay, Spear, & Brown, Coin, Set Of 4 .... 18.00
Silver, American, Teaspoon, Old English Pattern, Richard Humphreys, 1780, 4 .... 100.00
Silver, American, Teaspoon, Peacock In Bowl, Christian Wiltberger, C.1790, 4 .... 110.00
Silver, American, Teaspoon, Shell Tip, E.Whiton, Boston, C.1826, Coin, Set Of 6 .... 65.00
Silver, American, Tongs, Sugar, Seth Eastman, New Hampshire, 1820, Coin 38.00
Silver, American, Tongs, Sugar, Shell Ends, C.W.& H., Phila., 1790, Coin 55.00
Silver, American, Tongs, Tea, E.Watson, Boston, C.1820, Coin 35.00
Silver, American, Tray, Tea, Rectangular, Repousse, Views, F.& F., C.1850 .... 1300.00
Silver, American, Vase, Swirls, Flower Petals, Gorham, Coin, 7 1/2 In.High 30.00
Silver, Austrian, Beaker, Allover Embossed, Mythological Subjects, 4 In.High 250.00
Silver, Austrian, Box, Enamel, Royal Blue, Fleur-De-Lis, Sunbursts, Red Dots 165.00
Silver, Austrian, Buckle, Gilt, Jewels, Oval, Enamel, C.1850, Pair 125.00
Silver, Austrian, Ewer, Lapis Lazuli Mounted, Enamel Fruit & Foliage, C.1850 .... 500.00
Silver, Austrian, Salt Cellar & Spoon, Pierced, J.C.Klinkoch, C.1850, 12 .... 400.00
Silver, Austrian, Vase, Enamel, Pear Shape, Applied Filigree, C.1850 .... 650.00
Silver, Basket, Pierced, Tiffany, Circa 1902, 3 In.High 42.50
Silver, Bolivian, Dish, Sideboard, Round, Embossed Center, Fruit, Floral 100.00

Glass pitcher with straight narrow neck and ribbed handle, 19th century.

Satin glass vase, probably made in South Jersey, late 19th century.

Ornamental basket of overlaid glass with applied decoration, c. 1870.

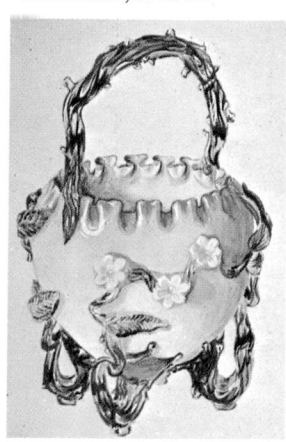

Mid-19th-century lamp with glass shade and font, metal wick holder.

Six-paneled loop font base with large round knop, c. 1850.

Glass lamp font, c. 1820–60.

Commercial coffee mill made by Enterprise Manufacturing Company of Philadelphia, c. 1850–1900.

Hose reel built by George Ruhl, 1851, for Neptune Hose Company of Philadelphia.

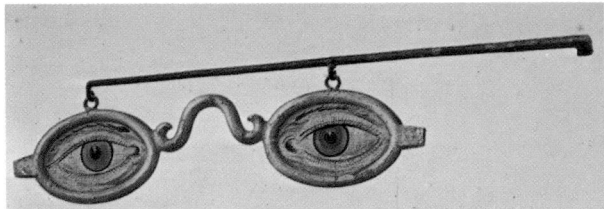

Optician's shop sign, c. 1875.

Cast-brass sewing bird, 19th century.

Textile picturing George Washington.

Stovepipe hat worn for firemen's dress parades, 19th century.

Sampler on canvas base, American, c. 1795.

Caswell carpet made by Zeruah
Higley Guernsey of Castleton,
Vermont, in 1835.

Hand-hooked rug of scroll design, c. 1850.

American coverlet woven on
Jacquard loom, c. 1835–40.

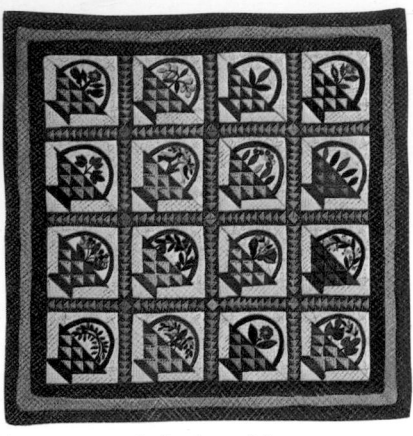

American quilt, basket-of-flowers pattern.

Wallpaper-covered bandbox depicting log cabin with riverboat and sunburst, c. 1830.

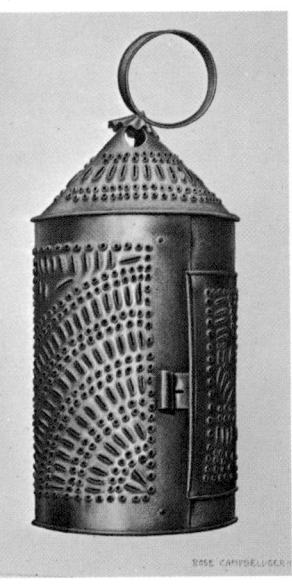

Toleware watering can decorated with tomato and petalous forms, mid-19th century.

American toleware teapot with floral motif, early 19th-century.

Pierced tin "Paul Revere" lantern. New England, late 18th century.

Tin American lard oil lamp, c. 1830.

Punched and painted tin picture frame made in the Southwest, late 19th century.

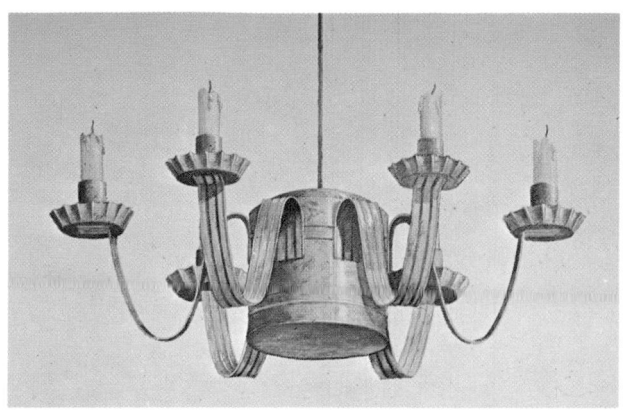

Tin American hanging light fixture, early 19th century.

American wind-up tin toy coach, mid-19th century.

Civil War drum with eagle design.

Punch and Judy mechanical bank, 1884.

Jonah and the Whale mechanical bank, c. 1888.

American mechanical music box, c. 1890.

Negro doll with carved wooden head and stuffed body, c. 1870.

Carousel deer, painted, carved wood, c. 1890.

American late-19th-century cow weather vane.

American carved-wood female ship's figurehead, mid-19th century.

Pennsylvania painted salt box, c. 1797.

American carved-eagle ship's stern piece, mid-19th century.

Folk art carving of sawing lumberjacks, c. 1885.

Various wooden mortars and pestles, 19th century.

Tavern figure of Bacchus, by John Russell, Windham, Connecticut, 1776.

19th-century American tobacconist's Indian figure.

Cigar-store Indian figure, "Squaw with Her Papoose," 19th century.

Tradesman's wooden figure, Punch, 19th century.

Santos, a carved holy image, made in the Southwest during the early 19th century.

Walnut cookie board made in Ohio by Swiss immigrants, 19th century.

Silver, American, Tea Set, S.Kirk & Son, Md., C.1890
See Page 518

Silver, American, Tea Set, William Thomson, N.Y., C.1830
See Page 518

Silver, Bolivian, Tureen, Soup, Covered, Round, Embossed Floral & Vines 190.00
Silver, Chinese, Cup, Tree Form Stem, Applied Birds, Cutsing, Canton, C.1860 .... 140.00
Silver, Chinese, Mustard Pot, Prunus Blossoms, Hinged Lid, Loop Handle 15.00
Silver, Chinese, Salt Dip, Pepper Shaker, Cutout Dragon, Blue Liner, Set Of 6 .... 50.00
Silver, Chinese, Salt Dip, Pepper Shaker, Woven Grass, Glass Liner, 2 Pair 22.00
Silver, Chinese, Teapot & Stand, Oval, Engraved, S.S., Canton, C.1790 .... 1000.00
Silver, Continental, Bowl, Shell Shape, Dolphin Stem, Chased, C.1900, Pair 225.00
Silver, Continental, Centerpiece, Boat Shape Bowl, Pierced, Chased, C.1900 .... 525.00
Silver, Continental, Cup, Covered, Embossed Judgement Of Solomon, C.1900 .... 325.00
Silver, Continental, Goblet, Dessert, Rustic & Village Scene, C.1900 .... 12.50
Silver, Continental, Salt Trencher, Gilt, Renaissance Style, C.1850, Pair 130.00
Silver, Continental, Spoon, Serving, Dutch Woman In Garden, Windmill Shank 12.50
Silver, Danish, Box, Spice, Gilt, Chased, Joachim Hendrich Dysterfijk, C.1760 .... 110.00
Silver, Dutch, Basket, Cake, Boat Shape, Reeded Rim, J.S., 1831 .... 200.00
Silver, Dutch, Basket, Cake, Rectangular, Pierced, Reeded Rim, 1841 .... 200.00
Silver, Dutch, Cup, Wedding, 925 Sterling, 7 In.High 85.00
Silver, Dutch, Cup, Wedding, 5 In.High 62.00

Silver, Dutch, Figurine, Windmill, Movable Vanes, 2 1/4 In.High 15.00
Silver, Dutch, Figurine, Woman, Yoke On Shoulders, Swing Pails, 1 1/2 In. 15.00
Silver, Dutch, Fork, Lemon, Movable Windmill On Handle, Marked 4.50
Silver, Dutch, Salt, Trencher, Miniature, Gilt, Paulus De Soomer, 1752 .... 250.00
Silver, Dutch, Spoon, Coffee, 19th Century, Set Of 8 .... 45.00
Silver, Dutch, Tea Ball & Stand 30.00
Silver, Dutch, Tea Caddy, Vase Shape, Heavily Embossed, 6 In. 68.00
Silver, English, Basket, Cake, Reeded Rims, R.Emes & E.Barnard, 1809, 12 In. 465.00
Silver, English, Basket, Cake, Thomas Gilpin, 1749 .... *Illus* 2200.00
Silver, English, Beaker, By Henry Chawner, 1790, 4 1/8 In.High 400.00
Silver, English, Candelabra, George III, 1791 .... *Illus* 3750.00
Silver, English, Case, Card, Embossed St.Paul's Cathedral, Thomason, 1848 .... 108.00
Silver, English, Castor, Queen Anne Style, Pear Shape, Pierced, 1880 .... 180.00
Silver, English, Cheese Scoop, Ornate 12.00
Silver, English, Clock, Footed, Columns & Spires, 1891, 8 In.High 185.00
Silver, English, Coaster, Wine, Hester Bateman, 1787, Pair 250.00
Silver, English, Coaster, Wine, Pierced, Engraved, 1799, Pair 300.00
Silver, English, Coaster, Wine, William Abdy, 1803, Pair 300.00
Silver, English, Coffeepot, Beaded Borders, Maker B.M., C.1783, 11 3/4 In. 1250.00
Silver, English, Coffeepot, George IV, Baluster, Charles Fox, London, 1826 .... 425.00
Silver, English, Coffeepot, Pear Shape, E.E., J.& W.Barnard, 1830 .... 450.00
Silver, English, Coffeepot, Queen Anne, Engraved Crest, 1710, 9 In.High 900.00
Silver, English, Coffeepot, T.Whipham, 1754 .... *illus* 1600.00
Silver, English, Cruet Stand, Robert Hennell, 1782 .... 150.00
Silver, English, Cruet, 4 Cut Glass Bottles, T.N., London, 1821 .... 100.00
Silver, English, Cup, Caudle, Engraved Crest, William Sheen, 1765 .... 100.00
Silver, English, Cup, 2 Double Scroll Handles, London, C.1750 .... 90.00
Silver, English, Dish, Meat, Armorial, Andrew Fogelberg, 1777, Pair 1300.00
Silver, English, Dish, Meat, Armorial, Paul Storr, 1808, Pair 2700.00
Silver, English, Dish, Meat, Oval, Armorial, William Fountain, 1880 .... 325.00
Silver, English, Dish, Meat, Oval, Crest, J.Angell, 1817 .... 350.00
Silver, English, Dish, Meat, Oval, Paul Storr, 1813, Pair 1450.00
Silver, English, Dish, Meat, Oval, Septimus & James Crespell, 1774 .... 850.00
Silver, English, Dish, Second Course, Armorial, James Young, 1791 .... 200.00
Silver, English, Dish, Serving, Gilt, Paul Storr, 1830, Pair 1400.00
Silver, English, Epergne, London, 1781, 25 In.High .... *Illus* 1500.00
Silver, English, Fish Set, Etched Blades, Ivory Handles, Wm.Bally, 24 Piece 75.00
Silver, English, Fork & Spoon, Serving, Bone Handles 45.00
Silver, English, Fork, Table, Paul Storr, 1812, Set Of 12 .... 450.00
Silver, English, Goblet, Peter & William Bateman, 1814 .... 200.00
Silver, English, Inkstand, Victorian, 2 Cut Glass Bottled, E.P., London, 1849 .... 225.00
Silver, English, Inkwell, Openwork, Diamond Cut Insert, C.1892 .... 50.00
Silver, English, Jug, Hot Water, Baluster, Herne & Butty, 1762 .... 450.00
Silver, English, Jug, Hot Water, Pear Shape, Charles Wright, 1776 .... 700.00
Silver, English, Kettle On Lampstand, London, 1745 .... *Illus* 1250.00
Silver, English, Knife & Fork, Dessert, Initial T, Crichton, 12 .... 200.00
Silver, English, Knife, Table, Engraved Crest, Moses Brent, 1798 .... 16.75
Silver, English, Knife, Table, Pistol Handle, Garrard, C.1770, Set Of 12 .... 400.00
Silver, English, Ladle, Chased & Engraved Handle, Grapes Inside, 1781-82 .... 50.00
Silver, English, Ladle, C.1817 .... 110.00
Silver, English, Ladle, Engraved Inside Cartouche, Stag's Head, G.Smith 1781 .... 55.00
Silver, English, Ladle, Soup, Armorials, Devonshire & Watkins, 1759 .... 400.00
Silver, English, Ladle, Toddy, Oval, Edward Aldridge, 1742 .... 150.00
Silver, English, Lamp, Alcohol, Sealing Wax Or Cigar Light, C.1790 .... 55.00
Silver, English, Mirror, Hand, Repousse, Beveled Mirror, 11 In.Long 45.00
Silver, English, Muffineer, Crest, 'Ut Sibi Sic Acter, ' Engraved, Embossed 75.00
Silver, English, Muffineer, Embossed Flowers, Marked Birmingham, 1890 .... 65.00
Silver, English, Mug, Baluster, Repousse, W.C., London, 1784 .... 170.00
Silver, English, Mug, Langlands & Robertson, Newcastle, 1783 .... 275.00
Silver, English, Mug, Leaf-Capped, Scroll Handle, Gilt Interior, T.Parr, 1739 .... 225.00
Silver, English, Pepperette, Vase Shape, Pierced, Blue Glass Liner, 1793 .... 75.00
Silver, English, Pillbox, C.1901 .... 20.00
Silver, English, Plate, Bread, Oval, Marked English Silver Mfg.CCRR 7.50
Silver, English, Rattle, Whistle, Repousse, Scrolls, Birds, Bells, 1899 .... 70.00
Silver, English, Salt & Pepper, Gadroon, Floral, Glass Insert, Spoons, 4 .... 120.00
Silver, English, Salt Cellar, George III, Pierced, Robert Hennell, 1780, 4 .... 170.00

Silver, English, Basket, Cake, Thomas Gilpin, 1749
See Page 520

Silver, English, Coffeepot,
T.Whipham, 1754
See Page 520

Silver, English, Epergne, London, 1781, 25 In.High
See Page 520

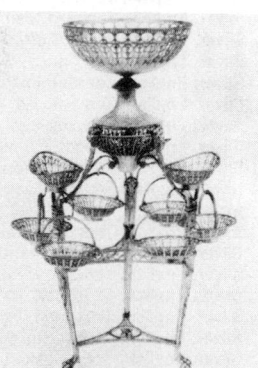

Silver, English, Candelabra, George III, 1791
See Page 520

Silver, English, Kettle On
Lampstand, London, 1745
See Page 520

Silver, English, Salt, Engraved, Gadroon Rim, London, 1814, Pair	100.00
Silver, English, Salt, Open, Victorian, In Case, Set Of 4	75.00
Silver, English, Salt, Pierced, R.& D.Hennell, London, 1767, Pair	140.00
Silver, English, Salt, Round, David Hennell, 1759, Set Of 4	350.00
Silver, English, Saltshaker, Cane, Mother-Of-Pearl Top	12.50
Silver, English, Salver, Armorials, Robert Abercromby, 1745	450.00

Silver, English, Salver, Engraved Armorials, John Carter, 1775 .... 475.00
Silver, English, Salver, Engraved Crest, R.Rew, London, 1763 .... 300.00
Silver, English, Sauceboat, Oval, Footed, S.M., 1747, Pair 525.00
Silver, English, Saucepan, Brandy, George I, Crest, James Smith, 1726 .... 225.00
Silver, English, Saucepan, Crest, Thomas Chawner, 1785 .... 450.00
Silver, English, Scoop, Marrow, Engraved Crest, Walls & Hayne, 1812 .... 75.00
Silver, English, Scoop, Marrow, Engravings, Walter Tweedle, 1778 .... 90.00
Silver, English, Spoon, Basting, Hanoverian, Elias Cachart, 1750 .... 200.00
Silver, English, Spoon, Chased, Peter & Wm.Bateman, C.1814 .... 55.00
Silver, English, Spoon, Chester Hallmark, C.S.W.F., C.1788 .... 30.00
Silver, English, Spoon, Dessert, Fiddle, Shell, Thread, Maker C.B., C.1868, 12 .... 300.00
Silver, English, Spurs, Chain & Stud Fittings, 1805, Pair 150.00
Silver, English, Stand, Lamp, Shell & Scroll Feet, Paul De Lamerie, 1741 .... 600.00
Silver, English, Stand, Teapot, Oval, Beaded Rim, London, 1782 .... 150.00
Silver, English, Strainer, Lemon, Pierced, S.Herbert & Co., 1754 .... 120.00
Silver, English, Sugar, Oval, Gilt Inside, Burwash & Sibley, 1807 .... 110.00
Silver, English, Tablespoon, Fiddle, Dated 1814 .... 30.00
Silver, English, Tablespoon, Hester Bateman, London, 1785 .... 65.00
Silver, English, Tablespoon, Thread Edge, Wm.Eley & Fearn, C.1800, Set Of 6 .... 180.00
Silver, English, Tankard, Baluster, Engraved, I.F., London, 1765 .... 475.00
Silver, English, Tankard, Baluster, Engraved, William & James Priest, 1770 .... 1100.00
Silver, English, Tea & Coffee Set, Reily & Storer, 1835, 4 Piece 1150.00
Silver, English, Tea Caddy, Scenic 35.00
Silver, English, Tea Set, Engraved, S.R., London, 1821, 3 Piece 500.00
Silver, English, Tea Set, J.& W.Barnard, 1828, 3 Piece 375.00
Silver, English, Tea Strainer, 5 In. 5.00
Silver, English, Teapot, Comes Apart, One Part Is Sugar, One Is Creamer 37.50
Silver, English, Teapot, George III, Oval Barrel, William Vincent, 1788 .... 250.00
Silver, English, Teapot, Oval, Engraved Crests, Henry Cooper, 1790 .... 225.00
Silver, English, Teapot, Oval, Engraved, B.M., London, 1787 .... 190.00
Silver, English, Teapot, Rectangular, Floral & Scrolls, A.K., 1810 .... 150.00
Silver, English, Teapot, Stand, Colonial, Chased, Applied Girdle, C.1830 .... 150.00
Silver, English, Teaspoon, Bateman, 1802 .... 24.50
Silver, English, Teaspoon, Initial, Peter & William Bateman, Set Of 6 .... 175.00
Silver, English, Teaspoon, Peter & William Bateman, 1808-09, Pair 20.00
Silver, English, Tongs, Sugar, Dated 1812 .... 36.00
Silver, English, Tray, Desk, 11 In.Long, Two Cobalt Bristol Ink Bottles 48.00
Silver, English, Tray, Tea, Oval, Chased Floral & Scrolls, 2 Handles, C.1825 .... 350.00
Silver, English, Tureen, Soup, Edward Farrell, 1846 .... *Illus* 2300.00
Silver, English, Tureen, William K.Reid, London, 1828 .... *Illus* 2700.00
Silver, English, Waiter, Armorials, Crouch & Hannam, 1755, Pair 525.00
Silver, English, Waiter, Chippendale Rim, John Trite, 1729 .... 200.00
Silver, English, Waiter, Chippendale Rim, Joseph Sanders, 1733 .... 335.00
Silver, French, Chocolate Pot, Gilt, Fluted, Laurel, L.Laper, C.1900 .... 180.00
Silver, French, Coffeepot, Cylindrical, Tapered, Laurel, Wreath, Risler, C.1900 .... 90.00
Silver, French, Coffeepot, Paris, C.1819 .... *Illus* 500.00
Silver, French, Coffeepot, Pear Shape, Joseph Bouillerot, 1789 .... 375.00
Silver, French, Cup, Stand, Gilt, Rococo, Pierced, Pink Porcelain Liner, C.1850 .... 44.50
Silver, French, Jar, Conserve, Paris, C.1809 .... *Illus* 1900.00
Silver, French, Ladle, Fiddle & Thread, Maker Lad, 1798-1809 .... 95.00
Silver, French, Ladle, Gravy, Oval Bowl, Monogram In Medallion 30.00
Silver, French, Ladle, Wine, Scalloped Bowl, Gold Wash Interior, Wood Handle 100.00
Silver, French, Meat Skewer, Swan Finial 25.00
Silver, French, Salt & Pepper, Vermeil Mushroom Shape, 1 In.High, 4 .... 40.00
Silver, French, Salt Cellar, Empire, Double, Eagle's Heads, 1809, Pair 250.00
Silver, French, Saucepan, Cylindrical, Ebony Handle, Paris, 1780 .... 200.00
Silver, French, Skewer, Pheasant Top, Hallmarked, 9 1/2 In.Long 15.00
Silver, French, Snuffbox, Scalloped, Engraved Hinged Lid, C.1810 .... 45.00
Silver, French, Tazza, Gilt, Hexagonal, Pierced, Scrolls, C.1900, Pair 325.00
Silver, French, Tea & Coffee Set, Applied Berries & Leaves, C.1900, 4 Piece 475.00
Silver, French, Tea & Coffee Set, Regence Style, A.Aucoc, C.1900, 4 Piece 300.00
Silver, French, Tea Set, Chased, Fluted, Swirls, Odiot, Paris, C.1890, 4 Piece 750.00
Silver, French, Tea Tongs, Woven Design, Engraved Paw Ends, Circa 1850 .... 42.00
Silver, German, Beaker, Cylindrical, Engraved, I.F., C.1690 .... 575.00
Silver, German, Beaker, Gilt, Cylindrical, Engraved, M.B., Augsburg, C.1700 .... 375.00
Silver, German, Beaker, Regence, Footed, Engraved, Strasbourg, C.1720 .... 300.00

Silver, German, Bowl, Portraits Louis XIV, XV, & XVI, Floral Urns 100.00
Silver, German, Candelabrum, 4-Light, Chased Leaves, Scroll Branches, C.1890 .... 200.00
Silver, German, Creamer, Cow, Chased Floral, C.1850 .... 120.00
Silver, German, Cup, Covered, Pineapple, Gilt, Warrior Support, C.1900 .... 225.00
Silver, German, Cup, Inset With 4 Coins, Chased, C.1900 .... 160.00
Silver, German, Dish, Sweetmeat, Fluted, Footed, I.V.G., C.1760 .... 350.00
Silver, German, Ewer, Augsburg, 1808 .... *Illus* 850.00

Silver, English, Tureen, Soup, Edward Farrell, 1846
See Page 522

Silver, English, Tureen,
William K.Reid, London, 1828
See Page 522

Silver, French, Coffeepot,
Paris, C.1819
See Page 522

Silver, French, Jar,
Conserve, Paris, C.1809
See Page 522

Silver, German,
Ewer, Augsburg,
1808

Silver, German, Tankard, Cylindrical, Chased, Running Hounds, C.1890 .... 325.00
Silver, German, Tankard, Cylindrical, Inset Coins, D.Vollgold & Sohn, C.1890 .... 900.00
Silver, Irish, Fork, Dessert, William Iv, T.Farnett & William Cummins, 1831 .... 22.75
Silver, Irish, Mug, Gilt, Williamson & Skinner, C.1750, Pair 500.00
Silver, Irish, Salt, Master, Crest, Initial, Wm.Bond, Dublin, C.1786, &air 120.00
Silver, Irish, Salver, Armorials, William Homer, C.1760 .... 775.00
Silver, Italian, Sugar, Covered, Round, Ring Handles, Pedestal, C.1850 .... 110.00
Silver, Jug, Clarte, Gilt & Glass, Etched, Chased, Scroll Handle, C.1890 .... 225.00
Silver, Knife, Serving, Butter, Initial, Pat.1861 .... 9.95
Silver, Ladle, Sauce, Tiffany, Audubon Series, Crimped Edge Bowl, Pat.1871 .... 35.00
Silver, Persian, Sugar & Creamer, Animals, Birds, Handmade 50.00
Silver, Portuguese, Bowl, Covered, Vase Shape, Engraved, Oporto, C.1855 .... 180.00
Silver, Portuguese, Candlestick, Gilt, Shell & Scrolls, Oporto, C.1900, 4 .... 700.00
Silver, Russian, Basket, Sugar, Gilded, Enameled Floral, Ivan Saltykov, 1880 .... 900.00
Silver, Russian, Beaker, Etched, Signed 84, Eagle, Maker, Dated 1879, 2 In. 28.00
Silver, Russian, Buckle, Belt, Three Belt Loops, Black Enamel, Marked, 1902 .... 115.00
Silver, Russian, Buckle, Shoe, Niello, Filigree, Marked, C.1865, Pair 60.00
Silver, Russian, Candlestick, Footed, Bowknot Ropes, C.1850, Pair 225.00
Silver, Russian, Cane Head, Inlaid Jade Type Stone, Carved Like Rose, 4 In. 85.00

Silver, Russian, Case, Cigarette, Coin Holder, Neillo, Rectangular, C.1850 .... 100.00
Silver, Russian, Case, Cigarette, Gilded, Rectangular, Repousse, K.B., C.1900 .... 140.00
Silver, Russian, Case, Cigarette, Gilded, Translucent Enamel, C.1900 .... 400.00
Silver, Russian, Coffee Set, Caspari, Riga, Embossed, C.1850, 3 Piece 300.00
Silver, Russian, Creamer, Gilded, Enameled Flowers, Ivan Saltykov, 1880 .... 700.00
Silver, Russian, Cup & Saucer, Parcel Gilt, Scroll Handle, Engraved, C.1880 .... 60.00
Silver, Russian, Cup, Kiddush, Chasing Of Judiac & Russian Motifs, Marked 65.00
Silver, Russian, Cup, Vodka, Multicolor Enamel 425.00
Silver, Russian, Flagon, Pavel Sazikov, Peasant Man Scene, St.Isaac's, 1858 .... 1300.00
Silver, Russian, Flask, Gilded, Enameled Flowers, Gustav Klingert, 1894 .... 1800.00
Silver, Russian, Fork & Spoon, Bright Cut On Handles, Back Of Bowl & Tines 28.00
Silver, Russian, Frame, Picture, Gilded, Enameled Flowerheads, C.1900 .... 1300.00
Silver, Russian, Garniture, Desk, Green Onyx, Ral & Company, C.1850, 18 Piece 3000.00
Silver, Russian, Goblet, Wine, Ceremonial, Cyrillic Hallmark, Pre-Revolution 30.00
Silver, Russian, Group, Equestrian, Nicholas Alexandrovich, P.F.Sazikov, 1853 .... 2400.00
Silver, Russian, Jardiniere, Cut Glass, Oval, Chased, Pierced, C.1880 .... 500.00
Silver, Russian, Kovtsch, Gilt Rim & Interior, Workmaster's Initials, Pair 185.00
Silver, Russian, Ladle, Signed By Maker, Double Eagle, Dated 1888, Marked 84 .... 135.00
Silver, Russian, Plate, Dinner, Orlov Service, Carl Johann Tegelsten, 1850 .... 1400.00
Silver, Russian, Plate, Dinner, Orlov Service, Nichols & Plinke, Gilt, 1859 .... 1400.00
Silver, Russian, Plate, Pavel Sazikov, Scalloped Rim, Engraved, 1864 .... 250.00
Silver, Russian, Salt, Engraved Floral, Ball Feet 45.00
Silver, Russian, Samovar, C.A., Gadrooned Lid, Pierced, Ivory Fittings, 1850 .... 1400.00
Silver, Russian, Snuffbox, Gilded, Niello, Rectangular, Napoleon, C.1820 .... 375.00
Silver, Russian, Spice Box, Footed Base, Steeple Shape, Flag On Top, Judaica 125.00
Silver, Russian, Spoon, Demitasse, Gilded, Initial G.St.Petersburg, 1861, 12 .... 120.00
Silver, Russian, Spoon, Enamel, Marked Klingert 90.00
Silver, Russian, Spoon, Gilded, Anton Kuzmetchev For Tiffany, Enamel, 1900, 2 .... 700.00
Silver, Russian, Spoon, Gilded, Enameled, Foliate, C.1900 .... 170.00
Silver, Russian, Spoon, Serving, Gilded, Enameled, C.1900 .... 275.00
Silver, Russian, Spoon, Serving, Marked AK1852-84 .... 25.00
Silver, Russian, Tablespoon, Fiddle & Shell Motif, Dated 1847, Coin, Pair 50.00
Silver, Russian, Tablespoon, Stag's Head Pierced By Arrow, C.1850, 10 .... 130.00
Silver, Russian, Tankard, A.W.W., Gilded, Pan-Slavic Style, Moscow, 1876 .... 350.00
Silver, Russian, Tea Set, Pavel Sazikov, Gilt Interiors, C.1865, 7 Piece 1200.00
Silver, Russian, Tea Strainer, Multicolor Enamel 325.00
Silver, Russian, Teaspoon, Gilded, Enamel, N.A., Moscow, C.1900, 6 .... 375.00
Silver, Russian, Tongs, Sugar, Gilded, Enamel Floral, C.1900 .... 90.00
Silver, Russian, Wine, Engraved, Village Scenes On Cartouche 85.00
Silver, Scottish, Fork, Dessert, 3 Prong, Patrick Robertson, 1771 .... 41.75
Silver, Scottish, Knife, Dessert, Cunningham & Simpson, 1810, Set Of 12 .... 175.00
Silver, Scottish, Vase, Victorian, Hamilton & Inches, Edinburgh, 1896, Pair 130.00
Silver, Sheffield, Basket, Cake, Victorian, Pierced, Henry Wilkinson, 1850 .... 160.00
Silver, Sheffield, Bowl, Grapevine Border, Monogram, Openwork Sides, Round 22.50
Silver, Sheffield, Bowl, Vegetable, Covered, Shell & Scroll Rim, Crest, C.1800 .... 80.00
Silver, Sheffield, Candelabra, 5-Light, Chased Leaves & Shells, C.1810, Pair 400.00
Silver, Sheffield, Candlestick, Armorial, John Watson, 1823, 4 .... 1200.00
Silver, Sheffield, Candlestick, Corinthian, Wreath Hanging From Top, 4 .... 450.00
Silver, Sheffield, Candlestick, Square Base, Baluster Stem, C.1830, Pair 110.00
Silver, Sheffield, Centerpiece, Cut Glass Bowl, Tripod Form, Foliage, C.1815 .... 150.00
Silver, Sheffield, Coffee Urn, Jas.Dixon & Sons, 20 In.High 350.00
Silver, Sheffield, Coffeepot, Baluster, Engraved Monogram, Chased, C.1815 .... 120.00
Silver, Sheffield, Cooler, Wine, Campana Shape, Armorial, W.R., C.1820, Pair 450.00
Silver, Sheffield, Cooler, Wine, R.Gainsford, 1823 .... Illus 750.00
Silver, Sheffield, Cruet, Egg, Revolving Frame, 4 Eggs, C.1820 .... 80.00
Silver, Sheffield, Dish, Entree, Covered, Stand, 1816, Pair 1550.00
Silver, Sheffield, Dish, Entree, Covered, Warming Stand, Engraved, C.1820 .... 120.00
Silver, Sheffield, Dish, Hot Water, Oval Ring Handle, M.Boulton & Co., C.1805 .... 27.50
Silver, Sheffield, Fork, Ice Cream, Marked MS Ltd., E.P.N.S., Eng., Set Of 6 .... 14.00
Silver, Sheffield, Knife & Fork, Dessert, Mother-Of-Pearl Handle, 12 .... 175.00
Silver, Sheffield, Liqueur Set, Glass Liners, Case, 7 Piece 70.00
Silver, Sheffield, Muffineer, Octagon, 8 1/4 In.High 25.00
Silver, Sheffield, Mustard, Cover, Blue Liner, Unmarked 35.00
Silver, Sheffield, Sconce, Candle, 2 Arm, C.1790 .... Illus 200.00
Silver, Sheffield, Stand, Quill, Rectangular Tray, 2 Glass Holders, Footed 50.00
Silver, Sheffield, Teakettle, Ornate, Bail, Engraved, E.P.N.A., J.Dixon & Sons 100.00

Silver, Sheffield, Cooler, Wine, R.Gainsford, 1823
See Page 524

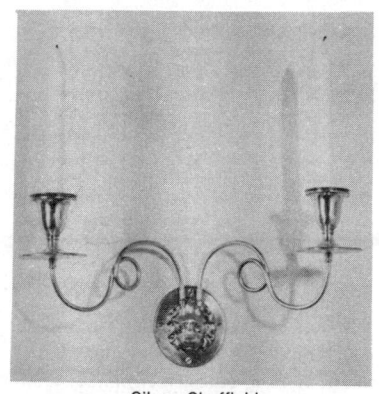

Silver, Sheffield,
Sconce, Candle, 2 Arm, C.1790
See Page 524

Silver, Sheffield, Teapot, Melon Shape, Floral Finial, Footed, Dixon & Sons	40.00
Silver, Sheffield, Teapot, Victorian, Spherical, Martin Hall & Co., 1867	100.00
Silver, Sheffield, Tongs, Sugar, Georgian, Cutout Design, John Munns, 1779	15.00
Silver, Sheffield, Tray, Engraved Floral Wreath & Bowknots, Wire Rim, Round	40.00
Silver, Sheffield, Tray, Inlay, Monogram, Applied Hallmark	125.00
Silver, Sheffield, Tray, Tea, Rectangular, Flowerheads, Engraved, C.1835	230.00
Silver, Sheffield, Tureen, Sauce, Covered, Bombe, Floral, Gadrooned, 1820, Pair	250.00
Silver, Sheffield, Urn, Coffee, Neoclassical, Vase Shape, Engraved, C.1800	140.00
Silver, Sheffield, Wine Cooler, Mother Bolton, Pair	750.00
Silver, Spanish, Tray With Inkwell, Art Nouveau, Signed Meneses, Madrid	25.00

Sterling Silver is made with 925 parts of silver out of 1, 000 parts of metal. The word sterling is a quality guarantee used in the United States after about 1860.

Silver, Sterling, Bag, Mesh, Mesh Handle	20.00
Silver, Sterling, Basket, Ornate Openwork Flowers Around Top & Handle	225.00
Silver, Sterling, Bell, Handle Has Relief Lady's Head, Flowers, 5 1/2 In.	27.50
Silver, Sterling, Bell, Lady Relief Handle, 7 1/2 In.	25.00
Silver, Sterling, Bonbon, Dutch Boy, Openwork	25.00
Silver, Sterling, Bonbon, Ornate Encrusted Border, Weighted	14.00
Silver, Sterling, Bowl, Black, Star, & Frost, Raised Shell & Floral	150.00
Silver, Sterling, Bowl, Centerpiece, Gold Washed, Floral Border, Victorian	140.00
Silver, Sterling, Bowl, Cutout & Repousse Border, Calt & Bros., 10 1/2 In.	65.00
Silver, Sterling, Bowl, Engraved Fruit Center, Monogram, Raised Fruit, Footed	150.00
Silver, Sterling, Bowl, Revere, Footed, 7 1/2 In.	70.00
Silver, Sterling, Bowl, Rose Pattern, By Stieff, 11 1/2 In.Diameter	425.00
Silver, Sterling, Bowl, Scalloped Rim, Gold Lined, Gorham, 8 In.Diameter	85.00
Silver, Sterling, Box, Cigar, Allover Scroll Engraving, Monogram	75.00
Silver, Sterling, Box, Repousse Figurals, Oval, Footed	75.00
Silver, Sterling, Box, Soap, Raised Fleur-De-Lis, Gold Wash Interior, Lid	39.00
Silver, Sterling, Box, Soap, Repousse, Roses, Leaves, 4 In.Long	40.00
Silver, Sterling, Brush, Baby's, Peter Rabbit	6.00
Silver, Sterling, Buttonhook, Embossed Handle, Hallmarks, 8 In.	15.00
Silver, Sterling, Buttonhook, Engraved	4.50
Silver, Sterling, Buttonhook, For Gloves	7.50
Silver, Sterling, Buttonhook, Mermaid, Flowing Hair	16.50
Silver, Sterling, Buttonhook, Ornate, Initials, 7 1/2 In.Long	3.95
Silver, Sterling, Buttonhook, 8 3/4 In.Long	3.75
Silver, Sterling, Candlesnuffer, Long Handle, Ornate End	19.00
Silver, Sterling, Candlestick, Encrusted, Weighted, 6 1/2 In., Pair	35.00
Silver, Sterling, Case, Card, Engraved Floral, Chain Handle, Scalloped Edges	20.00
Silver, Sterling, Case, Card, Hinged Lid, Filigree	30.00
Silver, Sterling, Case, Cigar, Shape Of Three Cigars, Gold Lined, Monogram	18.00
Silver, Sterling, Case, Cigarette, Signed R.& B., 1940s, 3 X 5 1/4 In.	25.00

Silver, Sterling, Case, Stamp, Art Nouveau	7.50
Silver, Sterling, Case, Stamp, Covered, Oxford University Insignia	12.00
Silver, Sterling, Castor, Tiffany & Co., Monogram, Crown Top, Openwork	60.00
Silver, Sterling, Chamberstick, Miniature, 3 X 3/4 In.High, Pair	18.00
Silver, Sterling, Chop Sticks, Pair	14.00
Silver, Sterling, Cigar Cutter, Bell Shape, Clapper Cuts Cigar	22.50
Silver, Sterling, Cigar Cutter, Dated 1910	11.50
Silver, Sterling, Cigar Cutter, Fish Shape, Fins Cut	22.00
Silver, Sterling, Cigar Cutter, Opens & Closes, Ring For Chain	6.50
Silver, Sterling, Cigar Cutter, Pocket, With Loop For Chain	4.95
Silver, Sterling, Cigarette Case, Figural, Elephant	125.00
Silver, Sterling, Coaster, 3 1/2 In., Set Of 6	10.00
Silver, Sterling, Coffee & Tea Service, Holloware, Frank Smith Co., 5 Piece	1000.00
Silver, Sterling, Coffeepot, Engraved, Ivory, Tiffany, Dated 1881	95.00
Silver, Sterling, Compact & Change Holder, On Chain, Art Nouveau	15.00
Silver, Sterling, Compote, Floral Design, Footed, Gorham, 2 1/2 In.High	28.00
Silver, Sterling, Creamer, Cow, Mouth Is Spout	130.00
Silver, Sterling, Creamer, Figural, Cow, Mouth Is Spout	130.00
Silver, Sterling, Cup & Saucer, Demitasse, Lenox Insert, Set Of 6	85.00
Silver, Sterling, Cup & Saucer, Swirl Design	40.00
Silver, Sterling, Cup, Child's, Engraved 'Frank'	7.50
Silver, Sterling, Cup, Demitasse, Engraved M.B., C.1895	18.50
Silver, Sterling, Cup, Demitasse, Gold Plated, Rose Leaf & Stem, C.1890	24.50
Silver, Sterling, Curling Iron	10.50
Silver, Sterling, Dish, Candy, Pierced Border, Dated 1914, 5 In.Diameter	12.00
Silver, Sterling, Dish, Mint, Pierced Side, Oval, Gorham	8.50
Silver, Sterling, Dish, Nut, Openwork Sides, 12	120.00
Silver, Sterling, Dish, Soap, Hinged	10.00
Silver, Sterling, Dresser Set, Art Nouveau, 11 Pieces	139.00
Silver, Sterling, Dresser Set, Enameled Blue, 2 Cut Glass Boxes, 11 Piece	200.00
Silver, Sterling, Dresser Set, Semidrape Nude, Flowing Hair, Wallace, 8 Piece	125.00
Silver, Sterling, Dresser Set, 9 Piece	49.50
Silver, Sterling, Dresser Set, 14 Piece	165.00
Silver, Sterling, Eraser	6.00
Silver, Sterling, Figurine, Knight, Sword, Shield, Ivory Face, 10 In.High	285.00
Silver, Sterling, Figurine, Owl, Horned, 3 In.High	37.50
Silver, Sterling, Flask, Indies, Miniature, 3 1/4 X 3 1/2 In.	30.00
Silver, Sterling, Flask, International Silver Co., 1/2 Pint	30.00
Silver, Sterling, Flask, Perfume, Hallmarked, Portrait, C.1830	99.00
Silver, Sterling, Flask, With Golfer	60.00
Silver, Sterling, Food Pusher	18.00
Silver, Sterling, Fork, Cold Meat, Victoria, Watson, Newell	20.00
Silver, Sterling, Fork, Dessert, Fiddle Shape, Engraved 'Mattie, 'F.Pieper	8.50
Silver, Sterling, Fork, Georgian Pattern, Patent Date 1898	6.50
Silver, Sterling, Fork, Lemon, Flared Prongs, Hallmarked	6.00
Silver, Sterling, Fork, Lettuce, Chased, Raised Work, 4 Prong	12.50
Silver, Sterling, Fork, Lily Of The Valley, Engraved Rev.T., 1906, Whiting	8.50
Silver, Sterling, Fork, Luncheon, Maryland Pattern, By Alvin, Set Of 10	55.00
Silver, Sterling, Fork, Salad, Audubon, Bird In Floral Spray On Handle, 12	84.00
Silver, Sterling, Funnel, Perfume, Ornate	25.00
Silver, Sterling, Funnel, With Golfer	30.00
Silver, Sterling, Goblet, Cocktail, Initial, Date, 4 1/2 In.High	6.00
Silver, Sterling, Hair Brush, Full Figure Woman Handle, Cupid, Rosebuds	85.00
Silver, Sterling, Hand Bag Frame, Heavy & Ornate Details	35.00
Silver, Sterling, Holder, Mint, Marked, Cup Shape, 3 In.High	12.00
Silver, Sterling, Holder, Pill, Tongs, Tiffany & Co., Rose Finial, Signed	55.00
Silver, Sterling, Holder, Place Card, Tiffany, Signed, Set Of 8	145.00
Silver, Sterling, Jar, Mustard, Hinged Lid, Cranberry Liner	42.50
Silver, Sterling, Knife Butter, F.W.Howard, Fredonia, N.Y., Case, Brass Trim	30.00
Silver, Sterling, Knife, Butter, Victorian	9.00
Silver, Sterling, Knife, Fruit, Pocket, Nut Pick	6.95
Silver, Sterling, Label, Decanter, Scotch, Rye, Sherry, & Bourbon, Set Of 4	50.00
Silver, Sterling, Ladle, Punch Bowl, Gold Wash Bowl, Whiting	75.00
Silver, Sterling, Ladle, Punch, Crosby, Morse, Script Name	85.00
Silver, Sterling, Ladle, Punch, King George Pattern, Gorham	75.00
Silver, Sterling, Ladle, Punch, Mark Gorham, Anchor Mark	125.00

Silver, Sterling, Ladle, Soup, Palm Pattern, Gorham, 1870 .... 68.00
Silver, Sterling, Letter Opener, Dagger Shape 7.50
Silver, Sterling, Letter Opener, Lavender Stone In End, 4 In.Long 7.50
Silver, Sterling, Letter Opener, Mother-Of-Pearl 6.50
Silver, Sterling, Lorgnette, Short, Engraved Handle, Snap Type 29.00
Silver, Sterling, Match Holder, Tray, Embossed 14.00
Silver, Sterling, Match Safe, Art Nouveau Floral 16.50
Silver, Sterling, Match Safe, Dated 1911 .... 15.00
Silver, Sterling, Match Safe, Embossed Edges, Initials, 1901 .... 23.00
Silver, Sterling, Match Safe, Embossed Figures Of Psyche, Presented In 1899 .... 45.00
Silver, Sterling, Match Safe, Embossed Horses & Fire Engine, Home Ins.Co. 10.00
Silver, Sterling, Match Safe, Floral Decoration, Place For Initial 18.50
Silver, Sterling, Match Safe, Initials T.H.C.C. 15.00
Silver, Sterling, Match Safe, Ornately Carved, Birmingham, 1909, 2 1/2 In. 22.50
Silver, Sterling, Match Safe, Oval Flowers, Bow & Horn Carving 18.00
Silver, Sterling, Match Safe, Scotch Plaid Carving 18.00
Silver, Sterling, Match Safe, Scrolling, Book Shape 20.00
Silver, Sterling, Match Safe, Striker, Convex, Step Design Border 15.00
Silver, Sterling, Matchbox, Victorian, English Hallmark, Engraved Initials 22.00
Silver, Sterling, Matchbox, Victorian, English Hallmark, Engraved, Flip Top 25.00
Silver, Sterling, Mirror, Hand, Embossed Cherubs, Looped Handle, Art Nouveau 45.00
Silver, Sterling, Mirror, Hand, Embossed Woman, Long Hair, Floral, Art Nouveau 50.00
Silver, Sterling, Mirror, Hand, Ornate, Beveled Glass, 16 X 4 3/4 In. 10.00
Silver, Sterling, Money Clip, Initials 4.50
Silver, Sterling, Money Clip, Raised Floral, Marked S.Kirk & Son 9.50
Silver, Sterling, Mug, Baby's, Clown, Drum, Monkey, Handle 35.00
Silver, Sterling, Mug, Miniature, Handle, 1 3/4 In.High 12.50
Silver, Sterling, Mustache Curler, Ornate Handle, Tiger Heads On End 12.00
Silver, Sterling, Mustard Pot, Covered, Handle, Filigree, Crystal Liner 20.00
Silver, Sterling, Mustard Pot, Ruby Glass Insert 30.00
Silver, Sterling, Nail File & Cuticle Tool 10.00
Silver, Sterling, Nail File, Child's, 3 In.Long 8.50
Silver, Sterling, Nail File, Raised Flowers 5.25
Silver, Sterling, Napkin Clip, Elephant On Front 21.00
     Silver, Sterling, Napkin Ring, see also Napkin Ring
Silver, Sterling, Napkin Ring, Engraved, Raised Chain-Like Borders 8.50
Silver, Sterling, Napkin Ring, Heavy Scroll, Ornate 8.50
Silver, Sterling, Napkin Ring, Pierced Beading 8.50
Silver, Sterling, Paper Clip, Signed Black Starr & Frost, Hand & Lace Cuff 29.00
Silver, Sterling, Paper Clip, Standing, Lady Gargoyles, Foods, Gorham, C.1915 .... 17.50
Silver, Sterling, Pencil, Mechanical, Engraved Design, Wahl Eversharp 6.00
Silver, Sterling, Pencil, Mechanical, Shaped Like A Spike 15.00
Silver, Sterling, Perfume, Flowers, Tiffany, 4 1/2 In. 42.50
Silver, Sterling, Pillbox, Moss Agate Inserts, Tan 95.00
Silver, Sterling, Pipe Tools To Hang On Watch Chain 25.00
Silver, Sterling, Pitcher, By Stieff, Heavy, 11 1/2 In.Tall 250.00
Silver, Sterling, Pitcher, Hand Hammered, Ribbon Handle Terminates In Heart 140.00
Silver, Sterling, Pitcher, Water, Simpson, Hall & Miller, Pre 1898, 3 Pt. 150.00
Silver, Sterling, Planter, Figures, Raised Enamel, Flared Sides 40.00
Silver, Sterling, Plate, Bread, Beaded Edge, Pierced Border, Gadroon Sides 45.00
Silver, Sterling, Plate, Bread, Etched, Beaded Edge, 12 In. 40.00
Silver, Sterling, Plate, Embossed Border, Art Deco, 11 In. 33.00
Silver, Sterling, Plate, Service, Scrollwork Rim, Chased, Gorham, N.Y. 100.00
Silver, Sterling, Porringer, Plain Bowl, Ornate Flat Handle 15.00
Silver, Sterling, Purse, Mesh, Engraved Frame, Chain, Marked Germany 125.00
Silver, Sterling, Purse, Mesh, Ornate Frame, Chain Handle, Marked H.M.M. 25.00
Silver, Sterling, Purse, Monogram, Attached Chain, Green Lined 9.50
Silver, Sterling, Rack, Toast, Holds Six Pieces Of Toast 75.00
Silver, Sterling, Rattle, Baby's, Teether, Dumbbell Shape 32.00
Silver, Sterling, Rattle, Baby's, Victorian, Bar Bell Shape, 4 In.Long 24.00
Silver, Sterling, Rattle, Rabbit Sits On Barrel, Ears Are Handle 18.00
Silver, Sterling, Salt & Pepper, Figural, Lighthouse 75.00
Silver, Sterling, Salt & Pepper, Marked 1866 .... 8.00
Silver, Sterling, Salt Cellar, Twisted Foot Frame, Salt Spoon, Pair 10.00
Silver, Sterling, Salt Dip, Openwork Festoons & Cupids, Blue Glass, Pair 50.00
Silver, Sterling, Salt Dip, Tiffany, Gold Interior, Footed, Pair 55.00

Silver, Sterling, Salt, Monogram 5.00
Silver, Sterling, Salt, Open, Cobalt Liner 10.50
Silver, Sterling, Salt, Open, Fluted, Spoon 9.50
Silver, Sterling, Seal, Uncut Bloodstone Base, Embossed Don Quixote Scenes 300.00
Silver, Sterling, Shaker, Talcum, 2 In. 6.50
Silver, Sterling, Shears, Grape, Fox Jumping For Grapes, German Blades 25.00
Silver, Sterling, Shoehorn, Chased 6.00
Silver, Sterling, Shoehorn, Monogram, Ornate Hollow Handle 8.00
Silver, Sterling, Snuffbox, Basket Weave, Engraved Cartouche, Marked 35.00
Silver, Sterling, Snuffbox, Niello Ground, Birds, Dragons, Flowers, Marked 35.00
Silver, Sterling, Spoon, ABC, 6 In.Long 9.00
Silver, Sterling, Spoon, Baby's, Teddy Bear In Swing In Bowl 16.50
Silver, Sterling, Spoon, Berry, Figural, Woman, Flowing Court Robe, 7 1/2 In. 20.00
Silver, Sterling, Spoon, Berry, Figure Of Lady In Court Dress, Hallmarked 20.00
Silver, Sterling, Spoon, Bonbon, Tiffany, Chrysanthemum 18.50
Silver, Sterling, Spoon, Demitasse, Lily Of The Valley, Leaf Handle 6.00
Silver, Sterling, Spoon, Demitasse, Lion Head Crown, Shell Bowl, 6 .... 24.00
Silver, Sterling, Spoon, Demitasse, Plush Case, Set Of 12 .... 48.00
Silver, Sterling, Spoon, Demitasse, Swedish, Enameled, Case, Set Of 12 .... 90.00
Silver, Sterling, Spoon, For Powdered Sugar 7.50
Silver, Sterling, Spoon, Full Figure Indian Handle, 5 1/2 In.Long 18.00
Silver, Sterling, Spoon, Full Figure Pere Marquette, 4 1/4 In.Long 15.00
Silver, Sterling, Spoon, Grapefruit, Monogram D, 12 .... 70.00
Silver, Sterling, Spoon, Grapefruit, Salem Witch, 6 In. 15.00
Silver, Sterling, Spoon, Iced Tea, Heart Shape Bowl, Cannonball End, Set Of 6 .... 45.00
Silver, Sterling, Spoon, Iced Tea, Prelude, International 6.50
Silver, Sterling, Spoon, Jelly, Thistle Mount 6.00
Silver, Sterling, Spoon, Salt, Classic Rose, Reed & Barton 2.75
Silver, Sterling, Spoon, Salt, Jade Handle, 3 In.Long 21.50
Silver, Sterling, Spoon, Serving, Hallmarked, London, 1822, 8 1/2 In.Long 60.00
Silver, Sterling, Spoon, Shakespeare Bust On Handle, 5 In.Long 20.00
    Silver, Sterling, Spoon, Souvenir, see Souvenir, Spoon
Silver, Sterling, Spoon, Stuffing, Tiffany Co., Pat.1902 .... 45.00
Silver, Sterling, Spoon, Tea Brewing, Hinged Lid, American, Marked P & B 13.50
Silver, Sterling, Spooner, Sugar, Blue, Glass Lined 89.50
Silver, Sterling, Strainer, Tea, Ebony Handle 10.00
Silver, Sterling, Stretcher, Glove, Engraved 15.00
Silver, Sterling, Sugar & Creamer, Footed, R.Wallace 29.00
Silver, Sterling, Sugar & Creamer, Openwork, Cobalt Liners 40.00
Silver, Sterling, Tatting Shuttle, Art Nouveau 20.00
Silver, Sterling, Tazza, 4 Orbs Between Semicircles, La Paglia, C.1925 .... 150.00
Silver, Sterling, Teapot & Coffeepot, Classic, Shaw & Fisher 450.00
Silver, Sterling, Tea Ball, Teapot Shape, Chain, Ring, 2 In.High 10.00
Silver, Sterling, Tea Caddy, Floral, Panels, Children, Trees, Octagon 55.00
Silver, Sterling, Tea Caddy, Repousse 65.00
Silver, Sterling, Teapot, On Standard, Embossed Tongue & Beads With Leaves 140.00
Silver, Sterling, Teaspoon, Beaded Rose, Set Of 6 .... 30.00
Silver, Sterling, Teaspoon, Full Female Figure, Cupid, Floral, Art Nouveau 12.50
Silver, Sterling, Teaspoon, Lily-Of-The-Valley, Set Of 6 .... 60.00
Silver, Sterling, Teaspoon, Nude Woman, Cherubs, 'Merry Xmas, ' Pat.1902 .... 8.00
    Silver, Sterling, Thimble, see Sewing Tool, Thimble
Silver, Sterling, Tongs, Iris On Handle, Claws, 3 1/2 In. 8.00
Silver, Sterling, Tongs, Sugar Cube, Dated 1895 .... 12.00
Silver, Sterling, Tongs, Tiffany & Co., Richelieu Pattern, Claw & Shell 60.00
Silver, Sterling, Toothbrush, Ivory Head, Flowers 6.50
Silver, Sterling, Toothpick, All Around Swirl 14.00
Silver, Sterling, Toothpick, Parasol 25.00
Silver, Sterling, Toothpick, Two Handles 12.00
Silver, Sterling, Tray, Card, Shape Of Turkey Wing, Turkey Sits On Tip 135.00
Silver, Sterling, Tray, Pin, Cupid Kissing Woman's Head, Art Nouveau 45.00
Silver, Sterling, Tray, Pin, Embossed Indian's Head, War Bonnet, Unger Bros. 150.00
Silver, Sterling, Tray, Pin, Floral, Roses, Scrolls, Ornate 9.00
Silver, Sterling, Umbrella Handle, Lady's, Heavy Work 12.50
Silver, Sterling, Umbrella Handle, Mother-Of-Pearl 15.00
Silver, Sterling, Vase, Art Nouveau Holder, 9 In.High 175.00
Silver, Sterling, Vase, Bud, 6 1/4 In.High 7.00

Silver, Swedish, Spoon, Engraved, Fig Shape Bowl, R.D., Stockholm, C.1650 .... 250.00
Silver, Swedish, Spoon, Tea Caddy, Rural Scene Bowl, Hallmarked, 1791 .... 35.00
Silver, Swiss, Box, Alpaca, Blue Medallion On Lid, Marked Bernforf 15.00
Silver, Tiffany, Bowl, Chased Scrolling Foliage On Coppered Ground 375.00
Silver, Tiffany, Butter Spreader, Wave Edge Pattern, 1884 .... 14.00
Silver, Tiffany, Butter, Covered, Raised Poppies & Leaves 65.00
Silver, Tiffany, Chatelaine, Greek Heads On Seal, Whistle & Coin Carrier 150.00
Silver, Tiffany, Cup, Hand Hammered, Handle, Marked 85.00
Silver, Tiffany, Desk Sponge Container, Engraved, Crystal Inset 39.00
Silver, Tiffany, Dish, Candy, Pierced Basket Weave, Shell & Flower Motif 35.00
Silver, Tiffany, Holder, Place Card, Set Of 8 .... 100.00
Silver, Tiffany, Inkwell, Mushroom Hinged Lid, Engraved, Signed 58.00
Silver, Tiffany, Muffineer, Pierced Top, 7 1/2 In.High 90.00
Silver, Tiffany, Penholder, Signed 15.00
Silver, Tiffany, Porringer, Engraved Baby Bess, 1884, Numbered 85.00
Silver, Tiffany, Salt & Pepper, Small 12.50
Silver, Tiffany, Salt & Pepper, 3 Feet, Initial M, Signed 45.00
Silver, Tiffany, Spoon, Demitasse, Persian, C.1872 .... 12.50
Silver, Tiffany, Spoon, Stuffing, Engraved Ivy Design, Shield, Initial 45.00
Silver, Tiffany, Sugar Shell 24.00
Silver, Tiffany, Tray, Card, 5 3/4 In.Diameter 17.50
Silver, Viennese, Candlestick, Gilt, Enamel Mythological Scenes, C.1850, Pair 500.00
Silver, Viennese, Knife, Tubular Handle, Enameled Cartouche Of Pan, C.1850 .... 70.00

Sinclaire cut glass was made by H.P.Sinclaire and Company of
Corning, New York, between 1905 and 1929. Pieces were made of crystal as
well as amber, blue, green or ruby. Only a small percentage of Sinclaire
glass is marked.
Sinclaire, Box, Silver Thread Pattern, Left Off Top, Signed, 3 1/2 In.Square 95.00
Sinclaire, Candlestick, Grape Design, Amber, S In Wreath Signed, 11 In.High 100.00

Slag Glass is streaked with several colors. There were many types made
from about 1880. Caramel or Chocolate Glass was made by the Indiana
Tumbler and Goblet Company of Greentown, Indiana, from 1900 to 1903.
Pink Slag was an American Victorian product of unknown origin. Purple
and Blue Slag were made in American and English factories. Red Slag
is a very late Victorian product. Other colors are known, but are of less
importance to the collector.
Slag, Blue, Basket, English Registry Mark, Round, Open Handles 18.00
Slag, Blue, Creamer, Fluted, 5 1/2 In.High 35.00
Slag, Blue, Mug, Troubadour, Opaque, Greentown 25.00
Slag, Blue, Stein, Troubador, Greentown 30.00
Slag, Blue, Vase, English Registry Mark, Footed, Ribbed Corners 16.75
Slag, Brown, Nappy, Leaf Bracket, Triangular 55.00
Slag, Caramel, Bowl, Cactus, Footed, 4 In.Diameter 45.00
Slag, Caramel, Bowl, Footed, 10 1/2 In. 47.50
Slag, Caramel, Breakfast Set, Leaf Bracket Pattern, 4 Piece 260.00
Slag, Caramel, Butter, Cactus 75.00
Slag, Caramel, Celery, Leaf Bracket, Scalloped, Four Ball Feet 65.00
Slag, Caramel, Celery, Sawtooth, Knob Stem 38.00
Slag, Caramel, Compote, Cactus ....95.00 To 110.00
Slag, Caramel, Compote, Jelly, Cactus, Greentown, 5 In.High 65.00
Slag, Caramel, Creamer, Cactus .... 55.00 To 65.00
Slag, Caramel, Cruet, Cactus, Stopper 100.00
Slag, Caramel, Cruet, Leaf Bracket, Greentown 85.00
Slag, Caramel, Dish, Cat On Hamper Cover, Shallow, Square, Greentown 225.00
Slag, Caramel, Dish, Hen Cover 200.00
Slag, Caramel, Jar, Cracker, Covered, Cactus 85.00
Slag, Caramel, Jug, Cactus, 5 1/2 In. 87.00
Slag, Caramel, Mug, Buttress, Herringbone, Greentown 32.50
Slag, Caramel, Mug, Cactus, Greentown, 3 1/2 In. 45.00
Slag, Caramel, Mug, Scene, Man & Woman In Windows, 4 3/4 In. 45.00
Slag, Caramel, Nappy, Beaded Fan 25.00
Slag, Caramel, Nappy, Cactus, Leaf Bracket, Footed, Greentown 45.00
Slag, Caramel, Nappy, Palm Leaf, Three Feet 35.00
Slag, Caramel, Nappy, Shell, Handle, Tricorner .... 35.00 To 55.00

Slag, **Caramel**, Nappy, Tricornered, Deep Cut 35.00
Slag, **Caramel**, Pitcher, Covered, Cactus, Miniature 47.50
Slag, **Caramel**, Pitcher, Expanded Rib, Greentown, 16 In. 130.00
Slag, **Caramel**, Pitcher, Squirrel 225.00
Slag, **Caramel**, Plate, Cactus, Scalloped Edge, 7 1/2 In.Diameter 38.00
Slag, **Caramel**, Salt & Pepper, Cactus, Greentown 65.00
Slag, **Caramel**, Sauce, Dewey, Flower Flange .... 22.00 To 25.00
Slag, **Caramel**, Sauce, Scroll 22.00
Slag, **Caramel**, Shade, 8 Panel, Flare Top, Tiffany Type, 22 .... 165.00
Slag, **Caramel**, Spooner, Acanthus 28.00
Slag, **Caramel**, Syrup, Cactus, Dewey Top, Greentown 65.00
Slag, **Caramel**, Syrup, Cactus, Lid .... 60.00 To 69.50
Slag, **Caramel**, Tankard, Hearts Of Loch Laven, 6 In. 45.00
Slag, **Caramel**, Toothpick, Cactus, Greentown 35.00
Slag, **Caramel**, Toothpick, English, 4 In.Square 25.00
Slag, **Caramel**, Toothpick, Pedestal, Marked 1831, Eagle 25.00
Slag, **Caramel**, Tumbler, Cactus .... 32.00 To 40.00
Slag, **Caramel**, Tumbler, Fleur-De-Lis 24.50
Slag, **Caramel**, Tumbler, Hearts Of Loch Laven 39.50
Slag, **Caramel**, Tumbler, Uneeda Milk Biscuit 50.00
Slag, **Green**, Basket, English Registry Mark, Quatrefoil, Open Handles 27.00
Slag, **Green**, Mug, Troubadour, Opaque, Greentown 25.00
Slag, **Green**, Pitcher, Lattice Edge 23.00
Slag, **Green**, Toothpick, Urn Stands On Square Base, Beaded Top 29.00
Slag, **Pink**, Cup, Punch 225.00
Slag, **Pink**, Lamp, Miniature 440.00
Slag, **Pink**, Sauce, Inverted Fan & Feather .... 155.00 To 172.50
Slag, **Pink**, Toothpick, Footed 350.00
Slag, **Purple**, Bell, Dinner 14.50
Slag, **Purple**, Boot 55.00
Slag, **Purple**, Boot With Spur 18.50
Slag, **Purple**, Bowl, Dart Pattern, Footed, 6 In.Diameter, 3 In.High 35.00
Slag, **Purple**, Bowl, Leaf, Paneled 95.00
Slag, **Purple**, Cake Stand, Dart Bar, 11 In.Diameter, 6 In.High 95.00
Slag, **Purple**, Cake Stand, 9 X 6 In.High 95.00
Slag, **Purple**, Celery, Fluted 39.75
Slag, **Purple**, Celery, Fluted Pattern, Pedestal 65.00
Slag, **Purple**, Celery, Paneled & Footed 85.00
Slag, **Purple**, Celery, Paneled, Scalloped Top, Footed 55.00
Slag, **Purple**, Compote, Jack-In-The-Pulpit, Tree Trunk Base 74.50
Slag, **Purple**, Compote, Jenny Lind 125.00
Slag, **Purple**, Compote, Lacy Edge, Basket-Weave Base 57.50
Slag, **Purple**, Compote, 9 X 6 3/4 In.High 70.00
Slag, **Purple**, Creamer 32.50
Slag, **Purple**, Dish, Candy, Ruffled 14.00
Slag, **Purple**, Dish, Crouching Lion On Cover, Pedestal Base, Dated Aug.1889 .... 55.00
Slag, **Purple**, Dish, Hen On Nest Cover 32.50
Slag, **Purple**, Dish, Soap 65.00
Slag, **Purple**, Goblet 120.00
Slag, **Purple**, Inkwell, Pair On Base, Floral, Brass Covers, Center Handle 50.00
Slag, **Purple**, Jelly, Threaded Stem 30.00
Slag, **Purple**, Match Holder 19.00
Slag, **Purple**, Match Holder, Square 28.50
Slag, **Purple**, Matchbox, Shape Of Saddlebag 55.00
Slag, **Purple**, Mug, Rose & Vine Pattern, Marbling 32.00
Slag, **Purple**, Pitcher, Water 38.50
Slag, **Purple**, Plate, Bread, Notched Edge 39.75
Slag, **Purple**, Plate, Closed Lattice Edge, 10 1/2 In.Diameter 95.00
Slag, **Purple**, Plate, Reticulated Border, 10 In. 60.00
Slag, **Purple**, Platter, Flowers On Notched Edge, 13 In. 75.00
Slag, **Purple**, Platter, Tam-O-Shanter 95.00
Slag, **Purple**, Salt, Open, English Registry Mark, Extended Handles, Ribbed 16.00
Slag, **Purple**, Spooner, Flower & Panel 42.00
Slag, **Purple**, Spooner, Marbled, Beaded, Scalloped Top 45.00
Slag, **Purple**, Spooner, 4 In.High 5.00
Slag, **Purple**, Sugar & Creamer, Shell & Coral Pattern, Footed 38.00

Slag, Purple, Sugar, Acanthus, 4 1/2 In.High 42.50
Slag, Purple, Sugar, Covered, Hexagon 30.00
Slag, Purple, Toothpick, Footed, Square, 3 3/4 In.High 25.00
Slag, Purple, Toothpick, Scroll With Acanthus, C.1885 .... 55.00
Slag, Purple, Toothpick, Thimble Shape, 'Just A Thimble Full' 60.00
Slag, Purple, Tray, Oblong 26.50
Slag, Purple, Tumbler, 'Imperial 1/2 Pint' Embossed On Bottom 25.00
Slag, Purple, Tumbler, Signed Sowerby, England .... 15.00 To 45.00
Slag, Purple, Urn, 6 In.High, Pair 55.00
Slag, Purple, Vase, Beads & Bark, Marbleized Mosaic Glass, Northwood 95.00
Slag, Purple, Vase, Tripod 37.50
Slag, Purple, Vase, Tulip Shape, On Leaf Pedestal 55.00
Slag, Red, Bowl On Black Base, Pair Candleholders 150.00
Slag, Red, Bowl, Dated 1924, Citizens Mutual Trust Co., Wheeling, W.Va. 65.00
Slag, Red, Bowl, Footed, 10 1/2 In. 75.00
Slag, Red, Bowl, 4 1/2 In.Diameter Base Flares To 8 In.Diameter Top 47.50
Slag, Red, Compote, Pedestal Base, Finial On Cover, 11 In.High 125.00
Slag, Red, Vase, Fan, Fluted 55.00
Slag, Red, Vase, Peacock & Floral, 7 1/2 In. 95.00
Slag, Tan, Basket, Daisies, C.1930, 10 X 3 In.Across 12.00
Slag, Turquoise, Tumbler, Cactus 16.50
Slag, White, Mug, Troubadour, Opaque, Greentown 18.00

Sleepy Eye Pottery was made to be given away with the flour products of
the Sleepy Eye Milling Co., Sleepy Eye, Minnesota, from about 1893
to 1952. It is a heavy stoneware with blue decorations, usually the famous
profile of an indian.
Sleepy Eye, Bowl, 6 5/8 In.Diameter 45.00
Sleepy Eye, Creamer, Barrel Label 47.50
Sleepy Eye, Mug, Blue & White, Signed Monmouth In Triangle, 4 1/2 In.High 45.00
Sleepy Eye, Vase, Blue, Gray, Signed, 9 In.High 35.00

Slip is a thin mixture of clay and water, about the consistency of sour cream,
that is applied to the pottery for decoration. If the pottery is made with
red clay, the Slip is mixed with yellow clay.
Slipware, Bowl, 'Annie Haines 1887' 90.00
Slipware, Bowl, Orange & Green Alternating Stripes, Shallow, 11 1/2 In. 275.00
Slipware, Bowl, Tulip Decoration, Signed J.L.Blaney, Cookstown, Pa. 400.00
Slipware, Bowl, Yellow Conventional Design, Crimped Edge, Round, Shallow 160.00
Slipware, Jar, Incised Decoration, Green & Cream, Dated 1811 .... 180.00
Slipware, Plate, Dark Brown, 9 In. 100.00

Smith Brothers Glass was made after 1878. The owners had worked for the
Mt.Washington Glass Company in New Bedford, Massachusetts, for
seven years before going into their own shop. Some of the designs were
similar.
Smith Brothers, Bowl, Hand-Painted Floral Border, Handled Silver Holder 145.00
Smith Brothers, Bowl, Melon Rib, Stylized Pansy Decoration, Beaded Rim 130.00
Smith Brothers, Bowl, Melon Shape, Cream Ground, Red, Pink & Green Floral 175.00
Smith Brothers, Bowl, Melon Shape, Purple & Yellow Floral On Cream, Green 275.00
Smith Brothers, Bowl, Melon Shape, Rust & Green Ivy, Silver Plate Rim 175.00
Smith Brothers, Box, Bridal, White, Embossed, 7 In.Square 175.00
Smith Brothers, Box, Covered, Melon Rib, Daisies, Rampant Lion Signature 225.00
Smith Brothers, Box, Powder, Melon Shape, Pansies, Green Leaves, Rampant Lion 175.00
Smith Brothers, Creamer, Melon Rib, Blue Pansies, Plated Spout, Rim, Handle 150.00
Smith Brothers, Humidor, Pansy Design, Mauve, Apricot, Gray, Yellow 145.00
Smith Brothers, Humidor, Pansy Design, Pink, Mauve, Apricot, Green, Cover 160.00
Smith Brothers, Jar, Biscuit, Floral, Red Rampant Lion Mark 295.00
Smith Brothers, Jar, Biscuit, Melon Rib, Gold Floral, Silver Lid & Bail 325.00
Smith Brothers, Jar, Candy, Rust Flowers, Red Rampant Lion Mark 295.00
Smith Brothers, Jar, Cookie, Jeweled, Signed 375.00
Smith Brothers, Jar, Cookie, Melon Rib, Water Lilies, Gold Outline, Metal Rim 350.00
Smith Brothers, Jar, Powder, Covered, Red Rampant Lion Mark 295.00
Smith Brothers, Lamp, Ribbed Shade & Base, Burmese Coloring, Roses, Leaves 150.00
Smith Brothers, Muffineer, Cream Color, Pansies, Ribbed, Rampant Lion Mark 297.50
Smith Brothers, Muffineer, Melon Ribbed, Floral & Leaf On Yellow To White 130.00

Smith Brothers, Muffineer, Melon Ribbed, Prunus Blossoms, Gold Enamel 150.00
Smith Brothers, Muffineer, Orange Flower On Orange & White 55.00
Smith Brothers, Muffineer, White Shasta Daisies On Ivory 135.00
Smith Brothers, Mustard Pot, Blue Ground, Blue Violets, Barrel Shape, Glossy 45.00
Smith Brothers, Mustard Pot, Pillar Ribs, Black & Gray Abstract Mottle 60.00
Smith Brothers, Mustard Pot, White Ground, Pink Flower Clusters 55.00
Smith Brothers, Mustard Pot, Winter Scene, Silver Lid & Bail 60.00
Smith Brothers, Plate, World's Fair, 1893, Santa Maria, Water, Clouds, Gulls 145.00
Smith Brothers, Rose Bowl, 'Compliments Of The Season' In Gold 225.00
Smith Brothers, Rose Bowl, Melon Rib, Pansies, Beaded Top 130.00
Smith Brothers, Rose Bowl, Trailing Bluets & Leaves On Old Ivory Ground 100.00
Smith Brothers, Salt & Pepper, Pansies, Aqua To White Ground, Pedestal Base 36.00
Smith Brothers, Salt, Open, Verre De Soie, Pedestal 60.00
Smith Brothers, Sugar & Creamer, Covered, Blue Pansies, Silver Rims, Handles 325.00
Smith Brothers, Toothpick, Melon Rib Base, Beaded Collar, Floral 55.00
Smith Brothers, Toothpick, White To Blue White, Columbine Type Floral 45.00
Smith Brothers, Vase, Albertine, Three Pinch, Signed 425.00
Smith Brothers, Vase, Enameled Daisies, Beaded Rim 115.00
Smith Brothers, Vase, Flask Shape, Pink Roses, Beaded Bluets 100.00
Smith Brothers, Vase, Flask Shape, Rose Clusters, Gold Splashes, Beaded Rim 135.00
Smith Brothers, Vase, Hummingbird, Spring Flowers, Script Signature 140.00
Smith Brothers, Vase, Light Green, Two Circles, Scenery, Robin, 10 In. 110.00
Smith Brothers, Vase, Old Ivory Ground, Trailing Violets, Leaves, Beads 200.00
Smith Brothers, Vase, Old Ivory Ground, Violets, Beaded Top, Triangular 225.00
Smith Brothers, Vase, Pink Opalescent, Stork Stands In Green Rush 95.00
Smith Brothers, Vase, Robin, Hand-Painted, 10 In.High 85.00
Snow Baby, Bisque, Outstretched Arms, Standing On Snowball 22.50
Snow Baby, Bisque, Yellow, Saxophone 39.00
Snow Baby, Box, Covered, Royal Bayreuth, Blue Mark .... 75.00 To 90.00
Snow Baby, Creamer, Girl, Boy Running, Dog In Snow, Royal Bayreuth 79.50
Snow Baby, Nappy, Ring Handle, Turned In Edges, Royal Bayreuth 60.00
Snow Baby, Nappy, Trefoil, Handle, Royal Bayreuth 65.00
Snow Baby, Plate, Royal Bayreuth, Blue Mark, 8 1/4 In. 75.00
Snow Baby, Polar Bear, 2 In.Tall 30.00
Snow Baby, Sitting, 1 1/2 In.Tall 28.00
Snow Baby, Sitting, 2 In.Tall 45.00
Snow Baby, Snow Man, 2 1/4 In.Tall 35.00
Snow Baby, Standing With Ski, 1 1/2 In.Tall 30.00
Snow Baby, Toothpick, Royal Bayreuth, Blue Mark 110.00
Snow Baby, Vase, Royal Bayreuth, Blue Mark, 5 In.High 75.00
Snow Bear, Bisque, Pebbly 20.00
Snow White & Dwarfs, Dishes, Tin, Child's, 26 Piece 15.00
Snow White, Book, Sketch, 1938, Wm.Collins Sons, London 70.00
Snow White, Figurine, Snow White & Dwarfs, Names Inscribed, C.1939, Set Of 8 .... 35.00
Snow White, Program, World Premiere, December 21, 1937 .... 35.00
Snuff Bottle, see Bottle, Snuff
Snuffbox, Black Lacquer & Pique, Cartouche Shape, Mother-Of-Pearl, C.1760 .... 230.00
Snuffbox, French, Carved Relief Of Louis Phillipe, Tortoiseshell Lined 85.00
Snuffbox, German, Rectangular, Enamel Figures, Scene, Galante, C.1760 .... 550.00
Snuffbox, Nickel Plated, Brass & Wood, Mother-Of-Pearl & Ivory, France 40.00
Snuffbox, Paris, Courtille Factory, Napoleon's Crest, Cartouche, 1777-1840 .... 90.00
Snuffbox, Round, French Enamel Floral Design On Top And Sides 23.00
Snuffbox, Russian, Gold & Enamel, Rectangular, David & Saul, Theremin, 1800 .... 2900.00
Snuffbox, Silver Gilt, Rectangular, T.P., R.M., London, 1914 .... 300.00
Snuffbox, Swiss, Gold & Enamel, Oval, Turkish Harbor Views, Urns, C.1810 .... 3000.00
Snuffbox, Swiss, Gold & Enamel, Rectangular, Classical Figures, C.1810 .... 3600.00
Snuffbox, Swiss, Gold & Enamel, Rectangular, Miniature Of 2 Lovers, C.1800 .... 1300.00
Snuffbox, Swiss, 18K Gold, Enameled Rialto Bridge, Venice, C.1860 .... 400.00
Snuffbox, Swiss, 3 Color Gold & Enamel, Engine Turned, Landscape, C.1810 .... 270.00

Soapstone is a mineral that was used for foot warmers or griddles because of
its heat-retaining properties. Chinese Soapstone Carvings of the
nineteenth and twentieth centuries are found in many antique shops.
Soapstone, Bookend, Basket Of Flowers, Brown Mottle, Carved, Pair 58.50
Soapstone, Bookend, Carved Foo Dogs, Gray, 6 In., Pair 42.00
Soapstone, Bookend, Carved Vine Flower Leaves, Pair 12.00

Soapstone, Bookend, Jade Color, Pair 50.00

Soapstone, Bottle, Snuff, Flask, Mottled Brown Gray, Carved Peach Tree, 1850 .... 40.00

Soapstone, Bottle, Snuff, Flattened, Mottled Brown, Carved Deer & Crane 30.00

Soapstone, Bowl, Monkeys, Red, Black, Green, Oval, 6 In.Diameter 18.00

Soapstone, Box, Carved Oriental Scene, House, Tree, Mountains 35.00

Soapstone, Box, Cigarette, Dragon On Top, Marked China 10.00

Soapstone, Candleholder, Carved Foo Dog, 8 1/2 In. 49.50

Soapstone, Carving, Religious Idol With Erotic Overtones, India 32.50

Soapstone, Compote, Blue Gray, Scalloped Edge, 11 1/2 In.High 37.50

Soapstone, Cup, Wine, Tumbler Shape, Oriental, Green Gray, Striations, Pair 18.00

Soapstone, Figurine, Bird, Gray, Black, 7 1/2 In.Long, 3 1/2 In.High 32.00

Soapstone, Figurine, Child & Dog 12.00

Soapstone, Figurine, Christ, 14 In.High 50.00

Soapstone, Figurine, Eskimo With Pack On Back, Alaskan, 6 In.High 32.50

Soapstone, Figurine, Monkey, See, Speak, Hear No Evil, Hand Carve .... 4.00 To 15.00

Soapstone, Foot Warmer, Bail 8.50

Soapstone, Jar, Hand Carved Design, Cover, China, 9 In.High 38.00

Soapstone, Lamp Base, Carved Birds, Flowers, Pink To Beige, 9 In.High 64.00

Soapstone, Match & Cigarette Holder, Flowers, Tan 5.50

Soapstone, Match Holder, Carved 9.00

Soapstone, Paperweight, House & Trees 12.50

Soapstone, Seal, Foo Dog On Top, 5 In.High 24.00

Soapstone, Seal, Hand, Foo Dog On Pedestal, Oriental Inscription On Front 39.00

Soapstone, Seal, Water Buffalo, Incised Initial On Bottom 17.50

Soapstone, Slipper, Carved, Etched Design, Black Stone, Oriental, 3 In., Pair 22.00

Soapstone, Teapot, Hand Carved, Nineteenth Century, China 75.00

Soapstone, Toothpick, Carved Floral, Vines 10.00

Soapstone, Toothpick, Three Monkeys .... 8.50 To 18.00

Soapstone, Vase, Animals, 5 3/4 In.High 23.00

Soapstone, Vase, Brown, Carved Flower & Leaf Design On Front 32.00

Soapstone, Vase, Carved Floral, Birds, Leaves Surround Three Open Jars, Gray 45.00

Soapstone, Vase, Dragon, Flowers, Carved 20.00

Soapstone, Vase, Floral Carvings, Marked China, 4 1/2 In. 26.00

Soapstone, Vase, Flowers, Bird, Berries, China, 8 3/4 In.High 95.00

Soft Paste, Coffeepot, Dome Cover, Decorated, Leeds 215.00

Soft Paste, Creamer, Pink Luster 30.00

Soft Paste, Creamer, Raised Decoration Of Dog & Flowers, Pink Luster Rim 100.00

Soft Paste, Creamer, Transfer Figures Of Children, Flowers & Leaves Top 60.00

Soft Paste, Cup & Saucer, Blue Bomb Pattern, Lowestoft, England 55.00

Soft Paste, Cup & Saucer, Handleless, Strawberry Pattern 125.00

Soft Paste, Cup & Saucer, Rosebud & Leaf Decoration 45.00

Soft Paste, Cup Plate, Blue Beaded Border, Impressed Riley, Circa 1820 .... 25.00

Soft Paste, Cup Plate, Blue Man & Child Scene Center, Raised Border, Rogers 25.00

Soft Paste, Cup Plate, Raised Bust Of Woman, Raised Floral, Cobalt, Orange 55.00

Soft Paste, Cup Plate, Red & Green Floral, Leeds 25.00

Soft Paste, Mug, Pink Luster, Luster Vine Decoration, England 25.00

Soft Paste, Pitcher, Milk, Floral Decoration In Color, 6 In.High 45.00

Soft Paste, Plate, Black Transfer, Disobedient Children 20.00

Soft Paste, Plate, Blue, Oriental Scene, Dated 1838, Spode, Set Of 6 .... 22.00

Soft Paste, Plate, Blue, Upper Ferry Bridge Over Run Schuylkill, Eagles 135.00

Soft Paste, Plate, Center Black Transfer Of Lafayette, Washington, & Eagle 110.00

Soft Paste, Plate, Coat Of Arms & Hanging Game Center, Scalloped, Leeds 55.00

Soft Paste, Plate, Lafayette, 7 In. 95.00

Soft Paste, Plate, Paintbrush Pattern, 8 In. 35.00

Soft Paste, Plate, Portuguese, Light Green Leaves, Lavender Veins, Pair 70.00

Soft Paste, Plate, Toddy, Powder Blue, Willow Pattern, Circa 1805, England 11.00

Soft Paste, Sugar, Peafowl, Leeds 130.00

Soft Paste, Sweetmeat, Blue Willow, Leaf Shape 14.00

Souvenir, Album, San Francisco, Philip Fry & Co., Gold Embossed, C.1870 .... 17.50

Souvenir, Album, Seattle, Washington Territory, Printed 1888, Gazzam's 7.00

Souvenir, Ashtray, Century Of Progress, 1933, Copper 2.00

Souvenir, Ashtray, World's Fair, 1939, New York, Brass, 4 1/2 In.Diameter 2.50

Souvenir, Basket, Evansville, Indiana, Gold On White, Germany, 3 3/4 In. 12.50

Souvenir, Bell, Cut Glass, Flowers, World's Fair 1893, Frosted Swirl Handle 65.00

Souvenir, Bell, 1936 German Olympics, White Porcelain, Wooden Base 37.50

Souvenir, Bottle, Chicago, Century Of Progress, 1933 .... 5.00

Souvenir, **Bowl**, Century Of Progress, Chicago, 1933, Bronze 4.95
Souvenir, **Bowl**, Lower Falls, Yellowstone Park, 4 In. 2.75
Souvenir, **Box**, Handkerchief, New York World's Fair, Walnut, Hinged 37.50
Souvenir, **Box**, Trinket, World's Fair, 1893, Filigree, Silver Plate 6.00
Souvenir, **Card**, Trade, Singer, Columbian Exposition, 1893, Set Of 36 In Box 35.00
Souvenir, **Chick & Egg**, Centennial Exhibit, 'Just Out, 'Gillinder, Camphor 35.00
Souvenir, **Creamer**, Aunt Belle, 1910, Colorado, Green, Gold 18.00
Souvenir, **Cup & Saucer**, Bunker Hill Centennial, 1775-1875, Washington 15.00
Souvenir, **Cup & Saucer**, Cohoes, N.Y., Gold Letters, Yellow, Roses 12.00
Souvenir, **Cup & Saucer**, Demitasse, Revere Beach, Mass., Gold In, Scene Out 5.50
Souvenir, **Cup**, Lacy Medallion, Emerald Green With Fold, 3 3/4 In. 22.00
Souvenir, **Cup**, Loving, Niagara Falls, 1905, Insert 65.00
Souvenir, **Dish**, Trinket, Lewis & Clark Expedition, 1905, Cobalt Blue, Gold 23.50
Souvenir, **Fork**, Benricksen & Greenberg, Portland, Ore., Columbia River, Boat 12.50
Souvenir, **Glass**, German Spa, Engraved, Dated 1834 .... 12.50
Souvenir, **Glass**, Champagne, Independence Hall, Rib, Acorns 25.00
Souvenir, **Glass**, Pan American Exposition, 1901, 2 1/2 In.Tall 12.50
Souvenir, **Goblet**, Columbian Exposition, Ring Stem 12.00
Souvenir, **Goblet**, G.A.R., 23rd Encampment, Milwaukee, 1889 .... 22.00
Souvenir, **Handkerchief**, St.Louis Exposition 6.50
Souvenir, **Hat**, Wilken Co.Court House, Breckenridge, Minn., Porcelain 12.00
Souvenir, **Hatchet**, Columbian Exposition, 1893, Vaseline, Libbey Glass Co. 55.00
Souvenir, **Hatpin**, Enameled Gopher, Bankers Convention, Minn., 1914 .... 7.00
Souvenir, **Knife**, Pocket, McKinley Monument & Buffalo, Brass, N.Y., 2 Blades 20.00
Souvenir, **Match Safe & Cigar Cutter**, Pan American Exposition, Buffalo, 1901 .... 20.00
Souvenir, **Medal**, Alaska-Yukon-Pacific Exposition, 1909, Seattle 19.75
Souvenir, **Medal**, B.P.O.E., New Orleans, Dallas, July, 1908, Sterling 12.00
Souvenir, **Mug**, Atlantic City, Drum & Eagle, Gold 11.00
Souvenir, **Mug**, Bayonne Carnival, 1906, Ruby Flashed, Buttons & Arches 10.50
Souvenir, **Mug**, Beer, Hobbs Brockunier Co., Philadelphia, 1876 .... 45.00
Souvenir, **Mug**, Button And Arches, Vida 1903, 31/2 In. 14.00
Souvenir, **Mug**, Columbian Exposition, German China 12.50
Souvenir, **Mug**, Cornell, Class Of 1908, Handled 25.00
Souvenir, **Mug**, Indian Congress, Pan American Exposition, 1901, Carlsbad 20.00
Souvenir, **Mug**, J.M.Peters, 94 Clement St., R.I., Eagle, Aug.3, 1905 .... 25.00
Souvenir, **Mug**, Princeton, 1904, Decennial, 1914, Orange & Blue Bands 25.00
Souvenir, **Mug**, Pueblo, Ruby Flashed 10.00
Souvenir, **Mug**, Shriner's, Atlantic City, 1904, Fish Handle 45.00
Souvenir, **Mug**, Watertown, New York, Button Arches, Ruby, Clear 12.00
Souvenir, **Mug**, Wellington, Kansas, Ruby Flashed, Buttons & Arches 8.50
Souvenir, **Pail**, Lard, Centennial, 1876, Tin, 2 In.High 25.00
Souvenir, **Pennant**, New York Yankees, Uncle Sam On It 3.00
Souvenir, **Picture**, Centennial, Views, Woven Silk, Signed Champromu, Frame 150.00
Souvenir, **Pin**, New York World's Fair, 1939, Red, White, Blue, Levelle & Co. 9.00
Souvenir, **Pincushion**, Slipper, Silver Plate, Washington, D.C. 5.00
Souvenir, **Pipe Holder**, Lake City, Michigan, Coal Scuttle, Ruby Stained Glass 11.00
Souvenir, **Pitcher**, Columbian Exposition, Machinery Building, Germany 10.50
Souvenir, **Pitcher**, Milk, Seattle, 1909, J.A.F.To A.Y.T., Button Arches, Red 35.00
Souvenir, **Pitcher**, Milk, Wychmere Bay, Harwichport, Mass., Porcelain 4.75
Souvenir, **Pitcher**, Niagara Falls, 1907, Red Flashing, Pattern Base 15.00
Souvenir, **Pitcher**, Peru, Nebraska, Red, Clear 13.00
Souvenir, **Pitcher**, Queen Victoria Jubilee, 1887, White Porcelain 25.00
Souvenir, **Pitcher**, Queen Victoria, 5 1/2 In. .... *Illus* 15.00
Souvenir, **Plaque**, Le Petit Palais, Exposition, 1900, Jasper, White On Blue 32.50
Souvenir, **Plate**, B & O Centennial, Thomas Viaduct, 1835, Blue, White 12.00
Souvenir, **Plate**, B.P.O.E. Elks, 1907 Reunion, Stag Center, Scenes, Tin 20.00
Souvenir, **Plate**, Bread, Iowa City, Elaine 59.00
Souvenir, **Plate**, Church, Rockaway, N.J., By Piper, Black & White 10.00
Souvenir, **Plate**, Glass, St.Louis World's Fair, 1904 .... 12.00
Souvenir, **Plate**, Home Of President Taft, Beverly, Mass., Advertisement 6.95
Souvenir, **Plate**, Lehigh University, 20 Year Reunion, June 3rd, 1916 .... 3.50
Souvenir, **Plate**, Natural Bridge, Va., Hand-Painted, 7 In. 3.95
Souvenir, **Plate**, Perry Memorial, Put-In Bay, Ohio, 1813-1913, Green & White 28.00
Souvenir, **Plate**, Salt Lake City, Picture Of Temple, Staffordshire 10.00
Souvenir, **Plate**, Salt Lake City, Utah, Mormon Temple, Eagle Gate, Monument 5.95
Souvenir, **Plate**, St.Louis Cathedral, New Orleans 10.00

Souvenir, Pitcher, Queen Victoria, 5 1/2 In.
See Page 534

Souvenir, Plate, Steamer Juniata Passing Out Of Lock, Sault Ste.Marie	4.75
Souvenir, Plate, West Baden, Ind., Marked Wheelock, Made In Germany	18.00
Souvenir, Plate, World's Fair Chicago 1893, Raised Design, 7 In.Diameter	35.00
Souvenir, Plate, 1939 World's Fair, 7 1/2 In.Diameter	22.50
Souvenir, Platter, Ontario Lake, Scenery, Blue, 18 X 14 In.	50.00
Souvenir, Purse, Change, Columbian Exposition, 1893, Mother-Of-Pearl	24.00
Souvenir, Shot Glass, Yellowstone, Etched With Cut Panels	4.50
Souvenir, Silk Square, Panama Exposition, San Diego, 1916, Buildings	15.00
Souvenir, Silk Square, Panama Pacific Exposition, 1915, Tower Of Jewels	15.00
Souvenir, Silk Square, World's Fair, Chicago 1893, Flag, Scenics	15.00
Souvenir, Spoon, Agricultural Bldg., World's Fair, 1893	2.50
Souvenir, Spoon, Boston, Paul Revere, Spirit Of 1776 In Gold Bowl	9.50
Souvenir, Spoon, Century Of Progress, Chicago Exposition, Court Of States	2.95
Souvenir, Spoon, Century Of Progress, Chicago Exposition, 1933, Gold Finish	3.75
Souvenir, Spoon, Century Of Progress, 1933, Science Court	3.50
Souvenir, Spoon, Columbian Exposition, Demitasse	18.50
Souvenir, Spoon, Copper, G.A.R.Encampment, Louisville, 1895, Cabin, Cannons	3.95
Souvenir, Spoon, Copper, Valdez, Alaska, Yukon Gold Fields, Engraved Bowl	12.00
Souvenir, Spoon, Machinery Hall, World's Fair, 1893	2.50
Souvenir, Spoon, Mae Murray	3.75
Souvenir, Spoon, Norma Shearer	3.75 To 8.00
Souvenir, Spoon, Queen Victoria	7.50
Souvenir, Spoon, Silver Plate, Adams	4.00
Souvenir, Spoon, Silver Plate, Admiral George Dewey, Standard	4.50
Souvenir, Spoon, Silver Plate, Bry's, Memphis, U.S.Silver Co.	4.50
Souvenir, Spoon, Silver Plate, Buffalo Hotel	4.00
Souvenir, Spoon, Silver Plate, Columbian Exposition	2.75
Souvenir, Spoon, Silver Plate, Dewey, Manila, 1898, Reverse Flag	4.00
Souvenir, Spoon, Silver Plate, Douglas Fairbanks, Oneida Community	6.00
Souvenir, Spoon, Silver Plate, Flower, Crab On Back, Rogers, 1847	4.50
Souvenir, Spoon, Silver Plate, Gerber Baby	3.00
Souvenir, Spoon, Silver Plate, Gloria Swanson, Oneida Community	3.50 To 8.00
Souvenir, Spoon, Silver Plate, Jefferson	4.00
Souvenir, Spoon, Silver Plate, Las Vegas Cowboy	1.00
Souvenir, Spoon, Silver Plate, Lois Wilson	3.50
Souvenir, Spoon, Silver Plate, Marion Davies, Oneida Community	3.50 To 6.00
Souvenir, Spoon, Silver Plate, Mary Pickford, Oneida Community	3.50 To 7.00
Souvenir, Spoon, Silver Plate, Mol Neurroy, Oneida Community	6.00
Souvenir, Spoon, Silver Plate, Monroe	4.00
Souvenir, Spoon, Silver Plate, Norma Talmadge, Oneida Community	3.75 To 8.00
Souvenir, Spoon, Silver Plate, Pinocchio	4.00
Souvenir, Spoon, Silver Plate, Pola Negri, Oneida Community	6.00
Souvenir, Spoon, Silver Plate, Ramon Navarro, Oneida Community	6.00 To 8.00
Souvenir, Spoon, Silver Plate, Richard Dix, Oneida Community	6.00
Souvenir, Spoon, Silver Plate, Roger Williams, Enameled, Twisted Handle	6.00
Souvenir, Spoon, Silver Plate, Skyline Of New York City	11.00

Souvenir, Spoon, Silver Plate, St.Louis Bridge In Bowl 3.50
Souvenir, Spoon, Silver Plate, Thomas Meighan, Oneida Community .... 3.75 To 6.00
Souvenir, Spoon, Silver Plate, White City, 1881, Rogers 4.50
Souvenir, Spoon, Silver Plate, World's Fair, 1893, Women's Building 2.75
Souvenir, Spoon, Sterling Silver, Albany, N.Y., Capitol Bldg., Demitasse 7.50
Souvenir, Spoon, Sterling Silver, Albuquerque, N.M., Alvarado Hotel 7.50
Souvenir, Spoon, Sterling Silver, Atlanta, Ill., June 30, 1892 .... 4.50
Souvenir, Spoon, Sterling Silver, Battle Of Lookout Mountain, Generals 9.50
Souvenir, Spoon, Sterling Silver, Boardwalk, Atlantic City, Fish Handle 9.50
Souvenir, Spoon, Sterling Silver, Brooklyn, N.Y., Views, Demitasse 9.50
Souvenir, Spoon, Sterling Silver, Catalina Island, Calif., Gold Wash Bowl 7.50
Souvenir, Spoon, Sterling Silver, Chicago World's Fair, 1893, Demitasse 8.00
Souvenir, Spoon, Sterling Silver, Chicago World's Fair, 1893, Indian Head 8.50
Souvenir, Spoon, Sterling Silver, Chicago, 1960 .... 8.00
Souvenir, Spoon, Sterling Silver, Christmas, Dated Dec.25, 1895, 6 .... 48.00
Souvenir, Spoon, Sterling Silver, Clinton, N.D. 5.00
Souvenir, Spoon, Sterling Silver, Coffee, English, Gun Club 5.50
Souvenir, Spoon, Sterling Silver, Colorado, Views, Demitasse 7.50
Souvenir, Spoon, Sterling Silver, Columbian Exposition, Chicago, 1893 .... 6.00
Souvenir, Spoon, Sterling Silver, Denver 6.00
Souvenir, Spoon, Sterling Silver, Des Moines, Iowa .... 8.50 To 10.00
Souvenir, Spoon, Sterling Silver, Detroit, Full Form Indian 8.50
Souvenir, Spoon, Sterling Silver, Ely, Minn. 5.00
Souvenir, Spoon, Sterling Silver, Embossed World's Fair & Ship 7.00
Souvenir, Spoon, Sterling Silver, Enameled 8.50
Souvenir, Spoon, Sterling Silver, Flatiron Building 7.00
Souvenir, Spoon, Sterling Silver, Florida 14.00
Souvenir, Spoon, Sterling Silver, Fort Sumpter 6.00
Souvenir, Spoon, Sterling Silver, Frankfort, Ky., State Monument 6.00
Souvenir, Spoon, Sterling Silver, Full Figure Girl Handle, Wears Cap & Gown 20.00
Souvenir, Spoon, Sterling Silver, Full Figure Of Statue Of Liberty Handle 14.00
Souvenir, Spoon, Sterling Silver, Grand Rapids, Mich. 5.00
Souvenir, Spoon, Sterling Silver, High Rock Spring, Saratoga, N.Y. 5.00
Souvenir, Spoon, Sterling Silver, Horticultural, Chicago, 1492-1892 .... 7.00
Souvenir, Spoon, Sterling Silver, Hot Springs, Va. 8.50
Souvenir, Spoon, Sterling Silver, Hudson River, Washington Irving Ship 7.50
Souvenir, Spoon, Sterling Silver, Idaho, Miners, Gold Wash Bowl 9.00
Souvenir, Spoon, Sterling Silver, Indian Handle, Saranac Lake, N.Y. 15.00
Souvenir, Spoon, Sterling Silver, Indiana 12.00
Souvenir, Spoon, Sterling Silver, Iowa 10.00
Souvenir, Spoon, Sterling Silver, Lafayette, Ind. 6.00
Souvenir, Spoon, Sterling Silver, Lansing, Michigan, New Auditorium 7.00
Souvenir, Spoon, Sterling Silver, Lewis & Clark 12.00
Souvenir, Spoon, Sterling Silver, Lick Observatory, California 6.00
Souvenir, Spoon, Sterling Silver, Lincoln, Nebraska, Capitol Building 6.50
Souvenir, Spoon, Sterling Silver, Los Angeles, California 12.00
Souvenir, Spoon, Sterling Silver, Louisiana, Eagle 6.50
Souvenir, Spoon, Sterling Silver, McKinley Memorial 9.50
Souvenir, Spoon, Sterling Silver, Memphis, Tenn., Demitasse 6.00
Souvenir, Spoon, Sterling Silver, Michigan 6.00
Souvenir, Spoon, Sterling Silver, Milwaukee 5.00
Souvenir, Spoon, Sterling Silver, Miner Handle, Struck It At Last, Michigan 20.00
Souvenir, Spoon, Sterling Silver, Minneapolis 6.00
Souvenir, Spoon, Sterling Silver, Mission San Jose, San Antonio 9.00
Souvenir, Spoon, Sterling Silver, Montreal, Enameled, Engraved 7.50
Souvenir, Spoon, Sterling Silver, New York City, Woolworth Bldg., Demitasse 6.00
Souvenir, Spoon, Sterling Silver, New York, Good Luck & Swastika 8.50
Souvenir, Spoon, Sterling Silver, Newburg, George Washington 12.00
Souvenir, Spoon, Sterling Silver, Newport, Old Stone Mill 6.00
Souvenir, Spoon, Sterling Silver, Niagara Falls 12.00
Souvenir, Spoon, Sterling Silver, Niagara Falls, Demitasse, Maple Leaf 8.00
Souvenir, Spoon, Sterling Silver, Niagara Falls, Indian 6.50
Souvenir, Spoon, Sterling Silver, North Platte, Neb., Cowboy Roping Steer 7.00
Souvenir, Spoon, Sterling Silver, Omaha 6.00
Souvenir, Spoon, Sterling Silver, Ostrich Farm, Utah, Demitasse 5.00
Souvenir, Spoon, Sterling Silver, Pan American Expo., 1901 .... 10.00 To 22.00

Souvenir, Spoon, Sterling Silver, Panama Pacific Exposition 8.50
Souvenir, Spoon, Sterling Silver, Parkersburg, W.Va., Cutout Scene 7.00
Souvenir, Spoon, Sterling Silver, Pasadena, Bear 8.00
Souvenir, Spoon, Sterling Silver, Philadelphia, Independence Hall 12.00
Souvenir, Spoon, Sterling Silver, Prince Edward Isle, Demitasse 7.00
Souvenir, Spoon, Sterling Silver, Riverside, Calif. 5.00
Souvenir, Spoon, Sterling Silver, San Diego City & Bay, 1910 .... 10.50
Souvenir, Spoon, Sterling Silver, San Francisco, 1915 .... 8.50
Souvenir, Spoon, Sterling Silver, Sioux City, Iowa, Ornate Raised Work 8.50
Souvenir, Spoon, Sterling Silver, Somerville, Mass., Powder House 6.50
Souvenir, Spoon, Sterling Silver, St.Louis Fair, Engraved Handle & Bowl 10.00
Souvenir, Spoon, Sterling Silver, St.Louis World's Fair, 1904 .... 10.00
Souvenir, Spoon, Sterling Silver, Temple, Mormon Angel, Salt Lake City 22.50
Souvenir, Spoon, Sterling Silver, Texas, Embossed Steer & Star 10.00
Souvenir, Spoon, Sterling Silver, The Alamo, Texas, Enameled Bowl 15.00
Souvenir, Spoon, Sterling Silver, Toronto, Enameled, Engraved 7.50
Souvenir, Spoon, Sterling Silver, Watertown, N.Y., Fish On Handle 4.50
Souvenir, Spoon, Sterling Silver, Wisconsin 6.00
Souvenir, Spoon, Sterling Silver, World's Fair, 1893, Gold Wash, Monogram 7.00
Souvenir, Spoon, Sterling Silver, Yellowstone, Bison Head, Elk In Bowl 13.50
Souvenir, Stickpin, St.Louis Centennial, 1909 .... 7.00
Souvenir, Tape Measure, Bend Oregon, Celluloid 3.00
Souvenir, Tapestry, Spirit Of St.Louis, Portrait, France ....65.00 To 100.00
Souvenir, Tie Clasp, Century Of Progress Expo., Chicago 1933 .... 2.75
Souvenir, Toothpick, N.Y.State Fair, 1908, Pitcher Shape, Ruby Flashed 12.00
Souvenir, Toothpick, Waldorf, Minn., Red With Clear Daisy & Button 16.00
Souvenir, Toothpick, World's Fair, 1893, King's Crown, Ruby Flashed 13.50
Souvenir, Toothpick, 100th Anniversary Wheeling, W.Va., The Stogie City 18.00
Souvenir, Torch, Fireplace, Centennial, Tin, Handle & Plunger, Label 8.00
Souvenir, Tray, Independence Hall, Liberty Bell, & City Hall, 1776-1926 .... 16.00
Souvenir, Tray, Omaha Exposition, 1898, Pewter 9.50
Souvenir, Tray, Pan American Exposition, 1901, Buffalo, Silver Plate, 5 In. 12.50
Souvenir, Tray, Pin, Hay Springs, Nebraska, Ruby Flashed, Gold Edge 7.00
Souvenir, Tray, St.Louis World's Fair, 1904, Aluminum, Scene, Have A Look 3.95
Souvenir, Tray, Washington, D.C., Scenes, 10 In. 25.00
Souvenir, Tray, World's Fair 1904, St.Louis, Four Children, Aluminum, Germany 3.75
Souvenir, Tumbler, Button And Arches, State Fair 1906, Mother 18.00
Souvenir, Tumbler, California, Metal, 3 1/2 In. 8.50
Souvenir, Tumbler, Columbia Exposition, Administration Bldg., Clear, Etched 14.00
Souvenir, Tumbler, Columbia Exposition, Woman's Bldg., Clear, Etched 14.00
Souvenir, Tumbler, Mason City, Iowa, Clambroth Arches, 2 Button 20.00
Souvenir, Tumbler, Omaha Exposition, 1898, Child's Size, Green, Gold 7.00
Souvenir, Tumbler, Pan American Exposition, 1898, Child's Size, Green, Gold 7.00
Souvenir, Tumbler, Texas Centennial, 1936, Cobalt 6.50
Souvenir, Tumbler, 1893 Exposition, Etched 18.00
Souvenir, Vase, Bewdley, Locke Worcester, 3 In. 12.50

*Spangle Glass is multicolored glass made from odds and ends of colored
glass rods. It includes metallic flakes of mica covered with gold, silver,
nickel, or cooper. Spangle Glass is usually cased glass with a thin layer
of clear glass over the multicolored layer.*
Spangle Glass, Basket, Yellow Gold, Cased, White Interior, Gold Flakes 175.00
Spangle Glass, Box, Trinket, Rainbow Colors, White Lining, Blown 24.00
Spangle Glass, Hat, Blown 36.00
Spangle Glass, Pitcher, Blue, 5 In.High 175.00
Spangle Glass, Pitcher, Hobbs, Brockunier, Silver Blue Mica, Clear, C.1884 .... 125.00
Spangle Glass, Rose Bowl, Pink With Deep Maroon Splotches 97.50
Spangle Glass, Rose Bowl, Red & White, Enameled Blue Flowers & Gold Leaf 75.00
Spangle Glass, Vase, Deep Rose, Brown, Crimped Top, 5 1/2 In. 50.00
Spangle Glass, Vase, Yellow, Pink, Clear, Silver Mica, Ruffled, 4 1/2 In., Pair 75.00

*Spanish Lace is a Victorian glass pattern that seems to have white lace
on a colored background. Blue, yellow, cranberry, and clear glass was made with
this distinctive white pattern.*
Spanish Lace, Basket, Bride's, Blue 125.00
Spanish Lace, Bowl, Bride's, Green Opalescent, Frilled Edge 32.00

Spanish Lace, Bowl, Clear & Opalescent 45.00
Spanish Lace, Cruet, Blue & White, Bulbous, Stopper 95.00
Spanish Lace, Cruet, Cranberry, Clear Handle, Blown Stopper 65.00
Spanish Lace, Cruet, Opalescent, Ruffled Top, Vaseline, 6 1/2 In.High 22.50
Spanish Lace, Cruet, Opalescent, Trefoil Lip, Opalescent Teardrop Stopper 45.00
Spanish Lace, Pitcher, Cranberry & Opalescent, 10 In.High 67.50
Spanish Lace, Pitcher, Green, Ruffled Edge, Applied Handle, 10 In. 65.00
Spanish Lace, Rose Bowl 30.00
Spanish Lace, Rose Bowl, Canary Opalescent, Fluted 55.00
Spanish Lace, Sugar & Creamer, Blue, Gold Tones 90.00
Spanish Lace, Sugar Shaker, Blue Opalescent 48.00
Spanish Lace, Sugar Shaker, Opalescent 55.00
Spanish Lace, Tumbler, Blue .... 22.50 To 24.00
Spanish Lace, Tumbler, Blue, Opalescent 20.00
Spanish Lace, Tumbler, Pink 28.00
Spanish Lace, Vase, Blue, Translucent, Crimped Rim, Clear Edge, 6 1/4 In. 35.00
Spanish Lace, Vase, Opalescent Blue, Ruffled, Turned Down Top, 6 1/2 In. 45.00

Spatter Glass is a multicolored glass made from many small pieces of
different colored glass.
Spatter Glass, Basket, Cased, White Lining, Applied Thorn Handle 55.00
Spatter Glass, Bottle, Cased, Crystal Stopper, Lined White, Ringed Body 35.00
Spatter Glass, Bottle, Pink, Swirls, Clear Cased, Blown Stopper, 11 1/2 In. 45.00
Spatter Glass, Bowl, Fruit, Pink & White, Ruffled Rim 65.00
Spatter Glass, Bowl, Star & Sunburst 125.00
Spatter Glass, Candlestick, Blue & White Rings, 9 1/2 In.Tall, Pair 40.00
Spatter Glass, Castor, Pickle, Footed Frame 75.00
Spatter Glass, Cologne, Marked Ricksicker's Sweet Clover, In Gold, Clear 35.00
Spatter Glass, Cruet, Cranberry, White, Clear Cut Stopper, Reed Handle 47.50
Spatter Glass, Ewer, End Of Day, Reds And White, Ruffled, Handle 38.00
Spatter Glass, Pitcher, Pink, Clear Pedestal Foot & Applied Handle, Signed 25.00
Spatter Glass, Pitcher, Pink, White, Inverted Thumbprint, Ruffled Square Rim 85.00
Spatter Glass, Pitcher, Rainbow, 4 1/2 In. 165.00
Spatter Glass, Pitcher, Water, Orange & White 65.00
Spatter Glass, Pitcher, Water, Red, White, Green, Pontil, Clear Handle 125.00
Spatter Glass, Plate, Red In Center, Blue Edge, Penna.Dutch, 9 In.Diameter 60.00
Spatter Glass, Rose Bowl, Bulbous Base, Pinched Sides, Cranberry & White 42.00
Spatter Glass, Rose Bowl, Pink, Blue 25.00
Spatter Glass, Salt & Pepper, Pink, Cranberry, White 27.50
Spatter Glass, Sugar Shaker, Cabbage Rose Shape, Pink & Yellow Shades 75.00
Spatter Glass, Tumbler, Inverted Thumbprint, Cranberry, Clear & White 15.00
Spatter Glass, Vase, Cased Rainbow, White Lining, Scalloped Top 78.00
Spatter Glass, Vase, Cased, Fluted Rim, Variegated Colors, 10 In.High 45.00
Spatter Glass, Vase, Gold Rim, 6 1/2 In.High 21.00
Spatter Glass, Vase, Pinched Sides, Sterling Top, England 38.00
Spatter Glass, Vase, Pink, White, Cased, Clear Applied Handles, Pair 50.00
Spatter Glass, Vase, Red To Rose, Green, Clear Ruffle, Cased, Rough Pontil 35.00
Spatter Glass, Vase, White Cased, Multicolor, 6 1/2 In.High 38.00
Spatter Glass, Washstand Set, 2 Piece 70.00

Spatterware is a creamware or soft-paste dinnerware decorated with spatter
designs. The earliest pieces were made during the late eighteenth century,
but most of the wares found today were made from 1800 to 1850. The
Spatterware dishes were made in the Staffordshire District of England
for sale on the American market.
Spatterware, Bowl, Soup, Green, American Eagle, C.1820 .... *Illus* 150.00
Spatterware, Bowl, Unglazed, Glazed Inside, Inside Border, Red, 9 1/4 In. 90.00
Spatterware, Creamer, Green, 3 1/2 In. 145.00
Spatterware, Creamer, Rainbow 110.00
Spatterware, Creamer, Rooster, Blue, 3 1/2 In. 32.50
Spatterware, Creamer, Rose, Purple & Blue, 3 1/2 In. 110.00
Spatterware, Cup & Saucer, Bull's-Eye 110.00
Spatterware, Cup & Saucer, Peafowl, Lavender 95.00
Spatterware, Cup & Saucer, Peafowl, Red 125.00
Spatterware, Cup & Saucer, Rose, Blue 135.00
Spatterware, Cup & Saucer, Tulip 150.00

Spatterware, Cup, Handleless, Adams	15.00
Spatterware, Cup, Handleless, Peafowl Decoration, Green	75.00
Spatterware, Pitcher, Blue, 4 In.	55.00
Spatterware, Pitcher, Brown On Yellow, Plain Handle, 7 1/4 In.High	27.50
Spatterware, Plate, House & Tree Center In Pink & Green, Blue Border	185.00
Spatterware, Plate, Old Fort Design, Blue Band, 7 1/2 In.Diameter	110.00
Spatterware, Plate, Peafowl Center, Blue, Tooled Edge, 8 1/2 In.Diameter	135.00
Spatterware, Plate, Peafowl Decoration, Red, 8 1/4 In.Diameter	150.00
Spatterware, Plate, Peafowl With Green Belly, 8 3/8 In.	125.00
Spatterware, Plate, Peafowl, Blue, 9 In.	90.00
Spatterware, Plate, Peafowl, Purple Allover Design, 8 1/4 In.Diameter	300.00
Spatterware, Plate, Peafowl, Red Border, 8 1/2 In.Diameter	45.00
Spatterware, Plate, Pennsylvania Dutch, Cock In Center, Signed A.Over W.	185.00
Spatterware, Plate, Port Noeuf, Red, Green *Illus*	38.00
Spatterware, Plate, Rainbow, 8 1/2 In.	100.00
Spatterware, Plate, Red, Green Belly Peafowl	125.00
Spatterware, Plate, Star Of Bethlehem Center, Blue, Octagonal	50.00
Spatterware, Plate, Stick Decoration, Blue Circles, Green Stars, 8 3/4 In.	40.00
Spatterware, Plate, White Star Pattern, Blue, 10 In.	20.00
Spatterware, Platter, Rectangular, Blue, Cut Corners, 12 X 15 1/2 In.	80.00
Spatterware, Platter, Red & Purple, 13 1/2 In.	225.00
Spatterware, Saucer, Peafowl Center, Red *Illus*	175.00

Spatterware, Dish, Soup, Green,
American Eagle, C.1820
See Page 538

Spatterware, Plate,
Port Noeuf, Red, Green

Spatterware, Saucer,
Peafowl Center, Red

Spatterware, Sugar & Stand, Covered, Black & Lilac Striping, C.1850	60.00
Spatterware, Sugar Sifter, Pink & White	47.50 To 50.00
Spatterware, Sugar Sifter, Pink, White, Pear Shape	45.00
Spatterware, Sugar, Blue, Red Rose, Green Leaves, Open Handles, C.1820	50.00
Spatterware, Sugar, Cluster Of Buds	110.00
Spatterware, Sugar, Covered, Adams	60.00
Spatterware, Sugar, Covered, Cock's Comb Pattern, Blue	120.00
Spatterware, Sugar, Covered, Octagonal, Red & Blue, 2 Blossoms, C.1850	110.00
Spatterware, Sugar, Covered, Plain, Blue	100.00
Spatterware, Sugar, Covered, Rainbow	70.00

Spatterware, Teapot, Peafowl, Blue 100.00
Spatterware, Toothpick, Pink, White, Frosted, Pleated Ribs At Base, Barrel 37.50
  Spinning Wheel, see Tool, Spinning Wheel
Spittoon, Black Ground, Raised Beige Flowers, Weller-Like, No Mark 35.00
Spittoon, Brass, Copper Bottom, Two Ornate Brass Handles, Circa 1850 .... 65.00
Spittoon, Brass, 4 1/2 In.High, 7 1/2 In.Diameter 15.00
Spittoon, Brass, 8 X 5 1/2 In. 18.00
Spittoon, Figural, Turtle, Step On Head, Back Lifts To Reveal Spittoon 35.00
Spittoon, Green Ground, Roses, Porcelain, Taylor, Smith, Taylor Mark 45.00
Spittoon, Hammered Sides, Three Legs, Brass 27.50
Spittoon, Iron, 8 1/2 X 5 1/2 In. 13.00
Spittoon, Lady's, Blue Opalescent Glass 22.00
Spittoon, Lady's, Blue, English, Richardson Glass, C.1860, Pair 90.00
Spittoon, Lady's, White Porcelain, Pink And Red Rose, Germany 45.00
Spittoon, Red & Black Swirl, Ironstone, Circa 1900 .... 65.00
Spittoon, White Enamel On Metal, Blue Enamel At Rim Base, C.1910 .... 12.50
Spittoon, White Pottery, Blue Stripes 15.00

Spode Pottery, Porcelain, and Bone China were made by the Stoke-on-Trent Factory of England founded by Josiah Spode about 1770. The firm became Copeland and Garrett from 1833 to 1847, then W.T.Copeland or W.T.Copeland and Sons until the present time. The word spode appears on many pieces made by the Copeland Factory. Most antique dealers include all the wares under the more familiar name of Spode.

Spode, see also Copeland
Spode, Basket, Fruit, Pierced, Blue Willow, Circa 1830, Handle, 8 X 6 In. 75.00
Spode, Bowl, Soup, Cowslip, Copeland, England 3.50
Spode, Bust, Churchill, 7 1/2 In.Tall 50.00
Spode, Cup & Saucer, Cobalt, Floral 60.00
Spode, Cup & Saucer, Cobalt, White & Gold Floral, Enameled Reserves, 1810 .... 75.00
Spode, Mold, Pudding, Creamware, Pineapple, Incised Mark 25.00
Spode, Plate, Armorial, Blue & Gold Floral, Coat Of Arms, Motto, 10 In. 45.00
Spode, Plate, Blue, Portland Vase In Center, Red Roses In Vase, Copeland 25.00
Spode, Plate, Cutty Sark, 1969 .... 25.00
Spode, Plate, Luncheon, Gold Band, Cobalt Band, Ovington Bros., Set Of 12 .... 250.00
Spode, Plate, Ruins, Flow Blue, C.1848, 12 In. 30.00
Spode, Platter, Bird, Tree, Chelsea, 10 X 14 In. 15.00
Spode, Platter, Mandarin 25.00
Spode, Platter, Meat, Blue Oriental Design, 20 In. 45.00
Spode, Tea & Coffee Set, Lilac, Iron, & Gilt Floral, No.889, C.1810, 48 Piece 550.00
Spode, Tea Set, Imari Colors, Circa 1800, Blue Printed Mark, 16 Piece 425.00
Spode, Tea Set, Japan Pattern, Iron, Blue, & Gilt, No.1409, C.1808, 36 Piece 800.00
Spode, Vase, Spill, Gray Ground, White Floral, England, 3 1/2 In.High 5.00

Spongeware is very similar to Spatterware in appearance. The designs were applied to the ware by daubing the color. Many dealers do not differentiate between the two wares and use the names interchangeably.

Spongeware, Bowl, Blue & White, 10 3/4 X 4 In. 40.00
Spongeware, Bowl, Blue & White, 12 X 7 In.Diameter 48.50
Spongeware, Bowl, Blue Design On Gray, 4 3/4 In.High 45.00
Spongeware, Bowl, Blue, White, Flat Rim, Bulbous, 5 X 9 In.Diameter 40.00
Spongeware, Bowl, Cream Ground, Brown & Green Decoration, 10 In. 35.00
Spongeware, Cup & Saucer, Farmer Scene, Blue, White 45.00
Spongeware, Dish, Soap, Blue & White 25.00
Spongeware, Pitcher, Blue & White, 9 In. 40.00
Spongeware, Pitcher, Blue Design On Gray, 8 3/4 In.High 30.00
Spongeware, Pitcher, Blue, 8 1/2 In.High 45.00
Spongeware, Pitcher, Milk, Blue & White, Tankard, 2 Quart 45.00
Spongeware, Plate, Blue & White, 7 In. 12.00
Spongeware, Plate, Blue & White, 9 In. 22.00
Spongeware, Plate, Blue, Raised Border Design, 9 In. 20.00
Spongeware, Plate, Dessert, Blue, Octagonal, 5 In. 20.00
Spongeware, Spittoon, Brown & Blue 35.00
Spongeware, Spittoon, Green & White, Gold Trim 25.00
Spongeware, Wash Basin, Blue 55.00
Spongeware, Water Filter, Blue, Nashville, 3 Piece 150.00

St.Louis, Box, Cameo, Flowers, Cranberry, Vaseline, Signed, 4 In.Diameter 125.00
St.Louis, Vase, Twisted Pink & Green Ribbons & Latticinio Strands 160.00

*Staffordshire is a district in England where pottery and porcelain have
been made since the 1900s. Thousands of types of pottery and porcelain have
been made in the hundreds of factories that worked in the area. Some of the
most famous factories have been listed separately. See Royal Doulton,
Royal Worcester, Spode, Wedgwood, and others.*

Staffordshire, see also Flow Blue
Staffordshire, Inkwell, see also Inkwell
Staffordshire Type, Font, Holy Water, Wall, Easter Lilies, Christ On Cross 6.75
Staffordshire, Bank, Figural, Dog's Head, White, Black, Gold Lock 20.00
Staffordshire, Bank, Puppy, Slot For Pennies, 2 X 1 1/2 In. 22.50
Staffordshire, Bell, Toby, English Chambermaid, 3 In. 25.00
Staffordshire, Bonbonniere, Egg Shape, Enameled Floral, Gilt, C.1770 .... 125.00
Staffordshire, Bowl, Chowder, Oriental Pattern, Blue & White, Gold, Marked 6.50
Staffordshire, Bowl, Dark Blue, Flower & Leaf Design, Flared, Footed 30.00
Staffordshire, Bowl, Dr.Syntax Series, Blue, 8 Sided 150.00
Staffordshire, Bowl, Fruit, Woven Pattern, Pink Roses, Pedestal Base 41.50
Staffordshire, Bowl, Fruit, Woven, Roses, Pedestal Base, Pink Handles 37.50
Staffordshire, Bowl, Soup, Florentine, Mayer, 10 In.Diameter 10.00
Staffordshire, Bowl, Vegetable, A Winter View Of Pittsfleld 275.00
Staffordshire, Bowl, Vegetable, Covered, Carolina, Pink, Pierced Handles 48.50
Staffordshire, Bowl, Vegetable, Military Academy, West Point, Wood 150.00
Staffordshire, Box, Match Or Pin, Oblong 2 X 3 1/4 X 4 1/2 In.Tall 18.00
Staffordshire, Box, Patch, Baby Reclining 85.00
Staffordshire, Box, Pin, Oval, Child In Pink Dress, Fruit, Oval 16.00
Staffordshire, Box, Red Riding Hood & Wolf 15.00
Staffordshire, Box, Roses 25.00
Staffordshire, Box, Trinket, Alice In Looking Glass 25.00
Staffordshire, Box, Trinket, Babies Sitting On Jester's Shoulders 27.50
Staffordshire, Box, Trinket, Boy, Dog 30.00
Staffordshire, Box, Trinket, Child Fallen Asleep In High Chair 30.00
Staffordshire, Box, Trinket, Crown & Sword On Table 10.00
Staffordshire, Box, Trinket, Girl At Spinet 38.00
Staffordshire, Box, Trinket, Girl, Blonde Hair, Holds Bunnies 50.00
Staffordshire, Box, Trinket, Hand On Lid 33.50
Staffordshire, Box, Trinket, Raised White Floral, Boy, Trumpet, Toy Dog 110.00
Staffordshire, Box, Trinket, Washington Standing Beside Horse, White, Gilt 32.00
Staffordshire, Box, Trinket, 4 In. .... *Illus* 35.00
Staffordshire, Can & Saucer, Coffee, Gros Bleu Border, Gilt Scrolls, C.1820 .... 12.50
Staffordshire, Candlestick, Classical Maiden, Ralph Wood Type, C.1770, Pair 150.00
Staffordshire, Coffeepot, Miniature, Pearlware, Lighthouse, Man & Camel, 1810 .... 90.00
Staffordshire, Creamer, Yuan Pattern, White With Blue, Wood & Sons 18.00
Staffordshire, Cup & Saucer, Bands Of Puce & Iron Garlands, Gold, C.1820 .... 13.50
Staffordshire, Cup & Saucer, Basket Of Flowers, Ephraim Wood, 1815 .... 60.00
Staffordshire, Cup & Saucer, Blue & White, Oriental Pattern 32.50
Staffordshire, Cup & Saucer, Blue, Wadsworth Tower, Wood's 155.00

Staffordshire, Box, Trinket, 4 In.

Staffordshire, Cup & Saucer, Blue, Washington At Tomb, Wood 200.00
Staffordshire, Cup & Saucer, Child's, Little Girl, Boy, Scenes 12.00
Staffordshire, Cup & Saucer, Dark Blue, Pair Of Birds 55.00
Staffordshire, Cup & Saucer, Demitasse, Handleless, Brown & Green 25.00
Staffordshire, Cup & Saucer, Floral, Gilt, Blue Bands, Vines, C.1820 .... 13.50
Staffordshire, Cup & Saucer, Handleless, Athens, Mulberry, W.Adams & Sons 30.00
Staffordshire, Cup & Saucer, Handleless, Deep Blue, Cottage Scene 27.50
Staffordshire, Cup & Saucer, Handleless, Jeddo, Mulberry, W.Adams & Sons 35.00
Staffordshire, Cup & Saucer, Handleless, Loretta, Mulberry, Alcock, 1830-59 .... 35.00
Staffordshire, Cup & Saucer, Handleless, Wm.Adams & Son, Registry Mark 1849 .... 30.00
Staffordshire, Cup & Saucer, Lafayette At Franklin's Tomb, Blue 155.00
Staffordshire, Cup & Saucer, Pink, Rose & Bird Pattern, Circa 1840 .... 25.00
Staffordshire, Cup & Saucer, White, Rose Decoration, Signed 3.50
Staffordshire, Cup Plate, Battery, New York, Trefoil Border 65.00
Staffordshire, Cup Plate, Black, White, Church, Lake, Trees, Man, Woman, Mark 13.50
Staffordshire, Cup Plate, Brown, Chinese Fountain 28.00
Staffordshire, Cup Plate, Cadmus, Trefoil Border 55.00
Staffordshire, Cup Plate, Carmine To Pink, Scenic Center, Castles, Ruins 12.50
Staffordshire, Cup Plate, Dark Blue, English Scene, Broadlands 37.50
Staffordshire, Cup Plate, Dark Blue, Lagrange Residence Of Lafayette 60.00
Staffordshire, Cup Plate, Dark Brown, Scene & Franklin Proverbs 30.00
Staffordshire, Cup Plate, Grecian Scenery, Circa 1830 .... 15.00
Staffordshire, Cup Plate, Scene, Woman Stands In Woods, Reg.Mark 1848 .... 12.00
Staffordshire, Cup Plate, Sprig Design, Green, Lavender, Marked, C.1840 .... 19.00
Staffordshire, Cup Plate, Transfer, Blue, Pompeii, Urn, Flower, J.& G.Alcock 12.00
Staffordshire, Dish, Cheese, White & Blue, English Scene 13.00
Staffordshire, Dish, Duck Cover, On Nest, 7 1/2 In.Long 110.00
Staffordshire, Dish, Hen Cover 150.00
Staffordshire, Dish, Hen Cover, Black To Gray, Weaved Base, Green Nest, Eggs 95.00
Staffordshire, Dish, Hen Cover, C.1871, 7 In. 135.00
Staffordshire, Dish, Hen Cover, On Nest, 5 Colors, 6 X 7 1/2 In. 97.50
Staffordshire, Dish, Hen Cover, 8 In.High .... *Illus* 115.00
Staffordshire, Dish, Sitting Hen Cover, R.I.Red Hen With 7 Chicks 40.00
Staffordshire, Figurine, Cat, Pair 135.00
Staffordshire, Figurine, Cat, Sits On Cobalt Cushion, 7 1/2 In.High, Pair 95.00
Staffordshire, Figurine, Cat, Sitting, Spatter Decorated 55.00
Staffordshire, Figurine, Cat, White, Green & Red Hearts, Green Eyes 45.00
Staffordshire, Figurine, Child, Basket Of Flowers, By Child, 18th Century 85.00
Staffordshire, Figurine, Cobbler, Woman, Jobson & Nell, Pair 150.00
Staffordshire, Figurine, Deer, White, Black, Gold, 14 In. 35.00
Staffordshire, Figurine, Dog, Copper Luster Spots 37.50
Staffordshire, Figurine, Dog, Copper Luster Trim, Front Legs Separate, Pair 100.00
Staffordshire, Figurine, Dog, Glass Eyes 65.00
Staffordshire, Figurine, Dog, Orange Muzzle, Black Eyes, 12 1/2 In.High 55.00
Staffordshire, Figurine, Dog, Sitting, 10 In.High 75.00
Staffordshire, Figurine, Dog, Standing 125.00
Staffordshire, Figurine, Dog, White, Black Face, 9 In.High, Pair 46.00
Staffordshire, Figurine, Dog, White, Brown Chain, 10 In., Pair 32.00
Staffordshire, Figurine, Dog, White, Copper Luster Decoration, 9 In., Pair 69.00
Staffordshire, Figurine, Four Seasons, C.1800, 7 3/4 In.High, Set Of 4 .... 325.00
Staffordshire, Figurine, General Sir Colin Campbell, On Horse 75.00
Staffordshire, Figurine, George Washington, 1800s .... *Illus* 450.00
Staffordshire, Figurine, Girl & Boy & Goat, Blue, Green 45.00
Staffordshire, Figurine, Jack, Jill, Pair 100.00
Staffordshire, Figurine, King & Queen Of Sardinia, Dalmation, 13 1/2 In. 75.00
Staffordshire, Figurine, Lamb, 3 In.High, 4 In.Long 12.00
Staffordshire, Figurine, Lion, Paw On Ball, Green Plinth, 1800 .... 245.00
Staffordshire, Figurine, Lovers Sitting In Bower, Scottish Costumes 35.00
Staffordshire, Figurine, Man Holding Grapes 22.00
Staffordshire, Figurine, Man In Kilts, Woman In Long Pleated Dress 40.00
Staffordshire, Figurine, Pair Collies, Rust & Gold, Glass Eyes, 10 In.High 65.00
Staffordshire, Figurine, Pair Dogs Sitting, Red Spots On White Coats, 7 In. 55.00
Staffordshire, Figurine, Poodle, Flower Basket In Mouth, Pen Holder On Base 50.00
Staffordshire, Figurine, Prince Of Wales, Marked, 18 In.High 50.00
Staffordshire, Figurine, Queen Victoria On Horse, White, Gold 82.00
Staffordshire, Figurine, Queen Victoria, Standing, Crowned, C.1850 .... 90.00

Staffordshire, Dish, Hen, 8 In.High
See Page 542

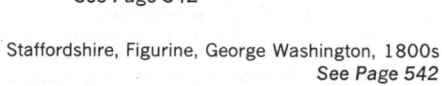

Staffordshire, Figurine, George Washington, 1800s
See Page 542

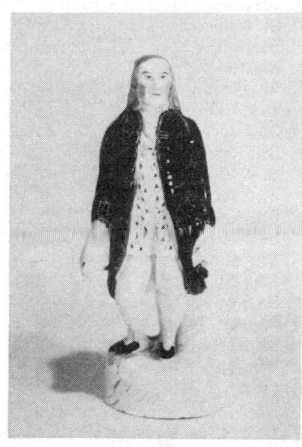

Staffordshire, Figurine, Rebecca At The Well	65.00
Staffordshire, Figurine, Red Riding Hood & Wolf, Orange Cape	28.00
Staffordshire, Figurine, Robin Hood	65.00
Staffordshire, Figurine, Sankey, White Suit, 16 In.High	85.00
Staffordshire, Figurine, Scotsman With Hunting Dog	75.00
Staffordshire, Figurine, Scottish Couple Standing Beside Clock, 13 In.	45.00
Staffordshire, Figurine, Sir Henry Havelock, On Horse	75.00
Staffordshire, Figurine, Tom King	50.00
Staffordshire, Figurine, Uncle Tom, 12 In.	150.00
Staffordshire, Figurine, Whippet, Brown & White, Blue Collar, 5 1/2 In.	45.00
Staffordshire, Figurine, Zebra, Early 19th Century, 6 1/2 In.High, Pair	185.C0
Staffordshire, Figurine, Zebra, Standing, Foliage Base, 5 In.High	20.00
Staffordshire, Figurine, 8 In. *Illus*	39.50
Staffordshire, Hen On Nest, 9 In.	180.00
Staffordshire, Hen, Highly Colored, Large Size	330.00
Staffordshire, Holder, Cigar, Hand Holding Cigars	21.00
Staffordshire, Inkwell, Cover, Brass Collar	18.00
Staffordshire, Inkwell, Dalmation Lying On Blue Ground	35.00
Staffordshire, Inkwell, Tree Stump, Chickens & Chicks	250.00
Staffordshire, Inkwell, Whippet Reclining On Cobalt Base	60.00
Staffordshire, Inkwell, White, Blue Floral, 3 1/4 In.Sq.	35.00
Staffordshire, Jar, Biscuit, Dark Blue, Gold Luster, Silver Lid & Bail	50.00

Staffordshire, Figurine, 8 In.

Staffordshire, Pitcher,
Boston State House, 8 In.High
See Page 544

Staffordshire, **Jug**, Apostle, Tan, Pewter Lid, Masked Handle, 1842	140.00
Staffordshire, **Jug**, Apostle, White, Masked Handle, 1842, 8 1/2 In.High	60.00
Staffordshire, **Jug**, Julius Caesar, Salt Glaze, C.1839, 9 1/2 In.Tall	85.00
Staffordshire, **Jug**, Rest, Farm Tools, Wheat, Silver Luster Outline, 1810	150.00
Staffordshire, **Ladle**, Blue Eagle Handle, Blue Rim On Bowl, Circa 1820, 6 In.	28.00
Staffordshire, **Lamp**, Fairy, Kitten, Eyes Light Up When Candle Burns	85.00
Staffordshire, **Match Holder**, Black Boots, Bootjack	26.50
Staffordshire, **Match Holder**, Dog Standing By Blue & White Basket	17.00
Staffordshire, **Match Holder**, Figural, Boots & Bootjack, Black, White	35.00
Staffordshire, **Matchbox**, Horse In Relief, Striker	25.00
Staffordshire, **Muffineer**, Gray & Blue Stripings, Footed	40.00
Staffordshire, **Mug**, Child's, Going To The Mill, 2 1/2 In.High	27.50
Staffordshire, **Mug**, Child's, Pink Luster, Schoolhouse Pattern	18.00
Staffordshire, **Mug**, Child's, Three Little Kittens, 2 1/2 In.High	45.00
Staffordshire, **Mug**, Child's, Transfer Print, Puppies & Kittens	15.00
Staffordshire, **Mug**, Frog Shape, Drinking Scene, 5 In.Tall	69.00
Staffordshire, **Mug**, Pink Luster Bands, 'Joseph'	20.00
Staffordshire, **Mug**, Scuttle, Rotary Cultivator Rickett, 1858	22.00
Staffordshire, **Mug**, Shaving, Scuttle, Flow Blue	35.00
Staffordshire, **Mug**, Wreath Decoration, Inscribed Mary	40.00
Staffordshire, **Necessaire**, Wedge Shape, Enameled Travelers, Gilt, C.1770	400.00
Staffordshire, **Penholder**, Figural, Greyhounds, Red Brown, Black Collars	50.00
Staffordshire, **Pepper Pot**, Blue Luster	62.00
Staffordshire, **Pitcher**, Arms Of The United States, C.1810, Ovoid, 5 5/8 In.	550.00
Staffordshire, **Pitcher**, Boston State House, 8 In.High .... *Illus*	275.00
Staffordshire, **Pitcher**, Franklin Tomb, Blue, 6 1/2 In.	385.00
Staffordshire, **Pitcher**, Landing Of Lafayette, Blue, 8 In.	300.00
Staffordshire, **Plate**, Andalusia, Pink, Adams, 8 In.	22.50
Staffordshire, **Plate**, Asiatic Palace, Dark Blue, Ridgway, 10 1/4 In.	27.50
Staffordshire, **Plate**, Athens, Mulberry, 14 Sided, Adams, 1849 .... 8.50 To 15.00
Staffordshire, **Plate**, Battle Of Lake Erie, Fruit, Foliage, Dated 1813, 10 In.	55.00
Staffordshire, **Plate**, Battle Of New Orleans, Blue, Marked England	12.00
Staffordshire, **Plate**, Boston State House, Blue, Wood	60.00
Staffordshire, **Plate**, Boston, Acorn & Leaf Border, Blue, Johnson Bros.	95.00
Staffordshire, **Plate**, British Views, Dark Blue, 8 1/2 In.	30.00
Staffordshire, **Plate**, Buckingham Palace, Blue, Morley, C.1845	15.00
Staffordshire, **Plate**, Cadmus Full Sail, Floral Garland Edge, Dark Blue	215.00
Staffordshire, **Plate**, Cake, Center Painting Of Alnwich Castle, Pierced Edge	47.50
Staffordshire, **Plate**, Canary, Black Transfer Of Women, Child, Flowers	90.00
Staffordshire, **Plate**, Cannon Hall, Riley, 1915, Blue	35.00
Staffordshire, **Plate**, Castles, R.Stevenson, Blue, 8 In.	30.00
Staffordshire, **Plate**, Child's, Blacksmith Center, He That Hath A Trade	35.00
Staffordshire, **Plate**, Child's, Docility, 6 In.	27.50
Staffordshire, **Plate**, Child's, Does It Rain, Daisy Border	12.50
Staffordshire, **Plate**, Child's, Farm Scene, 4 1/2 In.	17.50
Staffordshire, **Plate**, Child's, Hunter & Dog Transfer, Pink Luster Rim	22.50
Staffordshire, **Plate**, Child's, Luster Decoration, Proverb, 5 1/4 In.	35.00
Staffordshire, **Plate**, Child's, Proverb, 6 In.	35.00
Staffordshire, **Plate**, Child's, Rabbit Decoration, 5 In.	15.00
Staffordshire, **Plate**, Christmas Eve, Willkie Series, Blue, Clews, 9 In.	65.00
Staffordshire, **Plate**, De Soto's Discovery, Fruit, Flowers, Blue	32.00
Staffordshire, **Plate**, Dinner, Dr.Syntax Painting, Clews .... *Illus*	100.00
Staffordshire, **Plate**, Dinner, Ironstone, J.Clementson, 6 .... *Illus*	70.00
Staffordshire, **Plate**, Don Quixote, Dark Blue, 10 In.	120.00
Staffordshire, **Plate**, Dr.Syntax Reading His Tours, Clews, 9 In.	80.00
Staffordshire, **Plate**, Fairmont Near Philadelphia, Stubbs, Blue	65.00
Staffordshire, **Plate**, Famous Musicians & Composers, Blue, White, R.& M.	17.00
Staffordshire, **Plate**, Grecian Font, Adams, Pink, 9 1/4 In.	25.00
Staffordshire, **Plate**, Grecian, Toddy, Green	12.00
Staffordshire, **Plate**, Grecian, Transfer, Blue, 8 2n.	35.00
Staffordshire, **Plate**, Jackson, Shannondale Spring, Va., Brown, 9 In.	68.00
Staffordshire, **Plate**, Famous Musicians & Composers, Blue, White, R.& M.	17.00
Staffordshire, **Plate**, Jeddo, Mulberry, W.Adams & Sons, C.1845, Ironstone	20.00
Staffordshire, **Plate**, Landing Of Lafayette, Blue, Clews, 8 7/8 In.	175.00
Staffordshire, **Plate**, Landing Of Lafayette, Blue, Clews, 9 In.	155.00

Staffordshire, Plate, Dinner,
Dr.Syntax Painting, Clews
See Page 544

Staffordshire, Teapot, Lafayette,
Franklin's Tomb, Wood
See Page 546

Staffordshire, Plate, Dinne
Ironstone, J.Clementson,
See Page 544

Staffordshire, Plate, Landing Of Lafayette, Blue, 10 In. 185.00
Staffordshire, Plate, Macdonough's Victory, Wood, Blue 130.00
Staffordshire, Plate, Mansion, Grapes, Flowers, Couple, Blue, Enoch Wood & Son 29.50
Staffordshire, Plate, Military Sketches, Green, Circa 1840, 8 In. 8.00
Staffordshire, Plate, Mohawk Trail, Blue & White, 7 1/2 In. 7.00
Staffordshire, Plate, Monte Video, Connecticut, Pink, Adams, 6 3/4 In. 30.00
Staffordshire, Plate, Near Fishkill, Dark Blue, 8 In. 135.00
Staffordshire, Plate, Niagara Falls, Blue, White, 10 In. 30.00
Staffordshire, Plate, Oriental Scene, Openwork Border, Circa 1810, Pair 125.00
Staffordshire, Plate, Oyster, Marguerite Pattern 40.00
Staffordshire, Plate, Palestine, Adams, Pink, 9 1/2 In. 22.00
Staffordshire, Plate, Panoramic Scenery, Cathedral, Stevenson's, Blue 55.00
Staffordshire, Plate, Pastoral Scenes, Dark Blue, 10 In. 48.00
Staffordshire, Plate, Peace & Plenty, Clews, 8 7/8 In. 165.00
Staffordshire, Plate, Pelew, Mulberry, E.Challinor, C.1840, 14 Sided 10.00
Staffordshire, Plate, Peru, Mulberry, Holdcroft & Co., C.1846-52, 12 Sided 15.00
Staffordshire, Plate, Peruvian Horse Hunt, Purple, 19th Century 18.00
Staffordshire, Plate, Pittsfield Elm, Blue, 8 3/4 In.Diameter 135.00
Staffordshire, Plate, Plymouth Rock, Rolled Edge, R.&m. 19.00
Staffordshire, Plate, Rhone Scenery, Mulberry, T.J.& J.Mayer, C.1850 .... 15.00
Staffordshire, Plate, Ride Of Paul Revere, Browns, Dated, Royal Fenton 15.00
Staffordshire, Plate, River Scene, Waterfall, Dark Blue, C.1820, 10 In. 28.00
Staffordshire, Plate, Roche Abbey, Yorkshire, Blue, 10 In. 17.50
Staffordshire, Plate, Safari Scene, Clews, 10 In. 35.00
Staffordshire, Plate, Scenic View, S.Tams & Co., Dark Blue, 9 In. 35.00
Staffordshire, Plate, Scenic, Wild Rose Border, C.1810, Blue 15.00
Staffordshire, Plate, Seaweed, Ridgway, Dark Blue & Black, 9 1/2 In. 15.00
Staffordshire, Plate, Shannondale Springs, Adams, Pink, 8 In. 37.50
Staffordshire, Plate, Ship, Shell Border, Blue, Wood & Sons 80.00
Staffordshire, Plate, Soup, Mikado, 9 1/2 In. 15.00
Staffordshire, Plate, Souvenir Of Old Albany, Made For Van Heusen Charles 12.00
Staffordshire, Plate, State House, Boston, Medium Blue, 8 1/2 In. 70.00
Staffordshire, Plate, States, Clews, 8 1/2 In. 125.00
Staffordshire, Plate, States, Clews, Blue, 8 3/4 In. 150.00
Staffordshire, Plate, Sun Of Righteousness, Black, White, Wood, 9 1/2 In. 48.00
Staffordshire, Plate, Sundorn Castle, Ridgway, Lavender Transfer 12.00
Staffordshire, Plate, Texas Campaign, Brown, 9 1/4 In. 70.00
Staffordshire, Plate, Texas Campaign, Lavender, 7 1/2 In. 50.00
Staffordshire, Plate, The Capital, Rose Border, Marked Wedgwood 65.00
Staffordshire, Plate, The Elm At Cambridge, Washington Army, July, 3, 1775 .... 24.00
Staffordshire, Plate, Ventura, Blue, 7 1/2 In., Pair 10.00
Staffordshire, Plate, Venture, Mulberry, Ironstone By R.B., Central Scene 12.00
Staffordshire, Plate, View At Liverpool, U.S.Constitution, Dark Blue 150.00
Staffordshire, Plate, View Conway, New Hampshire, Adams, Pink, 9 In. 45.00
Staffordshire, Plate, View Of La Grange, Blue & White, Enoch Wood & Sons 115.00
Staffordshire, Plate, Villa Regents Park, Adams, Dark Blue, 9 In. 45.00

Staffordshire, Plate, Vue D'Une Ancienne Abbaye, Dark Blue, Woods, 9 1/4 In.	40.00
Staffordshire, Plate, West Point, American View, Sepia, 8 In.	28.50
Staffordshire, Plate, West Point, Hudson River, Purple, 8 In.	40.00
Staffordshire, Plate, White Floral, C.1815, Signed Riley, Blue, 10 In.	35.00
Staffordshire, Plate, Wild Rose, Blue, White, Marked E.M. & Co., Set Of 6	85.00
Staffordshire, Platter, Abbey Ruins, Signed, Lavender, 15 X 13 In.	30.00
Staffordshire, Platter, Blue Willow, Oval, 14 X 11 In.	18.00
Staffordshire, Platter, Blue Willow, 15 X 12 In.	40.00
Staffordshire, Platter, British Views, Dark Blue, 14 3/4 In.	88.00
Staffordshire, Platter, Castle Garden, Battery, N.Y., Enoch Wood & Sons	65.00
Staffordshire, Platter, Corinth, G.Phillips, Longport, Brown	35.00
Staffordshire, Platter, Deer & Kangaroos In London Zoo, Clews, Pink	78.00
Staffordshire, Platter, Dorney Court, Buckinghamshire, Well, Blue	40.00
Staffordshire, Platter, Franklin Flying Kite, Blue, 5 X 3 5/8 In.	35.00
Staffordshire, Platter, Gondola, Sailboats, C.1835, 17 1/2 In.Long, Pink	65.00
Staffordshire, Platter, Hermitage En Dauphine, E.Wood & Sons, Dark Blue	40.00
Staffordshire, Platter, Italian Scenes, Floral Border, Blue, 12 X 15 In.	35.00
Staffordshire, Platter, Napoleon Pattern, Brown, White, 15 1/2 In.	40.00
Staffordshire, Platter, Naval Battle Off Boston, Chesapeake & Shannon	385.00
Staffordshire, Platter, Pastoral Scene, Floral Border, Blue, 13 X 10 In.	68.00
Staffordshire, Platter, Peasant Girl Mistaken For The Lady Dulcinea, Blue	175.00
Staffordshire, Platter, Seaweed & Shell Series, Chesapeake & Shannon	395.00
Staffordshire, Platter, The White House, Scalloped Edge, Large	650.00
Staffordshire, Platter, Tyrolean Scene, WR.& Co., Blue	23.00
Staffordshire, Platter, View Of Greenwich, Grapevine Border, Woods, Blue	75.00
Staffordshire, Platter, Windsor Castle, Adams, Dark Blue	100.00
Staffordshire, Platter, Yale College, Four Section Floral Border, Scenes	125.00
Staffordshire, Saltshaker, Pearlware, Pyriform, Feathered Band, C.1850, 4	70.00
Staffordshire, Sauce, Blue Landscapes, People, White Ground, England	6.98
Staffordshire, Saucer, Oriental, 4 In.	6.00
Staffordshire, Shoe, Child Inside, Whistle In End, 2 1/2 In.	25.00
Staffordshire, Snuffbox, Rectangular, Transfer Landscape & Herdsman, C.1770	140.00
Staffordshire, Soup, Boston State House, Blue, Marked Rogers	90.00
Staffordshire, Soup, Fairmount Near Philadelphia, Eagle Border, Blue	115.00
Staffordshire, Soup, Falls Of Montmorency, Blue, Wood	135.00
Staffordshire, Soup, The Holme, Regent Park Series, Wood	63.00
Staffordshire, Sugar & Creamer, Jenny Lind Pattern	35.00
Staffordshire, Sugar, Chinoiserie, Dark Blue	80.00
Staffordshire, Swan, Miniature, Yellow Basket, 2 1/2 In.High	50.00
Staffordshire, Tea Set, Child's, Blue Transfer Printed, 3 Piece	27.50
Staffordshire, Tea Set, Child's, Lavender Peacocks, Floral	50.00
Staffordshire, Teapot, Brown Splash, Lavender Band Of Greek Figures, Signed	40.00
Staffordshire, Teapot, Globular, Blue & Yellow Flowering Branches, C.1830	70.00
Staffordshire, Teapot, Lafayette At Franklin's Tomb, 8 1/2 In.High	250.00
Staffordshire, Teapot, Lafayette, Franklin's Tomb, Wood *Illus*	175.00
Staffordshire, Teapot, Little May	15.00
Staffordshire, Teapot, Ribbed, Silver Luster, Domed Lid, Finial, Circa 1805	135.00
Staffordshire, Teapot, Shaped Like Man, 13 In. *Illus*	125.00
Staffordshire, Teapot, Toby, Seated, Cobalt, Red, Holds Mug & Pouch	110.00
Staffordshire, Toby Mug, Lord Nelson, 12 In.High	225.00
Staffordshire, Toby Mug, Man, Seated, Blue Coat, Yellow Breeches, Holding Jug	125.00
Staffordshire, Toby Mug, Marked Old Staffs Toby, Shorter & Sons, Ltd.	27.50
Staffordshire, Toby Mug, Miser, Coin In Fish, Green Coat, Yellow Pants	125.00
Staffordshire, Toby, Man Taking Snuff	125.00
Staffordshire, Toothpick, Artist Holding Palette & Painting	17.50
Staffordshire, Tray, Chateau, Trees, People, Brown, White, John Alcock, Hexagon	65.00
Staffordshire, Tureen Set, Italian Scenery, Blue, 2 Piece	360.00
Staffordshire, Tureen, Bank Savanna, Oval, Open Handles, Blue	180.00
Staffordshire, Tureen, English Rural Scene, Tray, Blue, C.1820	195.00
Staffordshire, Tureen, Miniature, 4 1/2 In. *Illus*	35.00
Staffordshire, Tureen, Oriental Motif, Lion Head Handles, Finial, Blue	185.00
Staffordshire, Tureen, Pigeon, Gray & Blue Plumage, Nest Of Straw, C.1835	300.00
Staffordshire, Vase, Cottage, 6 In.	10.00
Staffordshire, Washstand Set, Blue & White Floral On Cobalt, 2 Piece	95.00
Staffordshire, Washstand Set, Florette, 1883, 2 Piece	150.00
Staffordshire, Watch Holder, Figural, Castle, Pink, Green Grass	60.00

Staffordshire, Tureen,
Miniature, 4 1/2 In.
See Page 546

Staffordshire, Teapot,
Shaped Like Man, 13 In.
See Page 546

Stangl, Hummingbird, 3 1/2 In.

Staffordshire, Watch Holder, Girl, Boy, Dog, Bower Grapes, Leaves, 12 In.	85.00
Staffordshire, Watch Stand, Cottage Figure, Three Lambs	30.00
Staffordshire, Whistle, Owl	45.00
Stained Glass, Window, Four Colors, Bird In Circle, 16 X 14 3/4 In., Pair	150.00
Stangl, Ashtray, Oval, Bird Motif, Signed, 8 X 10 In.	15.00
Stangl, Bird Of Paradise	24.00
Stangl, Bird, Blue & Yellow, 2 3/4 In.High	30.00
Stangl, Bird, Blue, Black Beak, Red Berries Each Side Base, 4 1/2 In.	18.00
Stangl, Bird, Blue, Yellow Underside, Dark Blue Crown, 4 1/8 In.	28.00
Stangl, Bird, Double, Black, Pink, & Yellow, 6 In.High	60.00
Stangl, Bird, Double, Brown, Yellow, & White On Fancy Bower	49.00
Stangl, Bird, Double, Signed M.R.F., 5 1/2 & 5 In.	30.00
Stangl, Bird, Green & Yellow, Black Wing Tips, Tree Stump, Artist MV	18.00
Stangl, Bird, Green & Yellow, 3 1/2 In.High	30.00
Stangl, Bird, Green, Cream, & Brown, 3 In.High	35.00
Stangl, Bird, Mother Feeding 3 Babies, Marked	65.00
Stangl, Bird, Standing, Green, Blue, & Pink Base, 12 In.Long	95.00
Stangl, Bird, Yellow, Green Wings, Blue Beak, Artist's Initials, 4 In.Long	19.00
Stangl, Bluebird	28.00
Stangl, Bluebird, Spread Wings, Multicolored Base, Pink Flower	39.00
Stangl, Bluebirds	40.00
Stangl, Bluejay, Marked & Signed, 3 In.High	14.00
Stangl, Bluejay, 5 In.High	25.00
Stangl, Bowl, Blue & Brown Floral Panels	8.50
Stangl, Bunting, Painted	24.00
Stangl, Cardinal, Gray	16.00
Stangl, Cerulean Warbler	16.00
Stangl, Cockatoo, Artist Jacob, 12 In.High	80.00
Stangl, Cockatoo, Double, Pink, 9 In.High	75.00
Stangl, Cockatoo, Multicolored, Signed, 6 1/2 In.	36.00
Stangl, Cockatoo, Pink, 5 In.High	28.00
Stangl, Cockatoo, Signed, 6 1/2 In.	20.00
Stangl, Cockatoo, 11 In.	115.00
Stangl, Cockatoos On Base, Marked	55.00
Stangl, Double Wrens	42.00
Stangl, Hummingbird, Broadbill	30.00
Stangl, Hummingbird, Rufus	12.00
Stangl, Hummingbird, Sipping From Pink Morning Glory, 6 In.	40.00 To 42.00
Stangl, Hummingbird, Spread Wings	45.00
Stangl, Hummingbird, Two With Stalk Of Corn Center, Artist PS, 9 In.High	68.00
Stangl, Hummingbird, 3 1/2 In.	Illus 27.50

Stangl, **Kingfisher**, Blue, 3 In.High 25.00
Stangl, **Lovebirds** 20.00
Stangl, **Mother Thrush Feeding Two Babies** 48.00
Stangl, **Oriole** 12.00
Stangl, **Parakeet On Branch** 28.00
Stangl, **Parakeets On Branch Base**, Yellow, 5 1/4 In.High 58.00
Stangl, **Parrot**, Red & Blue, Marked & Signed, 7 In.High 20.00
Stangl, **Plate**, Bird, Pheasant, Incised Design, 11 1/2 In. 35.00
Stangl, **Plate**, Bird, Quail, Incised Design, 11 1/2 In. 35.00
Stangl, **Plate**, Cowboy, Cactus, Artist Signed, 9 In. 25.00
Stangl, **Plate**, Terra Rose, Incised Grapes 7.00
Stangl, **Rooster**, Green Ground, Black Mark, 9 1/2 In.High 65.00
Stangl, **Titmouse** 12.00
Stangl, **Two Birds On Base**, Leaves, Flowers, 10 1/2 In. 145.00
Stangl, **Two Parrots**, Signed 55.00
Stangl, **Two Wrens On Branch**, Signed 48.00
Stangl, **Vase**, Green, Lavender Interior, High Gloss Glaze, Impressed Mark 35.00
Stangl, **Vireo**, Blue Head 16.00
Stangl, **Western Tanager**, Dogwood, Green Base, Artist MW & VR 35.00
Stangl, **Wren** 12.00
Stangl, **Wrens** 45.00

*Star Holly is a milk glass type of glass made by the Imperial Glass
Company of Bellaire, Ohio, in 1957. The pieces were made to look like
Wedgwood jasperware. White holly leaves appear against colored borders of
blue, green, or rust. It is marked on the bottom of every piece.*

Star Holly, **Bowl**, Blue Ground, Pierced Rim, Satin Finish, 5 1/4 In.Diameter 50.00
Star Holly, **Bowl**, Satin Finish, 5 1/4 In.Diameter 50.00
Star Holly, **Bowl**, White, Signed IG, 6 1/2 In.Diameter 40.00
Star Holly, **Bowl**, White, Signed IG, 8 3/4 In.Diameter .... 50.00 To 250.00
Star Holly, **Cream & Sugar**, Signed 45.00
Star Holly, **Cup & Saucer**, White, Signed 35.00
Star Holly, **Sauce**, Blue, Cutouts Between Leaves, Signed Ig 75.00
Star Holly, **Sugar & Creamer**, White, Signed 45.00
Star Holly, **Wine**, White, Footed, Signed IG .... 50.00 To 55.00

*Steins have been used for over 500 years. They have been made of ivory,
porcelain, stoneware, faience, silver, pewter, wood, or glass in sizes up to nine
gallons. Although some were made by Meissen, Capo-di-Monte, and other
famous factories, most were made in Germany.*

Stein, **Mettlach, see Mettlach, Stein**
Stein, **Amber Glass With Applied Green Buttons**, Pewter Base & Lid, French 95.00
Stein, **Berlin** 40.00
Stein, **Blue**, Gray, Ceramic, Courting Scene, Metal Top 25.00
Stein, **Bowling Pin**, 1/2 Liter, Pottery, Porcelain Lined 110.00
Stein, **'Cafe Ostendorf Deutsche Juche Phila.,** ' Pewter Lid, Red, Black 30.00
Stein, **Carved Deer In Forest**, Carved Bone Lid & Thumbrest 165.00
Stein, **Courting Scene**, Inlaid Top, 1/2 Liter, Musterschutz 85.00
Stein, **Cream**, Open Top, Boston State House, Brown & Green 15.00
Stein, **Cream**, Panels, Raised Figures Of Knight, Lady, Man, 2 Liter, Germany 50.00
Stein, **Crystal**, Tall Dwarf Thumbpiece, 14 In.Tall 255.00
Stein, **Deer**, Purple Luster Bands, Porcelain, Lithophane Bottom, Lid 65.00
Stein, **Drinking Scene**, Zum Wohlstein, Pewter Lid, Germany, 1901, 1/2 Liter 35.00
Stein, **Earthenware**, Pewter Lid, 1/2 Liter, 'Pschoor-Brau, 'Munchen, Wheat 40.00
Stein, **Embossed Elks**, Foliage, Verse, Blue, Gray, Germany, 1/2 Liter 25.00
Stein, **Embossed Elves**, 1/2 Liter, M & W G 125.00
Stein, **Etched Bowling Scene**, Inlaid Top, 1/2 Liter 85.00
Stein, **Forest Drinking Scene**, Tree Trunk Handle, 1/2 Liter, Geschulzt 55.00
Stein, **French**, Enamel, 3 1/2 In.High 250.00
Stein, **German Texts**, Boy & Girl In Wheat Field, Pewter Lid, 10 Liter 20.00
Stein, **German**, Embossed German Scenes, Pewter Hinged Cover 16.00
Stein, **German**, Flower Design, Pewter Lid, Enamel, Amber, Initials, Date 1850 .... 90.00
Stein, **German**, Porcelain Insert, Metal Hinged Cover, Inscribed 25.00
Stein, **German**, Raised Figures, Signed A.H.Guido Schultze, 3 Liter 75.00
Stein, **German**, 1/2 Liter, Embossed Soldiers, Cream, Marked F&M N 5047 .... 35.00
Stein, **German**, 5 Liter, Drinking Scene, Pewter Lid 50.00

Stein, Geschutz, No.2181, 1/4 Liter	89.00
Stein, Gray Pottery, Printed North German Lloyds, Pewter Lid, Thumbrest	14.00
Stein, Gray Stoneware, 1 Liter, Marked B.No.1451, Pewter Top & Thumbrest	20.00
Stein, Gray, Monk Drinking, Cobalt Trim, Open Top, 4 1/4 In.	7.50
Stein, Gray, Munchen, Pewter Lid With Embossed Scene, 5 In.	35.00
Stein, Gray, Stoneware, Signed Arnold, 1910, 1/2 Liter	50.00
Stein, Hand-Painted Tavern Scene, Bavarian, 1/2 Liter	250.00
Stein, Hunting Scene, Pewter Top, Lion Couchant Thumbpiece, Germany	65.00
Stein, Kinghts Of Labor	21.50
Stein, Legation Of High Wheelers, Musterschutz, 1/2 Liter	195.00 To 200.00
Stein, Lithophane Of Cyclist On High Wheeler In Base, Musterschutz	225.00
Stein, Lithophane, Pewter Lid, Germany	58.00
Stein, Milk Glass, Hand Painted Roses, 18th Century, 1 Liter	195.00
Stein, Milk Maid, Musterschutz, 1/2 Liter	300.00
Stein, Miniature, French Enamel, 3 1/2 In.High	275.00
Stein, Miniature, Mary Gregory Figure Of Kneeling Boy, Green Thumbprint	85.00
Stein, Miniature, Pewter Lid, Signed Musterschutz, 3 In.High	45.00
Stein, Minneapolis Brewing Co., 1897, 4/10 Liter, Mercury Mark	35.00
Stein, Monk, Brown Robe, Lithophane, Porcelain	155.00
Stein, Monk, Lithophane, 1/2 Liter	95.00
Stein, Monk, 1/2 Liter, J.Reinemann, Munchen, Gesetzlich Geschutze	75.00
Stein, Munchen Maid On Keg, Holds Stein, Musterschutz, 1/2 Liter	300.00
Stein, Munich Maid, Black Robe, Lithophane, Porcelain	155.00
Stein, Munich Maid, Pottery, 1/2 Liter	75.00
Stein, Munich Maid, Twin Tower Thumbrest, 1/2 Liter	100.00
Stein, No.942, 1/2 Liter, Watchman, Elves, Sun Coming Up, Musterschutz	275.00
Stein, No.1741, 1/2 Liter, Gray, Blue Designs, Musterschutz	200.00
Stein, Outdoor Courting Scene, Etched, Musterschutz, 1/2 Liter	93.00
Stein, Oval Medallion, Embossed Man, Woman, Pewter Lid, Porcelain, Germany	59.00
Stein, Pewter, Glass Bottom, Dutch, 18th Century, 1/2 Liter	45.00
Stein, Pewter, Porcelain Insert Reads Zum-Namestag	30.00
Stein, Pewter, Tankard, English, 18th Century, 13 In.Tall	192.00
Stein, Pewter, Wicker Handle, Wooden Thumb Rest, Marked England, 1 3/4 Pint	65.00
Stein, Porcelain, Colored Pictures, Cannon On Top, Lithograph Base, 1903	125.00
Stein, Porcelain, Drinking Scene, 1 Liter	90.00
Stein, Porcelain, Fancy Lady Beautiful, P.U.G.1 Liter	110.00
Stein, Potato Head, White, Green Leaves, Musterschutz, 1/2 Liter	325.00
Stein, Pottery, 'Remember The Maine', Dated February 15, 1898	20.00
Stein, Pottery, German, Beige, Drinking Scene, Pewter Top, 1/2 Liter	32.50
Stein, Raised Fish Motif, 1/2 Liter, Wicke Werke Geschutz	145.00
Stein, Raised Monks' Feast, 1/2 Liter	125.00
Stein, Regimental, Lithophane, Dated 1898, 1/2 Liter, Pewter Top	150.00
Stein, Regimental, Lithophane, Two Soldiers On Top, Bird On Handle, 1902	110.00
Stein, Regimental, Second Batallion, 1919, Germany, 1/3 Liter	25.00
Stein, Regimental, Soldier On Horseback, Stoneware, Ornate Pewter Lid	68.00
Stein, Religious Decoration, Pouring, 4 Liter, C.1880	400.00
Stein, Rope Handle, Marked 'Bamboo, ' Pewter Lid, 1 1/2 Liter	85.00
Stein, Royal Berlin, Marked Koenig Forzellan Mfg., Eagle, Flower, C.1847	65.00
Stein, Royal Minton, 2 1/2 Liters	165.00
Stein, Royal Vienna, 'Wild, ' Signed, 9 In.High	375.00
Stein, Sad Turnip, Musterschutz	195.00
Stein, Salt Glaze, Gray, Blue Coachman Scene, Pewter Top, 1/2 Liter, Signed R	35.00
Stein, Scene, Two Jolly Men Drinking, Animal Heads At Base, 1/2 Liter	105.00
Stein, Silver, Tankard, English Hallmark, 5 In.High	125.00
Stein, Skull	65.00 To 75.00
Stein, Stoneware, Classic Figures In Relief, Pewter Top, German Inscription	30.00
Stein, Tavern Scene, Print Under Face, 1 Liter	125.00
Stein, White, Gold Beading, Pink Roses, Black Bands, Porcelain, Pewter Lid	16.50
Stein, Wine Picture, 12 Figures, Each Month With Verse Above Each Figure	700.00

Stereo Cards that were made for stereopticon viewers became popular after 1840. Two almost identical pictures were mounted on a stiff cardboard backing so that, when viewed through a stereoscope, a three-dimensional picture could be seen.

Stereo Card, Canadian & Foreign Views, Classical Statuary, Lot Of 51	9.95
Stereo Card, Comic, Scenic, American & Foreign, 30	25.00

Stereo Card, Europe, Color, 100	30.00
Stereo Card, Foreign Views, 150	42.50
Stereo Card, Humorous Approach To Marriage, 18	15.00
Stereo Card, Japan, Color, 100	30.00
Stereo Card, Juvenile, Color, 100	30.00
Stereo Card, Theodore Roosevelt's Inaugural, Color, Two Views	8.00
Stereo Card, U.S., Foreign Views, Lot Of 10	2.50
Stereo Card, Views Of Swiss Alps, Mountain Climbing, Underwood, 10	3.50
Stereo Card, Views Of U.S.A, 100	35.00
Stereo Card, Views Of World War I Battle Scenes, By Underwood, 40	15.00
Stereo Card, World War I Views, 100	45.00

Stereoscopes, or Stereopticons, were used for viewing the stereo cards. The hand viewer was invented by Oliver Wendell Holmes, although more complicated table models were used before his was placed in production in 1859.

Stereoscope, Double Viewer, Adjustable, Fruitwood, France	70.00
Stereoscope, Folding, Corte Scope, 40 Views Of Willys Overland Co., Case	50.00
Stereoscope, Graphoscope, Black, Inlaid Design, Circa 1870, 14 In.Long	125.00
Stereoscope, Graphoscope, Made In Germany, Patent 1895, 48 Cards	36.00
Stereoscope, Hand Held, Patent 1895, Holmes Style	18.00
Stereoscope, Hand Viewer, Slide Adjustment, Metal	8.75 To 12.50
Stereoscope, On Stand, Walnut Pedestal & Base, 12 1/2 In.High, 35 Views	20.00
Stereoscope, Slide Adjustment, Walnut, 9 Views	21.00
Stereoscope, Storage For Views, Hinged Viewer Section, Rosewood, 20 Views	65.00
Stereoscope, Viewer, Home, Wooden, Folding, 8 X 4 1/2 In.	15.00
Stereoscope, Viewer, Walnut, 20 Cards	10.00
Stereoscope, Walnut & Aluminum, 50 Views	16.50
Stereoscope, With 10 Cards	15.00
Stereoscope, With 18 Views	20.00
Stereoscope, With 34 Keystone Views, Includes President Mckinley, 1895, Box	35.00
Stereoscope, With 50 Views Of Sears Roebuck	25.00
Sterling Silver, see Silver, Sterling	

Steuben Glass was made at the Steuben Glass Works of Corning, New York. The factory, founded by Frederick Carder and T.C.Hawkes, SR., was purchased by the Corning Glass Company. They continued to make glass called Steuben. Many types of art glass were made at Steuben. The firm is still producing glass of exceptional quality.

Steuben, see also Aurene, Verre De Soie

Steuben, Ashtray, Green Jade, Alabaster Cable Loop Through Ring	71.00
Steuben, Atomizer, Blue & Gold Iridescent, Unsigned, 8 1/2 In.	85.00
Steuben, Basket, Bubbly Glass, Blue Threaded Top, Unsigned, 10 In.	49.00
Steuben, Bonbon, Orange Gold Iridescent, Calcite Foot, Paper Label	165.00
Steuben, Bookend, Gazelle, Signed, Clear, Pair	175.00
Steuben, Bottle, Aurene, Melon Shape, Rainbow Iridescence, Signed & Numbered	95.00
Steuben, Bottle, Bathroom, Square, Swirled Base, Cerise, Threaded Stopper	30.00
Steuben, Bottle, Cosmetic, Blue Threading & Flower Stopper	45.00
Steuben, Bottle, Hand Lotion, Verre De Soie, Pink Flower Stopper, Signed	45.00
Steuben, Bottle, Swirl Rib, Green, Unsigned, Stopper	55.00
Steuben, Bowl & Plate, Marine Blue, Signed	40.00
Steuben, Bowl & Underplate, Finger, Calcite, Gold, Pink	150.00
Steuben, Bowl, Amethyst Crystal, Signed Fleur-De-Lis, 10 In.Diameter, 5 In.	150.00
Steuben, Bowl, Amethyst, Cluthra, 6 X 4 In.High	360.00
Steuben, Bowl, Blue & Purple Iridescent, Rolled Sides, Carder, 10 1/2 In.	295.00
Steuben, Bowl, Blue Aurene, Signed, Paper Label, 9 In.Diameter	275.00
Steuben, Bowl, Blue Calcite, Low, Flaring	425.00
Steuben, Bowl, Blue Rim, Verre De Soie	45.00
Steuben, Bowl, Calcite, Blue, 3 1/2 In.High, 8 In, Wide	550.00
Steuben, Bowl, Calcite, Blue, 8 In.	550.00
Steuben, Bowl, Calcite, Blue, 8 X 3 1/2 In.	395.00
Steuben, Bowl, Calcite, Gold Aurene Lining, 5 1/2 In.	145.00
Steuben, Bowl, Calcite, Gold Iridescent Inside	225.00
Steuben, Bowl, Calcite, Gold, White Outside, Cone Shape, Rolled Top, 8 In.	150.00
Steuben, Bowl, Calcite, Green Highlights, Gold Lining, 7 In.Diameter	115.00
Steuben, Bowl, Calcite, Sterling Holder, 2 Handles, 4 In.Diameter	75.00
Steuben, Bowl, Centerpiece, Calcite & Gold Aurene, Rolled In Top, 10 1/2 In.	115.00

Steuben, Bowl, Centerpiece, Diamond-Quilted, Blue Reeding 135.00
Steuben, Bowl, Centerpiece, Green Jade & Alabaster, Signed, 12 In.Diameter 85.00
Steuben, Bowl, Centerpiece, Rosaline & Alabaster, Signed, 12 In.Diameter 98.00
Steuben, Bowl, Cerise, Fluted, Signed With Fleur-De-Lis, 14 In. 180.00
Steuben, Bowl, Clear Crystal, Grotesque, Signed, 6 1/2 In.High 65.00
Steuben, Bowl, Clear, Crystal, Oval, 6 In.Tall, 11 1/2 In.Long 70.00
Steuben, Bowl, Cluthra, Jardiniere Shape, White To Green Band At Top, Signed 350.00
Steuben, Bowl, Covered, Amethyst, Signed, 6 In.High 125.00
Steuben, Bowl, Crystal, Grotesque, Four Column 24.00
Steuben, Bowl, Crystal, Turned Down Top, Diagonal Swirl, 11 1/2 In. 37.00
Steuben, Bowl, Finger, Jade, Alabaster, Signed, Set Of 6 .... 150.00
Steuben, Bowl, Finger, Rosaline, 2 1/2 In.High 75.00
Steuben, Bowl, Flower, Clear, Scroll Handles, Pedestal, Signed 75.00
Steuben, Bowl, Gold Aurene & Calcite, Waffle Pontil 95.00
Steuben, Bowl, Green Shading To Clear, 5 1/2 In.Square 85.00
Steuben, Bowl, Green, Blown, Applied Foot, 12 In. 75.00
Steuben, Bowl, Grotesque, Clear To Green, Signed 250.00
Steuben, Bowl, Grotesque, No.9443, Crystal, Signed 95.00
Steuben, Bowl, Jade, Green, Acid Cut, Floral & Leaf Decoration, 7 3/4 In.High 550.00
Steuben, Bowl, Pedestal, Underplate, Bristol Yellow & Clear, Signed 40.00
Steuben, Bowl, Rosa, Cranberry, Crystal, Diagonal Swirl, Flared 37.00
Steuben, Bowl, Rosaline, Amethyst Base & Rim, Ground Bottom, Unsigned 350.00
Steuben, Bowl, Ruffled, Flare Top, Ivorene, Signed, 5 In.High 125.00
Steuben, Bowl, Threading, Ruffled Edge, Blue, 16 In. 75.00
Steuben, Bowl, Yellow Jade, Low 200.00
Steuben, Candleholder, Green, Hollow Mica Stem, Applied Curls, 12 In., Pair 165.00
Steuben, Candleholder, Ivory & Black, Mushroom Type, Signed, Pair 150.00
Steuben, Candlestick, Amber & Blue, Pair 50.00
Steuben, Candlestick, Aurene, Gold, Signed, 7 In. 120.00
Steuben, Candlestick, Blue, Carder, 8 1/4 In., Pair 175.00
Steuben, Candlestick, Bubbly Crystal, Green Threads At Top, Unsigned, Pair 125.00
Steuben, Candlestick, Controlled Bubbles, Green Threading At Top, Pair 175.00
Steuben, Candlestick, Diamond-Quilted, Mushroom Shape, Blue, Pair 95.00
Steuben, Candlestick, Gold, Ruby, Signed F.Carder, 10 In.High, Pair 250.00
Steuben, Candlestick, Green, Amber, Swirled Top & Foot, 12 In.High 55.00
Steuben, Candlestick, Swirl, Blue, 2 1/4 In.High, Pair 45.00
Steuben, Champagne, Clear Cup, Blue Ball Stem 9.50
Steuben, Cologne, Blue Threads, Blue Flower Stopper, Ground Pontil 35.00
Steuben, Compote, Amber, Blue Swirl Stem, Button Finial, Unsigned 75.00
Steuben, Compote, Amethyst, Ribbed, Folded Rim On Base & Top, Unsigned 36.50
Steuben, Compote, Calcite Gold Iridescent & Creamy White 115.00
Steuben, Compote, Clear, Air Bubbles, Footed, Unsigned 35.00
Steuben, Compote, Green Swirl, Alabaster Fittings, Signed, 7 1/4 In. 120.00
Steuben, Compote, Green, Amber Stem, Signed, 8 In.Tall 125.00
Steuben, Compote, Jade 135.00
Steuben, Compote, Pink, Swirls, Crystal, Signed 47.50
Steuben, Compote, Rosaline, Alabaster Pedestal, Unsigned 235.00
Steuben, Compote, Rosaline, Alabaster Stem & Foot .... 130.00 To 150.00
Steuben, Compote, V.D.S. Shape, 3234 .... 80.00
Steuben, Creamer, Crystal, Incised Signature 35.00
Steuben, Darner, Stocking, Green Jade 75.00
Steuben, Decanter, Amethyst, Ribbed, Blown Stopper, Label, 9 1/2 In.High 165.00
Steuben, Dish, Candy, Jade & Alabaster, Fluted, Footed, Unsigned 50.00
Steuben, Dish, Leaf, Blue Crystal, Applied Topaz Leaves Form Handle 27.00
Steuben, Dish, Nut, Gold Aurene On Calcite, Footed, Ruffled 125.00
Steuben, Figurine, Gazelle, Frosted, Galloping Over Wave, C.1935 .... 120.00
Steuben, Figurine, Gazelle, Frosted, Signed, Pair 395.00
Steuben, Figurine, Pigeon, Head Down On Extended Breast, Pair 275.00
Steuben, Flower Block, Crystal, Matted Nude Figure, Signed, 2 Piece 175.00
Steuben, Flower Block, Figural, Buddha, Bubbly Green Crystal, 9 In.Tall 185.00
Steuben, Flower Frog, Green Jade, Two Circles Of Openings 40.00
Steuben, Glass, Ice Tea, Ivory With Black Handle 45.00
Steuben, Globe, Calcite, Acid Etched, Medallion, Sway, Ribbon Pattern, 10 In. 150.00
Steuben, Goblet, Blue, Threaded Top And Stem 75.00
Steuben, Goblet, Bristol Yellow Crystal, Signed, 6 In.High 55.00
Steuben, Goblet, Carder, Amber, Green Punts On Base, Green Threaded Base 145.00

Steuben, Goblet, Celeste Blue & Topaz 35.00
Steuben, Goblet, Cut Leaf Pattern, Signed 45.00
Steuben, Goblet, Gold Aurene, Twisted Stem, Signed 250.00
Steuben, Goblet, Green Jade, Twisted Alabaster Stem, Green Base 110.00
Steuben, Goblet, Peach Color Bowl, Alabaster Stem & Foot, 5 In.High 90.00
Steuben, Goblet, Pedestal Stem, Signed Selenium 43.00
Steuben, Goblet, Selenium Red Crystal, Signed, 5 1/4 In.High 60.00
Steuben, Goblet, Water, Jade, Alabaster Stem & Foot, Signed 40.00
Steuben, Goblet, Water, Smoky Topaz, Venetian, Unsigned 22.50
Steuben, Goblet, Wheel Pattern, Green, Engraved 198.00
Steuben, Goblet, Wine, Green With Threading 22.00
Steuben, Jar, Blown Pear & Leaf, Amber Cover & Base 165.00
Steuben, Jar, Vertical Ribbed, Green, Signed, Cover, 7 In.Tall 125.00
Steuben, Jardiniere, Cluthra, White To Green At Top, Signed 350.00
Steuben, Lamp Base, White Jade, Relief Leaves, Stems, Vines, 7 In. 48.00
Steuben, Lamp, Cintra, Yellow, Acid Cut, Chrysanthemums, Wooden Mounts 675.00
Steuben, Lamp, Chrysanthemum, White Jade, Signed Fleur-De-Lis, 23 In.High 550.00
Steuben, Lamp, Double, Acid Cutback Shades 195.00
Steuben, Lamp, Flying Geese, Lavender Ground, Acid Cut, Cintra, Three Layers 1295.00
Steuben, Lamp, Jade Green, Chrysanthemums, Leaves, Acid Cut, 9 1/2 In.High 450.00
Steuben, Lamp, Jade, Green, Homogeneous, Acid Cut, Chrysanthemums, 9 1/2 In. 325.00
Steuben, Loving Cup, Clear, Pink Threads, Fleur-De-Lis Mark, 6 1/4 In. 110.00
Steuben, Mug, Lemonade, Green Jade, Swirls, Alabaster Handle, Signed 105.00
Steuben, Perfume, Lavender Hollow Blown Stopper, 8 In.High 85.00
Steuben, Perfume, Mandarin Yellow Jade, Stopper, 10 In.High 225.00
Steuben, Perfume, Melon Rib, Red Threads, Pointed Stopper, Signed 140.00
Steuben, Perfume, Oriental Poppy 750.00
Steuben, Perfume, Verre De Soie, Melon Rib, Engraved Floral Swags, Footed 250.00
Steuben, Plate, Blue, Wheel Engraved, Leaves, Signed Fleur-De-Lis 18.00
Steuben, Plate, Cake, Aurene, Signed, 8 In.Diameter 80.00
Steuben, Plate, Cased Crystal, Wheel Engraving, Wisteria .... *Color* 35.00
Steuben, Plate, Cerise Ruby Rim, Threading, 6 3/4 In. 11.00
Steuben, Plate, Yellow Jade, 6 In. 55.00
Steuben, Rose Bowl, Green Jade, Signed, 7 In.High .... 125.00 To 140.00
Steuben, Salt, Aurene, Blue, Signed 80.00
Steuben, Salt, Calcite & Gold Aurene, Pedestal .... 75.00 To 95.00
Steuben, Salt, Calcite, Footed 120.00
Steuben, Salt, Calcite & Gold Aurene, Pedestal 85.00
Steuben, Salt, Rosa, Pedestal, Signed 95.00
Steuben, Salt, Verre De Soie, Pedestal, Monogrammed 48.00
Steuben, Shade, Calcite, Bell Shape, Gold Iridescent, Signed, Pair 85.00
Steuben, Shade, Calcite, Gold Leaves, Threads, Gold Lines, 4 5/8 In., Pair 95.00
Steuben, Shade, Gas, Gold Iridescent, Signed 35.00
Steuben, Shade, Gas, Ivory Satin, Calcite Interior, Scalloped Rim, Signed 38.00
Steuben, Shade, Gold On Calcite, Unsigned, 5 1/2 In. 50.00
Steuben, Shade, Gold, Feather, Signed, 5 1/4 In.High, 2 1/4 In.Fitting 65.00
Steuben, Shade, Gold, Ribbed, Signed, 5 3/4 In.Long 30.00
Steuben, Shade, Green Feather With Gold Border On White, Signed 65.00
Steuben, Shade, Ivorene, Floral, Copper Wheel Engraving, Signed, 5 In. 29.00
Steuben, Shade, Ivorene, Gold Leaf & Vine, Unsigned, 4 1/2 In.High, Pair 70.00
Steuben, Shade, Ribbed Bell, Solid Gold, Signed 28.00
Steuben, Shade, Wide Rib, Iridescent, Flared, Scalloped, Signed 68.00
Steuben, Sherbet & Saucer, Calcite 110.00
Steuben, Sherbet & Underplate, Bristol Yellow & Clear, Signed 40.00
Steuben, Sherbet & Underplate, Calcite, Gold 125.00
Steuben, Sherbet & Underplate, Calcite, Gold Aurene, Pedestal 137.00
Steuben, Sherbet & Underplate, Gold Aurene, Twisted Stem, Signed 325.00
Steuben, Sherbet & Underplate, Green Jade & Alabaster, Unsigned 65.00
Steuben, Sherbet & Underplate, Rosaline, Alabaster Stem 215.00
Steuben, Sherbet & Underplate, Verre De Soie 50.00
Steuben, Sherbet, Calcite, Gold Interior, 4 In.High 50.00
Steuben, Sherbet, Cone Shape, Jade, Alabaster, Pedestal Base, Signed 25.00
Steuben, Sherbet, Pomona, Green 12.00
Steuben, Sherbet, White, Iridescent Highlights, Ground Pontil, Unsigned 17.00
Steuben, Tazza, Calcite & Gold Aurene, Flare Top, Pedestal 95.00
Steuben, Torchere, Alabaster, Acid Cut, Wired, Signed, 11 1/2 In.High 225.00

Steuben, Urn, Celeste Blue, Expanded Diamond, Crystal Handles 125.00
Steuben, Urn, Expanded Diamond, Reeding At Top, Green, Signed 85.00
Steuben, Urn, Gold Aurene, Signed Frederick Carder, 5 In.High 275.00
Steuben, Urn, Ivorene, Pink Highlights, Signed 295.00
Steuben, Urn, Ivorene, Signed 250.00
Steuben, Urn, Jade Green, Alabaster Handles, Unsigned 275.00
Steuben, Urn, Miniature, Footed, Celeste Blue, Floral Cutting 47.50
Steuben, Vase, Alabaster Ground, Green Oriental Motif, Acid Cut, 10 In. 750.00
Steuben, Vase, Amber, Signed, 6 In. 39.00
Steuben, Vase, Aurene, Gold Iridescent, Foliated, Ruffled Top, 5 1/4 In.High 185.00
Steuben, Vase, Aurene, White, Gold Pulled Decoration 575.00
Steuben, Vase, Bird Design, Jade, Alabaster, Green, 9 1/8 In.High 750.00
Steuben, Vase, Blue Diamond-Quilted Crystal With Opaque White Threading 85.00
Steuben, Vase, Blue Ribbed Crystal, Pedestal, Signed, 10 In.High 80.00
Steuben, Vase, Blue, Bubbly, Reeded Rim 45.00
Steuben, Vase, Blue, Green Highlights, Stretched Top, Signed, 6 In. 325.00
Steuben, Vase, Blue, Silvery Stripe, Squat, Signed 80.00
Steuben, Vase, Bubbly Crystal, Green Threads Upper Part, 9 In. 33.00
Steuben, Vase, Bubbly Crystal, Green Threads, 12 3/4 In. 65.00
Steuben, Vase, Bud, Blue, Aurene, Signed, 6 In. 150.00
Steuben, Vase, Bud, Signed Fleur-De-Lis 90.00
Steuben, Vase, Bulbous, Green 75.00
Steuben, Vase, Butterfly In Spider Web, Green, 8 3/4 In.Tall 165.00
Steuben, Vase, Cabinet, Crystal, Gold Threading & Prunts 35.00
Steuben, Vase, Calcite, Gold Lining, Footed, 4 1/2 In. 75.00
Steuben, Vase, Canary Yellow, 16 Pillars, 3 Applied Feet 68.00
Steuben, Vase, Celeste Blue, Signed, 8 1/2 In.Tall 85.00
Steuben, Vase, Chrysanthemum Pattern In Green Jade, Acid Cut, 12 In. 375.00
Steuben, Vase, Clear With Pink Threading At Top, Signed, 8 In. 100.00
Steuben, Vase, Clear, Applied Glass Decoration, Signed, 5 In. 45.00
Steuben, Vase, Clear, Flared, Bulbous Stem, Round Base, 5 In. 30.00
Steuben, Vase, Cluthra, Green, 10 In. 425.00
Steuben, Vase, Cobalt Blue, Signed, 8 1/2 In.Tall 105.00
Steuben, Vase, Cornucopia, Crystal, Block Base, 6 1/4 In. 37.50
Steuben, Vase, Cornucopia, Deep Amethyst, Signed, Pair 200.00
Steuben, Vase, Cosmos Pattern, Signed Sinclaire, 9 In.Tall 135.00
Steuben, Vase, Crystal To Amethyst, Etched Fleur-De-Lis On Base, 11 In.High 215.00
Steuben, Vase, Cuspidor Shape, Gold Aurene On Calcite, 9 1/2 In.High 175.00
Steuben, Vase, Cutback Floral, Buds, Leaves, Shades Of Amethyst, Carder 1750.00
Steuben, Vase, Engraved Stars, Amber 24.00
Steuben, Vase, Fan, Amber Gold, Signed, 11 In.High 145.00
Steuben, Vase, Fan, Bristol Yellow, Signed 95.00
Steuben, Vase, Fan, Clear Crystal, Signed, 8 1/2 In.High 50.00
Steuben, Vase, Fan, Topaz, Green Base, Signed, 8 1/2 In.High 85.00
Steuben, Vase, Flared Top, Red Threading, Signed, 5 3/8 In.High 35.00
Steuben, Vase, Flaring Top, Calcite, Gold Aurene Lining, 6 In. 95.00
Steuben, Vase, Fleur-De-Lis Design, Bulbous, Signed, 11 In.Tall 85.00
Steuben, Vase, Fleur-De-Lis, Green To Clear, 9 In.Tall 110.00
Steuben, Vase, Flying Geese, Lavender Ground, Acid Cut, Cintra, Three Layers 1395.00
Steuben, Vase, Frosted Yellow, Art Deco, 4 3/4 In. 295.00
Steuben, Vase, Gold Calcite, Green Feather Design, Gold Aurene Lined 38.00
Steuben, Vase, Gold Red, Etched Vintage, Amberina Ribbed .... *Color* 200.00
Steuben, Vase, Gold With Blue Iridescence, 6 1/4 In.High 160.00
Steuben, Vase, Gold, Aurene, Signed, Paper Label 200.00
Steuben, Vase, Golden Amber, Swirls, 7 In. 45.00
Steuben, Vase, Green & Alabaster, Acid Cut, 12 In.High 475.00
Steuben, Vase, Green & White Loopings, Verre De Soie Decoration, F.Carder 275.00
Steuben, Vase, Green Jade Over Alabaster, Birds, Acid Cut, Pedestal Foot 695.00
Steuben, Vase, Green Jade, Alabaster, Acid Cutback, Double Etched, 10 In. 750.00
Steuben, Vase, Green Jade, Diagonal Stripes, 11 1/4 In. 53.00
Steuben, Vase, Green Jade, Marked Fleur-De-Lis, 8 In.High 105.00
Steuben, Vase, Green Jade, Ovoid, Short Neck, Flaring Rim, Signed, 8 1/2 In. 325.00
Steuben, Vase, Handkerchief, Clear, Signed 60.00
Steuben, Vase, Iridescent, Threaded Top, Verre De Soie, 6 1/2 In. 100.00
Steuben, Vase, Ivorene, Ribbed, Pink Applied Rim, Signed 265.00
Steuben, Vase, Ivorene, Rosaline Edging, Signed, 3 In. 265.00

Steuben, Vase, Ivory, Acid Cutback, Stamford Pattern, Signed 925.00
Steuben, Vase, Ivory, Signed, 5 1/2 In.High 95.00
Steuben, Vase, Jack-In-The-Pulpit, Gold Aurene, Blue Toward Base, Signed 250.00
Steuben, Vase, Jack-In-The-Pulpit, Ivorene, Trilily 525.00
Steuben, Vase, Jack-In-The-Pulpit, Ivorene, Trilily, Pair 1195.00
Steuben, Vase, Jade Green, Signed With Fleur-De-Lis, 7 In.High 110.00
Steuben, Vase, Jade, Alabaster Base, Signed, 6 In., Pair 300.00
Steuben, Vase, Jade, Alabaster Handles, 10 1/2 In. 325.00
Steuben, Vase, Jade, Alabaster, Carved, Embossed Fleur-De-Lis, 10 In.High 750.00
Steuben, Vase, Jade, Fleur-De-Lis, Signed 350.00
Steuben, Vase, Open Flower, Gold Intaglio Cut Floral, Unsigned, 8 3/4 In. 150.00
Steuben, Vase, Oriental Poppy, 5 1/2 In.High 695.00
Steuben, Vase, Parfait, Jade & Alabaster, 8 In. 77.00
Steuben, Vase, Selenium Red, Polished Pontil, Signed, 6 3/4 In. 145.00
Steuben, Vase, Selenium Red, Swirl, Urn Form, Signed, 7 In.High .... 75.00 To 145.00
Steuben, Vase, Shape 541, V.D.S.Signed 85.00
Steuben, Vase, Stick, Gold Aurene, Blue Iridescence, Signed, 8 In.High 120.00
Steuben, Vase, Stick, Jade, 8 In. 45.00
Steuben, Vase, Stick, No.2556, Gold Aurene, Blue Highlights, Mint, Signed 115.00
Steuben, Vase, Swirl, Pink Amber, Signed FDL 100.00
Steuben, Vase, Swirled, Amber, Signed, 7 In.High, 6 In.Diameter 35.00
Steuben, Vase, Swirled, Bristol Yellow, Signed, 7 In.High, 6 In.Diameter 38.00
Steuben, Vase, Trumpet, Calcite, Gold Lining 175.00
Steuben, Vase, Tulip Shaped Top, Gold, Blue Tints, Marked Aurene 275.00
Steuben, Vase, Urn Shape, Green, Expanded Diamond, Threading At Top, Signed 85.00
Steuben, Vase, Vaseline, Blue Edge, Base, Top, Rings Hang Each Side, 12 In. 95.00
Steuben, Vase, Verre De Soie, Footed, Paper Label, 5 In.High 90.00
Steuben, Vase, Verre De Soie, Green Threading At Top, 6 In. 55.00
Steuben, Vase, Vintage Design, Intaglio Cut, Selenium Red, 12 In.High 245.00
Steuben, Vase, White & Aqua, Opalescent, Ribbing, Fleur-De-Lis Signature 295.00
Steuben, Vase, White, Jack-In-The-Pulpit, Aurene, 8 In. 250.00
Steuben, Vase, Wisteria, Crystal, Grotesque, Pedestal, Signed, 8 In.High 185.00
Steuben, Vase, Wisteria, Signed, 5 1/4 In.High 150.00
Steuben, Vase, Wisteric Crystal, Grotesque, Pedestal, Signed, 8 In.High 185.00
Steuben, Water Set, Silver Overlay In Green To Clear, Signed, 4 Piece 275.00
Steuben, Wine, Celeste, Clear, Unsigned 35.00
Steuben, Wine, Cut Leaf Pattern, Signed 35.00
Steuben, Wine, Green Bowl, Clear Hollow Stem & Base, Carder 225.00
Steuben, Wine, Jade Green Bowl, Alabaster Stem & Base, Unsigned 45.00
Steuben, Wine, Marine Blue, Yellow Stem, Signed, 4 In.High 30.00
Steuben, Wine, Smoky Topaz, Venetian, Unsigned 20.00

*Stevengraphs are woven pictures made like ribbons. They were manufactured
by Thomas Stevens of Coventry, England, and became popular in 1862.*

Stevengraph, Bookmark, A Blessing 35.00
Stevengraph, Bookmark, 'A Blessing, May Your Progress On Life's Road' 47.50
Stevengraph, Bookmark, A Friend's Blessing, 9 1/2 In.Long 16.75
Stevengraph, Bookmark, Albert & Alexandria, Married March 10, 1863, Silk 38.00
Stevengraph, Bookmark, Christmas Verse By E.Cook, Winter Scene, 1871 .... 37.00
Stevengraph, Bookmark, 'Happy Christmas, ' Tennyson Verse, Scene, Signed 35.00
Stevengraph, Bookmark, Home Sweet Home, Signed 12.50
Stevengraph, Bookmark, Landing Of Columbus 50.00
Stevengraph, Bookmark, To My Dear Sister, 5 1/2 In.Long 14.75
Stevengraph, Bookmark, Wishing A Happy Birthday 38.00
Stevengraph, Christmas Poem, Floral, Satin Leaf Border, 4 X 5 In. 20.00
Stevengraph, George Washington Bust, 1876, Silk 45.00
Stevengraph, McKinley Memorial, Framed 75.00
Stevengraph, The Good Old Days, Framed .... *Illus* 125.00
Stevengraph, The Start, Frame 75.00

Stevens & Williams of Stourbridge, England, made many types of art glass.

Stevens & Williams, Basket, Vasa Murrhina, Silver Mica, Crimped Edge 75.00
Stevens & Williams, Bowl Vase, Green, Iridescent, Textured, Drape & Cherries 85.00
Stevens & Williams, Bowl, Amber, Cut Panels At Base, Center Diamond Point 35.00
Stevens & Williams, Bowl, Banana, Olive Color, Clear Drippings, Footed 85.00
Stevens & Williams, Bowl, Cameo, White On Citron, Wafer Base, 8 In. 280.00

Stevens & Williams, Bowl, Finger, Mother-Of-Pearl Satin Glass, Swirled 95.00
Stevens & Williams, Bowl, Green Threads, Applique Violet, Clear, Swirl Ribs 35.00
Stevens & Williams, Bowl, Mother-Of-Pearl, Brown, Crimped Rim, 4 1/2 In. 175.00
Stevens & Williams, Bowl, Opaque Ground, Applied Amber Leaves, Red Cherries 55.00
Stevens & Williams, Bowl, Swirl Optic Ribbed Violet, Emerald Green Swirl 35.00
Stevens & Williams, Bowl, Yellow Casing, Deep Rose, Satin, Crimped Top, 5 In. 210.00
Stevens & Williams, Bowl, Zipper Pattern, Blue, Unsigned, 14 X 2 1/2 In.High 35.00
Stevens & Williams, Cup & Saucer, Demitasse, Rosaline, Amethyst Handle 50.00
Stevens & Williams, Decanter, Crystal, Tiffany Silver Stopper 125.00
Stevens & Williams, Dish, Jam, Double, Vaseline, Pink, White, Silver Holder 85.00
Stevens & Williams, Epergne, Ribbed Diamond Puffs, Silver Holder, Deer, Tree 110.00
Stevens & Williams, Ewer, Cased Peachblow Satin Glass, Enamel Bird, Gold 85.00
Stevens & Williams, Ewer, Cranberry & White Flower, Vaseline Stem Handle 35.00
Stevens & Williams, Ewer, Lime Green, Hand-Painted Flowers, Camphor Handle 70.00
Stevens & Williams, Ewer, Peachblow Color, Deeply Ruffled, 8 In.High 85.00
Stevens & Williams, Jar, Jam, Hobnail, Cranberry Glass 45.00
Stevens & Williams, Jar, Yellow Green, Applied Clear Finial 75.00
Stevens & Williams, Pitcher, Mother-Of-Pearl, White Handle, Signed, Patent 595.00
Stevens & Williams, Pitcher, Water, Mother-Of-Pearl, Wandering Rivulets 395.00
Stevens & Williams, Rose Bowl, Blue Opalescent Swirl, Pleated Top 80.00
Stevens & Williams, Rose Bowl, Clear, Registery Mark 55693 .... 35.00
Stevens & Williams, Rose Bowl, Cranberry & White Floral, Amber Leaves 50.00
Stevens & Williams, Rose Bowl, Pink, Gold Floral & Leaf Design 50.00
Stevens & Williams, Rose Bowl, Pull-Up, Rainbow, Pink, White, Green 225.00
Stevens & Williams, Rose Bowl, Red To Pink, Amber Leaves, White Floral 435.00
Stevens & Williams, Rose Bowl, Swirl Opalescent Base, Crystal Flowers 65.00
Stevens & Williams, Vase, Amber Crimped Leaf Across Front, Fan Shape 48.00
Stevens & Williams, Vase, Amber, Panels, Blue Glass Alligators, 5 In. 85.00
Stevens & Williams, Vase, Apricot Satin Ground, Enamel Floral, Butterfly 75.00
Stevens & Williams, Vase, Blue Satin, Enamel Floral, Coralene Leaves, Handle 65.00
Stevens & Williams, Vase, Blue, Mother-Of-Pearl, Box Pleat Top 200.00
Stevens & Williams, Vase, Bull's-Eye, Green Centers, Wavy Edge, 3 1/2 In. 24.00
Stevens & Williams, Vase, Cased Blue Satin Glass, Melon Ribbed, Floral 65.00

Stevengraph, The Good Old Days, Framed
See Page 554

Stevens & Williams,
Vase, Silveria,
Signed, 8 3/4 In.
See Page 556

Stevens & Williams, Vase, Ewer, Shaded Peach, Satin Glass 75.00
Stevens & Williams, Vase, Fan Type, Cut Crystal, Floral On Long Stems 75.00
Stevens & Williams, Vase, Flower Form Top, Pink To Apricot, Enamel Floral 65.00
Stevens & Williams, Vase, Flowers, Leaves, Coralene, Ribbed, Thorn Handles 82.00
Stevens & Williams, Vase, Green Satin Ground, White Enamel Grecian 45.00
Stevens & Williams, Vase, Lavender Satin Glass, Enamel, Gold 210.00
Stevens & Williams, Vase, Marbleized, Pink, Blue, Red, Gold 250.00
Stevens & Williams, Vase, Miniature, Pull-Up, Opaque White, Acid Finish 115.00
Stevens & Williams, Vase, Mother-Of-Pearl, Herringbone, Satin Finish 185.00
Stevens & Williams, Vase, Mother-Of-Pearl, Rose, Expanded Diamond 95.00
Stevens & Williams, Vase, Pink To Rose Color Top, Daisies, Leaves, Stems 65.00
Stevens & Williams, Vase, Rainbow Swirl, Ribbed, Blue, White, Green, 13 In. 225.00
Stevens & Williams, Vase, Ribbed, Camphor Satin Glass, Roses, Leaves 65.00

Stevens & Williams, Vase, Rosaline Flower Form Shape, Brass Holder 155.00
Stevens & Williams, Vase, Rose To Pink, Applied Camphor Feet, Floral Pontil 125.00
Stevens & Williams, Vase, Satin Glass, Frosted Ground, Ribs, White Pull-Ups 80.00
Stevens & Williams, Vase, Satin Swirl, Pink, Yellow, Camphor 75.00
Stevens & Williams, Vase, Silveria, Green Threading, 7 1/2 In. 195.00
Stevens & Williams, Vase, Silveria, Signed, 8 3/4 In. .... *Illus* 1000.00
Stevens & Williams, Vase, Six Panel Design, Blown, Signed, 10 In.Tall 135.00
Stevens & Williams, Vase, White, Opalescent, Ribbed, Enamel Heron, Floral 45.00
Stevens & Williams, Wine, Jade, Alabaster 25.00
Stiegel Type, Bottle, Enameled Floral, 6 In.High 150.00
Stiegel Type, Creamer, Clear, Footed, Broad Flutes, Applied Handle 85.00
Stiegel Type, Salt, Expanded Diamond, Acorn Shape, Medium Blue 100.00
Stiegel Type, Salt, Footed, Expanded Diamond Pattern, Cobalt Blue 110.00
Stiegel Type, Salt, Master, Diamond Pattern, Sapphire 95.00
Stiegel Type, Tumbler, Decorated 50.00
Stiegel Type, Tumbler, Enameled Daisy Panels 25.00
Stiegel Type, Vase, Engraved Flip 117.00
Stiegel Type, Wine, Blue Band, Gold & White Enamel, Clear 5.00
Stone, Figurine, Bacchante, Italian, Standing, 27 3/4 In.High, C.1750 .... 300.00

Stoneware is a coarse glazed and fired potter's ware that is used to make
crocks, jugs, etc.

Stoneware, Bed Warmer, Iron Bail 30.00
Stoneware, Bottle, Blue Gray, Dated 1874 .... 45.00
Stoneware, Bowl, Bulb, Geometric Design Under Celadon Glaze, China 250.00
Stoneware, Box, Salt, Gray, Blue Underglaze, Round, Hole To Hang 15.00
Stoneware, Churn, Quill Lines On Bands, Mark Whites, Utica, N.Y., 3 Gallon 100.00
Stoneware, Cooler, Blue Borders, Pewter Spigot, Cork, 1866, Ottman Bros. 250.00
Stoneware, Creamer, Gray, Blue Lining 4.00
Stoneware, Crock, Barrel Shape, Dark Glaze With Rings 15.00
Stoneware, Crock, Bird On A Trunk, Earred, 2 Gallon 75.00
Stoneware, Crock, Blue Bird, Handle, Ft.Edward Stoneware Co., 4 Gallon 45.00
Stoneware, Crock, Blue Bird, Handle, Unsigned, 1 1/2 Gallon 40.00
Stoneware, Crock, Blue Decoration Of Man's Face, D.Ack, Mooresburg, Pa. 380.00
Stoneware, Crock, Blue Decoration, J.Swank & Co. 80.00
Stoneware, Crock, Blue Eagle Stencil Decorated, Pennsylvania, 11 1/2 In. 70.00
Stoneware, Crock, Blue Floral, E.& L.P.Norton, Bennington, Vt., 2 Gallon 45.00
Stoneware, Crock, Blue Scrolls, Grocery & Hardware, Wheeling, W.Va., 8 Gallon 80.00
Stoneware, Crock, Butter, Cobalt Blue Letters 18.00
Stoneware, Crock, Chicken Pecking Corn, West Troy Pottery, 4 Gallon 65.00
Stoneware, Crock, Cobalt Decoration, Earred, Tankard, 1 Gallon 125.00
Stoneware, Crock, Cobalt Motif, Ear Handles, J.S.Taft & Co., 1 Gallon 30.00
Stoneware, Crock, Cobalt Snow Flake, Star, 4 Gallon 200.00
Stoneware, Crock, Cobalt, Underglaze Design, Hamilton & Jones, Greensboro 42.50
Stoneware, Crock, Cobalt Underglaze, Stenciled A.P.Donaghho, One Gallon 20.00
Stoneware, Crock, Eagles Carrying Banners, Incised In Cobalt Blue, 6 Gallon 75.00
Stoneware, Crock, Gray Salt Glazed, Cobalt Designs, Amber, Gallon 34.00
Stoneware, Crock, Gray, Blue Decoration, Incised Band, J.Swank & Co., Pa. 110.00
Stoneware, Crock, Gray, Blue Decoration, J.Swank & Co. 60.00
Stoneware, Crock, Gray, Ears, Blue Stenciled Eagle, Enterprise, New Geneva 110.00
Stoneware, Crock, Gray, Spread American Eagle, A.P.Donaghho, Pa. 90.00
Stoneware, Crock, Lion, Eagle With Spread Wings, 2 Gallon 250.00
Stoneware, Crock, Miniature, Bunches Of Grapes & Leaves For Handles 55.00
Stoneware, Crock, Ovoid, Earred, Cobalt Oak Leaf, C.Sherburne, 1858, 1 Gallon 60.00
Stoneware, Crock, Ovoid, Earred, Cobalt Trim, Goodwin & Webster, Circa 1810 .... 75.00
Stoneware, Crock, Vivid Pea Fowl, Ovoid, Circa 1820, 3 Gallon 300.00
Stoneware, Cuspidor, Blue, Flower Decoration 30.00
Stoneware, Dish, Gray Crackle Glaze, Crane, Tree, Butterflies, Cheng Hua Mark 85.00
Stoneware, Doorstop, Rampant Lion On Oval Base, Dark Brown Glaze 20.00
Stoneware, Figurine, Dog On Base, Standing, Tooled Decoration 360.00
Stoneware, Gray, Cobalt Floral, Sipe & Sons, Wmsport, Pa., Gallon 28.50
Stoneware, Inkwell, Marked Skey, England 5.00
Stoneware, Inkwell, Spout, Octagonal 65.00
Stoneware, Jar, Cobalt Fern Decoration, C.Boynton & Co., Troy, 1820s 45.00
Stoneware, Jar, Cobalt Underglaze Decoration, Hamilton & Jones, Handles 38.00
Stoneware, Jar, Ginger, Blue Underglaze Scene, House, Boat, Garden, Gray 38.00

Stoneware, Jar, Jam, Gray Salt Glazed, Cobalt Designs, Quart 32.00
Stoneware, Jar, Narrow Flared Neck, Blue Stripes & Wavy Lines 55.00
Stoneware, Jar, Tobacco, Brass Lid, Dated Clamp 25.00
Stoneware, Jar, Tobacco, Swami, Salt Glazed, 6 In.High 65.00
Stoneware, Jug, A.Hatke & Co., Whiskey, Gallon 25.00
Stoneware, Jug, Batter, Stemmed Flower & Leaves Under Spout, 9 In.High 45.00
Stoneware, Jug, Bird On A Leaf, 2 Gallon 50.00
Stoneware, Jug, Blue Design, Gray, White, Binghamton, 1 Gallon 23.00
Stoneware, Jug, Blue Design, 2 Gallon 30.00
Stoneware, Jug, Blue Peacock, Whites, Binghamton, 3 Gallon 75.00
Stoneware, Jug, Blue Shades, Windmill, 1 1/2 Qt. 20.00
Stoneware, Jug, Blue Shading, Embossed Windmill, 1 1/2 Qt. 28.00
Stoneware, Jug, Brown, Says Centennial July 4, 1876, 3 In. 17.50
Stoneware, Jug, Cobalt Christmas Tree Design, N.A.White, Utica, 1 Gallon 17.00
Stoneware, Jug, Gray, Flow Blue Lettering, F.J.Mcguire, Auburn, N.Y. 25.00
Stoneware, Jug, Gray, Ovoid, Charlestown, 2 Gallon 55.00
Stoneware, Jug, Impressed Swan Smeared In Cobalt, Gardner, Maine, 2 Gallon 60.00
Stoneware, Jug, Swan Design, Blue, Gallon 22.50
Stoneware, Jug, Water, Blue Decoration, J.Swank & Co., Johnstown, Pa., Spout 205.00
Stoneware, Jug, Whiskey, Ramsay's Old Scotch, Straus Bros., Chicago 30.00
Stoneware, Mallet, Cone Shape, Wooden Handle, Blue Band 25.00
Stoneware, Mug, Buffalo Design, Drinking Scene, White's Pottery, 1899 .... 15.00
Stoneware, Mug, Flaccus Bros., Wheeling, W.Va., Label 30.00
Stoneware, Mug, Open Handle 20.00
Stoneware, Mustard Pot, Men Figures, White, Silver Plated Top, 3 In.High 32.50
Stoneware, Pitcher, Blue & Gray, Horse Racing Figures In Relief, Germany 37.50
Stoneware, Pitcher, Blue & Gray, 17 In.High 150.00
Stoneware, Pitcher, Blue Decoration, Richey & Hamilton, Palatine, W.Va. 110.00
Stoneware, Pitcher, Dark Brown, Glazed Inside, 10 In.High 20.00
Stoneware, Pitcher, Two Blue Cows, Dorchester, Embossed Holstein Milk 35.00
Stoneware, Planter, Tree Stump, Bangor Stoneware Works, Me. 70.00
Stoneware, Pot, Cobalt Bird On Branch, 2 Gallon 80.00
Stoneware, Stein, Blue Decoration, Pewter Top 50.00
Stoneware, Stein, Symbols For Mountain Climber, 1/2 Liter 55.00
Stoneware, Stein, 1/2 Liter, Regimental, Pewter Lid, Munich Maid, Twin Towers 68.00
Stoneware, Sugar, Covered, Raised Decoration 150.00
Stoneware, Syrup, Men, Animals, Trees, White, Pewter Lid, 6 1/2 In.High 47.50
Stoneware, Urn, Footed, Saucer Base, Applied Ring Handles, Flared Top 20.00
Stoneware, Vase, Blue Decoration, Two Handles, 5 1/2 In.High 210.00
Stoneware, Washstand Set, Floral On Pitcher, Blue, Gray, 2 Piece 67.00
Stoneware, Water Cooler, Ear Handles, G.Arblaster Inscribed In Blue 170.00
Stoneware, Whistle, Rooster, Gray, Blue Decoration 180.00
   Store, see also Card, Advertising, Coffee Grinder, Tool, Scale
Store, Ashtray, Armstrong Tires, Embossed, Glass In Tire 4.50
Store, Ashtray, Bay Ridge Specialty Co., Inc., Trenton, N.J., Porcelain 1.50
Store, Ashtray, Crosfield's Pyramid Soap, Green On White, China 9.00
Store, Ashtray, Goodyear Tire, Green Glass Insert 5.00
Store, Ashtray, Hood Tires, Glass In Tire, Red Arrow 3.00
Store, Ashtray, Pepsi Cola, Decal, 1940s 9.00
Store, Ashtray, S.L.Allen & Co., Inc., Planet Jr.Flexible Flyer, China 5.00
Store, Ashtray, Soussa Cigarettes, American Tobacco Co., Rectangular, China 3.00
Store, Ashtray, Springfield Brewery Co., Mass., China, Rectangular 3.00
Store, Bag, Worcester Brand Salt, White 7.00
Store, Banner, Coon's Ice Cream, Painted On Canvas 15.00
Store, Barrel & Scoop, Ice Cream, Coon's Cream, Burlington, Wooden, Painted 65.00
Store, Barrel, Richardson's Liberty Root Beer, Embossed In Black, Porcelain 140.00
Store, Barrel, Stearn's Old Fashioned Root Beer, Wooden, 13 In.High 85.00
Store, Basket, Splint, Bushel Size 35.00
Store, Beer Set, Coor's, Pitcher, 6 Tumblers, & Tray 27.50
Store, Bin, Coffee, Atwood, Green Ground, Lettering, Tin 55.00
Store, Blotter, Arm & Hammer Soda .... .95
Store, Blotter, Ink, Carter's, Call For Carter's .... .15
Store, Bonnet Block, Wooden 39.50
Store, Bookmark, Elastica, Child On Rocking Horse, Celluloid 6.00
Store, Boot, Cast Iron, Painted Black 35.00
Store, Bootjack, Iron, 'Use Musselman's Bootjack Plug Tobacco, ' 10 In. 35.00

Store, Bowl, Pettijohn's Flaked Breakfast Food, Bear Lithograph, Bavarian 15.00
Store, Bowl, Planters Peanut, Set Of 3 .... 5.00
Store, Bowl, Soup, Uneeda Boy, Yellow Slicker, White China 30.00
Store, Box, A.Hoefner's Pure Ceylon Soap, Wooden, Dovetailed, Glass Inside 40.00
Store, Box, Adam's Pepsin Tutti Frutti Gum, Flat, Flip Top, Cardboard 6.00
Store, Box, American Pencil Co., 1902, Pie Shape, Black, Gold Lettering 1.00
Store, Box, American Table Cutlery, Landers, Frary, & Clark, Conn., Paper 10.00
Store, Box, Amoskegg Rolled Oats, Scene Of Waterfall, Round, Paper, 2 Pounds 30.00
Store, Box, Armour's Chicken Bouillon Cubes, 2 3/4 X 2 X 3/4 In. 10.00
Store, Box, Aunt Lydia's Carpet & Button Thread, Red .... 8.00 To 15.00
Store, Box, Baker's Caracas Chocolate, Stenciled, Dovetailed, Black 8.00
Store, Box, Baker's Caracas Sweet Chocolate, Baker Lady, Wooden 10.00
Store, Box, Baker's Chocolate, Green, Paper 5.00
Store, Box, Baker's Cocoa, 6 Drawer, Porcelain Knobs 150.00
Store, Box, Bigger Hair Tobacco, Cardboard, Tin Bottom 18.00
Store, Box, Borax Toilet & Bath Powder, 20 Mule Team, Cardboard Sides 6.00
Store, Box, Boy's Union Tool Chest, Hinged, Oak, Metal Grips, Tools, Pictures 35.00
Store, Box, Bromo Seltzer, Stenciled, Black Type, Dovetailed 10.00
Store, Box, Buttermilk Toilet Soap, The Cosmo Buttermilk Fine Soap Co. .... .50
Store, Box, Button Rings, Contents, 1 X 2 In. 1.50
Store, Box, Chas.S.Higgins, German Laundry Soap, Color Labels, Wooden 20.00
Store, Box, Cigar, Merry Christmas & Happy New Year, 1892, Wooden, Engraved 12.00
Store, Box, Cigar, Oak, Silver Metal Escutcheon & Key, Lettering 38.00
Store, Box, Cigar, Pitners Repeaters, 1910 Tax Stamp 3.50
Store, Box, Clarks'O.N.T.Spool Cotton, Hinged, Brass, Black Paint, Wooden 5.00
Store, Box, Colgate & Co., Glycerine Soap, Wooden, Dovetailed 12.00
Store, Box, Colgate's Petit Dentures, Flip Top, Label, Pictures Of Children 1.00
Store, Box, Collar, Album Collar, Shape Of Dictionary 1.50
Store, Box, Companion Pingsuey Tea, Wooden, Label, 10 Pounds 24.00
Store, Box, Cornstarch, Iron Handle, Paper Label, Orange, 7 1/2 In.High 15.00
Store, Box, Curly Blossom Tea, Scherr & Brewer Retailers, Cardboard Sides 3.00
Store, Box, Cuticura Anti-Pain Plastering, Flip Top, Red & Black 6.00
Store, Box, Diamond Finish Laundry Starch, R.L.Shennan & Co., Round 1.00
Store, Box, Display, A.B.Bruce Cracker & Biscuit, Train, Red & Beige, Label 35.00
Store, Box, Display, Aunt Lydia's Button & Carpet Thread, Extra Strong 65.00
Store, Box, Display, Aunt Lydia's Button & Carpet Thread, Wooden, Hanging 50.00
Store, Box, Display, National Biscuit Co., Paper Label, Green & Beige 10.00
Store, Box, Display, National Biscuit, Glass Front, Brass Lid, Tin 35.00
Store, Box, Display, Norris Biscuit & Crackers, Paper Label, Red & White 22.00
Store, Box, Display, Stickney & Poor's Mustard, Older People By Fireplace 35.00
Store, Box, Duryea's Superior Starch, National Starch Co., 1805, Paper 1.50
Store, Box, Fairbanks Gold Dust Washing Powder, Wooden, Lithograph Label 9.00
Store, Box, Foss Vanilla, Paper Label, White, Black Type, Wooden 10.00
Store, Box, Geo.W.Smith & Son, Wintergreen, Yellow .... .50
Store, Box, German's Sweet Chocolate, Walter Baker Co., Label 5.00
Store, Box, Gillette Safety Razor 2.00
Store, Box, Good Will Soap, Paper Label, Flowers, Red & Green, Wooden 15.00
Store, Box, H.D.Foss & Co., Peppermint Patties, Paper, White 1.50
Store, Box, Handsnap Buttons, Joseph P.Noyes & Co., Patent 1885, 1 X 2 In. 3.00
Store, Box, Hose, The Best Melba Fast Black, Red, 6 X 12 In. 3.00
Store, Box, John Hepburn, Pharmacist, Quinine, Main St., Flushing, Wooden 1.50
Store, Box, John Primble India Steel Works Pocket Knives, Cardboard 2.50
Store, Box, Kennedy Biscuits, Paper Label, Wooden, Blue 12.00
Store, Box, Kennedy's Biscuits, Hinged, Paper Label, Wooden 10.00
Store, Box, Kibbe's Gum Drops, 10 X 4 X 1 1/2 In. 1.00
Store, Box, Kingsford's Silver Gloss Starch, Wooden, 10 X 5 X 5 In. 5.00
Store, Box, Kraft Cheese, Wooden 3.00
Store, Box, Labeled Collard, Collar Shape, Embossed Horseshoes, Black 2.00
Store, Box, Lawrence Braid, Painted Lettering, Roll Front, Oak 45.00
Store, Box, Leather Marking Crayons, F.W.Whitcher & Co., Paper Label 3.00
Store, Box, Lucky Strike, Flat 50, Cardboard, Full 6.50
Store, Box, Macy's Brand Breakfast Cocoa, Paper Label, Cardboard Sides 12.00
Store, Box, Malden Coffee Blend, Paper Label, Eagle, Beige & Black, Cardboard 3.00
Store, Box, Maxwell House Tea, Paper Label, Cardboard Sides 3.00
Store, Box, Muff, C.G.Gunther & Sons, Furriers, N.Y., Lithograph, Round, Black 15.00
Store, Box, Nervease Headache Powder, Paper Label, Black Type, Paper 6.00

Store, Box, North Carolina Tobacco, Wooden, Paper Label, Black & Red 35.00
Store, Box, O-Bright Silver Polish, Powder Form, Color Label, Paper 1.00
Store, Box, Old Reliable Complete Outfit For Repairing Shoes, Wooden 65.00
Store, Box, Oswego Silver Gloss Starch, Lithograph Of Indian Maiden, Wooden 15.00
Store, Box, Pape's Cold Compound Tablets, Wooden, Round 3.00
Store, Box, Peerless Wafers Wintergreen, Red Label, Flit Top, Blue 8.00
Store, Box, Pencil, Picture Of Children Playing, Paper Label, Wooden 3.00
Store, Box, Philip Morris Cigarettes 2.00
Store, Box, Proctor & Gamble Lenox Soap, Paper Label, Dovetailed, Blue, Red 15.00
Store, Box, R.& G.Corsets, Metal Lacer, Paper, 2 X 14 In. 3.00
Store, Box, R.H.Macy & Co., Glace Fruit, Wooden, Paper Label 1.00
Store, Box, Royal Baking Powder, Paper Label, Red & Beige 8.00
Store, Box, S.S.Sleeper & Co.'s Eye Cigar, Lithograph Of Eye & Cigar 15.00
Store, Box, Sanford's Ginger, Black, Painted Label, Wooden, Dovetailed 12.00
Store, Box, Saunder's Face Powder, Paper Label, Round, Wooden 1.50
Store, Box, Sawyer's Crystal Bag, Blue, Paper Label, Wooden, Round 3.00
Store, Box, Schrafft's Chocolates, Blue Boy Picture 1.50
Store, Box, Selco Dry Cleansing Powder Spot Remover, Cardboard, Yellow 1.50
Store, Box, Sensible Tobacco, Paper, Brown & Beige 5.00
Store, Box, Slippery Elm Lozenges, Cathedral Window, Flip Top, Gold & Black 75.00
Store, Box, Spool, John Clark, Jr., Black Gold, 1862, Hinged Top, Blue Label 65.00
Store, Box, Spruce Gum, Slide Top, Paper Label, Wooden 5.00
Store, Box, Squirrel Brand Peanut Bars, Cardboard 35.00
Store, Box, Stearns Kingston Roll Braid, Cardboard 3.00
Store, Box, Stein Hirsh & Co., Starch, Indian Lithograph, Paper Label 12.00
Store, Box, Stickney & Poor's Allspice, Cardboard 5.00
Store, Box, Stickney & Poor's Tartar, Paper Label, Dovetailed, Red & Yellow 15.00
Store, Box, The Apollo Chocolates, Lady, Paper Label, Paper 2.00
Store, Box, The Mirror Candies, Original Mexican Kisses 1.00
Store, Box, The Victor Bubbler, Patent Feb.24, '03, Rob'T Gain Co., Bkln 5.00
Store, Box, Thomson's High Test Lye, Painted Paper Label, Wooden 9.00
Store, Box, Tiger Tobacco, Cardboard, Hinged Tin Lid, Tiger, Gold & Orange 35.00
Store, Box, Triumph Brand Coffee, Blue, White-Type, Cardboard 30.00
Store, Box, Tropical Lemon Peel, Wooden 3.00
Store, Box, Vapo-Cresolene For Throat & Lung Diseases 1.00
Store, Box, Walter Baker & Co., Premium, Chocolate, Wooden, Dovetailed 10.00
Store, Box, White Windsor Soap, F.R.Robinson's, 2 1/2 X 5 In. .... .50
Store, Box, Wm.Wilson & Son, Silversmiths Co., Indian Good Luck Sign Inside 1.50
Store, Box, Wrigley's Spearmint Pepsin Gum, Flip Top, Cardboard 6.00
Store, Branding Iron, For Wooden Boxes, City Of New York 5.00
Store, Breakstone's Home Made Cheese, Green & Yellow, Round, 5 Pounds 3.00
Store, Broadside, Civil War Recruiting, 'Flag Of America Shall Never Dim' 64.50
Store, Broadside, Clemen's Indian Tonic, American, Dated 1845 .... 29.50
Store, Broadside, Encouraging French Protestants To Transport, 1689 .... 39.50
Store, Broadside, English, Murder, Joseph Guinn, C.1820 .... 14.50
Store, Broadside, F.B.Underhill, Clothing Store, Paper, Mounted 45.00
Store, Broadside, Mont Storm's Breech-Loading Arms, Dated 1861 .... 6.50
Store, Broadside, Sharps Rifle, 1850, Hartford, Woodcut Illustration 54.50
Store, Brochure, Warner's Log Cabin Remedies, 32 Pages, 1887 .... 10.00
Store, Bucket, Buffalo Brand Peanut Butter, E.M.Hoyt & Co., Handle, Red 25.00
Store, Bucket, Climax Peanut Butter 12.00
Store, Bucket, Cottlene N.F.Fairband Co.Lard, Handle, Beige & Red, Tin 9.00
Store, Bucket, Dixie Peanut, Handle, Red & Gold, Tin 12.00
Store, Bucket, Long's Ox-Heart, Paper Label, Round, Wire Handle, Tin 20.00
Store, Bucket, Nut-Te-Na Peanut Butter, Handle, Red & White, Tin 25.00
Store, Bucket, Porster's Peanut Butter, Handle, Girl & Dog, Mustard & Red 25.00
Store, Bucket, Rajan Chocolate, Wire Handle, Red & Beige, Black Type, Tin 20.00
Store, Bucket, Sap, Maple, Wooden 6.50
Store, Bucket, Saple Brand Peanut Butter, Orange & Green, Round. Wire Handle 20.00
Store, Bucket, Sultana Peanut Butter, Boy & Girl, Handle 25.00
Store, Bucket, Swift's Jewel Brand Lard, Handle, Beige & Red, Tin 10.00
Store, Bucket, Swift's Silver Leaf Brand Lard, Leaved, Gold & Red, Tin 12.00
Store, Buttonhook, Shoe, Bone Handle 5.00
Store, Cabinet, Druggist's, Wooden, Humphrey's Specifics, Gold Lettering 70.00
Store, Cabinet, Druggist's, Wooden, Munyon's Homoeopathic Remedies, 36 Cures 55.00
Store, Cabinet, Dye, Putnam, Lithograph, Horses, Riders, Tags On Partitions 40.00

Store, Cabinet, Dye, Tin Front, Wood, Phoenix 85.00
Store, Cabinet, Johnson & Johnson, Black, Red Lettering, Tin, 4 Drawer 50.00
Store, Cabinet, Morison's English Veterinary Medicines, Hanging, Wooden 135.00
Store, Cabinet, Screw, Octagonal, 80 Drawers, 36 X 21 In. 375.00
Store, Cabinet, Shot Dispenser, Glass Front, Circa 1878 .... 125.00
Store, Cabinet, Spice, Lithograph Of Woman, 8 Drawers, Milk Glass Pulls 350.00
Store, Cabinet, Spool, Clark's, Oak, Flat Top, 5 Drawer 85.00
Store, Cabinet, Spool, Clark's, Swivel Base, Glass Doors, Lift Lid, Oak, 23 In. 145.00
Store, Cabinet, Spool, J.P.Coats, Celluloid Insert, Porcelain Knobs, 2 Drawer 65.00
Store, Cabinet, Spool, J.P.Coats, 4 Drawer, 8 Mellon Pulls, Desk Model 110.00
Store, Cabinet, Spool, Six Drawers, J.P.Coats, Cherry, Restored 125.00
Store, Cake Tin, Angel, Swansdown 2.50
Store, Calendar, Astrology, Quaker Oats, 1900, 6 X 6 In. 6.00
Store, Calendar, Bristol Steel Fishing Rods, 1904, Lithograph, Lady, Fish 50.00
Store, Calendar, Bristol Steel Fishing Rods, 1905, Lithograph, The Start 50.00
Store, Calendar, Bristol Steel Fishing Rods, 1909, Man & Lady In Boat, Kesch 50.00
Store, Calendar, Bristol Steel Rods, Men Fishing, Oliver Kemp 50.00
Store, Calendar, Fairbank's Fairy Soap, 1899 .... 10.00
Store, Calendar, Perpetual, Copyright 1880, Gold Frame 35.00
Store, Calendar, RC Cola, Miss Nehi Picture, 1939 .... 14.50
Store, Calendar, Swift's Products, Folds Into Ruler, 1919-1920 .... 3.75
Store, Can, Cream, Handle, Brass Label, Solon, Me., 1 Gallon 15.00
Store, Can, Milk, Gray Enamel, Wire Handle, Quart 5.00
Store, Canister, Coffee Co., Paper Label, Hinged Top, Red, Gold, & Black 40.00
Store, Canister, Coffee, Lithograph Of Lady, Red, 9 In.High 20.00
Store, Canister, Coffee, Winter Scene, Slide Up Opening, Coffee In Script 35.00
Store, Canister, Oblong Gunpowder, Refinished, Pair 50.00
Store, Canister, Pepper, Paper Label, Red, Round 3.00
Store, Canister, Spice, 7 Round Containers, Labeled, Wooden 25.00
Store, Canister, Zatek Chocolate Billets, 1907, Penna., Chocolate Glass 150.00
Store, Cap Remover, White Belt Dairy, Miami, Florida, C.1930, Metal 2.00
Store, Card, Pin, Nouss Bros., Aix-La-Chapelle, Children, Patent 3.00
Store, Carton, Sani-Tissue, Scott Paper Co., 3 Rolls 4.00
Store, Case, Cigar, Metal 3.50
Store, Case, Display, Burnham's Hardy Jelly Can, Glass, Filigreed Metal 85.00
Store, Case, Display, Collar, Simeon Sharaf, Concord, N.H., Glass, Metal 150.00
Store, Case, Display, La Garcia Grande Cigar, Tin, Slanted Glass Front 40.00
Store, Case, Display, Thread, Oak, 4 Tilt Down Glass Doors 60.00
Store, Case, Handcuff, Leather 2.95
Store, Case, Nonpareil Needle & Toilet Pin, Cherubs & Granny, British, Paper 3.00
Store, Cash Drawer, For Counter, Change Compartments, Bell, Combination Lock 20.00
Store, Cash Drawer, Under Counter, Combination Release & Alarm Bell 18.00
Store, Cash Drawer, Wooden, Tucker 10.00
Store, Cash Register, Barber Shop, Chrome Plated, One Cent To Ninety Cents 50.00
Store, Cash Register, Brass, Polished, Lacquered, Small 265.00
Store, Cash Register, Ideal, Miller Vastine Mfg.Co., Nickel On Brass 350.00
Store, Cash Register, National, Lithosteel & Wood, 3 Drawer 40.00
Store, Cash Register, Ornate, Polished & Lacquered, Brass 135.00
Store, Casket, Jewelry Cleaning, Dennison's, Quarter Oak 8.00
Store, Chair, Piedmont Cigarettes, Blue & White Tin Back, Folding 75.00
Store, Cheese Cutter, Iron Wheel, Wooden Handle, 23 In.Wide, 22 In.Tall 35.00
Store, Cheese Cutter, Wheel, Wire, 18 In.Wide, 21 In.High 22.00
Store, Chest, Elite Tool Chest For Boys, Wooden, Dovetailed, Tools 35.00
Store, Chest, Spool, Crowley's Needles, Oak, 2 Drawer, Porcelain Handles 45.00
Store, Chest, Spool, Eureka, Oak, 4 Drawer 55.00
Store, Chinese Ginger, Soldered Can, For U.S.Trade 10.00
Store, Cigar Cutter, Counter, A.B.Smith Co., Patent 1902, Iron 25.00
Store, Cigar Cutter, Counter, Cast Iron, Merit Davis, Syracuse, N.Y., Lighters 250.00
Store, Cigar Cutter, Scissors Type, Butterfly 8.50
Store, Cipher Box & Rule, Cryptographer's, Military, Wooden, Handmade, C.1850 ...... 110.00
Store, Clippers, Squeeze Action, Celluloid Calendar For 1908-09 On Handle 3.00
  Store, Coffee Grinder, see Coffee Grinder
Store, Compass, Dr.Scott's Electric Brush, Embossed 4.00
Store, Compote, Clark's Teaberry Gum, Glear Glass Pedestal Top 25.00
Store, Compote, Teaberry Gum, Hand-Painted Floral, Signed Landry, 10 3/4 In. 38.00
Store, Container, Cheese, Domed Top, Perforated Sides, Stenciled 75.00

Store, Container, Lipton Tea, Embossed Lion, Dated 1924, Brass 16.50
Store, Container, Pill, Doctor's, Leather Case, Bottles, Pewter Tops 7.00
Store, Cooler, Water, Crown Crock, Country School, 2 Gallon, Cobalt Trim 32.00
Store, Cork Sizer, Druggist's, Four Slots, Handle, Iron 25.00
Store, Corkscrew, Bar, Dallas 7.00
Store, Corkscrew, Gay 90s Lady's Stripped Legs 35.00
Store, Crate, Egg, Wooden, Carrying Handle, 12 Dozen Type 4.00
Store, Creamer, Marked Kellogg's Correct Cereal Creamer, Clear 3.75
Store, Creamer, Moxie, Girl, China 30.00
Store, Cup & Saucer, Heinz Pickle, 57 Varieties, Miniature, Lamberton China 15.00
Store, Cup, Armour's Vigoral, Red Carnations, 3 1/2 In.High 12.50
Store, Cup, Bouillon, Armour's Vigoral, Pink, Carnations, Porcelain 15.00
Store, Cup, Bouillon, Cudahy 15.00
Store, Cup, Cyclist's, Patent 1897, Collapsible, Nickel On Brass, Scene 15.00
Store, Cup, Measuring, Marked Cloverdale Quality, 3 Four Leaf Clovers, Clear 3.75
Store, Cup, Moxie, Girl 25.00
Store, Cup, Van Houten's, Delft Type Decoration, Porcelain 25.00
Store, Dentures, Demonstrator, Celluloid, Brass Hinges, Marked Pittsburgh 9.50
Store, Dish, Candy, Schrafft's, Square, Pressed Pattern 6.50
Store, Dish, Hot, Metal Dome Cover, Marked Empress Trademark, China Liner 35.00
Store, Dish, Schepp's New Improved Coconut, Embossed, Covered 150.00
Store, Dispenser, Daggett's Orangeade, Clear Top, Green Glass Base, Mottled 65.00
Store, Dispenser, Dixie Cup, Glass Top, Metal Base, Brass Letters, One Cent 20.00
Store, Dispenser, Dixie Dew, Milk Glass Base, Clear Acorn Shape Top 65.00
Store, Dispenser, Fowler's Cherry Smash, Our Nation's Beverage 165.00
Store, Dispenser, Matchbox, Wooden, Coin Operated 29.00
Store, Dispenser, Pill, Brass 2.25
Store, Dispenser, Ward's Lemon Crush, Lemon Form 125.00
Store, Dispenser, Ward's Lime Crush, Lime Form 125.00
Store, Dispenser, Ward's Orange Crush, Porcelain, 14 In.High 125.00
Store, Display Stand, Thimble, Holds 72 Thimbles, Boye Needle Co. 25.00
Store, Display, Shotgun, Engraving, 3 Times Normal Size, C.1900 .... 32.50
Store, Doctor's Cure All, Super Marvel, Generators, Hinged Box 21.00
Store, Dress Form, Acme, Cast Iron Wheel Base, Tan, Collapsible, Patent 1914 .... 20.00
Store, Dryer, Apple, 8 Drawers With Wire Bottoms 30.00
Store, Duster, Turkey Feather .... *Illus* 18.00
Store, Egg Tray, Star, 1903, Wooden 6.50
Store, Envelope, Old Honesty Plug Tobacco, Rich Mellow Chew, Cloth, Dog 3.00
Store, Eyecup, John Bull's, Green 12.00
Store, Fan, Alka Seltzer, Pasteboard 2.00
Store, Fan, Benjamin Moore Paints, 'Use Muresco Colorful Flowers' 3.00
Store, Fan, Calendar, 1896, 7 X 12 In. 8.00
Store, Fan, Mara-Cola, American Beauty, Lady, Fitchburg, Mass. 15.00
Store, Fan, Moxie, Cowboy & Man, Horse 12.00
Store, Fan, Moxie, Eileen Percy, Music 20.00
Store, Fan, Moxie, Frances Pritchard Holding Glass, 1915 .... 15.00 To 25.00
Store, Fan, Moxie, Lady & Man, 1915 .... 35.00
Store, Fan, Moxie, Lady, Man, 1924 .... 15.00
Store, Fan, Moxie, Man, Lithograph, Color, 1921 .... 15.00
Store, Fan, Moxie, Muriel Ostriche, Full Figure, Pink Dress, 1916 .... 25.00
Store, Fan, Moxie, Muriel Ostriche, Red Beret 15.00
Store, Fan, Moxie, Peggy, Picnic Scene 20.00
Store, Fan, Moxie, Woman, Man, 'sensible Drink, '1920s 15.00
Store, Fan, Putnam Dyes, Man On Horse 15.00
Store, Fan, Singer Sewing Machines, Boy, Girl 18.00
Store, Fan, Sunshine Biscuit, 'Tak-Hom-A-Biscuit, 'Wooden Handle 9.00
Store, Figure, Tobacconist, Zinc, American, C.1850, 50 In. .... *Illus* 800.00
Store, Figurine, Boy, Holding Newspaper, Gilt Metal, 'Extra 5 Cents' 150.00
Store, Figurine, Horse, White Horse, Plaster 8.00
Store, Figurine, Johnny Pfeiffer Beer 2.50
Store, Figurine, Lady, Moxie, Carved Wooden, Holding Tray, Blue Uniform 95.00
Store, Flour Scoop, Nickel Plate Over Brass, Wooden Handle 6.00
Store, Foot Warmer, Tin, Wood, 9 In. .... *Illus* 45.00
Store, Form, Dress Maker's, Thomasens Glove Fitting, Blue Velvet Top 55.00
Store, Glass, Bar, Columbia Beer 7.50
Store, Glass, Budweiser, Stemmed 5.00

Store, Glass, Embossed Nash Co., Clear 10.00
Store, Glass, Hire's Root Beer, Etched, 'RJ With Real Juices' 10.00
Store, Glass, Moxie, 'Drink Moxie Nerve Food, 'White Decal 25.00
Store, Glass, Moxie, Embossed, Handle 15.00
Store, Glass, Moxie, Red 10.00
Store, Glass, Moxie, Red Label, Handle 22.00
Store, Glass, Pabst Blue Ribbon Beer, Stemmed 12.00
Store, Glass, Schlitz 2.00
Store, Glass, Shot, Dr.C.Bouvier's Bucher Gln For The Kidneys, Clear 10.00
Store, Glass, Soda Water, Clicquot Club, Embossed, Weighted Base 8.00
Store, Glass, Soda, Canada Dry Ginger Ale, Etched, Clear 3.00
Store, Glass, Soda, Embossed Phoenix 5 In Shield, Clear 10.00
Store, Graduate, Apothecary's, Etched Gradations, Free Blown, Aqua 12.00
Store, Grater, Crank Type, Iron & Tin, Wooden Plunger & Handle 4.00
     Store, Gum Machine, see Store, Machine, Gum ball
Store, Hame, Horse, Metal, Pair 4.00
Store, Hammer, Cordove Cigar Co., Osmundo Cigars, Iron, 4 1/4 In.Long 7.50
Store, Handbill, Al.G.Barnes, 1923, Pink & Black 6.00
Store, Handbill, Circus, Florida Blossoms, 1915 .... 5.50
Store, Handbill, Circus, Gentry, 1913 .... 6.00
Store, Handbill, Circus, Great Wallace, 1905 .... 12.50
Store, Handbill, Circus, Mighty Haag, 1916 .... 5.50
Store, Handbill, Cole Circus, Auto Loop Act Featured, 1937 .... 4.50

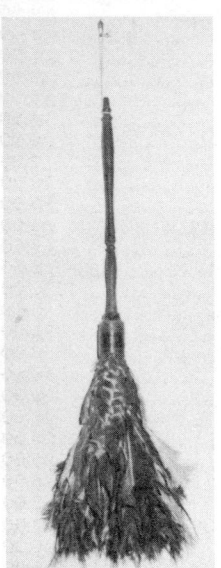

Store, Foot Warmer, Tin, Wood, 9 In.
See Page 561

Store, Figure, Tobacconist, Zinc,
American, C.1850, 50 In.
See Page 561

Store, Duster, Turkey Feather
See Page 561

Store, Handbill, De Rue Bros., American Minstrels, White 3.50
Store, Handbill, Golden Bros.4 Ring Animal Show, 1922, Brown & Cream 7.50
Store, Handbill, M.L.Clark Circus, 1920 .... 3.50
Store, Handbill, Rentz Bros.Circus, 1913 .... 3.75
Store, Handcuffs, Nickel Plated, 2 Keys 3.75
Store, Hat Block, Lady's, Wood 10.00
Store, Hat, Hard, Miner's 3.00
Store, Heater, Buggy, Charcoal 12.00
Store, Holder, Postcard, Metal Rack, Revolving 45.00
Store, Holder, String, Ball, Cast Iron, Fastens To Counter Top, 7 In.High 15.00
Store, Holder, Thread, Sarah's, 3 Spools, Cutters, Snap Top, Painted Label, Tin 18.00
Store, Horse Brasses, Enameled Flowers Under Glass 5.00
Store, Horseshoe, Take Simon's Liver Regulator, Brass 8.00
Store, Ice Cream Freezer & Butter Churn, Shephard's Lightning, Quart, 1891 .... 24.00
Store, Jar, Adam's Chewing Gum, Ground Top, Counter, 14 In.High 45.00

Store, Jar, Bagdad Tobacco, Picture Of Sultan, Porcelain 35.00
Store, Jar, Globe Tobacco Company, Detroit, Pat.Oct.10th, 1882, Amber, Barrel 22.50
Store, Jar, Gordon's, Red Truck Decoration, Metal Lid, 11 3/4 In.High 18.50
Store, Jar, Grand Union Marshmallow Cream, N.Y., Paper Label, Metal Lid 1.50
Store, Jar, Kiss Me Gum 15.00
Store, Jar, Lucky Strike Tobacco, Unopened, Dated July 1918 .... 50.00
Store, Jar, National Biscuit Company, Large Knob, Glass Lid, 2 Gallon 15.00
Store, Jar, National Biscuit Co., Lid, 10 3/4 In.High 32.50
Store, Jar, Planter's Peanut, Embossed, Mr.Peanut Decoration, Tin Lid 15.00
Store, Jar, Planter's Peanut, Leap Year, 1940 .... 16.00
Store, Jar, Planter's Peanut, 'Platner's, ' Glass Peanut Finial On Lid 35.00
Store, Jar, Planter's Peanut, Yellow Mr.Peanut On Alternation Panels 22.00
Store, Jar, Planter's Peanut, 4 Embossed Peanuts 125.00
Store, Jar, Prince Albert Tobacco 6.00
Store, Jar, Tilt, 'United States Nut Company, ' Metal Lid, 1 Gallon 10.00
Store, Jar, Tobacco, Glass, Square Sides, Dated 1900 .... 12.50
Store, Juicer, Sunkist, White 8.00
Store, Knife, Pocket, David Kohn Whiskeys, 1900, 3 1/2 In.Long 20.00
Store, Knife, Pocket, Warsaw Cheese Co. 10.00
Store, Lamp, Shop Torch, Iron, 1800s 32.00
Store, Lighter, Cigar & Cigarette, Manning-Bowman, 1911 Patent, Cast Iron 6.50
Store, Lighter, Cigar, Bossy Brand, Oil, Wall, Milk Glass, Black Cow 65.00
Store, Lighter, Cigar, Counter, Pewter, Shape Of Pipe, Brass Fixture 24.50
Store, Lock, D.M.& Co., Iron & Brass 4.50
Store, Lunch Box, Folding, Haywood & Hurlbuts, Patent 1863-1866, Tin 25.00
Store, Lunch Box, H-O Tobacco, Brown & Gold 35.00
Store, Lunch Box, Just Suits Tobacco, Red, Gold, Black 22.00
Store, Lunch Box, Mayo's Cut Plug 14.50
Store, Lunch Box, Patterson Seal 14.50
Store, Lunch Box, Tiger Tobacco, Double Handle, Red & Black .... 15.00 To 20.00
Store, Lunch Box, Union Leader Cut Plug .... 7.00 To 12.00
Store, Lunch Box, Union Leader, Double Handles, Basket Weave, Red & Gold 20.00
Store, Lunch Box, Union Leader, Eagle, Red & Gold 25.00
Store, Lunch Box, Winner Cut Plug Tobacco 35.00
Store, Lunch Pail, Tin, History Of Aviation, 1796-1940 .... 27.50
Store, Lunch Pail, Winner Cut Plug 30.00
Store, Machine, Clock 1350.00
Store, Machine, Digger, Counter Type 450.00
Store, Machine, Digger, Penny Arcade, Walnut, 1933 .... 595.00
Store, Machine, Digger, Upright 950.00
Store, Machine, Football Game 750.00
Store, Machine, Fortune Teller, Pedestal 850.00
Store, Machine, Gum Ball, Aluminum Base, Chrome Tray 27.50
Store, Machine, Gum Ball, Puritan Baby Vendor, Your Fortune, Embossed 225.00
Store, Machine, Gum Ball, Returns Token 125.00
Store, Machine, Gum Ball, Table Model, Shoot Penny From Gun, Three Ducks 75.00
Store, Machine, Gum, Ad Lee Co., Pat.Sept.15, 1908, Metal Base, Glass Globe 125.00
Store, Machine, Gum, Embossed Acorn On Glass Top, Steel Base, Oak Mfg. Co. 17.00
Store, Machine, Gum, Mansfield Automatic, Nickel Rings Bell, Glass Case 25.00
Store, Machine, Gum, One Cent, Dated 1873, Oak, Zeno 99.00
Store, Machine, Lift 500.00
Store, Machine, Match, Rosebud, Penny 40.00
Store, Machine, Moderne Vendor, Hershey, Chrome, 1 Cent 30.00
Store, Machine, Never Lose 100.00
Store, Machine, Northwestern Peanut Vendor, 1 Cent, Octagonal Base 22.50
Store, Machine, Peanut, Round, Tall 75.00
Store, Machine, Peanut, Smiling Sam, Iron .... *Illus* 350.00
Store, Machine, Penny Peg Game 95.00
Store, Machine, Pistol Game 125.00
Store, Machine, Pulver Gum 85.00
Store, Machine, Race Horse, Upright 650.00
Store, Machine, Silver Comet Cigarettes, 8 In.High 40.00
Store, Machine, Silver Queen Tab Gum Vendor, 5 Slot 75.00
Store, Machine, Slot, Bell Fruit, Takes Nickel, Dated 1933 .... 100.00
Store, Machine, Slot, Mills-Dewey 500.00
Store, Machine, Stamp 25.00

Store, Machine, Peanut, Smiling Sam, Iron
See Page 563

Store, Machine, Tire Recapping, Saleman's Sample, Compressed Air, 1940s 25.00
Store, Machine, Vending, Lighter Fluid, Gas Pump Shape, One Cent, 18 In.High 45.00
Store, Machine, Vending, Penny Cigarette, 6 X 6 X 8 In. 40.00
Store, Measure, Grain, Bushel Size, 18th Century 55.00
Store, Measure, Grain, Dated 1786 .... 90.00
Store, Medical Quack Gizmo, Violet Light Emanates, Glass Implements 150.00
Store, Mill, Sausage, Iron 5.00
Store, Mirror, American Express 30.00
Store, Mirror, Cincinnati, Ohio 9.00
Store, Mirror, Gavitt's System Regulator Pills 1.25
Store, Mirror, Kamp Jewelers, Appleton, Wisc. 8.00
Store, Mirror, Red Tractor, Joe Mitchell & Son, Artesia, New Mexico 10.00
Store, Mirror, Utica, N.Y. 9.00
    Store, Mold, see also Tin, Mold
Store, Mortar & Pestle, Brass, 2 In. 12.50
Store, Mortar & Pestle, Brass, 4 In.Diameter .... 17.00 To 35.00
Store, Mortar & Pestle, Burl Mortar, Raised Rings Around Mortar 150.00
Store, Mortar & Pestle, Druggist's, Maple, 8 1/2 In.High 30.00
Store, Mortar & Pestle, Glass 18.00
Store, Mortar & Pestle, Iron .... 10.00 To 22.75
Store, Mortar & Pestle, Lignum Vitae 28.00
Store, Mortar & Pestle, Squat Pedestal Base, Iron 15.00
Store, Mortar & Pestle, Stone, 7 In. High X 4 1/2 In.Wide 21.00
Store, Mortar & Pestle, Stoneware 35.00
Store, Mortar & Pestle, Two Knobs, Brass 45.00
Store, Mortar & Pestle, Walnut, Mortar 8 X 6 In.High, Pestle 13 In.Long 65.00
Store, Mortar & Pestle, Wooden, Hand Carved 14.00
Store, Mortar & Pestle, Wooden, 8 In.High 22.75
Store, Mug, Armour's Very Best Root Beer 20.00
Store, Mug, Bellwood Rye Whiskey, Haverhill, Mass., Red 25.00
Store, Mug, Blatz, Brown 5.00
Store, Mug, Borax Makes Real Strength, Dragon Handle 18.00
Store, Mug, Buckeye Root Beer, Pottery 8.00
Store, Mug, Compliments Frank X.Schwab, 655 Broadway, Buffalo 15.00
Store, Mug, Compliments Of Louis Reprecht, Scranton, Pa., Brown Script 25.00
Store, Mug, Fabaschers, Barrel Shape, 3 Sheafs Of Wheat 25.00
Store, Mug, Gehring's Root Beer, Cleveland, Ohio, Crockery 15.00
Store, Mug, Hires, Corset Shape, 6 In. 15.00
Store, Mug, Jayne's Hot Soda, Gold Lettering On White Porcelain 25.00
Store, Mug, Lash's Root Beer, Pottery 12.00
Store, Mug, Moxie, Glass 15.00
Store, Mug, Old Kentucky Malt, 'secretly Different, 'Tan & Black Banding 10.00
Store, Mug, Prosit-Wm.Knabe & Co., May 14, 1902, Red & Black Script 25.00
Store, Mustache Curler, Scissors Type, 6 In. 9.00
Store, Opener, Bottle, Crab, Cast Iron 2.00
Store, Opener, Bottle, Donkey, Laughing, Cast Iron 2.00

Store, **Opener**, Bottle, Drunk On Lamppost, Cast Iron 2.00
Store, **Opener**, Bottle, Duck, Redhead, Brass 2.00
Store, **Opener**, Bottle, Elephant, Sitting, Cast Iron 8.00
Store, **Opener**, Bottle, Fish, Brass 2.00
Store, **Opener**, Bottle, Hammer, Brass 8.00
Store, **Opener**, Bottle, Jester, Brass 8.00
Store, **Opener**, Bottle, Lady's Fancy Boot, C.1911 .... 6.00
Store, **Opener**, Bottle, Lady's Leg, Brass 8.00
Store, **Opener**, Bottle, Londonderry Ale 2.00
Store, **Opener**, Bottle, Mairer Brewing, Los Angeles, Saber Shape 5.00
Store, **Opener**, Bottle, Owl, Brass 2.00
Store, **Opener**, Bottle, Parrot On Perch, Cast Iron .... 3.00 To 8.00
Store, **Opener**, Bottle, Pelican, Cast Iron 8.00
Store, **Opener**, Bottle, Pretzel, Cast Iron 2.00
Store, **Opener**, Bottle, Schlitz, Embossed 1.50
Store, **Opener**, Bottle, Sea Gull, Cast Iron 2.00
Store, **Opener**, Bottle, Sitting Goat, Brass 8.00
Store, **Opener**, Bottle, Touring Car, C.1911 .... 6.00
Store, **Opener**, Letter, Hamel Leather, 1916-1926 .... 3.00
Store, **Opener**, Letter, Uneeda Biscuit Boy, Metal, Lithograph .... 9.00 To 15.00
Store, **Opener**, Palm Tree, Cast Iron 8.00
Store, **Orange Crate Label** .... .50 TO 3.95
Store, **Pack**, Egg, Foot Locker Style, Fragile, 6 Dozen, Tin 12.00
Store, **Package**, Royal Lion Tea, Paper 3.00
Store, **Pail**, Armour's Peanut Butter, Nursery Rhyme, 1 Lb. 14.50
Store, **Pail**, The Jewel, Bail, Reg.1876 .... 3.50
Store, **Peanut Warmer**, Wood & Glass, 36 In.High, 18 In.Square 95.00
Store, **Pen**, Fountain, Parker, Tortoiseshell 3.00
Store, **Pen**, Mother-Of-Pearl Handle, Gold Filled Point, 5 In. 9.50
Store, **Pen**, Waterman's, Lady's, 14k Gold Engraved Bands, Nov.29, 1909 .... 12.00
Store, **Pencil**, Gene Autry, Mechanical, Photograph Lights Up, Battery 3.00
Store, **Pickle Scoop**, Juice Drain Hold, Glass 10.00
Store, **Pill Maker**, Wooden 65.00
Store, **Pill Roller**, Apothecary, Wooden & Brass 35.00
Store, **Pillbox**, Doct.Herrick's Sugar Coated Vegetable Liver Pills, Wooden 2.00
Store, **Pinback**, Peters Superior Cartridges .... .50
Store, **Pitcher**, Henderson's Wild Cherry Beverage Free, Clear 35.00
Store, **Plate**, China, Kellogg's Corn Flakes, 7 1/2 In.Diameter 3.50
Store, **Plate**, Dove Brand Sugar Cured Meats, Lady, Dresden Art, 8 In. 25.00
Store, **Plate**, From Safe, Adams, Hammond & Co., Patent Salamander Safe, Bronze 25.00
Store, **Plate**, George Urban Milling, Liberty Flour, Buffalo, N.Y., Pink Glass 12.00
Store, **Plate**, Moxie, Boy, 5 1/4 In. 25.00
Store, **Plate**, Tin, Pretty Lady, Joseph Glennon Brewery, 1907 .... 25.00
Store, **Pouch**, H-O Tobacco, Cloth, Red & Black 9.00
Store, **Press**, Wine, Cast Iron & Metal, Screw Type, 3 Gallon Capacity 34.00
Store, **Pump**, For Barrel Of Vinegar, Wooden 25.00
Store, **Pump**, Water, Painted 12.00
Store, **Punching Bag** 400.00
Store, **Rack**, Hanging, Wall, Three Tiers 7.50
Store, **Razor**, Straight, Omega Solingen Steel, Set Monday To Sunday In Case 65.00
Store, **Razor**, Straight, Winchester Trade Mark 25.00
Store, **Razor**, Winchester, Straight Neck 35.00
Store, **Salt & Pepper**, R.C.A.Dogs 5.00
Store, **Scale**, Buffalo Hide 12.50
Store, **Scale**, Buffalo Scale Co., Painted, Brass Scoop & Weights 100.00
Store, **Scale**, Cast Iron, Counter Type, Brass Weights, Buffalo Scale Co. 19.00
Store, **Scale**, Drugstore, Brass, I.Marden, Baltimore 150.00
Store, **Scale**, Egg, Metal 2.75
Store, **Scale**, Fairbanks Standard, Red Painted Iron, Porcelain, Tray, Globe 55.00
Store, **Scale**, Gold, Brass, Mahogany Base, Drawers 85.00
Store, **Scale**, Gold, Pocket, Wooden Box With Hinged Cover, C.1852 .... 30.00
Store, **Scale**, Howe, Red With Gold Stencil, Brass Pan & Weights, 10 Lbs. 59.00
Store, **Scale**, Iron, Tin Scoop, Red Paint, 6 Weights 55.00
Store, **Scale**, Multiple, Signed T.Berg, N.Y.S., Brass & Iron 75.00
Store, **Scale**, Postal, Brass, Wood Base, 5 Weights 42.50
Store, **Scale**, Postal, Pocket 3.50

Store, Scale, Rag Picker's, Brass, Hanging, Marked Chatillons Balance, N.Y. 3.75
Store, Scale, Steel Yard 6.50
Store, Scale, Stillyard, J.S.Trowbridge Co., Boston, Brass 45.00
Store, Scale, Weight, Avoir Dupois 45.00
Store, Scoop, Jelly Bean, Brass 7.50
Store, Scoop, Tin, Large Size 20.00
Store, Scriber, Stanley, Brass 2.00
Store, Scrubbrush & Scour Soap, Scrub-E-Z, Paper Wrapped, Freed Fean & Co. 3.00
Store, Sealing Device, Stamp, Lead, American Eagle, Shield, Floral, C.1850 .... 12.50
Store, Separator, Cream, DeLaval, Tin 17.50
Store, Server, Peanut, Mr.Peanut, Carlton Silver Plate 5.00
Store, Shaker & Cup, Hamo Thompson Malted Milk, Embossed Writing, Tin Cover 6.00
Store, Shocking Device, Generator, Patent 1897 .... 35.00
Store, Shoe Stretcher, Wooden, Iron Vise 5.50
Store, Shoe, Child's, Black Leather, Etched Brass Adjustable Closing, Pair 50.00
Store, Shoe, Heineken's Beer, Wooden 5.00
Store, Shoe, U.S.Army Issue, Indian Wars, Brass Eyelets, C.1870 .... 24.00
Store, Shoes, High Top, Lace Up, Little Girl's Size 7.50
Store, Shredder, Fels Naptha Soap 2.00
Store, Sign, Allen & Ginter Tobacco, Va., State Flags, George Harris, C.1900 .... 135.00
Store, Sign, American Boat Builder's, Hinson & Stowman, C.1870, Pine 89.50
Store, Sign, American Central Ins.Co., St.Louis, Tin, Black & Gold, Oak Frame 35.00
Store, Sign, American Lady, Hamilton Brown Shoe Co., Lady, Roses, Tin 85.00
Store, Sign, American Shoemaker's, Outdoor, Leather Shoe, Military Type 135.00
Store, Sign, Apothecary, Yellow & White, Smoke Grained, Wooden 185.00
Store, Sign, Arm & Hammer Soda, Design Of 16 Fish Cards, 16 In.Diameter 35.00
Store, Sign, Armour's Corn Flakes, Yellow Box, Red Letters, Tin 40.00
Store, Sign, Atlantic & Pacific Tea Co., C.1886 .... *Illus* 250.00
Store, Sign, Austin's Dog Bread, Poodle & Bulldog, Tin, Repousse 275.00
Store, Sign, Auto Spoof, 'A Study In Horsepower, 'stuart Blackten, 1906 .... 75.00
Store, Sign, B Y's & Bury B's, Embossed, Picture Cigar, Tin, 16 X 28 In. 22.00
Store, Sign, Balm Of Gilead & Cedar Plaster, Mt.Asartney View, Tin, Sepia 75.00
Store, Sign, Barber, Hand-Forged Iron Straight Edged Razor, Wooden Handle 12.50
Store, Sign, Bartholomay Brewery Co., N.Y., Chromolithograph, Nude Lady, Hops 300.00
Store, Sign, Blacksmith's Shop, Silvered Wood Horse, C.1900's, 30 In.Long 275.00
Store, Sign, Blacksmith's, Hand-Forged Iron, C.1830, 20 Pounds 135.00
Store, Sign, Blatz, Girl Holds Two Cork Type Bottles, 1902, Tin 165.00
Store, Sign, Bonnie Whiskies, Hand-Painted, By Joel E.Frazier, Frame 65.00
Store, Sign, Boston Rubber Shoe Co., Boy, Huge Rubber Boots, Cutout 45.00
Store, Sign, Boxing, Perrins & Johnson To Decide Their Contest, 1889 .... 37.50
Store, Sign, Bryce Cigars, Ceiling Fan Ad .... .65
Store, Sign, Buchanan & Lyalls Tobaccos, Girl With Cross By Window, Wooden 125.00
Store, Sign, Buck Jones, White Eagle, 1941 Serial, 27 X 40 In. 8.00
Store, Sign, Buckeye Bear, Grandpa, Dog, Waiter, Tin, 15 X 20 In. 24.00
Store, Sign, Buckeye Beer, Tavern Scene, Tin, 20 X 15 In. 18.50
Store, Sign, Budweiser Beer, Custer's Last Fight, Oak Frame 250.00
Store, Sign, Budweiser Beer, Girl, Lithograph, Color, C.1890, Set Of 6 .... 6.50
Store, Sign, Buffalo Bill, Sells Flota, Dated 1914 .... 54.50
Store, Sign, Buffalo Bill's Wild West & Pawnee Bill's Far East, 1910 .... 79.50
Store, Sign, Butter-Nut Boy, 9 X 16 In., Paper 2.00
Store, Sign, Butter-Nut Boy, 1900, 12 Color Lithograph, Canvas 45.00
Store, Sign, Butterick Patterns, Wooden Frame, 36 1/2 X 12 1/4 In. 12.00
Store, Sign, C.& M.Orangeade, 'Plain 5 Cents, With Egg 10 Cents, 'Tin 15.00
Store, Sign, Carling's Ale, Tin, Nine Pints Of The Law, Color, Ti .... 27.00 To 35.00
Store, Sign, Central Union Plug, Red, Cardboard 15.00
Store, Sign, Champion Spark Plug, Picture Of Colorful Spark Plug, Porcelain 45.00
Store, Sign, Chase & Sanborn, Cardboard, Oak Frame 150.00
Store, Sign, Chase & Sanborn, Men In General Store, Lithograph, Cardboard 85.00
Store, Sign, Cherry Smash, John E.Fowler, Pink On Blue, Paper, Glass, Metal 12.00
Store, Sign, Chew Pay Car Scrap, Picture Of Street Car, Tin 15.00
Store, Sign, Chew Virgin Leaf Tobacco, Lady In Pink, Tin, D.H.McAlphin 150.00
Store, Sign, Circus, Great Kar-Mi Troop, Newport, Kentucky, 1914 .... 12.50
Store, Sign, City Club Special Beer, Tin, 14 X 39 In. 20.00
Store, Sign, Clicqout Club-Cyc-Kola, It Cures Bicycle Thirst, Cardboard 9.00
Store, Sign, Clockmaker's, C.W.Kaiser, Cast Iron & Tin Clock, C.1870 .... 145.00
Store, Sign, Cook's Beer, Tin, 14 X 28 In. 8.00

Store, Sign, Atlantic & Pacific Tea Co., C.1886
See Page 566

Store, Sign, Knox Gelatin, Canvas, Color, 1901
See Page 568

Store, Sign, Corona, Girl Holds Typewriter, Cardboard, 20 X 13 In. 10.00
Store, Sign, Dance Madness, Conrad Nager, Cardboard, 14 X 22 In. 7.50
Store, Sign, DeLaval Cream Separators, Little Victorian Girl, Tin 125.00
Store, Sign, Devilish Good 5 Cent Cigars, Tin, Babies Smoking, 10 X 14 In. 20.00
Store, Sign, Dr.Swett's Root Beer, Lady Holding Mug, 15 In.Diameter 185.00
Store, Sign, Drink Moxie 100 Percent, Tin, 6 X 18 In. 35.00
Store, Sign, Drink Pureoxia Ginger Ale, Green, Yellow, Tin 35.00
Store, Sign, Drum Five Cent Cigar, Big Drum, Red, White, Blue, Tin, 10 X 14 In. 14.00
Store, Sign, Duffee's Laxative, 9 X 13 In., Tin 7.00
Store, Sign, Dukes Cameo, The Best Cigarette, Woman, Lithograph, Paper 250.00
Store, Sign, Dutchess Trousers, Pollard & Carpenter, Tin, 6 X 20 In. 35.00
Store, Sign, Egyptian Beer, Lady, Tin, 17 In.Diameter 65.00
Store, Sign, Egyptian Luxury Cigarettes, Girl, Dutch Hat, Tin, 26 X 34 In. 200.00
Store, Sign, Egyptian Straight Cigarettes, Paper, Wood Frame 150.00
Store, Sign, Empire Tires, Touring Car, 2 Couples, Policeman, Wm.Bengar 135.00
Store, Sign, Epco Cigars, 7 X 16 In., 1922, Paper 2.00
Store, Sign, Exit, Leaded Glass, Lights Up, 3 1/2 X 3 X 8 In. 75.00
Store, Sign, Fatima Turkish Blend, Veiled Lady, Cardboard 25.00
Store, Sign, Fish Store, Wood Carved Fish, Yellow Paint, C.1820 ..... 79.50
Store, Sign, Five Brothers Plug Tobacco, Children Reading, Glass 25.00
Store, Sign, Foot Rest Hosiery, Little Girl On Swing, Tin, Pink Bow 75.00
Store, Sign, Foss Premier Chocolates, Girl On Phone, Banner, 1918, Fabric 150.00
Store, Sign, G.& W.Canadian Whiskey, Tin, Red, White Letters, Chicago 45.00
Store, Sign, General Store, Waggoner & Wisdom, Kentucky, Fall-Winter Goods 39.50
Store, Sign, Gold Medal Flour, Tin, Wood Frame & Stand, Red, Gold 85.00
Store, Sign, Gordon Dye Hosiery, 3 Victorian Girls In Underwear, Lithograph 150.00
Store, Sign, Grape-Ola, Bottle Illustration, Tin, 19 X 28 In. 30.00
Store, Sign, Green Mountain Boys Balm Of Giliad, Men In Woods, Sepia Tones 75.00
Store, Sign, Green River Whiskey, Paper Under Glass, 19 X 14 ..... 75.00
Store, Sign, Grocer & Girl, 11 X 13 In., Cardboard 1.50
Store, Sign, Hambone Cigar, Cartoon Negro In Airplane, 7 In.Diameter 4.00
Store, Sign, Hamm's Beer, Metal, St.Paul, 8 X 13 In. 10.00
Store, Sign, Hanley's Ale, Bulldog, Paper Under Glass, Frame, 13 X 20 In. 50.00
Store, Sign, Hanley's Ale, Bulldog, Tin, 9 X 13 In. 10.00
Store, Sign, Hanover Crackers, Victorian Child, 10 1/2 X 12 In. 10.00
Store, Sign, Harris' Boston Copper Weather Vanes & Emblematic Signs 135.00
Store, Sign, Hartshorn's Cough Balsam, 2 Victorian Girls, Tin, 16 X 20 In. 110.00
Store, Sign, Helmar Turkish Cigarettes, Girl In Mexican Hat, Embossed, Frame 200.00
Store, Sign, Hickey & Freeman & Co., 'Best Worn-Worn By The Best, '1905-07 ..... 200.00
Store, Sign, Hire's, Embossed, Girl With Red Derby, Tin, C.1920, 10 X 28 In. 35.00
Store, Sign, Hire's, Root Beer, Child Holds Mug, Oval, Tin, 20 X 24 In. 250.00
Store, Sign, Hood's Ice Cream, Brick On Glass Tray, 12 X 28 In. 50.00
Store, Sign, Huntley & Palmer, Cardboard 24.00
Store, Sign, Imperial Club
Store, Sign, Indianapolis Brewing, Flag Draped Women, Frame, 30 X 40 In. 275.00
Store, Sign, International Harvester Co.Of America, Farm Scene, Tin 125.00
Store, Sign, J.C.Davis Old Soap, Woman, Feeding Apple To Horse, Gilt Frame 125.00
Store, Sign, J.P.Coates, 'Best Silk Cord Cotton, 'Man & Lady Fishing 45.00
Store, Sign, Jack Frost Fontaine, 11 X 14 In., 1915, Cardboard 9.00
Store, Sign, Jersey Ice Cream, Reverse Painting On Glass, Gold, 11 X 22 In. 50.00
Store, Sign, Jolly Baker, 15 X 22 In., 1935 ..... 3.95
Store, Sign, Karmi Swallows A Loaded Gun Barrel, Dated 1914, Color 12.50
Store, Sign, King Kola, Thermometer, Round, 9 In. 6.00
Store, Sign, King Shoes, Brass, Tooled, Hanging 21.50
Store, Sign, Knox Gelatin, Canvas, Color, 1901 ..... *Illus* 150.00
Store, Sign, Knox Gelatin, Negro Fortune Teller & Little Girl, Roseland 150.00
Store, Sign, La Flor De Carvelhi Cigar, Tin, 15 X 21 In. 40.00
Store, Sign, La Linda Cigars, 1905, Colorful Lady, Tin, 19 X 28 In. 75.00
Store, Sign, Ladies Shoe Room Wrappers & Children's Dresses, Cardboard, Oak 50.00
Store, Sign, Las Amantes Cigar, 15 X 17 In., Cardboard 4.00
Store, Sign, Lenox Soap, 'Lathers Freely In Hard Water, 'Tin, Yellow, Black 25.00
Store, Sign, Lewis 66 Rye, For Sale At All Bars, Tin, 23 1/2 X 17 3/4 In. 32.00
Store, Sign, Lime Crush, Paper, 8 X 12 In. 15.00
Store, Sign, Lion Brand Yarns Are Best, Oak, Round, Sepia Lion 85.00
Store, Sign, Livery Stable, 'Teams To Let,' Painted Legend, 17 X 116 In. 60.00
Store, Sign, Lowney's Chocolates, Box Of Candy, Girl, Vase Of Red Roses, Tin 65.00

Store, Sign, Lowney's Chocolates, Victorian Girl & Man, Tin, Frame 350.00
Store, Sign, Mail Pouch, Porcelain, 1920, 3 X 12 In. 15.00
Store, Sign, Mason Root Beer, Tin, 20 X 30 In. 5.75
Store, Sign, McCormick Deering Line, Girl, Farm Machines, Tin, 13 X 17 In. 45.00
Store, Sign, Miller Beer, Reverse On Glass, Girl On Beer Case, Gold Leaf 350.00
Store, Sign, Miller Brewing, Milwaukee, Tin, Color, Signed J.F.Kernan 40.00
Store, Sign, Miller's High Life Beer, Man Fishing, Tin, 26 X 18 In. 27.50
Store, Sign, Mission Orange, Mirror, 3 1/2 X 12 In. 15.00
Store, Sign, Morton Salt, Girl With Umbrella, Tin, 19 X 27 In. 22.50
Store, Sign, Movie, Dietrich, Wayne, Seven Sinners, 1940 .... 6.00
Store, Sign, Moxie, Cutout Man, Red, Tin, 7 X 4 1/2 In. 45.00
Store, Sign, Moxie, Drink Moxie, Blue Writing, Tin 15.00
Store, Sign, Moxie, House, Palmer Cox Brownies, C.1900, Tin, 14 X 22 In. 115.00
Store, Sign, Moxie, Reverse Painting, Round, Red, Orange, Yellow, Gold 45.00
Store, Sign, Moxie, Reverse Painting On Glass, Girl, Red, 8 X 10 In. 45.00
Store, Sign, Moxie, The Texas Cattle King, American Show Print Co., 1910 .... 59.50
Store, Sign, Murad Cigarettes, Vanderbilt Cup Race, Dated 1909, Tin 65.00
Store, Sign, Nabisco Boy, Decal, Yellow Slicker, Glass, 7 X 18 In. 95.00
Store, Sign, Nabisco, Boy In Yellow Slicker, Uneeda Biscuit, Cardboard 65.00
Store, Sign, New York Times, 'All The News, 'sail Boats, Schofield Wickman 85.00
Store, Sign, Nonesuch Mince Meat, Cutout, Paper 15.00
Store, Sign, Norwich Union Fire Insurance, Enamel, 4 X 10 In. 5.00
Store, Sign, Okeefe's Beer, Thermometer, 9 X 12 In. 6.00
Store, Sign, Old Honesty Plug Tobacco, Calvert Lithograph Co., Tin 150.00
Store, Sign, Old Judge Cigarettes, Woman, Paper, Metal Tips 225.00
Store, Sign, Orange Crush, Paper, 8 X 12 In. 15.00
Store, Sign, Packard, Speedboat, Dirigible, 2 Seaplanes, C.1928, Tin 25.00
Store, Sign, Palmer Tires & Goodrich Tires, Earle Brenner, Lady, Red Ground 95.00
Store, Sign, Paul Jones Pure Rye Whiskey, Chromolithograph On Wood, 1901 .... 80.00
Store, Sign, Pepsi Cola, Standing Santa, Cardboard, Norman Rockwell, 20 In. 15.00
Store, Sign, Perfection Cigarettes, Lady, Cardboard, 24 X 30 In. 225.00
Store, Sign, Philip Morris, Johnnie, Tin, 15 X 44 In. 40.00
Store, Sign, Pleasant Valley Wine Co., Lithograph On Milk Glass, Frame, 1902 .... 100.00
Store, Sign, Pond's Extract Veterinary Remedy For Horses & Cattle, Tin 125.00
Store, Sign, Portsmouth Brewing Co., Girl, Flowers, Lithograph On Canvas 125.00
Store, Sign, Reid's Ice Cream, 1926, Lady With Cloche & Soda, Red, Pink, Cream 125.00
Store, Sign, Rice's Seeds, Paper, Color .... Illus 45.00
Store, Sign, Royal Lion Chop Japan Tea, Delano Potter & Co., Cardboard 25.00
Store, Sign, S.H.McAlpin & Co.'s Plug Tobaccos, Lady Holding Pair 75.00
Store, Sign, Saddler's, Pair Of White Metal Spurs, Western, Pair 37.50
Store, Sign, Sapolio Soap, Girl In Red, Leaning On Box Of Soap, Tin 18.00
Store, Sign, Satin Skin, 26 X 42 In., Dated 1903 .... 15.00
Store, Sign, Savage Arms Co., Hand-Carved Pine, Indian Head & Canoe, C.1900 .... 84.50
Store, Sign, Shultz Belting Co., Gold Leaf Frame, Lady, C.1900 .... 100.00
Store, Sign, Sidney Dillon Cigars, Horse & Racetrack, Tin, Lithograph 95.00
Store, Sign, Smoke Caton Quality Cigars, Tin, 3 1/2 X 11 1/2 In. 5.00
Store, Sign, Smoke Imperial Club Five Cent Cigar, Metal, Brass Chain 17.50
Store, Sign, Straight Cut No.1 & Virginia Brights Cigarettes, Bird Cards 175.00
Store, Sign, Strawbridge & Clothier Market, Phila., C.1930, Tin 10.00
Store, Sign, Sunshine Cigarette, 20 For 15 Cents, Yellow, Red, 13 X 17 In. 12.50
Store, Sign, Sunshine Stove & Ranges, Porcelain, White On Blue 28.00
Store, Sign, Surveyor's, French, Brass, Rural Code, Globe 150.00
Store, Sign, Sweet Caporal Cigarettes, Girl, Tin, 20 X 26 In. 120.00
Store, Sign, Sweet Caporal Cigarettes, Moose Hunt, Tin, 11 X 24 In. 125.00
Store, Sign, Swift's Premium Margarine, 1915, Cutout, Color 30.00
Store, Sign, Tavern, Jacobus Major, Pine, C.1780 .... 84.50
Store, Sign, Tiger Tobacco, Tiger On Blue, Tin, 24 X 30 In. 300.00
Store, Sign, Traphagen & Co., Clothing, Bookmark & Ruler, Tin, Black, Yellow 35.00
Store, Sign, Turkish Trophy Cigarettes, Girl, Turkish Headdress, Tin 250.00
Store, Sign, Tutor's, Carved Wood, School Boy In Breeches, C.1750 .... 395.00
Store, Sign, Tuttle's Family Elixir, Paper, Mounted, 3 X 5 Ft. 85.00
Store, Sign, Uncle John's Syrup, Old Man With Beard, C.1907 .... 3.00
Store, Sign, Union Metallic Cartridge Co., Kenney's Patent 27.50
Store, Sign, Union Workman Chewing Tobacco, Tin, 18 X 24 In. 10.00
Store, Sign, Valley Forge Beer, Cardboard 6.00
Store, Sign, Van Houten Cocoa, Portrait Of Lady, A.Pintz, Oak Frame 125.00

Store, Sign, Rice's Seeds, Paper, Color
See Page 569

Store, Sign, Veterinarian, Conn., C.1850, Wooden

Store, Sign, Veterinarian, Conn., C.1850, Wooden .... *Illus*	525.00
Store, Sign, Victor Record, Metal, 2 Sides, Record & Victrola Sign On Chain	37.50
Store, Sign, Virginia Cigarettes, Bathing Beauty, Tin	6.50
Store, Sign, Walter A.Wood, Mowing & Reaping, Lithograph On Canvas	250.00
Store, Sign, Ward's Lime Crush, Man In Straw Hat, Cutout, Cardboard	35.00
Store, Sign, Washburn-Crosby Gold Medal Flour, Tin, White On Blue, Gold	25.00
Store, Sign, Water Pump For Fires, A.D.Puffer, Boston, C.1865	27.50
Store, Sign, Wilbur's Tonic, Champion Horses, Paper	50.00
Store, Sign, Yankee Girl, 8 X 12 In., Cardboard	4.00
Store, Sign, Your Credit Is Good, Tin, Match Strike, Man Pointing Finger	80.00
Store, Sign, Zira Cigarettes, Girl, Alfred Everil Orr, Paris, 1912, Cardboard	125.00
Store, Slate, School	6.50
Store, Snuffbox, Sommer's, Paper Label, Round	5.00
Store, Spectacles, Gold Rimmed, C.1890, Optician's Leather Case	5.00
Store, Spigot, Barrel, Key To Lock	9.00
Store, Spill, Maple Syrup, Hand-Whittled	1.25
Store, Spoon, Apollo Chocolates, Embossed	5.00
Store, Spoon, Planters Peanut, Silverplate	5.00
Store, Spoon, Soup, Campbell Kids, Pair	11.00
Store, Spoon, Towle's Log Cabin	14.00
Store, Spoon, Walter Baker & Co., Ltd., Breakfast Cocoa, 1780, Mass.	12.00
Store, Stamp, Rubber, For Making Signs, Wooden Hinged Box	12.00
Store, Stamp, Sealing Wax, Hand	3.50
Store, Stand, Doughnut, Pressed Glass, 4 In.High	12.00
Store, Stapler, Carton, Hardware Mfg.Bridgeport Forged Steel, 3 Pounds	6.00
Store, Stapler, The Patent Novelty Paper Fastener, Patent 1866	7.75
Store, Stein, Good Cheer Cigar, Tin	6.00
Store, Stencil, Apple Crate, Brass	14.00
Store, Stereoscope, see Stereoscope	
Store, Stool, Ice Cream, Spring Seat .... 18.00 To	29.00
Store, Stopper, Bottle, Moxie	5.00
Store, Stopper, Moxie, Metal	2.00

Store, **Strainer**, Wheatlet For Breakfast, Self Embossed, Funnel Shape, Tin 10.00
Store, **Stretcher**, Glove, Bone, Holder 4.50
Store, **String Holder**, Beehive Shape, Raised Decoration, Ornate Work, Iron 22.00
Store, **Strop**, Razor, Barber's, Leather, Brass Ends 5.00
Store, **Tablet**, Elite Glasshead Toilet Pins, English, 6 Hatpins 3.00
Store, **Tablet**, Morris & Yeoman's Hatpins, Lithograph, 9 Hatpins 9.00
Store, **Thermometer**, Buick Car, Clinton Machine Works, 1915, Porcelain, Tin 65.00
Store, **Thermometer**, Dr.Daniel's Horse Medicine, A.C.Royder, Druggist 40.00
Store, **Thermometer**, Dr.Daniel's Horse Medicine, Davis Bros., Shoe Repair 25.00
Store, **Thermometer**, Dr.Daniel's Horse Medicine, F.M.Spalding & Co. 40.00
Store, **Thermometer**, Dr.Daniel's Horse Medicine, G.O.Thompson 40.00
Store, **Thermometer**, Dr.Daniel's Horse Medicine, H.B.Sawyer, Grocer 40.00
Store, **Thermometer**, Ginta Cigars, Oil, Painted Green, Cigar Band Insert 65.00
Store, **Thermometer**, Marvels Cigarettes, Tin, Porcelain, Cobalt Blue 35.00
Store, **Thermometer**, Moxie Man, 1920s 38.00
Store, **Thermometer**, Nash Automobile, John J.O'Hare, Wooden, White, Green 65.00
Store, **Thermometer**, Tin, Round 1.50
Store, **Thermometer**, Tums For The Tummy, Tin 7.00
Store, **Tin**, A.A.Valentine & Co.Stem Ginger, Flip Top, Painted Label 8.00
Store, **Tin**, Adam's Pepsin Gum, Picture Of Gum, Green & Red 65.00
Store, **Tin**, Adhesive Plaster, Miniature, 3/4 In. 5.00
Store, **Tin**, After Dinner Salted Peanuts, Orange & Red, Round 35.00
Store, **Tin**, Albert I .Rich's Crystallized Ginger, Brown & Cream 10.00
Store, **Tin**, Allen & Ginter's La.Perique Tobacco 12.00
Store, **Tin**, Allen & Ginter's Tobacco, Paper Label, Round, 2 1/4 In.High 25.00
Store, **Tin**, Ambero Coffee Berry, Dodge Co., Paper Label, Man In Sombrero 7.00
Store, **Tin**, Angelus Marshmallow, Beige & Red, Round 3.00
Store, **Tin**, Arcadia Tobacco, Green & Gold, 2 1/2 In.High .... 4.00 To 8.00
Store, **Tin**, Arcadia Tobacco, Green & Gold, 4 In.High 8.00
Store, **Tin**, Armour's Peanut Butter, Tin Label, Blue & Orange, Children 25.00
Store, **Tin**, Aster Tea, Painted Label, Square 5.00
Store, **Tin**, Aston Coffee, Blue Painted Label, Yellow Block Lettering, Round 5.00
Store, **Tin**, Autocrat Coffee, Paper Label, Red & Beige, Round 6.00
Store, **Tin**, B Plus B Baby Talc, Animal Decoration 1.50
Store, **Tin**, B.F.Gravely Superior Tobacco, Blue & Orange 8.00
Store, **Tin**, Bagley's Tobacco, Gold & Black, 4 In.High .... 10.00 To 15.00
Store, **Tin**, Baker's Cocoa, Woman Serving Cocoa, Paper, Cardboard, & Tin 3.00
Store, **Tin**, Barley & Oatmeal, Blue & White Dutch Scenes, Hinged, Pair 7.50
Store, **Tin**, Belfast Cut Plug, 3 X 6 X 4 In. 10.00
Store, **Tin**, Belwood Smoking Mixture 4.00
Store, **Tin**, Belwood Tobacco, Embossed, Blue & Gold 6.00
Store, **Tin**, Best Tobacco, J.G.Dill's Best, Green & Gold, 2 3/4 In.High 7.00
Store, **Tin**, Best Tobacco, Lady, Yellow & Green, 1 1/2 In.High .... 4.00 To 10.00
Store, **Tin**, Birnbaum's Social Comfort Tobacco, Crossed Pipes, Green 15.00
Store, **Tin**, Biscuit, Lift Lid, Shape Of French Chest Of Drawers, Gold Trim 65.00
Store, **Tin**, Biscuit, Octagonal, Pictures Of Ships, Handled, 9 1/4 In.Diameter 7.00
Store, **Tin**, Black Carnation Formosa Tea, Flower, Paper Label, 4 1/4 In.High 4.00
Store, **Tin**, Black Carnation Tea, Paper Label 3.00
Store, **Tin**, Bliss Coffee, Paper Label 2.25
Store, **Tin**, Blue Flame Coffee, St.Paul, Minn., 1 Lb. 3.00
Store, **Tin**, Bokar Coffee, Paper Label, Camels, Brown & Red 4.00
Store, **Tin**, Bootjack Plug Tobacco, Embossed Type, Silver 25.00
Store, **Tin**, Bootjack Plug Tobacco, Pocket, Aluminum 6.50
Store, **Tin**, Borden's Malted Milk, Beige & Red 35.00
Store, **Tin**, Brockton Tobacco, Shoe, Red & Black, 4 1/2 X 2 3/4 X 1 5/8 In. 25.00
Store, **Tin**, Buffalo Brand Fancy Peanut, Red & Yellow, 9 In.High 20.00
Store, **Tin**, Buffalo Brand Salted Peanuts, Buffalo Etching, Gold & Red, Round 45.00
Store, **Tin**, Burton's Assorted Shortbread, Scotch Plaid, Farm Decoration 12.50
Store, **Tin**, Butter Wafer, Renner Bros., Chicago 10.00
Store, **Tin**, Calabash Tobacco, Tin Label, Match Striker, Brown & Yellow 15.00
Store, **Tin**, California Nugget Tobacco 9.00
Store, **Tin**, Campfire Marshmallows, Red & Black, Round 9.00
Store, **Tin**, Campfire Marshmallows, Red & White Round 5.00
Store, **Tin**, Campfire Marshmallows, 15 In. 7.00
Store, **Tin**, Capstan Navy Cut Cigarettes, W.D. & H.O. Wills 3.00
Store, **Tin**, Carr's Carlisle Biscuits, Figural, Looks Like Trunk, Gold, Brown 9.00

Store, Tin, Centennial Java Coffee, Blue & Gold Paper Label 45.00
Store, Tin, Central Union Tobacco, Lunch Box, Handle, Face & Moon, Red & Gold 35.00
Store, Tin, Central Union Tobacco, Pocket, Lady In Moon, Orange, Brown, & Gold 15.00
Store, Tin, Chase & Sanborn Coffee, Paper Label 3.00
Store, Tin, Chase & Sanborn Seal Brand Coffee, Paper Label, 2 Pounds 3.50
Store, Tin, Chase & Sanborn Tea, Square, Orange & Green Paper Label 5.00
Store, Tin, Chase & Sanborn, Screw Top, Paper Label, Brown, Beige, & Black 15.00
Store, Tin, Chinese Tea, Round, Black, Picture, 8 In.High 4.00
Store, Tin, Climax Peanut Butter, Red & White 12.00
Store, Tin, Colburn's Black Pepper, Red Label, 4 In.High 6.00
Store, Tin, Colburn's Spices, Paper Label, Red & Beige, 5 In.High 12.00
Store, Tin, Cotartab Tobacco, Display, Figural, Young Girl & Veil, Greens 85.00
Store, Tin, Cross Swords Tobacco, Gold & Black, 3 1/4 In.High 10.00
Store, Tin, Cross Swords Tobacco, Green & Gold, 4 1/2 In.High 15.00
Store, Tin, Cross Swords Tobacco, Lady, Gold & Black .... 18.00 To 25.00
Store, Tin, Crown Teas, Alen, Shapleigh & Co., Paper Label, Round 12.00
Store, Tin, D.& L.Slade Pimento, Green Paper Label, 3 1/4 In.High 5.00
Store, Tin, Dan Patch Tobacco 5.00
Store, Tin, Delane Potter Coffee, Paper Label, Green & Beige, Round 4.00
Store, Tin, Dickerman & Co., Coffee, Handle, Bucket Style, Paper Label, Red 20.00
Store, Tin, Dill's Best Pocket Tobacco 7.00
Store, Tin, Dr.Hess Fly Chaser 2.50
Store, Tin, Dr.Hobb's Sparagus Kidney Pills, Picture 8.00
Store, Tin, Dr.Johnson Educator Crackers, Flit Top, Wheat Spray Motif, Tan 18.00
Store, Tin, Dr.Myer's Toilet Powder 2.00
Store, Tin, Dr.White's Cough Drops, Cupid, Green & Gold 50.00
Store, Tin, Dr.White's Cough Drops, Cupid, Red & Gold 50.00
Store, Tin, Dromedary Figs, Mustard & Brown, Round 3.00
Store, Tin, Drostee's Cocoa, Red & Gold, Dutch Boy & Girl 5.00
Store, Tin, Dupont Gunpowder, Label, 6 In. 12.50
Store, Tin, Durham Mustard, Portrait Of Woman, 7 3/4 X 6 X 10 In. 35.00
Store, Tin, Durham's Coconut, Paper Label, Lithograph With Negro 9.00
Store, Tin, Durkee's Ginger, Blue Paper Label, 1 Pound, 6 In.High 3.00
Store, Tin, Dy-O-La Dye, Ladies Dying Clothes, Lift Lid 35.00
Store, Tin, Eat-A-Good Peanut Butter, Handle, Red & Yellow, Tin 12.00
Store, Tin, Edgemont Crackers, Dayton, Ohio, Green & White, 8 In.High 10.00
Store, Tin, Edgewood Plug 3.00
Store, Tin, Edgeworth Plug Tobacco Slice 2.50
Store, Tin, Edgeworth Tobacco, Blue, Dark Blue, & Silver 6.00
Store, Tin, Edgeworth Tobacco, Striker, Silver & Blue 8.00
Store, Tin, English Bird's-Eye Tobacco, Gold & Red, 4 1/2 In.High 15.00
Store, Tin, English Bird's-Eye Tobacco, Gold & Red, 4 1/4 In.High 6.00
Store, Tin, English Bird's-Eye Tobacco, Lady, Green & Yellow 3.00
Store, Tin, Excelsior Coffee 1.50
Store, Tin, F.P.Garrettson Teas & Coffee, Green, Gold, & Black 10.00
Store, Tin, Famous Ginger Wafers, National Buscuit Co., Paper Label, Scene 18.00
Store, Tin, Faultless Biscuit, Paper Label, Little Boy & Top Hat 15.00
Store, Tin, Fi-Na-St.Peanut Butter, Red & Gold, Man 20.00
Store, Tin, Fi-Na-St.Peanut Butter, Red & White 25.00
Store, Tin, Flag Chop Tea, Paper Label, Flag, Red 5.00
Store, Tin, Flag Chop-Oolong Tea, Boston, Square, Red Paper Label 3.00
Store, Tin, Forest City Tea, Portland Maine, Square, 4 1/2 In.High 2.50
Store, Tin, Fougera Mustard Plasters Of Two Strengths, Red 8.00
Store, Tin, Four Roses Tobacco 2.00
Store, Tin, Freeman's Face Powder, Flower, Green 9.00
Store, Tin, Fry's Cocoa Extract, England, Golden Blue, 5 In.High 3.00
Store, Tin, G.N.Crouse & Co.Mustard, Lady Smoking Pipe, Gold & Black 75.00
Store, Tin, Game Finecut Tobacco, Scene, Game Birds, Front & Back 50.00
Store, Tin, George Washington Cut Plug, Lunch Box Type 6.00
Store, Tin, George Washington Tobacco 10.00
Store, Tin, Gibson's Linseed Lozenges, June 30, 1906, Flowers 45.00
Store, Tin, Ginger, Mustard & Brown, Round 5.00
Store, Tin, Glycerole For Oiling & Dressing Shoes, Red & Black 45.00
Store, Tin, Gold Bond Coffee, A-1, Jewett & Sherman, Wisconsin, 1 Lb. 4.00
Store, Tin, Gold Flake Peanut Butter, Gold & Black 10.00
Store, Tin, Golden Bean Cookies, Painted Label, Red & Black 9.00

Store, Tin, Golden Wedding Rye, Two Men Drinking, 13 X 20 In. 35.00
Store, Tin, Grandmother's Ceylon Tea, Taj Mahal, Green Painted Label 6.00
Store, Tin, Grandmother's Tea Bags, Green, Round 5.00
Store, Tin, Graun's Fire Extinguisher, 22 In.Long 14.00
Store, Tin, Green River Tobacco, Round, Green & White, Black Man & Horse 30.00
Store, Tin, H-O Tobacco, Red, Gold, Black, 6 In.High 15.00
Store, Tin, H.W.Clark & Co.Tea, Gold Rose, Blue & Beige 7.00
Store, Tin, Half & Half Tobacco, Telescoping 2.00
Store, Tin, Half & Half, Lucky Strike 5.00
Store, Tin, Havana Fives Cigar, Round 7.00
Store, Tin, Heinrich Halberlein Cookies, Houses & Castles, Browns & Gold 35.00
Store, Tin, Heinrich Halberlein, Bridge Scene ,,,,,,,,,,, ... 30.00
Store, Tin, Hershey's Chocolate & Cocoa, Silver On Brown, Round 20.00
Store, Tin, Hiawatha Tobacco, Indian Lithograph, Red & Yellow 18.00
Store, Tin, High Crown Java, Display, Wooden Hinged Top, Paper Label 65.00
Store, Tin, Home Of Good Nuts, Figural Of Home, Green & White 15.00
Store, Tin, Honest Labor Tobacco, Red & Yellow 5.00
Store, Tin, Honest Labor Tobacco, Strongarm, Gold, Black, & White 15.00
Store, Tin, Honey, Octagonal, Private Paper Label, Yellow 15.00
Store, Tin, Hung-Kee Chop, Paper Label, Red & Beige, 5 In.High 3.00
Store, Tin, Huntley & Palmer Biscuits, Bell 25.00
Store, Tin, Huntley & Palmer Biscuits, Bookcase, Two Tier Books 95.00
Store, Tin, Huntley & Palmer Biscuits, Books Between Bookends 75.00
Store, Tin, Huntley & Palmer Biscuits, Eight Books Strapped Together 110.00
Store, Tin, Huntley & Palmer Biscuits, Carved Wood, Inlaid Ivory & Silver 24.00
Store, Tin, Huntley & Palmer Biscuits, Fisherman's Creel 75.00
Store, Tin, Huntley & Palmer Biscuits, Orange Quarter Biscuit, 9 In.Square 22.00
Store, Tin, Huntley & Palmer Biscuits, Paper Label .... 5.00 To 14.00
Store, Tin, Huntley & Palmer Biscuits, Perambulator 95.00
Store, Tin, Huntley & Palmer Biscuits, Square 10.00
Store, Tin, Huntley & Palmer Biscuits, Syrian Table 40.00
Store, Tin, Huntley & Palmer Biscuits, Tan Hand Satchel 55.00
Store, Tin, Huntley & Palmer Tobacco, Portrait Of Winston Churchill 4.50
Store, Tin, Hungarian Pepper, Green & Orange 8.00
Store, Tin, Imperial Brand Tea, Paper Label, 3 5/8 In.High 3.00
Store, Tin, Imperial Granum, The Great Medicinal Food, Paper Label 5.00
Store, Tin, Ivin's Biscuit, Handle, Cookies, Red, Yellow, & Gold 10.00
Store, Tin, J.G.Dill's Best Tobacco, Lady, Striker On Bottom, Yellow & Green 9.00
Store, Tin, J.G.Dill's Best Tobacco, Lady, Yellow & Green 15.00
Store, Tin, J.G.Dill's Best Tobacco, Lady, 1 1/2 In.High .... 3.00 To 9.00
Store, Tin, J.W.Robert & Co., Boston, High Grade Formosa Teas, Floor 125.00
Store, Tin, J.Wright's Co.All Nation's Tobacco, Tin Label, Eagle & Flags 45.00
Store, Tin, J.Wright's Co.Winner Tobacco, Cut Plug, Paper Label, Red 25.00
Store, Tin, J.Wright's Tobacco, Black & Brown, Round 15.00
Store, Tin, J.Wright's Tobacco, Tin Label, Gold & Black 18.00
Store, Tin, Jacob & Co.Biscuit, Paper Label 8.00
Store, Tin, Java & Mocha Coffee, Paper Label, Red & Green, Round 7.00
Store, Tin, Java Red Seal Coffee, Paper Label 3.00
Store, Tin, John B.Carriere Tea, Red & Black, Round 6.00
Store, Tin, John Oakey & Son Knife Polish, Perforated Top, Cardboard Sides 12.00
Store, Tin, Jonathan P.Kent's Biscuit, Paper Label, Green & Black, 11 In. 20.00
Store, Tin, Jumbo Peanuts, 10 Lb.Size 10.00
Store, Tin, Jungle Chop Tea, Jungle Scenes, Paper Label 9.00
Store, Tin, Just Suits Tobacco, Red, Black, & Gold 18.00
Store, Tin, Kellogg's Drinket, Little Girl, 3 X 4 X 1 In. 10.00
Store, Tin, Kemp's Nuts, Tin 3.00
Store, Tin, Kennedy Biscuits, Labels, Blue, White Type 25.00
Store, Tin, Kennedy Biscuits, Paper Label, Black & Beige 15.00
Store, Tin, Kimball's Baby Powder, Cardboard, Tin Shaker Top 2.00
Store, Tin, Kipling Tobacco, Man & Wreath, Red, Blue, & Beige 22.50
Store, Tin, Kyanize Spar Boskin Varnish Co., Cork Stopper, Paper Labels 6.00
Store, Tin, LaBelle Chocolatiere, Baker & Co., Woman Serving Cocoa, Browns 6.00
Store, Tin, Lacto Dextrin Health Food, 8 1/2 In.High 3.50
Store, Tin, Lady Churchill Cigars, Flat, Tin 3.50
Store, Tin, Linseed Cough Lozenges, Flowers 45.00
Store, Tin, Lipton Tea, 4 1/2 In. 8.00

Store, Tin, Log Cabin Syrup .... 6.50 To 8.50
Store, Tin, Log Cabin, Syrup, Box In Doorway, Small 20.00
Store, Tin, Log Cabin Syrup, Cork, Red & Beige 25.00
Store, Tin, Log Cabin Syrup, Paper Label 10.00
Store, Tin, Lowney's Chocolate, 8 1/2 In.High 2.50
Store, Tin, Lucky Strike Cigarettes, Merrie Christmas, Holly 6.00
Store, Tin, Lucky Strike Tobacco, Cut Plug, Red & Green, 2 3/4 In.High 9.00
Store, Tin, Lucky Strike Tobacco, Red & Green, 4 1/2 X 2 5/8 X 3/4 In. 7.50
Store, Tin, Lucky Strike, Flat Fifty .... 2.50 To 5.00
Store, Tin, Lucky Strike, Flat Fifty, Picture Of Jean Harlow 10.00
Store, Tin, Luxury Tobacco, Fruit In Bowl, Round 8.00
Store, Tin, Mammy's Favorite Brand Coffee, Bucket, C.D.Kenny Co., Ky., 4 Lbs. 9.00
Store, Tin, Maple Butter, E.E.Post Co., Inc., Wire Handle, Silver Lettering 10.00
Store, Tin, Maryland Club Tobacco, Stone House, Green & Gold 15.00
Store, Tin, Matchless Brand Coffee, Coffee Bean Plant, Red & Green, Round 15.00
Store, Tin, Matchless Coffee, Green 4.00
Store, Tin, Mayo's Tobacco, Nutmeg Canister, Gold & Black, Round 25.00
Store, Tin, Mayo's Tobacco, Oatmeal Can, Round, Black & Gold, 6 1/4 In.High 35.00
Store, Tin, Mayo's Tobacco, Paper Label, Gold & Blue, 4 1/2 In.High 25.00
Store, Tin, Mayo's Tobacco, Pepper Can, Gold & Black, Round 25.00
Store, Tin, McCann's Finest Oatmeal, Gold, Black, & Beige, Round 15.00
Store, Tin, McLaughlin Coffee, Red Ground, Gold Letters, Bail, 17 In.High 22.50
Store, Tin, Melachrino, Egyptian Cigarettes 6.50
Store, Tin, Mellomints Confectionary, Red, Beige, & Black, Round 20.00
Store, Tin, Mellowmints, Red & Black, Oval 7.00
Store, Tin, Melrose Marshmallows, Roses, Beige & Blue, Round 3.00
Store, Tin, Melrose Marshmallows, Roses, Red, Blue, & Beige, Round 12.00
Store, Tin, Miles Mason Coffee, Blue Chinoiserie Decorated 19.00
Store, Tin, Mission Garden Tea, Green Painted Label, 4 In.Square 4.00
Store, Tin, Monadeneck, Tea Formosa, Kean, N.H., Paper Label, Square 3.00
Store, Tin, Monarch Cocoa, Lion, Blue & Cream 12.00
Store, Tin, Montclair Brand Cocoa, Paper Label, Red 18.00
Store, Tin, Montpelier Coffee, Me., Label, 2 Pound 6.00
Store, Tin, Mose's Cough Drops, Red & Gold 65.00
Store, Tin, Mozart Tobacco, Black, Gold, & Red 6.00
Store, Tin, N.B.C.Uneeda, Sheep Grazing On Lid 20.00
Store, Tin, N.L.Co.Lozenges, Glass Insert, Red, Black, & Gold 55.00
Store, Tin, National Biscuit, Brass & Tin 16.50
Store, Tin, National Biscuit, Uneeda Bakers Fruit Cake, Blue & Red, Round 3.00
Store, Tin, Nature's Remedy .... .98
Store, Tin, Necco Hard Candies, Lady Stencil, 10 In.High 4.00
Store, Tin, Necco Peach Blossoms, 9 In.High 3.00
Store, Tin, New Province Coffee, Red Paper Label, E.T.Cowdrey Co., Best 4.00
Store, Tin, North Pole Tobacco, Polar Bears, Beige & Black 45.00
Store, Tin, Nurnberger Lebkuchen Cookies, Man With Charger, Brown & Gold 25.00
Store, Tin, Old English Curve, 1910 .... 4.50
Store, Tin, Old English Cut Plug Tobacco, Display, Lift Lid, Red & Beige 75.00
Store, Tin, Old Reliable Peanut Butter, Gold, Black Type 25.00
Store, Tin, Ontario Peanut Butter, Blue & Gray 20.00
Store, Tin, Oriental Cookies, Yellow, Round 3.00
Store, Tin, Oriental Mixture Tobacco, Red & Yellow, 1 1/2 In.High 7.00
Store, Tin, Our Table Brand Tea, Scene Of Boston Tea Party, Red & Gold 25.00
Store, Tin, Paint & Varnish, Jemmen, Boston Varnish Co., Swing Cover 6.00
Store, Tin, Paragon Tea, Paper Label, Lady Serving Lithograph, Browns 7.00
Store, Tin, Patterson's Seal Cut Plug Tobacco, Fish In Gold, Flip Top 25.00
Store, Tin, Patterson's Seal Tobacco, Chest Shape, Orange & Black 20.00
Store, Tin, Patterson's Tobacco, Red & Gold 25.00
Store, Tin, Pekoe Tea 2.50
Store, Tin, Pepsi Cola, Red & White, Round 35.00
Store, Tin, Philip Morris Cigarettes 4.50
Store, Tin, Pickaninny Peanut Butter, Red & Gold 35.00
Store, Tin, Pickaninny Peanut Butter, Red, Gold, & Black, Child 45.00
Store, Tin, Pickwick Coffee 3.00
Store, Tin, Piper Heidsieck Champagne Chewing Tobacco, 2 Pounds 12.00
Store, Tin, Planter's Peanuts, Pennant, 9 1/2 In. .... 15.00 To 18.50
Store, Tin, Pond Brand Peanut Butter, Green & Yellow, Round 35.00

Store, Tin, Powder, Pear Shape, Red, Label 25.00
Store, Tin, Presto Hand Soap, Painted Yellow Label, Round 3.00
Store, Tin, Pride Of Virginia Tobacco, Brown, Beige, & Blue, 2 5/8 In.High 8.00
Store, Tin, Pride Of Virginia, Flying Banner, Blue & Brown, Flat 8.00
Store, Tin, Prince Albert Tobacco, Hinged Lid 1.00
Store, Tin, Pure Cocoa Powder, Paper Label, Gold 5.00
Store, Tin, Pure Dalmation Insect Powder, Painted Label, Monogram 3.00
Store, Tin, Pure Ground Cinnamon, Type, Gold & Red, 10 In.High 18.00
Store, Tin, Pure India Tea, Painted Label, India Scenes 9.00
Store, Tin, Putnam Dye 25.00
Store, Tin, Putnam Dye, Display, Man On Horse, Monroe Drug Co. 35.00
Store, Tin, Rawleigh's Cinammon, Red, C.1921, 4 3/4 In.High 3.00
Store, Tin, Rawleigh's Nutmeg, Brown & Gold 22.00
Store, Tin, Rawleigh's Pepper Co., Green & Gold, C.1921, 4 1/2 In.High 3.00
Store, Tin, Rawleigh's Salve, Art Nouveau, Orange, Red, & Gold, Round 35.00
Store, Tin, Red Cross Coffee, Paper Label, Black & Gold Stenciling 7.00
Store, Tin, Red Dot Cigar, Lid, Cameo Of Girl's Head On 2 Sides 6.00
Store, Tin, Red Lily Coffee, Screw Cap In Corner, Handle, Red Flower 45.00
Store, Tin, Rexall Orderlie's Laxative, Red & Blue 4.00
Store, Tin, Rexall Seidlitz Powder, Paper Label, Blue, Red Type 4.00
Store, Tin, Rich's Canton Ginger, Yellow & Black .... 8.00 To 12.00
Store, Tin, Rich's Crystallized Stem Ginger, Flip Top, Green & Gold 8.00
Store, Tin, Rich's Ginger, Gold & Black, 5 Pounds 12.00
Store, Tin, Ridgewood Candies, Glass Insert, Orange & Red, Round 25.00
Store, Tin, Rit Dye, Woman & Dye, 18 X 20 X 16 In. 35.00
Store, Tin, Rival Peanut Butter, Tin Label, Blue, Green, & Beige 20.00
Store, Tin, Robert J.Pierce's Tablets For Women, Green & Gold 6.00
Store, Tin, Rockwood & Co.Cocoa, Paper Label 8.00
Store, Tin, Roly Poly, Negro Mammy, Mayo 85.00
Store, Tin, Roly Poly, Set Of 6 .... 1600.00
Store, Tin, Roly Poly, Storekeeper, Mayo 60.00
Store, Tin, Rose Bud Coffee, C.H.Walrath & Sons, Syracuse, N.Y., Paper Label 12.00
Store, Tin, Royal Baking Powder, Paper Label, Round 2.50
Store, Tin, Royal Lion Tea Bags, Paper Label, Red Lion 5.00
Store, Tin, Runkel Bros., Pure Breakfast Cocoa, 4 1/2 In.High 14.00
Store, Tin, S.S.Pierce Co.London Mixture Tea, Red & Green, 4 1/2 In.High 8.00
Store, Tin, S.S.Pierce Co.Tea, Chinese Scenes, 6 In.High 10.00
Store, Tin, Saratoga Tobacco, Beige & Red, 4 1/4 In.High 18.00
Store, Tin, Schepp's Peanut Butter, Handle, Red Monkeys 50.00
Store, Tin, Scrub-Net Washing Compound, Paper Label, Women, Blue & Beige 6.00
Store, Tin, Seidlitz Powders, Yellow & Green 9.00
Store, Tin, Sensible Tobacco, Gold & Beige, 5 In.High 25.00
Store, Tin, Shilling Powder, Label 5.00
Store, Tin, Sir Walter Raleigh Smoke, Picture, 17 X 26 In. 20.00
Store, Tin, Skookum Tobacco, Paper Label, Beige & Gold 25.00
Store, Tin, Slade's Mustard, Camel, Yellow & Red 2.00
Store, Tin, Slade's Nutmeg, Blue, Red Writing, 4 In.High 7.00
Store, Tin, Sommer's Bros., Patent Apr.29, 1879, Lithograph, Green & Black 50.00
Store, Tin, Sozodent Powder, Figural, Gold, Black Type 15.00
Store, Tin, Spice Box, Hinged Lid, Mustard Color, Stencil Of Lady 35.00
Store, Tin, Spice, The Great American Tea Co., Green, Lithographed, Set Of 4 .... 6.95
Store, Tin, Spurr's Revere Mocha & Java, Paul Revere On Horse, Red & White 55.00
Store, Tin, Squirrel Peanut Butter, Red & Orange, Squirrel 20.00
Store, Tin, Stag, Pocket, 1910 .... 4.00
Store, Tin, Stanvar Standard Varnish Works, Clip On Cup, Swing Cover, Red 7.00
Store, Tin, Stickney & Poor's Allspice, Cardboard 5.00
Store, Tin, Stickney & Poor's Sage, Paper Label, Picture Of Child 5.00
Store, Tin, Stickney & Poor's Thyme, Yellow Label, 3 1/4 In.High 5.00
Store, Tin, Strictly Pure Spices, R.L.Craig & Co., Stenciling, Lift Lid, Red 25.00
Store, Tin, Sunshine Biscuit, Raised Type, 5 1/2 In.High 9.00
Store, Tin, Sunshine Clover Leaves Cookies, Impressed Printing, Flat, Long 5.00
Store, Tin, Sunshine Cookies, Boy, Girl, Dog, Octagon 4.50
Store, Tin, Sunshine Hydrox Biscuit, Viking Man, Paper Label 15.00
Store, Tin, Sunshine Krispy Crackers, Loose Wiles Co., Black, Gold Type 45.00
Store, Tin, Swain, Earle & Co.Tea, Lithograph, Red With Black, Round 20.00
Store, Tin, Sweet Burley Tobacco, Flat, Round 12.00

Store, Tin, Sweet Cuba Tobacco, Slant Top, Red Writing On Mustard 75.00
Store, Tin, Swift & Courtney Match, Blue & Red 25.00
Store, Tin, Talcum Powder, California Perfume Company 8.50
Store, Tin, Tea Gold Rule, Silver Stencil, 3 Pounds 8.00
Store, Tin, Tea, Used By Tea Merchants, Black, Oriental Figures, Brass Handle 65.00
Store, Tin, Tetley's Tea, Red & Yellow Flowers, 5 1/4 In.High 6.00
Store, Tin, Texaco Company, Oil, The Texas Company, C.1918 .... 3.00
Store, Tin, The Allenbury's Glycerine & Black Currant Pastilles, England 5.00
Store, Tin, Thomas Wood & Co., Queenbee, Formosa, Beveled Mirror, Octagon 150.00
Store, Tin, Thurber's Bird Seed, Hinged, Paper Label, Lithograph 45.00
Store, Tin, Tiger Tobacco, Round, Red & Gold, Hinged Lid 85.00
Store, Tin, Tiger Tobacco, Round, Red, Silver, & Black, 5 Pounds 55.00
Store, Tin, Towle's Log Cabin Syrup, Paint, Contents, Medium Size 15.00
Store, Tin, Towle's Log Cabin Syrup, Paint, Contents, Small Size 15.00
Store, Tin, Trout Line Tobacco, Pocket, Tin Label, Red & Green 55.00
Store, Tin, Tuxedo Tobacco, Patent 1906 .... 4.50
Store, Tin, Tuxedo Tobacco, Round 3.00
Store, Tin, Twin Oaks Tobacco, Silver & Red, 4 1/4 In.High .... 12.00 To 20.00
Store, Tin, U-All-No After Finner Mints, Embossed Type 12.00
Store, Tin, Union Leader, 3 X 6 X 4 In. 8.50
Store, Tin, Vance Cigars, Horses, 4 X 6 X 5 1/2 In. 25.00
Store, Tin, Vandervear & Holmes Biscuit Co., Glass Window, Painted Green 10.00
Store, Tin, Vanline's Canton Ginger, Red & Gold 4.00
Store, Tin, Vaseline, Paper Label, Black Type 8.00
Store, Tin, Virginia Picnic Peanuts, Children Riding Peanut, Orange, Black 18.00
Store, Tin, W.H.I.Haye's Tobacco, Man With Mustache, Green 25.00
Store, Tin, Walter Baker & Co., Ltd., Breakfast Cocoa, Paper Label 3.00
Store, Tin, Walter Baker & Co., Ltd., Stenciled, Black Type 10.00
Store, Tin, Washington, Mills Emery, North Grafton, Mass., Mustard Color 22.50
Store, Tin, Whitehouse Coffee, Paper Label 2.00
Store, Tin, Whitman's Candy, Chest Type 4.00
Store, Tin, Whitman's Lime Juice Drops, Figural, Etchings, Black 50.00
Store, Tin, Winner Tobacco, Racing Car, Beiges 75.00
Store, Tin, Wood's Ambeno Tea, Screw Cap, Paper Label, Cardboard Sides 5.00
Store, Tin, Wood's Primrose Tea, Paper Label, Red, Green Type 5.00
Store, Tin, Wood's Spice Herbs, Boston, Paper Label, 3 In.High 2.50
Store, Tin, WuLung Tea, Figural, Paper Label, Flowers, People 10.00
Store, Tin, Yale Tobacco, Green & Black, 4 1/2 In.High 18.00
Store, Tobacco Cutter, Guillotine Type, Home Made 12.50
Store, Tobacco Cutter, Star, Cast Iron 15.00
Store, Token, Green River Whiskey .... 8.00 To 12.00
Store, Token, Green River Whiskey, Man Holding Horse 5.00
Store, Tongs, Ice, Cast Iron 4.00
Store, Toothpick, Hartman Carpet & Furniture Co., Eureka Pattern 18.00
Store, Trailer, Circus, Big Dipper, Victorian, Chain Driven Motor, 31 In.Long 682.50
Store, Tray, Beer, Bartholomay Beers, Rochester, Victorian Lady, Tin, 12 In. 55.00
Store, Tray, Beer, Budweiser, Mississippi River Scene, Copyright 1914, 13 In. 65.00
Store, Tray, Beer, Buffalo Co-Operative Brewing Company, Beer, Ale, & Porter 25.00
Store, Tray, Beer, Christian Feigenspan Brewing Co., Round, 1900s Pin-Up 19.00
Store, Tray, Beer, Crown Beer, Bartels, Syracuse, N.Y., Tin, Flowers On Front 7.00
Store, Tray, Beer, Deer Park Brewing Co., Port Jervis, Elk, Tin, 12 In. 15.00
Store, Tray, Beer, Dixie-45 .... 11.50
Store, Tray, Beer, Edelweiss 11.50
Store, Tray, Beer, Grain Belt 5.00
Store, Tray, Beer, Hampden Mild Ale 13.00
Store, Tray, Beer, Henry Lutz & Son, Mineral Water, Tin, 10 X 13 In. 35.00
Store, Tray, Beer, Iron City, Teck, Duquesne, Metal 8.00
Store, Tray, Beer, Jacob Rupert Beer & Ale, 2 Hands & 2 Glassed, Oval 15.00
Store, Tray, Beer, Kloppitz-Melchers Brew, Detroit, Elves Brewing, C.1900 .... 35.00
Store, Tray, Beer, Lion Brewery, Cincinnati, Ohio, Brass 25.00
Store, Tray, Beer, Lone Star 5.00
Store, Tray, Beer, Maiden, Round, Hand-Painted, Tin 38.00
Store, Tray, Beer, Nortena, Superior, Carta Blanca, Mexico 5.00
Store, Tray, Beer, Pabst 4.50
Store, Tray, Beer, Schultz Beer & Ale, Tin, 4 In.Diameter 8.00
Store, Tray, Beer, Simon Pure Old Abbey Ale & Beer, 12 In.Diameter 10.00

Store, Tray, Bevo Anheuser Busch, Tin 15.00
Store, Tray, Carnation Milk, 5 1/8 In. 12.00
Store, Tray, Change, Emerson Hotel, Baltimore, Oval, Tin, 4 X 6 In. 3.00
Store, Tray, Change, Fairy Soap 23.00
Store, Tray, Change, Frank Jones Homestead Ale, 5 In. 5.00
Store, Tray, Change, German American Brewing Co., Buffalo, N.Y., Round, 5 In. 14.50
Store, Tray, Change, Goebel Deer, Detroit 17.00
Store, Tray, Change, King's Pure Malt, Picture Of Waitress 22.50
Store, Tray, Change, Lansburgh & Bro., Washington, D.C., Manhattan Pattern 12.00
Store, Tray, Change, Lenox Necco Chocolates, Tin, 4 In.Diameter 10.00
Store, Tray, Change, Marion Brewing, 1911, Lady, Roses, Round 30.00
Store, Tray, Change, Miller High Life Beer 5.00
Store, Tray, Change, National Cigar, Tin 27.50
Store, Tray, Change, Pharaoh's Horses, Advertising Wood Fencing 35.00
Store, Tray, Change, Prudential, Rock, Tin, 2 1/2 X 3 1/2 In. 8.00
Store, Tray, Change, Rochester Shoe Store 14.00
Store, Tray, Change, Rockford Watches, Portrait Of Girl 14.00
Store, Tray, Change, Seitz Beer, Color Eagle Decor 12.50
Store, Tray, Change, Stollwerck Cocoa & Chocolate, 1899, Painted, Tin 15.00
Store, Tray, Change, Sullivan Cigars, Brown, Tin, 7-20-4 .... 10.00
Store, Tray, Change, Universal Stoves & Ranges 17.00
Store, Tray, Change, Wellsbach Lamp 12.50
Store, Tray, Daggett's Boston Orangeade, Lady With Glass & Roses, Tin 30.00
Store, Tray, Dewar's White Label Whiskey, Man In Red Coat, Bottle 12.00
Store, Tray, Drink Sterling Ale, Red & Gold, Rectangular 4.00
Store, Tray, Edelweiss Brew, Redheaded Woman, C.1915 .... 23.00
Store, Tray, Jamestown Ice Cream, Woman With Dish Of Ice Cream, C.1920 .... 20.00
Store, Tray, Jersey Creme, Tin, Round, 12 In. 95.00
Store, Tray, Lawrence Welk 8.00
Store, Tray, Lennon Sisters 8.00
Store, Tray, Logan Jonson Co., Nafruco, Fruit Flavors Sodas, Macatee, 1911 .... 30.00
Store, Tray, Mardi-Gras Coffee & Tea, Boston, Silent Butler, Lithograph, Tin 22.00
Store, Tray, Meadow Gold Ice Cream, Red & Gold Girl, 1920s, Tin 30.00
Store, Tray, Moxie, Boy, Reverse Painting On Glass, Round 75.00
Store, Tray, Moxie, Face Of Lady, Holding Glass, 'I Just Love Moxie, ' Tin 55.00
Store, Tray, Moxie, Lady, Reverse Painting On Glass, Round 95.00
Store, Tray, Moxie, Man, Tan, Cardboard, 24 In.Square 15.00
Store, Tray, Moxie, Victorian Lady, Lavender Flowers, Tin, 6 In.Diameter 45.00
Store, Tray, Nu Grape, Woman Holds Bottle, C.1920 .... 25.00
Store, Tray, O.F.C.Bourbon, Round, Tin, Stag, 12 In. 22.00
Store, Tray, Pepsi Cola, 'Enjoy Pepsi Cola, 'Red, White, & Black 15.00
Store, Tray, Pepsi Cola, 1930s 15.00
Store, Tray, Progress Ale, Indianapolis, Circa 1905 .... 23.00
Store, Tray, Remember The Maine, Metal, Picture, Stenciling 20.00
Store, Tray, Seip Beer, Four People In Car, Mountains, Road, Beer Bottle 25.00
Store, Tray, Self Stirring Billy Baxter, Round, Red Raven, 12 In. 7.50
Store, Tray, Thompson's Whiskies, Boston, Elk's Head, Tin, 12 In. 35.00
Store, Tray, To The Patrons Of Granite Ironware, Girl, Cow, Paper 8.00
Store, Tray, White Rock, Tin, 4 1/2 X 6 1/2 In. 5.00
Store, Tube, Brigg's Marking Pens, Patent 1867, Round, Wooden, Paper Label 10.00
Store, Tumbler, Cook's Beer 3.00
Store, Tumbler, Moxie, Flared Top With Red Band 12.00
Store, Tumbler, Moxie, Licensed Only For Serving Moxie, Flared Top 15.00
Store, Vacuum Cleaner, Everybody's, Red Tin, Wood Handle, Dated 1913 .... 35.00
Store, Vending Machine, Match, Rosebud 45.00
Store, Vise, U.S.Cavalry Saddler's, Wooden, Iron, Brass Arm, C.1800 .... 14.50
Store, Whiskey Glass, David & Drake, Benedict Bye, Purest Of Whiskeys 6.00
Store, Whiskey Glass, Mutt & Jeff, Drink Monponsett, Etched 9.00
Store, Whiskey Glass, Old Cabinet Pure Rye Whiskey, Lonn Bros.Co., N.Y. 3.50
Store, Whiskey Glass, Shortell & Timmins, Green Mountain Rye 3.50
Store, Whistle, Keds, Wooden, Paper Label 10.00
Store, Whistle, Pol Parrot Shoes For Boys & Girls, Tin 6.00
Store, Whistle, Red Goose Shoes, Tin 2.50
Store, World War I Airplane, Kellogg's Pep Cereal, P-66 Vanguard, Wooden 6.00
    Stove, see Fire, Stove
    Strawberry, see Soft Paste

Stretch Glass, Hat, Ice Blue, 5 In.Tall, 4 1/2 In. Across 65.00
Stretch Glass, Plate, Lime, Reticulated Border, 12 In. 30.00
Stretch Glass, Vase, Fan, Vaseline, 8 X 10 1/2 In. 20.00
    Sulfide, Marble, see Marble, Sulfide

Sunbonnet Babies were first introduced in 1902 in the Sunbonnet Babies
Primer. The stories were by Eulalie Osgood Grover, illustrated by
Bertha Corbett. The children's faces were completely hidden by the
sunbonnets, and had been pictured in black and white before this time. The
color pictures in the book were immediately successful. The Royal
Bayreuth China Company made a full line of children's dishes decorated
with the Sunbonnet Babies.

Sunbonnet Babies, Book, Primer, Eulalie Osgood Grover, 1902 .... 45.00
Sunbonnet Babies, Book, 1902 Edition 30.00
Sunbonnet Babies, Bowl, Sand Babies, Diamond Shape, Royal Bayreuth 75.00
Sunbonnet Babies, Bowl, Sand Babies, Handle, Royal Bayreuth, Blue Mark 69.50
Sunbonnet Babies, Candlestick, Royal Bayreuth, Blue Mark 165.00
Sunbonnet Babies, Candlestick, Royal Bayreuth, Pair 275.00
Sunbonnet Babies, Candlestick, Washing Window & Floor, Royal Bayreuth 130.00
Sunbonnet Babies, Card, 'should Auld Acquaintance Be Forgot, ' 1906, Frame 18.75
Sunbonnet Babies, Card, Valentine, Three Boys & Girls, 11 1/2 In. 15.00
Sunbonnet Babies, Compote, Fishing, Pedestal, Royal Bayreuth, Blue Mark 125.00
Sunbonnet Babies, Creamer, Mending, Royal Bayreuth, Blue Mark 135.00
Sunbonnet Babies, Creamer, Washing, Ironing 96.50
Sunbonnet Babies, Cup & Saucer, Candy For My Mandy 65.00
Sunbonnet Babies, Cup & Saucer, Child's, Royal Bayreuth 80.00
Sunbonnet Babies, Cup & Saucer, Cleaning & Sewing, Blue Mark 155.00
Sunbonnet Babies, Cup & Saucer, Demitasse, Hanging Clothes, Germany 45.00
Sunbonnet Babies, Cup & Saucer, Feeding Calf 35.00
Sunbonnet Babies, Cup & Saucer, Kissing 45.00
Sunbonnet Babies, Cup & Saucer, Royal Bayreuth, Blue Mark 175.00
Sunbonnet Babies, Dish, Cheese, Miniature, Washing & Ironing 225.00
Sunbonnet Babies, Dish, Child's, 3 Babies, Marked R With V In Center 32.50
Sunbonnet Babies, Dish, Feeding, Child's, Washing, Hanging Clothes On Line 125.00
Sunbonnet Babies, Dish, Feeding, Fishing Scene, Blue Mark .... 110.00 To 150.00
Sunbonnet Babies, Dish, Feeding, 7 1/2 In.Diameter, Royal Bayreuth 125.00
Sunbonnet Babies, Door Stop, 7 1/2 In. 12.00
Sunbonnet Babies, Doorstop, Colorful Paint, Iron .... 15.00 To 18.00
Sunbonnet Babies, Doorstop, Pink & White 15.00
Sunbonnet Babies, Holder, Matchbox, Mending, Saucer 65.00
Sunbonnet Babies, Mug, Child's, Mending, Royal Bayreuth 90.00
Sunbonnet Babies, Mug, Child's, Washing, Royal Bayreuth 90.00
Sunbonnet Babies, Mug, Girls, Seashore, Silver Plate, Queen City Silver Co. 65.00
Sunbonnet Babies, Mug, Sweeping, Royal Bayreuth, Blue Mark 150.00
Sunbonnet Babies, Napkin Ring, Embossed Sailor Boy, Little Girl 22.50
Sunbonnet Babies, Nappy, Three Sand Babies, Triangular, Royal Bayreuth 58.00
Sunbonnet Babies, Picture, Signed, 1904, Framed, 8 1/2 X 6 1/2 In., Pair 45.00
Sunbonnet Babies, Pitcher, Cleaning, Royal Bayreuth, 4 In.High 140.00
Sunbonnet Babies, Pitcher, Fishing, Royal Bayreuth, Marked 115.00
Sunbonnet Babies, Pitcher, Ironing, Royal Bayreuth, Blue Mark, 11 In.High 90.00
Sunbonnet Babies, Pitcher, Ironing, Royal Bayreuth, 2 3/4 In. 85.00
Sunbonnet Babies, Pitcher, Japan 17.00
Sunbonnet Babies, Plaque, Five Babies, Burnt Wood, 9 X 12 In. 12.50
Sunbonnet Babies, Plaque, Full Figure In Relief, Brass On Wood 12.50
Sunbonnet Babies, Plaque, Ironing, Brass 16.50
Sunbonnet Babies, Plaque, Paying Toll, Kissing Boy At Garden Gate 15.00
Sunbonnet Babies, Plate, Beach Babies, Blue Mark, 8 1/4 In. 75.00
Sunbonnet Babies, Plate, Boy, Baby, Doll, Parasoled Carriage, 'Three Of Us' 47.50
Sunbonnet Babies, Plate, Calendar, Dated 1910, 7 1/2 In. 48.00
Sunbonnet Babies, Plate, Girl And Overall Boy, 6 In. 35.00
Sunbonnet Babies, Plate, Washing, Royal Bayreuth, 6 In. .... 50.00 To 55.00
Sunbonnet Babies, Plate, Washing, Royal Bayreuth, 8 In. 88.00
Sunbonnet Babies, Postcard, Day Of The Week 5.50
Sunbonnet Babies, Postcard, Days Of The Week, Set Of 7 .... 15.00 To 55.00
Sunbonnet Babies, Postcard, Days Of The Week, Set Of 7, Framed 72.00

Sunbonnet Babies, Postcard, Friday, Framed	8.00
Sunbonnet Babies, Postcard, Give Us This Day Our Daily Bread	5.50
Sunbonnet Babies, Postcard, Last Day Of Summer	7.50
Sunbonnet Babies, Postcard, Now I Lay Me Down To Sleep	5.50
Sunbonnet Babies, Postcard, Saying Grace	7.50
Sunbonnet Babies, Postcard, Sunbonnet Girl, No.1489	2.50
Sunbonnet Babies, Postcard, Sunbonnet Girl, Overall Boy, Ullman, 1906, 6	50.00
Sunbonnet Babies, Postcard, Ullman Nursery Rhyme, Months Of The Year	10.00
Sunbonnet Babies, Print, A.M., 12 M., 6 P.M., Three In Sectioned Frame, 1906	40.00
Sunbonnet Babies, Print, Bookplate, Color, Signed Bertha Corbett	7.00
Sunbonnet Babies, Print, Cleaning Day, B.Corbett, Frame	20.00 To 30.00
Sunbonnet Babies, Print, Summer, Frame, 5 X 7 In.	10.00
Sunbonnet Babies, Print, Winter, Frame, 5 X 7 In.	10.00
Sunbonnet Babies, Quilt, Full Size	175.00
Sunbonnet Babies, Quilt, White Ground, Pink Decoration, 72 X 83 In.	50.00
Sunbonnet Babies, Sugar, Sand Babies Running Barefoot On Beach, Handled	65.00
Sunbonnet Babies, Tankard, Fishing, Miniature, Royal Bayreuth, Blue Mark	125.00
Sunbonnet Babies, Tea Set, Child's, Metal, Painted, 23 Piece	72.50
Sunbonnet Babies, Tray, Pin, Fishing, Royal Bayreuth, 4 In.Square	72.50
Sunbonnet Babies, Vase, Bertha Corbett	75.00
Sunbonnet Babies, Vase, Sweeping, Two Handles, Royal Bayreuth	125.00
Sunbonnet Babies, Watercolor, Mending Day, Signed B.L.Corbett, Frame	35.00

*Sunderland Luster is a name given to a characteristic pink luster made by
Leeds, Newcastle, and other English firms during the nineteenth century.
The luster glaze is metallic and glossy and sometimes appears to have bubbles
as a decoration.*

Sunderland, Cup & Saucer, Bird On Cup, C.1835	35.00
Sunderland, Cup & Saucer, Lavender Trim, Deep Saucer	20.00
Sunderland, Cup & Saucer, Pink, C.1840	21.50 To 45.00
Sunderland, Jug, Sailor's Departure Verse, Compass, Circa 1820	225.00
Sunderland, Jug, Sailor's Farewell, Flying Cloud, 5 In.	65.00
Sunderland, Mug, Creamware, Applied Handle, C.1830	55.00
Sunderland, Mustache Cup & Saucer, Pink Luster, Ship, Compass, Pair	59.00
Sunderland, Mustache Cup & Saucer, Pink, Black Ship, Sailor, Luster	32.50
Sunderland, Plaque, Ship & Verse, Dixons, C.1800	150.00
Sunderland, Plaque, Thou God, See'st Me, Lavender Luster Border	25.00
Sunderland, Plate, English Scene, Ye Olden Days, Square, 6 In.	30.00
Sunderland, Plate, Pink	35.00
Sunderland, Tea Set, Sugar, Creamer, Four Cups & Saucers, Faith, Hope, Charity	275.00

*Teco Pottery is the art pottery line made by the Terra Cotta Tile
Works of Terra Cotta, Illinois. The company was founded by William
D.Gates in 1881. The Teco line was first made in 1902 and continued
into the 1920s. It included over 500 designs, made in a variety of colors
and glazes.*

Teco, Pitcher, Green Matte, Base Extends Up & Becomes Handle & Lip, Signed	20.00
Teco, Vase, Matte Green, Two Art Deco Shape Handles, 5 1/2 In.High	25.00
Telephone, Candlestick	20.00
Telephone, Candlestick, With Headset, Pat.1915, Western Electric	55.00
Telephone, Cradle Type, Black, Thin Pedestal, Property Of Western Electric	26.00
Telephone, Cradle Type, Dial Dated 1915, French	75.00
Telephone, Desk, Black Paint, Western Electric Patent 1915, Brass, Cord	35.00
Telephone, Desk, Magneto, Wall, Oak, Dovetail, 8 In.Box, Western Electric	22.00
Telephone, Mechanical, 'Holcomb's Private Line, ' Patent 1878, Walnut Box	14.00
Telephone, Wall, Dialing Mechanism Inside, No Shelf, Oak, Refinished	90.00
Telephone, Wall, Oak	45.00 To 50.00

Teplitz refers to art pottery manufactured by a number of companies in the

Teplitz-Turn area of Bohemia during the late nineteenth and early twentieth centuries. The Amphora Porcelain Works and the Alexandra Works were two of these companies.

Telephone, Wall, Oak	45.00
Teplitz, Ashtray, Cameo At Side	22.50
Teplitz, Basket, Arab Scene, Horse, Green	35.00
Teplitz, Ewer, Autumn Flowers Outlined In Gold On Ivory, Dolphin Handle	75.00
Teplitz, Figurine, Bust Of Girl, Green, Marked Bohemia, Amphora, 15 1/2 In.	185.00
Teplitz, Figurine, Comic Golf Caddy, Huge Feet, Amazed Look Of Disgust	35.00
Teplitz, Rose Bowl, Boy & Dog, Green	29.00
Teplitz, Shoe, Beige, Raised Gold Trim, Flare Top, 5 In.Long	22.50
Teplitz, Vase, Amphora, Bronze Finish, 8 In.	45.00
Teplitz, Vase, Amphora, Sculptured Motif, Blue & Tan, Bisquelike Surface	15.00
Teplitz, Vase, Amphora, Sculptured Water Lilies, Openwork, Austria, 7 In.	60.00
Teplitz, Vase, Art Nouveau, Landscape, Green & Royal Blue, Gold, 5 1/2 In.	35.00
Teplitz, Vase, Art Nouveau, Sea Dragon, Signed Amphora, 14 In.Tall	150.00
Teplitz, Vase, Boy Figure, Green, 3 1/2 In.	33.50
Teplitz, Vase, Dark Green, Gold, Jeweled, Signed Amphora	75.00
Teplitz, Vase, Figural, Fat Man, Arms Akimbo, Crazed, Marked Stellmacher, Pair	50.00
Teplitz, Vase, Figural, Imperial Mark, Amphora, 13 1/2 In.High	125.00
Teplitz, Vase, Flowering Lilac Branch, Brown Ground, Signed, 16 In.High	70.00
Teplitz, Vase, Green Panels, Raised Raspberries At Top, Signed, 11 In.	37.00
Teplitz, Vase, Green Shades, Applied Roses, Two Handles, Signed Austria	45.00
Teplitz, Vase, Kate Greenaway, 5 In. *Illus*	35.00
Teplitz, Vase, Landscape, Blue & Gold Floral, Bohemia	85.00
Teplitz, Vase, Portrait, Lady, Two Handles, 8 In.High	39.00
Teplitz, Vase, Woman's Face, Crown With Semiprecious Stones, Amphora Mark	85.00
Teplitz, Vase, Woman's Face, Floral, Blue, Gold, Tan, Art Nouveau, Pair	225.00
Terra-Cotta, Figurine, Man Standing On Pedestal, Pair	40.00
Terra-Cotta, Figurine, Virgin, Spanish Colonial, Standing, C.1850	120.00
Terra-Cotta, Group, The Rest On Flight Into Egypt, Italian, C.1750	275.00
Terra-Cotta, Plaque, Bas Relief, Benjamin Franklin, Nini, 1777, 4 3/4 In.	450.00
Terra-Cotta, Roundel, Putto Head, Blue & White Glaze, 16 In.Diameter	2900.00
Terra-Cotta, Spittoon, Etched Band, Marked F.G.W.& Numerals	10.50

Textile includes all types of table linens and household linens such as coverlets, quilts, fabrics, etc.

Textile, Altar Cloth, Russian, Silver & Gold Embroidered Velvet, C.1850	325.00
Textile, Bag, Embroidered 'Corset Bag, 26, 'White Linen, Hanging	7.50
Textile, Banner, Apotheosis Of McKinley, Silk, C.1901	190.00
Textile, Banner, Civil War, Hand-Painted American Eagle, Tan Linen	47.50
Textile, Bedspread, Blue & White, Hand-Loomed	95.00
Textile, Bedspread, Crochet, White Popcorn Pattern, 96 X 86 In.	45.00
Textile, Bedspread, Marseilles, Fringe, Floral, Scrolls, 88 X 95 In.	45.00
Textile, Bedspread, Marseilles, 6 Ft.10 In.Square	15.00
Textile, Bell Pull, Needlepoint, Birds & Floral Vine Spouting From Vase	80.00
Textile, Belt, Nez Perce, Hand Sewn Beads On Buckskin, Circa 1875	165.00
Textile, Bench Cover, Needlepoint, Foliage, Tan, Green, 33 1/2 In.Long	95.00
Textile, Blanket, Horse, Navy Blue & Plaid, Silver Medallion, 18th Century	100.00
Textile, Blanket, Indian, Wool, Black, Yellow, Blue, & Cream, Chilkat	2500.00
Textile, Blanket, Pendleton, Brown, Red, & Yellow, 1921, Fringe, 70 In.Square	200.00
Textile, Bookmark, Benjamin Harrison, Black & White, Silk	12.00
Textile, Bookmark, Black Eagle, Flag, George Washington Bust, Silk	30.00
Textile, Bookmark, Cottage & Beehives, Music & Words, 'Home Sweet Home, 'silk	2.20
Textile, Bookmark, La France & L'Amerique Paris Exposition, 1878, Silk	35.00
Textile, Bookmark, Lafayette Bust, Silk	30.00
Textile, Bookmark, Lafayette's Tomb, Silk, 7 In.	30.00
Textile, Bookmark, Lafayette's Tomb, Silk, 9 In.	45.00
Textile, Bookmark, Philadelphia International Exhibition, 1876, Silk	35.00
Textile, Cap, Lady's, Silk Brocade, Quilted, Linen Lined, Silver Thread, 1650	49.50
Textile, Carpet, Aubusson, Brown, Blue Diamond, 9 Ft.5 In.X 7 Ft.3 In.	950.00
Textile, Carpet, Aubusson, Brown, Central Rondel, 13 Ft.9 In.X 11 Ft.5 In.	2100.00
Textile, Carpet, Aubusson, Center Medallion, Browns, C.1850	1000.00
Textile, Carpet, Heriz, Beige, Interlaced Strapwork, 11 Ft.8 In.X 9 Ft.1 In.	1000.00
Textile, Carpet, Heriz, Blue, Vine & Palmette, 12 Ft.2 In.X 9 Ft.1 In.	1200.00
Textile, Carpet, Heriz, Brick Red, Blue Medallion, Strapwork, 10 X 14 Ft.	2400.00

Textile, **Carpet**, Kerman, Laver, Orange, Medallions, 26 Ft.7 In.X 18 Ft.6 In. 3400.00
Textile, **Carpet**, Kerman, Red Field, Central Medallion, 9 X 18 Ft. 900.00
Textile, **Carpet**, Oushak, Green, Flowering Vines, 16 Ft.6 In.X 12 Ft.1 In. 900.00
Textile, **Carpet**, Sarouk, Wine, Flowering Vines, 19 Ft.6 In.X 10 Ft.6 In. 600.00
Textile, **Carpet**, Savonnerie Style, Camel Field, Floral, 8 Ft.X 10 Ft.10 In. 1000.00
Textile, **Carpet**, Savonnerie, Beige, Central Paterae, 38 Ft.8 In.X 16 Ft. 3100.00
Textile, **Carpet**, Savonnerie, Brown, Floral Baskets, 18 Ft.3 In.X 13 Ft.8 In. 1400.00
Textile, **Carpet**, Sultanabad, Rust, Floral Vines, 11 Ft.3 In.X 10 Ft.10 In. 325.00
Textile, **Coat**, Cutaway, C.1890 .... 25.00
Textile, **Coat**, Man's, Prince Albert, C.1860 .... 15.00

Linen or wool coverlets were made during the eighteenth century. Most of
the coverlets date from 1800 to 1850. Four types were made, the double woven,
jacquard, summer and winter, and overshot.

Textile, **Coverlet**, Birds & Urns, House Border, Blue & White 160.00
Textile, **Coverlet**, Birds, Houses, Green, Gold, Red, White .... 110.00 To 150.00
Textile, **Coverlet**, Center Star, Floral, Eagles In Corners, Linen, Wool, 1840 .... 160.00
Textile, **Coverlet**, Cream & Rust, 4 X 8 Ft. 60.00
Textile, **Coverlet**, Eagle In Each Corner, Blue & White On Reverse 150.00
Textile, **Coverlet**, 'Liberty & Independence, Ithaca, 1838, ' Blue, White 138.00
Textile, **Coverlet**, Marseilles, Hemmed Edge, 82 X 72 In. 10.00
Textile, **Coverlet**, Marseilles, Scalloped, Cutouts For Bedposts, 81 In. 11.00
Textile, **Coverlet**, Marseilles, 84 X 56 In. 15.00
Textile, **Coverlet**, Medallion & Scrolls, Maroon, Red, & White 80.00
Textile, **Coverlet**, Medallion, Star, & Scrolls, Red, White, Blue, & Green 95.00
Textile, **Coverlet**, Muslin, President & Mrs.McKinley, Electric Tower 12.50

Teplitz, Vase,
Kate Greenaway, 5 In.
See Page 580

Textile, Banner,
Apotheosis Of McKinley,
Silk, C.1901
See Page 580

Textile, Handkerchief,
Printed Cotton, English, C.1800
See Page 582

Textile, **Coverlet**, Pine Tree, Blue & White 120.00
Textile, **Dress**, Flapper's, Lavender, Silver Beads & Brilliants, Size 12 .... 15.00
Textile, **Dress**, Flapper's, Pink, Beading, Circa 1920 .... 25.00
Textile, **Dress**, Heavily Beaded, Crepe De Chine, Gray, Circa 1920 .... 15.00
Textile, **Epaulette**, British Naval Officer's Full Dress, Gold, Pair 21.00
Textile, **Flag**, American Civil War, Silk & Cotton, Handmade, Wood Handle 17.50
Textile, **Flag**, Cavalry, Pennsylvania, Silk, Yellow, Hand-Painted, C.1870 .... 69.50
Textile, **Flag**, Civil War, Numeral 26 In Red In Center, Blue, Silk 34.50
Textile, **Flag**, Confederate, Red, White, Blue, Cross Of St.Andrew, Linen 22.50
Textile, **Flag**, Mass-E In Gold Letters, Red Linen 19.50
Textile, **Flag**, Silk, 36 Stars 7.50
Textile, **Flag**, Spanish American War Era Red Cross Medical, Field Tent 12.50
Textile, **Flag**, 1st Division In Gold Letters, American, Civil War, Silk 39.50
Textile, **Flag**, 48 Stars, Silk, 17 X 12 In. 20.00
Textile, **Glove**, Sealskin Fur, Brown Fur, C.1870, Pair 17.50

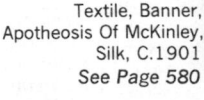

Textile, Handbag, Mesh, On Chain 8.00
Textile, Handkerchief, Linen, Hand Drawn Work & Lace Border, C.1887 .... 3.98
Textile, Handkerchief, Printed Cotton, English, C.1800 .... *Illus* 140.00
Textile, Hanging, Needlepoint, 3 Vertical Panels Of Floral, 8 Ft.3 In.Long 1600.00
Textile, Hat, British Rifle Officer's, Persian Lamb, Dress, Insignia, 1890s 32.50
Textile, Hat, Flapper, Scull Type, Black Velvet, Brocade, Jewels 5.00
Textile, Hat, Opera, Silk, Collapsible 11.00
Textile, Linsey-Woolsey, Blue Face, Brown & White On Back, Diamond Quilting 50.00
Textile, Linsey-Woolsey, Blue Face, Cream On Back, Lined Square Quilting 110.00
Textile, Linsey-Woolsey, Blue Face, Ecru On Back, Diamond Quilting 160.00
Textile, Linsey-Woolsey, Blue Face, Ecru On Back, Plume & Diagonal Line 90.00
Textile, Linsey-Woolsey, Blue Face, Sand On Back, Diamond Quilting 50.00
Textile, Linsey-Woolsey, Blue Face, Sand On Back, Fan & Scroll Quilting 70.00
Textile, Linsey-Woolsey, Blue Face, Sand On Back, Square & Quatrefoil 80.00
Textile, Linsey-Woolsey, Blue Green Face, Gold On Back, Diagonal Quilting 50.00
Textile, Linsey-Woolsey, Chocolate Face, Gold On Back, Diamond Quilting 50.00
Textile, Linsey-Woolsey, Chocolate Face, Russet On Back, Plume Quilting 350.00
Textile, Linsey-Woolsey, Cinnamon Face, Cream On Back, Plume Quilting 90.00
Textile, Linsey-Woolsey, Cinnamon Face, Gold On Back, Fish Scale Quilting 170.00
Textile, Linsey-Woolsey, Deep Blue Face, Gray Back, Plume & Star Quilting 40.00
Textile, Linsey-Woolsey, Gold Back, Plaid Patchwork Diamonds On Face 325.00
Textile, Linsey-Woolsey, Gold Face & Back, Floral Square Quilting 275.00
Textile, Linsey-Woolsey, Gold Face, Cream On Back, Plume & Circle Quilting 80.00
Textile, Linsey-Woolsey, Olive Face, Cream On Back, Interlocking Circle 200.00
Textile, Linsey-Woolsey, Russet Face, Cream On Back, Plume Quilting 425.00
Textile, Linsey-Woolsey, Sage Green Face, Ecru On Back, Diamond Pattern 50.00
Textile, Memoriam, Embroidered, Lady At Tomb, Gilt Frame 75.00
Textile, Napkin, Linen, Red & White, Hand Woven, Fringe, 12 In.Square, 11 .... 45.00
Textile, Needlepoint, Gray Cat, Black Ground, Wooden Frame 22.00
Textile, Needlepoint, Multicolor Flower Basket, Frame, Black Velvet, Gold 15.00
Textile, Panel, Needlepoint, French, Shepherd Piping, Sheep, C.1730 .... 300.00
Textile, Pennant, Civil War, 5th Connecticut Volunteers, Silk, Blue, Gold 39.50
Textile, Pennant, World War I, U.S.Artillery, Silk, Embroidered 17.50
Textile, Pillow Sham, Hand Embroidered Flowers, Verse, Pair 20.00
Textile, Quilt, Alphabet, Red, White, & Blue, Hand Quilted, 77 X 92 In. 85.00
Textile, Quilt, Applique, Butterflies, 49 Squares, Pink Back 60.00
Textile, Quilt, Applique, Flowers, Scalloped Edge, 80 X 92 In. 45.00
Textile, Quilt, Autograph, Red & White, Patchwork, Handmade, Double Bed Size 135.00
Textile, Quilt, Basket Pattern, Blue & White, 74 X 78 In. 120.00
Textile, Quilt, Basket Pattern, Red, Green, & White 210.00
Textile, Quilt, Block Pattern, Pink & Green, Orange Reverse 70.00
Textile, Quilt, Bride's, White 80.00
Textile, Quilt, Calico Designs, Multicolored 50.00
Textile, Quilt, Calico Print, Blue & White 70.00
Textile, Quilt, Calico, Red, Yellow, & White 150.00
Textile, Quilt, Country Lanes, Orchid & Yellow, 80 X 82 In. 35.00
Textile, Quilt, Cradle Size, Green, Blue, & White 110.00
Textile, Quilt, Crazy, American, Patty Hammond, 1884, 80 X 80 In. 100.00
Textile, Quilt, Crazy, Cotton, 76 X 68 In. 40.00
Textile, Quilt, Crazy, Ribbon Winner At 1920 Fair, 70 X 82 In. 30.00
Textile, Quilt, Crazy, Silk, 72 X 82 In. 45.00
Textile, Quilt, Crib Size, Deep Pink & White 50.00
Textile, Quilt, Diamond Triangle, Red, White, & Green, 64 X 84 In. 120.00
Textile, Quilt, Double Wedding Ring, Scalloped Edge, Pink Lined, 72 X 82 In. 50.00
Textile, Quilt, Floral, Red, Green, & White 600.00
Textile, Quilt, Floral, Scallops & Tassels, Blue & White 325.00
Textile, Quilt, Floral, Vine Border, Red, Green, & White 140.00
Textile, Quilt, Flowers & Leaves, Red, Green, Gold, & White 130.00
Textile, Quilt, Flowers, Applique, Yellow & White With Pink & Green 100.00
Textile, Quilt, Geometric Patchwork, Signed By 56 Makers, Dated 1899 .... 50.00
Textile, Quilt, Heart Pattern, Blue, Pink, & White 250.00
Textile, Quilt, Irish Chain, Made By Grandma Fenner, 1874, 100 X 108 In. 200.00
Textile, Quilt, Large Snowflake, Green & White 150.00
Textile, Quilt, Lavender, Pink, & Green .... *Illus* 550.00
Textile, Quilt, Lone Star Of Texas, Dark Green Border 150.00
Textile, Quilt, Lone Star, Yellow, Shaded Colors, 66 X 84 In. 50.00

Textile, Quilt, Necktie Pattern, 70 X 80 In. 35.00
Textile, Quilt, Off White Ground, Red, Brown, Vermont, Signed, 72 X 81 In. 55.00
Textile, Quilt, Patchwork 28.00
Textile, Quilt, Patchwork, Golden Linsey-Woolsey Back 120.00
Textile, Quilt, Patchwork, Handmade, Full Size 15.00
Textile, Quilt, Patchwork, Red, Green, & White 120.00
Textile, Quilt, Patchwork, White, Red, Beige, 76 X 86 In. 75.00
Textile, Quilt, Red, Green .... *Illus*   350.00
Textile, Quilt, Snowflake, Red, Blue, Yellow, & White 205.00
Textile, Quilt, Star Pattern, Red, Green, & White, 90 X 92 In. 100.00
Textile, Quilt, Stars, 4 In.Multicolor, 82 X 70 In. 40.00
Textile, Quilt, Tulips In Flowerpots, Large Size 95.00
Textile, Quilt, Tulips, Red, Green, & White 210.00
Textile, Robe, Buggy, Pink & Red Florals, Shaded Leaves, 48 X 56 In. 49.50
Textile, Rug, Bergamo, Beige Diamond Medallion, 3 Ft.8 In.X 4 Ft.7 In. 80.00
Textile, Rug, Chinese, Persian Style On Brown, 7 Ft.8 In.X 4 Ft.3 In. 325.00
Textile, Rug, Ganado Type, Red, Black, Cream, Wool, Circa 1890 .... 350.00
Textile, Rug, Ghiordes, Olive Green, Central Mirab, 7 Ft.X 4 Ft.6 In. 80.00
Textile, Rug, Gorovan, Red, Interlaced Vines & Floral, 4 Ft.4 In.X 3 Ft.9 In 120.00
Textile, Rug, Hamadan, Blue, Geometric Devices, 4 Ft.10 In.X 2 Ft.9 In. 100.00
Textile, Rug, Hamadan, Brown, Alternating Cones, 5 Ft.3 In.X 3 Ft.5 In. 50.00
Textile, Rug, Hamadan, Red, Diamond Latticework, Cones, 8 Ft.X 4 Ft.5 In. 150.00
Textile, Rug, Hamadan, Red, Diamond Pole Medallion, 5 Ft.11 In.X 3 Ft.6 In. 110.00
Textile, Rug, Hamadan, Red, Diamonds, Flowerheads, 5 Ft.7 In.X 3 Ft.7 In. 100.00
Textile, Rug, Hamadan, Rose, Diamond Medallions, 6 Ft.X 3 Ft.8 In. 70.00
Textile, Rug, Hooked, Beige, Floral, Blue Border, 3 Ft.8 In.X 1 Ft.10 In. 75.00
Textile, Rug, Hooked, Floral, Oval, 3 Ft.2 In.X 2 Ft.2 In. 5.00

Textile, Quilt, Lavender, Pink, & Green
See Page 582

Textile, Quilt, Red, Green

Textile, Rug, Hooked, Three Deer, Red, Black, Gray, Oval 22.50
Textile, Rug, Hooked, 2 Puppies, 3 Ft.2 In.X 1 Ft.6 In. 50.00
Textile, Rug, Kayseri, Silk, Wine, Floral Strapwork, 6 Ft.11 In.X 4 Ft.3 In. 120.00
Textile, Rug, Kazak, Blue, 3 Rectangular Medallions, 9 Ft.2 In.X 4 Ft.4 In. 750.00
Textile, Rug, Kazak, Red, Geometric Medallions, 7 Ft.2 In.X 6 Ft. 450.00
Textile, Rug, Kerman, Ivory Ground, Blue Center Medallion, Floral, 6 X 10 Ft. 500.00
Textile, Rug, Klagetoh, Navajo, Wool, Zigzag, C.1930, 101 X 47 1/2 In. 425.00
Textile, Rug, Kurdistan, Midnight Blue, Latticework, 9 Ft.4 In.X 3 Ft.8 In. 70.00
Textile, Rug, Moore, Navajo, Wool, Diamonds, Swastika, C.1915, 86 X 49 In. 450.00
Textile, Rug, Navajo Indian, Wool, Arrows, Birds, Swastikas, 103 X 69 In. 1200.00
Textile, Rug, Navajo Indian, Wool, Diamond Medallions, C.1900, 52 X 33 In. 300.00
Textile, Rug, Navajo Indian, Wool, Geometric Motifs, 51 1/2 X 32 In. 250.00
Textile, Rug, Navajo Indian, Wool, Geometric, Floral Pots, 72 X 53 In. 250.00
Textile, Rug, Navajo Indian, Wool, Triangular Panels, 59 1/2 X 39 1/2 In. 160.00
Textile, Rug, Navajo Indian, Wool, 1910, 60 X 38 In. .... *Illus*   325.00
Textile, Rug, Prayer, Anatolian, Red Mirab, Floral, Panels, 3 Ft.X 4 Ft.3 In. 100.00
Textile, Rug, Prayer, Daghestan, Blue Mirab, Flowers, 4 Ft.8 In.X 2 Ft.11 In. 250.00

Textile, Rug, Navajo Indian, Wool, 1910, 60 X 38 In.
See Page 583

Textile, Rug, Sarouk, Beige, Blue Pole Medallion, 7 Ft.2 In.X 4 Ft.7 In.	700.00
Textile, Rug, Sarouk, Beige, Central Pole Medallion, 4 Ft.3 In.X 6 Ft.9 In.	225.00
Textile, Rug, Sarouk, Red Ground, 4 X 5 Ft.	199.00
Textile, Rug, Shiraz, Diamond Medallions, Red, Beige, 8 Ft.3 In.X 5 Ft.7 In.	160.00
Textile, Rug, Shirvan, Beige, Gold, & Blue, Diamonds, 4 Ft.10 In.X 3 Ft.3 In.	50.00
Textile, Rug, Shirvan, Beige, Rows Of Flowerheads, 5 Ft.6 In.X 3 Ft.8 In.	325.00
Textile, Rug, Shirvan, Brown, Diamond Medallions, 4 Ft.2 In.X 3 Ft.7 In.	100.00
Textile, Rug, Shirvan, Brown, Star Devices, 4 Ft.10 In.X 3 Ft.6 In.	80.00
Textile, Rug, Teche Bohkara, Red, Circa 1903, 22 X 27 1/2 In.	118.00
Textile, Rug, Teec Nos Pas, Navajo, Wool, Medallions, C.1910, 85 X 52 1/2 In.	550.00
Textile, Rug, Velvet, Beige, Brown, Blue, Rust, Silk Fringe, 51 X 76 In.	50.00
Textile, Runner, Hamadan, Midnight Blue, Herati Design, 9 Ft.6 In.X 4 Ft.	160.00
Textile, Runner, Hamadan, Midnight Blue, Latticework, 204 X 44 In.	200.00
Textile, Runner, Hamadan, Red, Cones, Trees, Flowerheads, 21 Ft.8 In.X 3 Ft.	150.00
Textile, Runner, Hooked, Beige Tiles, 13 Ft.4 In.X 2 Ft.7 In., Pair	225.00
Textile, Runner, Hooked, Central Rectangle, Floral, 16 Ft.5 In.X 1 Ft.9 In.	60.00
Textile, Runner, Hooked, Central Rectangle, 11 Ft.9 In.X 2 Ft.8 In.	50.00
Textile, Runner, Hooked, Patchwork Diamonds, 16 Ft.11 In.X 1 Ft.4 In.	75.00
Textile, Runner, Kurdistan, Central Elongated Rectangle, 3 Ft.X 9 Ft.6 In.	325.00
Textile, Runner, Serabend, Gold, Cones, Flowerheads, 8 Ft.10 In.X 3 Ft.5 In.	110.00
Textile, Runner, Serabend, Midnight Blue, Herati, 16 Ft.3 In. X 6 Ft.5 In.	350.00
Textile, Runner, Table, Italian, Silk & Metal Thread Embroidered, 13 Ft.	60.00

Samplers were made in the United States during the early 1700s. The best examples were made from 1790 to 1840. Long narrow samplers are usually older than the square ones. Early samplers just had stitching or alphabets. The later examples had numerals, borders, and pictorial decorations. Those with mottoes are mid-Victorian.

Textile, Sampler, Alphabet, Numbers, Mercy Turner, Age 11, 1830, Houses, Frame	95.00
Textile, Sampler, American, Black & White, Dated 1857, Framed	40.00
Textile, Sampler, English, Birds, Flowers, Trees, 5 Royal Crowns, Dated 1799	70.00
Textile, Sampler, Flags, In Honor Shall Wave, Framed	30.00
Textile, Sampler, French, Needlework, Lovebirds, Figures, Floral, C.1850	110.00
Textile, Sampler, Old Homestead, Numerals, Frame, 15 X 11 In.	25.00
Textile, Sampler, Signed Emma Corben, 1844, Frame, 15 X 16 In.	65.00
Textile, Sampler, Strawberry & Vine Border, Made By H.M.Nash, 1813, Frame	95.00
Textile, Sampler, Strawberry Border, By Hannah Hunt, Born 1779, Frame	125.00
Textile, Seabag, Seaman's, Handstitched, 1850, 48 In.Long	17.50
Textile, Shawl, Allover Raised Design, Beige, Silk, Fringe	37.00
Textile, Shawl, Gray Plaid, Fringe, Homespun, Welsh, 36 In.Square	12.00
Textile, Shawl, Green Silk, Embroidered Flower Clusters, Long Fringe, 1920	20.00
Textile, Shawl, Paisley	40.00
Textile, Shawl, Paisley, 72 In.Sq.	45.00
Textile, Shawl, Piano, Black, Tan, Black Corner Tassels	42.50
Textile, Shawl, Silk, Pale Yellow, Embroidered Flowers, Fringe	10.00
Textile, Shawl, Silk, White, White Embroidery, China	12.00
Textile, Shawl, Spanish, Pink, Pink Embroidered Floral, Silk, Long Fringe	19.50
Textile, Shawl, Wool, Amish, Gray, 1 Yard Square	10.00
Textile, Spats, Gray Felt, Original Box	7.00
Textile, Stevengraph, See Stevengraph	
Textile, Straps & Epaulettes, Officer's, New York Insignia, Gilt, C.1900	12.50
Textile, Table Cover, Turkey Border, Homespun, Will Cover 8 Ft.Table	25.00

Textile, **Tablecloth**, Belgium Linen Inset, Hand Crochet, Six Napkins 80.00
Textile, **Tablecloth**, Red, Paisley Border, Fringe, 6 Ft.Square 37.00
Textile, **Tapestry**, Aubusson, Mythological, Chariot, Horses, 9 Ft.3 In., C.1650 .... 2600.00
Textile, **Tapestry**, Brussels, Figures, Hunters, Dogs, Game, 10 Ft.7 In., C.1550 .... 3250.00
Textile, **Tapestry**, Couple Holding Hands, House, Trees, Tulips, Belgian 600.00
Textile, **Tapestry**, Flemish, Seated Male, Standing Lady, 8 Ft.6 In., C.1550 .... 1100.00
Textile, **Tapestry**, Flemish, Verdure, Chateau, 9 Ft., C.1700 .... 1300.00
Textile, **Tapestry**, Fragment, French, Reclining Lady & Cornucopia, 9 1/2 In. 40.00
Textile, **Tapestry**, Needlepoint, English Court Scene, 40 X 52 In.High 450.00
Textile, **Tapestry**, Paris, Narcissus, Seated, 11 Ft., C.1650 .... 750.00
Textile, **Tapestry**, Petit Point, Vase & Floral Scene 35.00
Textile, **Tapestry**, Scene, Family, Goat, Dog, 33 X 25 In. 15.00
Textile, **Uniform**, Keystone Cop 25.00
Textile, **Woolwork**, Picture, Goat Herd, 1840 .... 110.00
Textile, **Woolwork**, Picture, Pastoral Scene, 1840 .... 125.00
Textile, **Woolwork**, Sailor's, Sailing Ship, Banner, With Love, Frame 185.00
Textile, **Woven Silk**, French Street Scenes, Signed N.F.& A.Perez, Pair 140.00
Textile, **Woven Silk**, Grandma & Grandpa Scene, A.Dimini, Black, Gray, Frame 44.50
Textile, **Woven Silk**, View Of Independence Hall, Phila., Horst-Mann, 1876 .... 45.00

Tiffany Glass was made by Louis Comfort Tiffany, the American glass
designer who worked from about 1879 to 1933. His work included iridescent
glass, art nouveau styles of design, and original contemporary styles. He was
also noted for his stained glass windows, his unusual lamps, and his bronze work.
Tiffany **Type, Inkwell**, Green & White Swirls, Copper Overlay, Apollo Studios 45.00
Tiffany **Type, Shade**, Birds, Fruit, 24 In.Wide 750.00
Tiffany **Type, Vase**, Pyriform, Green Iridescence, Blue Oil Spots, Silver 400.00
Tiffany, **Ashtray**, Artichoke Base, Bronze, Stand 295.00
Tiffany, **Ashtray**, Bronze, Semicircular, Shell Form, Reclining Female 175.00
Tiffany, **Bar**, Top Half, 11 Panels Of Leaded Glass, 7 Ft.High 4300.00
Tiffany, **Basket**, Mottled Green, Gold Handle, Reeded, Unsigned 95.00
Tiffany, **Blotter End**, Bronze, Signed, Pair 45.00
Tiffany, **Blotter End**, Zodiac, Bronze, Signed, Two Pieces 75.00
Tiffany, **Bonbon**, Queen, Ruffled Edges, Signed 225.00
Tiffany, **Bottle**, Bitters, Prism Bottom, St.Louis Diamond Top, Stopper 125.00
Tiffany, **Bowl & Underplate**, Finger, Blue, Signed 425.00
Tiffany, **Bowl & Underplate**, Finger, Gold Iridescent, Signed L.C.T. 130.00
Tiffany, **Bowl & Underplate**, Finger, Millefiori, Brown Iridescent, Floral 625.00
Tiffany, **Bowl & Underplate**, Finger, Pastel, Signed 200.00
Tiffany, **Bowl & Underplate**, Gold, Blue, Purple Highlights, Ruffled 265.00
Tiffany, **Bowl & Underplate**, Pink & White Pastel, Signed 250.00
Tiffany, **Bowl**, Applied S Shape Handles, Signed L.C.T.Favrile, 3 1/2 In. 165.00
Tiffany, **Bowl**, Blue, Iridescent, Floriform Shape, Pedestal, L.C.T. Favrile 850.00
Tiffany, **Bowl**, Blue, 5 In. 60.00
Tiffany, **Bowl**, Blue, 10 In. 875.00
Tiffany, **Bowl**, Bronze, Gold, Silver, Blue Iridescent, Scalloped, 4 1/2 In. 138.00
Tiffany, **Bowl**, Conical, Footed, Blue Iridescence, Inscribed L.C.T.Favrile 300.00
Tiffany, **Bowl**, Dore Bronze, Pedestal, Edge Pattern, 9 In.Diameter 49.00
Tiffany, **Bowl**, Etched Leaves, Iridescent Bronze Base, L.C.T., 12 In. 800.00
Tiffany, **Bowl**, Finger, Gold Iridescent, Marked L.C.T. 75.00
Tiffany, **Bowl**, Flower, Detachable Frog, Iridescent Blue Green, Favrile, 1785 .... 625.00
Tiffany, **Bowl**, Gadrooned Edge, Intaglio Cut Buttercups Interior, Favrile 200.00
Tiffany, **Bowl**, Gold Iridescent, Ribbed, Ruffled, L.C.T.Favrile, 6 1/2 In. 210.00
Tiffany, **Bowl**, Lily Of The Valley, Monogram, 5 In. 28.00
Tiffany, **Bowl**, Millefiori, Gold Iridescent, 4 1/4 In.Diameter, 2 In.High 450.00
Tiffany, **Bowl**, Nut, Fluted Edge, L.C.T., Gold Iridescence 100.00
Tiffany, **Bowl**, Nut, Gold, Iridescent, Onionskin, Stretch, Ruffled 245.00
Tiffany, **Bowl**, Pale Blue, White Feathers, Footed, 4 1/2 In. 225.00
Tiffany, **Bowl**, Pink Gold, Iridescent, Ruffled, Ribbed, L.C.T., 4 1/4 In. 125.00
Tiffany, **Bowl**, Red Iridescent, Swirls, Marked, 7 In. 300.00
Tiffany, **Bowl**, Red, Signed, 11 In. 350.00
Tiffany, **Bowl**, Silver Green Gold Iridescent, Intaglio Leaves, Flower Holder 525.00
Tiffany, **Bowl**, Swirls, Red Highlights, Signed, 4 1/2 In.Diameter 150.00
Tiffany, **Box**, Metal Cutout Overlay, Caramel Glass, Signed, 5 1/2 X 3 1/2 In. 115.00
Tiffany, **Box**, Patch, Silver, Pink Enamel, Mirrored Lid 38.00
Tiffany, **Bronze**, Kangaroo, Miniature, Signed 195.00

Tiffany, **Bronze**, Lion, Signed Tiffany Studios, Numbered, 5 In.Long 225.00
Tiffany, **Bronze**, Owl, Signed, No.892, 3 In.Tall 225.00
Tiffany, **Candelabrum**, Gilded Bronze, Floriform Handle, 2 Urn Form Sockets 225.00
Tiffany, **Candelabrum**, 4 Light, Urn Shape Socket, Green Glass, Bronze, Favrile 300.00
Tiffany, **Candleholder**, Flower Form, Bronze, Marked, 11 In.High, Pair 225.00
Tiffany, **Candlestick Vase**, Gold, In Metal Base, L.C.T., 10 In. 175.00
Tiffany, **Candlestick**, Bronze, Urn Shape Socket, In 3 Prongs, Round Base, Pair 225.00
Tiffany, **Candlestick**, Dore Bronze, 18 1/2 In., Pair 125.00
Tiffany, **Candlestick**, Opalescent, Pink, Clear, L.C.T.Favrile, 1927, Pair 435.00
Tiffany, **Candlestick**, Queen's Lace Pattern, Bronze, 17 In., Pair 300.00
Tiffany, **Candlestick**, 2 Arm, Pair 325.00
Tiffany, **Candlesticks**, Iridescent Tulip Form Shade, Bronze Base, Pair 325.00
Tiffany, **Case**, Spoon, Butterfly, Hinged, Brown Leatherette Cover, Marked 10.00
Tiffany, **Centerpiece**, Favrile, Carved Leaves, Iridescent, Signed, 4 In.Tall 525.00
Tiffany, **Centerpiece**, Flower Holder, Silver Gold Iridescence, Carved, Signed 525.00
Tiffany, **Champagne**, Opalescent White, Green Inside, Hollow Stem, Gold Foot 250.00
Tiffany, **Champagne**, Pastel Turquoise, Signed L.C.Tiffany, Favrile, 7 1/2 In. 250.00
Tiffany, **Chandelier**, Turtleback, 21 In.Diameter .... *Illus* 5750.00
Tiffany, **Cherubs**, Bronze Base, 34 In.High, Signed 600.00
Tiffany, **Clock**, Burnished Copper Mounting, 22 In.Long 385.00
Tiffany, **Clock**, Mantel, Bronze, Rectangular, Moorish Pattern, Chelsea Co. 375.00
Tiffany, **Clock**, Mercury Pendulum, Porcelain Face, Bevel Glass, French Works 350.00
Tiffany, **Compote**, Blue Aurene, Stemmed, Ruffled, Signed 290.00
Tiffany, **Compote**, Bronze Gold Iridescence, Red & Purple Highlights, Signed 500.00
Tiffany, **Compote**, Bronze, Enamel Rim, Signed, 10 In.Diameter 200.00
Tiffany, **Compote**, Diamond-Quilted, Signed L.C.Tiffany, 8 In. 350.00
Tiffany, **Compote**, Gold Iridescence, Fluted Rim, Pedestal, Signed, Label 225.00
Tiffany, **Compote**, Gold, Fluted Edge, Signed, 6 3/8 In.Diameter 250.00
Tiffany, **Compote**, Gold, Purple & Green Iridescent, Footed 155.00
Tiffany, **Compote**, Gold, Signed, 9 In.Diameter 225.00
Tiffany, **Compote**, Green, Opalescent, Ribs, Scalloped Rim, Morning Glory Shape 270.00
Tiffany, **Compote**, Iridescent Gold, Pedestal, Stretched Edge, Favrile 275.00
Tiffany, **Compote**, Miniature, Platinum Shade, Stretched Effect, Signed 295.00
Tiffany, **Compote**, Pastel Blue, Green, L.C.T.Favrile 325.00
Tiffany, **Compote**, Pastel Blue, Onionskin, White Diamond, L.C.T., 1871 .... 325.00
Tiffany, **Compote**, Stretched & Fluted Top, Iridescent, Pedestal, 5 In. 250.00
Tiffany, **Cordial**, Apricot, Iridescent, Signed L.C.T. 140.00
Tiffany, **Cordial**, Emerald Green Pastel Cup, Yellow Stem & Foot 115.00
Tiffany, **Cordial**, Gold, Signed 95.00
Tiffany, **Cup**, Loving, Three Handles, Gold, Iridescent, 4 1/4 In.High , ... 225.00
Tiffany, **Cup**, Punch, Blue Iridescent, Twisted Prunts, Signed 195.00
Tiffany, **Decanter**, Phoenician Style Glass, Signed & Numbered 695.00
Tiffany, **Desk Set**, Bronze & Abalone, Moorish, Tiffany Studios, 9 Piece 325.00
Tiffany, **Desk Set**, Bronze, Classical Motifs, Tiffany Studios, 11 Piece 375.00
Tiffany, **Desk Set**, Bronze, Zodiac, Signed, No.1009 .... 160.00 To 195.00
Tiffany, **Frame**, Picture, Blue Favrile Glass, Gold Bronze Mounting, Signed 350.00
Tiffany, **Frame**, Picture, Slag Liner, Ornate, Signed 72.00
Tiffany, **Globe**, Cream Ground, Blue & Green Pulls, 6 In.Tall 160.00
Tiffany, **Goblet**, Bronze, Silvered, Sailing Ship On Tooled Ground, Favrile 100.00
Tiffany, **Goblet**, Iridescent, Blue Toward Base, Signed 275.00
Tiffany, **Goblet**, Optic Pattern, Pastel Yellow, Twisted Stem, Signed 325.00
Tiffany, **Goblet**, Pastel Turquoise, Signed L.C.Tiffany, Favrile, 7 In.High 230.00
Tiffany, **Goblet**, Threaded, Gold Iridescence, 4 In. 140.00
Tiffany, **Goblet**, Venetian Sytle, Green Foot, Pink With White Strips, Signed 450.00
Tiffany, **Goblet**, Water, Pastel, Blue Purple, Signed 295.00
Tiffany, **Goblet**, Water, Stemmed, Yellow At Base To Iridescent Blue Purple 295.00
Tiffany, **Holder**, Blotter, Bronze, Zodiac, Signed 17.50
Tiffany, **Holder**, Calendar, Bronze, Zodiac, Signed 17.50
Tiffany, **Holder**, Pencil, Signed Bronze, 5 In.Tall, 2 1/2 In.Square 35.00
Tiffany, **Incense Burner**, Chinese Design, Signed, Bronze, 6 X 4 1/2 In. 60.00
Tiffany, **Inkwell**, Bronze, American Indian, Patina 145.00
Tiffany, **Inkwell**, Bronze, Crab, Octagonal 37.50
Tiffany, **Inkwell**, Bronze, Signed 60.00
Tiffany, **Inkwell**, Crystal, Sterling Hinged Lid, Signed Tiffany & Co. 59.00
Tiffany, **Inkwell**, Letter Holder, Blotter Ends, Calendar Holder, Bronze 98.50
Tiffany, **Inkwell**, Letter Opener, Calendar Holder, Geometric, Brass 100.00

Tiffany, Inkwell, 10 1/2 X 10 In. 125.00
Tiffany, Jar, Candy, Covered, Finial 32.50
Tiffany, Jar, Jam, Gold Iridescent, Silver Lid & Bail, Signed L.C.T. 595.00
Tiffany, Jar, Powder, Signed, Diamond-Quilted, Bronze Lid, 4 In. 350.00
Tiffany, Juice Glass, Applied Lily Pads, Signed 250.00
Tiffany, Lamp Base, Acorn Shape, Amber Iridescent Finial, Blue Zigzag 300.00
Tiffany, Lamp Base, Bridge, Bronze, Adjustable Scrolling Arm, 56 In.High 325.00
Tiffany, Lamp Base, Candle, Gold Iridescent, Twist Stem & Base, L.C.T., 7 In. 175.00
Tiffany, Lamp Base, Desk, Bronze, Signed, Ball Feet 300.00
Tiffany, Lamp Base, Enameled, Signed, 17 1/2 In.High 175.00
Tiffany, Lamp, Blue & Amber Loopings, Domical Shade, Bronze Bas .... 250.00 To 475.00
Tiffany, Lamp, Bridge, Dore Bronze Shade, Spherical Balance Weight, 55 In. 255.00
Tiffany, Lamp, Candle, Blue, Honeycomb Shade, Signed .... 695.00 To 850.00
Tiffany, Lamp, Candle, Damascene Shade, Signed .... 500.00 To 850.00
Tiffany, Lamp, Candle, Signed Shade & Base, 13 In.High 300.00
Tiffany, Lamp, Candle, Signed Shade & Base, 17 In.High 350.00
Tiffany, Lamp, Coach, Red, Green, Bronze, Signed, 17 1/2 In.Long, Pair 950.00
Tiffany, Lamp, Conical Shade, Radial Yellow Tiles, Greek Key Design, Bronze 1500.00
Tiffany, Lamp, Daffodil, Bronze Base .... Illus 2900.00

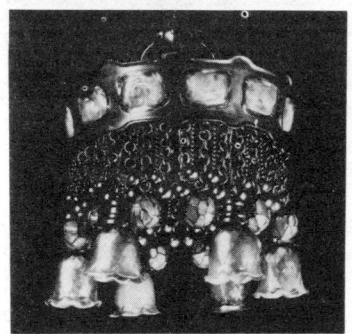

Tiffany, Chandelier,
Turtleback, 21 In.Diameter
See Page 586

Tiffany, Lamp, Daffodil, Bronze Base

Tiffany, Lamp, Desk, Amber Iridescent Favrile Shade, Bronze Pen Tray Base 425.00
Tiffany, Lamp, Desk, Blue Striated Shade 425.00
Tiffany, Lamp, Desk, Bronze Base, Gold Iridescent Quezal Shade 275.00
Tiffany, Lamp, Desk, Bronze Base, Green Favrile Fabrique Shade, Signed 600.00
Tiffany, Lamp, Desk, Gold Damascene, Numbered Shade, Signed Base, 7 1/2 In. 650.00
Tiffany, Lamp, Desk, Gold Dore, Chinese Pierced Design, Green & White, 16 In. 750.00
Tiffany, Lamp, Desk, Gold Shade, Ribbed Gold Bronze Base, Signed 485.00
Tiffany, Lamp, Desk, Harp Base, Decorated, Signed 575.00
Tiffany, Lamp, Desk, Swivel, Turtleback, Zodiac, Bronze, Two Shades 1250.00
Tiffany, Lamp, Dogwood, Leaded, Bronze Base, Ball Feet 3000.00
Tiffany, Lamp, Dragonfly, 14 In.Gold Shade, Gold Dore Base 3250.00
Tiffany, Lamp, Floor, Amber Glass, Fabrique, Signed Top & Bottom 750.00
Tiffany, Lamp, Floor, Mottled Yellow & White Domical Shade, Bronze Base 500.00
Tiffany, Lamp, Floor, Swirl Shade, Gold, Green, Bronze, 54 In.High 1500.00
Tiffany, Lamp, Geometric Mottled Shade, Bronze Base, Signed, 27 In.High 1500.00
Tiffany, Lamp, Geometric, Caramel Patina Shade, 20 In., Base & Shade Signed 1650.00
Tiffany, Lamp, Geometric, Patina Carved In Bronze, Orange, Brown, Ornate Base 1850.00
Tiffany, Lamp, Gold Shade, Pink Highlights, Signed, 14 In.High 695.00
Tiffany, Lamp, Gold Swirled Favrile Shade On Bronze Base, Signed, 27 In. 1500.00
Tiffany, Lamp, Green & Gold Linen Fold On Gold Dore Base, Signed, 21 In. 1500.00
Tiffany, Lamp, Green Iridescent Moire Shade, Signed Base & Shade, L.C.T. 625.00
Tiffany, Lamp, Green Leaded Shade, White Leaves On Bronze Base, 18 In.High 1650.00
Tiffany, Lamp, Green Shade, Turtleback Tiles In Bronze Base & Shade, 22 In. 3000.00
Tiffany, Lamp, Green Tiles, Conical Shade, Radial Leaf On Base, Bronze, 1913 .... 1200.00
Tiffany, Lamp, Leaded Shade, 20 In.Diameter, Teco Green Base 1475.00

Tiffany, Lamp, Lemon Leaf Band, Green, Gold, Orange Leaves, Gold Dore Base 2450.00
Tiffany, Lamp, Light Greens & Yellows, Signed Shade & Base, 16 In. 1400.00
Tiffany, Lamp, Lily, 3 Light, Amber Floriform Shades, Bronze Base 800.00
Tiffany, Lamp, Lily, 6 Light, Signed 400.00
Tiffany, Lamp, Mottled Amber Domical Shade, Geometric Border, Bronze Base 950.00
Tiffany, Lamp, Opalescent Domed Shade, Enameled, Bronze Base 250.00
Tiffany, Lamp, Petal Design, Green, Yellow, Signed, 25 1/2 In.Tall 1450.00
Tiffany, Lamp, Plain Squares, Gold Dove Base, Orange Glass, 16 X 22 In.High 2000.00
Tiffany, Lamp, Pomegranate Shade, Green & Orange Glass, 16 In.Diameter 1500.00
Tiffany, Lamp, Radial Green Tiles, Domical Shade, Tulips, Bronze Base 275.00
Tiffany, Lamp, Red & Green Ground, Red Poinsettia, Bronze Patina Base 1385.00
Tiffany, Lamp, Red, Yellow, & White On Green Domical Shade, Bronze Base 1600.00
Tiffany, Lamp, Signed Pottery Base, Unsigned Favrile Shade 750.00
Tiffany, Lamp, Stepped Shade, Blue Enameled Tiles, Bronze Base, Favrile 850.00
Tiffany, Lamp, Student, Copper Gauze Floral Enameled Shade, Bronze Base 475.00
Tiffany, Lamp, Student, Gold Damascene Shade, Signed & Numbered 650.00
Tiffany, Lamp, Student, Green & White Decorated Gas Shades, Signed 495.00
Tiffany, Lamp, Student, Two Arms, Pineapple Design, Gas Shades, Signed 475.00
Tiffany, Lamp, Student, Two Gold Iridescent Shades, Signed 475.00
Tiffany, Lamp, Tulip, 22 1/2 In.High .... *Illus* 3750.00
Tiffany, Lamp, Tyler, Green Glass Base .... *Illus* 5000.00
Tiffany, Lamp, Woodbine, Unsigned, 16 In. 1850.00
Tiffany, Lamp, 14 In.Gold Shade, Dragonflies, Gold Dore Base 3250.00
Tiffany, Letter Rack, Two Tier, Spider Web Design, Caramel Glass Inserts 110.00
Tiffany, Panel, Favrile, Green Mosaic, Oval Floral Medallion Center, 2 .... 3300.00

Tiffany, Lamp, Tulip,
22 1/2 In.High

Tiffany, Lamp,
Tyler, Green Glass Base

Tiffany, Paperweight, Bronze, Cougar, Impressed Tiffany Studios, 887 .... 180.00
Tiffany, Paperweight, Bronze, Glass, Pine Needle Pattern 65.00
Tiffany, Paperweight, Bronze, Lion, Reclining, Impressed Tiffany Studios 200.00
Tiffany, Parfait, Aqua, Opalescent, Signed L.C.Tiffany Favrile 195.00
Tiffany, Parfait, Blue Opalescent Iridescent Optic, Signed Tiffany 175.00
Tiffany, Parfait, Pastel Turquoise, Signed L.C.Tiffany, Favrile, 5 In.High 225.00
Tiffany, Perfume, Amber, Gold Filled Nozzle, Favrile, 3 In.High 85.00
Tiffany, Perfume, Gold Over Brass, Enamel Floral, Unmarked 75.00
Tiffany, Pillbox, Signed 25.00
Tiffany, Pitcher, Water, Gold Iridescent, Signed L.C.T., Favrile 1500.00
Tiffany, Plate, Gold Iridescent, Stretched Edge, 6 In.Diameter .... 75.00 To 85.00
Tiffany, Plate, Gold Washed Bronze, Signed, 8 1/2 In. 29.50
Tiffany, Plate, Iridescent, Ruffled, 7 In. 100.00
Tiffany, Plate, Pastel Turquoise, Signed L.C.Tiffany, Favrile, 8 1/2 In. 250.00
Tiffany, Plate, Pastel Turquoise, Signed L.C.Tiffany, Favrile, 10 1/2 In. 300.00
Tiffany, Prism 8.00
Tiffany, Rose Bowl, Decorated, Signed 425.00
Tiffany, Salt, Blue, Iridescent, Ruffled, L.C.T.Favrile, 1 In.Diameter 225.00
Tiffany, Salt, Blue, Low Pedestal, Signed L.C.T.Favrile 180.00
Tiffany, Salt, Bronze, Silver & Blue Iridescent, Crimped Edge, 2 1/2 In. 95.00
Tiffany, Salt, Crimped Top, Ground Base, L.C.T. 105.00

Tiffany, Salt, Footed, Kettle Shape, Gold Iridescent, Signed L.C.T. 75.00
Tiffany, Salt, Gold Iridescent, Blue, Signed 95.00
Tiffany, Salt, Gold Iridescent, Fluted Rim, Signed 95.00
Tiffany, Salt, Gold, Iridescent, Footed, L.C.T. 75.00
Tiffany, Salt, Gold Luster, Green Iridescent, Ruffled Edge, L.C.T. 95.00
Tiffany, Salt, Gold, Gold Swirls In Relief, Signed, Pair 140.00
Tiffany, Salt, Gold, Iridescent, Ruffled Top, Signed L.C.T. 75.00
Tiffany, Salt, Gold, Pink & Blue Highlights, Fluted Rim, 2 1/2 In. 45.00
Tiffany, Salt, Individual, Thorn Pattern 75.00
Tiffany, Salt, Lily Pad, Gold, Signed 125.00
Tiffany, Salt, Master, Blue, Iridescent, Ruffled, Swirl, Favrile .... 175.00 To 185.00
Tiffany, Salt, Master, Blue, Swirled, Signed 185.00
Tiffany, Salt, Master, Gold Iridescence 95.00
Tiffany, Salt, Master, Paperweight, Iridized Dark Topaz, Green Ribbon Design 145.00
Tiffany, Salt, Ruffled Top, Blue, Gold, Signed L.C.Tiffany, Favrile, 1255 .... 95.00
Tiffany, Salt, Thorn, Gold, Signed 100.00
Tiffany, Sconce, Lily, Gold Iridescent, Two Shades, Signed L.C.T. 400.00
Tiffany, Shade, Candle Lamp, Metal Filigree, Leaves, Vines, Signed 22.50
Tiffany, Shade, Daffodil, Domical, Yellow & Green On Green, Bronze 1600.00
Tiffany, Shade, Electric, Waffle Pattern, Gold, Signed, Set Of 2 .... 150.00
Tiffany, Shade, Gas, Bell Shape, Gold, Iridescent, Pair 175.00
Tiffany, Shade, Gas, Gold Iridescent, Platinum Feather, Signed 160.00
Tiffany, Shade, Gas, Green Leaves, Gold Iridescent, Signed 110.00
Tiffany, Shade, Gold Iridescent Lily, Signed 250.00
Tiffany, Shade, Green, Platinum, Wavy Over Pull-Ups, Peacock Blue, Unsigned 77.00
Tiffany, Shade, Hanging, Green, Geometric, Signed, 24 In. 1600.00
Tiffany, Shade, Leaded, Geometric, Yellow, Orange, Signed, 16 In. 650.00
Tiffany, Shade, Lily, Gold Iridescent, Signed .... 250.00 To 300.00
Tiffany, Shade, Openwork Silver Bronze, Grapevine, 6 1/4 X 3 1/2 In., Pair 135.00
Tiffany, Shade, Single Lily, Red To Green 175.00
Tiffany, Sherbet, Gold, Blue & Pink Highlights, Flared Bowl, Short Stem 95.00
Tiffany, Sherbet, Gold, Silvery Rim, Cut Fleur-De-Lis, L.C.T.Favrile 210.00
Tiffany, Sherbet, Pastel Blue, White, Stretch Edge, L.C.T.Favrile, No.1281 .... 225.00
Tiffany, Sherbet, Pastel Turquoise, Signed L.C.Tiffany, Favrile, 2 In.High 225.00
Tiffany, Sherbet, Pastel, Signed 120.00
Tiffany, Shield, Favrile, Metal Frame, Green Glass Brilliants 1300.00
Tiffany, Shot Glass, Gold Iridescent, Purple Highlights 110.00
Tiffany, Tazza, Blue, L.C.T., 1279, 7 1/2 X 4 In. 575.00
Tiffany, Tazza, Enameled Bronze, Green Circles In Leaves, Louis C.Tiffany 70.00
Tiffany, Tazza, Flashes, Irregular Rim, Opalescent Striations, Aqua, Favrile 300.00
Tiffany, Tazza, Gold & Lavender, L.C.T., 3 1/2 In.Stem X 6 1/2 In.Diameter 150.00
Tiffany, Tazza, Ruffled Rim, Baluster Standard, Blue Crackle Iridescence 375.00
Tiffany, Tile, Green, Unsigned 16.00
Tiffany, Tile, Impressed Designs, 1 1/2 In.Square 10.00
Tiffany, Tile, Marbleized Colors, Raised Cloverleaf, 3 In.Square 23.00
Tiffany, Tile, Red, 4 In, Square 30.00
Tiffany, Tile, Square, Blue Green, Leaf Motif, Favrile, Inscribed L.C.T., 1881 .... 60.00
Tiffany, Tile, Turtle, Blue, Iridescent, 6 In.Long 60.00
Tiffany, Toothpick, Attached Tray, Allover Floral Repousse, Signed 45.00
Tiffany, Toothpick, Geometric Design, Gold Metal, Signed 25.00
Tiffany, Toothpick, Gold, Signed 80.00
Tiffany, Toothpick, Pinched Sides, Gold, Signed 100.00
Tiffany, Tray, Brass, Art Glass Bottom, Brass Vines, Feet, 4 1/8 X 2 3/4 In. 85.00
Tiffany, Tray, Bronze, Rectangular, Green & Yellow Cut Glass Form Seaweed 375.00
Tiffany, Tray, Card, Dove, Gold, Signed 37.50
Tiffany, Tray, Pen, Zodiac, Proof Gold 125.00
Tiffany, Tray, Pin, Dark Topaz, Paperweight Decoration, Green Spirals 145.00
Tiffany, Tumbler, Vaseline Opalescent, Optic Laurel Leaf Pattern, Footed 175.00
Tiffany, Vase, Black Basalt, Signed Favrile, 13 In.High, 24 In.Around 175.00
Tiffany, Vase, Blue Aurene, Footed, Flared Top, Signed 260.00
Tiffany, Vase, Blue, Smocked, Signed, 4 In. 210.00
Tiffany, Vase, Bud, Auto, Gold, Sterling Bottom & Handle 45.00
Tiffany, Vase, Bud, Cylindrical, Blue Iridescent, L.C.Tiffany, Favrile 250.00
Tiffany, Vase, Bud, Green & Gold, Bronze Base, Signed, 11 1/2 In. 250.00
Tiffany, Vase, Bud, Green, White Leaf, Signed, L.C.Tiffany, Favrile 8854 D 235.00
Tiffany, Vase, Bud, Paperweight Base, Iridescent Gold, Blue & Green Leaves 350.00

Tiffany, Vase, Bud, White, Iridescent, Gold Leaf Design, Footed, L.C.T.Favrile 275.00
Tiffany, Vase, Cameo Cutting, Blue, Footed, Cased 400.00
Tiffany, Vase, Cameo, Pink Flowers, Pink Border, Intaglio Cut Floral, 10 In. 1150.00
Tiffany, Vase, Cameo, 7 1/2 In.High .... *Illus* 1300.00
Tiffany, Vase, Candle Shape, Gold, Brass Holder, 15 1/2 In. 225.00
Tiffany, Vase, Cypriote, Gold, Yellow, White .... *Illus* 800.00
Tiffany, Vase, Elongated Teardrop Form, Amber Iridescent, Ribbed, L.C.T. 225.00
Tiffany, Vase, Favrile Luster, Pulled Decorations In Green & Gold Luster 100.00
Tiffany, Vase, Flower Form, Gold To Green, White Leaves .... 795.00 To 895.00
Tiffany, Vase, Flower Form, Gold, Blue Highlights, 6 In. 350.00
Tiffany, Vase, Flower Form, Gold, Green Pulls, 8 In. 245.00
Tiffany, Vase, Flower Form, Gold, Pedestal, L.C.T., 9 1/2 In.High 350.00
Tiffany, Vase, Flower Form, Green & White, Pulled Feather, 15 In. 650.00
Tiffany, Vase, Flower Form, Green Stem, Amber Iridescent, Transparent 525.00
Tiffany, Vase, Flower Form, Green, Opalescent, Decorated Foot, Knob Stem 285.00
Tiffany, Vase, Flower Form, Green, White, Gold, Mirror Finish, 12 In. 600.00
Tiffany, Vase, Flower Form, Stem, Pedestal, Signed L.C.T.Favrile, 12 In. 950.00
Tiffany, Vase, Flower Form, Turquoise & White, 12 In. 550.00
Tiffany, Vase, Flower Form, White, Gold, Pulled Feather, 10 In. 500.00
Tiffany, Vase, Free Form, Dimpled, Amber, Signed, 4 1/4 In.High 225.00
Tiffany, Vase, Free Form, Gold, Pink & Lavender Highlights, L.C.T.607 .... 235.00
Tiffany, Vase, Geometric Pulled Glass Design, Clear, Opaque White, Signed 395.00
Tiffany, Vase, Gold Bronze Tone, Light Blue Base, Signed, 10 In. 275.00
Tiffany, Vase, Gold Iridescent, Dimpled, Signed, 5 In.High 275.00
Tiffany, Vase, Gold Iridescent, Green Ivy, Bulbous 425.00
Tiffany, Vase, Gold Iridescent, Pedestaled, 9 1/2 In.High, Signed 350.00
Tiffany, Vase, Gold Iridescent, Pulled Handles, Turned Collar, 1 3/4 In. 155.00
Tiffany, Vase, Gold Iridescent, Signed, 3 1/2 In. 175.00
Tiffany, Vase, Gold Iridescent, White Loopings, Signed & Numbered, 9 1/2 In. 425.00
Tiffany, Vase, Gold, Cut Green Cameo Leaves At Bottom .... 650.00 To 750.00
Tiffany, Vase, Gold, Green Leaves, Signed 400.00
Tiffany, Vase, Gold, Lily Pads, Light Green Base, 8 In.High 395.00
Tiffany, Vase, Gold, Ribs, Slender Base Swells Out & Tapers In On Top, 6 In. 225.00
Tiffany, Vase, Green Crystal Pedestal Becoming Paler At Top, Signed 125.00
Tiffany, Vase, Green, Iridescent, Button Pontil, 3 1/2 In.High 75.00
Tiffany, Vase, Handled, Butterscotch Gold, Signed L.C.T., N 194 .... 225.00
Tiffany, Vase, Iridescent Gold, L.C.T.Favrile, No.Y6808, 2 In. High 195.00
Tiffany, Vase, Iridescent Green Leaves, White Ground, Gold Base & Lining 425.00
Tiffany, Vase, Iridescent Moonstone, Flared, Footed, Pair 90.00
Tiffany, Vase, Iridescent Rainbow Colors, 3 1/4 In. 185.00
Tiffany, Vase, Iridescent, Metal Base, 14 In. 550.00
Tiffany, Vase, Jack-In-The-Pulpit, Iridescent Gold, Signed, Numbered, 21 In. 595.00
Tiffany, Vase, Jack-In-The-Pulpit, Signed 575.00
Tiffany, Vase, Miniature, Green, Silver Over White, Signed, Paper Label 395.00
Tiffany, Vase, Miniature, Pedestal, Gold & Platinum, L.C.Favrile, 9877 G 295.00
Tiffany, Vase, Morning Glory, Blue, White, Footed, L.C.Favrile, 9 In. 350.00
Tiffany, Vase, Moss Green Iridescent, Signed L.C.T., Favrile 2100.00
Tiffany, Vase, Opalescent, Iridescent, White, Two Small Handles 395.00
Tiffany, Vase, Paperweight, Green, Purple, 6 In.High .... *Illus* 1700.00
Tiffany, Vase, Paperweight, Signed & Numbered 1500.00
Tiffany, Vase, Paperweight, Signed V 428, L.C.Tiffany, Favrile 2800.00
Tiffany, Vase, Paperweight, Signed 1660 P, L.C.Tiffany, Favrile 3800.00
Tiffany, Vase, Paperweight, White Morning Glories On Amber, Favrile 900.00
Tiffany, Vase, Pastel, Signed & Numbered, 10 In. 175.00
Tiffany, Vase, Peacock Blue, Amber Handles, 9 3/4 In.High, Signed 1200.00
Tiffany, Vase, Peacock Blue, Veinings Of Reddish Gold, Signed L.C.T. 375.00
Tiffany, Vase, Red, Favrile, 4 1/4 In.High .... *Illus* 1500.00
Tiffany, Vase, Ribs, Ruffled, Gold Luster, Pink Highlights, Footed, 9 1/2 In. 375.00
Tiffany, Vase, Ruffled, Pulled Feather, Gold & Green Iridescent 350.00
Tiffany, Vase, Silver Over Melon, Paper Label, Signed, 4 In.High 495.00
Tiffany, Vase, Squat, Opalescent Striations Shading To Rose At Rim, Favrile 150.00
Tiffany, Vase, Stick, Green To Clear 145.00
Tiffany, Vase, Three Peacock Eyes, Multicolor Iridescent, 16 In. 750.00
Tiffany, Vase, Trumpet, Cream Opalescent, Iris Leaves In Bronze Base 400.00
Tiffany, Vase, Trumpet, Cutting On Sides, Gold Iridescent, 12 In.High 325.00
Tiffany, Vase, Trumpet, Favrile, Green, 6 In.High, 9 In.Wide 250.00

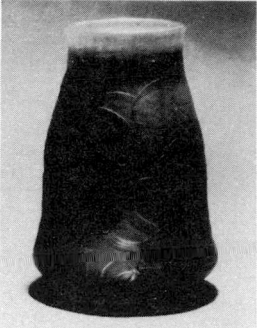

Tiffany, Vase, Cameo, 7 1/2 In.High
See Page 590

Tiffany, Vase, Cypriote,
Gold, Yellow, White
See Page 590

Tiffany, Vase, Paperweight,
Green, Purple, 6 In.High
See Page 590

Tiffany, Vase, Red, Favrile, 4 1/4 In.High
See Page 590

Tiffany, Vase, Trumpet, Gold Aurene, Footed, Favrile & Numbered, 12 In.High	325.00
Tiffany, Vase, Trumpet, Gold Iridescent, Signed, 14 In. High	359.00
Tiffany, Vase, Trumpet, Gold Iridescent, Signed, 17 In.High	225.00
Tiffany, Vase, Trumpet, Gold, Blue Highlights, Bronze Base, Enameled	185.00
Tiffany, Vase, Trumpet, Gold, Signed, Numbered	265.00
Tiffany, Vase, Trumpet, Yellow Pastel, Bronze Stem-Like Holder, 10 In.High	250.00
Tiffany, Vase, Trunk, Smoky Iridescence, 3 Openings, 17 1/2 In.	250.00
Tiffany, Vase, Twisted, Gold, Signed L.C., Favrile, No.547, 6 In.High	155.00
Tiffany, Vase, Urn Shape, Iridescent & Opalescent, Two Handles, 3 In.High	395.00
Tiffany, Vase, Violet & Blue Iridescent, Gold, Signed, 8 In.Tall	195.00
Tiffany, Vase, White Iridescent, Pulled Handles, Signed, 3 1/2 In.High	275.00
Tiffany, Vase, White, Signed L.C.T.Favrile, Numbered, 14 In.	280.00
Tiffany, Vase, Yellow Gold Iridescent, Signed L.C.T., Favrile	1800.00
Tiffany, Wine, Amethyst, Opalescent Stripes, Signed	135.00
Tiffany, Wine, Blue Opalescent, Iridescent Optic, 7 1/4 In.High	185.00
Tiffany, Wine, Gold & Blue Iridescent, L.C.T.Favrile, No.1209	125.00
Tiffany, Wine, Gold Iridescent, L.C.T.Favrile	125.00
Tiffany, Wine, Gold, Cut Amber Stem, Signed	175.00 To 195.00
Tiffany, Wine, Gold, Etched Border, Tall Stem, Signed	110.00
Tiffany, Wine, Pastel Green & White	175.00
Tiffany, Wine, Pink & White Stripes, Green Stem, Iridescent Ball In Stem	375.00

Tiffin Glass Company of Tiffin, Ohio, was a subsidiary of the United States Glass Co. of Pittsburgh, Pa. Black Satin glass, made by the company between 1923 and 1926, is very popular among collectors. Other types were also made.

Tiffin, Perfume, Paperweight, Clear Cut Encloses Ruby Glass, Ohio	220.00
Tiffin, Vase, Black, Satin, Red Poppies, Coralene	57.00

Tiffin, Wall Pocket, Black, Hanging, 9 In.Long 12.50
Tile, Broadmoor Pottery, Bird Of Paradise 5.00
Tile, Calendar, 1892, J.McDuffee 24.00
Tile, Calendar, 1910, Mayflower, J.McDuffee 28.00
Tile, Cherubs, High Relief, Signed H.Mueller, Green, 6 X 6 In. 55.00
Tile, Dutch, Blue, Purple, 5 X 5 In. 9.50
Tile, Green, Incised Flowers, Leaves, England 10.00
Tile, Impressed Leaf, Clear Glass 5.00
Tile, J.& J.G.Low Patent Art Tile Works, Chelsea, Mass., Pair 18.50
Tile, Lake Scene, Six Scalloped Feet, 5 1/2 In.Diameter 26.00
Tile, Mauve, Art Nouveau 8.00
Tile, Picture Of Old Man, Signed Isaac Abbott Senes 9.00
Tile, Polychrome Fruit, Leaves, Blossoms, Brown, England 17.50
Tile, Queen Isabella Pledging Jewels, Columbus 22.00
Tile, Ram's Head In High Relief, Teal Blue, England 17.50
Tile, Tea, Germany, Hand-Painted Pink & White Floral, Round 8.00
Tile, Tea, Green Rim, Water Lilies, Porcelain, Castle Mark, 7 1/4 In. 15.00
Tile, Tea, Onion Pattern, Marked Bonn, Castle Mark, 7 In. 12.50
Tile, Tea, Pink & Yellow Roses, Porcelain, Germany, 6 1/2 In. 12.50
Tile, Tea, Pink Luster, Black Transfer, St.Paul School, Concord, N.H. 17.00
    Tin, see also Store
Tin, Baby Nurser, With Spout 125.00
Tin, Basket, Picnic, Educator, Wooden Handles, 12 X 7 1/2 X 6 In. 8.50
Tin, Beater, Marshmallow, Marked, 6 In.Square, 9 In.High 20.00
Tin, Box, Candleholder Tinder, Damper, Strike, Flint, Round, 4 In.Diameter 165.00
Tin, Box, Document, Key 5.75
Tin, Box, Lunch, Four Sections, Dated 1884, 8 In.High 30.00
Tin, Box, Nursery Rhymes, Hinged Cover, Colorful, 4 1/2 In. 8.75
Tin, Box, Pencil, Jackie Coogan 8.50
Tin, Box, Pencil, Lindy Plane 5.00
Tin, Box, Soap, Lilies On Cover 3.50
Tin, Bucket, American Royal, Small Size 2.00
Tin, Can With Pump, Whale Oil Lamp Filling, 2 Quart 6.95
Tin, Can, Milk, Steel Bail, Metal Bands At Top & Bottom, 1 1/2 Gallon 6.50
Tin, Can, Oil, Long Spout 7.50
Tin, Candle Box, Marked Wax Vestas 10.00
Tin, Candle Device, Cone Sand Weighted, Step Lift 85.00
Tin, Candleholder, Street Light Shape, 18th Century 60.00
Tin, Candlestick, Push Up 15.00
Tin, Candlestick, Push-Up, Hog Scraper, Hand Wrought, Signed 17.50
Tin, Case, For Colonial Officer's Bicorne Hat, Gloves, & Stockings, Brass 35.00
Tin, Case, Map, Ship's, Cylindrical, Cover, 19 In. 5.95
Tin, Chamberstick, Double Heart, Gallery Type Pricket, 7 1/2 In.Long 65.00
Tin, Chamberstick, Saucer Base, 5 3/4 X 4 In.High, Pair 50.00
Tin, Chamberstick, Wedding Band, Notch Push-Up, 18th Century, 7 1/2 In.High 85.00
Tin, Coffeepot, Lighthouse Shape, Gooseneck Spout, Pin Prick Decor Of Tulip 950.00
Tin, Coffeepot, Pewter Lid, Rim, Gooseneck Spout, Metal Scroll Handle 59.00
Tin, Coffeepot, Strap Handle, Wire Bail, Copper Bottom 18.50
Tin, Cream Whipper, Churn Type 14.50
Tin, Cup, British Military Issue, Canteen R.A., C.1850 .... 12.50
Tin, Dipper, Long Handle 12.00
Tin, Ear Trumpet 25.00
Tin, Ear Trumpet, 20 5/8 In.Long 19.75
Tin, Egg Poacher, 1 Egg 5.50
Tin, Egg Poacher, 2 Egg 7.50
Tin, Flytrap, Pine's, Ketch The Flies, Save The Babies, Wire 18.00
Tin, Foot Warmer, Buggy, Carpet Covering, Drawer, Oval Ends, 14 In. 15.00
Tin, Foot Warmer, Carpet Covered .... 15.00 To 18.00
Tin, Foot Warmer, Pierced 30.00
Tin, Foot Warmer, Pierced, Wooden Frame 30.00
Tin, Foot Warmer, Yellow On Black, Painted, 5 1/2 X 6 3/4 In. 85.00
Tin, Hat, Slit Openings On Crown, American, C.1840 .... 70.00
Tin, Holder, Bill, Wire, Snap, Wall 3.50
Tin, Ink Sander, Straight Cylinder, 18th Century 20.00
Tin, Lamp Filler, 5 1/2 In.Tall, 4 In.Diameter 30.00
Tin, Lantern, Black, High Handle, Marked Globe, 7 1/2 In.High, Pair 10.00

Tin, Lantern, Paul Revere Type, Four Sides, Door, 13 1/2 In.Tall 18.00
Tin, Lighting Device, Egg Opens Into Traveling Lamp, Pierced, C.1750 .... 95.00
Tin, Match Holder, Double, Design 8.75
Tin, Match Holder, Hanging, Oval, Victorian 9.50
Tin, Match Safe, Diamond Match Co. 4.00
Tin, Match Safe, Wall, Two Compartments 3.95
Tin, Matchbox, Black 12.00
Tin, Matchbox, Embossed Fisherman, Boat Scenes, Pierced 10.00
Tin, Measure, Handle, Marked Mason, Pint 3.75
Tin, Mold, Candle, 2 Tube 50.00
Tin, Mold, Candle, 4 Tube, Side Handle 21.50
Tin, Mold, Candle, 6 Tube, Pennsylvania Dutch, Handle Ring 45.00
Tin, Mold, Candle, 6 Tube, Strap Handle .... 22.50 To 30.00
Tin, Mold, Candle, 8 Tube .... 10.00 To 35.00
Tin, Mold, Candle, 1i Tube 35.00
Tin, Mold, Candle, 11 Tube, Handle 36.75
Tin, Mold, Candle, 12 Tube .... 27.50 To 45.00
Tin, Mold, Candle, 12 Tube, Handle 28.00
Tin, Mold, Candle, 12 Tube, Pennsylvania Dutch, Handle Ring 55.00
Tin, Mold, Candle, 16 Tube 50.00
Tin, Mold, Candle, 28 Tube, Pine Frame, 12 In.Tall, 12 In.Wide 325.00
Tin, Mold, Candle, 36 Tube, Signed J.Walker, Red Frame, 11 X 13 X 11 In. 345.00
Tin, Mold, Candy, Prancing Pony, Clamps, 3 1/2 In.High 15.00
Tin, Mold, Chocolate, Bunny Pushing Wheelbarrow, 3 In. 7.00
Tin, Mold, Chocolate, Five Flowerpots, Germany, 1 5/8 In. 5.00
Tin, Mold, Chocolate, Four Goblets, Germany, 2 1/2 In. 9.00
Tin, Mold, Chocolate, Four Rabbits, Pewter Bracing, Germany 20.00
Tin, Mold, Chocolate, French Poodle, 3 In. 7.00
Tin, Mold, Chocolate, Heart, Mother, Germany, 7 1/2 In. 12.00
Tin, Mold, Chocolate, Heart, To My Valentine, Germany, 7 1/2 In. 12.00
Tin, Mold, Chocolate, Rabbit With Wheelbarrow Of Eggs, 5 1/2 In. 12.75
Tin, Mold, Chocolate, Rabbit, Running, Germany, 6 3/4 In. 10.00
Tin, Mold, Chocolate, Rabbit, Running, 8 1/4 In.Long 12.00
Tin, Mold, Chocolate, Rooster, Two Sides, 6 1/2 In. 18.00
Tin, Mold, Chocolate, Rooster, 4 In. 16.75
Tin, Mold, Chocolate, Rooster, 6 In. 10.00
Tin, Mold, Chocolate, Santa, 4 In. 10.00
Tin, Mold, Chocolate, Sitting Dog, 2 1/2 In. 5.00
Tin, Mold, Chocolate, Six Square Bottles, Germany, 1 3/8 In. 6.00
Tin, Mold, Chocolate, Standing Bunny With Open Basket, 6 In. 10.00
Tin, Mold, Chocolate, Standing Rabbit, U.S.A.Marking 22.00
Tin, Mold, Chocolate, Three Bells, Germany, 3 In. 12.00
Tin, Mold, Chocolate, Three Turkeys, Germany, 3 In. 12.00
Tin, Mold, Chocolate, Turkey, 4 In. 8.50
Tin, Mold, Chocolate, Twelve Cigars, Germany, 2 5/8 In. 8.00
Tin, Mold, Chocolate, Two Sitting Rabbits, 5 In., Germany 12.00
Tin, Mold, Chocolate, Two Touring Cars, Germany, 4 1/2 In. 20.00
Tin, Mold, Jelly, Bullet Edge, Corn In Bottom, Oval 5.50
Tin, Mold, Maple Sugar, Heart Shape, Fluted, Oval, Set Of 4 .... 9.50
Tin, Mold, Maple Sugar, Rabbit In Bottom, Fluted, Set Of 4 .... 12.00
Tin, Mold, Plum Pudding, Center Tube, Cover 4.75
Tin, Mold, Pudding, Fluted, Raised Fruit & Floral, England 12.00
Tin, Mold, Pudding, Melon Shape, Marked Kremer, 2 1/2 In. 1.00
Tin, Mold, Rabbit, 4 In. 7.50
Tin, Mold, Rooster, Double, 4 In. 16.50
Tin, Mold, Rose Design, 5 In. .... *Illus* 35.00
Tin, Mold, Two Boxer Rabbits, Germany, 6 In. 18.00
Tin, Mug, Inlaid Brass, Jessie, 18th Century, Label, 4 In. 59.00
Tin, Pail, Lard, Nophey's, 2 1/2 In. 5.00
Tin, Pitcher, Measuring, 4 Quart 18.00
Tin, Plate, Lithograph, Boy On Donkey, Children, Circa 1890, 6 In. 12.00
Tin, Plate, Nursery Rhyme 6.00
Tin, Plate, Red Riding Hood, Walking Beside Wolf 6.50
Tin, Rattle, Three Bells, Ivory Handle & Pacifier, Germany 25.00
Tin, Rum Warmer, Conical Shape 14.50
Tin, Sconce, Candle, Ball, Black, Flower Decoration, 13 In., Pair 10.00

Tin, Sconce, Candle, Single, Crimped Top, Hole For Hanging, 14 In., Pair 200.00
Tin, Sconce, Reflector, 15 In.Tall, , 9 1/2 In.Across Reflector, 18th Century 235.00
Tin, Scoop, Cranberry 18.00
Tin, Scoop, Square, Handmade 5.00
Tin, Scoop, Thumbrest, 7 1/2 In.Long 3.25
Tin, Smoking Caddy, Compartments For Cigars, Cigarettes, Matches 9.50
Tin, Tea Set, Child's, Ohio Art Co., Girl & Kitten, Signed Elaine 8.00
Tin, Tinderbox, Damper, Strike, Flint, Tinder, Candleholder, 4 In.Diameter 175.00
Tin, Toothpick, Arbee 2.00
Tin, Tray, Indian Decoration, 8 In.Diameter 30.00
Tischner, Ewer, Signed & Numbered, 10 In., Karlsbad 225.00
Toby Jar, Tobacco, Man, Seated, Cobalt Coat, C.1830, 5 In. 55.00

Toby Mugs have been made since the seventeenth century.
Toby Mug, see also Royal Doulton
Toby Mug & Pitcher, Man In Chair, Flow Blue Hat, Tunstall, 1933, 5 In. 40.00
Toby Mug, Coachman, Blue, Porcelain, Germany, 4 1/2 In. 40.00
Toby Mug, Coachman, Red & White, Porcelain, Germany, 6 1/2 In. 40.00
Toby Mug, English, Silver Resist Ware, C.1800 .... 75.00
Toby Mug, Hearty Good Fellow, Circa 1860, 11 In.High 150.00
Toby Mug, Lord Nelson, Circa 1820, 11 3/4 In.High 450.00
Toby Mug, Man Sitting On Chair With Stein, Removable Hat, English 165.00
Toby Mug, Man, Seated, Blue Willow, 5 1/2 In. 95.00
Toby Mug, Man, Seated, Brown & Green, Burlington Ware, 1959, 9 1/2 In. 35.00
Toby Mug, Mr.Pickwick, Standing, Lecturing, Extended Arm, 8 In. 38.50
Toby Mug, Mutton Chop Whiskers, Brown, Gray, 9 In.High 235.00
Toby Mug, Rockingham Type, New Jersey, C.1850 .... 45.00
Toby Mug, Scottish Bagpiper, Circa 1820, Chalkware, 5 In. 40.00
Toby Mug, Taking Snuff, Blue Coat, 9 In. 95.00
Toby Mug, Town Fool, Brown & Yellow, England, 6 1/2 In. 35.00
Toby Mug, Welsh Gin Woman, 9 1/4 In. 125.00
Toby Mug, Welsh Woman With Pitcher & Cup 38.50
Toby Mug, William Penn Treaty, Green Wreath Mark, 6 3/4 In.High 90.00
Toby Mug, William Penn, Indian Head Handle, 6 1/2 In.Tall 95.00
Toby Mug, Winston Churchill, 8 1/2 In.Tall 45.00
Toby Mug, Woman, White Ground, Blue & Mauve Decoration, C.1820, Delft 350.00
Toby Mug, Yale, Blue, 1933, Wedgwood, 6 1/2 In. 45.00
Toby Pitcher, Sitting Man, Holding Pitcher, Smile, 8 1/2 In.High 65.00

Tin, Mold, Rose Design, 5 In.
See Page 593

Tole, Coffeepot, Oliver Filley,
Conn., C.1800, 9 In.High
See Page 595

Toby Teapot, Luster Coat, Snufftaker 275.00
Toilet, Vieux Paris, White & Gold, U.S.Ships, Quadrangular, C.1850, Pair 200.00
Tole, Basket, Black, Ring Handles, 4 Ball Feet, Filled With Grapes 20.00
Tole, Basket, Victorian, Openwork, Painted Gold With Fruit, 12 In.Long 30.00
Tole, Box, Cutlery, American, Forks & Knives, Black, Red, Gold, C.1840 .... 22.50
Tole, Box, Deed, Black, Gold, Red Trim, 11 X 8 X 5 In. 10.00

Tole, **Box**, Document, C.1850 .... 12.00
Tole, **Box**, Rembrandt Scenes, 11 X 12 X 6 In. 10.00
Tole, **Cachepot**, French, Painted Burnt Amber, Medallion Farm Scene, Pair 70.00
Tole, **Cachepot**, Painted Medallion Of Dancing Female Figure 25.00
Tole, **Candleholder**, Saucer, 3 1/2 In.High 22.50
Tole, **Candlestick**, Saucer Base, Push-Up 15.00
Tole, **Canister**, Tea, Victorian, Chinese Servant & Rockeries On Green, C.1850 .... 150.00
Tole, **Coffeepot**, Gooseneck, Red Finish, Gold Stencils, House, Floral, Lid, Bail 42.00
Tole, **Coffeepot**, Oliver Filley, Conn., C.1800, 9 In.High .... *Illus* 200.00
Tole, **Cream Skimmer** 3.00
Tole, **Holder**, Flower, Lions, Painted Floral, Footed, Separate Holed Insert 12.00
Tole, **Lamp**, Whale Oil, Floral Decoration 4 In High 62.00
Tole, **Lantern**, Pole, Yellow, Glass Insert, Star Finial, Pair 50.00
Tole, **Lunch Box**, Pennsylvania, Decorated, Brass 200.00
Tole, **Mold**, Candle, 12 Tube 34.00
Tole, **Muffin Warmer**, Fabric Cover, Pat.1887 .... 13.50
Tole, **Pot**, Beverage, Red & Gold, Porcelain Knob On Top, Glass Window, 11 In. 75.00
Tole, **Tray**, Art Nouveau, Oval, 16 In. 6.50
Tole, **Tray**, Crumb, Wooden Brush Scraper, Scalloped Fluted Edge, Black, Gold 10.00
Tole, **Tray**, Fruit & Floral Center, Gilt Scroll Border, Signed B.H.B., 28 In. 60.00
Tole, **Tray**, Gold Fruit & Leaves, Red & Black Edge, Octagon, 23 In. 40.00
Tole, **Tray**, Octagonal, Decorated 12.50
Tole, **Tray**, Red & Yellow Roses, Tin Center, Round, 19 1/2 In.Diameter 25.00
Tole, **Tray**, Serving 3.00
Tole, **Tray**, Tea, Polychrome, Floral, Scene Of Indians, Boston Harbor 59.50
Tole, **Tray**, Yellow Honeysuckles, Roses, & Peacock On Red, Oblong, 1873 .... 59.00
Tole, **Watering Can & Lemonade Cooler**, Stenciled 38.00
Tom Mix, Card, Exhibit, Brown & White, Set Of 5 .... 10.00
Tom Mix, Gun, Wooden, Circa 1934 .... 75.00
Tom Mix, Picture, Tom & Indian, 8 X 10 In. 3.25
Tool, see also Kitchen, Store, Wooden, Iron, Tin
Tool, Adze, Bowl, 4 In.Wide Blade 45.00
Tool, Adze, Cooper's, Ship, C.1840, 9 In. 14.50
Tool, Adze, Hand, Cooper's, Wide Blade 15.00
Tool, Adze, Hand, Polled 30.00
Tool, Auger, Crank, Wrought Iron, 2 1/2 In. 6.00
Tool, Auger, Wood, Hand-Forged Steel Bores, 28 1/2 In.Long 28.00
Tool, Auger, Wooden Handle 3.50
Tool, Axe, Cooper's, 9 7/8 In.Blade, Early 60.00
Tool, Axe, Crow Chief, Hudson Bay, Wooden Handle 65.00
Tool, Axe, Goosewing, Marked M M, 12 1/4 In.Blade 110.00
Tool, Bee Smoker, Dated 1870s 14.50
Tool, Bee Smoker, Woodman's Bingham Co. 10.00
Tool, Bit Brace, Oak, With Pad 85.00
Tool, Boot Lacer, Bone And Wrought Iron 25.00
Tool, Box, Screw, 1 In. 20.00
Tool, Brace & Bit, Beechwood, Lignum Vitae Knob, Brass Throat, Initials S.F. 47.00
Tool, Brace, Carpenter's, Wooden, Brass, C.1840 .... 35.00
Tool, Broadax, Shapleigh Day & Co., Offset Handle 50.00
Tool, Brush, For Shoeing, Horse's Tail On Stick 22.50
Tool, Button Hole Cutter, Wrought Iron 10.00
Tool, Calipers, Birch & Brass 70.00
Tool, Carder, Sheep's Wool 3.50
Tool, Chain, Log, Ring At One End, Hook At Other, Cast Iron, 12 Ft.Long 25.00
Tool, Chisel, For Pinking Cloth, Serrated, 1/2 In. 4.00
Tool, Chisel, Knob For Palm, Wooden Hand, 27 1/2 In. Long, 4 In.Wide Blade 22.00
Tool, Chopper, Wrought Iron 10.00
Tool, Compass, Wood & Brass, Marked M.Leidel, N.Y. 28.00
Tool, Cooper's Wheel, C.1840 .... *Illus* 20.00
Tool, Corkscrew, Sterling Silver Cap On Antler Handle, 19th Century 6.00
Tool, Corn Dryer, Iron 3.00
Tool, Croze, Cooper's 20.00
Tool, Dentist's, Forceps 3.00
Tool, Dentist's, Gum Lancet, Tortoiseshell Handle 12.00
Tool, Dentist's, Tamping Tool, Ebony Handle 1.20
Tool, Dentist's, Tamping Tool, Ivory Handle 1.20

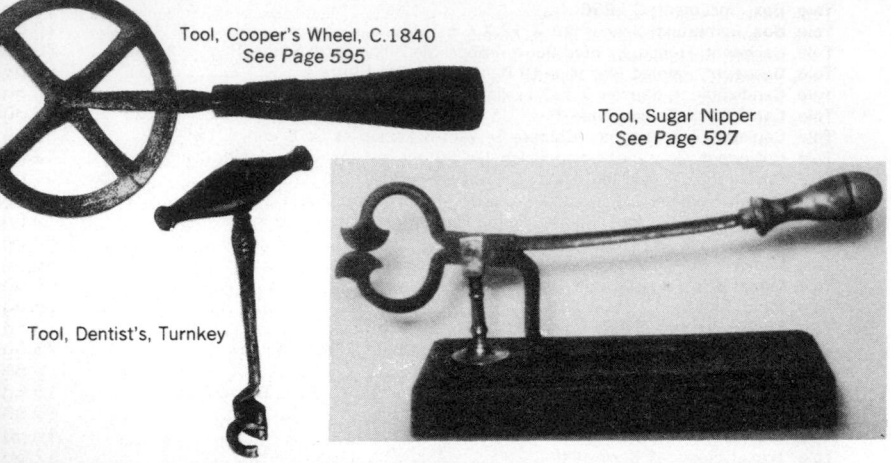

Tool, Cooper's Wheel, C.1840
See Page 595

Tool, Sugar Nipper
See Page 597

Tool, Dentist's, Turnkey

Tool, Dentist's, Turnkey	*Illus*	12.00
Tool, Dentist's, Turnkey, For Pulling Molars, Ebony Handle		14.00
Tool, Doctor, See Doctor		
Tool, Farrier's, Hand-Forged Iron, 8 Fold Out Tools, C.1750		22.50
Tool, Flax Breaker, Weathered Oak, 18th Century		20.00
Tool, For Leather, By C.I.Osborne, 70 In Chest, Four Drawers, C.1900		500.00
Tool, Framing Scriber, Threaded Wood Adjustment, Opens To 18 In., Wood		16.00
Tool, Frow, Splitting, Hand Forged, Hickory Handle, 15 In.Blade		18.00
Tool, Gauge, Double Mortise		8.00
Tool, Gauge, Mortise & Tendon, Rosewood, Brass, Double		7.50
Tool, Handsaw, Riveted Handle, Seven Points, 26 In.Long Blade, Circa 1850		6.50
Tool, Hatchet, Double Bevel Blade, Cast Steel		15.00
Tool, Hay Fork, Three Tines, Wooden		50.00
Tool, Howel, Large Size		50.00
Tool, Level, Cherry, Stanley, Dated 1906, Brass Hardware		17.00
Tool, Level, One Bubble, Marked L.R.Watts		30.00
Tool, Level, Wooden, 26 1/4 In.		4.00
Tool, Loom, Tape, 18th Century		50.00
Tool, Mallet, Cooper's, Wooden		3.50
Tool, Marking Gauge For Mortice & Tenons, Rosewood, Brass, Double		7.50
Tool, Niddy Noddy, Wooden, Pegged		9.00
Tool, Niddy Noddy, 3 Round Rungs, For Winding Yarn, 21 In.Long		26.00
Tool, Peel, Wooden, 48 In.Long		55.00
Tool, Pipe Wrench, Ornate Handle, 1897, 5 1/2 In.Long		10.00
Tool, Plane, Block		8.00
Tool, Plane, Carpenter's, Iron, 3 1/2 In.Long		4.75
Tool, Plane, Carpenter's, Wooden	3.50 To	15.00
Tool, Plane, Compass, Beech		6.00
Tool, Plane, Cooper's, Whaling Ship, Maple, Steel Blade		9.50
Tool, Plane, Molding, Adjustable, Wood, L.W.Raymond, 9 In.Long		17.00
Tool, Plane, Molding, Stanley No.55, Universal, 35 Bits		22.00
Tool, Plane, Molding, Wooden		4.00
Tool, Plane, Plow, Carved Out Saw Handle, Molded Fence Adjustment, Wooden		18.00
Tool, Plane, Skate, For Sharpening Skates, Lynch, Pat.1894		5.95
Tool, Plane, Smoothing, Bench, Winchester, Cherry Wood Handles, 11 In.Long		50.00
Tool, Plane, Smoothing, Round Sole		7.50
Tool, Plane, Stanley, Dated 1888, 15 In.		12.50
Tool, Plane, Stanley, No.45, Original Box, Instructions, 20 Blades		65.00
Tool, Plane, Sun, Three Way Adjustable Base, E.C.Simmonds, 10 1/2 In.Long		25.00
Tool, Plane, Tongue & Groove, Adjustable, Greenfield & Co., Pair		45.00
Tool, Plane, Wood, Signed Ogontz Tool Co., 22 In.Long		10.00
Tool, Planetarium, Mechanical, French, Orrery, C.1850		999.50
Tool, Plumb Bob, Brass, 18th Century		20.00
Tool, Pulley, Wheel, Wooden		2.00

Tool, Rake, Wooden Teeth, 6 Ft.High 10.00
Tool, Reamer, Wheelwright's, 28 In.Overall, 9 1/2 In.Long Bit 20.00
Tool, Router, Blade Bolted, Original Handles 50.00
Tool, Router, Coachmaker's, Massive 32.00
Tool, Sawhorse, Jointed, 18th Century 35.00
Tool, Saw, Buck, Wooden Frame 10.00
Tool, Saw, Panel, Disston, Twelve Points, Applewood Handle 4.50
Tool, Scissors Sharpener, Patent 1896 .... 4.00
Tool, Scorp, Turpentine Hack, Iron Ball On End 38.00
Tool, Sewing Machine, New Home, Domestic Scene, Dated 1897 .... 40.00
Tool, Spinning Wheel, Signed & Dated 185.00
Tool, Spinning Wheel, 42 In Diameter 125.00
Tool, Spinning Wheel, 56 In.High 45.00
Tool, Stilyards, Handmade, Initialed B.M., Dated 1768, Marked 134, 25 In.Long 95.00
Tool, Sugar Nipper .... Illus 90.00
Tool, Torch, Hand, Plumber's, Brass & Copper, Burnished 9.00
Tool, Trammel, Iron & Tin, Brass Button On Hook, Extends To 58 In. 75.00
Tool, Trap, Bear, Chain, 34 In.Long 75.00
Tool, Trap, Rat, Wire Cage Type 7.50
Tool, Vise, Harness Maker's, Wooden, Iron Screw To Open, 27 In.High 11.50
Tool, Wagon Jack, Dated 1807 .... 85.00
Tool, Wheel, To Measure Circumference Of Wagon Wheel, Wood & Iron 6.00
Tool, Wrench, Machinery, Derre 2.50
Tool, Wrench, Pipe & Monkey Combination, 15 In.Long 10.00
Tool, Wrench, Wagon Wheel 2.50

Toothpick Holders are sometimes called Toothpicks by collectors. The variously shaped containers made to hold the small wooden toothpicks are of glass, china, or metal. Most of the toothpicks are Victorian.
Toothpick, see also other categories such as Bisque, Slag, etc.
Toothpick, Animal, Tree Trunk, Glass 15.00
Toothpick, Beatty Opalescent Rib, Fiery 18.50
Toothpick, Blue Ground, Girl's Head, Porcelain 15.00
Toothpick, Blue, Colorado 20.00
Toothpick, Blue, Square Design, Porcelain 9.00
Toothpick, Bull Dog With Glass Eyes, Signed Derby Silver 50.00
Toothpick, Button Arches, Red, Clear, Says Goldie, 1916 .... 22.00
Toothpick, Button Arches, Ruby Flash, C.1887, Pair 29.00
Toothpick, Cherub, Barrel, Sapphire Blue 45.00
Toothpick, Chick & Wishbone, Silver .... 20.00 To 40.00
Toothpick, Chick & Wishbone, Silver Plate .... 13.00 To 15.50
Toothpick, China Girl & Dog, German, 3 3/4 In. 24.00
Toothpick, Clear Glass, Solid Bulbous Bottom, Sterling Base & Rim, Beaded 15.00
Toothpick, Clear, Galloway 12.50
Toothpick, Clear, Ruby Flashed Top, Beaded Swag, Name & Date 1902 .... 18.00
Toothpick, Cordova, Clear 9.50
Toothpick, Daisy & Button, Clear, Urn Shape 9.00
Toothpick, Daisy & Button, Pink, Urn Shape 11.00
Toothpick, Diamond Shape, Handle, Four Pink Feet, Porcelain 14.00
Toothpick, Elephant, Frosted 26.00
Toothpick, Elephant, Hand-Painted, Porcelain, Germany, C.1915 .... 10.00
Toothpick, Emerald Green, Gold Relief Flowers, Profusion 35.00
Toothpick, Emerald Green, U.S.Glass Co., 1901 .... 65.00
Toothpick, Eye Winker, Green 1.95
Toothpick, Fleur-De-Lis, Crystal, U.S.Glass Co., 1898 .... 12.00 To 12.50
Toothpick, Frog On Lily Pad 18.00
Toothpick, Green Lacy Medallion, 1908 .... 15.00
Toothpick, Green Stippled, Gold Flower Spray, Footed 65.00
Toothpick, Half Egg, Robin On Side, Wishbone Base, Best Wishes, Metal, Black 16.00
Toothpick, Hand, Flashed Red Iridescent, 4 In. 10.00
Toothpick, Hat Shape, Cobalt, 2 1/2 In. 4.00
Toothpick, Hobnail, Opalescent, Footed 10.00
Toothpick, Inverted Thumbprint, Daisy Band, Blue, Footed 10.00
Toothpick, Lacy Medallion, Green, Gold Trim, Souvenir 16.00
Toothpick, Latticinio Glass Color Swirls 65.00
Toothpick, Leaf Umbrella, Cased Yellow 45.00

Toothpick, Maize Pattern 24.00
Toothpick, Milk Glass, Phaeton Car 12.50
Toothpick, Monkey & Stump 18.00
Toothpick, Mule & Barrel, Metal 15.00
Toothpick, Paneled Cut, Yellow, Czechoslovakia 12.00
Toothpick, Pink, Square Design, Porcelain 9.00
Toothpick, Red & Clear Glass, Beaded Swag, Souvenir, 1908 .... 20.00
Toothpick, Red & Clear Glass, Button Arches, Star Base, Advertising, 1901 .... 25.00
Toothpick, Red & Clear, Beaded Drape, Star Base, 1908 .... 22.00
Toothpick, Ribbed Opal 27.00
Toothpick, Ribbed Opal, Blue Opalescent 19.50
Toothpick, Ribbed Thumbprint, Ruby Flashed Top, Name & Date 1909 ...... 16.00
Toothpick, Ribbed, Opalescent 6.00
Toothpick, Ruby Flash, York Herringbone 16.00
Toothpick, Ruby Flashed, Panels, Horizontal Ribs, Footed, Scalloped 8.00
Toothpick, Ruby, Kings Crown 14.00
Toothpick, Sapphire Blue Glass, Block Pattern, Held By Molded Children 32.00
Toothpick, Sapphire Blue, Enameled Floral, Wide Panels, Houghton, Mich. ... 22.00
Toothpick, Silver Plate, Cherub Design 16.00
Toothpick, Silver Plate, Ruffled Top, Raised Cherries, Vine, Webster & Son ... 18.00
Toothpick, Souvenir, High School, Monticello, Iowa, Cobalt Luster, Germany ... 15.00
Toothpick, Souvenir, Titusville, Pennsylvania, Ruby Glass 12.00
Toothpick, Tree Trunk, Monkeys Around Base, Clear Glass 12.00
Toothpick, U.S.Battleship Maine, Destroyed In 1898, Silver Plate 10.00
Toothpick, Webster's Dictionary, Clear 21.00
Toothpick, White Enamel Cutouts Over Clear Glass, Cameo Effect 20.00
Toothpick, White Enamel Overlay Designs, Cover 20.00
Toothpick, White Opaque, Bees 27.50

Tortoiseshell Glass was made during the 1880s and after by the Sandwich Glass Works of Massachusetts and some firms in Germany. Tortoiseshell has been reproduced.

Tortoiseshell Glass, Bowl, Ribbed, Rolled Edge, 12 In. 75.00
Tortoiseshell Glass, Bowl, Smocking, Pedestal, English, Flint 150.00
Tortoiseshell Glass, Case, Card 16.00
Tortoiseshell Glass, Case, Card, Carved Dragon 37.50
Tortoiseshell Glass, Hat, 7 1/2 In.Diameter Brim 60.00
Tortoiseshell Glass, Pitcher, Water, Sandwich, Amber Handle, 7 1/4 In. ... 250.00
Tortoiseshell Glass, Vase, Jack-In-The-Pulpit, Diamond Puff Body, Leaves ... 50.00
Tortoiseshell, Box, Patch, Carved White Jade Top, Mirror Inside 125.00
Tortoiseshell, Box, Snuff, Blonde Color, Ivory Miniature, Gold, Pair 175.00
Tortoiseshell, Box, Snuff, Depicting Death Of Socrates 43.50
Tortoiseshell, Box, Snuff, George Iii Profile, Gold & Silver Flowers 65.00
Tortoiseshell, Box, Snuff, Gold Pique Design, C.1790, France 60.00
Tortoiseshell, Box, Snuff, Grisaille Painting On Ivory, C.19th Century 45.00
Tortoiseshell, Case, Card, Gold Decorated, Chinese Style Birds, Scalloped ... 15.00
Tortoiseshell, Case, Card, Inlaid Mother-Of-Pearl 25.00
Tortoiseshell, Comb For Mantilla, Ornate 18.50
Tortoiseshell, Comb, Amber Stones 35.00
Tortoiseshell, Comb, Handmade, C.1830 .... 20.00
Tortoiseshell, Comb, High, Cut 27.50
Tortoiseshell, Lorgnette, Cutout Ornate Handle, 6 1/2 In. 35.00
Tortoiseshell, Snuffbox, Louis XV, Gold Mounted, Oval, Chased, Paris, 1760 ... 1900.00
Tortoiseshell, Snuffbox, Silver Gilt Mounts, Cartouche Shape, Carved, C.1750 ... 200.00
Tortoiseshell, Whistle, 2 1/2 In. 25.00

Toy, see also Card, Doll, Marble, Tin, Wooden
Toy, Acrobat, Flips Over Weighted Poles, Mechanical, Germany 30.00
Toy, Airplane, Iron, 4 In. 8.00
Toy, Airplane, Spirit Of St.Louis, Iron 25.00
Toy, Airplane, United Boeing AMC, Iron, 5 X 3 1/2 In. 18.00
Toy, Airplane, UX214, Tootsie Toy 5.00
Toy, Alphabet Blocks, Box, Van Benthusen Lithograph, Dated 1865 .... 15.00
Toy, Armchair, Doll's, Wicker, Brass Fittings At Feet, 3 1/2 X 8 In.High 12.50
Toy, Auto, Key Wind, Made In Germany, 1930, Tin 6.50
Toy, Auto, Tin, Coupe, Running Board, Orange, Red, 13 In.Long 25.00
Toy, Babies, Creeping, Windup, Celluloid, Japan 5.00

Toy, Badge, Police, Tootsie Toy	2.00
Toy, Balky Mule, Windup, Lehman	57.50
Toy, Band, L'il Abner, Windup, Original Box	115.00
Toy, Banjo, Tin, Plays When Plunger Is Pressed, Marked Made In Germany	12.00
Toy, Barn, Wooden, Red, Green Root, 1920, Animals & Accessories, 17 Pieces	22.50
Toy, Baseball Game, Hustler Toy Corp., Dated Dec.11, 1922	19.50
Toy, Bathroom Set, For Doll's House, Wooden, 3 Piece	5.75
Toy, Beaded Bag, Doll's	10.00
Toy, Bear, Forest, Ideal, Original Clothes	8.00
Toy, Bear, Winnie The Pooh, Large Size	12.00
Toy, Bed, Brass, Salesman's Sample, 19 In.Long	97.50
Toy, Bed, Doll's, Ornate Head & Foot Pieces, Bed Spring, Brass, 28 X 12 In.	37.50
Toy, Bed, Doll's, Tootsie Toy, 2 In.High X 3 1/2 In.Long	8.00
Toy, Bed, Doll's, Wicker, 16 In.Long X 13 In.High	16.50
Toy, Bed, Doll's, Wooden Frame, Four Brass Finials, Knob Type, Wire Mattress	25.00
Toy, Bed, Doll's, Woven Springs, Side Rails, Brass, Pad Mattress, 25 1/2 In.	47.50
Toy, Bell, Pulled By Metal Horse, Circa 1890	18.00
Toy, Bicycle, see also Bicycle	
Toy, Binoculars, Gold & Rose Luster Trim, Staffordshire	15.00
Toy, Bird, Feeding, Wind, Multicolored, Patent 1927	8.50 To 9.75
Toy, Bird, Hops, Wind, Tin, Occupied Japan	8.00
Toy, Bird, Pecking, Windup, 1927	8.00
Toy, Red Carpetbreast, Wind, Metal, C.1870	20.00
Toy, Birdcage, Bird Sings, Stand, Wind, Tin	25.00
Toy, Blocks, Wooden, A, B, Cs, Numbers, Animals, Set Of 64	9.00
Toy, Blocks, Wooden, House Of Sego, Wooden Box	4.95
Toy, Board, Wooden Spell, Red, Patent 1912	10.50
Toy, Boat On Wheels, Tin, 10 In.Long	20.00
Toy, Boat, Paddle Wheel, Marked Puritan, Iron, 10 1/2 In.Long	110.00
Toy, Boat, Pull, Columbus, Cast Iron, American, C.1850 *Illus*	80.00

Toy, Boat, Pull, Columbus, Cast Iron, American, C.1850

Toy, Buggy, Tin, 7 In.
See Page 600

Toy, Cat, Tin, U.S.A., 7 1/2 In.Long
See Page 600

Toy, **Bobsled**, Doll's, Runners, Red	10.00
Toy, **Bombo**, The Monkey, Somersaults From Tree, Unique Art, Circa 1930, Wind	29.00
Toy, **Bond Bread Wagon**, Wooden, Horse Drawn, Pull, Morrison Rice Toys, Ill.	150.00
Toy, **Bowl**, Berry, Child's, Lacy Daisy Pattern, Six Bowls	65.00
Toy, **Bowl**, Punch, Child's, Flattened Diamond & Sunburst, Six Cups	55.00
Toy, **Bowl**, Punch, Child's, Tulip, Sawtooth, 4 1/2 In.Diameter, Five Cups	35.00
Toy, **Box**, Powder, Lined, Silver Catch, Three Combs, Celluloid, Salesman Sample	25.00
Toy, **Buck Rogers Battle Cruiser**, Tootsie, Box	20.00
Toy, **Buck Rogers Duo Destroyer**, Tootsie, Box	20.00
Toy, **Bucket**, Wooden, Wire Bail, 2 1/2 In.	5.00
Toy, **Bug**, Lehmann, Tin	37.50
Toy, **Buggy**, Circa 1920, Tin, 4 In.Long	35.00
Toy, **Buggy**, Tin, 7 In. *Illus*	35.00
Toy, **Buick Roadster**, Blue Cloisonne Radiator Emblem, 45 X 21 In.	145.00
Toy, **Bull**, Brahma, Cast Metal, U.S.A., 4 In.High	5.00
Toy, **Bull**, Cow, & Calf, Hereford, Cast Metal, Made In U.S.	12.00
Toy, **Bull**, Pulling Boy, Tin, Windup	12.00
Toy, **Bureau**, Doll's, Victorian, Porcelain Knobs	60.00
Toy, **Bus**, Arcade, Iron Wheels, Cast Iron, 1 3/4 X 8 In.	30.00
Toy, **Bus**, Cast Iron, Says Bowen Motor Coach, Texas Centennial, 1936 On Top	25.00
Toy, **Busy Bridge**, Marx	42.50
Toy, **Butter**, Child's, Oval Star, Cover	22.00
Toy, **Butter**, Child's, Vine & Beads, Cover	25.00
Toy, **Cabinet**, China, Two Glass Doors, Mirror Back, Pine, 12 3/4 In.Tall	14.50
Toy, **Camping Set**, Tootsie	7.00
Toy, **Candlestick**, Child's, Colonial, 3 1/2 In.High, Pair	16.00
Toy, **Cannon Carrier**, Two Cannons, Drivers, Two Men On Horses, France, Tin	55.00
Toy, **Cannon**, Brass, Webster Crescent	25.00
Toy, **Cannon**, Brass, 10 1/2 In.Long	45.00
Toy, **Cannon**, Carbide, Cast Iron Wheels & Carriage, Mechanical, 18 In.	35.00
Toy, **Cannon**, Cast Wheels, 7 1/2 In.Long	75.00
Toy, **Cannon**, Etched, Brass, Wooden Cart, Iron Wheels	7.00
Toy, **Cannon**, Iron, 9 In.	25.00
Toy, **Cannon**, Tootsie Toy, 3 3/4 In.	10.00
Toy, **Car**, Celluloid, Metal Wheels, 3 In.	5.00
Toy, **Car**, Driver Training, Windup, Marx	20.00
Toy, **Car**, Driver, Windup, Marx, Original Box	22.00
Toy, **Car**, Edsel, 1958, Salesman's Sample, 8 1/4 In.	12.50
Toy, **Car**, G-Men, Tin, 3 1/2 In.	8.00
Toy, **Car**, Marked U.S.A., Iron, 5 In.Long	35.00
Toy, **Car**, Model T Ford, Rumble Seat, Steel Wheels, Blue Paint, Cast Iron	30.00
Toy, **Car**, Nylint, Windup, Metal, 14 In.Long	15.00
Toy, **Car**, Passenger, Buddy L, C.1920	55.00
Toy, **Car**, Race, Marx, Windup	7.00
Toy, **Car**, Rubber, 1938	2.00
Toy, **Car**, Rumble Seat, Open, Oldsmobile, Tootsie Toy	5.00
Toy, **Car**, Tootsie Toy, 1939	3.00
Toy, **Castor Set**, Concave Diamonds, Child's	39.00
Toy, **Cat Pushes Ball**, Pump Tail To Wind, Marx	16.50
Toy, **Cat**, Tin, U.S.A., 7 1/2 In.Long *Illus*	25.00
Toy, **Celluloid**, Wind Up, Negro Boy Eating Watermelon, 5 In.High	80.00
Toy, **Cement Mixer**, Buddy L., C.1930	30.00
Toy, **Chair**, Doll's, Chippendale, Cabriole Legs, Fan Carving, Wooden, 5 1/2 In.	15.00
Toy, **Chair**, Doll's, Swinging Tray, Wooden	8.00
Toy, **Chair**, Doll's, Wicker, Blue & Lavender Reeds Woven Into Back & Seat	12.50
Toy, **Chair**, Marked Arcade, Iron	5.95
Toy, **Chair**, Side, Iron, 2 1/2 In.High	4.95
Toy, **Charlie Chaplin**, Harry Richmond, Pull String, Doff Hats, Tin, Pair	10.00
Toy, **Chest Of Drawers**, Georgian, Brass Knobs, 8 1/2 In.Tall	60.00
Toy, **Chest**, Blanket, Doll's, Dovetail, Pine, Walnut, Four Ball Feet, C.1830	125.00
Toy, **Chest**, Whatnot Shelf, Two Tiger Maple Drawers, Cherry, 16 1/2 In.High	90.00
Toy, **Chicken**, Tin, Lays Eggs, Wyandotte, 6 1/2 In. *Illus*	18.00
Toy, **Chocolate Set**, Child's, Pink Roses, Germany, 15 Piece, Service For 4	49.50
Toy, **Circus Performers**, Clowns, Bareback Rider, Bisque, Heubach	325.00
Toy, **Circus**, Schoenhut, Seneca, N.Y., Boxed	125.00
Toy, **Clown & Jo Jo In Car**, Unique Arts	7.00

Toy, Chicken, Tin, Lays Eggs, Wyandotte, 6 1/2 In.
See Page 600

Toy, **Clown And Mule**, Wind, Lehmann 33.50
Toy, **Clown At Grinding Wheel**, Wind, Strauss 45.00
Toy, **Clown**, Playing Drum, Tin, Schuco, Windup 7.50
Toy, **Clown**, Playing Violin, Tin, Schuco, Windup 7.50
Toy, **Clown**, Playing Violin, Windup, Germany 15.00
Toy, **Clown**, Walks On Hands, Windup, Chein, Tin, 5 In. 10.00
Toy, **Clown**, Windup, Chein 12.00
Toy, **Clown**, Windup, German, Violinist 27.00
Toy, **Coach**, Driver, & 2 Horses, Hand-Carved Wood, 11 1/2 In.Long 70.00
Toy, **Coffee Grinder**, Wheel On Each Side, Middle Drawer, Arcade, Iron 40.00
Toy, **Coffeepot**, Creamer, Four Cups & Saucers, Porcelain, Roses, Circa 1850 .... 30.00
Toy, **Colander**, Three Legs, Tin, 4 In.Across 4.00
Toy, **Comic Cubes**, Box, McLoughlin Bros., Wooden 6.00
Toy, **Construction Set**, Wood, Buildo 6.00
Toy, **Coolie & Cart**, Nu Nu, Lehmann, Tin 40.00
Toy, **Cow**, Wooden Body, Skin Cover, Bell On Neck, Horns, Tail, 4 1/2 In. 15.00
Toy, **Cowboy On Horse**, Wyandotte 4.00
Toy, **Cowboy**, Lead 3.00
Toy, **Cradle**, Doll's, Oak, 23 1/2 In.Long 40.00
Toy, **Cradle**, Doll's, Wooden, Rockers, Hand-Painted Flowers, 24 In.Long 38.50
Toy, **Crib**, Doll's, Wicker, On Stand, 11 In.High 12.50
Toy, **Crib**, Doll's, Wood, Painted White, Brass Tips, 10 In.Long 24.50
Toy, **Cruet**, Child's, Pressed Glass, Swirl Pattern, Faceted Stopper, 4 In. 30.00
Toy, **Cup & Saucer**, Doll's, English Silver, Gold Lined 10.00
Toy, **Cup & Saucer**, Heart & Thumbprint, Pressed Glass 35.00
Toy, **Cup**, Punch, Child's, Miniature, Milk Glass, Little Red Riding Hood 15.00
Toy, **Cyclist**, Mechanical, Skippy Tricky, Cragstan 15.00
Toy, **Dancer**, Hawaiian, Celluloid, 1930s, Japan 9.00
Toy, **Dare Devil**, Rollover Motorcycle Cop, Falls Over, Rights Self, Circles 45.00
Toy, **Decoder**, Capt.Midnight, 1949 .... 15.00
Toy, **Dish**, Vegetable, Child's, Blue Willow, Cover, Two Handles, 5 In.Long 18.50
Toy, **Dishes**, Child's, Tin, Germany, 15 Piece 6.00
Toy, **Dog**, Schoenhut 25.00
    Toy Doll, see also Doll
Toy, **Dollhouse**, Furniture, Five Rooms, Petite Princess, 25 X 32 In. 250.00
Toy, **Dollhouse**, Lithograph On Metal, Six Rooms, Terrace 20.00
Toy, **Dollhouse**, New England, Colonial, 2 Story, Tiny-Tot Furnishings 3500.00
Toy, **Dollhouse**, 1940s, 28 X 18 X 12 In., 5o Pieces Of Furniture 125.00
Toy, **Donald Duck**, Windup, Celluloid, Key, Japan 15.00
Toy, **Donkey**, Wind, Tail Twists, Eyes Move 21.50
Toy, **Dresser**, Doll's, Ornate Mirror, 22 In.High 52.00
Toy, **Dresser**, Doll's, Three Drawers, Mirror, Wooden, C.1930, 13 In.High 22.50
Toy, **Dresser**, Mirror, Tootsie Toy, 16 X 4 3/4 In. 10.00
Toy, **Driver**, Seated, For Wagon, Iron, Top Hat, Insert Flange 10.00
Toy, **Drum**, Lithographs, Airplane, Flag Ship, Sailor, Tin, Circa 1915, 5 In. 12.50
Toy, **Drummer**, Chein, Tin, Windup 8.00
Toy, **Dry Sink**, Child's, Well & Drawer In Top, Doors Below, Pine, 20 In. 35.00
Toy, **Duck**, Joe Penner Wanna Buy A Duck, Wind, Tin 68.00
Toy, **Duck**, Windup, Chein 12.00
Toy, **Duck**, Windup, Chein, 2 1/2 In. 3.50

Toy, Dump Truck, Keystone, 1917, 26 In.	65.00
Toy, Dutch Girl, Painted, Iron, 3 3/4 In.High	7.50
Toy, Elephant, Mechanical, Tin	5.00
Toy, Engine & Tender, Friction, Painted, Tin	27.00
Toy, Engine, Steam, Weeden, Electric, Horizontal, Chrome Boiler	45.00
Toy, Felix The Cat, Jointed Body, Dated 1922, Wooden	35.00
Toy, Ferris Wheel, Herculis	35.00
Toy, Ferris Wheel, Six Seats, Key, Chein, Tin, 16 In.High	37.00
Toy, Fire Chief Car, Red Metal, Circa 1930, Friction, 15 In.	18.00
Toy, Fire Engine, Aerial Ladder	4.00
Toy, Fire Engine, Ladder, Driver, Fireman, Iron, 5 1/4 In.Long	16.75
Toy, Fire Engine, Pumper, Box, 12 In.	17.50
Toy, Fire Engine, Rubber	4.00
Toy, Fire Engine, Two Horses, Driver, Circa 1919, Iron, 13 1/2 In.	150.00
Toy, Fire Pumper, Two Horses, Two Men, Phoenix, Iron	225.00
Toy, Fireplace Set, Doll's House, Brass, Screen, Fender, & Tools	25.00
Toy, Flatiron, Step Up Grooves, Connected Handle, Iron	11.50
Toy, Flatiron, Wooden Handle	4.00
Toy, Frog, Tin, Hops, Windup, 5 In.Long	12.00 To 17.00
Toy, Frying Pan, Iron	3.50
Toy, Furniture, Commode, Doll's, Cherry Veneer, Marble Top, Olive Wood	85.00
Toy, Furniture, Doll's, Settee, 2 Chairs, Table, From Tree Limbs	12.50
Toy, Furniture, Dresser, Doll's, Oak, Round Mirror, 3 Drawers, 17 In.High	35.00
Toy, Furniture, Highchair, Doll's, Pine Seat, Red Leather Back, Pla-Doll Co.	8.00
Toy, G.I.Joe And K-9 Pups, Unique Art, Wind, 1941	29.00
Toy, Galloway, Rubber, 1945, 6 1/2 In.	5.00
Toy, Game, see Game	
Toy, Garden Seat, Doll House, Picture Of Cat, 3 In.	7.00
Toy, Gay Fiddler, Man, Top Hat, Coat, Checkered Pants, Hand-Painted, 1900, Wind	125.00
Toy, Girl Pushes Buggy, Celluloid, Baby, Umbrella Turns, Tin Base, Key Wind	8.00
Toy, Goose, Wind, Tole	32.00
Toy, Graf Zeppelin, Iron	14.00
Toy, Graf Zeppelin, 25 In.Long	35.00
Toy, Gun, Cap, Biff, Caps	4.00
Toy, Gun, Cap, Gene Autry, Holster	20.00
Toy, Gun, Cap, Invincible, Dated 1914, 50 Shot	12.50
Toy, Gun, Cap, Pluck, Iron, 3 In.	4.00
Toy, Gun, Cap, Two Hammers, Says 1880, Iron, 4 In.	18.00
Toy, Gun, Clicker, Tin, Holster, The Lone Ranger, Copyright 1938	20.00
Toy, Gun, Ray, Flash Gordon	40.00
Toy, Gun, Ray, Wyandotte, Uses Air, 7 1/2 In.Long	20.00
Toy, Hack With Horse & Driver, Cast Iron	80.00
Toy, Hen On Nest, Wind, Cackles, Lays Egg, Tin, 5 1/4 In.Long	9.75
Toy, Hen, Tin, Wind, Clucks, Lays Marble Eggs	15.00 To 18.00
Toy, High Chair, Doll's, Wicker, Cane Seat, 30 In.High	28.00
Toy, High Chair, Doll's, Wooden	3.00
Toy, Hobbyhorse, Mipony, Wooden, Wheels, 10 In.High	35.00
Toy, Hobbyhorse, On Wheels, Leather Harness, 3 1/2 X 4 In.	7.50
Toy, Hobbyhorse, Stuffed, Iron Bottom & Wheels, 20 In.Long	55.00
Toy, Hobbyhorse, Wood, Painted, American, C.1850	*Illus* 225.00
Toy, Horse & Rider, Wagon, Bell Center, 7 In.Long	50.00
Toy, Horse & Sulky, Cast Iron, Painted	80.00
Toy, Horse & Two Wheel Cart, Iron, 6 1/2 In.	15.00
Toy, Horse, Buggy, Driver, Tin, Clockwork, American, 1850	*Illus* 825.00
Toy, Horse, Carved Wood, Wooden Base, Tin Wheels, Pull	45.00
Toy, Horse, Dappled, On Wheels, Carved Wood, 5 In.Long, 5 1/2 In.High	45.00
Toy, Horse, Papier-Mache, 8 In.	*Illus* 45.00
Toy, Horse, Red Felt Saddle, Schoenhut	35.00
Toy, Hose Reel & 2 Horses, Cast Iron, Painted	130.00
Toy, Howitzer, Self-Propelled, 155 Mm., Tootsie Toy, 5 In.	18.00
Toy, Iron On Trivet	12.50
Toy, Iron, Child's, Detachable Handle Has Release Lever, 3 1/2 In.Long	12.50
Toy, Iron, Child's, Detachable Handle, Pat.May 22, 1900, 5 In.Long	10.00
Toy, Iron, Child's, Flat, Iron, 1 3/4 In.Long	5.50
Toy, Iron, Child's, Green, Electric, 'Utility Iron'	4.00
Toy, Jazzbo Jim, Banjo, Dances On Cabin Roof, Tin, Windup, Chein	55.00

Toy, Jeep, G.I.Joe, Art's, Tin, Windup	25.00 To 37.50
Toy, Jeep, Jumping, Marx	25.00
Toy, Jenny, The Balking Mule, Strauss, Wind	55.00
Toy, Jo Jangle, Dances, Tin	25.00
Toy, Jockey Cart With Driver, Iron	35.00
Toy, Jolly Nigger, Mechanical, Tin	50.00
Toy, Kaleidoscope, Wooden Frame, Knob Turns Colored Glass	18.00
Toy, Kayo, Cast Metal, Springy Head, Screw Under Each Foot, Painted	25.00
Toy, Kazoo, Tin	2.29
Toy, Kettle, Coal Scuttle, Shovel, Fry Pan, Sauce Pan, Child's, Iron, 1 1/2 In.	12.00
Toy, Kiddie Cyclist, Wind, Box	35.00
Toy, Ladder, Step, Iron, 9 In.Tall	4.95
Toy, Laddie, Dog Shakes, Moves, Lindstrom, Wind	16.00
Toy, Locomotive, Molded Engineers At Sides Of Cab, Red Paint, Iron	70.00
Toy, Locomotive, Tender, Lionel, No.2026	20.00
Toy, Log Puller, Horses, Kenton, Iron	250.00
Toy, Machine Gun, Cap, Hand Crank, Rapid Fire, Grey Iron Company	125.00
Toy, March Hare, Marionette, Walt Disney, Boxed	10.00
Toy, Metallophone, Schoenut, Box	9.00
Toy, Mickey Mouse, see Mickey Mouse	
Toy, Milk Truck, Tootsie, 3 In.Long	7.00
Toy, Milk Wagon, Horses, & Driver, Tin, Windup	35.00
Toy, Minnie Mouse Knitting & Rocking, Walt Disney Productions, Japan	15.00
Toy, Minnie Mouse, In Rocker, Mechanical, 7 In.Tall	27.50
Toy, Model Kit, Aircraft Carrier Wasp, Wooden, 18 In.	8.75
Toy, Monkey Drummer, Mechanical, Tin, 5 In.Tall	12.50

Toy, Hobbyhorse, Wood,
Painted, American, C.1850
See Page 602

Toy, Horse, Buggy, Driver, Tin, Clockwork,
American, 1850
See Page 602

Toy, Horse, Papier-Mache, 8 In.
See Page 602

Toy, Noah's Ark, Wood, Painted, C.1850, 34 Pieces

Toy, Piano, Schoenhut, 8 1/2 In.
See Page 605

Toy, Monkey, Straw Filled, Move Tail & Head Moves, 13 In.Tall	13.50
Toy, Monkey, Stuffed, 19 In.Long	10.00
Toy, Monoplane, Katz, Big Boy, 27 In.Wing Span	27.50
Toy, Mortimer Snerd, Tin, Windup, Tips Hat, Rolls Eyes, 6 In.	16.50
Toy, Motorcycle & Rider, Military, Marx	22.50
Toy, Motorcycle, Champion, Iron, 7 In.	80.00
Toy, Motorcycle, Cop, Marked Champion, Paint, Iron, 4 3/4 In.Long	20.00
Toy, Motorcycle, Harley, Rider's Head Turns, Iron, 7 1/4 In.	85.00
Toy, Motorcycle, Red, Black Tires, Iron, 4 1/4 In.	10.00
Toy, Motorcycle, Sidecar, Iron, 5 In.	45.00
Toy, Motorcycle, Sidecar, Passenger, Champion, Blue & Red, Iron	125.00
Toy, Motorcyclist, Orange Paint, 6 1/2 In.	45.00
Toy, Mouse In Clock, Chein	3.00
Toy, Mouse, Running, Gray, Tin, Windup	40.00
Toy, Mousetrap & Mouse, Tin, On Three Wheels	6.50
Toy, Movie Projector, Andy Panda	15.00
Toy, Mule, Schoenhut	22.50
Toy, Music Box, Upright, Glass Door On Front, Bells, Butterflies, Swiss	500.00
Toy, Noah's Ark, Wood, Hand-Painted, 6 People, 60 Animals	50.00
Toy, Noah's Ark, Wood, Painted, C.1850, 34 Pieces .... *Illus*	125.00
Toy, Organ, Cathedral, Tin, Lithograph, Plays, Chein	12.50
Toy, Pencil, Big Magic Multiplying, Wooden, 6 In.	4.00
Toy, Percolator, Three Cups, Saucers, Plates, Spoons, Aluminum, Circa 1933, Box	25.00
Toy, Piano Stool, Refinished, Seat 8 In.Diameter, 9 1/2 In.High	50.00

Toy, **Piano**, Player, Side Wind, Hand-Painted Wood Nymphs, Tin, Four Rolls 48.00
Toy, **Piano**, Schoenhut, 8 1/2 In. .... *Illus* 35.00
Toy, **Pick Up Sticks**, Schoenhut, Cylinder Box 5.00
Toy, **Pig**, Windup, Chein 12.00
Toy, **Pinocchio**, Balances On Ladder, Iron 12.50
Toy, **Pistol Horn**, Gene Autry 5.00
Toy, **Pistol**, Buck Rogers, U-235 Atomic, Gold & Black, Box 110.00
Toy, **Pistol**, Cap, Colt, Patent 1890, Iron, 6 In. 20.00
Toy, **Pistol**, Cap, Cowboy, Iron, 4 In. 7.50
Toy, **Pistol**, Cap, Dick Tracy 6.00
Toy, **Pistol**, Cap, Iron, Mark Challenge, Single Shot 9.95
Toy, **Pistol**, Cap, Iron, Percussion Hammer, Fires 1 Cap 6.95
Toy, **Pistol**, Cap, Iron, 4 In. 7.50
Toy, **Pistol**, Cap, King, C.1920, Iron 10.00
Toy, **Pistol**, Cap, Mark Model Patent June 17th, 1890, Iron, Single Shot 9.95
Toy, **Pistol**, Cap, Mark, Doc Patent 1923, Iron, 5 In.Long 6.95
Toy, **Pistol**, Cap, Marked Buffalo Bill, Lacquered Finish, 7 1/2 In. 20.00
Toy, **Pistol**, Cap, Mountie, Hubley 5.00
Toy, **Pistol**, Cap, Repeating, Ebony Handle, Gene Autry, Iron 14.50
Toy, **Pistol**, Cap, Single Shot, Marked Pat.1870, Iron 6.75
Toy, **Pistol**, Cap, Tin, Germany, 3 In. 8.00
Toy, **Pistol**, Cap, 7 1/4 In. 10.00
Toy, **Pistol**, Gene Autry, Smokes, Gold Finish 35.00
Toy, **Pistol**, Lone Ranger 5.00
Toy, **Pistol**, Pirate, Iron 15.00
Toy, **Pistol**, Pop, Black Tin, 1935 .... 1.50
Toy, **Pistol**, Radio Repeater, Flash Gordon, Tin, Lithograph 65.00
Toy, **Pistol**, Water, Buck Rogers, Liquid Helium, 1936 .... 85.00
Toy, **Plane**, Lindy, 1930, 11 X 13 In.Wingspread, Iron 90.00
Toy, **Plane**, Marked Lindy, Iron, 4 1/2 In.Long 9.95
Toy, **Plane**, 1918 Model, Pilot 35.00
Toy, **Pop Gun**, Boy's, Tin, Painted Green 5.00
Toy, **Popeye**, Pull, Beats Spinach Can, Dated 1928, Wooden 28.00
Toy, **Porky Pig**, Twirls Umbrella, Wind, 1939, Marx 45.00
Toy, **Potato Masher**, Child's, Wooden, 4 In. 5.00
Toy, **Printer's Press**, Salesman Sample, 10 In.High 17.00
Toy, **Pull**, Two Horses, Two Bells, Tin, Iron Wheels, C.1890, Repainted Base 135.00
Toy, **Pump**, Lithographed 7.50
Toy, **Pumper & Three Horses & Men**, Cast Iron 130.00
Toy, **Pups**, G.I.Joe, Art's, Tin, Windup 32.00
Toy, **Rabbit**, Pushing Wheelbarrow, Glass Eyes, Papier-Mache, Germany 9.50
Toy, **Racer**, Cast Iron, Rubber Wheels 10.00
Toy, **Racer**, Hubley, Iron Art, Iron, 6 3/4 In. 5.00
Toy, **Range**, Gas, Marked Royal, Iron 9.95
Toy, **Rattle**, Doll's, Sterling, Bone Handle 22.00
Toy, **Rattle**, Tin, Perforated Handle, Embossed 'For A Good Child, 'Alphabet 15.00
Toy, **Register**, Play-Store 10.00
Toy, **Roadster Touring Car**, Friction, Circa 1925, Tin, 18 In. 25.00
Toy, **Roadster**, W.V., Circa 1930 .... 25.00
Toy, **Rocket**, Buck Rogers, Police Patrol, Marx, Windup, 1927, 13 In.Long 60.00
Toy, **Roller Coaster**, Wind, Box 22.00
Toy, **Roller Coaster**, Wind, Chein 10.00
Toy, **Rookie Cop**, Siren, Motorcycle, Marx, Circa 1930, Wind 23.00
Toy, **Rooster Pulling Bunny On Egg**, Tin 35.00
Toy, **Running Scotty**, Dog, Marx, Wind 18.00
Toy, **Sadiron**, Child's 2.25
Toy, **Sadiron**, Double Pointed, Iron 4.75
Toy, **Sadiron**, Iron, 2 3/4 In.Long 5.95
Toy, **Sadiron**, On Trivet 9.50
Toy, **Sadiron**, One Piece, Handle, 2 In.High 5.50
Toy, **Sadiron**, Rope Style Handle, Iron, 4 1/4 In.Long 5.95
Toy, **Sadiron**, Swan Shape, Iron, 2 3/4 In.Long 7.95
Toy, **Sadiron**, Triangular Shape, Iron, 2 1/8 In.Long 4.75
Toy, **Samovar**, Handles, Hood, Spigot, Brass, Russian, 7 In.High 32.50
Toy, **Sand Shovel**, Tin, Iron Roller & Wheels, Painted Tan, 17 In.High 20.00
Toy, **Sandy Andy Football Player**, Kicks Marble 125.00

Toy, Scrub Board & Washtub, Wooden, Circa 1830, 3 In. 50.00
Toy, Seal, Clown Clothes, Wind, Walks On Hands, Chein, Tin 7.50
Toy, Seaplane, Windup, Chein 12.00
Toy, Sedan, Graham, 16 In. 17.50
Toy, Settee, Doll's, Painted To Simulate Wooden Frame, Pillows, Iron 30.00
Toy, Sewing Machine, Blue, Tin, Nickle Plate, Gold Eagle, Iron Wheel, Germany 14.00
Toy, Sewing Machine, Child's, Betsy Ross 6.00
Toy, Sewing Machine, Child's, Singer, Iron 12.50
Toy, Sewing Machine, Child's, 4 X 5 In. 12.00
Toy, Sewing Machine, German .... 8.50 To 12.00
Toy, Sewing Machine, Hand Turn, Maker Lindstrom, Patent Number 11.00
Toy, Sewing Machine, Scalloped Base, Handle On Wheel, Steel & Nickle 12.00
Toy, Shooting Gallery, Windup, Wyandotte, Original Box .... 30.00 To 35.00
Toy, Shovel, Child's, Tin 2.00
Toy, Skates, Ice, Clamp On 4.00
Toy, Skates, Ice, Curled Steel Toe With Acorn On End, Pair 35.00
Toy, Skates, Ice, Rosewood & Steel, Brass Trim 22.00
Toy, Skates, Ice, Winchester, Signed 6.00
Toy, Skates, Ice, Wood Base, Straps, Pair 9.00
Toy, Skates, Roller, Winchester, Boxed 23.00
Toy, Ski Boy, Wind, Chein, Box 15.00
Toy, Skillet, Iron, Long Handle 4.50
Toy, Slate, Wooden Frame, Pat.1872, 10 1/2 X 7 1/2 In. 17.50
Toy, Sled, Child's, Wooden, Painted, Turned Up Runners, Turned Front Support 30.00
Toy, Sleigh, Doll's, Wicker 15.00
Toy, Sofa, Heart In Center Of Back, Victorian, Iron, 6 In.Long 15.00
Toy, Soldier, American, Lead, Lot Of 10 .... 12.00
Toy, Soldier, Assorted Positions, Red & Gray Uniforms, England, 1901, 33 .... 50.00
Toy, Soldier, Cannon, Tent, Horse, World War I, Lot Of 17 .... 26.00
Toy, Soldier, Lead, Khaki Uniform, Rifle On Shoulder, C.1940, Group Of 90 .... 25.00
Toy, Soldier, Movable Arms, Weapons, Lead, Paint, Marked France, Lot Of 10 .... 22.50
Toy, Soldier, Pair Of Stretcher Bearers With Stretcher, Pre-World War II 15.00
Toy, Soldier, Rifleman, Pre-World War II 7.50
Toy, Soldier, World War I, Mess Hall & Tents, Lead, 100 Pieces 200.00
Toy, Steam Engine, Tin Wheels, Key Wind, Cast Iron, 3 In.High 32.50
Toy, Steam Shovel, Buddy L, C.1920 .... 75.00
Toy, Steam Shovel, Keystone 45.00
Toy, Steam Shovel, Paint, Buddy L .... 75.00 To 78.00
Toy, Step Ladder, Iron, 3 In.High 4.95
Toy, Store, Utensils & Implements, Iron 75.00
Toy, Stove, Allover Raised Acorns & Leaves, Chimney, Two Pans, Tin 15.00
Toy, Stove, Child's, Cast Iron, Muffin Pan, Teakettle, 5 1/2 In.High 145.00
Toy, Stove, Child's, Cast Iron, Royal Esther, Mount Penn Stove Works 220.00
Toy, Stove, Child's, Lid Lifter, Three Iron Pans, Gem, Iron, 5 X 6 In. 57.50
Toy, Stove, Child's, Poker Lids, 'Bird' By Kenton, Iron, 6 1/2 X 9 In. 40.00
Toy, Stove, Cook, Iron 85.00
Toy, Stove, Doll's House, Cast Iron, Champion, Geneva, 3 1/4 In. 12.00
Toy, Stove, Four Holes, Reservoir, Lids, Skillet, Coal Hod, Pot, 'Eagle, ' Iron 45.00
Toy, Stove, Four Openings, Three Lids, Lifter, Kettle, Frying Pan, Iron 50.00
Toy, Stove, Heating, Salesman's Sample, Tin, 12 In.High 72.00
Toy, Stove, High Legs, Oven, Electric, Empire, C.1924, Salesman's Sample 55.00
Toy, Stove, Little Fanny, Grates 125.00
Toy, Stove, Marked Star, Iron, 3 3/4 In. 9.95
Toy, Stove, Oven Opens, Metal, Circa 1940, 8 X 4 1/2 In. 8.00
Toy, Sugar & Creamer, Child's, Pennsylvania, Cover 48.00
Toy, Sugar & Creamer, Child's, White, Embossed, Cover, Ironstone 5.00
Toy, Sugar & Creamer, English Silver, 5/8 In.High 12.50
Toy, Sugar, Creamer, Butter, Diamond Type Pattern, Milk Glass, Circa 1890 .... 25.00
Toy, Sugar, Creamer, Covered Butter, Flat Diamond & Sunburst, Child's 38.00
Toy, Sugar, Creamer, Spooner, Butter, Child's, Tulip Honeycomb 42.50
Toy, Table Set, Child's, Diamond & Sunburst, 4 Piece .... 52.00 To 65.00
Toy, Table Set, Child's, Tulip & Honeycomb, 4 Piece 72.00
Toy, Table, Doll's, Pedestal, Round, Oak 7.50
Toy, Tank, Army, Wind, Tin, Marx, 4 X 10 In. 9.00
Toy, Tank, Doughboy, Wind, Tin, Marx 35.00
Toy, Tank, World War I, Wind, Soldier Comes Out, Marx 45.00

Toy, Taxi, Amos & Andy, Fresh Air, Windup, Tin 65.00
Toy, Tea Set, Child's, Blue Willow, Covered Casserole, Gravy Boat, 25 Piece 15.00
Toy, Tea Set, Child's, Children Motif, Unmarked Royal Bayreuth, 21 Piece 510.00
Toy, Tea Set, Child's, Oval Star, 4 Piece 68.00
Toy, Tea Set, Child's, Nippon, White Silhouettes Of Girls Playing, 22 Piece 45.00
Toy, Tea Set, Child's, White Porcelain, Gold Trim, Japan, 23 Piece 19.00
Toy, Tea Set, Doll's, Germany, 20th Century, Original Box 12.50
Toy, Teapot, Cup, Saucer, Child's, Wedding Band, Melto, Japan 10.00
Toy, Teapot, Doll's, English Silver, Wooden Handle, Hinged Lid, Gold Lined 25.00
Toy, Teapot, Sugar, Creamer, Child's, Pink Luster Color, Children Playing 18.00
Toy, Teapot, Sugar, Creamer, Four Cups & Saucers, Doll's, Floral, Blue Bands 45.00
Toy, Teapot, Sugar, Creamer, Four Cups, Saucers, Child's, Porcelain, Moss Rose 18.00
Toy, Teddy Bear, Straw Filled, 24 In.High 45.00
Toy, Telephones, Red Tin, 1935 .... 2.00
Toy, Telescope, Jack Armstrong, Explorer 20.00
Toy, The Tireless Top, No String, Spring Or Ring, Spins On Pedestal 3.95
Toy, Threshing Machine, Painted Gray 70.00
Toy, Tombo, Alabama Coon Jigger, Strauss Mfg.Co., May 24, 1910 .... 65.00
Toy, Top, Gyroscope Center, Patent 1868, Brass 18.00
Toy, Top, Singing, Disney Figures, Red & Blue Paint, Tin, 10 In.Diameter 8.50
Toy, Top, Spins, 1927 Movie, Palmer Cox Brownies, Tin 25.00
Toy, Top, Wood, 2 1/2 In.High 5.00
Toy, Touring, Parker, 1926 .... 5.00
Toy, Tractor, Caterpillar, Bulldozer Blade, Stake, Dump Wagon, Louis Marx Co. 22.00
Toy, Tractor, Fordson, 7 In.Long 45.00
Toy, Tractor, McCormick, Deering, 6 In.Long .... 45.00.
Toy, Train Engine, Friction, Iron, 7 1/4 In. 60.00
Toy, Train Engine, Tender, Wood Smoke Stacks, Lantern, Metal, Marked Dewey 210.00
Toy, Train Station, Bing, Hornby Series, Tin 75.00
Toy, Train, American Flyer, O Gauge, No.1096, Tin Plate, C.1927 .... 20.00
Toy, Train, Army, Cannon, Searchlight, Two Switches, Wind, Marx 30.00
Toy, Train, Caboose, Open Vestibules, Cupola, Red, Iron 30.00
Toy, Train, Circus, Wooden, Taylor, Circa 1935, 15 In.Long, 5 Piece 12.50
Toy, Train, Diesel, Electric, Marx, Circa 1950, Box 45.00
Toy, Train, Engine, Four Cars, Tracks, Control Tower, Unique, Windup 20.00
Toy, Train, Four Cars, Tracks, Transformer, Lionel, No.258 .... 85.00
Toy, Train, Franconia, West Germany, Tin, Windup, Tender, Car, Track, & Key 15.00
Toy, Train, Hofner, Windup, Wyandotte, 4 Piece 10.00
Toy, Train, Lionel, Engine With Tender, No.221, Torpedo Block 25.00
Toy, Train, Lionel, Engine With Tender, No.224 .... 22.50
Toy, Train, Lionel, Engine With Tender, No.229 .... 22.50
Toy, Train, Lionel, Engine With Tender, No.300-A.C. 18.00
Toy, Train, Lionel, Engine With Tender, No.301, Metal 8.00
Toy, Train, Lionel, Engine With Tender, No.303, Metal 8.00
Toy, Train, Lionel, Engine With Tender, No.307, Metal 8.00
Toy, Train, Lionel, Engine With Tender, No.310 .... 20.00
Toy, Train, Lionel, Engine With Tender, No.312 .... 20.00
Toy, Train, Lionel, Engine With Tender, No.736, Big 2, 8, 48 & Whistle Tender 45.00
Toy, Train, Lionel, Engine With Tender, No.1055, Diesel 10.00
Toy, Train, Lionel, Engine With Tender, No.1110, Metal 8.00
Toy, Train, Lionel, Engine With Tender, No.1654 .... 10.00
Toy, Train, Lionel, Engine With Tender, No.1666 .... 22.50
Toy, Train, Lionel, Engine With Tender, No.1668, Torpedo Block 25.00
Toy, Train, Lionel, Engine With Tender, No.1684 .... 15.00
Toy, Train, Lionel, Engine With Tender, No.1688-E, Whistle Tender, Gray 30.00
Toy, Train, Lionel, Engine With Tender, No.1688, Torpedo Gray 22.5C
Toy, Train, Lionel, Engine With Tender, No.2016 .... 22.5
Toy, Train, Lionel, Engine With Tender, No.2018 .... 25.C
Toy, Train, Lionel, Engine With Tender, No.2025 .... 25.
Toy, Train, Lionel, Engine With Tender, No.2026 22
Train, Lionel, Engine With Tender, No.2037 .... 2?
Train, Lionel, Engine, No.21085, 4 6, 2, Plastic 1
ain, Lionel, No.370, Diesel, Switcher ....
n, Marx, Set In Original Box ....
Meteor, Streamline, Silver, Mechanical ....
Pull, Engine, Tender, Two Box Cars, Caboose, Iron, Pratt Letchworth ....

Toy, Train, Seven Cars, Tracks, Transformer, Commodore Vanderbilt, Marx 35.00
Toy, Train, Steel Engine, Tin Tender, Four Cars, Track, Transformer, Lionel 40.00
Toy, Train, Three Cars, Tin, Wind, Marx 25.00
Toy, Train, Unique Art, Electric 35.00
Toy, Train, Unique Art, Windup 35.00
Toy, Train, Windup, Bing 110.00
Toy, Train, Windup Engine, Iron, Tin Tanker, Freight, Caboose, Coal Car, Tracks 50.00
Toy, Tray, Doll's, English Silver, 5 1/2 In.Long 15.00
Toy, Tricycle, Child's, Two High Back Wheels, Small Front Wheel, Iron 300.00
Toy, Trivet, Child's, Cathedral, Handle, Iron 4.75
Toy, Trivet, Child's, With Release Iron 9.00
Toy, Trolley, Painted, Iron, 8 In.Long 32.00
Toy, Truck, Army, Khaki Color, Buddy L, Wooden, Circa 1940 .... 7.25
Toy, Truck, Country Produce 4.00
Toy, Truck, Dump, Buddy L, 20 In. .... 40.00 To 45.00
Toy, Truck, Dump, Horses, Driver, Circa 1950, Iron 45.00
Toy, Truck, Dump, Wyandotte, 13 In. 3.00
Toy, Truck, Fire, Chemical, Pressed Steel, Hose, Rubber Tires 75.00
Toy, Truck, Fire, Hook & Ladder, Keystone, 29 In.Long 105.00
Toy, Truck, Fire, Hose, Buddy L, C.1920, 25 In.Long 75.00
Toy, Truck, Fire, Ladder, Buddy L, C.1920, 39 In.Long 85.00
Toy, Truck, Fire, Rubber 3.00
Toy, Truck, Gasoline, Iron, 5 1/4 In.Long 16.75
Toy, Truck, Ice, Buddy L, 26 In.Long 75.00
Toy, Truck, Pickup, Wind, Tin, Courtland Mfg. Co. 15.00
Toy, Truck, Sand & Gravel, Marx, Windup 7.50
Toy, Truck, Stake, Two Horses, Driver, Iron, 14 1/2 In.Long 95.00
Toy, Truck, Stake, 12 In. 12.50
Toy, Truck, Telephone Maintenance, Buddy L., C.1930 .... 35.00
    Toy, Trunk, See Trunk
Toy, Trunk, Mail, Armored 4.00
Toy, Tureen, Lid, Underplate, Gravy Boat, Underplate Attached, Blue Willow 15.00
Toy, Tureen, Platter, Pitcher, Six Plates, Child's, Czechoslovakia 10.00
Toy, Typewriter, Simplex 12.50
Toy, Violin, Tin, Case, 13 1/2 In. 18.00
Toy, Wagon, Bell Ringer, Ladder, Drivers, Horses, Iron, Paint, C.1885, 21 In. 225.00
Toy, Wagon, Covered, Marked Prairie Schooner, Wood, 17 1/2 In.Long 8.00
Toy, Wagon, Horse, Driver, Iron, 12 1/2 In.Long 75.00
Toy, Wagon, Ice, 2 Dapple Grays, Snipped Tin 85.00
Toy, Wagon, Stake, Two Horses, Driver, Iron, 14 1/2 In.Long 95.00
Toy, Wagon, Two Oxen, Iron, 15 3/4 In. 125.00
Toy, Wagon, Wooden, Spoke Wheels, Circa 1920, 15 X 7 3/4 In. 25.00
Toy, Washboard, Basket, Rack Dryer, Hand Wringer, Tub, Wood Compartment 35.00
Toy, Washing Machine, Tin & Glass 12.00
Toy, Washstand Set, Child's, Chrysanthemum Pattern, Gold Edge 85.00
Toy, Watercolors, Child's, Frost & Adams Co., Boston, 4 X 6 In.Box 3.00
Toy, Wheel Bell, Iron, Pull Toy 10.00
Toy, Wheelbarrow, Red, Stenciled, Wooden, 27 In.Long 30.00
    Trap, see Tool, Trap

    Treen are small wooden objects such as mugs, spoons, and bowls. The term is
    early English but is used in the United States in many areas.
Treen, Bowl, 37 In.Diameter 100.00
Treen, Mortar & Pestle, Cylindrical Vessel, Ring Turned Neck & Foot, 8 In. 40.00
Treen, Vessel, Cylindrical, Flaring Lip, Integral Handle, 10 1/4 In. 20.00

    Trivets are now used to hold hot dishes. Most of the late nineteenth and
    early twentieth century trivets were made to hold hot irons. Iron or brass
    reproductions are being made of many of the old styles. The H-xx number
    refers to the book 'Trivets' by Dick Hankerson.
et, **Advertising**, Folded Asbestos, 5 1/4 X 3 In. 8.50
t, **Beaded Hearts**, Iron, Handle 6.95
, **Brass**, Chinese, Pierced, 5 In.Diameter 4.00
Brass, Flat Circular Band, Ball Feet 12.50
Brass, Openwork Center Design, Footed, Marked China .... 4 ⁻
Brass, Signed Fleur-De-Lis On Bottom ....

Trivet, **Brass**, 3 Masted Sailing Ship, Handwrought, 1860, 6 In. 20.00
Trivet, **Bust Of George Washington Center**, Cast Iron 25.00
Trivet, **Cathedral**, Handle, Iron 5.95
Trivet, **Child's**, Cathedral, Handle, Iron, 4 1/4 In.Long 4.75
Trivet, **Child's**, Iron 12.50
Trivet, **Claw Feet**, Brass, Art Nouveau Tile Inset 20.00
Trivet, **Clear Glass**, Silver Overlay, Scalloped Edge, 7 3/4 In.Diameter 22.50
Trivet, **Crown**, Maltese Cross, Royal, Iron 4.95
Trivet, **Enterprise Bar**, Iron 3.95
Trivet, **Enterprise E**, Iron, No.114 .... 3.95
Trivet, **Ferro Steel Urn**, Iron 4.95
Trivet, **Fire Bar**, Brass, Porcelain Handle, Flowers & Leaves, Georgian Period 62.50
Trivet, **Fireplace**, Hangs From Pot Hook To Hold Kettle, Iron 45.00
Trivet, **Fireplace**, Movable Holder, 18th Century, Iron 85.00
Trivet, **Flatiron**, Says 'Best On Earth' 5.00
Trivet, **Geometric Design**, Handle, Brass 26.00
Trivet, **Good Luck**, Horseshoe, Star In Circle, Eagle At Top, Iron 9.75
Trivet, **Heart**, Initial, Handle, Iron 6.95
Trivet, **Hearth**, Ornamental Top Plate & Handle, Brass & Iron, English 32.50
Trivet, **Hearts**, Paw Feet, Circular, Iron 5.95
Trivet, **Horseshoe Shape**, Star In Circle, Eagle At Top, , Good Luck, ' Iron 9.75
Trivet, **Humphrey**, Iron 4.95
Trivet, **Iron**, Colebrookdale Crown & Maltese Cross 5.95
Trivet, **Iron**, Footed, Round, Openwork Designs 9.50
Trivet, **Iron**, Humphrey Gas Iron 5.95
Trivet, **Iron**, I Want U, Spade 4.95
Trivet, **Iron**, Imperial In Center, Consolidated Gas Iron Co., N.Y. 5.95
Trivet, **Iron**, No.134, B & D 3.95
Trivet, **Iron**, Oblong Waffle 5.75
Trivet, **Iron**, Round, Footed, Cricket, Handwrought 35.00
Trivet, **Iron**, W Center, Scrolls, Oval 6.00
Trivet, **Lacy Design**, Footed, Iron, 5 1/2 In.Diameter 18.00
Trivet, **Lacy Urn Variant**, Iron 5.95
Trivet, **Letter C**, Iron 4.95
Trivet, **Lilies Form Scrollwork**, Iron 6.00
Trivet, **Lion & Unicorn**, Dieu Et Mon Droit, Four Legs, Brass, 6 In.Sq. 24.00
Trivet, **Mule Shoe**, Iron 4.95
Trivet, **Oblong Waffle**, Iron .... 4.95 To 8.00
Trivet, **Ocean Waves**, Iron, H-84 .... 4.95
Trivet, **Ornate Design**, Brass, English, 11 1/2 In.Long, 4 1/2 In.Wide 19.50
Trivet, **Rope Border**, Center Says Ives & Allen, Montreal, Iron 15.00
Trivet, **Rose Design**, Green, Mark Bonn Germany 6.50
Trivet, **San Francisco**, California, Marked S.E.A.Co., Iron 9.00
Trivet, **Soapstone**, Flat, Iron Shape 3.00
Trivet, **Spiderweb**, Iron, No.90 .... 3.95
Trivet, **Target**, Handle, Iron .... 4.95 To 5.95
Trivet, **Two Children**, Donkey, Chickens, Enamel, Porcelain, French, 5 1/2 In. 65.00
Trivet, **Two Hearts**, Iron 15.00
Trivet, **Vulcan**, Iron, H-121 .... 4.95
Trivet, **Waffle**, Oblong, Iron 4.75
Trivet, **Want U Comfort**, Iron, H-148 .... 4.95
Trivet, **Wrought Iron**, Folding Handle, Rack At End, Engraved 60.00
Trivet, **Wrought Iron**, Wooden Handle 24.00
Trunk, **Doll's**, Camelback, Pine, Lined With Blue Paisley, 10 In.High 39.00
Trunk, **Doll's**, Dome Top, Embossed, Tin 28.00
Trunk, **Doll's**, Drawers, Hangers, Travel Labels, Lining 10.50
Trunk, **Doll's**, Ivory, Hand-Carved, C.1812, 3 In.Long, 2 In.High 45.00
Trunk, **Doll's**, Lithograph Scene, Says Little Favorite, 1870, Pine 28.00
Trunk, **Doll's**, Pine, Dome Top, 14 In. 35.00
Trunk, **Dome Top**, Pine, Lock, 8 X 12 In. 25.00
Trunk, **Dome Top**, Wood, Leather, N.Y., C.1820 .... *Illus* 275.00
Trunk, **Leather**, Painted, Coffered Lid, Handles, Chinoiseries In Gold, Red 225.00
Trunk, **Miniature**, Wooden, Leather, Brass Handle, C.1800, 6 X 11 X 5 In. 22.50
Tucker, **Cup & Saucer**, Floral, Circa 1820 .... 135.00
Tucker, **Teapot**, Floral Band, 8 3/4 In.High 240.00
Typewriter, **Blickensderfer** .... *Illus* 25.00

Trunk, Dome Top, Wood, Leather, N.Y., C.1820
See Page 609

Typewriter, Blickensderfer
See Page 609

Val St.Lambert, Vase, Acid Cut Back, Lavender On Clear
See Page 611

Typewriter, Blickensderfer, Stamford, Conn., Original Wooden Case	95.00
Typewriter, Corona, Folding	20.00
Typewriter, Corona, Portable, No.3	9.00
Typewriter, Crandall, Pearl Inlaid	50.00
Typewriter, Franklin, 1891	25.00
Typewriter, Hammond, 60 Years Old	15.00
Typewriter, Oliver, 1912	15.00
Typewriter, Remington, Portable, Case	25.00
Typewriter, Remington, Smith Premier, Model 10-A	75.00
Typewriter, Rex M, American Model, 20th Century	20.00
Typewriter, Smith Premier	12.00
Umbrella, Handle, Gold Filled, Mother-Of-Pearl, Etched, 1914	10.00
Umbrella, Handle, Porcelain, Blue, Hand-Painted, Transfer, Floral, Figures	22.50
Umbrella, Parasol, Child's, Rosebud Cotton Print, Blue Ruffles	3.00
Umbrella, Parasol, Silk, Black, Lady's	7.50
Umbrella, Nautical, George Washington & Eagle, Brass Fittings, C.1840	29.50

Val St.Lambert Cristalleries of Belgium was founded by MESSIEURS   Val St Lambert
Kemlin and Lelievre in 1825. The company is still in operation.

Val St.Lambert, Bowl, Clear, Open Handles	9.00
Val St.Lambert, Box, Cameo, Cranberry Cut To White, Floral Festoons, Lid	63.00
Val St.Lambert, Box, Green, Signed, Cover, 2 X 3 In.	24.00
Val St.Lambert, Box, Powder, Cameo, Cranberry	85.00
Val St.Lambert, Candelabra, 3-Light, Facet Cut, Clear, Signed, Pair	55.00
Val St.Lambert, Centerpiece, Shell Shape, 2 Geometric Handles, Green, C.1930	40.00
Val St.Lambert, Dish, Clear, Octagon, Shallow, 3 1/2 In., Set Of 4 In Box	15.00
Val St.Lambert, Perfume, Acid Cut & Frosted Ground, Cranberry Cut Floral	45.00
Val St.Lambert, Perfume, Cameo, Cranberry, Cut Glass Stopper, Signed	85.00

Val St.Lambert, Perfume, Cut & Frosted, Cranberry Floral, Jeweled Stopper 65.00
Val St.Lambert, Perfume, Flowers, Cranberry, Frosted, Signed, 6 In. 45.00
Val St.Lambert, Plate, Game Bird Center, Frosted, Marked, 8 In.Diameter 22.50
Val St.Lambert, Plate, Pilgrim Fathers, 1969 .... 200.00
Val St.Lambert, Vase, Acid Cut Back, Lavender On Clear .... *Illus* 500.00
Val St.Lambert, Vase, Brown Frieze Of Apple Blossoms & Berries On Green 110.00
Val St.Lambert, Vase, Cameo, Carved Cranberry, Green Scroll Grround, 1873 .... 85.00
Val St.Lambert, Vase, Cameo, Frosted, Purple Scene, Mountains, Water, Tree 145.00
Val St.Lambert, Vase, Squat, Lavender Blossoms In Pale Lavender, Signed 275.00
Val St.Lambert, Vase, Two Colors 250.00
Vallerystahl, Bowl & Plate, Hexagon, Aqua, Stippled Floral, Signed 42.50
Vallerystahl, Dish, Elephant & Rider Cover, White, Milk Glass 100.00
Vallerystahl, Dish, Rabbit On Egg Cover, Oval Base, Milk Glass, Stippled 27.50
Vallerystahl, Dish, Setter Dog Cover, Signed, Milk Glass .... 55.00 To 95.00
Vallerystahl, Eggcup, Opaque, Marked 8.50
Vallerystahl, Salt, Hen On Nest, Amber 15.00
Vallerystahl, Sherbet, Underplate, Gold Star Border, Fiery Blue, Opalescent 35.00

*Van Briggle Pottery was made by Artus Van Briggle in Colorado
Springs, Colorado, after 1901. Mr.Van Briggle had been a decorator at
the Rockwood Pottery of Cincinnati, Ohio, and he died in 1904. His
wares were original and had modeled relief decorations with a soft dull glaze.*

Van Briggle, Bookend & Ashtray Combination, Indian Chief Shape, Blue, Pair 50.00
Van Briggle, Bookend, Peacock Design, Aqua, Pair 12.50
Van Briggle, Bowl, Art Nouveau, Turquoise, Acorns, Leaves, Dated 1920 .... 30.00
Van Briggle, Bowl, Flower Holder, Pair Candlesticks, Blue Matte Glaze 65.00
Van Briggle, Bowl, Frog, Blue Shades 10.00
Van Briggle, Bowl, Glossy Rust, Stylized Tulip, Relief Pattern, 4 In. 16.00
Van Briggle, Bowl, Turquoise Ground, Raised Tulip Pattern, 8 1/2 In. 10.00
Van Briggle, Bowl, Wine Shades, Acorns, 6 In. 17.50
Van Briggle, Candleholder, Double, Number 37 On Bottom 14.00
Van Briggle, Candleholder, Tulip Decoration, Green Shading, Dated '35, Pair 10.00
Van Briggle, Candleholder, Tulips, Shaded Green, Pair 15.00
Van Briggle, Candleholder, Turquoise, Signed, 2 Candle, Pair 35.00
Van Briggle, Candlestick, Double, Blue, Pair 20.00
Van Briggle, Candlestick, Double, Purplish, Signed, Pair 12.50
Van Briggle, Console Set, Deep Rose With Blue, Duck On Frog, Oval Bowl 32.50
Van Briggle, Cup & Saucer, Demitasse, Blue 15.00
Van Briggle, Ewer, Rose Shades, Signed, 8 3/4 In. 20.00
Van Briggle, Figurine, Fawn, Raspberry, Signed, 4 In.High 16.00
Van Briggle, Flower Frog, Turtle Crawls Over Rock, Green Blue, 14 Hole 15.00
Van Briggle, Lamp, Figural, Dog, 9 In.High 30.00
Van Briggle, Lamp, Light Blue, Shade, Electric 27.50
Van Briggle, Mug, Signed Anna 45.00
Van Briggle, Planter, Blue Shell 12.00
Van Briggle, Plate, Five Long Neck Birds Spirling Into Three Webbed Feet 45.00
Van Briggle, Rose Bowl, Blue To Green, Scalloped, Footed, Signed 16.50
Van Briggle, Rose Bowl, Rose Color, Footed 20.00
Van Briggle, Seashell, Plum Color 25.00
Van Briggle, Seashell, Wine & Blue, 8 1/2 In.Long 17.50
Van Briggle, Sugar & Creamer, Shaded Green 12.00
Van Briggle, Vase & Bowl, White Matte, Tan Gloss Inside, Dated 1905 .... 65.00
Van Briggle, Vase, Aqua, Conch Shape, 3 1/2 In.High 16.00
Van Briggle, Vase, Blue Shading, Signed, 3 In. 16.50
Van Briggle, Vase, Blue To Green, 7 In. High 8.00
Van Briggle, Vase, Bud, Dark Rose, Dated 1924, 6 In.High 8.00
Van Briggle, Vase, Butterfly, Signed, 3 In. 7.50
Van Briggle, Vase, Embossed Dragonflies, Blue Green, 7 In. 10.00
Van Briggle, Vase, Hat Shape, Turned In Brim, Aqua, Blue Drippings, 6 1/2 In. 15.00
Van Briggle, Vase, Maroon, Blue, Indian Faces At Top 75.00
Van Briggle, Vase, Maroon, Green, 2 1/2 In. 8.00
Van Briggle, Vase, Persian Rose, Embossed Leaves & Floral, 4 1/2 In.High 12.00
Van Briggle, Vase, Persian Rose, 3 In. 10.00
Van Briggle, Vase, Shaded Turquoise, Bulbous, Marked Original, 4 1/2 In. 10.00
Van Briggle, Vase, Three Faces, Signed 35.00
Van Briggle, Vase, Turquoise, Matte, Embossed Flower, 4 In.High, Pair 20.00

Van Briggle, Vase, Wall, Turquoise, Bow Shape 37.50
Van Ruyckevelt, Figurine, Colonel Of The Noble Guard 750.00
Van Ruyckevelt, Figurine, Passion Flower 950.00

*Vasa Murrhina is the name of a glassware made by the Vasa Murrhina
Art Glass Company of Sandwich, Massachusetts, about 1884. The
glassware was transparent and was embedded with small pieces of colored glass
and metallic flakes. Some of the pieces were cased. The same type of glass
was made in England. Collectors often confuse Vasa Murrhina Glass
with Aventurine, Spatter, or Spangle Glass. There is much confusion
about what actually was made by the Vasa Murrhina Factory.*

Vasa Murrhina, Base, Bud, Yellow, Mica Dust, Swirled Brown Bands 30.00
Vasa Murrhina, Basket, Cranberry, Overlay, Red On White, Silver Specks 100.00
Vasa Murrhina, Basket, Thorn Handle 48.00
Vasa Murrhina, Bride's Basket, Blue, Silver Mica Threads, Bronze Holder 125.00
Vasa Murrhina, Bride's Basket, Rose To White, Enamel Floral, Silver Holder 115.00
Vasa Murrhina, Dish, Tricornered, Deep Ground Pontil 70.00
Vasa Murrhina, Lamp, Amber & White Spatters, Silver Mica, Swirl Amber Shade 55.00
Vasa Murrhina, Pitcher, Milk, White, Pink, Green Swirls, Green Mica, Cased 28.00
Vasa Murrhina, Pitcher, Water, Amber, Mica, Forget-Me-Nots, Amber Handle 225.00
Vasa Murrhina, Rose Bowl, Gold, Gold Mica, White Lining 65.00
Vasa Murrhina, Tumbler, Blue & White Spatters, Silver Mica 23.00
Vasa Murrhina, Vase, Bud, Yellow, Gold Mica Dust, Swirled Bands, 2 1/4 In. 35.00
Vasa Murrhina, Vase, Bud, 5 1/4 In. 17.50
Vasa Murrhina, Vase, Burgundy, White Spatter, Amber Cased, Mica, 8 In.High 90.00
Vasa Murrhina, Vase, Cranberry, Allover Silver Mica, Applied Leaves & Feet 55.00
Vasa Murrhina, Vase, Cranberry, Cylinder Shape 55.00
Vasa Murrhina, Vase, Cranberry, Gold Mica, Swirled, 9 In.High 48.00
Vasa Murrhina, Vase, Jack-In-Th-Pulpit, Apricot, Bulbous, 5 In.Tall 42.00
Vasa Murrhina, Vase, Jack-In-The-Pulpit, Apricot, Ruffled, White Base 45.00
Vasa Murrhina, Vase, Maroon & White Spatter, Mica Flakes, Amber Casing, Pair 65.00
Vasa Murrhina, Vase, Multicolor, Cased, 7 In. 40.00
Vasa Murrhina, Vase, Orange, Gold Fleck, Cased, Hexagon, 4 1/2 In. 38.00
Vasa Murrhina, Vase, Pink Cased, Silver Mica, White Lining, Crystal Petals 55.00
Vasa Murrhina, Vase, Pink, Maroon, Yellow Spatter, Mica Flakes, 12 In., Pair 95.00
Vasa Murrhina, Vase, White Ground, Blue, Pink, Amber, Flecked White Lining 40.00
Vasa Murrhina, Vase, White, Gold Flecks, Cranberry Swirl, Pair 200.00

*Vasart is the signature used on a late type of art glass made by the
Streathearn Glass Company of Scotland.*

Vasart, Basket, Cloudy White, Blue Rim, Signed 35.00
Vasart, Basket, Smoky Blue To Yellow, Twisted Handle 20.00
Vasart, Basket, Smoky Blue & Yellow, Loop Handle 15.00
Vasart, Bowl, Pink Body, Green Rim, Open Handles, 6 In. 30.00
Vasart, Box, Jewel, Crimson Pink Mottle, Cover, Unsigned 35.00
Vasart, Dish, Lavender To Opaque White, Ruffled, Signed, 5 In. 22.50
Vasart, Vase, Gray, Multicolor Splotches Turning To Pink At Top, Label 35.00
Vasart, Vase, Pale Yellow To Pink, Bulbous, Flared, 8 In. 60.00
Vasart, Vase, Scalloped Top, Grayish White, Pinkish Top 35.00

*Vaseline Glass is a greenish yellow glassware resembling petroleum jelly.
Some Vaseline Glass is still being made in old and new styles. Pressed
Glass of the 1870s was often made of vaseline-colored glass. The old glass
was made with uranium, but the reproductions are being colored in a different
way. See Pressed Glass for more information about patterns that were also
made of vaseline-colored glass.*

Vaseline Glass, Basket, Cactus, Twist Handle 59.00
Vaseline Glass, Basket, Floral, Silver Plate Holder 28.00
Vaseline Glass, Basket, Opalescent Stripe, Applied Floral, Twisted Handle 70.00
Vaseline Glass, Basket, Opalescent Swirl, Miniature, Thorn Handle 60.00
Vaseline Glass, Bottle, Captain Type, Ground Bottom, Hand Blown 65.00
Vaseline Glass, Bowl, Berry, Iris In Meander, Opalescent 45.00
Vaseline Glass, Bowl, Berry, Opalescent, Fluted, Scrolls 32.50
Vaseline Glass, Bowl, Cracker, Three Panels, Button Band, Pedestal 33.50
Vaseline Glass, Bowl, Curved In Top, Satinized Finish, Bulbous, 9 1/2 In. 48.00
Vaseline Glass, Bowl, Daisy & Button, Plain Paneled Corners, Square 18.00

Vaseline Glass, Bowl, Daisy & Button, 6 In.Diameter 12.00
Vaseline Glass, Bowl, Fluted Rim, Footed, 7 1/2 In. 32.00
Vaseline Glass, Bowl, Hobnail, Ruffled Rim 25.00
Vaseline Glass, Bowl, Maple Leaf, Oval, Footed 25.00
Vaseline Glass, Bowl, Ribbed Spiral, Opalescent, Flared, 7 In.Diameter 18.75
Vaseline Glass, Butter, Covered, Opalescent, Wreathed Shell 55.00
Vaseline Glass, Butter, Fish Shaped Cover ...: 45.00
Vaseline Glass, Butter, Maple Leaf, Oval, Covered, Tree Bark Feet 49.50
Vaseline Glass, Butter, Opalescent, Floral Pattern, Footed, Flower Finial 85.00
Vaseline Glass, Butter, Panels, Gold Band Trim, Knob Finial On Cover 36.00
Vaseline Glass, Cake Stand, Cathedral 52.00
Vaseline Glass, Candleholder, Opalescent, 2 1/2 In.High 45.00
Vaseline Glass, Castor, Pickle, Daisy & Button 115.00
Vaseline Glass, Celery, Daisy & Button 19.50
Vaseline Glass, Celery, Daisy & Button With V Ornament 40.00
Vaseline Glass, Celery, Sunken Buttons 28.00
Vaseline Glass, Celery, Two Panel 37.50
Vaseline Glass, Clock, Mantle, Daisy & Button, 14 X 4 In.Wide 75.00
Vaseline Glass, Compote, Candy, Swag With Brackets, Opalescent 30.00
Vaseline Glass, Compote, Covered, Engraved Flower & Ribbon Design 45.00
Vaseline Glass, Compote, Daisy & Button, Panels, Footed, 11 X 7 In.High 57.50
Vaseline Glass, Compote, Diamond Quilt 17.00
Vaseline Glass, Compote, Nine Deep Scallops, Knob Stem 75.00
Vaseline Glass, Compote, Rose Sprig Pattern, Tall Standard 35.00
Vaseline Glass, Compote, Seashell Design, Opalescent, Rolled Edge, Footed 42.00
Vaseline Glass, Compote, Swag & Bracket, Opalescent Scalloped Edge 32.00
Vaseline Glass, Compote, Three Panel, Low 22.00
Vaseline Glass, Compote, 16 Beaded Panels, Scalloped Edge, Knobbed Stem 48.50
Vaseline Glass, Console Set, 7 In.Candlesticks 59.00
Vaseline Glass, Creamer, Alaska 47.00
Vaseline Glass, Creamer, Opalescent, Fluted, Scrolls 32.50
Vaseline Glass, Cruet, Panels, Gold Band Trim, Faceted Stopper 48.50
Vaseline Glass, Cruet, Ribbed, Applied Clear Handle, Blown 48.50
Vaseline Glass, Cruet, Swirl 12.00
Vaseline Glass, Cup, Miniature, Enameled Floral, Applied Handle 40.00
Vaseline Glass, Decanter, Wine, Resilvered Cap & Base 40.00
Vaseline Glass, Dish, Candy, Opalescent, Fluted Scrolls, Footed 17.50
Vaseline Glass, Dish, Doughnut, Center Post, Blue Decoration 20.00
Vaseline Glass, Dish, Stick, Stretched, 5 In. 7.00
Vaseline Glass, Epergne, Lily, Thorn, Leaves, Ruffled Bowl, 17 In.Tall 125.00
Vaseline Glass, Goblet, Daisy & Button With Crossbar 22.00
Vaseline Glass, Goblet, Daisy & Button With Panel, Opalescent Top 16.50
Vaseline Glass, Goblet, Fine Cut .... *Illus* 20.00
Vaseline Glass, Goblet, Mitered Diamond 22.50
Vaseline Glass, Goblet, Oval Panels 22.00
Vaseline Glass, Goblet, Tegman's Inverted Thumbprint 17.50

Vaseline Glass, Goblet, Fine Cut

Vaseline Glass, Goblet, Two Panels	22.50
Vaseline Glass, Goblet, Wildflower, Opalescent Rim	22.50
Vaseline Glass, Gum Stand, Teaberry, Signed	15.00 To 18.75
Vaseline Glass, Hat, Daisy & Button, 5 In.High	65.00
Vaseline Glass, Jar, Jam, Plaid, Silver Plate Lid	32.00
Vaseline Glass, Mug, Chicks, Dogs, Grass, Embossed	22.50
Vaseline Glass, Mug, Daisy & Button	24.00
Vaseline Glass, Mug, Jewel & Dewdrop	16.50
Vaseline Glass, Paperweight, Hatchet, Raised Indian Head	9.50
Vaseline Glass, Pitcher, Amber Handle, 8 In.High	30.00
Vaseline Glass, Pitcher, Canary, Copper Luster & Green Raised Leaves, Fruit	50.00
Vaseline Glass, Pitcher, Cobalt Threading Around Rim & Neck, Cobalt Handle	30.00
Vaseline Glass, Pitcher, Water, Daisy & Button With Crossbar	55.00
Vaseline Glass, Pitcher, Water, Honeycomb Pattern	39.50
Vaseline Glass, Pitcher, Water, Two Panels	45.00
Vaseline Glass, Pitcher, 8 1/2 In.	74.00
Vaseline Glass, Plate, Bread, Daisy & Button, Open Handles	40.00
Vaseline Glass, Plate, Bread, Garfield Memorial	40.00
Vaseline Glass, Plate, Bread, Grant Memorial	40.00
Vaseline Glass, Plate, Cake, High Standard, Molded Heavy Pedestal	49.50
Vaseline Glass, Plate, Grant, Peace	35.00
Vaseline Glass, Plate, Maple Leaf, 11 In.Diameter	27.00 To 35.00
Vaseline Glass, Plate, Octagonal	4.00
Vaseline Glass, Plate, Stretch, 8 In., Pair	15.00
Vaseline Glass, Plate, Wildflower, Square, 9 3/4 In.	16.00
Vaseline Glass, Platter, Deer & Pine Pattern, 13 In.	38.50
Vaseline Glass, Platter, Maple Leaf, Oval	30.00
Vaseline Glass, Relish, Daisy & Button With Crossbar	17.50
Vaseline Glass, Relish, Dewey	25.00
Vaseline Glass, Relish, Open Rose	27.00
Vaseline Glass, Rose Bowl, Diamond-Quilted, Scalloped Top	25.00
Vaseline Glass, Rose Bowl, Opaline Stripes, Green Edge	55.00
Vaseline Glass, Rose Bowl, White Spatters	44.00
Vaseline Glass, Salt & Pepper, Cactus	25.00
Vaseline Glass, Salt Dip	6.50
Vaseline Glass, Salt Dip, Opalescent, Footed, English, Pair	35.00
Vaseline Glass, Salt Dip, Ribbed, Opalescent Crimped Waist Band	17.50
Vaseline Glass, Salt, Master, Valencia Waffle	16.00
Vaseline Glass, Salt, Opalescent, Oval, Footed, Circa 1865, Pair	35.00
Vaseline Glass, Salt, Oval, Two Panel	7.50
Vaseline Glass, Sauce, Alaska Pattern, Opalescent	25.00
Vaseline Glass, Sauce, Daisy & Button	9.00 To 11.50
Vaseline Glass, Sauce, Daisy & Button With Thumbprint, Footed	10.00
Vaseline Glass, Sauce, Daisy & Button, Paneled	13.00
Vaseline Glass, Shoe, Daisy & Button, Eyelets, Patent Oct.1886	31.50
Vaseline Glass, Shoe, Daisy & Button, Oxford, Dated Oct.19, 1886, Pair	55.00
Vaseline Glass, Spill, Double Elongated Ovals, Footed, Ground Pontil	50.00
Vaseline Glass, Spooner, Beaded, Double Handles	25.00
Vaseline Glass, Spooner, Diamond-Quilted	27.50
Vaseline Glass, Spooner, Inverted Thumbprint With Rope Band	18.50
Vaseline Glass, Spooner, Wild Flower	17.50
Vaseline Glass, Spooner, Wreathed Shell, Footed, Opalescent	32.00
Vaseline Glass, Sugar & Creamer, Cover, Palm Beach, Opalescent	75.00
Vaseline Glass, Sugar & Creamer, Miniature, Sugar 1 In., Creamer 2 In.High	27.50
Vaseline Glass, Sugar, Cover, Log Cabin	145.00
Vaseline Glass, Sugar, Open, Alaskan, Opalescent	28.00
Vaseline Glass, Syrup, Baby Inverted Thumbprint	46.00
Vaseline Glass, Syrup, Raindrop, Pewter Lid, Dated 1872, 9 In.Tall	29.00
Vaseline Glass, Syrup, Removable Cover, Plate	21.50
Vaseline Glass, Toothpick, Daisy & Button, Hat Shape	9.50 To 25.00
Vaseline Glass, Toothpick, Opalescent, Crimped Top, Three Handles	45.00
Vaseline Glass, Toothpick, 1, 000-Eye	19.00
Vaseline Glass, Tray, Jewel, Opalescent, Alaska, Northwood	35.00
Vaseline Glass, Tray, Water, Basket Weave, Scenic Center	30.00
Vaseline Glass, Tray, Water, Cloverleaf	45.00
Vaseline Glass, Tray, Water, Daisy & Button, Triangular, 2 Tab Handles	29.50

Vaseline Glass, Tray, Water, Daisy & Button, 11 1/4 In.Round 36.00
Vaseline Glass, Tumbler, Daisy & Button 14.00
Vaseline Glass, Tumbler, Daisy & Button With Crossbar 28.00
Vaseline Glass, Tumbler, Daisy & Button, Wide Margin 18.00
Vaseline Glass, Tumbler, Hobnail 22.00
Vaseline Glass, Tumbler, Opalescent Northwood 28.00
Vaseline Glass, Tumbler, Windflower 25.00
Vaseline Glass, Vase, Bigler Pattern, Scalloped Top, 9 1/2 In., Pair 475.00
Vaseline Glass, Vase, Celery, Opalescent, Panels, Flared Top, 7 In. 35.00
Vaseline Glass, Vase, Flute, Etched Chrysanthemums 19.50
Vaseline Glass, Vase, Four Mold, Urn Shape, Beaded Design, Scalloped 25.00
Vaseline Glass, Vase, Hobnail, Opaline Edge, Fluted, 5 1/2 In.High 55.00
Vaseline Glass, Vase, Opalescent, Fluted, Ruffled Edge, Bulbous, 5 In. 24.00
Vaseline Glass, Vase, Swirl Opalescent, Pinched Ruffle Top, Fiery, 10 In. 20.00
Vaseline Glass, Vase, Trumpet, Blown 12.50
Vaseline Glass, Wine, Diamond-Quilted 18.00
Vaseline Glass, Wine, Diamond-Quilted, Canary 17.00
Vaseline Glass, Wine, Inverted Thumbprint 14.50
Vaseline Glass, Wine, Two Panel 19.50

*Venetian Glass has been made near Venice, Italy, from the thirteenth to
the twentieth century. Thin, colored glass with applied decorations is favored
although many other types have been made.*
Venetian Glass, Bottle, Water, Emerald Green, Gold, Tumbler And Tray 135.00
Venetian Glass, Bowl, Applied Threads, Red, White, 19th Century, 11 In. 130.00
Venetian Glass, Bowl, Latticinio, White Twists, Goldstone 45.00
Venetian Glass, Bowl, Rose Color, Swirls, Ruffled, Footed, 9 1/2 In. 25.00
Venetian Glass, Candlestick, Gold Flecked Crystal, Blue Rims 15.00
Venetian Glass, Candlestick, Green, Gold Flecked, Low, Pair 12.00
Venetian Glass, Candlestick, Hollow Stem, Blue Jade Ball, Prunts, Signed 120.00
Venetian Glass, Candlestick, Turquoise, Gold Flecks, Swirl Stem, 5 In., Pair 28.00
Venetian Glass, Compote, Blue, Threaded With Hollow Stem, Signed 85.00
Venetian Glass, Cruet, Enameled Floral, Pink Rose Stopper 21.50
Venetian Glass, Decanter, Multicolored Jeweled, Snake Handle, Five Glasses 200.00
Venetian Glass, Dish, Candy, Flower Center, Ruffled Edge, Brass Wire Holder 13.50
Venetian Glass, Jar, Candy, Enamel Roses, Leaves, Ribs, Gold Trim, Finial 16.00
Venetian Glass, Jar, Candy, Enameled Pink Roses, Purple Floral, Finial 22.50
Venetian Glass, Paperweight, Red & White Rods, White Filigree, Goldstone 90.00
Venetian Glass, Perfume, Square, White Latticinio, Goldstone Panels 35.00
Venetian Glass, Rose Bowl, Allover Enameled Floral, Pleated Top 24.50
Venetian Glass, Swan, Blown 25.00
Venetian Glass, Urn, Covered, Rear Finial, Amber, 10 In., Signed 125.00
Venetian Glass, Vase, Blue, Ruffled Edge, Blown, White Lilies-Of-The-Valley 12.00
Venetian Glass, Vase, Bud, Swan Stem, Blown, Opalescent 20.00
Venetian Glass, Vase, Coin Gold Motif, Blue & White Floral, Pedestal Base 85.00
Venetian Glass, Vase, Mustard Ground, Paperweight Millefiori Inlaid 150
Venetian Glass, Vase, Pink To Red Top, Fluted, 11 In., Pair 5
Venetian Glass, Vase, Winged Serpent, Applied Red Tongue, Cornucopia Holder ....

*Verlys Glass was made in France after 1931. Verlys was also made in the
United States. The glass is either blown or molded. The American
glass is signed with a diamond-point-scratched name, but the French pieces
marked with a molded signature.*
Verlys, Bowl, Amber Color, Octagon Base, Signed, 1o In. ....
Verlys, Bowl, Butterfly, Frosted, Signed ....
Verlys, Bowl, Dragonflies, Wild Roses, Frosted, 13 1/2 In.Diameter ....
Verlys, Bowl, Dusty Rose, Double Signed ....
Verlys, Bowl, Flying Duck, Fish, Molded Signature, 13 In. ....
Verlys, Bowl, Fruit, Opalescent, Swimming Fish Motif, Signed ....
Verlys, Bowl, Orchid, Crystal, Etched, Signed ....
Verlys, Bowl, Pinecone, Footed, Molded Signature ....
Verlys, Bowl, Pinecone, Script Signed ....
Verlys, Bowl, Poppies, Frosted, Signed ....
Verlys, Bowl, Stems Of 6 Stylized Thistles In Relief, Script Signat'
Verlys, Bowl, Thistle, Frosted, Signed ....
Verlys, Bowl, Thistle, Topaz, Signed ....

Verlys, Bowl, Water Lilies, Crystal, Etched, Signed	90.00
Verlys, Bowl, Wild Ducks, Blue Satin, Signed	275.00
Verlys, Bowl, Wild Ducks, Clear Satin With Blue Cast, France	275.00
Verlys, Box, Amber, Etched Floral On Lid, Signed, 5 1/4 In.Diameter	65.00
Verlys, Box, Opalescent, Butterflies On Lid, 2 X 6 1/2 In.Diameter	89.50
Verlys, Candlestick, Frosted Leaves, Signed, Pair	25.00
Verlys, Centerpiece, Pheasant, Green Topaz, Signed, France, 18 In.Long	400.00
Verlys, Figurine, Mary & Her Lamb, Artist Signed & Dated	275.00
Verlys, Plaque, Three Fish, 10 In.Diameter	90.00
Verlys, Plate, Flowers, Frosted, Concave, Signed, 14 In.Diameter	95.00
Verlys, Tray, Buffet, Crystal, Leaves Pattern, Etched, 15 In.Diameter	45.00
Verlys, Vase, Fan Shape, Frosted Lovebirds, Signed In Script, 4 1/2 In.	75.00
Verlys, Vase, Frosted Blue, Butterflies, Signed, 5 In.High	75.00
Verlys, Vase, Frosted Figures, Winter, Spring, Summer, Fall, Carl Schmitz, Pair	145.00
Verlys, Vase, Frosted Ground, Large Clear Berries, Signed, 6 In.	55.00
Verlys, Vase, Gems Pattern, Inverted Bell Shape, 6 In.	60.00 To 65.00
Verlys, Vase, Gems Pattern, Signed, 6 1/2 In.High	52.00
Verlys, Vase, Lance, Crystal, Etched, Signed	75.00
Verlys, Vase, Lovebirds, Signed, 4 1/2 In.	37.50
Verlys, Vase, Mandarin, Signed	175.00
Verlys, Vase, Oriental Scene, Floral, 8 1/4 In.High	175.00

*Verre De Soie Glass was first made by Frederick Carder at the
Steuben Glass Works from about 1905 to 1930. It is an iridescent glass
of soft white or very, very pale green. The name means glass of silk, and it
does resemble silk. Other factories have made Verre De Soie, and some of
the English examples were made of different colors. Verre De Soie is an
art glass and is not related to the iridescent pressed white carnival glass
mistakenly called by its name.*

Verre De Soie, see also Steuben

Verre De Soie, Basket, Ribbed, Double Rope Handle, Flower On Handle, 9 In.	95.00
Verre De Soie, Bottle, Hand Lotion, Pink Flower Stopper, Steuben	35.00
Verre De Soie, Bowl & Underplate, Finger, Chartreuse, White Loopings	78.00
Verre De Soie, Bowl & Underplate, Finger, Protruding Ribs	38.00
Verre De Soie, Bowl, Flower, Gold Metal Rim & Frog, Ripple Pattern	48.00
Verre De Soie, Candlestick, Low, Cranberry Threading, Steuben, Signed	85.00
Verre De Soie, Goblet, Pedestal Stem, Steuben, 6 1/4 In.	21.00
Verre De Soie, Lamp, Enameled Birds On Shade, Amber Rim & Base, Handles	185.00
Verre De Soie, Perfume, Ball Shape, Flat At Base, Cerise Ruby Stopper	145.00
Verre De Soie, Perfume, Inverted Cone Shape, Celeste Blue Stopper	145.00
Verre De Soie, Perfume, Melon Rib, Flame Stopper, Steuben, 4 1/2 In.	85.00
Verre De Soie, Perfume, Melon Rib, Flame Stopper, Steuben, 7 In.	100.00
Verre De Soie, Perfume, Melon Rib, Green Jade Stopper, Steuben	125.00
Verre De Soie, Perfume, Melon Rib, Green, Steeple Stopper, Steuben, Label	125.00
erre De Soie, Perfume, Melon Shape, Blue Flame Stopper, Steuben	50.00
re De Soie, Perfume, Rosaline Stopper	165.00
e De Soie, Pitcher, Water, Iridescent, Blown Free Form, 4 Tumblers	125.00
De Soie, Rose Bowl, Diamond Pattern, Unsigned, 3 1/4 X 2 1/2 In.High	35.00
e Soie, Salt, Pedestal, Steuben	70.00
Soie, Sherbet & Underplate, Steuben	35.00
oie, Tumble-Up, Cobalt Blue Handle	150.00
ie, Tumbler, Blue, Elongated Herringbone Type Air Traps	45.00
Tumbler, Iced Tea, Engraved Floral, Bows, Steuben, Hawkes	38.00
Vase, Applied Cherries, 10 In.	60.00
se, Atomic Cloud, Iridescent, 6 X 3 1/2 In.High	68.00
e, Bowl, Nipped In Waist, Fluted Rim, Dimpled Sides	35.00
Jack-In-The-Pulpit, Twisted Stem, Turnback Top, Pair	120.00
Steuben, 12 In.	135.00
ick, Hawkes Flower Design, Iridescent, 8 In.	70.00
/4 In.High	75.00
Busch, Lady With Rose In Hair, 1905, Wagner	50.00
1907, Harvard Brewing Co.	75.00
Lodge Reunion, Phila., July 1907, Handled, Tin	12.00
Cupids, 10 In.	12.00 To 16.00
illary, Louisville, Ky., 1905	65.00
er, 1905	35.00

Vienna Art, Plate, Tin, Girls' Faces, 1908 .... 25.00

*Vieux Paris, or Old Paris, are porcelain wares that are known to have
been made in Paris in the eighteenth or early nineteenth century but have
no identifying manufacturer's mark.*
Vieux Paris, Bottle, Toilet, White & Gold, U.S.Ships, Quadrangular, 1850, Pair 200.00

*Villeroy & Boch Pottery of Mettlach, Germany, was founded in 1841.
The firm made many types of pottery, including the famous Mettlach Steins.*
Villeroy & Boch, see also Stein
Villeroy & Boch, Bowl, Signed Villeroy Boch Dresden, Germany, 1900 .... 85.00
Villeroy & Boch, Bowl, Stylized Geometric Border, Blue Ground, Art Nouveau 25.00
Villeroy & Boch, Candlestick, Art Nouveau, Castle Mark 24.00
Villeroy & Boch, Creamer, Dresden Saxony No.6802 .... 18.00
Villeroy & Boch, Jar, Tobacco, Mottled, Soft Colors, Signed 24.00
Villeroy & Boch, Mold, Fish, White & Brown, 7 X 8 In. 30.00
Villeroy & Boch, Plaque, Wall, Blue & White Castle Scene, Signed Wartburg 300.00
Villeroy & Boch, Plaque, Windmill, Lake, Ships, Birds, Blue, 10 1/2 In. 55.00
Villeroy & Boch, Plate, Cottage Scene, Blue On White, Wallerfanger, 8 In. 17.50
Villeroy & Boch, Plate, Harvest Scene, Pierced For Hanging, 12 In. 70.00
Villeroy & Boch, Plate, Pastoral, Sheep, Pierced For Hanging, 12 In. 70.00
Villeroy & Boch, Plate, Wallerfangen, 8 1/4 In. 9.00
Villeroy & Boch, Platter, Blue & White Floral, 16 In. 25.00
Villeroy & Boch, Sugar, Dresden Pattern 15.00
Villeroy & Boch, Tile, Blue & White, Delft Style, Water, Boats, Marked 15.00
Villeroy & Boch, Tureen, Napoleon Pattern, White, Green Decoration 20.00
Villeroy & Boch, Tureen, Soup, Blue, White Design, 1 Gallon 55.00
Volkstadt, Figurine, Clown, Sad, Guitar, 13 1/2 In.High 220.00
Volkstadt, Figurine, Prussian Soldier & Drummer Boy, Marked, Pair 110.00
Wallendorf, Compote 350.00

*Warwick China was made in Wheeling, West Virginia, in a pottery factory
founded in 1887.*
Warwick, Mug, Bulldog Decoration 38.00
Warwick, Mug, Ioga, Signed Ch.Rodney Stone, Circa 1887 .... 16.50
Warwick, Plate, Portrait, Queen Louise, 9 1/8 In. 20.00
Warwick, Vase, Ioga, Clover Shape, 3 Legs, Beige To Green, Flowers 35.00

*Watch Fobs were worn on watch chains. They were popular during
Victorian times.*
Watch Fob, Airplane, Car, Motorcycle, No Strap 2.95
Watch Fob, Antique Car, Silver, Leather Strap 10.00
Watch Fob, Blue Enameled Initial, New Strap 3.75
Watch Fob, Blue Ground, Eagle, Initials, No Strap .... 2.50 To 2.75
Watch Fob, Brockway Trucks, No Strap 2.75
Watch Fob, Buick 2.50
Watch Fob, Carnelian, Carved, Openwork Gold Frame, Portrait Of Lady 15.00
Watch Fob, Caterpillar, Strap .... 2.00 To 3.50
Watch Fob, Chicago Exposition, 1893, Keystone Co., Sterling 10.00
Watch Fob, Elk's Tooth, Elk With Red Glass Eyes, Gold Chain 12.50
Watch Fob, Embossed Indian's Head, Wears War Bonnet, Unger Bros., Silver 125.00
Watch Fob, Falion, Strap Type 6.00
Watch Fob, Ford 2.50
Watch Fob, Ford Motor, C.1930 .... 2.50 To 4.25
Watch Fob, Garlock Packing Co., Girl's Head, No Strap 4.75
Watch Fob, Gold Filigree Ball, Three Turquoise Inserts, Rope Chain, Dated 17.50
Watch Fob, Great Seal Of The U.S., No Strap 3.95
Watch Fob, Great Seal Of U.S.In Bronze, Blue & White Porcelain, Strap 2.75
Watch Fob, Hyster, Construction Machine, No Strap 2.75
Watch Fob, International Harvester, Strap Type 3.00
Watch Fob, Knights Of Columbus, Gold 40.00
Watch Fob, Knox Auto 12.75
Watch Fob, Man On Motorcycle, Tin 6.00
Watch Fob, Maxwell Belie 2.50
Watch Fob, Mesh, Gold Filled 22.50
Watch Fob, National Woolen Mills, Brass 12.00

Watch Fob, Nude Lady 4.25
Watch Fob, **Orange Rifle Powder**, Ornate 5.00
Watch Fob, **Packard Tourister** 4.50
Watch Fob, **Rumeley Oil Pull Tractor**, Slogan 15.00
Watch Fob, **Seagram's Marked On Tiny Barrel**, Mesh, Gold Filled 11.00
Watch Fob, **Silver Medallion**, Raised Alligator, Says Florida, Strap 3.50
Watch Fob, **Syracuse Plow Company** 5.95
Watch Fob, **Taft**, Strap 10.00
Watch Fob, **Texaco**, Strap 7.00
Watch Fob, **Town Of Stoughton**, Mass.200th Anniv., 1726-1926, Strap 3.95
Watch Fob, **Vest Pocket Chain Type**, Uncut Seal 12.50
Watch Fob, **Vintage Medallion**, Marked Sterling, Initial 7.00
Watch Fob, **Woodsmen Of The World** 8.50
Watch, **Swiss**, Alice In Wonderland, New Haven Clock & Watch Co., C.1951 .... 25.00
Watch, **American**, Man's, Pocket, Gold Hunting Case, Stem Wind, 15 Jewels 85.00
Watch, **Annie Oakley**, Animated 50.00
Watch, **Bambi**, U.S.Time 50.00
Watch, **Barrand & Lund**, Cornhill, London, 1838, Gold Open Face, White Dial 70.00
Watch, **Book Form**, Silver, Engraved Masks, Foliage, Horsemen 350.00
Watch, **Breguet A Paris**, Gold, Enamel Peacock Feathers, Open Face, C.1800 .... 525.00
Watch, **Breitling**, Navigational Chronograph, Open Face, Chrome, 16 Jewel 75.00
Watch, **Bugs Bunny**, Band 12.00
Watch, **C.H.Meylan**, Chronograph, Open Face, 15K Gold, Seconds 275.00
Watch, **Cabrier**, London, Silver Pair Case, Repeating, Pierced, Chased, C.1730 .... 475.00
Watch, **Calendar**, Hunting Case, Dials On Both Sides, 18K Gold 350.00
Watch, **Calendar**, Open Face, Sweep Second Hand, Silver Engraving, 18 Jewel 120.00
Watch, **Captain Marvel**, White Circular Dial, Captain Marvel Picture, 1948 .... 80.00
Watch, **Centennial**, Says '1776-1876' On Back, 'Centennial' On Dial 60.00
Watch, **Charles Frodsham**, England, Hunting Case, Silver, Chain Driven, C.1860 .... 350.00
Watch, **Chronograph & Stop Watch Combination** 90.00
Watch, **Chronograph**, Open Face, Silver Engraved Case 65.00
Watch, **Cinderella**, U.S.Time, Band 20.00
Watch, **Coach**, Cabrier, London, Silver, Striking, Repeating, Chased, C.1760 .... 2700.00
Watch, **Coin Silver Hunting Case**, Porcelain Face, Perrett Watch Co., Boston 65.00
Watch, **Columbia**, Hunging Case, 7 Jewels 45.00
Watch, **Daisy Duck**, Band, Square 50.00
Watch, **Dechaudens**, Open Face, Key Wind & Set, Engraved, Silver 80.00
Watch, **Doxa**, Open Face, Chiseled Antique Automobile, 15 Jewel 225.00
Watch, **Elgin**, Engraved, Dated 1870, 14K Gold & Black Enamel Slide, Pearl 125.00
Watch, **Elgin**, Hunting Case, Diamond In Center, 18K 125.00
Watch, **Elgin**, Hunting Case, Pocket, 14K Gold Chain, Hardstone 180.00
Watch, **Elgin**, Hunting Case, Ruby In Center, 18K 125.00
Watch, **Elgin**, Hunting Case, 14K Gold, Engraved, 11 Jewel 125.00
Watch, **Elgin**, Hunting Case, 14K Yellow Gold, Engraved, 8 Diamonds, 17 Jewel 275.00
Watch, **Elgin**, Louis XIV, 3 Color, Yellow Gold Filled Case, 15 Jewel 150.00
Watch, **Elgin**, Open Face, Gold Filled 17.50
Watch, **Elgin**, Open Face, Silveroid Bezel, Metal Dial, Gold Filled, Size 16 .... 16.00
Watch, **Elgin**, Open Face, 17 Jewel, Gold Numerals, Engraved Rim, 14K 80.00
Watch, **Elgin**, Pocket, Engraved Gold 48.50
Watch, **Elgin**, Silveroid Open Face, Stem Wind, Size 18 .... 15.00
Watch, **Elgin**, Sterling Silver Case, 7 Jewels 50.00
Watch, **Elgin**, 3 Color Gold Filled Case, 15 Jewel 150.00
Watch, **Ellicot**, London, No.5452, 1764, Pierced, Engraved Mask, Gold Pair Case 1200.00
Watch, **English**, Lady's Fob Watch, Engraved Gold Case, C.1900 .... 105.00
Watch, **English**, Man's, Chronograph, Sterling, Key Wind, Chain, C.1890 .... 75.00
Watch, **English**, Man's, Hallmarked Sterling, Key Wind, Enamel Dial, C.1860 .... 80.00
Watch, **English**, Man's, Pocket, Sterling Case, Key Wind, Chain, C.1855 .... 95.00
Watch, **English**, Man's, Pocket, Sterling Case, Key Wind, Chain, C.1890 .... 75.00
Watch, **Engraved Building In Center Of Floral Wreath**, Nickel Case, Elgin 40.00
Watch, **Engraved Trains On Case & Works**, N.H.W.Co., Chain, Gold 45.00
Watch, **French**, Digital 95.00
Watch, **French**, Empire, Gold & Enamel, Cypher Of Napoleon, C.1810 .... 1300.00
Watch, **French**, Open Face, Plays Quadrille Des Lanciers On Hour, C.1800 .... 2250.00
Watch, **Fromanteel & Clark Calendar**, 1680-1722 .... 400.00
Watch, **Gene Autry**, Animated Pistol 77.50
Watch, **Gene Autry**, Swiss, 'Always Your Pal, Gene Autry, '1948 .... 40.00

Watch, Gilt Metal & Silver, Iron Plates & Serpentine Cock, Chased, C.1600 .... 475.00
Watch, Gold, Automaton, Repeating, Scene Galante, White Enamel, C.1800 .... 3750.00
Watch, Hamilton, Open Face, Arabic Numerals, 21 Jewel, Gold Filled 55.00
Watch, Hamilton, Open Face, Gold Dial, 17 Jewel, Gold Filled 32.00
Watch, Hamilton, Open Face, Gold Filled, Size 12 .... 22.00
Watch, Hampden, John F.Duber On Dial, Gold Filled Hunting Case 55.00
Watch, Hand Engraved Case, Scenic, C.Bornard & Co., Geneva, Circa 1810 .... 275.00
Watch, Hebdomas, Open Face, Visible Balance, 8 Day 55.00
Watch, Henry Capt, Geneva, Gold Hunting Case, Blue Enamel, 19 Jewel, C.1900 .... 170.00
Watch, Hopalong Cassidy, Good Luck From Hoppy, U.S.Time .... 25.00 To 45.00
Watch, Hot Wheels, 2 Race Cars Circle Dial 8.00
Watch, Howdy Doody, Picture Of Howdy Doody, 'say Kids What Time Is It' 12.95
Watch, Hunting Case, E.Howard, Stem Wind 65.00
Watch, Hunting Case, Eagle, Scroll, Plan Watch Co., Coin Silver 25.00
Watch, Hunting Case, Engraved, 15 Jewel, Longines, Nelson & Anderson, 1892 .... 100.00
Watch, Hunting Case, Engraved, 15 Jewel, Waltham 65.00
Watch, Hunting Case, Hand Engraved, Key Wind, National Watch, Elgin, C.1866 .... 250.00
Watch, Hunting Case, Lady's, Gold, Key Wind 155.00
Watch, Hunting Case, Roman Numerals, Key Wind, Circa 1870, Gold Filled 65.00
Watch, Hunting Case, Silver, Porcelain Dial, Roman Numerals 35.00
Watch, Hunting Case, Size 18, Seth Thomas, Gold Filled 75.00
Watch, Hunting Case, Waltham, 14K, 54 In.Chain, Slide, Opals & Pearls 315.00
Watch, Hunting Case, 15 Jewel, Crown Watch Co., Made By Keystone 80.00
Watch, Hunting Case, 15 Jewel, Elgin, Circa 1914 .... 85.00
Watch, Hunting Case, 15 Jewel, 1894, Waltham 65.00
Watch, Illinois, Open Face, 17 Jewel, Porcelain Dial, 14K Gold 37.00
Watch, Illinois, 14K White Gold Case, Gold Numerals & Hands, 21 Jewels 45.00
Watch, J.F.Bautte & Cie, Rue De La Paix, No.8, Paris, Gold, Thin, C.1850 .... 60.00
Watch, J.Fieret, Montpellier, Oval, Silver, Engraved Fruit Baskets, C.1620 .... 4250.00
Watch, J.L.Rey, Geneva, Gilt Metal, Octagonal, Pierced Case 325.00
Watch, John Drawtag, London, Silver Pair Case, Chain, Key, Dutch Verge, 1780 .... 80.00
Watch, John Jones-Wales, Chronograph, Open Face, Silver Case, Chain Driven 90.00
Watch, Key Wind, Cylinder Movement, M.J.Tobias, England, Circa 1859 .... 65.00
Watch, Key Wind, Ernest Duval, Coin Silver 40.00
Watch, Key Wind, Paul Breton, Silver 25.00
Watch, Key Wind, Swiss, Black Enamel, Engraved, Closed Face, 1850, 18K 225.00
Watch, Lady's, Chain & Slide, Gold Filled, Blue Sapphires 23.00
Watch, Lady's, Cross Hatch Engraving, Scene, Flowers, Gold, Hampden, Dueber 150.00
Watch, Lady's, Elgin, Closed Case, Chain, Two Opals, Seed Pearls, Pin 125.00
Watch, Lady's, Hampden, Engraved Case, Slide, Chain, Gold 150.00
Watch, Lady's, Lapel, Enamel Case, Rose Cut Diamonds, Pearls, Fob, C.1800 .... 260.00
Watch, Lady's, Open Face, Engraved Back, Country Scene, Key Wind, 18K 95.00
Watch, Lady's, Pendant, Brass Case, Hand Tooled 19.50
Watch, Lady's, Relief Peacock, Fence, Flowers, Lady Robin, Gold, 1 1/2 In. 195.00
Watch, Lady's, Size 0, Elgin, Hunting Case, Porcelain Dial, Floral, Scrolls 65.00
Watch, Lady's, Size 0, Hunting Case, Engine Turned Ground, Floral Leaf 58.00
Watch, Lady's, Size 0, Waltham, Gold Filled Hunting Case, Engraved Design 55.00
Watch, Lapel, Lady's, French Enamel, Inlaid Gold & Silver Floral, 1 In. 35.00
Watch, Le Roi A Paris, Silver Gilt, Rock Crystal, Octagonal, Engraved 275.00
Watch, Le Roi A Paris, White Enamel Dial, Gilt Metal, C.1760 .... 160.00
Watch, Little Orphan Annie, Round 50.00
Watch, Longines, Open Face, Key Wind & Set, Silver Case, 15 Jewel 75.00
Watch, Louis XV, White Enamel Dial, Stones, Turquoise, 3 Color Gold, 1770 .... 225.00
Watch, M.I.Tobias & Co., Liverpool, Gold Open Face, Chased, Gold Dial, C.1830 .... 250.00
Watch, Man's, Closed, Engraved, New York Standard, 20 Year 60.00
Watch, Man's, Size 16, Open Face, Elgin 60.00
Watch, Man's, Sterling Case, Key Wind, Enamel Dial, 19th Century 60.00
Watch, Mary Marvel, Flying Pose, Fawcett Pub.Inc., 1948 .... 50.00
Watch, Masson A Paris, Gilt Metal, Pierced, Birds & Strapwork, Floral 400.00
Watch, Millogg, Vienna, Silver, 2 Figures Holding Candle On Dial, C.1750 .... 225.00
Watch, N.Y.Standard, Lady's, Gold Filled Hunting Case, Roman Numerals 42.00
Watch, N.Y.Standard, Porcelain Face, Roman Numerals, Engraved Scene, Size 18 .... 20.00
Watch, New York Standard, Worm Drive 300.00
Watch, Open Face, Chinese Duplex, Jump Second Hand, Silver 145.00
Watch, Open Face, New York Standard Chronograph, Silveroid, 7 Jewel 40.00
Watch, Open Face, White Gold Filled 17.50

Watch, **Patek Philippe & Cie**, Geneve, Gold, Split Second, Chain, Gold Hands 1000.00
Watch, **Patek Philippe & Co.**, Geneva, Lady's, Fob, Gold & Enamel, C.1860 .... 575.00
Watch, **Patek Philippe**, Pocket, 18k Gold Open Face, 20 Jewels 200.00
Watch, **Peter Paulson**, London, No.362, Silver Gilt Pair Case, Engraved, C.1780 .... 100.00
Watch, **Pluto**, Original Box & Instructions, C.1951 .... 60.00
Watch, **Pocket**, Closed Face, Waltham, 14K 175.00
Watch, **Pocket**, Donald Duck, Circa 1930 .... 95.00
Watch, **Pocket**, Graf Zeppelin 100.00
Watch, **Pocket**, Locomotive Engraving, Large Size 19.75
Watch, **Pocket**, Locomotive On Case 30.00
Watch, **Pocket**, Open Face, Admiral, Swiss, 15 Jewel, Winds On 3 .... 35.00
Watch, **Pocket**, Open Face, 15 Jewel, Elgin 15.00
Watch, **Pocket**, Waltham, Open Face, Engraved, 14K Gold 65.00
Watch, **Prevost**, Paris, Gilt Metal & Enamel, Oignon, Pierced, Chased, C.1690 .... 3400.00
Watch, **R.Johnstone**, London, Brass, Engraved, Chain Driven 10.00
Watch, **Railroad**, Hamilton, 21 Jewel, Gold Plate Hunting Case, Vest Chain 150.00
Watch, **Railroad**, Hampden Special, 21 Jewel 90.00
Watch, **Railroad**, Hampden, 14K Gold Filled Case 85.00
Watch, **Railroad**, Illinois, Closed Engraved Case, 20 Year 140.00
Watch, **Railroad**, Illinois, Open Face, Coin Silver, 15 Jewel 65.00
Watch, **Richardson**, London, No.9920, Stand, Silver Gilt & Enamel, Engraved 950.00
Watch, **Rockford**, Open Face Silver Case, 3 Step Porcelain Dial, Size 18 .... 32.00
Watch, **Sam Gimalde**, No.1, Somerstown, Gold Open Face, Chain, Fob, 1809 .... 900.00
Watch, **Shell Oil**, Girard Perragaux, Skeletonized 140.00
Watch, **Silver Case**, Scrolled Silver Face, M.J.Tobias, Key Wind 55.00
Watch, **Smitty** 45.00
Watch, **Snoopy** 10.00
Watch, **Size 8**, Elgin, Gold Filled Hunting Case, Scene, 15 Jewel 48.00
Watch, **Swiss**, Chronograph, Open Face, Sterling Case, Separate Seconds 90.00
Watch, **Swiss**, Gold & Enamel, Ball Form, Pendant, Blue & White, C.1890 .... 650.00
Watch, **Swiss**, Gold & Enamel, Vinaigrette Pendant, Kidney Shape, C.1800 .... 4500.00
Watch, **Swiss**, Gold Hunting Case, 21 Jewels 165.00
Watch, **Swiss**, Gold Open Face, Minute Repeating, Pocket, Stem Wind, C.1900 .... 675.00
Watch, **Swiss**, Lady's Fob Watch, Engraved Sterling Case, Key Wind, C.1880 .... 45.00
Watch, **Swiss**, Lady's, Pendant, Open Face, Engraved Silver Case 40.00
Watch, **Swiss**, Man's, Pocket, Rolled Gold Hunting Case, Stem Wind, C.1910 .... 70.00
Watch, **Swiss**, Open Face, Silveroid, 15 Jewel 80.00
Watch, **Swiss**, Open Face, 2 Dials, 18K Gold 200.00
Watch, **Swiss**, Pocket, Miniature Of Alexander III, 18K Gold, C.1890 .... 160.00
Watch, **Swiss**, Principal 22.50
Watch, **Thomas Tompion**, London, No.2875, Silver Pair Case, Pierced, C.1700 .... 1350.00
Watch, **Tiffany**, Key Wind, Inscribed Inside Cover 165.00
Watch, **Tom Corbett**, Space Cadet, Circular Dial .... 18.50 To 40.00
Watch, **Vacheron & Constantin**, Geneve, 14K Gold Hunting Case, Pocket, 1884 .... 190.00
Watch, **Walham**, Hunting Case, Hinged Bezel Face, Blank Cartouche, Key, 1860 .... 55.00
Watch, **Waltham**, Bartlett, Key Wind, Hunting Case, 14K Gold 95.00
Watch, **Waltham**, Coin Silver Open Face, Key Wind 30.00
Watch, **Waltham**, Engraved Open Face Coin Silver Case, Size 18 .... 22.00
Watch, **Waltham**, Equity, Silveroid Case, 7 Jewels 25.00
Watch, **Waltham**, Gold Filled Case, Open Face, 21 Jewels 45.00
Watch, **Waltham**, Gold Filled Hunting Case, Carved Rose On Back, Size 18 .... 45.00
Watch, **Waltham**, Hunting Case, Floral, Scroll, Gold Filled, Size 0 .... 55.00
Watch, **Waltham**, Lady's, Gold Filled Hunting Case, Roman Numerals 47.00
Watch, **Waltham**, Lady's, 14K Gold Open Face, Rose Diamonds, Fleur-De-Lis 125.00
Watch, **Waltham**, Open Case, Key Wind, Bartlett Movement, Silverine, Size 18 .... 27.50
Watch, **Waltham**, Open Face, Floral, Leaf, Porcelain Dial, Red Numbers, Size 18 .... 25.00
Watch, **Waltham**, Open Face, Silveroid Case, Size 18 .... 17.00
Watch, **Waltham**, Silveroid Case, Key Wind & Set, 7 Jewels 40.00
Watch, **Waltham**, Yellow Gold Hunting Case, 7 Jewels 60.00

*Waterford Type Glass resembles the famous glass made in the Waterford
Glass works in Ireland. It is a clear glass that was often cut for
decoration. Modern glass is still being made in Waterford, Ireland.*
Waterford, **Bowl**, Punch, Cut Crystal, Circa 1800, 15 In.High X 12 In.Across 200.00
Waterford, **Celery**, Turned Down Rim 95.00
Waterford, **Chest**, Sweetmeat, Hinged Sheffield Cover & Cage 275.00

Waterford, Creamer, Marked Penrose-Waterford, C.1790 .... 275.00
Waterford, Decanter, Faceted, Rigaree & Diamond Cut, Mushroom Stopper, 1800s 160.00
Waterford, Glass, Goblet, Heavy Diamond Cut And Paneled 45.00
Waterford, Honey Jar, Diamond Pattern, Deep Cut, Plate 110.00
Waterford, Lamp, Dome Shape Shade, Cut Glass Shade & Base, 29 In. 950.00
Waterford, Salt, Master, Urn Shape, Cut Crystal, Circa 1840 .... 30.00
Waterford, Vase, Flare Top, Pedestal Base, Signed, 7 In.Tall 50.00

Wavecrest Glass is a white glassware manufactured by the Pairpoint
Manufacturing Company of New Bedford, Massachusetts, and some French
factories. It was then decorated by the C.F.Monroe Company of
Meriden, Connecticut. The glass was painted pastel colors and decorated
with flowers. The name Wavecrest was used after 1898.

Wavecrest, Bowl, Baby Chicks, Signed, 3 1/2 In. 65.00
Wavecrest, Bowl, Blue, Rabbits 35.00
Wavecrest, Bowl, Flowers, Enamel, Puffed, Signed, 3 In.Square, 2 In.Tall 55.00
Wavecrest, Bowl, Flowers, Gold Rim & Handle, Marked, 7 In.Diameter 173.00
Wavecrest, Bowl, Metal Rim 30.00
Wavecrest, Bowl, Ormolu Trim, Signed 135.00
Wavecrest, Bowl, Pastel Flowers, Gold Ormolu Rim & Handles, 7 In. 173.00
Wavecrest, Bowl, Pink & White Scrolls, Enameling, Ormolu Rims & Handle 70.00
Wavecrest, Bowl, Rose Design, Handles, Signed, Pink, Blue 110.00
Wavecrest, Bowl, Swirl, Floral Sprays, White, Pink, Brass Collar, 7 1/2 In. 70.00
Wavecrest, Box, Beading, Pink & Blue Ground, Floral, Puffed Top, Bottom 350.00
Wavecrest, Box, Blue Swirl, Floral, Hinged 95.00
Wavecrest, Box, Blue, Green, Yellow Flowers, Red Mark, Footed 250.00
Wavecrest, Box, Blue, 4 In.High, 4 1/2 In.Diameter 155.00
Wavecrest, Box, Bronze Ormulu Feet, Hinged, Unsigned 475.00
Wavecrest, Box, Cigarette, Gold Rim, Handles, & Footed Base, Lavender Florals 70.00
Wavecrest, Box, Collars & Cuffs, 6 1/2 X 6 In. 300.00
Wavecrest, Box, Covered, Blue, Enamel Floral, Signed, 5 1/2 X 3 1/2 In. 165.00
Wavecrest, Box, Covered, Brass Ormolu Footed Base, Pink, Florals, Signed 165.00
Wavecrest, Box, Covered, Ivory, Hinged, Round, 5 In. 160.00
Wavecrest, Box, Covered, Oval, Blue With Floral, Signed, 5 1/4 X 3 1/2 In. 125.00
Wavecrest, Box, Covered, Yellow & White, Roses, Boy & Girl On Cover, Signed 235.00
Wavecrest, Box, Cream Ground, Pink Rose On Lid, Hinged, Unsigned 70.00
Wavecrest, Box, Cuff Link, Signed, Red Mark 68.00
Wavecrest, Box, Cuff Link, Slanting Ormolu Top, Signed, Open 65.00
Wavecrest, Box, Embossed Blue Flowers, Floral Ormolu Rim, Signed, Open 58.00
Wavecrest, Box, Embossed, Forget-Me-Nots, Signed, 3 1/2 In.Square 120.00
Wavecrest, Box, Embossed, Painted Flowers, Robin's Egg Blue, Brass Collar 225.00
Wavecrest, Box, Floral, Hinged, 4 In.High, 7 1/2 In.Diameter 400.00
Wavecrest, Box, Flower & Cigar Design, Hinged, Square 195.00
Wavecrest, Box, Flowers, Lady, Tree, White, Round, Hinged 75.00
Wavecrest, Box, Glove, Child's, White Medallions, Portrait Of Cherubs, Floral 135.00
Wavecrest, Box, Glove, Lacy, Scrolls, Yellow, White, Pink Roses, Gold Lining 325.00
Wavecrest, Box, Green, Signed 59.00
Wavecrest, Box, Helmschmied Swirl Pattern, Blue & White Panels, Blossoms 375.00
Wavecrest, Box, Hinged Lid, Boy, Girl, Scrollwork, Floral, 6 In.Diameter 350.00
Wavecrest, Box, Hinged, Blue Flowers 95.00
Wavecrest, Box, Hinged, Scrollwork, 5 3/4 In.Diameter 325.00
Wavecrest, Box, Jewel, Blue, White Daisies, Swirls On Lid, Clasp, Unmarked 130.00
Wavecrest, Box, Jewel, Floral, Puffy, Metal Bands, Clasp, Unsigned 65.00
Wavecrest, Box, Jewel, Gold Plated Rims, Banner Mark, Lid, 4 In.Diameter 145.00
Wavecrest, Box, Jewel, Gray, Pink, Blue Sprays, Relief Enamels, Red Mark 198.00
Wavecrest, Box, Jewel, Hand-Painted Flowers, Puffy, Metal Bands, Clasp 85.00
Wavecrest, Box, Jewel, Open, Blue & White With Pink Blossoms, Brass Collar 85.00
Wavecrest, Box, Jewel, Oval, Signed, 4 In. 135.00
Wavecrest, Box, Jewel, Pastel Coloring, Signed 350.00
Wavecrest, Box, Jewel, Pastels, Enamel Floral Sprays, Ormolu Reliefs, Lid 225.00
Wavecrest, Box, Jewel, Pink Enamel Trim, Brass Top & Bottom, 3 Footed 45.00
Wavecrest, Box, Jewel, Reliefs, Color Floral, White Enamels, Hinged Lid 195.00
Wavecrest, Box, Jewel, Round, Pink & Blue Flowers, Brass Band & Hinge 195.00
Wavecrest, Box, Jewel, Swirls, Ivory Ground, Lining, Cover, Not Signed 110.00
Wavecrest, Box, Jewel, White, Swirls, Enamel Pink Clover, Polychrome Leaves 245.00
Wavecrest, Box, Jeweled, Footed, Unsigned 350.00

Wavecrest, Box, Letter, Brass Ormolu Corners & Feet, Red Banner Mark 250.00
Wavecrest, Box, Lock & Key, Cupids Painting At Easel, Signed 195.00
Wavecrest, Box, Open, Blue Floral, Double Handles, Brass Rim, Red Banner Mark 75.00
Wavecrest, Box, Open, Panels, Floral, Raised Scroll, Ormolu Collar & Rim 145.00
Wavecrest, Box, Oval, Hinged, Brass Base, Ormolu Feet, Signed 190.00
Wavecrest, Box, Panels, Daisies, Hinged Lid 250.00
Wavecrest, Box, Pansies, Hinged, 3 In.High, 5 1/2 In.Diameter, Unsigned 150.00
Wavecrest, Box, Pastel Green, Meadow Scene, Stream, Bridge, Pink Cloth Lining 125.00
Wavecrest, Box, Photo Holder, Red Banner Mark, Footed, Violet Decoration 195.00
Wavecrest, Box, Pin, Open, Ormulu Trim & Handles, Red Banner Mark 65.00
Wavecrest, Box, Pink, Shell Design, Hand-Painted Rose, Bud, White Dots 185.00
Wavecrest, Box, Portrait, Cupids Painting At Easel, Lock, Key 195.00
Wavecrest, Box, Powder, Hinged, Floral, Scrolls, Shell Design, Red Banner Mark 190.00
Wavecrest, Box, Raised Pansy Design, Banner Mark, 4 1/4 X 3 In. 125.00
Wavecrest, Box, Raised Shell, Blue & Pink Floral, Brass Collar, Red Banner 130.00
Wavecrest, Box, Raised Shell, Pink, Blue, Marked, 2 1/2 X 3 In. 175.00
Wavecrest, Box, Ring, Blue Floral, Scrolls, Round, Red Banner Mark 175.00
Wavecrest, Box, Rosy Beige, Tan Flowers, Swirl, Lined, Hinged Lid, No Mark 145.00
Wavecrest, Box, Scene, Boy Proposing To Girl In Garden, Hinged Lid 375.00
Wavecrest, Box, Scenic, Mill, Water Wheel, Bridge, Stream, Signed, 4 In. 185.00
Wavecrest, Box, Scroll Design, Floral On Pastel, Yellow, Pink, 4 X 2 3/4 In. 200.00
Wavecrest, Box, Shell Pattern, Pink & Blue Flowers, Red Banner Mark 110.00
Wavecrest, Box, Shell Pattern, Signed, 3 1/2 In. 100.00
Wavecrest, Box, Square, Hinged, Blue Flowers, 3 1/2 In. 95.00
Wavecrest, Box, Trinket, Brass Band, Blue Embossed, Pink Rose & Leaf Motif 160.00
Wavecrest, Box, Trinket, Hand-Painted Floral, Brass Collar, 5 In. 39.50
Wavecrest, Box, Trinket, Lily-Of-The-Valley Decoration, Brass Collar 45.00
Wavecrest, Box, Trinket, Ormolu, Brass Collar, 4 In. 55.00
Wavecrest, Box, Trinket, Pale Blue Scroll, Floral, Brass Collar, Signed 59.00
Wavecrest, Box, Trinket, Shell Design, Red Banner Mark, Cover 125.00
Wavecrest, Case, Jewel, Ivorene, Enamel Floral, Brass Hinge, Satin Lined 200.00
Wavecrest, Casket, Jewel, Hinged, Yellow, Scrollwork & Floral, Pink Banner 155.00
Wavecrest, Dish, Dresser, Open, Embossed Shell Design, Silver Rim, Floral 65.00
Wavecrest, Dish, Dresser, Open, Swirled, Puffy Base, Blossoms, Gold Color Rim 55.00
Wavecrest, Dish, Dresser, Open, Yellow Green Ground, Floral, Not Signed 55.00
Wavecrest, Dish, Dresser, Swirl Base, Floral, Gold Color Rim, Open, Signed 60.00
Wavecrest, Dish, Dresser, Swirl Base, Floral, Gold Color Rim, Open, Unmarked 45.00
Wavecrest, Dish, Pin, Cream, Daisy, Brass Ormolu Collar & Handle 80.00
Wavecrest, Dish, Pin, Raised Ornate Scrolls, Pink Shaded, Enamel Floral 55.00
Wavecrest, Ewer, Metal Base, Handle, & Spout, Yellow Shading, Ferns 140.00
Wavecrest, Fernery, Blue Flowers, White Dots, Brass Rim, Removable Insert 175.00
Wavecrest, Fernery, Relief Scrolls, Brass Rim, 8 In.Square 85.00
Wavecrest, Fernery, Small Blue Floral, Insert, Banner Mark 165.00
Wavecrest, Flower Center, Blue Ground, Pink & Purple Wild Roses 155.00
Wavecrest, Holder, Hair Brush, Floral, Brass Cuffs Each End, Velvet Lined 250.00
Wavecrest, Holder, Letter, Purple Violets, Gold Feet, Red Banner Mark 195.00
Wavecrest, Humidor, Cigar, Green, Baroque Medallions, Floral Sprays, Lid, Lock 365.00
Wavecrest, Jar, Biscuit, Bulbous, Apple Blossoms, 8 Panels, Silver Lid 350.00
Wavecrest, Jar, Biscuit, Enameled Floral & Gold Scrolls On Blue, Silver 115.00
Wavecrest, Jar, Biscuit, Enameled Floral & Gold Scrolls On Green, Silver 115.00
Wavecrest, Jar, Biscuit, Flowers, Leaves, Pink, Green, Silver Cover & Bail 95.00
Wavecrest, Jar, Biscuit, White Satin, Streamers, Yellow Floral, Silver Top 140.00
Wavecrest, Jar, Blue Flowers, Hinged Lid, 3 1/2 In.High 125.00
Wavecrest, Jar, Blue Shading, Flower Sprays, Bail, Open 58.00
Wavecrest, Jar, Cookie, Floral On Ivory, Silver Plate Handle, Collar, & Cover 175.00
Wavecrest, Jar, Cookie, Floral, Silver Plate Cover, Marked 89.00
Wavecrest, Jar, Cookie, Robin's Egg Blue, Flowers, Silver Plate Handle 195.00
Wavecrest, Jar, Cookie, Square, Yellow, White Panels, Florals 85.00
Wavecrest, Jar, Cracker, Blue Pansies & Raised Scrolls, Silver Rim & Bail 115.00
Wavecrest, Jar, Cracker, C.F.M.Co. 185.00
Wavecrest, Jar, Cracker, Cream Ground, Enameled, Silver Collar & Handle 75.00
Wavecrest, Jar, Cracker, Cream Ground, Pink Floral, Curlicues, Unsigned 75.00
Wavecrest, Jar, Cracker, Egg Crate Pattern, Yellow, Lavender Floral 245.00
Wavecrest, Jar, Cracker, Enamel Decoration, Hand-Painted Floral, Puffy Type 99.00
Wavecrest, Jar, Cracker, Flowers, Scrolls, Green, Red 75.00
Wavecrest, Jar, Cracker, Hand-Painted Flowers, Embossed Scrolls, Silver Bail 88.00

Wavecrest, **Jar**, Cracker, Portrait, Two Victorian Women, Silver Collar, Cover 85.00
Wavecrest, **Jar**, Cracker, Silver Lid & Bail, Soft Colors 135.00
Wavecrest, **Jar**, Cracker, Yellow, Floral Panels, Square, Unsigned 90.00
Wavecrest, **Jar**, Open, Flowers, Metal Rim & Handles, Marked, 3 X 2 In. 50.00
Wavecrest, **Jar**, Open, Signed, 4 1/4 In.Wide 42.50
Wavecrest, **Jardiniere**, White Ground, Pink Chrysanthemum, Leaves 135.00
Wavecrest, **Lamp**, Banquet, Cherubs With Outspread Wings, Floral, Satin Glass 250.00
Wavecrest, **Planter**, Blue Flowers, Pink & White Ground, Brass Insert, 8 In. 135.00
Wavecrest, **Planter**, Creamy Ground, Floral, Puffy Shape, Brass Liner 125.00
Wavecrest, **Planter**, Floral, Red, Metal Insert, Signed 190.00
Wavecrest, **Planter**, Pink & Blue, Embossed, Oblong, Brass Collar 195.00
Wavecrest, **Planter**, Pink On White, Blue Daisies, Copper Insert, Signed 150.00
Wavecrest, **Planter**, Red, Octagonal Shape, Signed 325.00
Wavecrest, **Pot**, Mustard, Covered, Tole Collar, 2 1/2 In. 12.50
Wavecrest, **Pot**, Mustard, Yellow To White, Purple & Red Violets, Scrolls 50.00
Wavecrest, **Salt & Pepper**, Enameled Floral On Pink, Signed 75.00
Wavecrest, **Salt & Pepper**, Floral 39.00
Wavecrest, **Salt & Pepper**, Puffed Pattern, Black Trade Mark, Signed 75.00
Wavecrest, **Salt & Pepper**, Red Blossoms On White, Pewter Top, Pair 39.00
Wavecrest, **Saltshaker**, Molded Floral, Hand-Painted Sprays, Metal Top 39.00
Wavecrest, **Saltshaker**, Silver Plated Holder, Pair 115.00
Wavecrest, **Saltshaker**, Yellow & White Swirls, Hand-Painted Floral 35.00
Wavecrest, **Shaker**, Sugar, Buff Ground, Blue Ribbons, Gold Outline, Pansies 165.00
Wavecrest, **Sugar & Creamer**, Cupid & Flowers On Off-White, Silver Handles 165.00
Wavecrest, **Sugar & Creamer**, Ornate Silver, Pink, Swirls, White Floral 295.00
Wavecrest, **Sweetmeat**, Blue Decoration, Ornate Bail & Handle 225.00
Wavecrest, **Syrup**, Ivory Ground, Blue Floral, Sepia Scrolls 125.00
Wavecrest, **Toothbrush Holder**, Blue To White, Raised Scrollwork, Floral 250.00
Wavecrest, **Toothbrush Holder**, Curlicues, Red Banner Mark, 7 In. 295.00
Wavecrest, **Toothbrush Holder**, Decorated, 7 In.High, Signed 295.00
Wavecrest, **Toothbrush Holder**, Red Banner Mark 350.00
Wavecrest, **Toothpick**, Pansies, Footed, Signed 90.00
Wavecrest, **Vase**, Blue, Enamel Decoration, Raised Scrolls, Footed Holder 245.00
Wavecrest, **Vase**, Bluish White, Pink Flowers, White Beading, Signed 185.00
Wavecrest, **Vase**, Embossed Ormolu, Floral Painting, Signed, 12 In., Pair 775.00
Wavecrest, **Vase**, Floral, Enamel Beading, Raised Molded Design, 5 1/2 In. 135.00
Wavecrest, **Vase**, Lacy & Reticulated Metal Base 190.00
Wavecrest, **Vase**, Panels, Yellow To White, Wine Mallows, Flower Form, 13 In. 58.00
Wavecrest, **Vase**, Pink, Floral, 12 In.High, Pair 65.00
Weapon, **Adapter**, Muzzle Of Rifle, Bronze, Confederate, Richmond, Va., 1861 .... 44.50
Weapon, **Battle-Axe**, African, Crow Bill, Hand-Forged Iron, Wooden Handle 22.50
Weapon, **Bayonet**, British, Sheath, Brass, Engraved, Wilkinson, 1836 .... 125.00
Weapon, **Bayonet**, Civil War, Triangular, Marked U.S., Steel, 20 1/2 In. 12.00
Weapon, **Bayonet**, Leather & Brass Scabbard 12.75
Weapon, **Bayonet**, Socket, Iron, Used On Flintlock, C.1680 .... 39.50
Weapon, **Belt**, Cartridge, U.S.Infantry, Brass Fittings, 100 Rounds, C.1880 .... 6.00
Weapon, **Blunderbuss**, Swivel, Brass, Double Barrel, C.1830 .... 395.00
Weapon, **Boomerang**, Throwing Instructions Included 1.80
Weapon, **Box**, Cartridge, Leather, Engraved Silver, British Officer's, C.1850 .... 59.50
Weapon, **Brass**, Holland, Isa'H Jennings, Patent, N.Y., Flint Lock, .50 Caliber 1450.00
Weapon, **Breastplate**, Hinged Skirt, Iron, C.1580, 20 Pounds 225.00
Weapon, **Bullet**, Lead, Marked U.S., 1906, In Leather Belt Cartridge Case 20.00
Weapon, **Cannon**, India, Fuse Ignited, Muzzle Loading, Swivel, Iron Bands 89.50
Weapon, **Cannon**, Muzzle Loading, Handmade, 2 Iron Wheels, Silver Paint, C.1850 ...... 27.50
Weapon, **Cannon**, Muzzle Loading, 2 Cart Iron Wheels, C.1850 .... 29.50
Weapon, **Cannon**, Oak Carriage, Iron Bindings, Cannonball Mold 500.00
Weapon, **Cannon**, Winchester, Firearm Breach, Firing Pin, On Iron Wheels, Iron 200.00
Weapon, **Carbine**, German, Inlaid Walnut Stock, Stag Horn, Grotesque, C.1600 .... 1700.00
Weapon, **Case**, Carrying, For Colt Revolver, Leather, Black, 2 Piece, C.1851 .... 94.50
Weapon, **Cutlass**, British Naval, Iron Guard, Brass Pommel, Sheath, C.1850 .... 185.00
Weapon, **Cutlass**, British Naval, Iron Hilt, Guard & Grips, Ribbed, C.1840 .... 64.50
Weapon, **Dagger**, European, Brass Hilt, Figure Of Priest, Iron Blade, C.1880 .... 22.50
Weapon, **Dagger**, German Marine Military Type, Leather Sheath, 15 In.Long 14.50
Weapon, **Dagger**, German, Garde Du Corps, Rifle Officer's, Brass, C.1880 .... 54.50
Weapon, **Dagger**, Indo-Persian Jambiya, Iron Hilt, Etched 14.50
Weapon, **Dagger**, Italian, 1 Piece Horn Handle, Ribbed, C.1750 .... 17.50

Weapon, Dagger, Japanese Military Dress, Brass Handle, Iron Sheath, C.1900 .... 26.00
Weapon, Dagger, Katar, Armor Piercing, India, Peacock Handle, C.1700 .... 175.00
Weapon, Dagger, Kirpan, Silver, Tiger, Engraved Handle, Etched Blade, 14 In. 7.00
Weapon, Dagger, Left Hand, Main Gauche, Wood Handle, Carved, Iron, C.1890 .... 22.50
Weapon, Dagger, Malayan, Kriss, 8 In.Long 2.40
Weapon, Dagger, Nationalist Chinese Army Officer's Dress, Sheath, C.1920 .... 21.00
Weapon, Dagger, Naval Officer's, Orange Handle, WKC Mfg. 85.00
Weapon, Dagger, Presentation, Silver Gilt, Chased, German, C.1750 .... 2000.00
Weapon, Dirk, British Naval Officer's, Brass Hilt, Sheath, C.1790 .... 74.50
Weapon, Dirk, British Naval Officer's, Ivory Handle, Sheath, C.1800 .... 57.50
Weapon, Dirk, British Naval, Brass Hilt, Lion's Head Pommel, C.1790 .... 150.00
Weapon, Dirk, British Naval, Brass Hilt, Lion's Head Pommel, Sheath, C.1840 .... 125.00
Weapon, Dirk, British Naval, Gilt Finish, Brass Handle, Maltese Cross, C.1840 .... 110.00
Weapon, Dirk, British Naval, Iron Hilt, Pommel, & Guard, Ivory Grips, C.1790 .... 94.50
Weapon, Dirk, Imperial German Naval, Nickel On Brass Hilt, C.1900 .... 49.50
Weapon, Dirk, Miniature, Scottish Highland, Silver Pommel, Ebony Handle, 1850 .... 29.50
Weapon, Dirk, Naval Officer's, Ivory Grips, Brass Pommel, Engraved, C.1800 .... 115.00
Weapon, Dirk, Naval, American, Bone Grips, Brass Sheath, C.1810 .... 54.50
Weapon, Dirk, Naval, Sheath, German Silver Mountings, Ivory Grips, C.1850 .... 47.50
Weapon, Flask, Bead, Rib, Copper, Holds 1 1/2 Lb.Gun Powder, Dixon Sheffield 85.00
Weapon, Fowler, Signed Ketland & Co., Curly Maple, Flint Lock, Brass, Carved 400.00
Weapon, Guidon Pole, European, Cavalry, Iron Blade, C.1850 .... 19.50
Weapon, Gun, Allen & Thurber Pepper Box, 31 Cal., Percussion, 1845, 6 Shot 135.00
Weapon, Gun, Army, Colt, Serial 29183, .45 Caliber, Made In 1883 .... 135.00
Weapon, Gun, Bacon Ring Trigger, Single Shot 75.00
Weapon, Gun, Burnside, Carbine 195.00
Weapon, Gun, Carbine, Winchester, Circa 1866 .... 395.00
Weapon, Gun, Colt Lightning, .38 Caliber, Made In 1878 .... 95.00
Weapon, Gun, Colt Lightning, .41 Caliber, Made In 1878 .... 85.00
Weapon, Gun, Colt 45, Black Powder, Known As Peach Maker, C.1880 .... 265.00
Weapon, Gun, Colt, Lee, Grant, 1851, Navy Commemorative, Presentation Box, Both .. 475.00
Weapon, Gun, Full Stock, Long Barrel, Iron Patch Box & Flint Lock 450.00
Weapon, Gun, Full Stock, Tiger Stripe Maple, Silver Eagle Inlaid, Patch Box 350.00
Weapon, Gun, Kentucky Shutzzen, Signed J.Lehnert, Louisville 550.00
Weapon, Gun, Kentucky, Full Stock, Walnut, Long Barrel 225.00
Weapon, Gun, Percussion, Derringer, Washington Arms, 31 Cal., Engraved 79.50
Weapon, Gun, Rampart, India, Matchlock, Relief Designs, C.1750 .... 39.50
Weapon, Gun, Williamson, .41 Derringer, Brass Frame, Engraved, Crack In Stock 115.00
Weapon, Gun, Winchester, Brass Frame, Carbine, Dated 1860 .... 375.00
Weapon, Hanger, Rifle, Stevens Marksman 15.00
Weapon, Hunting Horn, Copper & Brass, English, Leather Case, 44 In.Long 65.00
Weapon, Hunting Horn, Pewter Rim 15.00
Weapon, Knife, Barlow Type, M.Kleins & Sons 5.00
Weapon, Knife, Bolo, World War I Type, 10 1/2 In.Blade 4.50
Weapon, Knife, Bowie, G.Wostenholm & Sons, Sheffield, Silver Guard 55.00
Weapon, Knife, Bowie, Iron Cross Guard & Mounts, Stag Handle, C.1900 .... 19.50
Weapon, Knife, Bowie, Manhattan Cutlery Co., Sheffield, Silver Guard, C.1900 .... 29.50
Weapon, Knife, Bowie, Says 'Texas Bowie' In Scroll, 11 1/4 In.Long 75.00
Weapon, Knife, British Commando, Brass Handle, Sheffield, England 6.80
Weapon, Knife, Colonial America, Leaf Shape Blade, Wood Handle, Iron Guard 54.50
Weapon, Knife, Cub Scout, Silver Cub On Handle 6.00
Weapon, Knife, Fighting, Military, Iron Hilt, Ebony Grips, C.1840 .... 49.50
Weapon, Knife, French Rifleman's, M1831, Brass Hilt, Engraved 29.00
Weapon, Knife, Ghurka, Inlaid Bone Handle, Leather Sheath, 12 1/2 In. 9.95
Weapon, Knife, Girl Scout, Green Handle, 1940s 4.00
Weapon, Knife, Hari-Kari, Hand-Lacquered, 7 In.Blade 85.00
Weapon, Knife, Imperial, Sheath, Jackknife Attached In Separate Case 5.00
Weapon, Knife, India National, Inlaid Bone Handle, Leather Scabbard, 9 In. 8.95
Weapon, Knife, Pen, Lady's Shoe 15.00
Weapon, Knife, Philippino Borong, Carved Briar & Bone Grips, 16 In.Blade 75.00
Weapon, Knife, Plains Indian, Sheath, Pierced Wood, Steel Blade, Beads, Paint 205.00
Weapon, Knife, Pocket, Black & Silver, Schrade Walden, 2 Blade 10.00
Weapon, Knife, Pocket, Bone Handle, 3 Blades 8.50
Weapon, Knife, Pocket, Comus, Bone, 3 Blades 10.00
Weapon, Knife, Pocket, Gold Plated, Dated 1914 .... 5.00
Weapon, Knife, Pocket, Mother-Of-Pearl, 3 Blades 20.00

Weapon, Knife, Pocket, Remington, 3 Blade 18.00
Weapon, Knife, Pocket, Scout, Bone Handle, Camping Tools & Blade 15.00
Weapon, Knife, Pocket, Two Blades, White, Silver Hardware, Remington Arms 75.00
Weapon, Knife, Pocket, Winchester, No.3016 .... 45.00
Weapon, Knife, Remington, Pocket 25.00
Weapon, Knife, Remington, Two Blades, Wooden Handle, U.M.C.In Circle 6.50
Weapon, Knife, Rigger's, Russell 35.00
Weapon, Knife, Sioux Indian, Sheath, Antler Haft, Steel Butt Plate, Beads 375.00
Weapon, Knife, Solingen, German, Combat Bowie, 10 In.Long 18.50
Weapon, Knife, Solingen, German, Companion Bowie, 6 In.Long 7.50
Weapon, Knife, Solingen, German, Original Bowie, 0 In.Long 12.50
Weapon, Knife, Solingen, German, Remington Pattern, Frontier Blade, Saw Back 8.60
Weapon, Knife, Solingen, German, Remington Pattern, Frontiersman, 10 In. 12.95
Weapon, Knife, Solingen, German, Remington Pattern, Hunter, 7 In.Long 8.95
Weapon, Knife, Solingen, German, Royal Bowie, 8 In.Long 14.00
Weapon, Knife, Solingen, German, Royal Buffalo Skinner, 5 In.Long 8.50
Weapon, Knife, Solingen, German, Royal Original Bowie, 5 In.Long 8.50
Weapon, Knife, Solingen, German, Texas Fighting Bowie, Engraved, 10 In.Long 35.00
Weapon, Knife, Solingen, German, Texas Hunter, Engraved, 9 3/4 In.Long 29.95
Weapon, Knife, Solingen, German, Woodsman, Remington Pattern, Woodsman, 8 In. 9.95
Weapon, Knife, Solingen, German, Youth, Steel Scabbard, 10 In.Long 5.50
Weapon, Knife, Solingen, Germany, Pearl Handle, Handmade 6.50
Weapon, Knife, Solingen, Germany, Premium Stock, Bone Handle, Handmade, 4 In. 7.50
Weapon, Knife, Survival, Leather Sheath, Honing Stone, 5 In.Blade 4.85
Weapon, Knife, Winchester, Trademark 2.00
Weapon, Knife, Winchester, Western 2.00
Weapon, Knife, Winchester, 15 1/4 In. 18.00
Weapon, Lance & Guidon Pole, European, Cavalry, Iron, C.1860 .... 29.50
Weapon, Lance, Cavalry, Iron Blade & Integral Shaft, C.1850 .... 19.50
Weapon, Lance, Cavalry, Wood Shaft, C.1850 .... 24.50
Weapon, Loading Tool, Winchester 20.00
Weapon, Measure, Powder, Arabian Miguelet Pistol, Iron, Engraved, C.1750 .... 24.00
Weapon, Measure, Powder, Cannon, Copper, Brass Handle, 4 1/2 In. 45.00
Weapon, Musket, Brown Bess, Artillery Musketoon Size, Double Barrel, C.1800 .... 89.50
Weapon, Musket, Cap & Ball, 70 Cal., Pewter Forecaps, Lane & Read, Manchester 79.50
Weapon, Musket, German, Military, Matchlock, .70 Caliber, C.1550 .... 895.00
Weapon, Musket, India, Matchlock, Inlaid Ivory, Brass, Octagon Muzzle 195.00
Weapon, Musket, India, Rosewood Grain Stock, Brass, Double Barrel 125.00
Weapon, Musket, Lock Marked Augme, Flint, Metal, Circa 1750 .... 395.00
Weapon, Musket, U.S.Presentation, Harpers Ferry, 1841, German Silver Bands 495.00
Weapon, Musketoon, French, Percussion, M1825, Automatic Capping Device 150.00
Weapon, Pistol, Boot, Percussion 13.50
Weapon, Pistol, British Hardware Mask Butt, Gen.Holland Williams Rev., Pair 5000.00
Weapon, Pistol, Flint Lock, Chased, Floral, Silver Mount, Manceaux A Paris 235.00
Weapon, Pistol, Gambler's, Boot 42.00
Weapon, Pistol, Percussion, Marked Tower 180.00
Weapon, Pistol, Repeating, Cap & Ball, 1854, Bullet Mold, Box 285.00
Weapon, Pistol, Revolutionary War, Grotesque Mask, Converted To Percussion 200.00
Weapon, Pistol, Walnut Grips, 41 Caliber, Circa 1830 .... 65.00
Weapon, Pouch, Bullet, British Officer's, Leather, Silver Embroidery 29.50
Weapon, Pouch, Cartridge, British Officer's, Silver & Gold, Victorian Era 24.50
Weapon, Pouch, Cartridge, Leather, Silver Covered, British Officer's, C.1850 .... 64.50
Weapon, Pouch, Cartridge, Prussian, Leather, 18th Century 32.50
Weapon, Pouch, Cartridge, Royal Artillery, British Seal, Gold, Leather 24.50
Weapon, Pouch, Powder, Leather, Brass Measure 22.50
Weapon, Pouch, Shot, Leather, Oval 12.50
Weapon, Powder Can, Pewter, Some Dents, Dated 1786 .... 25.00
Weapon, Powder Flask, Brass Dispenser, Raised Design, Dogs, Woods, Copper 24.75
Weapon, Powder Flask, Civil War, Cow's Horn, Marked Frary Benham & Co. 25.00
Weapon, Powder Flask, Dead Game Decoration, Brass, Dixon .... 35.00 To 42.00
Weapon, Powder Flask, Eagle, Clasped Hands, Stars, Shield, Flags, Brass 47.00
Weapon, Powder Flask, Fluted, Measure Top, Scrolls, Flowers, Brass & Copper 35.00
Weapon, Powder Flask, Hunter, Top Hat, Two Dogs, Copper, Brass Top, Cord 48.00
Weapon, Powder Horn, Carved Spout, Scrimshaw 58.00
Weapon, Powder Horn, Carved, Indian Shooting Deer, R.F.1847 .... 85.00
Weapon, Powder Horn, Carved, Ships, Fish, Snakes, Yellow Patina, 7 1/2 In. 85.00

Weapon, **Powder Horn**, Engraved Initials & Date 1807, Leather, Wood 27.00
Weapon, **Powder Horn**, For Kentucky Rifle, No Markings, 9 1/2 In. 25.00
Weapon, **Powder Horn**, Kentucky Rifle, Signed Zephinah Tubs, Pre-1800 .... 80.00
Weapon, **Powder Horn**, Leather .... *Illus* 45.00
Weapon, **Powder Horn**, Made From Horn, 14 1/2 In. 19.75
Weapon, **Powder Horn**, Masonic Symbols & Kentucky-Ohio-1834, Carved 90.00
Weapon, **Powder Horn**, Miniature, Silver Ornaments, C.1850 .... 65.00
Weapon, **Powder Horn**, Translucent, Carved Out Spit, Leather Loop For Cord 14.00
Weapon, **Revolver**, Civil War, Whitney, .36 Caliber, Percussion 145.00
Weapon, **Revolver**, Colt .44, Charcoal Blue Finish, Civil War 195.00
Weapon, **Revolver**, Marlin, Brass Frame Bottom, Rosewood Grips, 1875 .... 65.00
Weapon, **Revolver**, Wooden, Handmade, Gettysburg, C.1870 .... 9.50
Weapon, **Rifle Bayonet**, Leather Scabbard, U.S.Springfield, 1906 .... 15.00
Weapon, **Rifle**, Brass Frame, Blue On Barrel, Henry, 1860 .... 2600.00
Weapon, **Rifle**, Buffalo, Winchester, Blue On Barrel, 1876 .... 650.00
Weapon, **Rifle**, Colt Lightning, Safety & Tang, .38 .... 395.00
Weapon, **Rifle**, Hungarian Military, Cal.8x, 57 Mm Mauser 80.00
Weapon, **Rifle**, Kentucky Flint Lock, Colonial Revolutionary, Curly Maple 495.00
Weapon, **Rifle**, Kentucky, Curly Maple, Flint Lock, 41 In.Barrel 700.00
Weapon, **Rifle**, Percussion, Silver Star On Barrel, Engraved Patch Boxes 650.00
Weapon, **Rifle**, Seal Hunting, Cast White Metal, Dated 1871, 38 In.Harpoons 245.00
Weapon, **Rifle**, Sharps & Hankins Navy Model, .52rf, Leather Covered, 1859 .... 795.00
Weapon, **Rifle**, Sporting, Percussion, Florida, C.Oak & Son, Jacksonville, 1870 .... 695.00
Weapon, **Rifle**, Springfield Model 1884, With Bayonet, Blue 210.00
Weapon, **Rifle**, Springfield, Bayonet, U.S.Model, No.10618, 1873 .... 165.00
Weapon, **Rifle**, Springfield, .50-70 Caliber, Trapdoor, 1868 .... 85.00
Weapon, **Rifle**, Three Inlays, Full Stock, Signed J.Fordney, 46 In. 475.00
Weapon, **Rifle**, Union Snipers, Percussion, Octagon Double Barrel, .50 Caliber 425.00
Weapon, **Rifle**, Winchester, Engraved Inscription, Sling Swivel, 1873 .... 650.00
Weapon, **Saber**, British Officer's, Scabbard, Brass Hilt, Grotesque Pommel 69.50
Weapon, **Saber**, German Dragoon, Brass Basket Hilt, Ball Pommel, C.1750 .... 185.00
Weapon, **Saber**, Spanish Cavalry, Chrome Plated Metal Scabbard, Gold Trim 22.36
Weapon, **Sabre**, Scabbard, Civil War, Etched Blade, Engraved U.S.Eagle, Scrolls 55.00
Weapon, **Scabbard**, For Entrenching Tool, U.S., Leather, C.1880 .... 54.50
Weapon, **Scabbard**, For Triangular Bayonet, U.S., Civil War, Brass, Copper 34.50
Weapon, **Scabbard**, Lever Action Carbine, Fort Worth, Texas, Black, C.1860 .... 22.50
Weapon, **Scabbard**, Spencer Carbine, Black Leather, C.1860 .... 24.50
Weapon, **Scabbard**, Spencer, U.S.Cavalry Issue, Black Leather, C.1870 .... 24.50
Weapon, **Scabbard**, Winchester Carbine, 1873, Black Leather, Iron, C.1830 .... 29.50
Weapon, **Scabbard**, Winchester, Moran Bros., Montana, Brown Leather, C.1860 .... 34.50
Weapon, **Scabbard**, Winchester, W.E.Baughan, Texas, Brown Leather, Tooled, 1860 ...... 19.50
Weapon, **Scabbard**, Winchester, 1873, Brown Leather, Saddle 34.50
Weapon, **Shield**, Masai Warrior, African, Leopard Hide, Fur, C.1870 .... 27.50
Weapon, **Shield**, Persian, Elephant Hide, Hand-Painted Polychrome Decoration 12.50
Weapon, **Shot Pouch**, Leather, Wooden Stopper 12.50
Weapon, **Shotgun Loader**, Attaches To Table Edge 5.50
Weapon, **Shotgun**, Percussion, Twist Barrel, Inlays, Engraved, England 125.00
Weapon, **Spear Head**, Engraved, Ethiopian, Iron 12.00
Weapon, **Stiletto**, Folding, 9 In.Long 2.45
Weapon, **Stiletto**, Italian, Iron Hilt, C.1650 .... 29.50
Weapon, **Sword Cane**, Carved Face On Handle 75.00
Weapon, **Sword**, Ambassador, The, Relief Gold Handle, Antique Finished Blade 9.95
Weapon, **Sword**, British Foot Officer's, Brass, Lion's Head Pommel, C.1800 .... 145.00
Weapon, **Sword**, British Officer's, Brass Basket Hilt, Engraved, C.1820 .... 225.00
Weapon, **Sword**, Child's, British Naval Officer's, Brass Hilt, Wilkinson 54.50
Weapon, **Sword**, Child's, French Artillery Officer's, Brass Hilt, Iron Sheath 54.50
Weapon, **Sword**, Civil War, Brass Hilt & Guard Marked Ames 1864 .... 32.00
Weapon, **Sword**, Dated 1869, 39 In., Leather Scabbard 45.00
Weapon, **Sword**, Double Scissors, British, German Silver, Pierced, C.1850 .... 225.00
Weapon, **Sword**, El Capitan, Gold Wire Wrapped Black Handle, 35 1/2 In. 9.95
Weapon, **Sword**, English, Brass Hilt, Engraved Shell, Fan, & Floral, C.1750 .... 69.50
Weapon, **Sword**, Falchion, Saxon Janissary Infantry, Brass Hilt, C.1690 .... 475.00
Weapon, **Sword**, Fencing Foil, Engraved & Hand Enameled Blade & Guard 10.75
Weapon, **Sword**, Fencing Foil, Gold Trimmed, Mirror Polished Blade, 43 In.Long 8.50
Weapon, **Sword**, Fish, American, Wood Hilt, Bone, Militia Drill 24.50
Weapon, **Sword**, French Grenadier, 1767 Pattern, Brass Hilt & Grips, American 185.00

Weapon, Sword, German Artillery, Brass Hilt, Lion's Head Pommel, C.1800	27.50
Weapon, Sword, German Military, Pioneer, Iron Hilt, Stag Grips, C.1820	94.50
Weapon, Sword, German Officer's, Presentation, Iron Hilt, Ebony Grips	165.00
Weapon, Sword, Guardsman, The, Eagle Shaped Gold Handle, 33 On.Long	9.95
Weapon, Sword, Horstmann & Sons, Brass Handle, 19th Century, 38 In.	35.00
Weapon, Sword, India, Crow Bill Tipped, Talwar, Serpentine Shape, C.1700	54.50
Weapon, Sword, Indo-Persian, Silver Hilt, Sheath, Serpents, Fleur-De-Lis	295.00
Weapon, Sword, Italian, Viva Garibaldi, Brass Mounted Leather Sheath, 1850	84.50
Weapon, Sword, Japanese Type, Scabbart, Leather Grips, Copper Wire, C.1850	17.50
Weapon, Sword, Japanese, White Carved Bone Handle & Sheath	24.00
Weapon, Sword, Kirpan, Military, Hand-Forged Blade, Scabbard, 39 In.Long	14.00
Weapon, Sword, Lion Head Handle, Silver Over Brass, 22 In.	75.00
Weapon, Sword, Naval, Child's, Pierced Floral Guard, C.1860	19.50

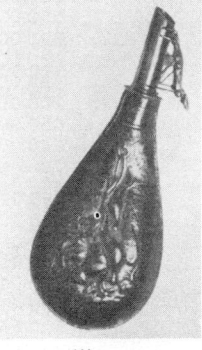

Weapon,
Powder Horn, Leather
See Page 626

Weather Vane, Dog, Copper, American, C.1850, 47 In.Long
See Page 628

Weather Vane, Horse & Rider,
Iron, American, C.1850
See Page 628

Weapon, Sword, Nepal, Ceremonial, 19th Century	13.00
Weapon, Sword, Nimcha, Moroccan, Presented To Adm.F.Campbell, C.1850	145.00
Weapon, Sword, Officer, British, Gold Gilt Handle, Fluted Ivory Grips, C.1790	175.00
Weapon, Sword, Samurai Warrior's, Lacquered Scabbard, Cloth Case, 35 In.	36.60
Weapon, Sword, Scabbard, German, Dress, Siegfried Blade, Swastika, Oak Leaves	350.00
Weapon, Sword, Spanish Artilleryman's, Iron Hilt, Pistol Iron Pommel, C.1900	12.50
Weapon, Sword, Spanish Cavalry, Cup Hilt, Eagle Crest, Crown, Circa 1870	85.00
Weapon, Sword, Spanish, Scabbard, Gold, Enamel, Libertad 15 De Set'E 1821	295.00
Weapon, Sword, Tennessee Toothpick, Indian Head Pommel, Leather Scabbard	4.50
Weapon, Sword, U.S.Officer, Helmet Head, Pearl Handle, Scabbard, C.1820	185.00
Weapon, Sword, Wakizashi, Japanese, Carved Ivory Hilt, 19th Century, Pair	211.50
Weapon, Sword, War Of 1812 Infantry, Brass Handle, Bird's Head Pommel	22.50
Weapon, Sword, Wilkinson, Official British Infantry, Etched Blade & Guard	148.50
Weapon, Sword, Wilkinson, Official Diplomatic, Scabbard	72.00
Weapon, Sword, Wilkinson, Official Presentation, Etched Blade	36.00
Weapon, Sword, Wilkinson, Official Royal Airforce, Dress, Etched Blade	181.50
Weapon, Swork, Punjab, Short, Teakwood Handle, Brass Fittings, 20 In.	10.00

Weather Vane, **Arrow**, Iron, Black 19.50
Weather Vane, **Copper Spire**, Amethyst Ball, Lightning Rod, 1893 ....85.00 To 145.00
Weather Vane, **Dog**, Copper, American, C.1850, 47 In.Long .... *Illus* 325.00
Weather Vane, **Dog**, Pointer, Sheet Iron, 8 1/4 In.High, 21 In.Long 75.00
Weather Vane, **Eagle**, Gilded Copper, On Orb, Spread Wings, American, C.1850 .... 750.00
Weather Vane, **Eagle**, 24 In.Wing Span, Gold Leaf On Ball & Arrow, Copper 350.00
Weather Vane, **Horse & Rider**, Iron, American, C.1850 .... *Illus* 450.00
Weather Vane, **Horse**, Bronzed, Scroll On Arrow, Brass, Iron, 32 In.Long 38.50
Weather Vane, **Horse**, Running, Copper 175.00
Weather Vane, **Horse**, Two Ball Ornaments On Standard, Copper, 76 X 29 In. 400.00
Weather Vane, **Human Hand**, Copper, American, C.1900's, 40 3/4 In.Long 350.00
Weather Vane, **Lightning Rod**, Copper Spire, Amethyst Glass Ball, Pat.1893 .... 145.00
Weather Vane, **Man In Roadster**, White Milk Glass Ball & Stand, 5 In.High 185.00
Weather Vane, **Rooster**, Arrow, N.E.S.W., Zinc, 21 1/4 In.Long 75.00
Weather Vane, **Rooster**, Copper, American, C.1900's, 30 1/2 In.Long 275.00
Weather Vane, **Rooster**, Copper, Gilded Body, American, C.1900's, 24 In.High 550.00
Weather Vane, **Rooster**, Red Ball, Rod, Tin, 9 In.High 125.00
Weather Vane, **Sulky**, Complete 390.00
Weather Vane, **Tin Cow**, Brass Fittings, Milk Glass Ball, 31 X 61 In.High 135.00

Webb Glass was made by Thomas Webb & Sons of Stourbridge, England.
Many types of art and cameo glass were made by them during the Victorian
era.

Webb Burmese, **Hat**, Acid, 2 3/8 In.High, 3 3/8 In.Diameter 495.00
Webb Burmese, **Lamp**, Fairy 135.00
Webb Burmese, **Lamp**, Fairy, S.Clarke Patent Trade Mark Fairy 250.00
Webb Burmese, **Lamp**, Fairy, Shaded Coloring, Clarke Base 125.00
Webb Burmese, **Lamp**, Fluid, Signed, 7 1/8 In.High .... *Illus* 600.00
Webb Burmese, **Perfume**, Bulbous, Full Cut With Matching Stopper 60.00
Webb Burmese, **Ruffled Top**, Applied Yellow Trim, Yellow Edge, 5 In. 500.00
Webb Burmese, **Tumbler**, Juice, Ivy Vine, Green Leaves, Acid 250.00
Webb Burmese, **Vase**, Bowl Shape, Satin Finish, 6 Sided Top 195.00
Webb Burmese, **Vase**, Cabinet, Enameled, 3 1/4 In.High .... *Illus* 300.00
Webb Burmese, **Vase**, Five Pointed Star, Bulbous, Footed, Signed, 5 In.Tall 325.00
Webb Burmese, **Vase**, Flower Form Top, Pink Swirls To Lemon Yellow, 3 1/4 In. 450.00
Webb Burmese, **Vase**, Ruffled, Crimped, Ruffled Foot, Acid, 3 3/4 In. 295.00
Webb Burmese, **Vase**, Trumpet, Ivy Leaves Trail Down Front To Backside, 9 In. 675.00

Webb Burmese, Lamp,
Fluid, Signed,
7 1/8 In.High

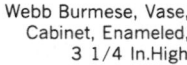

Webb Burmese, Vase,
Cabinet, Enameled,
3 1/4 In.High

Webb, **Basket**, Mother-Of-Pearl, Pink To Rose, Coralene, Camphor Handle 950.00
Webb, **Basket**, White Satin Glass, Applied Blue Ribbon & Floral 95.00
Webb, **Bowl & Underplate**, Finger, Diamond-Quilted, Mother-Of-Pearl, Signed 350.00
Webb, **Bowl**, Citron Yellow, Ginko Branches, Butterflies, Unsigned, 9 In. 840.00
Webb, **Bowl**, Finger, Deep Rose, Crimped, Green Mother-Of-Pearl Lily Pad Plate 335.00
Webb, **Bowl**, Honeycomb, Amber Cameo Cut Roses, Buds, Leaves, England, 9 In. 145.00
Webb, **Bowl**, Mother-Of-Pearl, Diamond-Quilted, Blue Satin, Coin Gold Floral 320.00
Webb, **Bride's Basket**, Flowers, Butterflies, White, Melon, 10 X 3 In. 225.00
Webb, **Cologne**, Peachblow, Floral Enamel, Clear Stopper, 7 In.High 155.00

Webb, Compote, Camphor Satin, Cased White, Blue Satin Inside, Silver Base 85.00
Webb, Compote, Satin Glass, Blue To White, Crimped Edge, Applied Edge 110.00
Webb, Epergne, Fan Shape Trumpet, Intaglio Cut Flowers, Silver Holder 60.00
Webb, Epergne, Three Bowls, Porcelain Portraits, Signed 400.00
Webb, Ewer, Gold Decoration 175.00
Webb, Ewer, Mother-Of-Pearl, Pink To Rose, Coralene 750.00
Webb, Ewer, Mother-Of-Pearl, White Raindrops, Camphor Handle 145.00
Webb, Ewer, Rose To White At Base, Crimped Top, Applied Camphor Handle 85.00
Webb, Ewer, Shaded Blue, Classical Woman, Holds Sword, Cream Lining 135.00
Webb, Goblet, Thistle Pattern, Signed 30.00
Webb, Jar, Cookie, Fluted Pattern, White Inside, Silver Top And Bail Handle 195.00
Webb, Lamp, Kerosene, Cameo, Yellow, Carved Butterfly, Honeysuckle, 7 In. 695.00
Webb, Mayonnaise, Thistle Pattern, Signed 65.00
Webb, Mug, Coronation, 1953, Engraved ER, Crown, Flowers, Thistles 35.00
Webb, Nappy, Swirled Candy Stripes, Applied Rigaree, Side Handle 48.00
Webb, Peachblow, Rose Bowl, Red To Flesh Color, Acid Finish, Miniature 225.00
Webb, Peachblow, Vase, Pink, Gold Decoration, Prunus Blossoms 225.00
Webb, Peachblow, Vase, Stick, Bulbous Body, Butterfly, Prunus, Gold Encrusted 275.00
Webb, Peachblow, Vase, 6 In. 70.00
Webb, Perfume, Cameo, Citrus, White Cut Floral, Laydown, Silver Top 210.00
Webb, Perfume, Laydown, Red Matte, Carved Floral Sprays In Cameo, Signed 575.00
Webb, Perfume, Turquoise Ground, Cut White Floral, Sterling Top 485.00
Webb, Pitcher, Mother-Of-Pearl, Melon Rib, Blue, Camphor Thorn Handle 250.00
Webb, Pitcher, Water, Blue To White, Cased, Clear Handle 210.00
Webb, Rose Bowl, Cranberry, Gold Dragonflies, Ferns, Four Crystal Feet 115.00
Webb, Rose Bowl, Crystal, Optic Rib, Raised Gold Floral, Jules Barbe 50.00
Webb, Rose Bowl, Gold Prune Blossoms, Leaves, Scrolls, Clear Ground 55.00
Webb, Rose Bowl, Miniature, Queen's Burmese, Decorated .... 395.00 To 450.00
Webb, Rose Bowl, Peachblow, Coralene Flowers, Signed 140.00
Webb, Rose Bowl, Satin, Yellow, Three Layers, Gold Decoration, 2 1/2 X 3 In. 185.00
Webb, Rose Bowl, Vaseline To Amber, White Lining, Triangle Ruffled Top 110.00
Webb, Rose Bowl, White Ground, Flowers & Leaves, Pink Lining 250.00
Webb, Sugar & Creamer, Cranberry, Melon Shape, Ribbed, Crimped Top 65.00
Webb, Sugar & Creamer, Fish Scale, Deep Pink, Creamy Lining 125.00
Webb, Tray, Card, Mother-Of-Pearl, Coin Spot Pattern, Crimped Edge 85.00
Webb, Vase, Acid Crystal, Wheel Cut Royal Blue Tulips, 9 In. 365.00
Webb, Vase, Acid Cut Back In Green, Signed, 7 X 7 In. 185.00
Webb, Vase, Acid Cut Ground, Cameo Wheel Cuttings Of Blue Florals, 9 In. 300.00
Webb, Vase, Alexandrite, Amber To Blue, 4 In.Tall 450.00
Webb, Vase, Allover Enamel Decoration, White Lining, 9 1/2 In.High 125.00
Webb, Vase, Amber, Acid Cut Floral Design, 6 1/2 In. 58.00
Webb, Vase, Black Teardrops, Berries, Enamel Floral, Bird In Nest, Pair 165.00
Webb, Vase, Blue Satin, White Lining, Gold Floral & Butterflies, Jules Barbe 135.00
Webb, Vase, Blue, Signed Thomas Webb And Sons, Cameo 395.00
Webb, Vase, Bronze Glass, Classic Shape, Greenish Color, 9 In.High 145.00
Webb, Vase, Bronze, Blue 75.00
Webb, Vase, Bronze, Iridescent, 7 In. 135.00
Webb, Vase, Bud, Satin Glass, Three Colors, Pinched Neck, Fluted Top 75.00
Webb, Vase, Burmese, Painted Leaf Design, Signed Queen's Burmese Ware 595.00
Webb, Vase, Cameo Insert In Swirled Crystal, 3 In. 225.00
Webb, Vase, Cameo, Blue Floral, Engraved & Stippled Crystal Ground, 7 In. 395.00
Webb, Vase, Cameo, Blue Ground, 5 In.High 525.00
Webb, Vase, Cameo, Citron & White Apple Blossoms, 6 1/2 In. 950.00
Webb, Vase, Cameo, Clear Fish Scale Ground, Green Carved Floral, 6 1/2 In. 375.00
Webb, Vase, Cameo, Cranberry, White Carvings, Passion Flower, Dragonfly 795.00
Webb, Vase, Cameo, Raisin, Signed, 4 1/2 In.High 523.00
Webb, Vase, Cameo, Red Ground, White Sweetpeas, Cylindrical Shape, 11 1/2 In. 400.00
Webb, Vase, Cameo, Rose Spray, Four Layer, 3 3/4 In.Tall 385.00
Webb, Vase, Cameo, White On Brown, 5 3/8 In.High .... *Illus* 1200.00
Webb, Vase, Cobalt, Encrusted Gold Prunus & Butterflies, Overlay, Pair 195.00
Webb, Vase, Coralene, Mother-Of-Pearl, Orange Shading, Blue Seaweed 350.00
Webb, Vase, Crystal, Cut, Intaglio, 14 In. 160.00
Webb, Vase, Diamond-Quilted, White & Pink Stripes At Top, Gold Leaves, Feet 350.00
Webb, Vase, Enamel Hummingbird, White Flowers, Green Leaves, Mark 120.00
Webb, Vase, Flower Design, Cameo, Signed, Acid Cut, Blue, 7 In.Tall 395.00
Webb, Vase, Gold Design, White, Satin, 4 1/2 In.High 110.00

Webb, Vase, Cameo, White On Brown, 5 3/8 In.High
See Page 629

Webb, Vase, Gold Floral, Pink Geometric Designs, Enameled Floral	85.00
Webb, Vase, Gold Prunus Blossoms, Butterfly, Verre, Opaline	150.00
Webb, Vase, Intaglio Cut, Dancing Cupids, Candy Cane Legs, Signed	550.00
Webb, Vase, Iridescent, Green, Squatty, 6 In.	37.00
Webb, Vase, Iris, Marigold, Iridescent, Pinched Sides, Stretched Rim	375.00
Webb, Vase, Mother-Of-Pearl, Diamond-Quilted, Melon Rib, Blue Shades, 7 In.	175.00
Webb, Vase, Mother-Of-Pearl, Nodules Around Base, Chartreuse Lining	145.00
Webb, Vase, Mother-Of-Pearl, Rose To Pink White, Green Liner, Camphor Trim	145.00
Webb, Vase, Peachblow, Beige To Dark Pink, Cased, Slim Neck, 14 3/4 In., Pair	500.00
Webb, Vase, Peachblow, Satin Finish, Unsigned, 6 In.	145.00
Webb, Vase, Pink Ground, Enamel, Gold Wash	125.00
Webb, Vase, Pink Mother-Of-Pearl, Diamond-Quilted, Bird Of Paradise Handles	212.50
Webb, Vase, Pink, Blue Seaweed, Coralene, Signed, 7 1/2 In.	200.00
Webb, Vase, Polychrome, Enamel, 11 In.High	895.00
Webb, Vase, Satin, Green To Camphor, Coralene Icicles, 13 In.	55.00
Webb, Vase, Satin, Green To Yellow, Prunus Blossoms, Butterflies, Jules Barbe	365.00
Webb, Vase, Tulip Shape, Cobalt To Clear, Signed, 4 In.	60.00
Webb, Vase, Verre Opaline, Coin Gold Floral, Leaves, Enameled Beading	290.00
Webb, Vase, White Birds & Floral On Yellow, Signed Thomas Webb & Sons	700.00
Webb, Vase, White, Gold Enamel, Moonstone, Brown, Cased, 6 In.High	225.00
Webb, Vase, Yellow, Puffed Coralene Flowers, Signed	175.00
Webb, Wine, Thistle Pattern, Signed	25.00

*Wedgwood Pottery has been made at the famous Wedgwood Factory in
England since 1759. A large variety of wares has been made, including the
well-known Jasperware, Basalt, Creamware, and even a limited amount of
porcelain.*

Wedgwood, see also Basalt, Creamware, Jasperware

Wedgwood, Bank, Green Jasper, Prince Of Wales, 1969	50.00
Wedgwood, Bell, Green Jasperware, White Classical Figures, Signed	29.50
Wedgwood, Biscuit Barrel, Blue, Ladies, Cherubs, Trees, Silver Top & Handle	75.00
Wedgwood, Biscuit Barrel, Dark Blue With White	55.00
Wedgwood, Biscuit Barrel, Dark Blue, White Classical Pattern, Signed	90.00
Wedgwood, Biscuit Barrel, Dark Blue, White Decoration, Ornate Cover	100.00
Wedgwood, Biscuit Barrel, Dark Blue, White Figures, Jasper, Silver Mounts	110.00
Wedgwood, Biscuit Barrel, Pale Green, Grecian Scenes, Ball Feet, Marked	75.00
Wedgwood, Bowl, Basalt, Turned In Rim, 12 In.	125.00
Wedgwood, Bowl, Basalt, 12 In.Diameter	125.00
Wedgwood, Bowl, Blue & White, C.1860	145.00
Wedgwood, Bowl, Blue, Gold Dragons, Green Inside, Coiled Serpent	115.00
Wedgwood, Bowl, Covered, Fish, Caning Effect, Signed	88.00
Wedgwood, Bowl, Fairyland Luster, Bats, Dragons, Gold, Red, Marked	135.00
Wedgwood, Bowl, Fairyland Luster, Blue Ground, Gold Dragons, Border, Floral	165.00
Wedgwood, Bowl, Fairyland Luster, Blue, Gold Birds, Green Bird Center	175.00
Wedgwood, Bowl, Fairyland Luster, Blue, Orange Interior, Fruit, 3 1/4 In.	129.00
Wedgwood, Bowl, Fairyland Luster, Center Bird, Gold Bird Border, 3 1/4 In.	185.00

Wedgwood, Bowl, Fairyland Luster, Dragon, Mother-Of-Pearl Interior, Mark 105.00
Wedgwood, Bowl, Fairyland Luster, Dragons, Bats, Peaches, 6 In.Diameter 225.00
Wedgwood, Bowl, Fairyland Luster, Dragons, Red, Gold, Marked, 6 In.Diameter 225.00
Wedgwood, Bowl, Fairyland Luster, England, 7 In. 350.00
Wedgwood, Bowl, Fairyland Luster, Fruit Design, Blue, Orange, Portland Mark 145.00
Wedgwood, Bowl, Fairyland Luster, Gold Dragons & Scrolls On Blue, Signed .....: 200.00
Wedgwood, Bowl, Fairyland Luster, Gold Stars Between Fairies, 5 In. 300.00
Wedgwood, Bowl, Fairyland Luster, Green, Gold Dragons, Blue Interior 235.00
Wedgwood, Bowl, Fairyland Luster, Octagonal, Oriental Pattern, Green, Gold 125.00
Wedgwood, Bowl, Flying Cranes, Fu-Ku-Ro-Ku-Ju Rides Crane, Gold Dragons 150.00
Wedgwood, Bowl, Game, Caneware, Raised Design, Cauliflower Shape Cover 145.00
Wedgwood, Bowl, Green, Butterflies, Mottled Orange Inside, Butterfly, Footed 115.00
Wedgwood, Bowl, Luster, Dragon, Blue, Green Lining, Octagon 425.00
Wedgwood, Bowl, Mottled Blue, Gold Trim, Mottled Orange Inside, Hummingbird 80.00
Wedgwood, Bowl, Mottled Orange, Gold Butterflies, Dragons Inside 138.00
Wedgwood, Bowl, Octagon, Blue, Gold Dragons, Green Inside, Dragons, Footed 140.00
Wedgwood, Bowl, Salad, Blue Ground, Allover Classical Figures, Silver Rim 110.00
Wedgwood, Bowl, Salad, Classical Figures, Blue, White, 9 In.Diameter, 4 In. 110.00
Wedgwood, Box, Black Basalt, Classical Figures, Acorns 85.00
Wedgwood, Box, Cigarette, Etruria 8.50
Wedgwood, Box, Classical Figures, Black Basalt Cover, 4 1/2 In.Diameter 85.00
Wedgwood, Box, Heart Shape, Blue, Classical Figures, Cover 25.00
Wedgwood, Box, Orchid, White Decoration, Cupid On Lid, 4 In.Square 30.00
Wedgwood, Box, Serpentine, Dancing Cupids, Blue, England, 4 1/2 In.Long 20.00
Wedgwood, Bust, Churchill, By Arnold Machin, 1940, 7 1/2 In.High 140.00
Wedgwood, Bust, Winston Churchill, Black Basalt, Signed, 7 In.Tall 75.00
Wedgwood, Candlestick, Black Jasperware, White Classic Figures, 8 In., Pair 195.00
Wedgwood, Candlestick, Classical Figure Design, Blue, White, 6 In.High, Pair 110.00
Wedgwood, Candlestick, Queensware, Blue On White, 7 1/2 In. 15.00
Wedgwood, Chamberstick, Blue & White Jasper, Circa 1784 .... 85.00
Wedgwood, Charger, Willow Pattern, 10 X 8 1/4 In. 17.50
Wedgwood, Chess Piece, King & Queen, Basalt, England 72.00
Wedgwood, Coffeepot, Drabware, Arabesque & Scroll, Dog Finial 225.00
Wedgwood, Coffeepot, Flaring Handle & Spout, Footed, Basalt, Impressed Mark 145.00
Wedgwood, Compote, Portrait Medallion, Coin Gold Floral, Lid, Set Of 3 .... 750.00
Wedgwood, Creamer, Black Basalt, Ornate Design 65.00
Wedgwood, Creamer, Black Basalt, Thistle, Harp, Shamrock, 4 In. ....70.00 To 75.00
Wedgwood, Creamer, Caneware, Basket Weave Pattern, Signed 85.00
Wedgwood, Creamer, Cauliflower, Majolica 16.00
Wedgwood, Creamer, Creamware, Purple Feathering, Rose Sprays 35.00
Wedgwood, Creamer, Fairyland Luster, Butterflies, Green & Blue, 2 In. 84.00
Wedgwood, Creamer, Jasper, Maroon Ground, White Classic Figures, England 60.00
Wedgwood, Creamer, Small Majolica With Rustic Design 35.00
Wedgwood, Creamer, Town Of Lindsay, 4 In.Tall 25.00
Wedgwood, Cup & Saucer, Creamware, Green Transfer Design, Circa 1834 .... 28.50
Wedgwood, Cup & Saucer, Demitasse, Embossed Queensware, Made In England 4.00
Wedgwood, Cup & Saucer, Fluted White Ground, Rust, Blue & Gold Border 22.00
Wedgwood, Cup & Saucer, Octagon, Bone 20.00
Wedgwood, Cup & Saucer, Sybil 25.00
Wedgwood, Cup & Saucer, Trophy, Red Medallions, White On Blue 600.00
Wedgwood, Cup Plate, Willow Pattern, Yellow, Cobalt, Orange 12.00
Wedgwood, Cup, Flower Design, Blue, Red, Gold, Marked, 2 1/4 In. 15.00
Wedgwood, Dish & Underplate, Cheese, White Females & Cherubs On Blue 120.00
Wedgwood, Dish, Nut, Fairyland Luster, Duck, Mother-Of-Pearl Lining 85.00
Wedgwood, Dish, Nut, Fairyland Luster, Rooster, Mottled Blue, Gold Trim 85.00
Wedgwood, Dish, Pie, Game, Caneware, 8 1/2 In. Long 125.00
Wedgwood, Figurine, Bust Of Scott, Basalt, Wedgwood Only Mark, 14 In.High 550.00
Wedgwood, Figurine, Kangaroo Figures, Signed By Skeaping, 9 In. 195.00
Wedgwood, Figurine, Sea Lion On Rock, Signed J.Skeaping, Basalt 375.00
Wedgwood, Figurine, Seal, Signed Skeaping 185.00
Wedgwood, Figurine, Tiger With Antelope In Mouth, Signed Skeaping 195.00
Wedgwood, Figurine, Tiger, Sheep In Mouth, Yellow, Wooden Base, 13 In.Long 155.00
Wedgwood, Fish Set, Blue, White, Platter, Six Plates, Impressed Mark 175
Wedgwood, Holder, Matchbox, Medium Blue ....
Wedgwood, Inkwell, Blue, In Bronze Base, 9 In.Diameter ....
Wedgwood, Jam Pot, Yellow, Black Garlands, White Bands, Silver Lid & Spoon ....

Wedgwood, Jar, Biscuit, Blue Jasperware, England, Silver Lid & Bail 65.00
Wedgwood, Jar, Biscuit, Blue, Metal 'Biscuit' On Top, Signed 117.50
Wedgwood, Jar, Biscuit, Blue, White Classic Figures, Silver Trim, Feet, Handle 67.50
Wedgwood, Jar, Biscuit, Lilac, White, Silver Rim, Bail, Lid 165.00
Wedgwood, Jar, Cookie, Blue Jasper, Marked Wedgwood 65.00
Wedgwood, Jar, Cracker, Classical Figures, Blue Jasper, Silver Bail & Cover 100.00
Wedgwood, Jar, Cracker, Dark Blue Ground, White Classic Figures 165.00
Wedgwood, Jar, Green, Grecian Figures, Acorn Finial, England 55.00
Wedgwood, Jardiniere, Basalt, 6 In.High, 7 In.Diameter 200.00
Wedgwood, Jardiniere, Blue, White Classical Figures, Signed 187.50
Wedgwood, Jardiniere, Classical Figures, Dark Blue, Lions' Heads, 7 In. 55.00
Wedgwood, Jardiniere, Figures, Blue & White, 7 In.High 85.00
Wedgwood, Jardiniere, Lions Heads, Grapes, Leaves, Blue, 10 In.Diameter 165.00
Wedgwood, Jug, Dark Blue Jasperware, White Classical Figures, Handle 90.00
Wedgwood, Jug, Dark Blue Jasperware, White Classical Figures, Rope Handle 57.50
Wedgwood, Jug, Milk, Green And White, Pewter Top, 5 1/2 In. 75.00
Wedgwood, Luncheon Set, Cornflower Center, Cobalt & Green Banding, 4 Place 37.50
Wedgwood, Match Holder, Scratcher, Brown, Green, Cream Glaze, Marked 17.50
Wedgwood, Matchbox, Covered, White Classical Groups On Blue, Round 43.50
Wedgwood, Pitcher, Basalt, Raised Design 40.00
Wedgwood, Pitcher, Blue, Classic Figures, Signed, 8 In. 75.00
Wedgwood, Pitcher, Blue, Classical Figures, Trees, Foliage, Roman Key Bands 85.00
Wedgwood, Pitcher, Blue, White Classical Figures, Signed, 5 In. 72.50
Wedgwood, Pitcher, Blue, White Figures, 6 1/2 In.High 65.00
Wedgwood, Pitcher, Brown, Gray, Turquoise Jewel Beads, Verse, 1869, Majolica 175.00
Wedgwood, Pitcher, Centennial, 1776-1876, Mocha Ware, 13 States Emblem 200.00
Wedgwood, Pitcher, Creamware, Silver Luster, 5 In.High 22.50
Wedgwood, Pitcher, Dark Blue Jasper, White Design, Portland, 9 In.High 375.00
Wedgwood, Pitcher, Gold Luster, Fallow Deer, 4 In. 35.00
Wedgwood, Pitcher, Green, Bulbous, 6 In. 70.00
Wedgwood, Pitcher, Green, Classic Figures, 8 In. 65.00
Wedgwood, Pitcher, Light Blue, Classical Figures, Circa 1890, 6 In. 75.00
Wedgwood, Pitcher, White Ground, Green Leaves, Berries, Floral 60.00
Wedgwood, Plaque, Blue, White, Louis XVI, Marie Antoinette, Square, Pair 200.00
Wedgwood, Plaque, Bringing In The Game, Black, Lilac, White, 1800, 4 X 12 In. 995.00
Wedgwood, Plaque, Choice Of Hercules, Green Jasper, White, 19 X 7 In. 750.00
Wedgwood, Plaque, Green, Figure & Pedestal, Velvet Frame, Gold Edge 95.00
Wedgwood, Plaque, Green, White Classical Figure, Gold Frame, Signed 95.00
Wedgwood, Plate, Amherst College Scene, Blue, White, 10 1/2 In. .... 8.00 To 8.50
Wedgwood, Plate, Bennington Battle Monoment, Made For Datman & Wood, 1891 ...... 20.50
Wedgwood, Plate, Bennington Battle Monument, Blue, White, England, 10 In. 14.50
Wedgwood, Plate, Boston Tea Party, 9 In. 14.00
Wedgwood, Plate, Cake, Blue, White Floral, Gold, Footed, 6 Dessert Plates 185.00
Wedgwood, Plate, Cake, Sparrow & Bamboo, Dated 1968, 9 1/2 In. 30.00
Wedgwood, Plate, Cattle, Flow Blue, 10 In. 25.00
Wedgwood, Plate, Cobalt Jasper, White Cherubs, Circa 1840, 7 In. 35.00
Wedgwood, Plate, Commemorating Bridges Hall Of Music, Blue Monochrome 20.00
Wedgwood, Plate, Eastern Flowers, 10 In. 35.00
Wedgwood, Plate, Flow Blue, Floral, Incised Mark, Backstamp, 1796-1800 .... 30.00
Wedgwood, Plate, Fort Ticonderoga, 1755-1955, 9 1/4 In. 14.00
Wedgwood, Plate, Friar Tuck Entertains Black Knight, 10 In.Diameter 28.50
Wedgwood, Plate, Friar Tuck Exchanges Buffs With Black Knight, Blue, White 20.00
Wedgwood, Plate, General Grant, Floral Border, 9 In. 22.00
Wedgwood, Plate, George Washington, Blue & White 26.00
Wedgwood, Plate, Green Glaze, Majolica, 8 1/2 In. 15.00
Wedgwood, Plate, Hand-Painted, Fox, Reticulated Border, Signed 85.00
Wedgwood, Plate, Home Of The Fairbanks Family In America 18.50
Wedgwood, Plate, Historical, Blue, 9 In.Diameter 17.50
Wedgwood, Plate, Ivanhoe & Powona, Blue, White, 10 In. 26.00
Wedgwood, Plate, Ivanhoe, Blue, 10 In.Diameter 24.50
Wedgwood, Plate, Ivanhoe, Flow Blue, England, 8 3/4 In. 22.50
Wedgwood, Plate, Ivanhoe, Rebecca Repelling The Templar .... 18.50 To 28.00
Wedgwood, Plate, Longmeadow Town, Settled In 1644, Floral, Blue & White 19.00
Wedgwood, Plate, M.I.T., Blue & White 6.50
Wedgwood, Plate, McKinley Home, Blue, 9 1/4 In. 18.00
Wedgwood, Plate, Mt.Holyoke, Skinner Hall, 10 1/2 In. .... 9.00 To 12.00

Wedgwood, Plate, Nantucket, Blue & White 18.50
Wedgwood, Plate, Old Man Of The Mountains, Blue & White 18.50
Wedgwood, Plate, Old North Church, Boston, 1889 Series, 10 1/4 In. 13.00
Wedgwood, Plate, Onion Pattern 8.00
Wedgwood, Plate, Oyster, Shell & Seaweed, Majolica, Petal Feet 35.00
Wedgwood, Plate, Pierced Rim, Majolica, Marked 1878 .... 50.00
Wedgwood, Plate, Pink Luster, Raised Enameled Floral Border, Circa 1826 ..... 65.00
Wedgwood, Plate, Portrait, Lincoln, Marked, Etruria, England 14.00
Wedgwood, Plate, Queensware, Embossed Border, 12 1/2 In. 22.50
Wedgwood, Plate, Shell Shape, Pink Luster, Pearl Ware, 9 In.Diameter 45.00
Wedgwood, Plate, Slate Blue, Pearl Stone China, Dated Apr.2, 1849 .... 75.00
Wedgwood, Plate, Societas Cincinnatorum Emblem, Blue Border 21.00
Wedgwood, Plate, Soup, Creamware, 10 1/2 In. 18.50
Wedgwood, Plate, South African Leopard, Gray, Black, 10 1/2 In.Diameter 15.00
Wedgwood, Plate, Souvenir, Half Moon On The Hudson, Rose Border 30.00
Wedgwood, Plate, Souvenir, World's Columbian Expo., Building, Etruria 4.75
Wedgwood, Plate, St.Pauls, 1941, 1st Edition 45.00
Wedgwood, Plate, Teddy Roosevelt, Blue & White, Floral Border, 9 In. 22.00
Wedgwood, Plate, Town Of Framingham Library, Blue & White 18.50
Wedgwood, Plate, Town Of Milton, Blue & White 18.50
Wedgwood, Plate, University Of Chicago, Queensware, Set Of 4 .... 28.00
Wedgwood, Plate, Vine, Hand-Painted, Luster, C.1907, 10 1/2 In. .... 9.00 To 12.00
Wedgwood, Plate, West Point, 1931, Military Border, Pink, Etruria, 10 1/2 In. 1.00
Wedgwood, Plate, Willow Pattern, Marked, 10 In.Diameter 6.50
Wedgwood, Platter, Grape & Shell, Queensware, 12 X 16 In. 20.00
Wedgwood, Platter, Majolica, Basket Weave, Butterfly 52.00
Wedgwood, Platter, Pale Green, Darker Edge, Overall Leaves Outlined In Gold ... 80.00
Wedgwood, Platter, Shell & Seaweed, 12 X 9 1/2 In. 40.00
Wedgwood, Pot, Mustard, Leaf & Flower Design, Brass Lid, Marked, 4 In.High ... 65.00
Wedgwood, Pot, Mustard, Light & Dark Blue Jasper, White Mounted Warriors ... 225.00
Wedgwood, Potpourri, Blue, White, Raised Relief, Pierced Lid, Footed, 1830 ... 500.00
Wedgwood, Ring Tree, Dark Blue & White, Signed 60.00
Wedgwood, Salt, Light Blue, White Decoration, Pedestal, Pair 18.00
Wedgwood, Salt, Master, Dark Blue Jasper, White Figures, Silver Rim 35.00
Wedgwood, Sauceboat, Covered, Etruria, Black Transfer On Cream 25.00
Wedgwood, Saucer, Cherub Groups On Border, Light Blue, England 25.00
Wedgwood, Soup, Blue, White, Gold Trim, C.1890 .... 12.00
Wedgwood, Sugar & Creamer, Blue & White, Classical Decoration, Silver Rim ... 70.00
Wedgwood, Sugar & Creamer, Classical Figures, White, Blue, England, Open ... 55.00
Wedgwood, Sugar & Creamer, Commemorating St.John's, Basalt, Green Enamel ... 48.00
Wedgwood, Sugar & Creamer, Dark Blue & White Jasper 95.00
Wedgwood, Sugar & Creamer, Jasperware, Dark Blue 75.00
Wedgwood, Sugar, Basalt, Covered, Raised Design 75.00
Wedgwood, Sugar, Eastern Flower Pattern, Cover 8.50
Wedgwood, Sugar, Hexagon, Creamer, Octagon, Brown Luster, Floral, Gold Borders ... 95.00
Wedgwood, Sugar, Light Blue, White Trees, Maidens, Cover, Signed 16.50
Wedgwood, Teapot, Ball-Shape, Ship, Eagle, Wreath, England, 5 1/2 In.Tall ... 59.00
Wedgwood, Teapot, Blue, Grecian Design 7.00
Wedgwood, Teapot, Classical Figures, Blue Jasper 97.00
Wedgwood, Teapot, Covered, Raised Flaxman Figures, Black Basalt 105.00
Wedgwood, Teapot, Creamer, Sugar, Drabware, Blue Floral 575.00
Wedgwood, Teapot, Jasper, Blue, White Figures & Window Finial, C.1870 ..... 110.00
Wedgwood, Teapot, Jasperware, Dark Blue 95.00
Wedgwood, Teapot, Pink Poppy, Gold Trim, 3 1/4 In.High 22.50
Wedgwood, Teapot, Sugar, Creamer, Three Cups & Saucers, Gold, Blue, Brown ... 250.00
Wedgwood, Teapot, Two Cups & Saucers, Tray, Pearlware, Cream Ground 200.00
Wedgwood, Tile, Brown & White Stylized Flower Forms, Brass Corners, Feet ... 13.00
Wedgwood, Tile, Calendar, 1896 .... 75.00
Wedgwood, Tile, Calendar, 1897, Made For Jones McDuffy & Stratton 95.00
Wedgwood, Tile, Calendar, 1900, Made For Jones McDuffy & Stratton 80.00
Wedgwood, Tile, Calendar, 1904, Frigate Constitution In Chase 30.00
Wedgwood, Tile, Calendar, 1907 .... 32.00
Wedgwood, Tile, Calendar, 1907, Made For Jones McDuffy & Stratton 40.00
Wedgwood, Tile, Calendar, 1914 .... 29.00 To 32.00
Wedgwood, Tile, Calendar, 1918 ....
Wedgwood, Tile, Calendar, 1918, Made For Jones McDuffy & Stratton ....

Wedgwood, Tile, Gaming Scene, Blue, White, Marked, 8 In.Square 38.00
Wedgwood, Tile, July, Blue, White, 8 In.Square 65.00
Wedgwood, Tile, October, Blue, White, 6 In.Square 40.00
Wedgwood, Toothpick, Blue Jasper, Medallion Of Josiah Wedgwood, 1900 .... 19.00
Wedgwood, Tray, Dark Blue, White, Classical Figures, 6 1/2 X 9 1/4 In. 97.50
Wedgwood, Tray, Majolica, Sea Motif, Coral, Seals, Waves, Signed Wedgwood 65.00
Wedgwood, Tumbler, Dark Blue, Classic Figures 65.00
Wedgwood, Tureen, Brown Transfer, Cover, Diamond Registry Mark 1883 .... 15.00
Wedgwood, Urn, Blue Jasper, White, Two Handle, 11 In.Tall 295.00
Wedgwood, Urn, Dip, Blue, Jasper, Classical Figures, Square Base, Anthemion 100.00
Wedgwood, Vase, Black Basalt, Thistle, Harp, Shamrock, 9 1/2 In. 100.00
Wedgwood, Vase, Blue & White, Scenes, Impressed Wedgwood Only, 5 In.High 55.00
Wedgwood, Vase, Blue Dragon, Luster, 8 3/4 In.High 225.00
Wedgwood, Vase, Blue Hummingbird, Luster, 8 3/4 In.High 225.00
Wedgwood, Vase, Classical Figures, Tree, Blue, White, 7 In.Tall 52.00
Wedgwood, Vase, Covered, Jasperware, 13 1/2 In.High .... *Illus* 800.00
Wedgwood, Vase, Creamware, Embossed White Flowers, Portland Blue, Footed 37.50
Wedgwood, Vase, Dragon Luster, Blue, Gold Dragons, Phoenix Birds 145.00
Wedgwood, Vase, Dragon Luster, Blue, 5 In.High 160.00
Wedgwood, Vase, Dragon Luster, Blues, Large Gilt Dragon, 8 1/4 In. 238.00
Wedgwood, Vase, Dragon Luster, Orange, Blue Lining, Gilt Dragons, 8 1/2 In. 450.00
Wedgwood, Vase, Dragon Luster, Portland Vase Mark, Pair 8 In., One 11 In. 565.00
Wedgwood, Vase, English Landscape, White Handles, Etruria 54.00
Wedgwood, Vase, Fairy Luster, Butterflies, Blue, Green, Red, Portland, 4 In. 125.00
Wedgwood, Vase, Fairy Luster, Elves, 8 1/4 In.High 425.00
Wedgwood, Vase, Fairyland Luster, Gold Dragons & Edging, Blue Ground, Marked 155.00
Wedgwood, Vase, Fairyland Luster, Panels, Elves, Gnomes, Phoenix Bird, 8 In. 650.00
Wedgwood, Vase, Fairyland, Peacock Design, Orange, Portland Mark, 5 In.Tall 127.00
Wedgwood, Vase, Hummingbird Luster, Mottled Flame Lining, 4 3/8 In. 235.00
Wedgwood, Vase, Jasper, Black, White Classical Figures, 5 In.High 85.00
Wedgwood, Vase, Jasperware, Blue, White Children In Relief, Signed 48.00
Wedgwood, Vase, Jasperware, Portland, Blue, White Figures, Signed 250.00

Wedgwood, Vase, Covered, Jasperware, 13 1/2 In.High

Wedgwood, Vase, Luster, Orange, Gilt Butterflies, Blue Inside, 4 1/4 In. 120.00
Wedgwood, Vase, Mottled Blue, Butterfly, Dragonfly, Aqua & Gold Inside 135.00
Wedgwood, Vase, Pale Blue & White Jasper, Classic Figures, Handles 195.00
Wedgwood, Vase, Portland, Dark Blue And White, 6 In. 175.00
Wedgwood, Vase, Spill, Black Basalt, Classical Figures & Flowers, Signed 75.00
Wedgwood, Vase, Spill, Black Basalt, Classical Figures, England, 7 3/4 In. 125.00
Wedgwood, Vase, Spill, Blue Jasper, Classical Figures, Silver Rim, C.1891 .... 65.00
Wedgwood, Vase, Victoria Ware, Blue Medallions On Blue Green, Pearlware 310.00
Wedgwood, Vase, Victoria Ware, White & Gold On Dark Blue Green, Pearlware 310.00
Wedgwood, Vase, Victoria Ware, White & Gold On Green Blue, Pearlware 180.00
Wedgwood, Vase, White Classical Figures, Blue Jasperware, 1860, 6 In.High 100.00
Wedgwood, Washstand Set, Iris, Rectangular Bowl, Signed, 3 Piece 95.00

Weller pottery was first made in 1873 in Fultonham, Ohio. The firm

moved to Zanesville, Ohio in 1882. Art wares were first made in 1893.
Hundreds of lines of pottery were made including Louwelsa, Eocean,
Dickens, and Sicardo before the pottery closed in 1948.

Weller, Basket, Brown, Yellow & White Flowers, Twig Handle, Signed	17.00
Weller, Basket, Hanging, Embossed Pink Floral, Grapes, Green Ground	15.00
Weller, Basket, Roba, White, Green Base, Embossed Floral, Twigs Handle	25.00
Weller, Basket, Woodcraft, 3 Cherries In Relief With Ribbon, Pedestal	20.00
Weller, Basket, Yellow Green, Roses, Rope Handles, Block Signature	50.00
Weller, Bowl, Ardsley	18.00
Weller, Bowl, Drippy Maroon On Green, Two Handles, Incised Mark, 10 In.	16.00
Weller, Bowl, Flower, Iris Pattern, Deep Green, 15 In.Long, 2 1/4 In High	27.50
Weller, Bowl, Flower, Raised Black Lattice & Rim, Green Leaves, Pastel Fruit	14.00
Weller, Bowl, Rosy Tan, Wild Rose Sprig, Ear Handles, Marked G, 8 In.	8.00
Weller, Bowl, Squirrel Sitting On Edge, 8 In.Diameter	22.00
Weller, Bowl, Triangular, Acanthus Leaves Form Sides, Yellow, Script-Signed	12.00
Weller, Bowl, Woodcraft, Basket Type, Pink Roses On 2 Sides, Signed	25.00
Weller, Box, Pansy Design, Star Shape, Brown Glaze	45.00
Weller, Cachepot, Embossed Apples On Lattice, Glossy Black Ground	14.00
Weller, Candleholder, Louwelsa, Miniature, Artist V.A., Floral, Green To Tan	20.00
Weller, Candlestick, Louwelsa, Floral Decoration, High Glaze, 5 In.High	76.00
Weller, Candlestick, Louwelsa, Floral, 9 In.	73.00
Weller, Candlestick, Pansies, Signed, Louwelsa, 5 In.Tall	25.00
Weller, Console Set, Blue, Cameo Centerpiece, Pair 15 In.Candlesticks	29.50
Weller, Console Set, Marvo, 2 In.Candleholders, 4 Piece	27.50
Weller, Cruet, Louwelsa, Yellow Flowers	125.00
Weller, Dish, Baby, Ducks, Hand-Painted, Marked	18.00
Weller, Dish, Feeding, Brown Rabbit, Bluebird, Embossed	12.00
Weller, Ewer, Aurelian, Berries, High Glaze, Artist Initials, 8 1/2 In.	75.00
Weller, Ewer, Chess Players, Dickensware, Peach & Gray Colors	325.00
Weller, Ewer, Dickensware, Antlered Elk Decoration, Matte Finish, 7 In.	90.00
Weller, Ewer, Embossed Floral, Matte Finish, Ribbed Bottom, Handle, 7 In.	19.00
Weller, Ewer, Yellow Roses, 6 1/2 In.	55.00
Weller, Figurine, Pheasant, Pair	75.00
Weller, Flower Frog, Lizard, Signed	14.00
Weller, Jar, Tobacco, Dickensware, Oriental Man	195.00
Weller, Jar, Tobacco, Louwelsa, Pipe & Match Scene, Brass Top, Artist-Signed	75.00
Weller, Jardiniere, Blue Ground, Yellow Figures, 9 1/2 X 8 3/4 In.High	85.00
Weller, Jardiniere, Bluebirds	65.00
Weller, Jardiniere, Dickensware, Brown, Nasturtiums, Dark Cream Inside	65.00
Weller, Jardiniere, Floral Decoration	65.00
Weller, Jardiniere, Forest In Relief	35.00
Weller, Jardiniere, Forest, Impressed Weller In Block, 9 In.High	45.00
Weller, Jardiniere, Gray, Green, Brown, Raised Jewels & Circles, 13 1/2 In.	72.00
Weller, Jardiniere, Green Brown Ground, Orange Iris Decoration, 8 1/2 In.	45.00
Weller, Jardiniere, Louwelsa, Daffodil, Signed N.D.Garmo, 10 1/2 In.	85.00
Weller, Jardiniere, Majolica Type Design, Rose, Green, Brown	27.00
Weller, Jardiniere, Pansies On Chocolate Ground	59.00
Weller, Jardiniere, Raised Rustic Scene, Dull Glaze, 7 In.Diameter	12.00
Weller, Jardiniere, Rozane, Iris Design, Glossy, 8 X 9 1/2 In.	45.00
Weller, Jug, Aurelian, Blackberry Decoration, Handle	75.00
Weller, Jug, Dickensware, Advertising, Mt.Vernon Bridge Construction Co.	265.00
Weller, Jug, Dickensware, Green & Brown, Embossed Corn, Painted Cherries	20.00
Weller, Jug, Dickensware, Green & Orange Leaves With Berries, Cork	95.00
Weller, Jug, Louwelsa, Artist H., Cherries & Leaves On Brown	40.00
Weller, Jug, Monk Design, Handle, Dickens, Second Line	165.00
Weller, Jug, Mt.Vernon, Ohio Bridge Building Co., Dickensware	265.00
Weller, Jug, Rum, No.330, Grapes, Leaves, Louwelsa	45.00
Weller, Lamp Base, Bulbous, Circa 1880	115.00
Weller, Lamp, Owl, Tree Trunks, Flowers, Woodcraft Line, Block Letter Mark	65.00
Weller, Mug, Beige, Leaf Decoration, Handled, 4 3/4 In.High	9.00
Weller, Mug, Blackberries, Signed, 6 1/4 In.Tall	60.00
Weller, Mug, Grapes, Vine, Signed, Louwelsa, 6 In.Tall	50.00
Weller, Mug, Louwelsa, Dark Brown, Underglaze Cones & Foliage, Handle	42.50
Weller, Mug, Portrait Of Monk, Signed L.J.Burgess	50.00
Weller, Pitcher, Basket Weave, Beige, Glazed, 7 In.High	15.00
Weller, Pitcher, Blue Ground, Yellow Flowers, Green Twig Handle, 6 1/2 In.	7

Weller, Pitcher, Etna, Gray & Blue Decoration, 6 In.	34.50
Weller, Pitcher, Etna, Gray Ground, Purple Grapes, Tankard, 14 In.High	95.00
Weller, Pitcher, Green, Embossed Flowers & Leaves, Stem Handle, 5 In.	13.00
Weller, Pitcher, Horizontal Impressed Lines, Pink, 5 In.Tall	15.00
Weller, Pitcher, Louwelsa, Depicts An Ear Of Corn, Tankard, 14 In.	110.00
Weller, Pitcher, Louwelsa, Straw Flower Decoration, Footed, 5 1/2 In.	49.00
Weller, Pitcher, Milk, Ribbed, Pink, 5 5/8 X 5 1/8 In.	6.00
Weller, Pitcher, Rose Design, Mark	12.50
Weller, Pitcher, Seminude Woman, Matte Finish, 8 In.	56.00
Weller, Pitcher, Woman Golfer, Tankard, Dickensware, 11 In.High	125.00
Weller, Planter, Blue Green, Brown Oak Leaves, Label, 6 In. X 12 In.Long	18.00
Weller, Planter, Forest, 2 Handles, 3 1/4 In.High	10.00
Weller, Plaque, Bust Of Ulysses S. Grant, Matte Finish, 5 In.Oval	44.50
Weller, Rose Bowl, Palm Trees, Sea, Sunset, Signed, 3 1/2 In.Tall	75.00
Weller, Rowboat, Marked Weller, Gray Green, 9 1/2 In.High, 3 1/2 In.Wide	16.00
Weller, Spittoon, Dickensware, Dark Green Ground, Leaf Decoration, Signed	95.00
Weller, Spittoon, Louwelsa, Flower Design, Yellow, Ladies, 3 In.Tall	65.00
Weller, Tankard, Etna, Signed, 14 In.High	95.00
Weller, Tankard, Floretta, 16 1/2 In.High	85.00
Weller, Teapot, Rose Design, Pink, Gold, 5 X 8 In.	20.00
Weller, Tub, Grape Clusters On Sides, Two Handles, 8 1/2 In.Diameter	25.00
Weller, Umbrella Stand, Louwelsa, Three Large Mums	98.00
Weller, Vase Planter, Gold, Brown, Green, 1912, 4 1/2	14.00
Weller, Vase, A.Ansel, Blue, Pink, Yellow & Blue Flowers, Mark, 7 In.	15.00
Weller, Vase, Allover High Relief Floral, Tan, Green Interior, 8 In.	65.00
Weller, Vase, Ardsley, Flaring Top, 9 In.High	10.00
Weller, Vase, Art Nouveau Tulip, Bulbous, Blue, Green, Iridescent, 16 In.Tall	175.00
Weller, Vase, Art Nouveau Woman's Figure Across Front, Matte	57.50
Weller, Vase, Art Nouveau, Matte, Female On Front & Back, 16 In.High	85.00
Weller, Vase, Aurelian, Kidney Shape, Grapes, Signed E.Roberts	325.00
Weller, Vase, Baldwin, Blue Ground, Apples, 12 1/2 In.	85.00
Weller, Vase, Baldwin, Similar To Woodcraft, Impressed Weller In Block	25.00
Weller, Vase, Blue Drapery, Matte Glaze, 4 1/2 In.	8.00
Weller, Vase, Blue, White Dogwood, Two Handles, Marked, 6 In.High	9.75
Weller, Vase, Blue, White Floral, Two Handles At Base, 9 In.	15.00
Weller, Vase, Bonita, Berry, Leaf On Cream Ground, Signature Ferrell	60.00
Weller, Vase, Bronze Ware, Marked, 9 In.High	52.75
Weller, Vase, Brown Shades, Flowers, High Glaze, 4 In.	25.00
Weller, Vase, Bud, Louwelsa, Brown Glaze, Yellow Floral, 4 1/2 In.	44.00
Weller, Vase, Bud, Rose Horseshoe, Ivory, Three Prongs, 8 1/2 In.	13.00
Weller, Vase, Bud, Tree Trunk, Joined Limbs, Two Prongs, Brown, 7 In.	15.00
Weller, Vase, Bulbous, Olive Green, Signed Breton, 6 In.High	10.00
Weller, Vase, Burntwood, Floral, Unmarked, 8 1/2 In.	32.00
Weller, Vase, Chase, Dark Blue, White Hunt Scene, 5 1/2 In.	45.00
Weller, Vase, Climbing Salamander, Matte, 6 1/2 In.	40.00
Weller, Vase, Clown Taking A Bow, Dickensware, 7 In.	150.00
Weller, Vase, Comet, Stars On Blue Ground, Matte, Marked, 5 1/4 In.	15.00
Weller, Vase, Copper & Green Floral, Tapers At Neck, Signed Sicard	185.00
Weller, Vase, Coppertone, 6 1/2 In. _Illus_	19.00
Weller, Vase, Cornish, Mottled Brown, Berries, Leaves, 7 3/4 In.	32.50
Weller, Vase, Cream Color, Etched Daisies, Matte Glaze, 10 In.	15.00
Weller, Vase, Dark Blue, Pink Floral, Green Leaves, Mark, 9 1/2 In.	60.00
Weller, Vase, Dark Brown Glaze, Leaves, Two Handles, 8 1/2 In.	45.00
Weller, Vase, Darsie, Light Blue, Scalloped Rim, 8 In.	12.00
Weller, Vase, Dickensware, Gibson Girl Playing Golf, Flask Shape, 7 1/2 In.	150.00
Weller, Vase, Dickensware, Sea Gulls, 8 In.High	130.00
Weller, Vase, Dickensware, Sheep Herder, White Sheep, Trees, Mountains, 12 In.	300.00
Weller, Vase, Dickensware, Woman Golfer, Signed, 10 In.	115.00
Weller, Vase, Dogwood Design, Branch Handle, Bulbous, Pink, Green, 5 1/2 In.	18.00
Weller, Vase, Dogwood Design, Globe Shape, Pink, Green, 5 1/2 In.Tall	18.00
Weller, Vase, Double, Handle Connects, Green, Wild Rose, Artist Initials	15.00
Weller, Vase, Drapery, Fan Shape, 4 In.High	12.50
Weller, Vase, Eocean, Pink To Gray To Green & Brown, Purple & White Pansies	42.50
Weller, Vase, Eocean, Red Thistles & Green Stems On Gray To White	100.00
Weller, Vase, Etna, Dark To Light Gray, Red Thistles, Embossed	38.00
Weller, Vase, Etna, Flowers, Vines, Gray To Rose, 6 1/4 In.High	35.00

Weller, Vase, Etna, Pink Flowers On Gray To White Ground, 8 1/2 In.High 65.00
Weller, Vase, Etna, 8 1/2 In. .... *Illus* 55.00
Weller, Vase, Floral On Blue To Green Ground, Script Inscribed, Matte 85.00
Weller, Vase, Floretta, Cherry Motif, 6 In.High 32.00
Weller, Vase, Floretta, Grape Decoration, Brown, Pair 75.00
Weller, Vase, Floretta, Grape Decoration, 10 1/2 In. 40.00
Weller, Vase, Floretta, Grays, Raised Pink Floral, Signed, 4 1/2 In.High 15.00
Weller, Vase, Floretta, Green Flowers & Yellow Berries, Root Handles 55.00
Weller, Vase, Floretta, Tan, Brown, Grape Design, 7 1/2 In. 40.00
Weller, Vase, Flower Design, Blue, Pink, Yellow, Signed, 3 3/4 In.High 43.00
Weller, Vase, Flower Design, Brown, Orange, Triangular Shape, 4 In.Tall 25.00
Weller, Vase, Flower Design, Pink, Blue, & Gray, Signed Kennedy, 8 In.High 40.00
Weller, Vase, Flowers, Green To Orange, Crackle Glaze, Signed, 9 1/2 In.Tall 95.00
Weller, Vase, Golfer, Dickensware, Club Ready To Swing, Marked 200.00
Weller, Vase, Grape & Leaf Decoration, Artist FDD 60.00
Weller, Vase, Gray To Mauve To Pink, Gray Border, Floral, 3 3/4 In.High 43.00

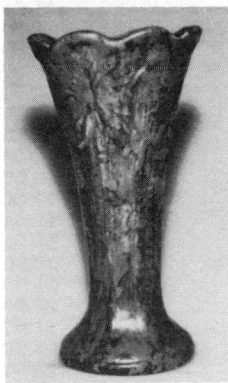

Weller, Vase, Coppertone, 6 1/2 In.
See Page 636

Weller, Vase, Etna, 8 1/2 In.

Weller, Vase, Green & White With Flowers, Handled, Signed, 12 In.High 23.00
Weller, Vase, Green Red Leaf Decorations, Marked Louwelsa, 4 In. 52.50
Weller, Vase, Hudson, D.England, Blue, Blueberries 59.00
Weller, Vase, Hudson, Daisy, Pale Blue Ground, Signed Pillsbury 85.00
Weller, Vase, Hudson, Grape And Leaf, Artist Signed, Frank Didonatis 63.00
Weller, Vase, Hudson, Gray Ground, Pink Cascading Flowers, 12 In.High 23.00
Weller, Vase, Indian Pattern, Black, Tan, Beige, 7 In.High 75.00
Weller, Vase, Ivoria, Two Handles, Urn Shape, Impressed Script Mark, 6 In. 14.00
Weller, Vase, L'Art Nouveau Line, Matte, Marked In Circle, 12 1/4 In. 69.50
Weller, Vase, Lasa, Rose Bowl Type, Scenic, Iridescent 58.00
Weller, Vase, Lasa, Scenic, Abstract, Iridescent, 9 1/4 In. 110.00
Weller, Vase, Lasa, Scenic, Iridescent, Red, Green, Purple, Gold, 8 1/2 In.High 115.00
Weller, Vase, Lasa, Scenic, Signed, 5 In. 135.00
Weller, Vase, Lasa, Scenic, 8 In.High 125.00
Weller, Vase, Lessell, Trees, Sky, Land, Water, Gold & Silver Ground 60.00
Weller, Vase, Lizard Design, Green, Pink, Signed Block Letters, 4 1/2 In.Tall 55.00
Weller, Vase, Louwelsa, Blue, White Flowers, Minnie Mitchell, 8 In. 47.00
Weller, Vase, Louwelsa, Brown & Green Glaze, Floral, 9 In. 51.00
Weller, Vase, Louwelsa, Brown Glaze, Cherries, 3 In. 25.00
Weller, Vase, Louwelsa, Brown To Green Glaze, Underglaze Floral, 9 In. 51.00
Weller, Vase, Louwelsa, Cylinder, Wild Roses & Stems, Signed LS, 11 In. 40.00
Weller, Vase, Louwelsa, Dark Brown, Olive, Yellow Floral, Artist R.S., 7 In. 92.50
Weller, Vase, Louwelsa, Floral, Flattened Gourd Form, Ruffled, 5 In. 49.00
Weller, Vase, Louwelsa, Floral, One Left-Handed, One Right-Handed, Pair 85.00
Weller, Vase, Louwelsa, Floral, Signed, 8 In. 70.00
Weller, Vase, Louwelsa, Floral, Wide Base, Triangle Top, 3 1/2 In. 56.50
Weller, Vase, Louwelsa, Grapes, Signed E.R., 24 In.High 425.00
Weller, Vase, Louwelsa, Green, Brown, Artist-Signed, 6 1/2 In.High 35.00
Weller, Vase, Louwelsa, Leaf Design, Signed WM, 11 In. 60.00
Weller, Vase, Louwelsa, Panting Dog, Signed Wilson, 15 In.High 375.00

Weller, Vase, Louwelsa, Pillow, Blue, Floral	185.00
Weller, Vase, Louwelsa, Yellow Daffodils, Signed Mary Pierce, 10 In.	75.00
Weller, Vase, Maroon, Marbelized, Small Handles On Sides, Mark, 7 In.	14.00
Weller, Vase, Maroon, Two Handles, Incised Mark Under Glaze	12.00
Weller, Vase, Mint Green, Raised Yellow Daisy Decoration, 7 In.	8.00
Weller, Vase, Pale Blue Ground, Daisies, Two Handles, Artist Pillsbury	85.00
Weller, Vase, Palm Vines, Orange & Green Ground, 12 In., Pair	55.00
Weller, Vase, Pillow, Dickensware	300.00
Weller, Vase, Pillow, Dickensware, Monk, Artist's Initials	115.00
Weller, Vase, Pink & Maroon Apple Blossoms On White, Blue Rim, Signed	45.00
Weller, Vase, Pink Luster, Bulbous, 6 In.	20.00
Weller, Vase, Pitcher Type, Louwelsa, Flowers & Leaves, Artist Signed	185.00
Weller, Vase, Pitcher Type, Louwelsa, Flowers On Gray To White, Signed	55.00
Weller, Vase, Portrait Of Dog, Signed, 7 1/2 In.	175.00
Weller, Vase, Roma, Cameo Center, Garlands Of Roses, 16 In.Long Handles	34.50
Weller, Vase, Roma, Cameo, Square, 4 In.High	12.50
Weller, Vase, Roma, Incised Red Flowers, Triangular, 9 In.High	17.50
Weller, Vase, Rudlor, Green, White Floral	15.00
Weller, Vase, Sicard, Allover Purple & Green Floral	185.00
Weller, Vase, Sicard, Bulbous, Silver Snowflakes On Blue Red Ground, 6 In.	115.00
Weller, Vase, Sicard, Dragonflies, Green, Lavender, Gold, 4 1/2 In.High	125.00
Weller, Vase, Sicard, Flower Design, Signed, 5 1/4 In.High	140.00
Weller, Vase, Sicard, Green & Purple Iridescent, Signed, 5 In.	245.00
Weller, Vase, Sicard, Green Iridescent, Molded Daisies, Signed	165.00
Weller, Vase, Sicard, Insects, Iridescent, Green, Lavender, Signed	135.00
Weller, Vase, Sicard, Iridescent, Multicolor Swirls, Pyriform, Unsigned	70.00
Weller, Vase, Sicard, Iridescent, Signed, 7 1/4 In.	92.00
Weller, Vase, Sicard, Signed, 6 1/2 In.	100.00
Weller, Vase, Sicard, Squat, Paneled, Contiguous Handles, Tooled, Blue	150.00
Weller, Vase, Silvertone, Artist A., Pastel Type Finish, Stamped Weller Ware	35.00
Weller, Vase, Silvertone, Handled, Signed, 6 1/2 In.Tall, 3 In.Across	35.00
Weller, Vase, Snowberry, Beige, Bulbous, Script-Signed, 9 In.High	20.00
Weller, Vase, Stick, Louwelsa, Floral Decoration	32.00
Weller, Vase, Tree Trunk	15.00
Weller, Vase, Tree Trunks, Green, Beige, Brown, Signed, 10 1/2 In.	25.00
Weller, Vase, Trees, Scenic, Signed, 8 1/2 In.Tall	110.00
Weller, Vase, Wall, Donatello, 12 In.	15.00
Weller, Vase, Woodcraft, Bark, Leaves, Owl, Tree Section, Marked, 10 In.	37.50
Weller, Vase, Woodcraft, Single Long-Stemmed Pink Rose In Relief, Signed	15.00
Weller, Vase, Woodcraft, Tree Trunk, Red Cherries, 2 Openings For Flowers	12.50
Weller, Vase, Woodcraft, 8 3/4 In.High	12.50
Wells Fargo, Express Bag, 12 X 18 In.	15.00
Wells Fargo, Safe, Office, Iron, Wood, Brass, Delano Patent, Rivets, C.1860	125.00
Wells Fargo, Sealing Device, Brass, Guilford, Mo., Wood Handle	54.50
Western Stoneware Co., Vase, Green, Stamped, Ill., 10 In.High	75.00
Wheeling Pottery, Plate, Blue	8.00
Whieldon, Plate, Brown & Green, Splotching, Scalloped Border, 9 1/2 In.	50.00
Willow, see Blue Willow	
Witch's Ball, Red Glass, Cane Holder	12.00
Witch's Ball, Round, Clear, Hole In Top, Colored Stripes	49.00
Wooden, see also Kitchen, Store, Tool	
Wooden, Ashtray, Carved Owl, Amber Glass Eyes	12.00
Wooden, Barrel, Biscuit, Porcelain Liner, Silver Trim, Lid, S N Mark	43.00
Wooden, Barrel, Carved From Single Log, 18th Century, 19 In.High	90.00
Wooden, Basket, Fruit, Carved, Ram's Head Handles, Openwork, Pair	375.00
Wooden, Bellows, Blacksmith, Red Paint, Leather & Iron Hardware, 1870, 7 Ft.	75.00
Wooden, Bootjack, Folding, Walnut	12.50
Wooden, Bootjack, Lyre Shape, Spring At Top	5.00
Wooden, Bowl, Burl, Bird's-Eye Maple	65.00
Wooden, Bowl, Burl, 8 1/4 In.	70.00
Wooden, Bowl, Butter, Oval, 9 X 16 In.	22.50
Wooden, Bowl, Butter, Round, Blue & Gray Paint, Double Bottom	65.00
Wooden, Bowl, Draw Shaved, 17 1/2 In.Long	27.00
Wooden, Bowl, Inlaid, Pedestal, 2 1/4 In.High	4.00
Wooden, Bowl, Salad, Kiaat Wood, Hand-Carved, South Africa	15.00
Wooden, Bowl, 13 1/2 In.Diameter	60.00

Wooden, Box, Elephant Shape, Hand Carved, Hinged Top	40.00
Wooden, Box, Pencil, Dome Top, Polished, Jeweled	10.00
Wooden, Box, Tobacco, Pipe Rack Ends	9.00
Wooden, Bust, Emperor, Dressed In Armor, 29 In.High	100.00
Wooden, Bust, Lady, Italian, Gilt, Central Jewel In Collar, C.1650	100.00
Wooden, Bust, Virgin, Italian, Polychrome, 16 In., C.1650	425.00
Wooden, Candle Box, Wall, Slopes, Red, 16 In.Long	81.00
Wooden, Candle Box, Wall, Two Compartments, White Pine	50.00
Wooden, Candlestick, Circa 1923, 12 In., Pair	12.00
Wooden, Candlestick, Italian, Carved, Gilt, Triangular Base, Pair	80.00
Wooden, Candlestick, Italian, Renaissance Style, Gilt, Carved, 27 In.	60.00
Wooden, Candlestick, Mahogany, Brass Insert, 8 In.High, Pair	15.00
Wooden, Candlestick, Turned, Red Paint, Pair	110.00
Wooden, Candlestick, Unmarked Pairpoint Hurricane Shade, 14 In., Pair	500.00
Wooden, Cannon, Barrel, British, Naval, Presentation, Nelson's Victory, 1850	97.50
Wooden, Case, Carrying, Brass Trimmed, 17 X 10 X 9 In.	28.00
Wooden, Cherub, Italian, C.1670, Worm Holes, 16 X 10 In.High	350.00
Wooden, Chest, Hunters, Castles, Hand-Carved, Iron Hinges, 12 1/2 X 7 In.	100.00
Wooden, Child's Face, Pine, Carving	120.00
Wooden, Corkscrew, Carved, Figure Of Man	7.50
Wooden, Deer, Reclining, Hand-Carved, 6 In.High	7.00
Wooden, Desk, Lap, Compartments	16.00
Wooden, Dipper, Drinking, Maple, One Piece	80.00
Wooden, Doorstop, Owl, Hand-Carved, 8 In.High	4.00
Wooden, Eagle, American, Gilt, Maurice Decker, Maine, Pair, Carved	950.00
Wooden, Eagle, Fighting Coiled Snake, C.1860, 15 In.High, Carved	79.50
Wooden, Eagle, Gilt, American, C.1850, 51 In.Wide *Illus*	700.00
Wooden, Eagle, Gilt, Rockwork Base, Wings Spread, C.1750, 13 In.High	300.00
Wooden, Figurine, Angel, Standing, Polychrome, 28 1/4 In., C.1750	150.00
Wooden, Figurine, Armorial, Cromwellian Helmet, Walnut, Oak, C.1870	125.00
Wooden, Figurine, Bust Of Poet Dante, 13 In.High	135.00
Wooden, Figurine, Christ, Dead, Spanish, Polychrome, 16 5/8 In., C.1790	90.00
Wooden, Figurine, Christ, French, Man Of Sorrows, Polychrome, C.1530	650.00
Wooden, Figurine, Classical, Poplar, American, 1800, Pair *Illus*	650.00
Wooden, Figurine, Four Seasons, 16th Century, 14 In.Long, Set	650.00
Wooden, Figurine, John The Baptist, Italian, Polychrome, Standing, C.1750	625.00
Wooden, Figurine, King David, Seated, 44 3/4 In., C.1750	325.00
Wooden, Figurine, Kuan Yin, Gilded, Polychrome, Jeweled Tiara, Ming Dynasty	700.00
Wooden, Figurine, Magus, South German, Polychrome, Standing, C.1730	700.00
Wooden, Figurine, Monastery Figure, Italian, C.1550, 40 In.High	265.00
Wooden, Figurine, Peasant, Italian, Creche, Walking, Polychrome, C.1750	250.00
Wooden, Figurine, Saint, Spanish Colonial, Polychrome, Standing, Male, C.1750	50.00
Wooden, Figurine, Two Frogs On Rocks, Boxwood, Oriental, 6 In.High	115.00
Wooden, Figurine, Virgin & Child, Italian, Standing, 19 In., C.1790	130.00
Wooden, Figurine, Virgin, Italian, Standing, Polychrome, C.1750, 18 In.High	275.00
Wooden, Group, Equestrian, Flemish, Polychrome & Gilt, Relief, C.1550	550.00
Wooden, Group, Pieta, Seated Virgin, 16 1/2 In.High, C.1550	425.00
Wooden, Group, St.Anne, Virgin, & Child, Flemish, Polychrome, C.1550	1200.00
Wooden, Group, Virgin & Child, French, Standing Figure, Polychrome, C.1350	2500.00
Wooden, Horn, Carved, Bearded Man, 8 1/2 In.Tall	35.00
Wooden, Ice Cream Freezer, Child's, Alaskan, Hand Crank	19.50
Wooden, Horse, see Carousel Horse	
Wooden, Lioness On Rock, Patinated Wood, 5 1/2 In.High	65.00
Wooden, Mold, Butter, Carved Flower, Square, Case	20.00
Wooden, Mold, Butter, Leaf, Rectangular	10.00
Wooden, Mold, Butter, Sheaf Of Wheat	17.50
Wooden, Mold, Butter, Star, Handle	70.00
Wooden, Mold, Butter, Swan Pattern, 1 Pound	32.00
Wooden, Mold, Cigar, Manufacture's, 20 Hole	6.50
Wooden, Mold, Cigar, 12 In.Long	25.00
Wooden, Mold, Cigar, 20 In.Long, 4 1/2 In.Wide	15.00
Wooden, Mold, Cigar, 20 Tube, Dated 1882	25.00
Wooden, Mold, Cigar, 22 In.Long	17.50
Wooden, Mold, Maple Sugar, Dog, Two Parts	62.00
Wooden, Mold, Maple Sugar, Flower In Center	45.00
Wooden, Mold, Maple Sugar, Rooster, 2 Equal Parts, 2 1/2 In.High	50.00

Wooden, Eagle, Gilt, American, C.1850, 51 In.Wide
See Page 639

Wooden, Figurine, Classical, Poplar,
American, 1800, Pair
See Page 639

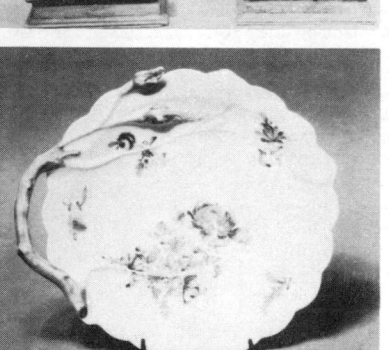

Worcester, Basket, Oval, Pierced, 7 1/2 In.Long
See Page 641

Worcester, Dish, Sweetmeat, Blind Earl Pattern
See Page 641

Wooden, Mold, Maple, Squirrel Shape, Three Piece	32.50
Wooden, Mold, Miniball, Hand Whittled, 18th Century	45.00
Wooden, Mug, Maple, American, 13 1/2 In.Tall	150.00
Wooden, Nutcracker, Carved Squirrel	25.00
Wooden, Ornamental Piece, Head Of Beast, C.1650, 24 1/2 In.	250.00
Wooden, Peacock, Boxwood, 8 In.High, Carved	95.00
Wooden, Plaque, Bronze Profile Head Of Lincoln, Oval, 8 In.	15.00
Wooden, Plaque, Eagle, Spread Wings, Rockwork Base, C.1800, 20 1/2 In.Long	400.00
Wooden, Plaque, Mother-Of-Pearl Floral Inset, 8 X 13 In.	65.00
Wooden, Plate, Bread, Hand Carved, Penna.Dutch, Gib Uns Unser Taglich Brot	14.50
Wooden, Rooster, Schimmel, 8 1/4 In.High	400.00

Wooden, Shell Ornament, Gilded, 13 Segments, Horizontal Ribbing 200.00
Wooden, Sap Bucket, Iron Bands At Top & Bottom, Wire Tree Holder 10.00
Wooden, Shoehorn, Hand-Painted, Marked China, 16 In.Long 10.00
Wooden, Skif, For Removing Lather From Horses, Primitive 12.00
Wooden, Spigot For Cask 6.00
Wooden, Stagecoach, 2 Coachmen, Woman & Child, 19th Century 375.00
   Wooden, Telephone, see Telephone
Wooden, Tiger, Glass Eyes, Oriental Signature At Base, 12 In.Long 135.00
Wooden, Toothpick, Hand-Carved, Bird At Side 11.75
Wooden, Tray, Maple, Turned, 18th Century, 20 In.Diameter 130.00
Wooden, Tub, Carved From Single Log, Iron Bail Across Top, 18th Century 225.00
Wooden, Yoke, Animal, Hickory, Iron Bell 35.00
Wooden, Yoke, Animal's, Iron Bell 35.00
Wooden, Yoke, Goat's 5.00
Wooden, Yoke, Ox, American Black Walnut, Ring, Irons, 1870, 50 In.Long 75.00
   Worcester, see also Royal Worcester
Worcester, Basket, Blue & White, Oval, Pierced, Applied Floral, 1st Period 375.00
Worcester, Basket, Oval, Pierced, 7 1/2 In.Long .... Illus 1200.00
Worcester, Bowl, Blue Scale, Cartouche Panels, Gilt, Kakiemon, 1st Period 325.00
Worcester, Bowl, Chamberlain Armorial Crest, Blind Earl Pattern, 1811 .... 285.00
Worcester, Bowl, Round, Puce Floral Garlands, Gilt, 1st Period 225.00
Worcester, Bowl, Tea, Saucer, Overglaze Blue, Gilt Floral, Festoons, 1775 .... 95.00
Worcester, Cider Set, Blue, White, Willow, Pair Handled Mugs, Pitcher, Tray 150.00
Worcester, Coffeepot, Fence Pattern, Pear Shape, Floral, 1st Period 190.00
Worcester, Coffeepot, Pear Shape, Bouquets Of Tiger Lilies, 1st Period 275.00
Worcester, Cup & Saucer, Blue, White, Dr.Wall, Handleless, Circa 1780 .... 100.00
Worcester, Cup & Saucer, Blue, White, Gold, Handleless, Circa 1780 .... 50.00
Worcester, Cup & Saucer, Coffee, Floral, Gilt Scrolls, Pansies, 1st Period 200.00
Worcester, Cup & Saucer, Coffee, Florettes, Gilt Foliate, C.1800 .... 12.50
Worcester, Cup & Saucer, Floral Garlands In Pink, Puce, & Iron, 1st Period 200.00
Worcester, Cup & Saucer, Flowers, Gold, Marked, C.1810 .... 79.50
Worcester, Cup & Saucer, Fluted, Lilac Urn, Fruit Festoons, 1st Period 175.00
Worcester, Cup & Saucer, Gilt & Blue Motif, Blue Crescent Mark, Dr.Wall 100.00
Worcester, Cup & Saucer, Quail Pattern, Fluted, Kakiemon Palette, 1st Period 400.00
Worcester, Cup & Saucer, Rose & Yellow Floral, Circa 1907, Matte 37.50
Worcester, Dish, Muffin, Allover Rosebud Decoration, Chamberlain 95.00
Worcester, Dish, Shell, Gold Shading On Edge, Matte, Circa 1890 .... 42.50
Worcester, Dish, Sweetmeat, Blind Earl Pattern .... Illus 300.00
Worcester, Jardiniere, Oriental Motif, Blue, White, Small Feet, 4 In.High 39.00
Worcester, Jug, Milk, Bleu De Roi, Ovoid, Panels, Floral Garlands, 1st Period 200.00
Worcester, Jug, Milk, Covered, Japan Pattern, Pear Shape, 1st Period 300.00
Worcester, Jug, Milk, Fluted, Pear Shape, Parrot In Peony Tree, 1st Period 70.00
Worcester, Jug, Milk, Japan Pattern, Covered, Pear Shape, Gilt, Red, 1st Period 180.00
Worcester, Match Holder, Gold Lizard Climbing, Dated 1874, 2 1/2 In.High 55.00
Worcester, Muffineer, Bird Design, Sterling Cap, Circa 1900, Box, Silk Lining 98.00
Worcester, Mug, Blue & White, Cylindrical, Apple & Floral, 1st Period 150.00
Worcester, Mug, Blue Scale .... Illus 350.00
Worcester, Mug, Gros Bleu Border .... Illus 225.00
Worcester, Mug, Transfer Print .... Illus 475.00
Worcester, Parian Bust, Soldier, 8 1/2 In.High, Dated 1858, Signed 85.00
Worcester, Pitcher, Floral, Pink, Blue, Yellow, Matte, Circa 1889, 4 1/2 In. 70.00
Worcester, Pitcher, Palm Leaf, 1876, 6 1/4 In.High 80.00
Worcester, Plate, Bouquets & Floral Sprays, Gild Edge, Molded Border, Marked 175.00
Worcester, Plate, Chamberlain, White, Deep Cobalt Blue, Imperial Mark 30.00
Worcester, Plate, Cobalt & Gilt Border, Boar Head Center, Chamberlain's 125.00
Worcester, Plate, Kakiemon Style, Fluted, Birds Center, 1st Period 250.00
Worcester, Plate, Oriental Pattern, Crescent Mark In Gold, Circa 1770 .... 375.00
Worcester, Plate, Ornithological, Birds, Landscape, 1st Period 175.00
Worcester, Plate, Sir Joshua Reynolds Pattern, Scrolls, 1st Period, Pair 700.00
Worcester, Plate, Soup, Gilded Turquoise Bands, Dated 1842 .... 6.50
Worcester, Saucer, Underglaze Blue Transfer, Two Figures In Temple, 1780 .... 25.00
Worcester, Stand, Blue Scale, Oval, Scalloped, Kakiemon Style, 1st Period 200.00
Worcester, Stand, Teapot, Bengal Tiger Pattern, Hexagonal, 1st Period 200.00
Worcester, Stand, Teapot, Fluted, Floral Sprigs, Medallion, 1st Period 225.00
Worcester, Stand, Teapot, Hexagonal, Spiral Festoons, Puce Floral, 1st Period 130.00
Worcester, Stand, Teapot, Japan Pattern, Hexagonal, Gilt, 1st Period, Pair 275.00

Worcester, Mug, Transfer Print
See Page 641

Worcester, Mug, Blue Scale
See Page 641

Worcester, Mug, Gros Bleu Border
See Page 641

Worcester, Sucrier, Covered, Floral Medallion, Gilt, Kakiemon, 1st Period 200.00
Worcester, Sucrier, Covered, Floral, Fluted, Gilt, 1st Period 190.00
Worcester, Sucrier, Covered, Fluted, Panels Of Floral, 1st Period 160.00
Worcester, Sucrier, Covered, Gros Bleu, Panels, Medallions, 1st Period 325.00
Worcester, Sucrier, Covered, Japan Pattern, Floral, 1st Period 250.00
Worcester, Sucrier, Covered, Turquoise Husks, Gray, Pink, & Yellow, 1st Period 110.00
Worcester, Tea & Coffee Set, Floral, Insects, Gros Bleu, C.1790, 56 Piece 675.00
Worcester, Tea Caddy, Blue Scale, Covered, Ovoid, Kakiemon, 1st Period 250.00
Worcester, Tea Caddy, Covered, Fluted, Ovoid, Floral Sprigs, 1st Period 130.00
Worcester, Tea Caddy, Covered, Turquoise Bands, Scrolls, Gilt, 1st Period 200.00
Worcester, Tea Caddy, Fluted, Ovoid, Enamel Floral, Gilt, 1st Period 160.00
Worcester, Tea Caddy, Fluted, Ovoid, Floral Enamel Sprays, Gilt, 1st Period 150.00
Worcester, Tea Caddy, Fluted, Ovoid, Iron Parrot On Peony Tree, 1st Period 120.00
Worcester, Tea Caddy, Gros Bleu, Ovoid, Famille Rose Floral, Gilt, 1st Period 200.00
Worcester, Tea Caddy, Japan Pattern, Ovoid, 1st Period 275.00
Worcester, Teapot, Barrel Shape, Fluted, Garlands & Bouquets, 1st Period 300.00
Worcester, Teapot, Chinoiserie, Globular, Figures, Building, 1st Period 350.00
Worcester, Teapot, Covered, Barrel Shape, Iron Carnations, Roses, 1st Period 130.00
Worcester, Teapot, Covered, Stand, Japan Pattern, 1st Period 300.00
Worcester, Teapot, Ovoid, Bouquets Of Garden Flowers, Pink Rose, 1st Period 150.00
Worcester, Teapot, Sir Joshua Reynolds Pattern .... *Illus* 975.00
Worcester, Teapot, Sugar, Creamer, Patent 1889 .... 245.00
Worcester, Tray, Spoon, Hexagonal, Fluted, Floral, Pink Rose, 1st Period 210.00
Worcester, Tray, Spoon, Hexagonal, Gilt Medallion, Bands, 1st Period 90.00
Worcester, Tray, Spoon, Hexagonal, Lilac Trellis, Medallion, 1st Period 150.00
Worcester, Tray, Spoon, Hexagonal, Medallion Of Hen In Landscape, 1st Period 575.00
Worcester, Tray, Spoon, Japan Pattern, Hexagonal, Blue Bands, 1st Period 130.00
Worcester, Tray, Spoon, Queen Charlotte Pattern, Hexagonal, 1st Period 160.00
Worcester, Tub, Butter, Covered, Blue Scale, Oval, 1st Period, Pair 650.00
Worcester, Tub, Butter, Covered, Stand, Blue & White, Bouquets, 1st Period 400.00
Worcester, Tumble-Up, Hand-Painted Leaves & Ferns, Circa 1889 .... 110.00
Worcester, Tureen, Black, Gold, Marked, C.1800, 5 1/2 In.Long & Tall 135.00
Worcester, Tureen, Sauce, Covered, Blue Scale, Oval, Shell Handles, 1st Period 525.00
Worcester, Vase, Made To Resemble Carved Ivory, Cranes, Dated 1875 .... 150.00
Worcester, Vase, Spill, Rose, Yellow, Blue Floral, Handle, Circa 1896 .... 50.00
Worcester, Vase, Thistles, Green & Orange Base, Handles, 11 1/2 In., Pair 250.00

Worcester, Teapot,
3h Joshua Reynolds Pattern
See Page 642

Worcester, Vegetable, Oriental Design, Dome Cover, Gold Fruit Knob	175.00
World War I, Bayonet, Spike	1.50
World War I, Binoculars, French Artillery Officer's, Ministry Of War	29.50
World War I, Blouse, French Artillery Officer's, Gray Worsted Wool, Brass	22.50
World War I, Blouse, U.S.Army, Wool, Bronze Eagle Buttons	5.75
World War I, Bucket, Water, Field, U.S.Army, Canvas	6.00
World War I, Bugle, U.S.Regulation, Brass	15.00
World War I, Cap, Canadian, Scottish Type, Wool, Leather, Silk, Dated 1918	12.00
World War I, Clock, Aviation, Ansonia, La Guerre, 1918, Signed Helice Paris	75.00
World War I, Coat, Frock, Prussian Officer's, Blue Wool, Red Collar, Brass	12.50
World War I, Eagle, Brass, From German Helmet, 'Mit Gott Fur Koenig'	15.00
World War I, Handkerchief, Silk, Lace, Souvenir De France	4.50
World War I, Hat, U.S., Winter Campaign, Wool, Earlaps	7.50
World War I, Helmet, Belgian, Metal Lion Frontplate	11.00
World War I, Helmet, Doughboy's, Steel, Liner	4.75
World War I, Helmet, French, Poilu, Brass Insignia, Medical Service	11.00
World War I, Helmet, French, Poilu, Steel, Trench, Black, Initials S.R.B.	9.50
World War I, Helmet, Prussian, Jaeger, Shako, Black Felt Covering, C.1900	47.50
World War I, Helmet, Trench, American, Face Visor, Experimental, 1918	84.50
World War I, Helmet, Trench, Emperimental, 1918	97.50
World War I, Helmet, Trench, Portuguese, Steel Crown, 1917	8.95
World War I, Jardiniere, Comic War Scenes, Marked Belgium	36.00
World War I, Knife, Pocket, Picture On Handle, Uncle Sam, I Need You	27.00
World War I, Lighter, Cigar, Bulldog, Metal, German	12.50
World War I, Lighter, Cigarette, Brass Shell Casing, Clemenceau On One Side	45.00
World War I, Lighter, Cigarette, Tank, Dated 1919	20.00
World War I, Lighter, Cigarette, Trench	1.75
World War I, Lighter, Cigarette, 75mM.Shell, Alsace, Strasbourg Cathedral	35.00
World War I, Medal, M.Lordonnois, Bronze	5.00
World War I, Mug, Victory, Porcelain	12.00
World War I, Overcoat, German, Gray Wool, Full Length, Dated 1917	27.50
World War I, Overcoat, U.S.Army, Wool, Bronze Buttons	12.50
World War I, Plate, Peace, June 28, 1919, The Great World War, 1914-19	8.00
World War I, Poster, Before Sunset Buy A Bond, 20 X 30 In.	15.00
World War I, Poster, Berlin Or Bust, Pershing, Uncle Sam	10.00
World War I, Poster, Brave Boys Of 1918, Wilson, Washington, Lincoln, Flag	10.00
World War I, Poster, Columbia Calls, 1916, 30 X 40 In.	48.00
World War I, Poster, Discharge, Infantry, Columbia Gives To Her Son, 1919	4.00
World War I, Poster, For Home And Country, 30 X 40 In.	15.00
World War I, Poster, I Summon You To Comradship, Wilson's Photo	15.00
World War I, Poster, Navy, Men Enlist, 20 X 30 In.	15.00
World War I, Poster, Our Colored Heroes, 1918, 1i X 15 In.	38.50
World War I, Poster, Red, White, Blue, Big 'V, ' 'Invest'	3.50
World War I, Poster, The Greatest Mother In The World, Red Cross Nurse	25.00
World War I, Poster, The Kaiser's Finish, Portraits, Joffre, Pershing, Haig	37.50
World War I, Print, Welcome Home, Negro, Framed	25.00
World War I, Projectile For Big Bertha, German Gun Of 1918, 2 Handles	39.50

World War I, Shovel, Austrian Infantryman's Field, Dated 1918, Iron	9.50
World War I, Shovel, Trench, German Infantryman, Steel, Wooden Handle	9.50
World War I, Trousers, Riding, German Cavalryman's, Gray Wool	22.50
World War I, Uniform, French Cavalryman's, Gray, Bronze Buttons	22.50
World War I, Washbasin, Rubber, Folding, U.S.Issue, Black Canvas	7.50
World War Ii, Boots, Nazi Wehrmacht Army, Black Leather, Pair	11.00
World War II, Canteen, Japanese, Iwo Jima	4.50
World War II, Canteen, Japanese, Metal, Enamel, Harness & Shoulder Strap	12.50
World War II, Cap, German Officer's, Black Patent, Gold Band	17.50
World War II, Coat, Frock, Japanese Naval Officer's, Blue, Brass Buttons	22.50
World War II, Compass, U.S.Army, Mark VII, Sperry Gyroscope Co.	7.50
World War II, Coveralls, Flight Suit, Japanese, Aviator's, Fur Lining	29.50
World War II, Flag Harness, U.S.Marine Corps, Brass Plaque, White Leather	19.50
World War II, Flag, Japanese, Silk, 20 X 30 In., Wooden Shaft	28.00
World War II, Flashlight, Nazi Wehrmacht, Signal, 3 Sliding Reflectors	5.95
World War II, Goggles, Desert, Rommel's Afrika Korps, Paperboard Box, Pair	22.50
World War II, Insignia, Helmet, Nazi Motorcycle Rider's, NSKK At Top	5.00
World War II, Kit, Rifle Cleaning, German Army, Mauser, Tin Container	3.75
World War II, Knapsack, Nazi Army, Mountain Troop, Brown Animal Fur	12.50
World War II, Knapsack, Polish Army, Green Web, Straps, 12 X 14 In.	5.90
World War II, Knife, Facist Symbol On Metal Sheath, Carved Swastika	28.00
World War II, Mask, Gas, Dutch, Dated 1939, Canister	5.00
World War II, Mask, Gas, Italian Army, Canister, Metal Case	11.00
World War II, Mask, Gas, Japanese Army, Canister, Label	12.50
World War II, Mask, Oxygen, U.S.Air Force, Dated 1944	5.00
World War II, Poster, Back The Attack, 20 X 30 In.	9.50
World War II, Poster, Hitler Wants Us To Believe That	10.00
World War II, Poster, Save Freedom Of Speech, Norman Rockwell, 30 X 40	13.50
World War II, Poster, She's Ready Too, Buy War Bonds, Cardboard, Date 1942	12.00
World War II, Poster, War Bond, Norman Rockwell	12.50
World War II, Shell, Tikkakoski, 1939	3.00
World War II, Sword	15.00
World War II, Trousers, German Cavalry, Gray Green Wool	12.50
World War II, Uniform, Imperial Japanese Navy, Full Dress	60.00
World War II, Wine, Engraved Nazi Insignia, Round Bowl, Low Base, 6	88.00
World's Fair, Ashtray, 1933, Buckingham Fountain, Scenes, Bronze	11.00
World's Fair, Bottle, N.Y.1939, Opaque White, 9 In.High 9.75 To	12.00
World's Fair, Bottle, 1939, Embossed Map	6.00
World's Fair, Bottle, 1939, Gilt	8.00
World's Fair, Compact, Chicago	8.00
World's Fair, Creamer, 1893, Red, Clear, Button Arches, Individual	25.00
World's Fair, Dish, Nut, 1939, Planter's Peanut, Tin, Set Of 4	7.00
World's Fair, Doll, Seattle, China, Dressed, 8 In.Tall	10.00
World's Fair, Figurine, 1893, Columbus, Frosted	75.00
World's Fair, Glass, 1893, Hatchet, Libbey	35.00
World's Fair, Guide, 1933 Chicago Exposition, 225 Pages, Hardbound	12.50
World's Fair, Hatchet, Washington, 1893, Clear, Marked Libbey Glass Co.	50.00
World's Fair, Lamp Base, Metal, Chicago, 1933	6.00
World's Fair, Lamp, 1939, Camphor Glass, 7 In.High	25.00
World's Fair, Mug, 1893, Red Block	22.50
World's Fair, Mug, 1893, Red Block, Inscribed Phoebe	18.00
World's Fair, Mug, 1893, Red Block, 3 In.	18.00
World's Fair, Mug, 1904, Enameled Decoration	10.00
World's Fair, Mug, 1904, Ruby, 'Mamie'On Back	15.00
World's Fair, Paperweight, 1893	5.00
World's Fair, Paperweight, 1904, Advertising, Heron & Ellis	20.00
World's Fair, Paperweight, 1904, Palace Of Transportation, St.Louis	8.50
World's Fair, Penknife, 1934, Chicago	8.50
World's Fair, Pitcher, 1939, George Washington, Marked American Potters	30.00
World's Fair, Plaque, 1939, Miniature, Copper, 1 3/4 In.	2.00
World's Fair, Plate, 1904, Turkey, St.Louis, Bisque	9.00
World's Fair, Playing Cards, 1904, Scenes, Louisiana Purchase	17.00
World's Fair, Ring, 1939, New York, Peking Enamel On Silver, Marked China	35.00
World's Fair, Salt & Pepper, 1909, Button Arches, New Tops	20.00
World's Fair, Spoon, 1893, Administration Bldg., Demitasse	2.50
World's Fair, Spoon, 1893, Agricultural Bldg., Demitasse	2.50

World's Fair, Spoon, 1893, Machinery Hall, Demitasse 2.50
World's Fair, Teaspoon, 1933, Silver Plate 3.00
World's Fair, Tie Clip, New York, 1939 .... 3.00
World's Fair, Toothpick, 1893, Ruby, Thumbprint 20.00
World's Fair, Toothpick, 1933, Pedestal, Wooden 11.00
World's Fair, Tray, Chicago, 1933, Brass, 7 X 10 In. 12.00
World's Fair, Tray, 1933, Chicago, Copper 14.00
World's Fair, Tray, 1939, Caffe Medaglia D'Oro, Lady, View, 10 X 13 In. 15.50
World's Fair, Tumbler, 1904, Clear, St.Louis 12.00
World's Fair, Umbrella, 1933, Chicago, 30 In.Long 7.50
World's Fair, Watch, Pocket, 1939, New York 125.00
World's Fair, 1904, St.Louis, Clear Glass, Scene, Festival Hall, Gardens 12.00
World's Fair, 1904, Tumbler, Ruby Flashed, Button Arches 12.50
Wurzburg, Cup & Saucer, C.1775 .... *Illus* 1450.00

Zsolnay Pottery was made in Hungary after 1855.

Zsolnay, Bowl, Cream Ground, Gold Traced Multicolor Flowers, 5 1/4 In. 75.00
Zsolnay, Bowl, Rose & Gold, Gold Decoration, Scalloped, Panels, 7 In. 65.00
Zsolnay, Centerpiece, Amber Green Iridescence .... *Illus* 175.00
Zsolnay, Centerpiece, Art Nouveau, Ovoid, Exotic Bird, Amber Iridescence 140.00
Zsolnay, Centerpiece, Clove Shape, Flower Design, Castle Mark, Signed 85.00
Zsolnay, Compote, Enamel, Gilt, Persian Flower Pattern, Pedestal 95.00
Zsolnay, Dish, Floral, Fan Shape, Curved Handle 55.00
Zsolnay, Dish, Iridescent Blue, Pink, Gold, Reticulated Edge, Oval 45.00
Zsolnay, Ewer, Creamy Ground, Rose Colored Floral, Filigree Neck, Handle 55.00
Zsolnay, Figurine, Blue & Purple Iridescent, 6 In.High 150.00
Zsolnay, Figurine, Cat, Iridescent Gold 45.00
Zsolnay, Figurine, Porcupine, Gold & Blue Iridescent, 2 1/2 In.High 45.00
Zsolnay, Group, Woman & Child, Cubist Style, Yellow To Green, Signed, C.1930 .... 250.00
Zsolnay, Jug, Persian Shape, Floral Design, Signed, 11 1/2 In. 85.00
Zsolnay, Jug, Persian Shape, Floral, Signed Pecs, 11 1/2 In.High 75.00
Zsolnay, Vase, Art Nouveau, Baluster, Iridescent, Nymph, Blue Green 200.00
Zsolnay, Vase, Art Nouveau, Bulbous, Ribbed, Red Iridescent, Signed, Pair 40.00
Zsolnay, Vase, Art Nouveau, Floral, Applied Decoration, 8 In. 78.00
Zsolnay, Vase, Art Nouveau, Ovoid, Iridescent, Landscape In Red, Blue, & Amber 170.00
Zsolnay, Vase, Enamelled, 10 In.High 45.00
Zsolnay, Vase, Hand-Painted Flowers, Hourglass Shape 55.00
Zsolnay, Vase, Iridescent Gold, Green, Blue, Signed, 5 In. 50.00
Zsolnay, Vase, Multicolor Hues, 5 In. 45.00
Zsolnay, Vase, Openwork Box In Bird Form, Yellow, Green, 9 In.High 125.00
Zsolnay, Vase, Peacock Blue, Green Iridescence, 4 Handles, Signed, 9 In.High 100.00
Zsolnay, Vase, Reticulated Pink & Blue Floral, Beige Ground, 14 In., Pair 130.00
Zsolnay, Vase, Tiffany Type Peacock Blue Iridescence, 3 Handles, 8 In. 75.00

Wurzburg,
Cup & Saucer, C.1775

Zsolnay, Centerpiece, Amber Green Iridescence

The Complete Antiques Price List

by Ralph and Terry Kovel

SIXTH EDITION • OVER 500 ILLUSTRATIONS

The most complete, accurate, and authoritative price guide in the field, the sixth edition of this indispensable volume has been completely updated, with every price reviewed and with so many items added that it is a "must" for every collector. Included are a listing of glass and pottery marks; information about the dates of manufacture, location, and artists making the antiques listed; new categories, including many of the American art pottery factories, Galle pottery, Shaker items, Corona ware, celebrity listings, and patent models; and limited edition plates and figurines. The book contains many more cross references than past editions, as well as over 500 excellent photographs, almost 100 in full color, and 42,000 entries—more than ever before. A practical working guide to the antiques market for 1973-1974, THE COMPLETE ANTIQUES PRICE LIST will prove invaluable for all museums, collectors, and dealers who want to verify the price of any collectible.

Ralph and Terry Kovel are nationally known for their expert advice on all matters pertaining to antiques. Their nationally syndicated column "Know Your Antiques" is known to hundreds of thousands of readers. In addition, their award-winning show on educational television, syndicated throughout the country, has made them one of the most popular and sought-after lecture teams to appear on television, at museums, and at collectors' groups in every part of the United States. They are the authors of many books on antiques, including *Know Your Antiques; Dictionary of Marks; Pottery and Porcelain; A Directory of Silver, Pewter, and Silver Plate;* and *American Country Furniture: 1780-1875.*

WHAT THE CRITICS SAID ABOUT THE OTHER EDITIONS OF

The Complete Antiques Price List

". . . not only an indispensable tool for use by those who collect, but a fascinating compilation of knowledge about those things which make 'the world of antiques' as well."
—*NATIONAL ANTIQUES*

". . . the most popular, definitive guide to the antiques market . . . an invaluable reference book—an essential aid to every museum, dealer, and collector."
—*MURFREESBORO NEWS-JOURNAL*

". . . helpful to dealers and collectors." —*THE ANTIQUES JOURNAL*

". . . from the start this computer-evolved list has been the most inclusive price listing of antiques in the country." —*THE DALLAS MORNING NEWS*

"Invaluable for professionals, dealers, collectors." —*INSIGHT*

Crown Publishers, Inc., 419 Park Avenue South, New York, N.Y. 10016

$5.95

ISBN: 0-517-506068